OUR ENVIRONMENT

A Canadian Perspective

FOURTH EDITION

DIANNE DRAPER
University of Calgary

MAUREEN G. REED
University of Saskatchewan

NELSON EDUCATION

NELSON / EDUCATION

Our Environment: A Canadian Perspective, Fourth Edition

by Dianne Draper and Maureen G. Reed

Associate Vice President, Editorial Director:
Evelyn Veitch

Editor-in-Chief:
Anne Williams

Executive Editor:
Paul Fam

Senior Marketing Manager:
Sean Chamberland

Developmental Editor:
Heather Parker

Photo Researcher and Permissions Coordinator:
Natalie Barrington

Senior Content Production Manager:
Natalia Denesiuk Harris

Production Service:
ICC Macmillan Inc.

Copy Editor:
Marcia Gallego

Proofreader:
Barbara Storey

Indexer:
Maura Brown

Manufacturing Coordinator:
Pauline Long

Design Director:
Ken Phipps

Managing Designer:
Katherine Strain

Interior Design Modifications:
ArtPlus Ltd.

Cover Design:
Dianna Little

Cover Images:
Dianne Draper, Maureen Reed

Compositor:
ICC Macmillan Inc.

Printer:
Courier

Library and Archives Canada Cataloguing in Publication Data

Draper, Dianne Louise, 1949–

Our environment : a Canadian perspective / Dianne Draper and Maureen G. Reed. — 4th ed.

Includes bibliographical references and index.
ISBN 978-0-17-610529-7

1. Canada—Environmental conditions—Textbooks. 2. Environmental policy—Canada—Textbooks. 3. Environmental degradation—Canada—Textbooks. I. Reed, Maureen Gail, 1961– II. Title.

GE160.C3D73 2008
363.700971   C2008-902810-4

ISBN-13: 978-0-17-610529-7
ISBN-10: 0-17-610529-8

BRIEF CONTENTS

CONTENTS

Chapter 9
Forests and Forestry 356

**PART 4   GETTING TO
TOMORROW**

CANADA AND THE WORLD

P R E F A C E

Environmental education is a lifelong process, and no one textbook or course can cover in depth every element relevant to a full understanding of environmental issues. This book is intended as a learning tool so that students, today and tomorrow, may be better informed about—and able to make scientifically grounded and socioeconomically balanced decisions on—environmental issues. Canadian students generally care a great deal about the world in which they live. Many want to be challenged to think critically about, and to act responsibly with respect to, the environment. We sincerely hope that the fourth edition of this book helps make environmental science meaningful and relevant to Canadian (and other) students so that they may meet the challenge of sustaining a healthy and productive Earth environment as well as a just and prosperous society.

OBJECTIVES

The purpose of this fourth edition of *Our Environment: A Canadian Perspective* is to provide a contemporary introduction to scientific and social concepts that are important to the study and understanding of the ecological functioning of our global environment. The book also aims to present current information on environmental issues we face in Canada. If our efforts to resolve these issues are to succeed, we need to think critically and in an integrated fashion about them and about the relationships between people and Earth's ecosystems. Thus, information presented here integrates physical and human dimensions, and reflects a broad, interdisciplinary approach to the study of global and local environments. This is why discussion of issues such as water appears in chapters dealing not only with water but in chapters on agriculture, forests, mining, and energy resources.

Canadians' experiences with environmental issues vary from east to west and north to south. This book is intended to help students understand the breadth of human activities and their effects on the environment in different resource sectors and regions of the nation. In addition, examples selected from across the country and internationally are intended to help students appreciate the range of opinion on, and approaches that have been taken to resolve, environmental concerns in Canada and beyond.

Canada is a global citizen with respect to issues of environment and development. We have achieved some notable successes in certain environmental matters, but we also have fallen behind other nations in our efforts to address environmental change. We cannot become complacent about what remains to be done. In this regard, a number of key themes thread through the text, including the importance of scientific research and critical reflection on environmental matters, the involvement of local people in identifying and addressing environmental changes in their region, the place of stewardship and cooperative problem solving in environmental action, and a focus on sustainability and on the future.

ORGANIZATION

The book contains 14 chapters, grouped into four parts. In Part I, students are introduced to environmental and social science concepts through discussion of our constantly changing global environment and the major, if contested, sources of environmental problems. The role of science and social science in understanding our environment and in moving toward a sustainable future is considered, as are the roles of worldviews, environmental values, and ethics.

In Part II, the focus is on fundamental features of, and interconnections in, the ecosphere, as well as on human population and development issues. We examine concerns for population and development at global and national scales and point to the increasing role that Aboriginal people play in Canadian environmental and resource management.

Part III focuses on Canada's natural resource endowment and associated human activities. Chapters on the atmosphere, agroecosystems and land resources, fresh water, oceans and fisheries, forests and forestry, minerals and mining, energy, and biodiversity each deal with fundamental scientific concerns related to assessing the abundance and quality of the resources, and the effects of human activities on them. Each chapter also identifies a range of Canadian responses to the challenges encountered through resource development and use of environments. These responses identify international and national actions, and discuss the activities, partnerships, and local actions of individuals, environmental nongovernmental organizations, industry, and governments.

Part IV considers issues associated with living in urban environments, the effects of our lifestyle choices, and some of the ways we can move toward sustainable environments in the future.

Canada and the World, the final section of the book, is new to the fourth edition. Canada's performance in environmental management is compared against other countries' performance using indicators that are part of the Environmental Performance Index, newly compiled by researchers at the Yale Center for Environmental Law and Policy and the Center for International Earth Science Information Network at Columbia University, in collaboration with the World Economic Forum and the Joint Research Centre of the European Commission.

FEATURES

Our Environment, Fourth Edition, contains several special features to help students. Each chapter begins with a list of *Chapter Objectives* so that students are aware of the concepts they will come to understand as they read and study the chapter. *Key terms* appear in bold throughout the text; definitions for these terms are found in the *Glossary.* Case studies in each chapter not only provide real illustrations of environmental problems but also demonstrate how people have applied the principles and concepts discussed in the text to the resolution of environmental issues at several geographic scales. These cases should help students understand how economic, social, political, and environmental elements interconnect, and how they relate to our scientific and traditional ways of understanding our environment when efforts are made to tackle environmental challenges.

Enviro-Focus boxes identify a range of personal interest/impact issues ranging from increases in skin cancer cases in Canada and the challenges in managing the discharge of municipal sewage to our ocean environment, to the competition between wild species and humans for habitat that affects grizzly bears in Banff National Park. *Future Challenges* sections, in the resource sector chapters, are intended to stimulate and extend our thinking about local environmental problems to the future of the world we live in and share with others.

Each chapter ends with a list of *Chapter Questions*; some questions review material presented in the chapter, others engage students in development of observational and critical thinking skills. A list of *References* containing research sources also appears at the end of each chapter.

WHAT'S NEW IN THIS EDITION

Many changes in our understanding of environmental issues have occurred since the publication of the third edition. To reflect these changes and to emphasize how dynamic a process it is to deal with environmental issues, new topics and updated statistics have been added to make the text as current as possible. We also have placed increased emphasis on social issues that attend changes in environmental conditions and policy.

Two new features are included in this edition. *Making a Difference* boxes at the end of each chapter provide brief profiles of people who are active in their communities and who, in various ways, either individually or in groups, are helping to make an environmental difference in Canada and the world. Some people are well known, many are not. These people have inspired our own thinking and actions; we hope they will inspire yours, too.

As noted above, *Canada and the World* is a new section in the book. In a series of figures, descriptions, and tables drawing upon the Environmental Performance Index, Canada's performance is compared to that of 19 other countries around the world. Reviewing our environmental performance in this way may raise questions about where we are leading and where we are lagging. Students also should consider the utility and limitations of such data gathering, aggregation, and monitoring exercises within and across nation-states.

Chapter 1 offers a Canadian-centred focus on our use of natural resources and ecosystems. We have provided definitions for resources and explained challenges associated with the use of both renewable and nonrenewable resources. We have expanded the discussion of how we might conceptualize sustainability and the kinds of tools we have to try to achieve it.

Chapter 2 provides a discussion of science and the environment, and explains the relationship among various disciplines in environmental studies and sustainable development. Several new topics, including political ecology, a citizens panel on plant molecular farming, and music and the environment, have been added.

Chapter 3 focuses on fundamental features and interconnections of the Earth's life-support systems. This chapter helps students understand why learning to work with nature—such as using lichens as indicators of air quality changes—is essential to achieving a sustainable future.

Chapter 4 identifies global population dynamics, including the roles of consumption and technology as pressures on the Earth's resources and ecosystems. We consider how Canada has used its resources for development and the role of the resource cycle in contributing to fluctuations in economic and social well-being. We also discuss the increasing role of Aboriginal people in environmental management and resource development. Our discussion encourages readers to examine the extent to which global population/development issues are present in Canada.

Chapter 5 provides updated information and data on atmospheric science and its relation to climate change and air quality, as well as information on modelling climate change. The international scientific consensus that global warming is a result of the increase in anthropogenic greenhouse gas concentrations is highlighted, as is the vulnerability of Canada's North to climate change.

Chapter 6 considers the complex nature and importance of the agriculture industry to Canadians. Updated data on agricultural operations, challenges associated with the production of biofuels and their utility as alternative sources of energy, the uses and risks of pesticides, and the growth of very large livestock farms near major cities are among the issues considered. The diversity of interconnected environmental concerns—from the effects of genetically modified foods, to bovine spongiform encephalopathy (BSE), to the place of agriculture in Canada's metropolitan areas—reflects the nature of contemporary Canadian agroecosystems.

Chapter 7 makes connections between the physical availability of water and the measures we take to use and manage it. The water budget and the cycling of water through freshwater ecosystems are explained. New information on the use of water for industrial purposes (e.g., oil sands development) and for export also is provided. The challenges of providing safe and secure water supplies in Canada are considered in relation to new regulations and source-protection measures throughout the country.

Chapter 8 provides new and expanded information on oceans and fisheries, including updated statistics on global and Canadian catches. Potential effects of climate change on the ocean, marine biodiversity, and fish harvests, and improvements in international efforts to control illegal and unregulated fishing are discussed, as are conservation of wild salmon, and the treating sewage discharges, federal government's focus on modernization of the Fisheries Act.

Chapter 9 discusses the use of forested ecosystems to illustrate how environmental science is intertwined with social and cultural issues. We discuss why tropical rain forests are overexploited and consider resource use in Canada with a focused discussion of volume-based and value-based forestry practices. Updated information is provided on the establishment of allowable cuts and on the creation of management regimes to protect forest ecosystems and rural communities and to encourage Aboriginal involvement. Information on measures such as eco-certification and community forestry experiments across Canada is updated, and we focus on the implications of the mountain pine beetle for the boreal forests of western Canada to illustrate the uncertainty within which forestry is undertaken. Impacts of harvest changes on workers, uses of forests beyond timber, and impacts of tourism as an alternative economic generator in forested ecosystems also are discussed.

Chapter 10 discusses the classification of mineral resources according to their economic availability. Linking to general issues raised in Chapter 4, discussion of "the staples trap" explains how this process contributes to boom and bust cycles in mining towns. We consider how communities can overcome this trap through initiatives such as amenity-based tourism or by establishing regional centres from which workers commute to mine sites. The diamond mining discussion is updated, and the environmental implications of exploitation of coalbed methane are identified.

Chapter 11 includes updated material on energy use, production, and sustainability. The offshore oil and gas industry, Alberta's oil sands development, remediation of the Sydney tar ponds, buying green power in Canada, growth in emerging renewable energy technologies such as wind farms, and the intent to achieve a carbon neutral Olympic and Paralympic Winter Games in Vancouver in 2010 are among the new topics discussed.

Chapter 12 defines biodiversity, provides examples of how scientists try to measure biodiversity, and discusses the scientific challenges associated with understanding the patterns and processes of biodiversity. We discuss the locations where there are concerns about the protection of biodiversity and consider how urban land conversion affects biodiversity. The challenges of protecting biodiversity as climatic conditions changed are raised, while new initiatives to meet these challenges are discussed.

Chapter 13 provides several definitions of "urban" to illustrate how difficult it is to make generalizations about what cities are and what their effects are on the environment. A short history of urban development and a discussion of its implications for our environment are provided, along with a discussion of the global rise of mega-cities. Our discussion of alternatives for providing ecosystem services such as water in urban environments includes a summary of debates surrounding private and public systems and private–public partnerships in water provision. We also explain how sustainable urban planning and "smart growth" may be used as tools to promote urban sustainability.

Chapter 14 begins with one person's story about growing up in the area of the Sydney tar ponds and then turns to Canada's record in safeguarding the Canadian environment. We suggest that there is a need to reconceptualize environmental problems to address questions related our motivations, beliefs, and behaviours. We discuss how science, values, and public policy making often are combined in decisions about environment, and note that this mix creates challenges for taking action. Next, we describe how various groups—governments, Aboriginal peoples, private firms, and ENGOs—can and do take responsibility for the environment. Embedded in this discussion are strategies that have worked and that can continue to improve our prospects for achieving sustainability. Our final section recounts some specific Canadian success stories and emphasizes how individuals and collectives can work together to pursue the goal of sustainability.

INSTRUCTOR'S RESOURCES TO FACILITATE TEACHING AND LEARNING

A rich variety of instructional resources supplement the book, giving instructors the tools to create a dynamic, exciting, and effective course.

Instructor's CD-ROM. The Instructor's CD-ROM contains the Instructor's Manual/Test Bank, Computerized Test Bank, and PowerPoints. See below for more details about each supplement.

Instructor's Manual/Test Bank. The instructor's manual consists of two parts. Part 1 includes a section on using the book's support package and integrating items such as the website into the classroom. The bulk of Part 1 provides teaching suggestions, chapter lecture outlines, activities, and exercises for students on a chapter-by-chapter basis. Part 2 contains the Test Bank. Multiple-choice, true/false, short-answer, and fill-in-the-blank questions are included for every chapter.

Computerized Test Bank. Available only on the Instructor's CD-ROM, all questions from the Test Bank are available in Examview for Windows and Mac format. Examview allows instructors to create, deliver, and customize texts (both print and online) in minutes with this easy-to-use assessment and tutorial system.

PowerPoint® Slides. PowerPoint slideshows recap the major topics discussed in each chapter and incorporate figures from the text to enhance classroom presentation. These files are available on the Instructor's CD-ROM and also can be downloaded from the password-protected Instructor's Resource area of our website.

Environmental Science on the World Wide Web. The dynamic website that accompanies this text can be found at www.ourenvironment4e.nelson.com. The site gives students access to helpful learning resources such as practice quizzes, chapter-specific Web links, study tips, information on degrees and careers in environmental science, and much more.

InfoTrac® College Edition. Gain access to InfoTrac, our online database of scholarly and popular journals available for downloading from the Web. Simply enter your password (included on the card in this text) for immediate access to full-text articles from *Maclean's, The Ecologist, Environmental Action Magazine, Geographical Journal,* and other environmental and geographical magazines, reviews, and journals.

ACKNOWLEDGMENTS

The authors have benefited greatly from the assistance of many people in preparing this edition of *Our Environment.* We would like to extend special thanks to Vicky Falk and Kim Sanderson, who provided effective research assistance to this project. In particular, we acknowledge the essential research and writing contributions of Sharla Daviduik in bringing to fruition the "Making a Difference" and "Canada and the World" components.

Lorn Fitch, Dave Irvine-Halliday, Wil Holden, Lawrence Nkemdirim, and Kees Vanderheyden kindly took the time to write specific materials for this edition; thank you for your willingness to contribute your expertise. Many people responded to requests for information and photographs; thank you for your contributions.

We are very grateful for the assistance of the talented members of the editorial and production team at Nelson Education. We would like to express our sincere gratitude to Paul Fam and Heather Parker for their advice and professional assistance. Others at Nelson helped in other ways, and we'd like to thank them, too: Natalia Denesiuk Harris, Susan Calvert, and Natalie Barrington, as well as Gunjan Chandola at MPS. We greatly appreciate and thank Marcia Gallego for her assistance.

We would like to thank the reviewers who pointed out errors and made important suggestions for improvements in this book. Although remaining errors and deficiencies are ours, we extend our thanks to Ann Zimmerman, University of Toronto; Barry Weaver, Camosun College; Roxanne Richardson, Saint Mary's University; Mark Hanson, University of Manitoba; Ben Bradshaw, University of Guelph; and Darren Bardati, Bishop's University, along with other reviewers who asked to remain anonymous. Thank you for your help.

Finally, we thank our families for the commitment and support they have given us during this project. Maureen would especially like to thank Michael, Louis, and Bruce. We would like to dedicate this edition to all who have nurtured our love for this Earth and our place within it. We also would like to challenge ourselves, and every reader of *Our Environment*, to examine our motivations, beliefs, and behaviours with respect to the environments within which we live our everyday lives, and to take those actions we can in moving our society and environment toward a sustainable future.

Dianne Draper
Calgary, Alberta

Maureen G. Reed
Saskatoon, Saskatchewan

PART 1

Our Environment

CHAPTER 1

Our Environment: Interpretations, Challenges, and Strategies

Chapter Contents

"Although it is only a little planet it is hugely beautiful and surely the finest place in the world to be."

Lawrence Collins (in Brower, 1975, p. 127)

INTRODUCTION

From the feel of earth under our feet, to the light of sun and sky in our eyes; from the flaming colours that greet us in autumn woods, to the shimmering oceans, lakes, and streams that flow around us—Canadians know they inhabit some special places on a beautiful planet. The challenge is that many of our activities in this country and on this planet are rapidly altering its beauty and its ecological functioning. Increasing industrial development and international trade, as well as exponential growth in resource consumption and in human population, have caused forests, wetlands, and grasslands to disappear, topsoil to be blown or washed away, oceans and water bodies to be poisoned, and wildlife species to be driven to extinction. The good news is that we are learning to think and act differently to sustain, rather than degrade, our planet.

The focus of this book is on learning about the impacts human activities have on the quality of our environment, about how environmental and social scientists understand the changes happening in our environment, and about the actions we can take to achieve sustainability of the Earth and its inhabitants. This book helps us to think critically about environmental challenges that face us as Canadians and global citizens. It also discusses efforts that individuals, groups, industries, and government agencies are making to solve existing problems and to improve the ways we interact with the ecosystems of the planet. Although many problems are significant ones, and sometimes people feel powerless to change them, it is important to remember that individual and combined actions do make a difference. Each one of us can improve our ecological knowledge and understanding of how the world works so that our individual and collective decisions and actions in the future will be less harmful to the environment. Industries and governments, too, can be challenged to develop new approaches to conserving the planet's basic life-support systems and to ensure the long-term sustainability of species and resources.

In addition to providing an overview of the nature of environmental challenges facing Canadians in this chapter, we introduce some of the linkages humans have with Earth's interconnected ecosystems, consider the complexity of environmental problems, and illustrate how our definition of natural resources affects the ways in which we approach the natural environment. We also consider the ideas behind the concept of sustainability and some of the principles and strategies that help us work toward it.

Chapter Objectives

After studying this chapter you should be able to

- identify a range of local, regional, and international environmental issues of relevance to Canadians and all citizens of the planet

- appreciate the ways in which humans are linked with Earth's ecosystems

- describe the complexity of environmental problems

- define and classify resources

- discuss the concepts of sustainable development and sustainability, illustrating their commonalities and distinctions

- identify and summarize the guiding principles of sustainability

- discuss tools and strategies we can use to advance sustainability

Photo 1–1

Winter storms in December 2006 brought near-hurricane-force winds and inflicted unprecedented damage on Vancouver's natural environment. Stanley Park lost 1000 trees. Climate change may mean that fierce storms such as this one will occur more frequently than in the past (see Chapter 5).

Photo 1–2

The Palliser Triangle of the Prairie region is the area at greatest risk of loss of biodiversity in Canada. In 2003, bison were reintroduced to the southern Prairies, after years of work by private individuals, environmental organizations, foundation funding, and government agencies (see Chapters 6, 12, and 14).

Photo 1–4

Although Canada has an abundance of freshwater, our supplies are limited. Yet, Canadians are among the world's largest consumers of water, and we export water and hydroelectric power for economic development. Furthermore, the quality of our water supplies is at risk in many rural areas. How can we protect our water supply for current and future generations (see Chapters 7, 11, 13)?

Photo 1–5

Although environmental management is fraught with uncertainties, we can employ strategies from which we can continue to learn and adjust. Adaptive management has been adopted by the British Columbia Forest Service (Chapters 1, 9).

Photo 1–3

Aboriginal people have been recognized only recently as important participants in the management of Canada's environment and resources. Today, Aboriginal people are involved in resource extraction and resource decision making across many sectors (see Chapters 4–12).

Photo 1–6
Canadians are profligate consumers of environmental resources, including water, foodstuffs, minerals, and fossil fuel. Each person can take responsibility for reducing consumption. A single cyclist who travels 100 kilometres reduces emissions of carbon dioxide by 4 to 6 kilograms over a car driver. In the course of a year, this number may be as high as 8.5 tonnes (see Chapter 13).

THE CHANGING GLOBAL ENVIRONMENT

Television and video programs have brought each of us face to face with the tragic images of environmental refugees fleeing famine, disease, and death as ecological deterioration overtakes their homelands. Through news photography we have seen images of the aftermath of nuclear explosions at Chernobyl and Three Mile Island; cyanide and heavy-metals mining spills on the Danube River system; burning tropical rain forests in Central and South America; oil escaping from tankers plying the oceans; and elephants, rhinos, and other African wildlife slaughtered by poachers. Canadian news media have carried stories about the shrinking Arctic ice pack; severe smog events in major cities; illness and death from contaminated water supplies; the collapse of cod and salmon fisheries; the spread of "mad cow" disease; and the use of genetically altered plants to produce drugs and vaccines. These images and stories carry the same underlying message—in a very short time, humans have greatly accelerated environmental change.

While it is true that Earth's history reveals periods of major environmental changes (such as when glaciation transformed landscapes, and catastrophic volcanic eruptions

and floods destroyed species and ecosystems), these events generally occurred over long time frames and provided for relative stability in ecological processes. In contrast, human activities have increased the pace of environmental change and have had dramatic impacts on the quality and productivity of the planet's **ecosystems.** Canadians are becoming increasingly aware of how human demands for and increased consumption of resources have resulted in events such as the collapse of the Atlantic cod fishery as well as the reduction of old-growth temperate rain forests by over 50 percent, prairie grasslands by about 80 percent, and Ontario's Carolinian forests to less than 15 percent of their former expanses. These numbers are estimates because there is considerable debate about definitions and measurement techniques that are used to derive these figures.

As people have continued to pursue economic growth, concerns about environmental quality have increased. For instance, acidic atmospheric pollutants from Canadian and U.S. industrial sources have destroyed fish in many lakes in eastern Canada; Arctic **country foods** (local meat and fish) have been contaminated by polychlorinated biphenyls (PCBs); and Labrador has been the recipient of long-range transport of radioactive particles from Chernobyl. Depleted soils, Arctic haze, large die-offs of neotropical migrant birds, increased levels of greenhouse gases such as carbon dioxide in the atmosphere, and rare forms of cancer in residents downstream from oil sands plants have resulted from discharges of industrial and community wastes as well as from agricultural, forestry, and mining practices.

Such results of our activities have alerted people to the fact that we are not separate from our **environment** but are an integral part of Earth's interconnected ecosystems. Perhaps we can understand the profound impacts that population growth and economic development have on the global ecosystem (the **ecosphere**) when we realize that "the world's population has multiplied almost fivefold since the early 1900s [and that during that same time period] the world's economy has grown by 20 times, the consumption of fossil fuels by 30 times, and industrial production by 50 times" (Government of Canada, 1996).

Ecosystems have finite productive capacities and assimilative abilities, and they are affected by human activities. As human populations and consumption levels grow, for example, they increase demands on energy supplies for industrial development, transportation, and housing. If the productivity and quality of our environment are to be retained, it is important to acknowledge our complex relationships with Earth's ecosystems and to act in ways that will not put intolerable pressure on natural resources and life-support systems of the ecosphere. Impacts of human activities often transcend political boundaries and can lead to serious social, economic, and environmental problems. This is why Vancouverites should care about what happens in the Arctic, why New Brunswickers should be concerned about pollution in Eastern Europe, and why Inuit in Nunavut should be interested in the Brazilian rain forest.

Photo 1–7a
Rocky Mountain meadow, Alberta.

Photo 1–7b
Great blue heron, British Columbia.

Photo 1–7c
Boreal forest and tundra, Yukon Territory.

Photo 1–7d
Ocean environment.

Photo 1–8a

Photo 1–8b

The productive capabilities of different environments are affected by natural limitations (a: deserts) and human activities (b: deforestation).

Many people in the Western world are troubled by the current impacts of their own activities on the environment, and worried about how future environmental changes might affect their health and socioeconomic well-being. Among these concerns are effects of nuclear waste disposal, toxic emissions, acid precipitation, genetically modified plant crops, deforestation, habitat loss and fragmentation, greenhouse gases, and global climate change in general.

At the individual level, many Canadians are concerned about whether their well water is contaminated with pesticides or agricultural runoff; whether enough trees are being replanted to replace all those that have been cut; whether sufficient high-quality habitat is being

Photo 1–9

One example of the impact that human activity can have on wildlife.

protected for wildlife; the degree to which pollution from other countries is affecting Canada's air and water quality; and whether exotic species introduced accidentally (or deliberately) can be controlled. Increasingly, people around the world are asking how they can balance the need for economic and social development with the need to sustain those resources on which such development rests. To put it another way, people want to know what actions to take individually and collectively, as well as how to achieve a balance among the social, economic, and environmental dimensions of activities such as mining,

fishing, agriculture, forestry, and tourism. Indeed, scientists around the world were so alarmed at the rate and scope of human impacts, they signed a collective statement to try to influence politicians to take serious action to reduce the human impact on the Earth.

The 1992 "World Scientists' Warning to Humanity" identified critical stresses facing the Earth's environment and noted what we must do to avoid irretrievably mutilating our planet (see Enviro-Focus 1). This warning was part of a long-term campaign by the Union of Concerned Scientists to increase awareness of the threat that global environmental degradation poses to humanity's life-support systems. By 1993, more than 1670 scientists from 71 countries, including 104 Nobel laureates, had signed the warning. Among Canadian scientists who signed the warning were Paul-Yves Denis, Gerhard Herzberg, Digby McLaren, Brenda Milner, Lawrence Mysak, John Polanyi, and Betty Roots. Five years later, 1500 scientists from 63 countries (including 100 Nobel laureates and 60 U.S. National Medal of Science winners) signed another petition, the "World Scientists' Call for Action at the Kyoto Climate Summit." Their hope, in part, was to influence leaders of nation-states to strengthen the 1992 Framework Convention on Climate Change and sign an international treaty on climate change at Kyoto, Japan. The fact that scientists felt so strongly that they took these actions sends a powerful message, even more than a decade later.

ENVIRO-FOCUS 1

World Scientists' Warning to Humanity

Introduction Human beings and the natural world are on a collision course. Human activities inflict harsh and often irreversible damage on the environment and on critical resources. If not checked, many of our current practices put at serious risk the future that we wish for human society and the plant and animal kingdoms, and may so alter the living world that it will be unable to sustain life in the manner that we know. Fundamental changes are urgent if we are to avoid the collision our present course will bring about.

The Environment The environment is suffering critical stress:

The Atmosphere. Stratospheric ozone depletion threatens us with enhanced ultraviolet radiation at the earth's surface, which can be damaging or lethal to many life forms. Air pollution near ground level and acid precipitation are already causing widespread injury to humans, forests, and crops.

Water Resources. Heedless exploitation of depletable groundwater supplies endangers food production and other essential human systems. Heavy demands on the world's surface waters have resulted in serious shortages in some 80 countries, containing 40 percent of the world's population. Pollution of rivers, lakes, and groundwater further limits the supply.

Oceans. Destructive pressure on the oceans is severe, particularly in the coastal regions, which produce most of the world's food fish. The total marine catch is now at or above the estimated maximum sustainable yield.

(continued)

Some fisheries have already shown signs of collapse. Rivers carrying heavy burdens of eroded soil into the seas also carry industrial, municipal, agricultural, and livestock waste—some of it toxic.

Soil. Loss of soil productivity, which is causing extensive land abandonment, is a widespread byproduct of current practices in agriculture and animal husbandry. Since 1945, 11 percent of the earth's vegetated surface has been degraded—an area larger than India and China combined—and per capita food production in many parts of the world is decreasing.

Forests. Tropical rain forests, as well as tropical and temperate dry forests, are being destroyed rapidly. At present rates, some critical forest types will be gone in a few years, and most of the tropical rain forest will be gone before the end of the next century. With them will go large numbers of plant and animal species.

Living Species. The irreversible loss of species, which by 2100 may reach one-third of all species now living, is especially serious. We are losing the potential they hold for providing medicinal and other benefits, and the contribution that genetic diversity of life forms gives to the robustness of the world's biological systems and to the astonishing beauty of the earth itself.

Much of this damage is irreversible on a scale of centuries, or permanent. Other processes appear to pose additional threats. Increasing levels of gases in the atmosphere from human activities, including carbon dioxide released from fossil fuel burning and from deforestation, may alter climate on a global scale. Predictions of global warming are still uncertain—with projected effects ranging from tolerable to very severe—but the potential risks are very great.

Our massive tampering with the world's interdependent web of life—coupled with the environmental damage inflicted by deforestation, species loss, and climate change—could trigger widespread adverse effects, including unpredictable collapses of critical biological systems whose interactions and dynamics we only imperfectly understand.

Uncertainty over the extent of these effects cannot excuse complacency or delay in facing the threats.

Population The earth is finite. Its ability to absorb wastes and destructive effluent is finite. Its ability to provide food and energy is finite. Its ability to provide for growing numbers of people is finite. And we are fast approaching many of the earth's limits. Current economic practices which damage the environment, in both developed and underdeveloped nations, cannot be continued without the risk that vital global systems will be damaged beyond repair.

Pressures resulting from unrestrained population growth put demands on the natural world that can overwhelm any efforts to achieve a sustainable future. If we are to halt the destruction of our environment, we must accept limits to that growth. A World Bank estimate indicates that world population will not stabilize at less than 12.4 billion, while the United Nations concludes that the eventual total could reach 14 billion, a near tripling of today's 5.4 billion. But, even at this moment, one person in five lives in absolute poverty without enough to eat, and one in ten suffers serious malnutrition.

No more than one or a few decades remain before the chance to avert the threats we now confront will be lost and the prospects for humanity immeasurably diminished.

Warning We the undersigned, senior members of the world's scientific community, hereby warn all humanity of what lies ahead. A great change in our stewardship of the earth and the life on it is required, if vast human misery is to be avoided and our global home on this planet is not to be irretrievably mutilated.

What We Must Do Five inextricably linked areas must be addressed simultaneously:

1. **We must bring environmentally damaging activities under control to restore and protect the integrity of the earth's systems we depend on.** We must, for example, move away from fossil fuels to more benign, inexhaustible energy sources to cut greenhouse gas emissions and the pollution of our air and water. Priority must be given to the development of energy sources matched to Third World needs—small-scale and relatively easy to implement.

   We must halt deforestation, injury to and loss of agricultural land, and the loss of terrestrial and marine plant and animal species.

2. **We must manage resources crucial to human welfare more effectively.** We must give high priority to efficient use of energy, water, and other

materials, including expansion of conservation and recycling.

3. **We must stabilize population. This will be possible only if all nations recognize that it requires improved social and economic conditions, and the adoption of effective, voluntary family planning.**

4. **We must reduce and eventually eliminate poverty.**

5. **We must ensure sexual equality, and guarantee women control over their own reproductive decisions.**

The developed nations are the largest polluters in the world today. They must greatly reduce their overconsumption, if we are to reduce pressures on resources and the global environment. The developed nations have the obligation to provide aid and support to developing nations, because only the developed nations have the financial resources and the technical skills for these tasks.

Acting on this recognition is not altruism, but enlightened self-interest: whether industrialized or not, we all have but one lifeboat. No nation can escape from injury when global biological systems are damaged. No nation can escape from conflicts over increasingly scarce resources. In addition, environmental and economic instabilities will cause mass migrations with incalculable consequences for developed and underdeveloped nations alike.

Developing nations must realize that environmental damage is one of the gravest threats they face, and that attempts to blunt it will be overwhelmed if their populations go unchecked. The greatest peril is to become trapped in spirals of environmental decline, poverty, and unrest, leading to social, economic, and environmental collapse.

Success in this global endeavour will require a great reduction in violence and war. Resources now devoted to the preparation and conduct of war—amounting to over $1 trillion annually—will be badly needed in the new tasks and should be diverted to the new challenges.

A new ethic is required—a new attitude toward discharging our responsibility for caring for ourselves and for the Earth. We must recognize the Earth's limited capacity to provide for us. We must recognize its fragility. We must no longer allow it to be ravaged. This ethic must motivate a great movement, convincing reluctant leaders and reluctant governments and reluctant peoples themselves to effect the needed changes.

The scientists issuing this warning hope that our message will reach and affect people everywhere. We need the help of many.

We require the help of the world community of scientists—natural, social, economic, political;

We require the help of the world's business and industrial leaders;

We require the help of the world's religious leaders; and

We require the help of the world's peoples.

We call on all to join us in this task.

SOURCE: *World Scientists' Warning to Humanity,* The Union of Concerned Scientists, 1993, Cambridge, MA: Author. Reprinted with permission.

In addition to these scientists, many individuals are aware that achieving the future we desire for human society, as well as the plant and animal kingdoms, means we must improve our knowledge of the ecosphere. Better understanding through science and social science research will enable all of us to cooperatively, and more effectively, plan and manage environmental resources. However, as the Union of Concerned Scientists has determined (with respect to the United States' government agencies), the integrity of scientific research can be compromised through political interference. Political interference means that scientific research can be

manipulated, suppressed, and/or distorted, and that the best available information may not inform policy decisions relating to the protection of our environment. Since 2004, nearly 15 000 scientists have signed the Union of Concerned Scientists' call to action to end political interference; they succeeded in having landmark scientific integrity legislation introduced into the senior levels of their political system. Vigilance on the part of scientists and citizens in Canada will help avoid this problem and help ensure the continued contributions of science and social science research to sound environmental policy decisions.

LINKAGES: HUMANS AS PART OF ECOSYSTEMS

Although our intellectual characteristics distinguish us from other species, humans play essentially the same role as any other species within ecosystems. That is, humans rely—as do other species—on clean air, water, soil, and a continuing supply of plant and animal products, some of which they consume and convert to meet their own physiological needs. The wastes humans discharge become part of the Earth's cycles of decay and renewal (see Chapter 3).

Humans, however, are unlike other species in that we have the ability to cause drastic changes in the ecosystems on which we depend. Our technologies enable us not only to extract and use resources and ecosystem products faster than the **biosphere** can renew them, but also to discharge wastes from our production processes faster than the ecosphere can assimilate them. Such actions cause a decline in the natural productivity of ecosystems that may be permanent and irreversible. If this happens, we are said to be living off the **natural capital** (see Box 1–1) of our environment rather than the interest. This is a significant reason for learning to sustain environmental resources so that they will be available in the future.

Unlike other species, humans have been successful in minimizing or overcoming factors such as extreme climates, other predators, and diseases that formerly limited our numbers. These successes have contributed to an expanding world population that continues to put increasing pressure on Earth's natural resources, life-support, and socioeconomic systems. It is important to recognize that humans are an integral and interdependent part of Earth's ecosystems and are subject to the same constraints as other living creatures. The way we lead our lives has a significant impact on the environment we share with them.

Consider how quickly our lives would end without the plants and animals that supply the products we consume every day—the oxygen we breathe, the food we eat, the timber for our houses, our cotton and linen clothing, the fibres in the pages of this book, our shoe leather, and the wool of our sweaters and socks, to name a few (Figure 1–1). People have always used the environment's resources to provide food, clothing, shelter, and other commodities. Often, we measured our progress by our success in exploiting these resources—fish, animals, land, water, and trees—but without realizing that all of these things were interconnected. The use of one environmental resource always affects the status of another resource or ecosystem, either immediately or in the longer term.

As our understanding of how the Earth works as a system continues to improve, people are realizing how they are a part of the ecosystem and are beginning to appreciate the importance of caring for the entirety of their ecosystem, their Earth home. Some people are also realizing how much knowledge is needed to understand the effects of our ongoing activities, so that we can determine which activities are sustainable (that is, which

Figure 1–1

Human–environment connections: An anthropocentric view of planet Earth's provision for human life and activities

Humans can be viewed as being part of three integrated systems or worlds:

- Natural systems
- Biological systems
- Sociocultural systems

Human production, consumption, and waste processes have a variety of direct and indirect effects on Earth's systems that induce environmental change.

ones will help maintain environmental resources so they continue to provide benefits for people and other living things).

Today, even though many people remain ignorant or unconcerned about environmental matters, many others have accepted the environment as one of humanity's major social and political issues. With the help of technology, "ordinary" citizens, scientists, businesspersons, and government agencies are trying to find solutions to the problems our activities have created. Part of the task of determining appropriate solutions is to understand that the environmental problems we face are complex, requiring multiple strategies that reinforce one another.

THE COMPLEXITY OF ENVIRONMENTAL PROBLEMS

Natural and social scientists have long debated the complex human–society interactions that give rise to environmental problems. In the late 1960s, the exponential growth in human populations during the 20th century led scientists to suggest that human population growth was the fundamental issue of the environment—environmental damage occurs simply because of the very large number of people now on Earth. The logic of this argument is that exponential rates of population intensify the competition among people as they try to gain their share of the Earth's water, land, food, and other resources. United Nations statistics indicate that about four-fifths of the more than 6 billion people now living on Earth do not have adequate food, housing, and safe drinking water. Each day, almost 110 000 people die from starvation or related illnesses. While most of the severe stress occurs in developing countries, even in industrialized nations such as Canada there are people who do not have enough food to eat and who cannot afford a warm, dry place in which to live.

Yet, the emphasis on human population numbers fails to explain how human activities, political and economic development processes, consumption patterns, and technology have contributed to environmental problems. Our technology has allowed humans to extract and use resources so efficiently that some people have been able to satisfy their ever-increasing wants in addition to their needs. This is particularly true of the affluent population that lives in developed nations (Western Europe, countries of the former Soviet Union, the United States, Australia, Japan, and Canada); composing about 20 percent of the world's population, people in these nations consume nearly 80 percent of the world's resources each year. The remaining 80 percent of the world's population survives on about 20 percent of the planet's ecological output. Overconsumption of this **natural capital** (Box 1–1) by rich North Americans, Europeans, and others not only affects the quality of life of poorer people but also threatens the Earth's productive capacity (Wackernagel & Rees, 1996).

Canadians are among the world's most profligate consumers. Although there are significant differences among people of different socioeconomic status, the average Canadian still typically consumes three to five times more resources each year than the average person on a global basis (see Table 1–1). In the next two to three decades, as developing nations strive to attain standards of living closer to those of Canada and other industrialized nations, resource use and associated impacts are expected to rise sharply, significantly increasing the risk to Earth's ecological assets and biophysical systems.

The effects of political-economic processes, technology, and consumption also are seen in the way in which

BOX 1-1
WHAT IS NATURAL CAPITAL?

Three forms of capital—*produced, human,* and *natural* capital—are essential for our economic system to operate effectively. *Produced capital* (sometimes called built capital) refers to the machinery, equipment, infrastructure, investment financing, and other items that are used to produce goods and services for businesses and consumers. *Human capital* refers to the human resources, talents, and skills that are applied productively to advance the economy and improve society. *Natural capital,* a different term for natural resources, not only includes water, minerals, timber, and oil and gas that are used to produce manufactured goods, but also the soil and clean air and water that secure our quality of life and support economic activities such as agriculture, forestry, tourism, and recreation. Natural capital also includes living ecosystems such as grasslands, wetlands, forests, and oceans, elements of our environment that provide important ecosystem services, including clean water and air, fertile soils, flood control, and climatic stability. Humans can cause the deterioration of natural capital—if we permit excessive growth and waste, if we extract too much of a particular resource, or if we modify our landscapes too greatly, for instance. Economic well-being and quality of life depend on natural capital; in turn, our management of natural capital must be undertaken with long-term interests (i.e., sustainability) in mind.

TABLE 1-1
AVERAGE CONSUMPTION OF SELECTED RESOURCES IN SELECTED COUNTRIES

Annual Consumption per Person	Canada	USA	Sweden	Japan	Cuba	India	World
Domestic water use (m³/yr) [1]	271 (1996)	203 (2000)	109 (2002)	136 (2000)	138 (2000)	47 (2000)	n/a
Carbon dioxide emissions (metric tonnes), 1998	15.3	19.9	5.5	9.0	2.3	1.1	4.1
Paper (kilograms/yr), 2000	263	331	280	250	8	4	53
Meat (kilograms/yr), 1998	99	122	71	42	24	4	38
Motor gasoline (litres), 2000	1221	1697	600	449	45	9	179
Coffee (kilograms), 2001	n/a	4	9	3	1	0	n/a

[1] Obtaining comparable data for this statistic is very difficult. We selected the data from the same report so the methods of analysis would be comparable, although the years of their sources vary and are included here in parentheses. Domestic uses include household, municipal, commercial, and government uses. This excludes industrial use, which for countries like Canada and the United States, increases use levels several-fold. The results should be used with caution and are for illustrative purposes only.

SOURCES: Adapted from *Freshwater Withdrawal by Country and Sector,* Worldwater.org, Pacific Institute, 2007, http://www.worldwater.org/data20062007/Table%202.pdf; and *EarthTrends 2003: Country Profiles,* World Resources Institute, 2007, Washington, DC: Author, http://earthtrends.wri.org

pollutants have entered our ecosystems. Media coverage of dramatic events such as the 1984 release of methyl isocyanate from Union Carbide's pesticide production facility in Bhopal, India; the 1986 Chernobyl nuclear plant disaster in the Soviet Union; the 1989 Exxon *Valdez* oil spill in Prince William Sound, Alaska; the 1991 oil slick in the Persian Gulf; the 1995 tailings dam break at the Omai gold mine in Guyana; the 2000 *Esmeralda* cyanide mining spill into the Danube River; the 2001 oil spill from the tanker *Jessica* off the Galápagos Islands; and the sinking of the *Prestige* off the coast of Spain in 2002 has promoted international awareness of pollution problems.

Far more insidious, perhaps, are the less dramatic but longer-term releases of toxic chemicals, sewage, carcinogens, hormone residues, pesticides, nuclear contaminants, and other harmful substances into our atmosphere, rivers, oceans, and soils. These sorts of industrial and municipal pollution problems have resulted in dead fish on stream banks, vanishing species, recreational beach closures, restrictions on shellfish consumption, dying lakes and forests, birth defects, and other debilitating or fatal conditions such as organ and nerve damage, and lung and bone marrow cancers. Through emissions, spills, dumps, and discharges of waste products, humans affect not only the health of other components of ecosystems, but also their own long-term health and well-being.

Pollutants—substances that adversely affect the physical, chemical, or biological quality of the Earth's environment or that accumulate in the cells or tissues of living organisms in amounts that threaten the health or survival of these organisms—may originate from natural or human (anthropogenic) sources. Volcanoes, fires ignited by lightning, decomposition of swamp materials, and other natural processes contribute to pollution of Earth's air, water, and soil. But as human populations have grown, technological capabilities advanced, and consumption of resources and consumer goods increased, large numbers and volumes of anthropogenic pollutants—including substances not previously found in nature—have been released into the environment. It has become increasingly difficult for the environment to absorb and process these substances.

Many pollution problems are global in scope: increases in greenhouse gases, a decline in stratospheric ozone, and acidification of soils, forests, and lakes are among the most prominent of current global pollution issues. International cooperative action, including overcoming political inertia and socioeconomic barriers that hamper progress, is required to solve these global pollution problems. Other pollution issues occur on regional scales (such as industrial pollution in Eastern Europe) and local scales (such as air pollution in Mexico City) and also require cooperative efforts to resolve.

Many of these problems are intensified in urban areas, where 50 percent of the world's population and 80 percent of Canada's population live. People living in cities and towns have dramatic effects on ecosystems by paving over farmland and natural areas, altering drainage patterns, endangering wildlife, and so on. Urban areas have not been studied intensely from an environmental quality perspective, but they experience air and water pollution, waste-disposal problems, social unrest, and other environmental stresses. Increasingly, the liveability of cities and quality of life for urban residents, the balance we strike between economic development and urbanization, and efforts we

Photo 1–10a

Photo 1–10b
Historically, humans have discharged their wastes without due regard for the long-term and cumulative impacts on the environment. Our challenge for the future is to change our attitudes and work toward sustainability as a primary goal.

make to maintain our physical health and well-being, will be important focuses in future sustainable environments.

Expanded scientific knowledge is necessary to address contemporary environmental problems and to move toward future sustainable environments. As subsequent chapters describe, there are many gaps in our understanding of the natural environment—from basic understanding of how ecosystems function to clear and concise ways to assess measurements of and interpret ecosystem change. But we

Photo 1–11
Even in Canada, where population pressures are less intense than in other areas, urban growth and development continue to encroach on limited agricultural land and natural habitats.

need more than facts and scientific understanding regarding a particular issue. While scientific knowledge is an integral part of environmental decision making, so too are our value systems, ethical concerns, and moral commitments to fellow human beings as well as to other living things, both for today and for future generations. Achieving sustainability will require an understanding of how many people depend on our ecosystems; the ways they use those ecosystems; the political and economic systems of production, trade, and development; and, ultimately, the values that people hold toward one another and other living systems. Several kinds of questions emerge for consideration: for example, What kind of life do we want for ourselves and our descendants? What kind of environment do we want for them? For people in developing nations? For our neighbours living in inner cities? If we know what our values are and which potential solutions are socially just, we should be able to apply our scientific knowledge and determine an acceptable, sustainable solution for each specific issue.

Before pursuing a discussion of sustainability, a description of what constitutes a resource illustrates how humans, particularly in Western industrialized nations, have viewed the dynamic between humans and their environment.

CLASSIFYING AND DEFINING NATURAL RESOURCES

The notion that environmental problems arise from a complex mix of human–environment interactions is given greater force when we consider our definition of resources. Resources typically are classified as renewable or nonrenewable resources (see Table 1–2). Technically, all resources are renewable, although over very different

TABLE 1-2
CLASSIFICATION OF RESOURCES

Resources	Nonrenewable	Nonrenewable	Nonrenewable	Renewable	Renewable
Characteristics	Consumed by use	Theoretically recoverable	Recyclable	Critical zone	Noncritical zone
Examples	Oil, gas, coal	All nonmetallic elemental minerals (e.g., potash)	All metallic minerals (e.g., copper)	Fish, timber, animals, soil, water in aquifers	Solar energy, tides, wind, waves, water, air

SOURCE: Adapted from *Natural Resources: Allocation, Economics and Policy,* 2nd Edition, Judith Rees, 1995, Routledge. Figure 2.1, page 15. Used with permission of the publisher.

time periods. **Renewable resources** (also known as renewable **natural capital**) such as forests, solar energy, and livestock are replaced by environmental processes in a time frame that is meaningful to humans. Provided they are not used more quickly than they are restored, these resources will continue to supply goods and services that meet human needs into the future. **Nonrenewable resources** are finite in supply or are replaced so slowly (in human terms) by the environment that, practically speaking, their supply is finite. Another important characteristic of nonrenewable natural capital, such as coal, oil, and other fossil fuels, is that their supply is depleted with use or transformed into a form that can no longer be captured for human consumption (e.g., from liquid to gas). Ironically, our practices often have resulted in unsustainable levels of use of renewable resources. In some cases, these practices have so decimated local populations (e.g., Atlantic cod), that the ability of these species to renew themselves has been seriously undermined or even destroyed, placing renewable resources at great risk of depletion. Because there are no ready substitutes for many renewable resources (e.g., clean water), their depletion may be more serious than depletion of nonrenewable resources for which substitutes can be found more readily (e.g., fossil fuels).

DEFINING NATURAL RESOURCES

But what exactly do we mean by natural resources? A simple definition is that **natural resources** are components of nature that are useful to us and are available at a price we are willing to pay. Whether a component of nature is made into a resource depends on how society is organized, institutional and legal arrangements, cultural norms, technological know-how, and whether there is sufficient demand for the materials and services produced from the resource. This process of transformation is a societal one, as illustrated in Figure 1–2. Unless these characteristics combine to create a practical demand for

the resource, physical substances in the environment remain, in the words of Erich Zimmerman (1951), "neutral stuff."

In short, our human abilities and demands create resource value, not the mere physical presence of environmental elements. This emphasis on humans' interpretations of their environment has interesting implications. In the words of Zimmerman (1951, p. 15), "resources are not, they become; they are not static but expand and contract in response to human wants and needs". Figure 1–2 illustrates that the transformation of nature into resources or waste products is based on society and culture. Because society and culture are human characteristics, some have suggested that "even though the total physical endowment of the earth is essentially fixed, resources are dynamic with no known or fixed limits" (Rees, 1990, p. 11). The idea that resources are dynamic is borne out by a realization that some elements of nature have only recently become resources, while others were

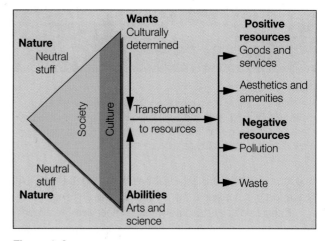

Figure 1–2
A Functional Interpretation of Resources

SOURCE: Adapted from Zimmermann, E (1951) *World Resources and Industries: A Functional Appraisal of the Availability of Agricultural and Industrial.* New York: Harper.

once considered resources and have since declined in use. For example, oil and natural gas, upon which the Canadian economy depends, is mainly a product of the 20th century. Cultural taboos in Hindu culture against the eating of beef preclude the use of cattle as a food source throughout much of India.

Such interpretations of natural resources are considered functional and anthropocentric. That is, resources are defined by their function or utility to humans. While this anthropocentric interpretation predominates, it sustains three key criticisms. Firstly, while our interpretation of the natural environment expands and contracts over time and across space, only finite amounts of certain elements exist in nature. Furthermore, for some elements there are no substitutes. For example, we cannot find substitutes for clean water and air. Overconsumption will reduce the availability of resources over time and also will reduce the options of future generations to achieve sustainability. We have been more successful in finding substitutes for some nonrenewable resources (minerals and fuels) than we have for renewable resources.

Secondly, this interpretation focuses solely on the value humans attribute to nature. Nature provides several ecological services, such as productive functions (for food and fibre used by other species), carrier functions (provision of habitat or water), buffering functions (ability to cleanse pollutants, to absorb or neutralize toxins), and information functions (capacity to pass along genetic information, to educate and provide experience). While these services also may be useful to humans, only recently have we considered how (such as through carbon credits) such functions may be given economic value and even exchanged in the marketplace (see Chapter 11). Consequently, resources that provide these services historically have been degraded because there has not been an economic incentive to conserve or protect their quality.

Finally, all of this discussion has emphasized nature's utility. Spirituality that may be associated with nature is not considered. Furthermore, nature's **intrinsic value** or inherent worth is not considered in these definitions (see Chapters 2 and 12). Understanding how resources are defined and classified can help us understand how we can use the environment more sustainably.

CONCEPTUALIZING SUSTAINABILITY

Sustainability is a major challenge related to the future of our lives and of the planet. As a concept, environmental **sustainability** refers to the ability of an ecosystem to maintain ecological processes and functions, **biodiversity**, and productivity over time (Kaufmann et al., 1994). Sustainability also has economic, political, social, and cultural components. In practice, the meaning of sustainability has varied, but there is agreement that people must learn how to sustain environmental resources so that they continue to provide benefits to us, to other living things, and to the larger environment of which we are a part. Sustainability is related to, but is not the same as, sustainable development.

The concept of **sustainable development** entered the public domain with the 1980 publication of the World Conservation Strategy (International Union for the Conservation of Nature and Natural Resources [IUCN], United Nations Environment Programme [UNEP], & World Wildlife Fund [WWF], 1980). The World Conservation Strategy (WCS) aimed to achieve sustainable development through the conservation of living resources. Living resource conservation had three main objectives: (1) maintaining essential ecological processes and life-support systems, (2) preserving genetic diversity, and (3) ensuring the sustainable use of species and ecosystems.

The WCS promoted integration of conservation and development to ensure that "modifications to the planet do indeed secure the survival and wellbeing of all people" and "to meet the needs of today without foreclosing the achievement of tomorrow's [needs]" (IUCN et al., 1980, p. 1). To be sustainable, the WCS declared, development must be sensitive to short- and long-term alternatives; take social, economic, and ecological factors into account; and include living and nonliving resources.

The publication of *Our Common Future* (World Commission on Environment and Development, 1987), also known as the Brundtland Report, propelled the concept of sustainable development into widespread usage as a global objective. The definition most cited from this report is "development that meets the needs of the present generation without compromising the ability of future generations to meet their own needs" (World Commission on Environment and Development, 1987, p. 43). Generally, most definitions of this concept mention the need for people to live equitably within the means of the ecosphere. Unfortunately, in popular usage the term *sustainable development* sometimes is misused or misunderstood because the two words contained in the term mean different things to different people. Some people tune in to the *sustainable* part of the term and understand that sustainable development calls for ecological and social transformation to a world of environmental stability and social justice. Other people identify more with the *development* part of the term and interpret it to mean more growth, or more sensitive growth, or a reformed version of the status quo.

The trouble with the term *sustainable development* is its failure to distinguish clearly between mere growth and true development. Growth generally means increasing in size, while development means improving quality or getting better. If we apply this understanding to the term, sustainable development means progressive

Photos 1–12a, b
The 1992 Earth Summit illustrates that, despite the appearance of cooperation among international leaders, political inertia often can be overcome only by the actions of individuals and nongovernmental organizations.

social betterment without growing beyond the ecological carrying capacity. Put another way, sustainable development means improving the quality of life while remaining within the carrying capacity of supporting ecosystems (World Conservation Union et al., 1991).

Some people use the broad term *sustainability*. Sustainability echoes the need to balance environmental and developmental concerns, to take an ecological approach to decisions, and to stay within carrying capacity. Sustainability also suggests that excessive material and energy consumption by people in wealthy societies compromises the opportunities for consumption by others. Not everyone accepts the implications of such a concept, namely that levels of consumption in wealthy nations must decrease so that people in poorer nations may consume more in order to improve their quality of life. And, if the world is already at the limit of its carrying capacity, providing adequately and fairly for everyone will be a considerable challenge.

Efforts to achieve sustainability may well affect the economic choices we make. Even though our economies are rooted in the ecosphere, and our lives depend on the maintenance of ecological life support, as citizens of wealthy nations we may find it difficult to acknowledge that if we over-consume today we will have less natural capital and lower natural income tomorrow. In 2003, for example, the World Wildlife Fund estimated that humanity's consumption of the global capacity of the biosphere (to provide the resources we use and to absorb our waste) exceeded supply by about 25 percent (World Wildlife Fund International, Zoological Society of London, & Global Footprint Network, 2006). This consumption is not evenly distributed, as "between 1992 and 2003 … the average per person [consumption level] increased by 18 percent" while "the average per person [consumption level] in low- and middle-income countries changed little" (World Wildlife Fund et al., 2006, p. 18) . We also may find it difficult to acknowledge that "every decision resulting in

the appropriation of more resources by those who already consume more than their fair share is a conscious choice against ecological, social and economic sustainability" (Wackernagel & Rees, 1996, p. 156). This imbalance in consumption is sometimes discussed under the topic of *environmental justice*. Environmental justice may be defined as the right to a safe, healthy, productive and sustainable environment for all, in which "environment" is viewed in its totality and includes ecological (biological), physical (natural and built), social, political, aesthetic, and economic components (Draper & Mitchell, 2001). The distribution of costs and benefits of resources and the environment form part of the concerns of environmental justice.

As people work toward a sustainable future, one important mechanism to help them achieve their goals is increased cooperation and collaborative effort among individuals, organizations, government agencies, and nation-states. A good example of cooperative global action toward sustainability was the development and subsequent adoption of treaties dealing with climate change and biological diversity, as well as Agenda 21 and the Earth Charter, at the 1992 Rio de Janeiro Earth Summit. National representatives attending the Earth Summit (officially, the second United Nations Conference on Environment and Development [UNCED]) discussed and debated a number of international environmental problems, including deterioration of the Earth's atmosphere and oceans from pollution, forest destruction, and loss of biodiversity.

Negotiations on these topics, treaties, and agreements began years before the Earth Summit was held. Agenda 21, for example, is a complex document outlining actions and programs to support sustainable development for the 21st century. Although developed nations did not commit nearly enough financial assistance to help developing countries industrialize without harming the environment, Agenda 21 itself was developed through the collective action and shared responsibility of both developed and developing nations. For a brief overview of Agenda 21, see the summary description in Box 1–2.

Attended by more than 100 heads of state, including Canada's prime minister, the Earth Summit was the largest international gathering ever to concentrate on serious environmental issues. Because the Earth Summit and the Global Forum (a parallel citizens' conference held in conjunction with the United Nations meeting) received so much international attention, they not only increased worldwide awareness of global issues, but also became the most visible expression of international awareness of sustainability ever seen. Progress (or lack of it) in achieving the objectives established at the 1992 Earth Summit was considered at the Earth Summit +5 sessions held in New York in 1997 and in the World Summit on Sustainable Development in Johannesburg, South Africa, in 2002 (see Table 1–3). In 2007, the United Nations also hosted a global conference on climate change in Bali, Indonesia, to review progress and maintain international attention on this important issue (see Chapter 5).

Canada has been involved in international efforts to define and refine the concept of sustainability and in domestic efforts to promote the concept. Table 1–3 identifies some of the major milestones in international growth of the sustainability concept, as well as selected Canadian efforts to support sustainability.

GUIDING PRINCIPLES OF SUSTAINABILITY

Development activities that increase the capacity of the environment to meet human needs, that improve the quality of human life, and that protect and maintain life-support systems are appropriate points from which to progress toward sustainability in Canada. Progressive improvement in human and environmental affairs should lead to (1) people who are healthy, well nourished, adequately clothed and housed, employed in productive work, and able to enjoy leisure and recreational pursuits; and (2) biologically diverse environments that are fully functional from an ecological perspective and that can be monitored for sustainability. These and other desired benefits, however, must be maintained indefinitely to be considered sustainable.

Efforts to achieve sustainability likely will entail a complex mixture of activities incorporating various social, economic, and environmental objectives; the exploitation of Earth's natural capital assets; and the intellectual resources to help people reach their full potential and enjoy a reasonable standard of living. Efforts by the Canadian federal government to establish sustainability strategies are discussed briefly in Box 1–3 on page 19.

One of the major principles of sustainable action, found in the initial WCS and reiterated in *Our Common Future* and Agenda 21 of the Earth Summit, involves ethical issues

---

BOX 1–2
AGENDA 21: A BRIEF OVERVIEW

Agenda 21 is a plan of action for the world's governments and citizens. It sets forth strategies and measures aimed at halting and reversing the effects of environmental degradation and promoting environmentally sound and sustainable development throughout the world. The Agenda contains 40 chapters and totals more than 800 pages. In the words of UNCED's Secretary General Maurice Strong, "It is the product of intensive negotiations among Governments on the basis of proposals prepared by the UNCED Secretariat, drawing on extensive inputs from relevant United Nations agencies and organizations, expert consultations, intergovernmental and nongovernmental organizations, regional conferences and national reports, and the direction provided through four sessions of the Preparatory Committee of the Conference." Agenda 21 is based on the premise that sustainable development is not just an option but an imperative, in both environmental and economic terms. While the transition toward sustainable development will be difficult, it is feasible.

UNCED has grouped Agenda 21's priority actions under seven social themes:

1. The Prospering World (revitalizing growth with sustainability)
2. The Just World (sustainable living)
3. The Habitable World (human settlements)
4. The Fertile World (global and regional resources)
5. The Shared World (global and regional resources)
6. The Clean World (managing chemicals and waste)
7. The People's World (people participation and responsibility)

For an overview of Agenda 21 and summaries of these themes, refer to UNCED's publication *The Global Partnership for Environment and Development: A Guide to Agenda 21*. Canada's International Development Research Centre also has published *IDRC, An Agenda 21 Organization: A Backgrounder on Current Activities*. In implementing Agenda 21, IDRC focuses on capacity building, that is, helping local communities in developing nations to enhance their environmental knowledge, decisions, and policies.

SOURCE: *Agenda 21: Green Paths to the Future*, International Research Development Centre, 1993, Ottawa: IRDC. Reprinted with permission.

TABLE 1-3

MAJOR MILESTONES: SUSTAINABLE DEVELOPMENT AND SUSTAINABILITY

Year(s)	Document or Process	Agency
1980	World Conservation Strategy	International Union for the Conservation of Nature and Natural Resources, United Nations Environment Programme, and World Wildlife Fund
1987	*Our Common Future* (the Brundtland Report) • Sustainable development gained international prominence as a global objective. • In 1985, the Brundtland Commission held hearings in Canada.	World Commission on Environment and Development
1989	Preparatory discussions began for the United Nations Conference on Environment and Development (UNCED).	United Nations
1989, 1990	Roundtables on the environment and the economy • National, provincial, and territorial roundtables established in response to Brundtland Report; cross-sectoral issues discussed.	National, provincial, and territorial governments in Canada
1991	*Caring for the Earth* • A more broadly based version of the first WCS. • In 1986, Canada supported the IUCN Conference on Conservation and Development that evaluated the WCS and led to publication of *Caring for the Earth*.	World Conservation Union (IUCN)
1992	Earth Summit (UNCED) in Rio de Janeiro. Treaties and agreements signed included *Climate Change*: to curb CO_2 emissions and reduce greenhouse effects; *Biological Diversity*: to decrease the rate of extinction of species; *Agenda 21*: an action plan for sustainable development; and *EarthCharter* (the Rio Declaration): a statement of philosophy about environment and development. The Commission on Sustainable Development (CSD) was established to ensure effective follow-up from the Earth Summit.	United Nations
1994	A new Earth Charter Initiative was launched in The Hague to complete the Earth Charter (unfinished business, 1992 Rio Earth Summit).	Maurice Strong, secretary general of the Earth Summit and chairman of the Earth Council, and Mikhail Gorbachev, president of Green Cross International, with support from the Dutch government
1997	Earth Charter Commission was established to oversee completion of the Earth Charter	Earth Charter Secretariat was established at the Earth Council, Costa Rica
2000	Final version of the Earth Charter released, providing fundamental principles for building a just, sustainable, and peaceful global society • Individuals and organizations from all regions of the world helped draft this document. • The Earth Charter circulated globally, promoting awareness and commitment to sustainable ways of life.	Earth Charter Commission
2002	World Summit on Sustainable Development established three key documents, including the Johannesburg Declaration on Sustainable Development affirming the importance of this concept to the world community, an implementation plan outlining actions and priorities, and a statement of partnerships for sustainable development that provided commitments to coalitions among private, civil, and public-sector organizations.	United Nations

TABLE 1–3
(CONTINUED)

Year(s)	Document or Process	Agency
2003	The Commission on Sustainable Development (CSD) set out its work plan (2003–17) with two seven-year cycles focusing on thematic clusters of issues, including energy, climate change, agriculture, transport, waste management, mining, forests, and oceans. In 2016–17, there will be an overall appraisal of implementation of Agenda 21 and the Johannesburg Plan of Implementation.	United Nations
2007	United Nations Conference on Climate Change was held in Bali, Indonesia, and culminated in adoption of the Bali Roadmap, which focuses on enabling the international community to fight climate change successfully.	United Nations

SOURCES: Adapted from *The State of Canada's Environment—1996,* Government of Canada, 1996, Ottawa: Supply and Services Canada; "Higher Education and the Earth Charter Initiative," Association of University Leaders for a Sustainable Future, 2000, *The Declaration, 4*(1), pp. 1, 16–20; and *Canada at the World Summit on Sustainable Development,* Government of Canada, 2002, www.canada2002earthsummit.gc.ca; *Multiyear Programme of Work for CSD: 2004/2005 to 2017–2017,* United Nations, 2008, http://www.un.org.esa/sustdev/csd/csd11/CSD_multiyear_prog_work.htm; *The United Nations Climate Change Conference in Bali,* United Nations, 2007, http://unfccc.int/meetings/cop_13/items/4049.php

BOX 1–3
SUSTAINABILITY AND THE CANADIAN FEDERAL GOVERNMENT

In late 1990, the Canadian government announced a $3 billion, five-year environmental action plan called the Green Plan. The initial focus of the Green Plan was to design a planning process for ecological resources that would change the way the government made its decisions. The initiative was unsuccessful, and the Green Plan was gradually abandoned after 1993.

However, in 1995, the concept of sustainable development was integrated into federal legislation and into amendments to the Auditor General Act that (1) created the position of the Commissioner of the Environment and Sustainable Development, and (2) required federal government departments to table Sustainable Development Strategies (SDSs) in Parliament and to update them every three years. The 1995 *Guide to Green Government* provided the framework that assisted federal departments in developing their SDSs and the action plans to achieve their sustainable development objectives. The goal of SDSs was to make environmental protection and sustainable development an integral part of federal government departments and agencies, and to develop action plans that would serve as benchmarks for measuring progress toward sustainable development. Environment Canada played a coordinating role in this initiative, and the first SDS was tabled in 1997.

The *Guide to Green Government* identified the following sustainable development objectives:

- Sustaining our natural resources—sustainable jobs, communities, and industries
- Protecting the health of Canadians and of ecosystems

- Meeting our international obligations
- Promoting equity
- Improving our quality of life and well-being

In April 2005, the Office of Greening Government Operations (OGGO) was created within Public Works and Government Services Canada (PWGSC). The purpose of OGGO was to implement and accelerate a government-wide approach to the greening of government activities and operations. In working closely with 35 other federal departments, including Environment Canada, a wide range of areas were targeted:

- Energy efficiency
- Reduction of greenhouse gas and other air-polluting emissions
- Green procurement
- Remediation of contaminated sites
- Waste management strategies
- Environmental performance of the vehicle fleet

The 2007 annual report from the Commissioner of the Environment and Sustainable Development (see http://www.oag-bvg.gc.ca/internet/English/aud_parl_cesd_2007_e_26831.html) called the SDSs a major disappointment and criticized the federal government for failing to conduct a thorough review of its SDSs since they were introduced in 1995. The commissioner indicated that there was no sustainable development strategy for the federal government as a whole, and that the lack of

(continued)

BOX 1-3
(CONTINUED)

continuity in the federal goals from one set of strategies to the next made it difficult to understand what long-term outcomes the government wanted to achieve. Key weaknesses in the guidance given to departments included the lack of clearly defined standardized monitoring and reporting functions, and the lack of baselines or targets.

The commissioner requested that Environment Canada conduct a thorough review of the government's approach and, in the course of the review, identify specific federal goals, performance expectations, indicators, and targets. Environment Canada was asked to identify how department and agency SDSs contribute to the overall federal sustainability goals, and to ensure that opportunities are acted on. Environment Canada agreed to complete its review by October 2008. Watch for the commissioner's response to this review!

SOURCES: *A guide to green government: Fact Sheet*, Environment Canada, n.d. http://www.ec.gc.ca; *Sustainable Development Strategy 2001–2003*, Environment Canada, 2002, http://www.ec.gc.ca/sd-dd_consult/index_e.cfm; and *Office of Greening Government Operations (OGGO)*, Public Works and Government Services Canada, 2008, http://www.pwgsc.gc.ca/greening/text/index-e.html

such as equity and respect for the rights and welfare of other people (Box 1–4). Other major principles are those of ecological sustainability, social sustainability, and economic sustainability (Table 1–4), as well as the precautionary principle. These principles are discussed briefly below.

Ecological Sustainability

Ecosystems are the source of all life's vital requirements—water to drink, air to breathe, sun for warmth, soils for plant growth—and are the structures within which these life-supporting processes occur (see Chapter 3). If an ecosystem is damaged (for instance, if soils cannot regenerate, or if carbon, oxygen, and other elements cannot circulate), its ability to sustain the life of people, plants, and animals may be reduced or destroyed. Since people depend on Earth's ecosystems, we need to learn how ecosystems support us and how environmental change affects them. Furthermore, because "the human economy is a fully dependent sub-system of the ecosphere" (Wackernagel & Rees, 1996, p. 4), it is vital that our developments incorporate the concept of **ecological sustainability**. To that end, we briefly consider the concept of carrying capacity and link this concept to the idea of the ecological footprint.

Carrying Capacity In simplistic terms, **carrying capacity** is the number of organisms that an area can

BOX 1-4
ETHICS AND THE ENVIRONMENT

The environment is something in which all people share a common interest and by which all may be affected. Not surprisingly, ethical concerns lie at the heart of many environmental issues.

Ethics refers to the principles that define a person's duty to other people and, indeed, to other living things with which we share the planet. Such principles are based on respect for the rights and welfare of other people, including those whom we may never meet and those who are as yet unborn. People look to ethics to decide if an action is right or wrong.

Socioeconomic development that affects the environment and even entire ecosystems also has ethical dimensions. Decisions about development are usually based on estimates of the present and future costs and benefits to society. Such assessments take into account the likely environmental, economic, and social effects of the development. To assess options, every effort is made to define effects in measurable terms and to identify who may gain and who may lose. Such a process is an indispensable means of assembling relevant information and can provide an invaluable basis for identifying the ethical dimensions involved.

However, many ethical issues cannot be quantified. It is difficult to fit ethical factors into the conventional framework of environmental decision making in the same way as more tangible factors such as economic and biophysical data. What is necessary, then, is for people to consider the broad implications of any development—its present and future impacts on other people, on other species, and on ecosystems. Access to full and accurate information about the development and about experiences with similar activities will guide people in deciding about the options that are available. Views on ethics are an essential supplement to the hard, measurable data in the decision-making process.

SOURCE: *The State of Canada's Environment—1996*, © Her Majesty the Queen in Right of Canada, Environment Canada, 1996. Box 1.1. Reproduced with permission of the Minister of Public Works and Government Services Canada, 2008. http://www.ec.gc.ca/soer-ree/English/SOER/1996report/Doc/1-5-2-5-4-1.cfm#box1.1

TABLE 1-4
PRINCIPLES OF SUSTAINABILITY

Ecological Sustainability	Social Sustainability	Economic Sustainability
• Conserve life-support systems. • Conserve biological diversity (genes, species, and ecosystems). • Anticipate and prevent adverse environmental impacts. • Practise full-cost accounting (environmental and social costs). • Accept responsibility to protect the global environment. • Respect the intrinsic value of nature.	• Aim for equitable distribution of benefits and costs of resource use and decisions (among nations and generations). • Ensure future generations have environmental assets equal to or greater than previous generation. • Promote a good quality of life (through opportunities for livelihood, education, training, social, cultural, and recreational services, and a quality environment). • Involve the public in land use and related resource and environmental decisions.	• Increase capacity to meet human needs and improve quality of life, while using a constant level of physical resources. • Encourage diversified, efficient resource use. • Ensure renewable resources are used sustainably and nonrenewable resources continue to provide for future generations. • Assimilate wastes from economic activity within ecosystem capacity. • Promote environmentally sound economic activity (through education, political, and legal instruments).

SOURCE: Adapted from *Off Course: Restoring Balance between Canadian Society and the Environment*, D. M. Taylor, 1994, Ottawa: International Development Research Centre. Reprinted with permission.

support indefinitely. An expanded definition, which reflects the importance of all ecosystem components and ecological processes, indicates that carrying capacity is the capability of an ecosystem to support healthy organisms while maintaining its productivity, adaptability, and capability for renewal (World Conservation Union et al., 1991).

The concept of carrying capacity sometimes is used to suggest the number of people who can be supported by the environment over time, or to define what levels of human impact might be sustainable. However, the idea of carrying capacity was developed by population biologists in their study of nonhuman populations, so the concept applies to human populations only by analogy. As a result, and because there is no universally agreed-on equation to calculate the carrying capacity for human populations, we do not know the human carrying capacity of the Earth at this time. Carrying capacity calculations increase in complexity when wealthier places import locally scarce resources (such as water, fertilizers, and fossil fuels) to supplement their natural carrying capacity. The carrying capacity of ecosystems in poorer places is more likely to be defined by their natural limitations.

Despite these difficulties, the carrying capacity concept is useful in debating whether ecosystems define natural limits to growth and whether humans already have exceeded the Earth's carrying capacity. Some observers believe that growth in per capita consumption is the most significant reason that Earth's carrying capacity is shrinking. Mathis Wackernagel and William Rees (1996) coined the phrase "ecological footprint" to describe a measurement of the land area required to sustain a population. They analyzed water and energy use; uses of land for infrastructure, agriculture, energy, and other materials; and waste assimilation, and converted these uses into an estimate of "land-equivalent."

Ecological Footprint Analysis An ecological footprint analysis (see discussion below) by Wackernagel and Rees (1996) showed two conflicting trends: one in which the available ecologically productive land (and water) has decreased and the second, in which our demand on the Earth's resources has grown. Calculations undertaken in 2006 based on 2003 data suggested that existing biological capacity of the Earth, the area of land and water that is biologically productive, is 1.8 hectares per person. This figure does not consider the need to protect land and resources for other species. By contrast, on a global basis, our consumption of biological resources is 2.2 hectares per person (World Wildlife Fund et al., 2006).

As illustrated in Table 1–5, both biologically productive areas and rates of use vary tremendously from country to country. While growth in population is a significant issue in some countries, these data suggest that rates of consumption in high-income countries need to be controlled if sustainability objectives such as greater equity among the world's people and other species are to be achieved. Why do you think Canada, one of the largest per capita consumers of energy, water, and other resources, does not register an ecological deficit? Calculate your own footprint using the guide at the Redefining Progress website (www.redefiningprogress.org).

In contrast to the viewpoint that consumption is the major contributor to the loss of carrying capacity, many people believe that technology and resource substitution provide endless possibilities for procuring the raw materials for continued economic growth. This perspective equates sustainable development with expansion and rapid economic growth in all nations. The assumption is that economic growth will lead to diversification and better distribution of income. In combination, these factors will assist developing countries to mitigate environmental stresses that derive from economic growth. Unfortunately, according to the United Nations, income disparities between countries and within countries widened throughout the 20th century. In countries such as Canada and the United States, these disparities have also increased, particularly since the early 1960s.

Regardless of which perspective people support, there can be little debate about the impacts of human, resource-related, technological, and economic development: widespread environmental degradation, serious depletion of some resources and resource stocks, and loss of many species. Many of these environmental changes are permanent and irreversible, and, since the economy is dependent on the ecosphere (the bottom line of the economy, so to speak), it follows that we may have overshot local and global carrying capacity and that current economic growth patterns may not be sustainable. If we believe that social and economic benefits attained through economic growth (such as increased average life spans, reduced physical work effort, and the multitude of consumer products available) are outweighed by the environmental costs and the danger of living at the ecological edge, then we must conclude that humans are living unsustainably, especially those in material-rich Western societies.

Most Canadians live in cities and towns, where it is easy to forget that human life is very tightly entwined with nature. Urban living tends to break our connections with the ecosystems that provide us with a host of basic materials we need for life—from the air we breathe to the wood we use to build houses and make paper prod-

ucts. Ecosystems also absorb our wastes, protect us from ultraviolet radiation, and provide a wide range of other functions (see Figure 1–3).

A dramatic metaphor for humanity's continuing dependence on nature, an ecological footprint allows people to visualize the impacts of their consumption patterns and activities on ecosystems. The ecological footprint for a particular human population or economy is an estimate of the total area of land and water (ecosystems) needed to produce all the resources consumed and to assimilate all the wastes discharged by that population or economy. Box 1–5 briefly describes the ecological footprint concept using the footprint of the Lower Fraser Valley in British Columbia as an example.

Figure 1–3
Humans and the Ecosphere

BOX 1–5
THE ECOLOGICAL FOOTPRINT CONCEPT

Most of us have looked at our footprints in the sand on a beach, in the dirt of a field, or in new-fallen snow, but how many of us have considered looking at the footprints our communities leave on their surroundings? That's one of the ideas William Rees and Mathis Wackernagel explored through the Task Force on Planning Healthy and Sustainable Communities at the University of British Columbia.

In considering a city's impact, or footprint, on the environment, it is important to consider our reliance on ecosystems as well as on the more obvious buildings, roads, industrial parks, and housing areas that are spread over the landscape. Ecological footprints measure the load that any given community or population imposes on the ecosystems that support it. Footprints are expressed in terms of the land area necessary to sustain current levels of resource consumption and waste discharge by that population. According to Wackernagel and Rees (1996, p. 9), "ecological footprint analysis is an accounting tool that enables us to estimate the resource consumption and waste assimilation requirements of a defined human population or economy in terms of a corresponding productive land area."

Much of the work involved in determining the footprint is aimed at estimating appropriated carrying capacity—the amount of land it would take to produce all the goods and services that are used by people living in a city. It is impossible to take every factor into account, and the calculations are complex, but a rough idea of a city's—or your individual—ecological footprint can be revealing.

In 1996, Wackernagel and Rees estimated the ecological footprint for residents of British Columbia's densely populated

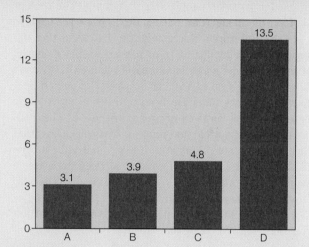

Box Figure 1–2

Comparison of ecological footprints by type of household

A Single parent with child—annual household expenditure $16 000

B Student living alone—annual household expenditure $10 000

C Average Canadian family, 2.72 people—annual household expenditure $37 000

D Professional couple, no children—annual household expenditure $79 000

SOURCE: *Our Ecological Footprint By Mathis Wackernagel and William Rees, New Society Publishers © 1996.* Used with permission.

NOTE: Although the information above is now "outdated," these individual comparisons have not been reproduced. It is important to consider the relative differences among different groups rather than the absolute numbers presented here.

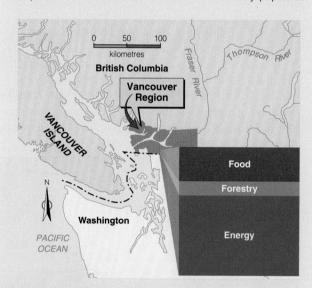

Box Figure 1–1

Lower Mainland/Greater Vancouver area

SOURCE: *Our Ecological Footprint By Mathis Wackernagel and William Rees, New Society Publishers ©1996, illustrated by Philip Testemale.* Used with permission.

Lower Fraser Valley (Vancouver to Hope) and determined that this region depended on a land area 19 times larger than that contained within its boundaries to satisfy consumption levels of food, forest products, energy, and carbon dioxide assimilation. In 1996, they calculated that each individual Canadian required 4.3 hectares of land to support her or his lifestyle. The footprint for an average American was estimated at 5.1 hectares. They concluded that "if everyone lived like today's North Americans, it would take at least two additional planet Earths to produce the resources, absorb the wastes, and otherwise maintain life-support. Unfortunately, good planets are hard to find" (p. 15).

Since Wackernagel and Rees's groundbreaking work, new analyses have illustrated that Canada's ecological footprint has grown even larger (see Table 1–5). Several ecological footprint calculators are now available on the Internet; using a calculator, it is possible to update the absolute numbers and to compare your ecological footprint to that of your parents or other people you know. Try calculating your own ecological footprint by logging on to http://www.myfootprint.org.

SOURCES: *The State of Canada's Environment—1996*, Government of Canada, 1996a, Ottawa: Supply and Services Canada; *1996 Report of Canada to the United Nations Commission on Sustainable Development*, Government of Canada, 1996b, http://www.ec.gc.ca/agenda21/96/part1.html; *Our Ecological Footprint: Reducing Human Impact on the Earth*, M. Wackernagel & W. Rees, 1996, Gabriola Island, BC: New Society.

Calculating an ecological footprint is a complex process, given that world trade in foodstuffs, forest resources, and minerals, as well as the products manufactured from those raw materials, facilitates international interaction between people and ecosystems. The ecological footprint model (discussed in Box 1–5 and in Chapters 4 and 13) interprets this complexity by calculating the resources an individual, city, or nation consumes and by determining how much land area is required to provide those resources on a sustainable basis. How much land does the average Canadian need in order to provide the materials, food, and energy resources he or she consumes? An ecological footprint analysis suggests that our lifestyle is not sustainable. If every individual on the Earth consumed as many resources as does the average Canadian, we would need at least two more planets to provide for everyone (see Figure 1–4).

The concept of an ecological footprint is important in guiding our efforts to achieve sustainability because it helps us understand that our individual actions can and do affect the global environment. While it is true that small communities in the developing world may have smaller ecological footprints (because they rely less on trade and technology) and may live at a level close to the carrying capacity of their local environmental resources, the same cannot be said of small communities in the industrialized

Photo 1–13
The ecological footprint for residents of the Lower Fraser Valley has been estimated at 19 times the land area they occupy.

world. Even in the Canadian North, for instance, just a few decades ago people in small communities lived in harmony with their local environment and extracted quality country food, yet they now purchase many imported foodstuffs and goods from southern Canada. This is partly because of concern about bioaccumulation of toxins in some fish and animal species eaten (see Chapter 3).

Calculating ecological footprints across different places or social groups can direct attention to the relative lack of fairness in the global distribution of resource use. Table 1–5, for example, illustrates that the size of Japan's and Sweden's footprints is about half that of the United States, even though both are highly developed and industrialized nations. Cuba, whose footprint is a fraction of Canada's, rates very highly for its human and social development (see Chapter 4). At a global level, one could debate allocation strategies to ensure that the footprints of nations are coordinated with the carrying capacity of the Earth (also called biocapacity). One might consider assigning allocations of the Earth's biocapacity on current regional use, or on the biocapacity of regions, or on

Figure 1–4
Wanted: more planet Earths
If every person on Earth consumed as much as every Canadian and American, we would need at least two more planets to sustain us.

SOURCE: *Living Planet Report—2006*, World Wildlife Fund International, Zoological Society of London, and Global Footprint Network, http://www. footprintnetwork.org/download.php?id=303

Photo 1–14
Urban infrastructure such as transportation systems contributes to a city's ecological footprint.

a per capita basis. Each way of assigning resources would have different implications for rich and poor nations and the people within them. For example, Canada may be favoured in the first two strategies, but it would assume a much smaller footprint if the last strategy were employed. The ecological footprint approach helps us see the ecological reality of our actions and challenges and directs us toward debating what measures are necessary to live more sustainably (see also Chapter 13).

Ecological sustainability, although vital to our survival, is difficult to measure. Achieving it will raise concerns for social justice. If we are to live within our means, ecological sustainability must be coupled with social sustainability, the subject of the next section.

Social Sustainability

Social constraints on development are just as difficult to measure as ecological limits, and just as important. **Social sustainability** refers to ensuring that basic needs are met, culture is protected, and ways of earning a living are fostered. Social sustainability requires acceptable governance systems that provide a collective sense of well-being and distributional equity in environmental and land use decisions. Social sustainability also promotes good quality of life, by assuring means to obtain education and training; to access social, cultural, and recreational services; and to make decisions in a fair and equitable manner (Robinson et al., 1990; Commission on Resources and Environment [CORE], 1994).

Reflecting the values attached to human health and well-being, social constraints (or social norms) are based on the traditions, religions, and customs of people and their communities. Sometimes these powerful social values are written in law. Often, they are invisible and not put in writing. For example, beliefs about what is considered right or wrong in a community or in relation to the environment may be strongly held, yet they are not given formal legal status. Other social norms may be made more concrete through the passing of policies, programs, and funding arrangements to provide social welfare, language, and education.

Like many other nations, Canada is undergoing rapid social and economic changes. Today's pervasive pressures for change, as well as the multicultural nature of Canada's varied communities, have compounded the difficulties in defining, measuring, and evaluating the changes occurring in social norms and in the limits they entail regarding development. Development activities may be considered socially sustainable if they conform to a community's social norms or do not stretch them beyond the community's tolerance for change. Conversely, socially unsustainable development may be indicated when antisocial behaviour occurs, such as property damage, violence, and other community disruptions.

While most norms will change over time, some social norms are extremely persistent; no matter what development activity is proposed, some people will oppose or resist it. Even though they are not measured easily (if at all), these are the norms or constraints that must be respected in assessing whether social sustainability will be achieved. For instance, in communities where traditional ways of life depend on the natural resource base (minerals, fish, land, and forests), people often are extremely resistant to change. Their strong social norms insist, for example, that the values they place on fish and fishing for a livelihood must be respected, even though outsiders (often developers) do not appreciate these same values. Unless these values are addressed in development decision making, people in such communities will continue to resist change.

Attention to social sustainability means that actions taken to protect environmental resources must consider the effects on local human populations. The lives and livelihoods of indigenous people around the world have been threatened by the pace and scale of industrial expansion. In Canada, the lifestyles and cultural traditions of First Nations, Métis, and Inuit people (collectively called Aboriginal people) frequently have been placed at risk by governments restricting the amount of land to which they have access, degrading the quality of their land and water resources by dumping wastes there, or allowing other parties, such as forestry and mining companies and hydroelectric utilities, to use their lands without consultation. Attention to social sustainability means that these inequalities in the distribution of harmful practices associated with resource exploitation must be addressed.

People who live in rural places who are involved in the extraction and processing of environmental resources also must be considered. They often share similar social histories and cultural norms. For example, efforts to curb logging will affect the livelihood and the well-being of loggers and all who have helped to build forestry communities such as families, community service providers, shopkeepers in forestry towns, professional foresters, and public servants. Environmental decisions affect not only the pocketbooks of these people, but also their identities as rural people. Often these people share common ideas about rural work and life that include living close to nature, doing hard physical work, and being self-reliant and independent. For example, decisions to reduce access to timber for harvesting and to impose job losses in forestry directly challenge the ability of people to live their lives based on these ideas and thereby threaten the very fabric of collective identity. The strength of social norms and their potential to place constraints on development activity means that they must be taken into account in planning for sustainability. The people in affected communities must be part of the process of defining social limits to development and to sustainability (refer to Table 1–4). As many of the examples discussed in later chapters demonstrate, the importance of cooperation and collaboration with groups or communities concerned cannot be underestimated if we are to move toward a sustainable future.

Economic Sustainability

Even though it is as difficult to predict and is affected by as many variables, **economic sustainability** is more easily measured than ecological or social sustainability. This is because economic sustainability requires economic benefits (defined usually in monetary terms) to exceed or at least balance costs.

Economic sustainability reflects the interplay of supply and demand factors. In general, supply-side factors include the availability, cost, and transport of raw materials, as well as the energy, labour, and machinery costs relating to their extraction or processing. Since ecological factors ultimately limit sustainability, economic development must use resources in ways that do not permanently damage the environment and must not impair the replenishment capacity of renewable resources (Government of Canada, 1996). This statement suggests that economic sustainability will be attained only if we use nonrenewable resources sparingly, if we reduce the content of nonrenewable resources in the goods we produce, and if we reduce the energy consumed in their production.

On the demand side, sustainability is threatened because of the increasing rate of human consumption of resources. Nowadays, whether prices are high, because of the heightened value of a scarce resource, or low, because of efficient harvesting technology, stocks continue to be overharvested. If prices stay high, harvesters may maintain pressure on the resource in order to generate maximum profit, and if prices are low while demand is high, overharvesting may reduce stocks to below-recovery levels. Neither high nor low market prices for resources are good indicators of sustainability. Instead of considering only price, it is possible to consider a set of more provocative indicators (e.g., proximity of residents to public transportation) that could be used to track consumption levels more closely and thereby demonstrate how to put values associated with sustainability into action. Some Canadians have been involved in efforts to identify sustainability indicators appropriate for their communities. We consider some of these efforts in more detail in Chapter 13.

Balancing costs and benefits to achieve sustainability is a complex task. In the pollution control field, for example, regulations may require a plant owner to install costly new equipment or to adjust production procedures to meet new emissions standards. Balancing costs and benefits is difficult when, as is frequently the case, unexpected cost savings derive from installation of such new equipment or procedures.

Economic, ecological, and social sustainability are equally important principles. Economic sustainability, however, may receive disproportionate emphasis (in the media, at least) because it is the basis of all forms of income distribution and returns on investment within a society (Government of Canada, 1996). New efforts to document social benefits and costs of environmental change are challenging the supremacy of economic indicators as the sole measures of societal well-being (see the following section).

The Precautionary Principle

Canada and many other nations lack adequate data and records regarding environmental change. Environmental information collected in the past is not always relevant today because it was not directed toward the problems and issues that concern us now, nor was it collected with sustainability objectives in mind. Appreciating that lack of data is currently (and, for some time into the future, likely to continue to be) a serious hindrance to environmental protection and achievement of sustainability, countries attending the 1992 Earth Summit, including Canada, adopted the precautionary principle.

The **precautionary principle** states that when there are threats of serious or irreversible damage to the environment, the "lack of full scientific certainty shall not be used as a reason for postponing cost-effective measures to prevent environmental deterioration" (Government of Canada, 1996). This principle means that, as long as the weight of evidence suggests action is appropriate, a country should take such action to protect its environment. For instance, if action were not already being taken in regard to global climate change, the precautionary principle would provide impetus for such action to commence even though disagreement existed about the specific details regarding climate change.

TOOLS AND STRATEGIES FOR SUSTAINABILITY

It is easy to be caught up in depressing images and imaginings of current and future environmental scenarios. Despite record changes to our environment, we also have enormous capacity to learn from and to address the changes in our environment. In this section, we explore four sets of tools and strategies that we can use to advance sustainability. These strategies involve individuals, organizations, governments, and nation-states. Throughout the textbook, more specific examples are provided of individuals and efforts that are making a positive contribution to sustainability in Canada and beyond.

THE ECOSYSTEM APPROACH

Historically, we have managed the environment by trying to manage one resource at a time. Governments at all levels created separate agencies or departments to manage water, timber, or minerals. This sectoral approach is associated with at least two types of problems. First, we now realize that humans do not really manage the environment; rather, people try to manage human uses and impacts. People are an integral part of ecosystems and the focus needs to be on managing humans rather than on individual sectors of the environment. This realization requires more explicit attention to human values and to ensuring that people most directly affected by environmental management decisions (called stakeholders) would have some say in management decisions and activities. Second, we now understand that human effects on ecosystems are interrelated. For example, managing timber requires an understanding of aquatic and atmospheric systems, and vice versa.

During the late 20th century, attention was placed not only on individual species, but also on the interconnections among them, including connections between humans and other components of nature. This approach, termed the **ecosystem approach**, involves the study and management of living species (including humans) and their physical environment in a holistic way, including component parts and the linkages among them. Frequently, scientists and managers who adopt an ecosystem approach attempt to understand environmental problems within natural boundaries, such as watersheds, rather than within political boundaries, such as municipalities. The ecosystem approach also directs attention to how decisions and actions at one level interact with biological, physical, and social components both locally and at other scales, for present and future generations. Some natural and social scientists also emphasize that such considerations require the establishment of ethical principles as well as scientific criteria to guide decision making.

The ecosystem approach requires a fundamental shift in thinking, reflecting a whole-Earth ethic in which our decisions and actions take into account the interdependencies within and among ecosystems, as well as the connections between biological and physical components of the ecosphere. The ecosystem approach emphasizes restoring and maintaining ecosystem and human health and well-being. For example, we cannot improve management of our fish stocks unless we understand both the aquatic environment in which the fish live and the human activities on land and in water that affect the aquatic environment. Finally, advocates of the ecosystem approach frequently recommend that affected individuals, groups, firms, and agencies become involved in collaborative processes to make decisions and to take actions that protect the environment. Essentially, the ecosystem approach is consistent with the idea of "shared governance" discussed later in this chapter.

In practice, the ecosystem approach is also referred to as ecosystem-based management. Perhaps the first application of ecosystem-based management on a large scale in Canada occurred in the Great Lakes. During the 1960s and 1970s, the devastating impacts of human activi-

ties in the Great Lakes region included high levels of contaminants from industrial and urban sources, increasing numbers of invasive species, and loss of critical habitats and biodiversity. Canada and the United States signed agreements and worked together to reduce toxic substances, manage contaminated sediment, restore and protect habitat and natural areas, monitor the health of the lakes, and protect human health. For over 30 years, efforts to manage the basin have included all levels of government, industry, and citizens in decisions and stewardship activities. Together, they focused on reducing or eliminating sources of pollution, identifying "hot spots" around the Great Lakes, sharing information, monitoring change, increasing scientific knowledge, and reporting regularly to other politicians and citizens. While much remains to be accomplished, the ecosystem approach has contributed to improvements in ecosystem and human health that could not have been achieved by individual sectoral management of air, water, or land-based resources and activities. Additional examples of the ecosystem approach are described in Chapters 6, 9, 12, and 13.

MEASURING, MONITORING, AND REPORTING

"We measure what we value" is a saying that applies to our environment. In Canada, at the time of Confederation, there seemed no need to monitor or measure our resources. It seemed impossible that we might run out of our ecological endowment. Yet, extinctions of species, reductions in aquifers, and increases in noxious air emissions and other wastes point to the need to keep better track of how we are using our natural environment.

One significant challenge in environmental management is monitoring the changes that take place in the environment. Counting environmental components and their interactions is not as simple as counting money in the bank. Often we are surprised to discover that basic information about environmental change is lacking, even in Canada. Or, where data are available, sometimes they are not in a format that is easily compared from one jurisdiction to another. For example, in Chapter 7, the water runoff data provided is an estimate, and we document some of the difficulties encountered in calculating an accurate reading of runoff. Yet, this statistic is important because it tells us how much water is available in a given year. Similarly, government agencies in charge of forestry have used estimates of forest cover to determine how much timber can be cut down each year on a sustainable basis. Yet, determining the actual volume is tricky, because estimators must account for factors such as age of the trees, growing conditions, potential or actual disease infestations, and volume losses as a result of fire or floods. Calculations become complex when we try to figure out how these factors are interrelated and how they will influence change over time.

Measuring, monitoring, and reporting our ecological endowment and services also builds awareness among members of the general public and policy makers. Government agencies and nongovernmental organizations have used measuring devices and reporting formats to inform the public and generate campaigns to improve environmental quality. Beginning in the 1990s, Environment Canada has prepared state of the environment (SOE) reports. In 1989–1990, in the wake of heightened concern about Canada's environmental health, the federal government began developing environmental indicators based on four themes: ecological life-support systems, human health and well-being, natural resources sustainability, and pervasive influencing factors. After 10 years of tracking, there is now a usable database for assessing Canada's environmental trends. In 2003, Environment Canada published *Environmental Signals: Canada's National Environmental Indicator Series 2003* in collaboration with Agriculture and Agri-Food Canada, Health Canada, Natural Resources Canada, and Statistics Canada. The document provides information on progress made in addressing key environmental issues and describes actions taken to date, as well as challenges remaining (see also Chapter 14). This publication is significant because it is one of the first governmental initiatives to assess the effectiveness of Canada's environmental policies over the longer term. The environmental indicator series is significant because it marks our progress in thinking our environment is sufficiently precious that we want to track changes and assess their implications.

Other government agencies also provide data on the status of the environment and resources. For example, each year the Canadian Council of Environment Ministers publishes a compendium of forestry statistics. Provincial and municipal governments now frequently publish state of the environment reports. At the regional level, the Fraser Basin Council in British Columbia tracks links among the health of residents, the state of local ecosystems, and the state of the regional economy.

In 2003, the National Round Table on Environment and Economy recommended that the federal government extend its system of national accounts (which publishes information about gross domestic product) to include measures of natural, human, and social capital. Such an initiative is extremely complex because many of the components of the accounting system are difficult to express in monetary terms, but a key benefit is the potential role this accounting system would play in raising awareness and debate among the general public, industry, and policy makers about environmental and sustainability issues.

Several nongovernmental organizations are involved in measuring, monitoring, and publicly reporting on environmental quality with the express purpose of changing government, industry, and public actions. For example, the Sierra Legal Defence Fund now reports regularly on the quality of drinking water and wastewater treatment in cities and provinces to induce local decision makers to improve their

Photo 1–15
Measuring, monitoring, and reporting environmental changes are key to making informed decisions about the environment.

infrastructure (see Chapter 7). The World Wildlife Fund Protected Spaces Campaign (1990–2000) helped spur governments across the country into increasing the proportion of land dedicated to protected areas. GPI (Genuine Progress Index) Atlantic, a nonprofit research agency, has worked to develop indicators and measures of "genuine progress" and to assess the economic value of nonmarket social and environmental assets that are not usually contained in conventional economic statistics. Their efforts, along with related initiatives, are described in Chapters 4 and 14.

ENVIRONMENTAL IMPACT ASSESSMENT AND ADAPTIVE MANAGEMENT

Environmental Impact Assessment (EIA) is a decision-making tool first employed in Canada in the early 1970s. Federal, provincial, and territorial governments have since enacted legislation requiring environmental reviews of projects that have potential impacts on the environment within their jurisdiction. Chapter 10 describes the steps and stages of environmental assessment. As a "scientific" decision tool, EIAs offer a systematic means to identify, determine the significance of, and address impacts of human activities on the environment. As a "political" decision tool, EIAs sometimes have resulted in placing significant constraints on development. Perhaps the most significant EIA decision in Canada was made by then Justice Thomas Berger, who, in 1977, called for a 10-year moratorium on oil and gas development in the Arctic. A landmark decision in its day, Berger's decision was based on the need to resolve outstanding land claims with Aboriginal people and to improve the technical understanding of dealing with transporting oil and gas across permanently frozen territory.

The uneven application of EIA processes (both in terms of the kinds of projects that qualify for review and the terms of reference given to reviewers) has, in some cases, made EIA a highly politicized activity. Provincial and federal governments sometimes go to court to determine which level of government has jurisdiction to determine whether an assessment is necessary. Other EIAs have been so narrow in scope as to be almost meaningless.

Increasingly, however, there is interest in "strategic" environmental assessment, where we move from assessments of specific projects to assessments of policies and programs of government and industry. For example, Saskatchewan's forestry policy has been subject to strategic environmental assessment. Life-cycle assessment (described in Chapter 14) is also an innovation that helps us think about and address the impacts of developing a product from the acquisition of raw materials, through to its use and final disposal. Expansion of the tools of EIA can help consider the connections between our immediate use of the environment and long-term and extensive effects, and think about how we might adapt to changing future conditions.

Adaptive management is an experimental approach to environmental management whereby management interventions are designed to test clearly expressed ideas (hypotheses) about the ways ecosystems are changed through human use, so that our knowledge may grow and adjustments may be made as more information becomes available. This is not simply a trial-and-error approach to making resource management decisions, but one that requires the initiator (government agency, industry, scientist, citizen) to articulate predictions about environmental change and then determine if the predictions came true. Adaptive management is suggested for situations where there are gaps in our data or knowledge about environmental change. For example, New Brunswick introduced an adaptive management approach to a spruce budworm infestation in the 1970s. Adaptive management

was introduced in the British Columbia Forest Service in the 1990s and continues to guide forest management practices (see Box 1–6). In fisheries, adaptive management has been used in the Great Lakes to learn how to restore habitat and improve fish stocks. Contemporary research is also taking place in the field of "adaptive co-management," an approach that combines the learning dimension of adaptive management with a desire to share rights and responsibilities of environmental management among government, industry, and citizens. This sharing of rights and responsibilities is considered in the following section.

SHARED GOVERNANCE

Since the 1970s, all of these efforts—the ecosystem approach; measuring, monitoring, and reporting; and adaptive management and environmental impact assessment—have placed an increasing emphasis on sharing management actions and decision making with stakeholders and government. An emphasis on sharing also implies sharing of rights and responsibilities, and broadening responsibility for the environment from "government" to "governance." Governance refers to a broad system of arrangements in which government works with the private sector and nongovernmental organizations to determine the rules and procedures by which actions are taken.

Canada's federated system of governance has split jurisdiction for the environment between provincial and federal governments. Municipalities also have important roles to play, particularly in urban areas; however, their powers are delegated to them by provincial governments. As described in Chapters 4 and 14, this split jurisdiction poses opportunities and challenges for governance. Canada's Aboriginal people also have a significant role to play in environmental governance, both as rightholders

---

BOX 1–6
ADAPTIVE MANAGEMENT IN ACTION: THE BRITISH COLUMBIA FOREST SERVICE

The British Columbia Forest Service has established that adaptive management should guide decision makers in situations where optimal policies or practices are uncertain.

The B.C. Forest Service defines adaptive management as a formal process for continually improving management by learning from the outcomes of operational plans, and identifies six critical steps in the process:

1. Acknowledging uncertainty about which policy or practice is "best" for a particular management issue

2. Thoughtfully selecting the policies or practices to be applied

3. Carefully implementing the plan of action

4. Monitoring key response indicators

5. Analyzing the outcome in light of the original objectives

6. Incorporating the results into future decisions.

The B.C. Forest Service believes that adaptive management is particularly important where demands for change do not allow the luxury of intensive, process-level research before starting widespread implementation of new approaches. Current issues in British Columbia that have been identified as high priorities for adaptive management include harvesting techniques and silvicultural systems that provide alternatives to conventional clear-cutting, methods for protecting riparian habitat and streams, landscape and stand-scale practices for maintaining biological diversity and sensitive wildlife values, and watershed restoration techniques.

under treaties and the Canadian Constitution, and as residents who frequently are the first to feel the effects of environmental resource exploitation. Forestry, mining, fishing, and even protected area management are activities that affect the livelihoods and well-being of Aboriginal people.

Private individuals, local communities, and non-governmental organizations are important players in new arrangements for environmental management. Their roles may vary, ranging from simply being informed of environmental issues at the time of elections, to participating in monitoring (e.g., taking part in Christmas bird counts), understanding stewardship and restoration activities for degraded environments or habitats, engaging in public awareness campaigns or direct action, or sitting on advisory committees or boards that make recommendations to government or industry. Although there are several names given to shared governance arrangements (e.g., collaborative natural resource management, civic science), we consider two options here: co-management and collaborative stewardship.

Co-management

Co-management is a process of shared action and decision making typically taking place between government and citizens about environmental and resource management. Through co-management, resource users can work cooperatively with government regulators to conserve resources and halt environmental degradation, providing, at the same time, economic, environmental, and social benefits and improving relations between government agencies and resource users. Where the status of an environment is contested, one benefit of co-management is improved communication between user groups—there is an opportunity to explain the sources of data along with their limitations and assumptions, and local residents can contribute directly to data gathering and information sharing. Direct interaction can help groups learn from one another and build trust in each other to improve the chances that new practices or regulations will be sensitive to local concerns and that residents will comply with such changes.

In Canada, co-management frequently applies to legal agreements between Aboriginal people and provincial or federal governments to share responsibility and authority for policy and program decisions related to the environment. These formal agreements may arise because of the constitutional, treaty, or Aboriginal rights of indigenous peoples. In this sense, Aboriginal people are not just stakeholders, but also rightholders. The 1975 James Bay and Northern Quebec Agreement established the first formal co-management agreement for fish and wildlife management between Aboriginal and non-Aboriginal governments in Canada. Many First Nations and Inuit people of northern Canada now have co-management arrangements embedded into their contemporary treaties with the

federal government. Joint management boards composed of federal and Aboriginal representatives are responsible for making decisions about fish, wildlife, forests, and protected areas within their jurisdiction and for determining whether and how environmental impact assessments will be carried out. Co-management committees have been established across Canada, including the Northwest and Yukon territories and Nunavut, at Haida Gwaii National Park Reserve in British Columbia, in the Temagami region of northern Ontario, and at the Bras d'Or watershed in Nova Scotia. These initiatives illustrate the growing recognition of Aboriginal interests in and responsibility for managing Canada's environment (see also Chapter 4).

Stewardship Activities

Co-management is not the only route to shared governance. Stewardship is also an important principle in achieving sustainability. The perception that governments and corporations in Canada have not been able to protect the environment effectively has persisted over the past generation. That perception, as well as fears that damage to the environment and human health could be irreversible, has prompted individuals and groups of people to demand comprehensive, proactive planning for environmental quality and sustainability in their region and the country (Lerner, 1994).

Many local group members who provide conservation, rehabilitation, and other care for threatened and special places in their communities demonstrate active citizen participation through environmental stewardship. These people and their groups place pressure on decision makers to act in environmentally responsible ways (Lerner, 1994). Through active participation in caring for and maintaining the well-being of a place, many people have learned that they are part of nature. They also learn how vital it is to maintain ecosystems, not only for the benefits they bring to people and other organisms, but also for the sake of ecosystems themselves. The Atlantic

Photo 1–16
Government–citizen collaboration on the Atlantic coast helps to protect valued coastal and marine ecosystems.

Photo 1–17
Toronto residents demonstrate stewardship in a local effort to clean up the Don River.

Coastal Action Program is a community–government initiative that has been in place for almost two decades and relies on local involvement and government support to restore and sustain watersheds and coastal areas. A more detailed example of stewardship activities is the Swan Lake Christmas Hill Nature Sanctuary on Vancouver Island (see Chapter 7).

Stewardship permits people to take leadership roles and act responsibly when a threat to a locally valued place or environment occurs. Local people who feel a sense of stewardship may be found cleaning up their natural areas, challenging polluters to do things differently, and demanding action and accountability from their governments. Stewardship also promotes working in partnership with other individuals and environmental nongovernmental groups, as well as with government or private-sector programs. Stewardship helps everyone understand the importance of accountability in regard to ecosystem sustainability. In short, stewardship is "active earthkeeping" (Lerner, 1993) that helps promote sustainability.

TOWARD SUSTAINABILITY

Throughout the remainder of this book, we will continue to promote the idea that our individual and collective actions will help move us toward sustainability. Individuals make a tremendous difference, and in Canada, several have done so already. At the end of each chapter, we feature an individual or a group that has made a substantial contribution to environmental and sustainability issues. You may know about some of these people, but likely not many of them. The first of these personal profiles (Making a Difference 1) describes some of the work of the Group of Seven, internationally renowned Canadian artists who promoted the environment through their landscapes and whose artwork influenced generations of Canadian and global citizens to notice the wonders of this planet—and confirmed the need to protect it. However, we emphasize that you do not have to be a famed artist or a David Suzuki (Making a Difference 2) to make a difference and benefit the planet. In each of the remaining chapters, we profile individuals who have worked for many years, often without recognition, to protect and maintain the quality of Canada's environment so that we all may enjoy and benefit from it.

MAKING A DIFFERENCE 1
THE GROUP OF SEVEN

Quickly, think of five Canadian paintings that capture our landscape and our country.

Those images in your mind—chances are that one or more was created by a member of the Group of Seven. But in their time, Canadian artists weren't so widely celebrated. Although Canada had been a dominion for a half-century by the 1920s, most Canadians continued to maintain a colonial mindset, looking to Europe for the latest trends in culture, with a belief that European art was innately superior to anything that could be produced in Canada. Only 2 percent of the paintings sold in Canada in 1924 were by Canadian artists.

This outlook was rejected by the group of artists who became known as the Group of Seven. While their portrayal of the Canadian landscape is now synonymous with Canadian art for many people, both the public and critics considered their work "freakish" and "hideous" when it was first exhibited (Smith, n.d.). The Group of Seven rejected European pastoralism as too sedate and instead portrayed "the rugged nature of the Canadian landscape … [using a] bolder, more vigorous painting style and a heightened use of colour." Nature was depicted as "a powerful force shaping the character of the country" (Centre for Canadian Studies, 2001).

The founding members of the Group of Seven, which came together formally in 1920 (and disbanded in 1933), were Lawren Harris, Arthur Lismer, Alexander Young (A.Y.) Jackson, James (J. E. H.) MacDonald, Frank

(continued)

Photo 1–18
The members of the Group of Seven (from left): Fred Varley, A. Y. Jackson, Lawren Harris, friend Barker Fairley, Frank Johnston, Arthur Lismer, James MacDonald. Missing: Franklin Carmichael.

Photo 1–19
Franklin Carmichael

Johnston, Frederick H. Varley, and Franklin Carmichael. The work of another influential artist, Tom Thomson, was often included in their exhibitions (although Thomson died in 1917 and was never a member of the Group). Later members of the Group of Seven included Alfred Joseph (A. J.) Casson, Edwin Holgate, and Lionel LeMoine (L. L.) Fitzgerald.

The artists travelled throughout the wilderness, preparing sketches in places such as Algonquin Park during the summer and producing their finished canvases in Toronto studios during the winter. Through conversations and shared sketching trips, the Group of Seven developed a unique artistic vision and style of painting that expressed their feelings for the rough, vibrant expanses of Canada's distinctive landscapes. They presented nature as a powerful force that shaped both the physical environment and the people of Canada.

While their favourite sketching locales included Algonquin Park, Algoma, Georgian Bay, and the north shore of Lake Superior, members of the Group of Seven also painted images of the Laurentians and the Canadian Rockies, the Pacific Coast, the lower St. Lawrence, the Maritimes, Northern Ontario, and the Arctic. Some also painted the urban or less wild areas where they lived.

Despite the initial resistance to their work, over time the Group of Seven's style has been recognized and respected as Canada's national school of art. These artists' contributions to the forging of a new Canadian way of viewing the landscape in which we live continue to be recognized today. In a very real way, the Group of Seven helped Canadians to define "Our Environment" and to recognize and care about our landscapes.

Have you ever been inspired by the landscape and spirit of Canada to try your hand at painting, poetry, or photography? Share your words and images with others—perhaps you will be the catalyst for another unique artistic record of our country!

May the work of the Group of Seven and the artists who have followed them inspire you too to care about the land and space in which we live.

SOURCES: *Nationalism and the Arts: The Group of Seven,* The Centre for Canadian Studies, Mount Allison University, 2001, http://www.mta.ca/faculty/arts/canadian_studies/english/about/study_guide/artists/group_of_seven.html; *The Collection—The Group of Seven,* McMichael Canadian Art Collection, n.d., http://www.mcmichael.com/collection/seven/index.cfm; *Group of Seven,* The Artchive, Dale Smith, n.d., http://www.artchive.com/artchive/groupseven.html

Attaining sustainability is an important Canadian goal that requires political will as well as individual and collective action. New ways of thinking—about the ecosphere and about our local environment, about ecosystems and the interactions and interdependencies that characterize them, and about how sustainability can be achieved now and for the future—are bringing about new means of achieving desired, sustainable futures. As we will see throughout the chapters regarding Canada's environment, we face distinct challenges, and we have a growing toolbox of strategies with which to address them.

Chapter Questions

The following statements are intended to get you to think critically about some of the upcoming topics in the textbook. Do you agree or disagree with these statements? For some statements, you may want to qualify your answer. Or, you may find you do not yet know enough to make an informed judgment. If this is the case, what would you do if you were a politician and had to make a decision? Feel free to browse through upcoming chapters to see what they say about these issues. Pair up with a fellow student and let the debates begin!

- Renewable resources are at greater risk of depletion than nonrenewables (Chapter 1).
- Better environmental decisions require better environmental science (Chapter 2).
- Vegetarians tread more lightly on the Earth than do people who like to eat meat (Chapter 3).
- Aboriginal people in Canada should be more involved in decisions about environmental management (Chapter 4).
- Canadians should grow trees instead of wheat on the Prairies to alleviate global warming (Chapter 5).

- Growing biofuel crops is just as important as growing foodcrops (Chapter 6).
- We should charge everyone equally for water use to curb consumption (Chapter 7).
- The only option for meeting future demand for fish is farming them (Chapter 8).
- Labelling a product as "certified wood" is merely a marketing scheme (Chapter 9).
- There is no such thing as sustainable mining (Chapter 10).
- Carbon taxes are the most effective way to reduce our emissions of greenhouse gases (Chapter 11).
- The Prairie region is at the greatest risk for loss of biodiversity in Canada (Chapter 12).
- Landfilling is the best way to get rid of Canadians' solid waste (Chapter 13).
- My university's sustainability policy is effective in raising awareness of sustainability issues on campus (Chapter 14).

references

Brower, D. (Ed.). (1975). *Only a little planet*. New York: Friends of the Earth/Ballantine Books.

Commission on Resources and Environment (CORE). (1994). *Vancouver Island land use plan, volume I*. Victoria: Commission on Resources and Environment.

Draper, D., & Mitchell, B. (2001). Environmental justice considerations in Canada. *Canadian Geographer, 45*(1), 93–98.

Government of Canada. (1996). *The state of Canada's environment—1996*. Ottawa: Supply and Services Canada.

International Union for the Conservation of Nature and Natural Resources (IUCN), United Nations Environment Programme (UNEP), & World Wildlife Fund (WWF). (1980). *World conservation strategy: Living resource conservation for sustainable development*. Gland, Switzerland: International Union for the Conservation of Nature and Natural Resources.

Kaufmann, M. R., Graham, R. T., Boyce, Jr., D. A., Moir, W. H., Perry, L., Reynolds, R. T., Bassett, R. L., Mehlhop, P., Edminster, C. B., Block, W. M., & Corn, P. S. (1994). *An ecological basis for ecosystem management*. Fort Collins, CO: U.S. Department of Agriculture Forest Service, Rocky Mountain Forest and Range Experiment Station and Southwestern Region. USDA Forest Service General Technical Report RM-246.

Lerner, S. (Ed.). (1993). *Environmental stewardship: Studies in active earthkeeping*. Waterloo, ON: University of Waterloo Department of Geography Publication Series No. 39.

Lerner, S. (1994). Local stewardship: Training ground for an environmental vanguard. *Alternatives, 20*(2), 14–19.

National Round Table on the Environment and the Economy. (2003). *State of the debate: Environment and sustainable development indicators for Canada*. Ottawa: Author.

Rees, J. (1990). *Natural resources: Allocation, economics and policy* (2nd ed.). London: Methuen.

Robinson, J., Francis, G., Legge, R., & Lerner, S. (1990). Defining a sustainable society: Values, principles, and definitions. *Alternatives, 17*: 36–46.

Wackernagel, M., & Rees, W. (1996). *Our ecological footprint: Reducing human impact on the earth*. Gabriola Island, BC: New Society.

World Commission on Environment and Development. (1987). *Our common future*. Oxford: Oxford University Press.

World Conservation Union (IUCN), United Nations Environment Programme (UNEP), & World Wildlife Fund (WWF). (1991). *Caring for the earth: A strategy for sustainable living*. Gland, Switzerland: International Union for the Conservation of Nature and Natural Resources.

World Resources Institute. (2007). *EarthTrends 2003: Country Profiles*. http://earthtrends.wri.org. Washington, DC: Author.

World Wildlife Fund International, Zoological Society of London, and Global Footprint Network. (2006). *Living planet report—2006*. http://www.footprintnetwork.org/download.php?id=303

Zimmermann, E. (1951). *World resources and industries: A functional appraisal of the availability of agricultural and industrial materials*. New York: Harper.

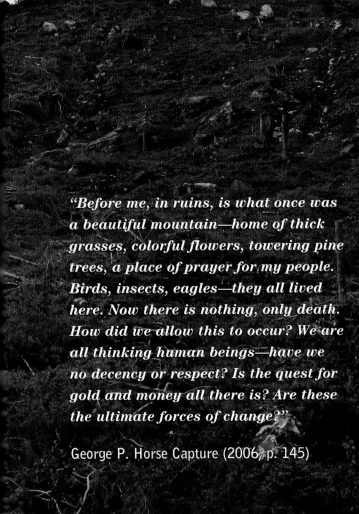

"*Before me, in ruins, is what once was a beautiful mountain—home of thick grasses, colorful flowers, towering pine trees, a place of prayer for my people. Birds, insects, eagles—they all lived here. Now there is nothing, only death. How did we allow this to occur? We are all thinking human beings—have we no decency or respect? Is the quest for gold and money all there is? Are these the ultimate forces of change?*"

George P. Horse Capture (2006, p. 145)

CHAPTER 2

Environmental Studies: Science, Worldviews, & Ethics

Chapter Contents

Chapter Objectives

After studying this chapter you should be able to

- appreciate why a scientific understanding of our environment is important in making decisions about sustainability
- outline the basic methods of science
- identify the different values and worldviews that characterize environmental controversies
- discuss the key historical approaches to conservation as well as current approaches to environmentalism
- understand the practical and moral reasons for valuing environments
- describe the concerns associated with environmental ethics

INTRODUCTION

In Chapter 1 we noted some fundamental features of life at the beginning of the 21st century: how people have changed the global environment; how ecosystems are under increasing threat from human population growth and resource consumption, pollution, and other environmental abuses; how uncertainty about global changes highlights the importance of sustainability as a counterbalance to these changes; and how both knowledge and values are vital in solving contemporary environmental problems.

In this chapter we discuss the historical and current roles and influences of science, worldviews, and ethics in environmental studies. The significance of multidisciplinary and interdisciplinary science in generating new environmental knowledge and understanding is stressed, as is the importance of the social sciences in understanding human attitudes, values, and beliefs in order to address root causes of environmental problems. Attention also is given to the growth in support for environmental action, particularly the "environmental revolution."

SCIENCE AND THE ENVIRONMENT

Early inhabitants of Canada depended on their knowledge of the environment for their survival; careful observations of wildlife habits and migration routes, weather patterns, and other natural events were crucial to their continued well-being. To some extent this reliance on environmental knowledge continues among occupations that depend on the natural environment (such as fishing, hunting, and trapping), but for most Canadians, especially those living in urban settings, the environment is not something we think about scientifically each day. However, the environment continues to play a vital role in our everyday lives.

As unaccustomed as we might be to thinking scientifically about the environment, there are several reasons why science, as a process for refining our understanding of how the natural world works, is important. The systematic observation and analysis underlying both science and social science has provided us with a great deal of understanding about ecosystems, their functioning, and human interactions with our environment. These are the kinds of knowledge that can be applied to prevent negative effects or better manage human impacts on the environment. With improved knowledge and understanding, we can learn how to avoid inappropriate choices and identify courses of action that will be positive and sustainable in the long term.

Photo 2–1
Before European settlement, Aboriginal peoples depended directly on land and water resources for life's necessities. Today, climate and other environmental and socioeconomic changes have reduced reliance on "country foods," often to the detriment of people dependent on these resources.

Environmental decision making reflects the interactions of society, politics, culture, economics, and values, as well as scientific information. To demonstrate why thinking critically (scientifically) about the environment is important to making decisions about environmental sustainability, the next sections discuss what science is (and is not), the importance scientists place on measurement, the methods of science, and the role of science in decision making. Since science alone is not sufficient to resolve environmental problems, some social science aspects of environmental management are considered later in the chapter. Different worldviews (ways of perceiving reality) are explored, as are the roles of the 1960s environmental revolution and the subsequent (1985–onward) wave of environmentalism in stimulating a reassessment of human relationships with the natural world.

WHAT IS SCIENCE?

Science is a process used to investigate the world around us—a systematic attempt to understand the universe. By repeatedly asking questions about how the natural environment works, conducting orderly observations (including experiments), and analyzing their findings, scientists attempt to reduce the complexity of our world to general principles that provide new insights or solve

problems. Thinking about environmental issues involves thinking scientifically.

While science provides one way of looking at the world, it is not the only way of viewing the world. Religious, moral, aesthetic, cultural, and personal values, for example, provide different and valuable ways of perceiving and making sense of the world around us. In general, scientists focus on rigorous observation, experimentation, and logic in developing an integrated and objective understanding of our world. However, science is not value-free: that is, scientists have their own values, interests, and cultural backgrounds that may influence their interpretation of data. This means that we need to be able to evaluate the statements they make about the environment: Are these statements based on observations and data? Are they a systematic, or "expert," interpretation of data, or are they subjective, personal opinion or assertion? In order to determine an answer for ourselves, we need to understand more about what science is and is not.

Modern science does not deal with metaphysical questions (What is the purpose of life?) or with questions that are answered by morals or values (What is beauty?), but rather with things that are observable and testable. In terms of the natural world, scientists must be able to make observations from which they develop a **hypothesis** (explanation) that can be accepted until it is disproved. Such hypotheses are based on certain assumptions that scientists make about the world.

Photo 2–2
Like all scientific theories, Darwin's theory of evolution involves a degree of belief. Alternative explanations about the way our natural world works continue to be proposed and tested.

Assumptions in Science

Scientists make five basic assumptions about the natural world they study: (1) people can understand the patterns of events in the natural world through careful observation and analysis; (2) the same rules or patterns of behaviour that describe events in the natural world apply throughout the universe; (3) science is based on inductive reasoning that begins with specific observations of, and extends to generalizations about, the natural world; (4) these generalizations can be subjected to tests that try to disprove them—if no such test can be devised, then a generalization still cannot be treated as a scientific statement (because it is true only until new, contrary evidence is found); and (5) existing scientific theories can be disproved by new evidence, but science can never provide absolute proof of the truth of its theories (Botkin & Keller, 1995).

Thinking Scientifically

Scientists use two kinds of reasoning: inductive and deductive. When scientists draw conclusions about their observations of the natural world by means of logical reasoning, they are engaging in **deductive reasoning** (thinking). In this process, a specific conclusion flows logically from the definitions and assumptions (the premises) set initially by the scientists. If a conclusion follows logically from the premises, it is said to be "proved." Deductive proof does not require that the premises be true, only that the reasoning be logical. This means that logically valid but untrue statements can result from false premises, as the following example illustrates:

Humans are the only tool-using organisms.

The Egyptian vulture uses tools.

Therefore, the Egyptian vulture is a human being.

The final statement must be true if the two preceding statements are true, but we know that this conclusion is untrue. If the second statement is true (and it is: some African populations of Egyptian vultures break ostrich eggs by dropping rocks on them), then the first statement cannot be true and the conclusion must be false. Because the rules of deductive logic deal only with the process of moving from premises to conclusions, in this example the conclusion that the Egyptian vulture is human follows logically from the series of statements (even though it is nonsensical).

This problem of false conclusions is why science requires not only logical reasoning but also correct premises. If these three statements were expressed conditionally, they would be scientifically correct:

If humans are the only tool-using organisms,

and the Egyptian vulture uses tools,

then the Egyptian vulture is a human being.

When a scientist (or anyone else) draws a general conclusion based on a limited set of observations, that person is engaging in **inductive reasoning**. Let us say, for example, that we are observing fruits with particular characteristics, such as tomatoes, and we observe that such fruits are always red. We may make the inductive statement (or generalization) that "all tomatoes are red." This really means that all the tomatoes we have ever seen are red. Since it is highly unlikely we will observe all the world's tomatoes, we do not know if the next observation we make may turn up a fruit that is like a tomato in all respects except that it is yellow. In inductive reasoning, then, people (scientists included) can state only what is usually true—for example, that there is a very high degree of probability that all swans are white—but we cannot say so with absolute certainty. Inductive reasoning produces new knowledge, but is error prone.

Probability is one way scientists express how certain (or uncertain) they are about the quality of their observations and how confident they are of their predictions. If they are highly confident in their conclusions, scientists may state the degree of certainty as "There is a 99.9 percent probability that..." This is about as close as scientists can get to stating proof of their theories—but it is still not proof.

The concept of correlation provides another way in which scientists can express their uncertainty. *Correlation* describes the degree to which one variable is related to another variable; for example, we know that climate and crops are closely correlated.

Proving something using inductive reasoning is different from demonstrating proof using deductive reasoning, and science needs both types to help analyze whether the conclusions reached are valid. Both ways of thinking are complementary and important in improving understanding of our environment.

Scientific Measurement

Perhaps more than anyone else, scientists appreciate that every measurement they make is an approximation. Depending on the instruments used and the people who use the instruments, all measurements contain some limitations. These limitations or uncertainties can be reduced, but they can never be eliminated completely.

To make their measurements meaningful, particularly to decision makers, scientists provide an estimate of the uncertainty associated with their measurements. Consider the case of a wildlife biologist who is asked to determine the impact on a caribou herd if the flow rate of a river they cross during their migration were to double due to a proposed hydroelectric development. If the wildlife biologist calculates that doubling the flow in the river will reduce the caribou population by 100 animals, decision makers still do not have enough information to determine whether construction of the hydro plant should proceed. In addition

Photo 2–3

The drowning of 9600 caribou in northern Quebec in October 1984 is thought to have resulted from increased flow in the Caniapiscau River, due in part to the operation of dam systems.

to information about the average population size of the particular herd affected (what proportion of the herd does 100 animals represent?), decision makers need to know the uncertainty associated with the loss of 100 animals. In this case, the statistical definition of significance likely would be used in interpreting results. *Statistical significance* describes the probability of whether or not the event or relationship has a greater potential to occur with more frequency than simple random chance. If the uncertainty were 1 percent, their decision might be different than if it were 10 percent.

In addition to uncertainty, scientists may encounter systematic and random measurement errors during their research. Random errors occur by chance, but if a scientist's instrument had been calibrated incorrectly and consistently provided inaccurate readings, a systematic error would result. *Standard error* calculations show us the degree to which results vary from sample to sample and are used to help determine whether errors are random or systematic. (Numerically, standard error is the square

root of variation in the sample population divided by the individual sample size.) Obviously, it is important to avoid such errors and to make and report measurements as accurately and precisely as possible.

If a scientist's measurement is accurate, it will correspond to the value scientists have already accepted for that feature; if that scientist's measurement is precise, the feature will have been measured with a high degree of exactness. Note that it is possible to make very precise measurements that are not accurate. For instance, the accepted value for the boiling point of water at sea level is 100.000°C (or 212.000°F); if you measure the boiling point of water as 99.885°C, your measurement is as precise as the accepted one (because both are recorded to the nearest 0.001°), but your measurement is still (slightly) inaccurate. It is important, too, not to mislead others by reporting measurements with more precision than is warranted.

Careful choice of research and statistical procedures, adoption of standard measurement procedures, and improvements in instrumentation will all help to reduce measurement errors and uncertainties. Given that errors will continue to occur in research, however, it is important to be informed about and understand the nature of measurement uncertainties so that we may read reports of scientific research critically and evaluate their validity.

The increased use of aerial photography and satellite remote sensing during the past 30 years has contributed greatly to our ability to map, inventory, and monitor the environment (thus reducing error and uncertainty). Similarly, the data storage, display, and analysis capabilities of geographic information systems (GIS) have been vital in enabling researchers to contribute to environmental management decisions. As satellite transmitters became small enough to slip over the shoulders of peregrine falcons, researchers were able to track some of these birds as they migrated more than 14 000 kilometres from their breeding grounds in Alaska and northern Canada to their wintering grounds in Central and South America. The data gathered using this technology not only fill large gaps in knowledge based on previous leg-banding programs, but also enable production of flight-path maps to determine whether peregrines are travelling to areas where potentially dangerous pesticides are used. In turn, this information has helped in decision making about removing the bird from the endangered species list (Yoon, 1996).

THE METHODS OF SCIENCE

As noted above, **observations**—made through any of our five senses or instruments that extend those senses—are the fundamental basis of science. When scientists check for accuracy in science, they compare their observations with those made by many other scientists, and when all (or almost all) of them agree that an observation is correct, they call it a **fact.**

Observations and facts provide a basis for **inferences**—conclusions derived either by logical reasoning from premises and/or evidence, or by insight or analogy based on evidence. Before inferences are accepted as facts, they must be tested (accepting untested inferences is sloppy thinking) and they must be repeatable (when the same methodology is followed). When scientists test an inference, they convert it into a hypothesis, a statement that they can try to disprove. Often, the hypothesis is stated in negative terms, called the null hypothesis, because in science it is assumed that there are no absolute truths (this is why assumptions 4 and 5, noted previously, regarding generalizations and scientific theories can only be disproved, not proved). By attempting systematically to demonstrate that certain statements are not valid—that is, are not consistent with what has been learned from observation—scientists learn which general principles governing the operation of the natural world are true. Invalid statements are rejected, while statements that have not been proved to be invalid are retained until such time as they are found to be incorrect.

Hypotheses are stated typically in the form of "If … then" statements—for example, "If I apply more fertilizer, then my pumpkin plants will produce larger pumpkins." This statement relates two conditions, namely the amount of fertilizer applied and the size of pumpkins produced. Because each of these conditions can vary, they are called variables. The size of pumpkins is called the **dependent** (or *responding* or y-axis) **variable** because it is assumed to depend on the amount of fertilizer applied, which is the **independent** (or *manipulated* or x-axis) **variable**.

Many variables may exist in growing pumpkin plants. Some can be assumed to be irrelevant, such as the position of the planet Mars, while others, such as length of the growing season, average temperatures during the growing period, and daylight hours, potentially are relevant. To test the stated hypothesis (above), a scientist would want to run a **controlled experiment.** A controlled experiment is designed to test the effects of independent variables on a dependent variable by changing only one independent variable at a time. For each variable tested, there are two setups—an experiment and a control—that are identical except for the independent variable being tested. If there are differences in the outcome between the experiment and the control (relating to the dependent variable), then these differences are attributed to the effects of the independent variable tested. It can be a challenge to properly design control tests and to isolate a single variable from all other variables.

It is also important to ensure that variables are defined in ways that enable their exact meaning to be understood by all scientists. The vagueness of the variable "size of pumpkins," for example, might cause one scientist to interpret it as weight, another as diameter. Both independent and dependent variables must be defined operationally before an experiment is carried out. **Operational**

Photo 2–4
Taking measurements and collecting data are integral parts of the scientific method. Here a researcher tests for dissolved oxygen.

definitions tell scientists what to look for or what to do in order to carry out the measurement, construction, or manipulation of variables. In that way, scientists know how to duplicate an experiment and how to check on the results reported: for example, they would know whether "size of pumpkins" was to be measured in kilograms or in centimetres.

Keeping accurate records of independent and dependent variables during experiments is an important element in science. These values, or data, are referred to as either **quantitative data** (numerical) or **qualitative data** (non-numerical). In the pumpkin example, above, qualitative data would record the size of pumpkins as small, medium, or large, while quantitative data would record each pumpkin's weight in grams or diameter in centimetres. There is a long-standing bias in science toward quantitative data, but many fields with relevance to environmental issues collect data in qualitative forms (for instance, sociology, psychology, animal behaviour, human geography, and environmental policy analysis).

Scientific research continues to contribute to the growing body of knowledge pertaining to the natural environment. As knowledge accumulates in both quantitative and qualitative dimensions, scientists develop explanations or models to illustrate how the natural environment works. Different types of models exist, from actual working models to mental, computer, mathematical, and laboratory models. All models may be revised or replaced as knowledge increases and currently accepted hypotheses are modified in light of new understanding. Models that offer broadly conceived, logically coherent, and well-supported concepts are labelled *theories*. Einstein's theory of relativity and Newton's theory of gravity are examples of strongly supported theories that are unlikely to be rejected in the future. However, science does not guarantee that future evidence will not cause even these theories to be revised.

It is worth noting that while theories usually grow out of research, theories also may guide research. In fact, scientists make their observations in the context of existing theories. On occasion, scientific revolutions occur when a growing discrepancy between observations and accepted theories forces replacement of old theories by new or revised ones. Perhaps the shift in thinking about Lovelock's Gaia concept—its shift from hypothesis to theory—may be viewed in this light.

MISUNDERSTANDINGS ABOUT SCIENCE

Use of Language

As we have seen, researchers use a variety of scientific methods, as well as their imagination and insight, to increase knowledge and understanding about the natural world. We also appreciate that while scientists may disprove things, they cannot establish absolute truth or proof. So, when you encounter statements that something has been "proved scientifically," it is important to recognize this inaccurate use of scientific language. The claim being made falsely implies that science yields absolute proof or certainty. This situation may occur when people do not understand the nature and limitations of science, or when language is misused deliberately.

Also, be alert to use of the term **theory**. In everyday language, people use the term to indicate a guess or a lack of knowledge ("it's just a theory") and do not accord theory the prestige it is given in science. Development of a theory is among the greatest achievements in science. It is only after considerable debate, speculation, and sometimes controversy that scientists develop theories based

Photo 2–5
Dolly the sheep, the first mammal to be cloned from an adult cell (genetic engineering), was euthanized in February 2003 at the age of six and a half years. She had developed arthritis and a progressive lung disease, a problem common in 10- to 12-year-old sheep. DNA evidence in some cloned mammals, including Dolly, indicates they age much faster than their non-cloned counterparts.

on their consensus about explanations of phenomena. The significance of scientific consensus is often undervalued by the public and the media as well; this consensus gives even more credence to the message of the "World Scientists' Warning to Humanity" (see Chapter 1).

Value-Free Science

Earlier in this chapter we noted that science is not value-free, that scientists are influenced by their social environment. This does not mean that objectivity is not a goal of scientists, but it means we need to recognize that scientists have biases that must be identified explicitly. Perhaps we need to estimate the effects of these biases, too. Controversial issues, from endangered species preservation to genetic engineering and vehicle emission standards, give rise to conflicts among science, scientists, technology, and society. While it is appropriate for different scientists and other individuals to express their values, science does not permit sloppy or fuzzy thinking. It is necessary to think critically and logically about science and social issues, for without such thinking it is more likely that pseudoscientific (false) ideas of the Earth and how it works will be believed. Pseudoscience constitutes a weak basis for making important environmental decisions with long-term, serious consequences.

Given that science is an open process of continual investigation and advances in knowledge, it is sometimes difficult to determine which scientific ideas will become accepted and which will not. Evidence for ideas and models at the frontiers of science is more ambiguous than for those ideas accepted by the scientific community, but some of these frontier-type ideas will be picked up before they have been verified fully (or discarded). In particular, media reports on scientific issues frequently deal with new discoveries, frontier science, and science beyond the fringe. As potential consumers of such information, we need to be able to analyze both media and scientific reports and decide if they are based on objective interpretation of observations and data or on subjective opinion (see Box 2–1). While expert opinion is valuable, accepting

BOX 2-1
THINKING CRITICALLY

With all the competing views and claims about environmental issues, how can we know which ones to believe? How can we determine what piece of evidence or interpretation is valid and what we should do about an issue? Critical thinking skills help us avoid jumping to conclusions by developing a rational basis for systematically recognizing and evaluating the messages that are conveyed. Critical thinking skills include the ability to recognize assumptions, hidden ideas, and meanings; to separate facts and values; and to assess the reasons and conclusions presented in arguments. These are useful tools in our everyday lives, not just in terms of the environment.

Each one of us has used critical thinking skills at some point. A common example is questioning the information conveyed on television ads. What does a particular beverage company mean when it labels its product as "good tasting"? According to whose taste buds? What does the product's "new and improved taste" involve—more salt and sugar? In addition to your "well-being," what motivations are behind the ads? If you have ever asked questions like these, you have used critical thinking skills.

Critical thinking involves questioning and synthesizing what has been learned; it is a deliberate effort to think and plan how to think about or analyze a problem rationally. To do this well, we need to be willing to question authority (because even experts are wrong sometimes); to be open-minded and flexible enough to consider different points of view and explanations; to seek full information about an issue; to focus on the main point(s); to be sensitive to the knowledge, feelings, and positions of people involved in the discussion of an issue; and to take a stand on an issue when the evidence warrants it, remembering that we, too, could be wrong and have to rethink our assessment later.

There are a number of steps we need to practise, and many questions to ask ourselves, if our critical thinking is to be effective:

1. Examine the claims made: On what premise or basis are they made? Is there evidence to support the claims? What conclusions are drawn from the evidence? Are the conclusions true?

2. Identify and clarify use of language: Are the terms used clear and unequivocal, or do they have more than one meaning? Is everyone using the same meaning? Are there any ambiguities in the language used? Could those ambiguities be deliberate? Are all the claims true simultaneously?

3. Separate facts and values or opinions: If the claims that are made can be tested, then they are factual statements and should be verifiable by evidence. If claims are made about the worth or lack of worth of something, they are value statements or opinions and may not be verified objectively.

4. Identify the assumptions and determine potential reasons for the assumptions, evidence, or conclusions people present: Does anyone have a personal agenda or "an axe to grind" on a particular issue? Are there gender, racial, economic, or other issues clouding the discussion?

5. Establish the reliability or credibility of an information source: What special knowledge or information do the experts bring? What makes the experts qualified in this specific issue? How can the accuracy, truth, or plausibility of the information they offer be determined? Is information being withheld?

6. Recognize the basic beliefs, attitudes, and values that each person, group, or agency holds: In what ways do these beliefs and values influence the way these people view themselves and the world around them? Are any of these beliefs and values contradictory?

If we use the preceding questions to examine the logic of the arguments people offer about an environmental issue, we should be able to determine what to believe even when facts seem confused and experts disagree. This is not to say that critical thinking is easy, but the skills come with practice and will improve with time. Look for opportunities to think for yourself and use those critical thinking skills.

SOURCE: Adapted from unpublished work by Karen J. Warren, Philosophy Department, MacAlester College, St. Paul, MN. Used by permission.

a statement as fact simply because it was made by a scientist is contrary to the nature of science (particularly if that person has not studied the topic as a scientist).

The Scientific Method

Usually students are informed that the series of steps scientists take to carry out their research is called the **scientific method**, and that it consists of steps similar to those in Figure 2–1. However, it is important to realize that not all research fits into such a neatly defined, step-by-step process. While discovering general principles about how the world works is quite often a result of inductive reasoning, accidental discoveries (serendipity), creativity, and flashes of insight also play roles in advancing knowledge and understanding.

The myth of a single scientific method dies hard, even though the disciplines of science undertake research differently. For instance, chemists or physicists use a different research logic to guide their research than biologists or geographers. Even within single disciplines, evolutionists conduct their research differently than ecologists, and hydrologists work differently than geomorphologists. In reality, there are many methods of science rather than one scientific method.

Complexity, Values, and Worldviews

In science, the more complex a system or problem being studied, the less certain are the hypotheses, models, and theories used to explain it. When we combine this fact with the knowledge that most environmental problems involve complex mixtures of data (or lack of data), hypotheses, and theories in the physical and social sciences, we realize that we really do not have sufficient information to understand them well or fully. It is in this context that advocates of any particular action (or inaction) regarding an environmental issue or problem can use incomplete information to support their beliefs, claiming scientific support for their perspective. Alternatively, an insistence that we fully understand a problem before taking action may lead to "paralysis by analysis." If we think this way, the inherent limitations of science and the complexities of environmental problems force us into an irresolvable situation.

Since environmental problems are not about to go away, there comes a point when people have to evaluate available information and make a political or economic decision about what to do (or not do). Often, these decisions are based on intuition, values, or common sense (claimed by all sides, of course!). This explains why we find different values and worldviews at the heart of most environmental controversies—people with different worldviews and values can take the same information, examine it in a logically consistent fashion, and come to completely different conclusions. (Worldviews, values, and ethics are examined later in this chapter.)

a. Common Steps in the Scientific Method

1. Observe and develop a question about your observations.
2. Develop a hypothesis—a tentative answer to the question.
3. Design a controlled experiment or model defining independent and dependent variables to test your hypothesis.
4. Collect data and record it in an organized manner (such as a table or graph).
5. Interpret the data.
6. Draw a conclusion from the data.
7. Compare your conclusion with your hypothesis to determine whether your results support or disprove your hypothesis.
8. If you accept your hypothesis, conduct further tests to support it.
9. If you reject your hypothesis, make additional observations and construct a new hypothesis.

b. Feedback Processes in Scientific Investigation

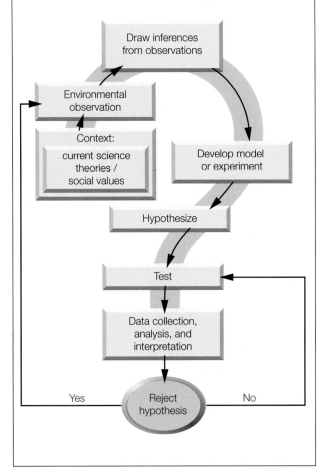

Figure 2–1

Common steps and feedback processes in the scientific method.

ENVIRONMENTAL DECISION MAKING

Just as we can identify a series of steps in the scientific method, we can portray the process of making decisions about the environment as a series of steps (see Table 2–1). While this procedure can help guide rational decision making, it is rather simplistic. In real-world environmental issues, for example, both social and scientific data frequently are incomplete and their interpretation sometimes is controversial. Consequences of particular courses of action are very difficult to anticipate, and unintended consequences are even more difficult to envision, particularly if decisions are based on a personal perspective or only on the economic bottom line. The trend to incorporate public participation processes in environmental decision making may appear to accentuate the conflicting, often emotionally charged, interests of different groups. Often, however, highly effective decisions result after stakeholders have been given an opportunity to build a consensus about appropriate courses of action (assuming implementation strategies are operationalized). Citizens' panels provide a useful example of consensus decision making (see Enviro-Focus 2).

TABLE 2–1
A SIMPLIFIED DECISION-MAKING PROCESS

Steps in Environmental Decision Making

1. State the issue as clearly and concisely as possible.

2. Research the issue, gathering pertinent social and scientific data and information.

3. Identify all possible courses of action (including alternatives developed through public participation processes).

4. Predict the outcome of each course of action with reference to the positive and negative consequences of each.

5. Predict the probability of occurrence of each course of action.

6. Evaluate the alternatives and choose the most sustainable one (followed by implementation).

ENVIRO-FOCUS 2

A Citizen's Panel on Plant Molecular Farming

Plant molecular farming (PMF) is a controversial emerging biotechnology that involves genetically modifying plants to produce drugs, vaccines, and industrial compounds. The plants are not intended for direct consumption by humans or animals, but are being developed experimentally to include drugs, vaccines, and industrial compounds for use in oil, plastic, and cosmetic products. For example, insulin is being produced in safflower, and drugs for use in treatment of Crohn's disease are being developed in tobacco. Concerns have been raised about why and how products are being made from PMF, and their long-term effects on the environment and human health. While PMF has potential benefits for Canadian and international communities, without addressing adequately the risks associated

with it, this biotechnology could cause significant harm to our natural and socioeconomic environments. As of 2007, Canada had not enacted policy or established regulatory frameworks to govern the research, development, and commercialization of PMF products.

Canadian citizens have both a right and a responsibility to be involved in decisions that affect their lives. One way in which "ordinary" Canadians have become involved in issues such as food biotechnology and PMF, and through which they have contributed to national policy and regulations, is by participation in a public engagement process known as a citizens' panel. Citizens' panels bring people together to study and develop in-depth understanding of complex technological, environmental, and social issues. One rationale behind the citizens' panel is that science-based assessments of the risks of new technologies provide an inadequate standard by which to determine policy. With respect to PMF, for instance, the Canadian Food Inspection Agency has undertaken risk assessments

(continued)

---

only on safety issues. Often, only easily quantified variables have been examined (e.g., loss of farmland used for food production), whereas additional criteria and a broader, multidisciplinary approach are needed to examine the risks that are more difficult to quantify. If public policy is to be credible and implemented successfully, citizens' perspectives must be sought early and included in development of policies and regulations respecting controversial emerging biotechnologies such as PMF.

In 1998–99, a group of 12 Canadians had joined a citizens' panel to examine food biotechnology (see Canadian Citizens' Final Report, 1999). Those same citizens reconvened in 2006–07 to investigate PMF issues. Acting independently of government, academia, and, in this case, the biotechnology industry, panel members discussed important questions about environmental and other complexities of PMF with experts and specialists, read research papers and policy documents, identified a range of benefits and risks of PMF, and worked together to produce a report outlining their policy recommendations.

The 2007 citizens' panel report noted that PMF's potential benefits include the development of additional vaccines that may be administered orally (avoiding the need for refrigeration and syringes), transported more easily to other countries, and stockpiled (in a dried form that has a long shelf life). However, a number of risks to

human and animal health exist that must be defined and understood early in development of PMF. For instance, because accidental contamination of the food chain could result in harm (or death) to humans or animals, formal regulations need to be enacted to reduce such risks, including prohibiting the use of major food and feed crops (e.g., corn, canola, soybeans, wheat) as PMF platforms, and isolation of PMF crops from non-PMF crops (e.g., use of confined enclosures for PMF crops). Since the long-term effects of human consumption of genetically modified foods have not been studied, and there is no benchmark for the long-term impacts of consumption of PMF pharmaceuticals, risk management strategies must be developed within the context of public health planning and sustainability.

Since PMF and other biotechnology developments involve value judgments and ethical choices, and have implications for sustainability, the citizens' panel members suggested that a "Public Engagement Bill of Rights" might help ensure ongoing, meaningful public involvement in biotechnology decisions that affect Canadians. The long-standing challenge of having public engagement as the norm rather than the exception in determining resource policies remains, but as Canada's citizens continue asking questions of regulators and strongly expressing their views to policymakers, perhaps the hoped-for paradigm shift will occur.

SOURCES: *Citizens' Final Report*, March 7, 1999, report presented at the Canadian Citizens' Conference on Food Biotechnology, http://www.acs.ucalgary.ca/~pubconf/report.html; *Pharming the Future: A Citizens' Panel Perspective on Plant Molecular Farming*, 2007, Canadian Biotechnology Secretariat, Agriculture and Agri-Food Canada and Genome Canada, www.fp.ucalgary.ca/pharmingthefuture/resources/Pharming%20the%20Future%202.pdf; *Biopromise? Biotechnology, sustainable development and Canada's future economy*, 2006, Ottawa: Canadian Biotechnology Advisory Committee, http://www.cbac.gc.ca/epic/site/cbac-cccb.nsf/en/ah00605e.html
Related information: See UNESCO's Ethics of Science and Technology Programme (www.unesco.org/shs/est), the Union of Concerned Scientists (http://www.ucsaction.org), and the International Council for Science (www.icsu.org).

While there are no easy answers here, it is essential to develop sound, critically evaluated approaches to environmental decisions that include sustainability principles and that reflect a commitment to environmental democracy (Mason, 1999). In practice, environmental democracy recognizes the basic right of humans to a safe and healthy environment and incorporates "an attitude of respect towards other living things, nonviolence and global forms of democratic self-understanding" (Mason, 1999, p. 51). Environmental and social sciences have key roles in positively promoting societal awareness and

understanding of the importance of making environmentally sound decisions. For instance, scientific research has identified a range of health effects of human exposure to toxic substances. Governments have used these data to make difficult decisions about regulating human exposure to hazardous substances. This is a good example of how addressing environmental issues from scientific and societal perspectives can be a powerful means of achieving mutual gain, as well as educating citizens about their common interests in accepting responsibility for the social and environmental costs of their consumption.

Photo 2–6
Environmental decision making should incorporate all possible worldviews and values. Matthew Coon-Come spoke for the Cree during the James Bay hydroelectric development hearings.

In Canada, governments play important roles in science and environmental decision making through involvement in international research agreements, and through domestic support of various research agencies, research councils, Crown agencies, and private-sector interests. In place of the former Technology Partnerships Canada program that helped fund development of environmental technologies, the federal government has established a new program, Funding Technologies for the Environment, to provide information about funding (not financial investment) that is expected to "help advance projects along the technology innovation continuum" (Environment Canada, 2007).

Even though government priorities have reduced monetary support for environmental research, government agendas still drive many research programs. Since most environmental policy decisions are made through the political process, decisions generally are made by political leaders and citizens, and only rarely by the scientists who possess some of the best understanding of environmental problems. This gap emphasizes the need for environmental and scientific education of all those in government and business, particularly policymakers, as well as all citizens.

WORLDVIEWS AND VALUES

Worldviews are "sets of commonly shared values, ideas, and images concerning the nature of reality and the role of humanity within it" (Taylor, 1992, pp. 31–32). Each society's worldview is reflected in and transmitted through its culture (see Box 2–2). Beliefs, ideas, values, and assumptions about knowledge that each culture transmits help to shape attitudes toward nature and human–environment relationships. These attitudes, in turn, lead to lifestyles and behaviours that may or may not be compatible with natural systems and that may or may not cause environmental problems.

Groups of many political persuasions—from ecofeminists and deep ecologists to advocates of maximum resource development—have adopted the term *sustainable development* as a guiding force in their activities. However, each of these groups operates with a different, sometimes conflicting, worldview. Different worldviews lead to different interpretations of sustainability and, in turn, to different decisions about use of the environment to achieve various goals. The two major competing worldviews that characterize Western society—expansionist and ecological—are described briefly below.

EXPANSIONIST AND ECOLOGICAL WORLDVIEWS

Two approaches to conservation in the early part of the 20th century have evolved into two major competing worldviews that exist today. The first of these, the expansionist or Western worldview, is based on the values of the 18th-century Enlightenment tradition. The newer and

Photo 2–7
Crowded and unsanitary urban conditions in 19th-century Europe were a direct result of the Industrial Revolution.

BOX 2-2
A FIRST NATIONS VIEW OF THE NATURAL WORLD

The earth is central to our values. We consider ourselves part of a family that includes all of creation. We refer to the earth as Mother Earth, the giver of all life. We refer to the sun as our eldest brother and the moon as our grandmother. We consider the animal and plant life our brothers and sisters. We consider the waters of the world to be the bloodlines of Mother Earth.... We must make sure that those are always clean so that there will not be a heart attack some day to our mother.

We believe that all of creation has been given instructions by the creator. These instructions are meant to ensure that all of creation can live in harmony and peace.... The waters of the world have been instructed to quench the thirst of all life. It is said that when we drink each cold glass of water, when our throat is so dry, that there isn't a more wonderful feeling of peace and [tranquillity] than what that fresh cold glass of water can do....

Our philosophies are based on the circle of life. To us, all life is seen as revolving in a circle and interrelated. Because movement is circular, any activity or decision made in the present will be felt in the future. In this circle, we do not see ourselves as separate or above the rest of the natural world, but an integral part of it.

Our lifestyles reflect our closeness to the natural world. We are fishers, trappers, hunters, gatherers, and farmers. These lifestyles keep us in touch with the natural world, spiritually, mentally, and physically, on a daily basis. Our close dependence on the natural world means that we must be thankful that the different parts of the natural world are fulfilling the instructions given to them by the creator. It also reminds us that we must also fulfill our instructions as well.

Because of the close relationship we have with the natural world, we cannot have healthy communities unless we have a healthy environment. Our ancestors have always understood this.... We have always recognized the importance of water. The rivers and lakes are used to transport our people from one community to the next. Fish and waterfowl have long been the major source of food for our people. The plants along its shores are the source of our medicines.

We have always followed the natural laws of the world. These laws are rooted in common sense. They say that if something you plan to do could be detrimental to the natural world, [then] don't do it. If we look at all of creation as part of our family, [then] the decisions we make must ensure that our family will come to no harm either today or in the future. Our dependence on the natural world requires us to follow these laws....

....When the Europeans first came to North America, they could not understand why First Nation people would not sell their land. For us, it was an issue of would you sell your mother? Today we cannot understand why it is okay to discharge pollutants into the waters of the world. It is akin to allowing drugs to be injected into [your] mother's blood and [then] saying it is okay because the blood will dilute it.

SOURCE: *Water Is Life,* by J. W. Ransom, September 1995, Technical Bureau Supplement to *Water News,* Canadian Water Resources Association. Reprinted by permission.

still-evolving ecological worldview is based on values of the Counter-Enlightenment and Romantic traditions. A little of the historical nature of both worldviews follows, in order that we may understand their contemporary forms and their links to sustainability.

The Expansionist Worldview

The Enlightenment was a period of profound economic, political, and social changes in society. Capitalism, an economic system based on accumulation of personal wealth, gained wide acceptance. Democracy, established through political revolutions in North America and France, asserted the rights of individuals to determine their own destinies through law making, the ownership of property, and the development of resources on private property.

The Industrial Revolution (beginning in England at the end of the 18th century) brought urbanization, accelerated use of resources, and pollution. As workers clustered

Photo 2–8
Early European immigrants to North America extensively exploited surrounding natural resources.

in industrial areas and became separated physically from direct, daily contact with the land, knowledge of nature was no longer transmitted to succeeding generations. The quality of life in urban areas declined as coal-burning industries polluted the air, as sewage and other wastes were poured into rivers and streams, and as contagious diseases spread quickly in the crowded, unsanitary conditions.

Many Europeans who migrated to North America during this era took their expansionist worldview with them. The roots of this worldview emphasized the following: faith in science and technology to control nature for human ends; belief in the inherent rights of individuals; accumulation of wealth so that material wants could be satisfied and progress could occur; and exploitation of nature and resources to achieve these ends. Arriving in a new land that seemed to have unlimited natural resources, and having the technological means to make maximum use of this resource base, these settlers aggressively exploited their surroundings. With their frontier mentality, European settlers spread across the continent, trying to tame the wilderness. Many of the Native North Americans whose land was taken over and whose cultures were fragmented or destroyed as settlement spread had lived lifestyles based on a very different worldview—a deep respect for the land, its animals, and other resources.

The Ecological Worldview

People who espouse the contemporary ecological worldview have built their opposition to the fundamental assumptions of the expansionist worldview on historical and philosophical traditions from both Western and non-Western sources. To varying degrees, people have accepted concepts from India and China that stress the unity of human life with nature; beliefs from Aboriginal people about the importance of kinship and the relatedness of all life forms; and ideas from the early animistic and mystic traditions of Celtic, Nordic, and Germanic societies (Taylor, 1992).

As well, the Counter-Enlightenment and Romantic thought of the late 18th and early 19th centuries influenced the ecological worldview. In particular, the ecological viewpoint protested the Enlightenment assumption that the universe was a great machine that rationalized and mechanized humans and nature and separated them from their intrinsic spiritual value. According to the expansionist worldview at that time, quantities (measurability) mattered, not qualities. Values, emotions, instincts, and all non-measurable aspects of the environment were of secondary importance compared with science and reason. Body and mind, and spirit and nature, were separate entities. On the contrary, Romanticism (part of the Counter-Enlightenment position) emphasized the importance of emotions, instincts, and the irrational. Romantics reacted against urbanization and technology and celebrated the world of nature and all that was not artificial. They tried to unify those elements

expansionists had separated—body and mind, and the supernatural and natural (Taylor, 1992).

During this Counter-Enlightenment period, the roles of human emotions, independence, and freedom of expression were elevated, sometimes above the claims of reason and science. Poets such as William Wordsworth extolled the values of beauty and tranquillity in nature and denounced artificial and urban realms. Other writers of the 1800s, such as Thoreau and Emerson, promoted individuals' rights to access universal truths through personal communion with nature and criticized the existing political structures for standing in the way of these truths. Writing in the 1860s, when deforestation was the major environmental preoccupation, George Perkins Marsh, a physical geographer, warned of the destructive effects of dominant cultural beliefs and practices on the environment.

Conservation in the Early 20th Century

The conservation movement was a reaction to "the excesses and wastefulness of an expanding industrial society," but by the early 20th century conservationists were viewing the problems from two competing worldviews (Taylor, 1992, p. 30). "Wise-management" conservationists such as Clifford Sifton in Canada (see Box 2–3) and Gifford Pinchot in the United States were allied with the expansionist worldview and pitted against the "righteous-management" conservationists such as Americans John Muir and, later, Aldo Leopold and Rachel Carson (see Figure 2–2, pp. 50–51). Both Leopold and Carson spoke of human responsibility for the Earth, echoing the older Christian concept of **stewardship**. Some of the key perspectives of each approach to conservation are presented in Table 2–2 on page 49. (For a definitive history of the conservation movement, see the book by Hays [1959] listed in the References section of this chapter.)

In addition to the features noted in Table 2–2, members of the wise-management school of preservation made it known that they were not preservationists but promoted sustainable exploitation, in which forests, soils, water, and wildlife could be harvested as if they were renewable crops. In contrast, righteous-management conservationists rejected the expansionist emphasis on viewing the world principally in economic and utilitarian terms. Preservationists believed that, in nature, humans could realize their inner spiritual, aesthetic, and moral sensibilities. Believing that physical nature, particularly wilderness, was a benchmark against which to judge the state of human society, the preservationists suggested that large areas of the natural world should be preserved and protected against human interference (Taylor, 1992).

During the period 1900 to 1960, the values of the Enlightenment tradition remained dominant in conservation theory in both Canada and the United States. Nature was seen as a storehouse of resources used to satisfy the

Clifford Victor Sifton was born in 1861 on a farm about two kilometres east of the tiny village of Arva, just north of London, Ontario. Although little is known of his early childhood, he had an outstanding record at school and won the gold medal when he graduated from Victoria College in Cobourg, Ontario, in 1880.

Ambitious and well educated, Sifton articled with a Winnipeg law firm and was called to the Manitoba bar in 1882. His legal practice in Brandon soon flourished, and he became the city solicitor. Like his father before him, Clifford Sifton entered politics, running as a Liberal candidate in the North Brandon riding. Successful in his bid for the seat, Sifton entered the Manitoba legislature in 1888, rising to become attorney general in the government of Thomas Greenway in 1891.

In January 1896, Sifton masterminded Greenway's victory in the provincial election, and in June 1896, the Liberals under Wilfrid Laurier won the federal election. In late 1896, Laurier appointed Clifford Sifton minister of the interior and superintendent general of Indian affairs in the federal Cabinet.

As minister of the interior, Sifton earned his place in Canadian history for his aggressive promotion of immigration to settle the west. But he also was one of the few public officials who knew about the conservation movement in other countries and realized Canada should do something—even though its resources seemed inexhaustible, they were not unlimited. Almost as soon as he became minister of the interior, Sifton placed forests under federal control and in 1902 created a separate forestry branch of the Department of the Interior. Sifton had also organized the Canadian Forestry Association in 1900.

By this time, conservation had gained national importance in Canada, as it had in the United States. In May 1909, the Canadian government established a Commission of Conservation and appointed Sifton as chairman. Although it had no formal power, the Commission set up a wide range of studies on topics including fisheries, forestry, lands, minerals, game and fur-bearing animals, water and water power, and public health.

In Sifton's day, conservation focused more on efficient management and the best way to exploit resources, rather than on preservation. The forest industry, for example, was governed by only a few, poorly enforced government regulations. The Commission of Conservation was determined to demonstrate that Canada would benefit from sensible conservation regulations in the long term. Sifton believed that forests should be preserved not just for the sake of their beauty but also because, in practical business terms, conservation techniques made economic sense. A successful businessman himself, Sifton argued that private enterprise operated in its own self-interest and that government control was needed to protect the public interest.

Sifton campaigned strongly against free trade and the practice of selling Canada's resources to the United States. In 1910, on behalf of the Commission, Sifton persuaded the Canadian government to veto a U.S. plan to construct a hydroelectric dam on the St. Lawrence River at the Long Sault Rapids above Cornwall. Sifton was convinced the project would lock Canada into permanently supplying power for U.S. industries. Following a similar dispute over another power project, Sifton resigned from the Commission in 1918. Without his leadership, the Commission carried little influence and was abolished by the government in May 1921.

Sifton's public contributions to Canadian life were recognized by King George V, who knighted him on January 1, 1915. Following the First World War, Sifton was no longer in government, but he served from 1924 to 1928 on the Canadian National Advisory Committee on the development of the St. Lawrence Seaway for shipping and hydroelectric purposes. Once again Sifton argued that the international section of the river should not be developed for hydropower until Canadian demand was sufficient to warrant development.

Sir Clifford Sifton died in a New York hospital from the effects of abdominal cancer on April 17, 1929. Two days later, the father of conservation in Canada was buried in Toronto's Mount Pleasant Cemetery.

SOURCES: *Clifford Sifton*, D. J. Hall, 1976, Don Mills, ON: Fitzhenry & Whiteside; "Sir Clifford Sifton," D. J. Hall, 1988, *Canadian Encyclopedia* (2nd ed.), pp. 1999–2000.

continually increasing material needs of an ever-growing population. The expansionist worldview equated material growth with development, which, in turn, was seen as a prerequisite for human happiness and prosperity. Proponents of the expansionist worldview continue to believe that scientific and technological advances will ensure increased global standards of living, employ renewable and other environmentally friendly sources of energy, increase food production, solve the problems created by previous technologies, create substitutes for depleted resources, and replace damaged environments (Taylor, 1992). Although the expansionist worldview originated with capitalism, today both capitalist and socialist countries apply the basic tenets of the expansionist position.

ENVIRONMENTALISM

In the 1960s and 1970s, a reassertion of Counter-Enlightenment and Romantic values occurred within the conservation movement. In fact, during this time of environmental revolution, both Canadian and U.S. governments began to recognize the value of qualitative and eco-centric approaches to conservation. The late 1960s and early 1970s were years of idealism and optimism—environmental awareness (including interest in worldviews held by other cultures) was growing among all segments of the population, major issues such as pollution and nuclear power were receiving media attention (see Table 2–3), and various pieces of legislation respecting environmental

TABLE 2-2
A COMPARISON OF EARLY-20TH-CENTURY APPROACHES TO CONSERVATION

Expansionist Worldview	Ecological Worldview
"Wise management" is based on the values of the Enlightenment tradition:	"Preservation" or "righteous management" is based on the values of the Counter-Enlightenment tradition:
• Nature is a resource to be used, not preserved.	• The universe is nondualistic, a totality with all of its parts interrelated and interlocked.
• Conservation must work together with the dominant values of the surrounding society, not against them.	• The biotic community and its processes must be protected.
• The primary value of natural areas lies in their value to modern society.	• Nature is intrinsically valuable—animals, trees, rock, etc., have value in themselves.
• Conservation should work against the wastefulness and environmentally disruptive excesses of a developing society.	• Human activities must work within the limitations of the planet's ecosystems.
• Conservation is equated with sustainable exploitation.	• Preservation works against the dominant societal values.
	• Nature provides a forum to judge the state of human society.

SOURCE: Adapted from "Disagreeing on the Basics: Environmental Debates Reflect Competing World Views," D. M. Taylor, 1992, *Alternatives, 18*(3), p. 29. Reprinted courtesy of Alternatives Journal: Environmental Thought, Policy and Action.

TABLE 2-3
ENVIRONMENTAL ISSUES AND CHARACTERISTICS OF THE FIRST AND SECOND WAVES OF ENVIRONMENTALISM

Environmental Issues	Characteristics and Emphases
First Wave (1968–76)	***First Wave (1968–76)***
• Pollution	• Tendency for individuals and groups to alienate themselves, to detach from social, political, and economic order
• Energy crisis	• Anti-technological character
• Offshore oil drilling, tanker spills	• Tendency to millennialism (escapism)
• Nuclear power	• Regulatory, "end-of-pipe" solutions favoured by decision makers (standards for emissions)
• Population	• Building awareness of problems
• Resource depletion, especially of oil	
• Urban neighbourhood preservation	
Second Wave (1985 onward)	***Second Wave (1985 onward)***
• Global warming	• Re-emergence of preservationist issues
• Ozone depletion	• Globalized concerns
• New wilderness and habitat concerns: old-growth forests, tropical rain forests, animal rights	• Acceptability of some environmental ideas within economic and political elites
• Waste reduction, recycling	• Professional character of major environmental organizations
• Hazardous wastes, carcinogens, pollution	• Split between those inclined to compromise and those opposed
• Resource depletion, especially of forests, fisheries, and biodiversity	• Multiple tools approach
• Oil tanker spills	
• Urban planning, automobiles, land use	
• Indoor air quality	

SOURCE: Adapted from "Eco-history: Two Waves in the Evolution of Environmentalism," R. Paehlke, 1992, *Alternatives, 19*(1), p. 22. Reprinted courtesy of Alternatives Journal: Environmental Thought, Policy and Action.

Figure 2–2

Key early figures in
20th-century conservation

John Muir
(1838–1914)

- Explorer, naturalist, writer
- Crusaded for establishment of
  parks and preservation of forests
- Instrumental in establishment of
  Yosemite and Sequoia National Parks

Gifford Pinchot
(1865–1946)

- Forester and politician
- Introduced principles of scientific
  forest management
- Worked with F. D. Roosevelt in
  establishing many National Forests

Clifford Sifton
(1861–1929)

- Lawyer and politician
- Minister of Interior—created separate
  forestry branch (1902)
- Considered father of conservation
  in Canada

founded
Sierra Club

The Yosemite

*The Fight for
Conservation*

estab. Cdn. Forestry Assoc.

| *1890* | 1892 | 1898 | 1900 | 1909 | 1910 | 1912 | 1918 | *1920* | *1930* |

Chief of U.S. Forest Service

Chair of Commission of Conservation

protection were promoted. The first Earth Day and environmental teach-in, bringing together scientists, environmentalists, politicians, students, government officials, and citizen groups, was held in the United States on April 20, 1970. In 1971 the Canadian government established the Department of the Environment. Since then, Environment Week in Canada has been an important way to promote environmental awareness and the benefits of environmental protection among Canadians (see Box 2–4).

However, long-lasting change in understanding nature and the place of humans in the environment did not occur during this first wave of environmentalism (1968–76). When inflation and an economic downturn began to drive the monetary costs of a clean environment upward, many people (especially in economically disadvantaged regions) began to argue that jobs were more important than environmental controls (Paehlke, 1992).

By the 1980s, the idealism of the 1960s and 1970s had given way to an emphasis on individual well-being, especially economic well-being. In both Canada and the United States, eco-centric values in conservation were increasingly difficult to maintain as the idea of limits to growth was rejected, eco-centric values were pitted against development values, and economic goals took precedence in environmental and resource management decisions (Taylor, 1992). For example, in 1987, when *Our Common Future* (the Brundtland Report) was published and

Photo 2–9

A windmill and an inflatable globe serve as visual props in encouraging ecology at an Earth Day celebration on the lawn of the Capitol Building, Washington, D.C.

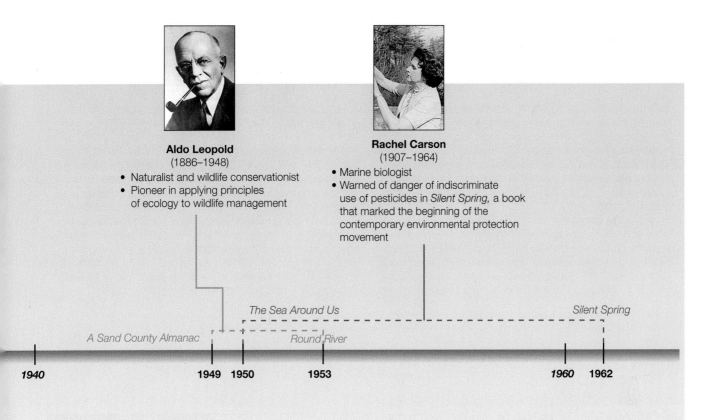

Aldo Leopold
(1886–1948)

- Naturalist and wildlife conservationist
- Pioneer in applying principles of ecology to wildlife management

Rachel Carson
(1907–1964)

- Marine biologist
- Warned of danger of indiscriminate use of pesticides in *Silent Spring,* a book that marked the beginning of the contemporary environmental protection movement

The Sea Around Us

Silent Spring

A Sand County Almanac

Round River

1940   1949 1950   1953   1960   1962

BOX 2–4
ENVIRONMENT WEEK IN CANADA

Canadian Environment Week is held in early June each year to coincide with World Environment Day (proclaimed by the United Nations in 1972, and celebrated on June 5). Initiated in 1970 on former prime minister John Diefenbaker's suggestion that a week should be set aside to focus on environmental issues, Canada's Environment Week was established through a private member's bill introduced by British Columbia member of Parliament Tom Goode. Given royal assent in March 1971, Environment Week in Canada provides an opportunity for concerned citizens to focus on environmental issues and to help conserve and protect our country's natural heritage. A key purpose of Environment Week is to urge all Canadians to make activities that preserve the Earth a part of their daily lives.

The theme of Environment Week has varied, but from 2004 the focus has been on "Taking Action for our Environment." People are encouraged to make small changes such as using less water and electricity.

Over the more than 35 years of its history, two themes emerged and became annual events during Canada's Environment Week, namely the Commuter Challenge and Clean Air Day. Provincial and municipal jurisdictions, workplaces, and a variety of other organizations issue challenges to citizens, employees, and members to walk, cycle, roller blade, skateboard, use public transportation, and car pool during Environment Week. The Commuter Challenge previously was linked closely to the federal government's One Tonne Challenge, an initiative that encouraged every Canadian voluntarily to reduce their current greenhouse gas (GHG) emissions by one tonne. Since half of Canada's GHG emissions come from vehicles, we personally could reduce GHGs significantly by driving less, driving fuel-efficient vehicles, and using biofuels and ethanol-enhanced fuel. However, the One Tonne Challenge program was cancelled in April 2006. Clean Air Day aims both to increase our awareness of air quality and climate change and to celebrate and promote actions, such as tree planting and recycling, that improve air quality and address climate change (see http://www.climatechange.gc.ca/plan_for_canada/challenge).

Be sure to watch for Environment Week activities in your community. Better yet, become involved personally. To find out more about Environment Week activities, go to your local and provincial government environment websites or to Environment Canada's website (where, unfortunately, you now need to use the search function to find Environment Week information).

BOX 2-5

THE UNITED NATIONS AND GLOBAL WATER INITIATIVES

International efforts to resolve the world's water problems date back several decades, and work continues today to help ensure that a growing number of people have access to safe drinking water and adequate sanitation. Commencing on World Water Day, March 22, 2005, the General Assembly of the United Nations proclaimed the years 2005 to 2015 as the International Decade for Action, "Water for Life" (and 2008 as the International Year of Sanitation).

Every three years, UN-Water (the interagency group that coordinates all United Nations agencies working in the area of freshwater resources) publishes its flagship World Water Development Report (WWDR). UN-Water's World Water Assessment Programme (founded in 2000) monitors water problems, develops case studies for discussion, and provides recommendations to help meet future demand. Two reports have been published to date: *Water for People, Water for Life* was released in 2003 as part of the International Year of Freshwater, and *Water: A Shared Responsibility* was presented at the fourth World Water Forum held in Mexico in March 2006. Subsequent editions of the report are anticipated in 2009, 2012, and 2015, and are expected to help monitor progress toward achieving the targets set at the Millennium Summit and the World Summit for Sustainable Development.

Since achieving water sustainability is a shared responsibility, and since "sound water governance should be open and transparent, inclusive and communicative, coherent and integrative, and equitable and ethical," it is vital to continue the international momentum and leadership of the UN-Water's World Water Assessment Programme (WWAP, 2006, p. 92).

SOURCE: *Water: a shared responsibility*. World Water Assessment Programme (WWAP). (2006). New York: United Nations Educational, Scientific and Cultural Organization (UNESCO)/Berghahn Books. http://www.unesco.org/water/wwap/wwdr1/table_contents/index.shtml

nations were challenged to develop sustainable development strategies, the Canadian government replied "within the framework of the Expansionist" worldview (Taylor, 1992, p. 28). Although neoconservative or expansionist values were dominant among federal politicians, poll after poll showed North Americans wanted to continue efforts to ensure a clean, safe environment for their children and themselves (see Dunlap, 1987).

This latent interest in environmental matters and concern for the state of the environment generated a second wave of environmentalism from 1985 onward. Not only were Counter-Enlightenment and Romantic values back again, but this time deep ecology and sustainable development entered the debate (Paehlke, 1992; Taylor, 1992). As illustrated in Table 2–3, issues of concern in the second wave of environmentalism often were global in perspective (particularly global warming and ozone depletion), and frequently dealt with nature, wilderness, and biodiversity. Earth Day 2000, the 30th anniversary event, was celebrated worldwide as a global expression of support for environmental action. In 2007, Earth Day organizers initiated a three-year, worldwide theme—"Urgent Climate Action"—with the goal of educating consumers, corporations, and governments on the pressing need to take immediate concrete steps on climate change. Other issues that are global in extent also are receiving longer-term attention from agencies such as the United Nations (see Box 2–5).

Deep Ecology, Sustainable Development, and Green Alternatives

Neither *deep ecology* nor *sustainable development* were familiar terms prior to the second wave of

Photo 2–10

The long-standing protest at Greenham Common, in England, against U.S. nuclear missile storage may be seen as an early expression of ecofeminism. Following decommissioning of the U.S. nuclear facilities, area residents formed Greenham Common Trust and purchased the area in 1997. The Common has been restored and reopened to the public to enjoy again.

Established in 1992 by the United Nations General Assembly, World Water Day (WWD) provides an opportunity to raise awareness of global water challenges. In recognition of WWD, March 22, 2003, seven people from different UN agencies, including UN University, wrote an editorial that began with bleak messages about water shortages, contaminated water, water-borne diseases, and the prediction of "impending calamity." However, they also offered a message of hope that

- the cooperation evidenced in watershed management will continue,

- investment will continue in water treatment facilities that have helped formerly "dead" rivers in North America and Europe to support fish spawning and migration,

- improvements in sanitation systems in Asia (which provided clean water to 220 million people in 1990) will be extended to the 800 million people still without safe and healthy supplies of drinking water.

These authors noted clearly that the world does not need any more declarations on how to achieve sustainability. Rather, what is needed is action on these declarations, such as the Plan of Implementation established at the 2002 World Summit on Sustainable Development. Responsible stewardship to safeguard the world's freshwater resources will require integrated management at all levels, from the individual to the international.

Efforts continue toward water sustainability. For instance, the theme for WWD 2007 was "Coping with Water Scarcity," a focus that highlighted the significance of cooperation and the importance of an integrated approach to water resource management at local and international levels. In dealing with limited water resources, issues of equity and rights, culture, and ethics, must be addressed as effectively as issues of the degradation of groundwater and surface water quality. The WWD's 2008 theme is sanitation, coinciding with the UN declaration of 2008 as the International Year of Sanitation.

SOURCES: *A Glass Half Empty? An editorial by United Nations Agencies and UN University for World Water Day, 22nd March 2003,* N. Desai, M. M. Brown, K. Toepfer, K. Matsuura, A. Tibaijuka, C. Bellamy, & H. van Ginkel, 2003, http://update.unu.edu/archive/issue24_18.htm; *About WWC,* World Water Council, n.d., http://www.worldwatercouncil.org/

environmentalism. Deep ecology states that humans are only one species among many, and that nature and non-human species are as valuable in their own right as are humans (Devall & Sessions, 1985). These assertions are labelled, respectively, the *principle of self-realization* (an awareness of one's ultimate inseparability and wholeness with the nonhuman world) and the *principle of biocentric equality* (the belief that all organisms and entities in the ecosphere have intrinsic worth and are part of the interrelated web of life). In the deep ecologist's view, at least implicitly, these principles mean that sometimes wild nature must be chosen over human habitat and human well-being. In contrast, sustainable development gives priority to global human needs (Paehlke, 1992).

Throughout North America and Europe, other green alternatives have developed that criticize the assumptions underlying modern society. Like deep ecology, ecofeminism is based on the biocentric equality principle but also tries to address the "hierarchical and dominance relationships that it sees as endemic to patriarchy" (Taylor, 1992, p. 30). Ecofeminism argues that the ongoing domination of nature and the ongoing domination of women are systemically related (Hessing, 1993; Salleh, 1984). Similarly, social ecologists argue that all forms of human domination are related directly to the issue of ecology. That is, as long as hierarchy and domination occur in human society, then the domination

of nature will continue and lead the planet to ecological extinction (Bookchin, 1980).

Ecological worldview adherents also have found the study of general systems theory to be useful, in that its view of the universe as a systemic hierarchy, or as organized complexity, pictures a "myriad of wholes within wholes, all of them interconnected and interacting" (Taylor, 1992, p. 31; Prigogine & Stengers, 1984). This perspective has appeared in James Lovelock's Gaia hypothesis, which explained the Earth and its living organisms in terms of a single, indivisible, self-regulating process (Lovelock, 1988). Lovelock's theory provided impetus to the concern that human expansionist activities at local levels were threatening Gaia's health and all the life contained on the planet.

Environmentalism is, primarily, a social movement; it embodies numerous environmentalist ideologies (as above) and organizational diversity (as you will note throughout this book). The major contribution that environmentalism has made to sustainability has emanated from efforts of numerous people to have nonhuman species and the interests of future generations included on political agendas and within democratic decision-making processes (Mason, 1999). In challenging existing models of democratic politics, environmentalism has created "tension between democratic means and green ends" (Mason, 1999, p. 31). Since ecological degradation affects everyone, we all share a common interest in addressing environmental problems. How society prioritizes these environmental interests that constitute the basis of our physical survival and well-being, and how society includes human rights to a healthy and safe environment, are part of the challenge of achieving environmental democracy (see the section "Science and Environmental Decision Making" earlier in this chapter).

Toward the Future

The second wave of environmentalism brought about remarkable changes. Environmental ideas now are widely promoted within the North American and international political elites. Today, blue boxes, composting, and other recycling programs generate economic returns for municipalities. In the business world, being perceived as environmentally concerned is important to a company's corporate image and perhaps to business success. Unfortunately, in some instances these changes reveal that the concept of sustainable development has been "co-opted by individuals and institutions to perpetuate many of the worst aspects of the expansionist model under the masquerade of something new" (Taylor, 1992, p. 32). However, sustainability does carry the hope that society will be able to transform its political, economic, and social institutions in keeping with what is socially and environmentally sustainable.

The expression of worldviews in the political sphere of the 1990s is illustrated in Figure 2–3. The horizontal axis shows that political opinions held by environmentalists or nonenvironmentalists can be either left or right.

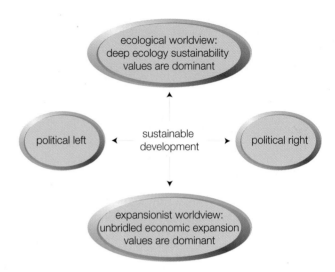

Figure 2–3

Worldviews in the political sphere at the turn of the 21st century

SOURCE: After "Eco-history: Two Waves in the Evolution of Environmentalism," R. Paehlke, 1992, *Alternatives, 19*(1), p. 22. Reprinted courtesy of Alternatives Journal: Environmental Thought, Policy and Action.

The vertical axis places ecological (sustainability) and expansionist (economic) worldviews at opposite ends, with sustainable development somewhere in the middle. There is tension between these ecological–sustainable development–expansionist values and ways of looking at the world; the challenge for the future is to identify and reach win-win conditions that will allow simultaneous improvement in equity, economy, and ecology.

The term *sustainable development* provides an opportunity for a dialogue between enthusiasts of economic growth, environmentalists, and advocates of greater equity among peoples and within nations. However, the real challenge lies in integrating new ideas for ecological protection and sustainability with a workable set of transformations of society and economy (Mason, 1999; Paehlke, 1992). For many people, current environmental problems reflect a cultural or worldview crisis, a concern for current national and international policies and values as they affect the long-term viability of social and natural systems. Thus, understanding the struggle between the entrenched expansionist worldview and the rising ecological worldview is important in helping us move toward both environmental and societal sustainability in the future.

Making decisions about our environment and planning effectively to meet the needs of the future require us to place a value on all aspects of our environment. As we attempt to deal with the expanding human population, meet the needs of an urban world, sustain resources for future generations, and preserve our environment on a global level, we need to know how we

Photo 2–11

Increasing awareness and changing attitudes result in a broader acceptance of environmental initiatives, such as the Blue Box recycling campaign.

Environmental degradation, conservation practices, environmental conflicts over resource uses and user groups—these are some of the topics studied by political ecologists. Political ecology is a field of study conducted by geographers, anthropologists, ecologists, historians, and sociologists, among others. Political ecologists contend that environmental problems do not simply emerge from simple explanations of "overpopulation" or "overconsumption." Rather, they are caused and affected by political and economic inequalities among people. Thus, political ecologists pay attention to identifying the groups who have power to control, develop, and distribute resources and how environmental decisions affect environmental quality and well-being for different groups and across different places. Political ecologists accept the idea that costs and benefits associated with environmental change typically are distributed unequally among groups of people and across different geographic places. Changes in environmental quality may reinforce or reduce existing social and economic inequalities and will reflect dominant political and economic interests. For example, the creation of parks to protect biodiversity may have adverse effects on local populations who need to use lands for crop or livestock production. In many societies, including Canada, women and men may have differential access to specific resources and to decision-making forums. In both cases, how do these differences in political, social, and economic powers affect the transformation and use of the environment? These are the kinds of issues political ecologists typically tackle.

are changing the environment, how we can rectify the problems we have caused, and what factors are most important to us. To these ends, the following section provides a brief discussion of environmental values and environmental ethics.

Photo 2–12
Family fishing endeavours in Canada's coastal communities, particularly in Newfoundland, have suffered as a result of declining fish stocks.

ENVIRONMENTAL VALUES AND ETHICS

ENVIRONMENTAL VALUES

Placing a value on some aspect of our environment—for example, healthy fish populations in Canada's rivers and oceans, clean air in industrialized regions of the country, scenic beauty, or the preservation of natural landscapes—may be based on utilitarian, ecological, aesthetic, or moral categories. The utilitarian and ecological categories deal with practical reasons such as economic benefit or our own survival. A **utilitarian justification** for the conservation of nature states that the environment, ecosystem, habitat, or species provides individuals with direct economic benefits or is directly necessary to their survival. Fishers, for example, derive their livelihood from the oceans and need a supply of fish so that they may continue to earn their living.

An **ecological justification** for conserving nature is based on the knowledge that a species, an ecological community, an ecosystem, or the Earth's biosphere provides specific functions necessary to the persistence of our life. The ability of trees in forests to remove carbon dioxide produced through burning fossil fuels is a public benefit and an important element in the argument to maintain large areas of forest. Enlightened self-interest also would suggest that dealing with the problems of polluted air in parts of Eastern Europe (caused by burning lignite and poor-quality coal) would be beneficial ecologically. Similarly, even if individuals do not benefit immediately, there is value in action designed to counter the production of greenhouse gases that lead to climate change affecting the entire Earth.

Science and economics may direct us toward global environmental protection, but music is a powerful motivator for humans that helps inspire action to protect the Earth. Much emotive music has been written in response to composers' personal experiences in nature—from Beethoven's symphonies such as the Sixth (*Pastoral*) Symphony, to Great Big Sea's "Fisherman's Lament." In environmental terms, we can say that Beethoven's Sixth dramatizes weather concepts, while Great Big Sea's Lament describes resource issues associated with the crisis in the Newfoundland cod fishery—but both pieces of music are much more powerful than these descriptors. Music lyrics often contain references to ecological crises and their effects on people, and speak to the linkages (or disconnections) between society and environment. Joni Mitchell (2007) clearly captures a key disconnect in "This Place," a

sentiment that echoes G. Horse Capture's words at the outset of this chapter:

You see those lovely hills
They won't be there for long
They're gonna tear 'em down
And sell them to California
Here come the toxic spills
Miners poking all around
When this place looks like a moonscape
Don't say I didn't warn ya....

Money, money, money...
Money makes the trees come down
It makes mountains into molehills
Big money kicks the wide wide world around.

Aesthetic arguments for the conservation and protection of nature are made on the basis that nature is beautiful and that beauty is of profound importance and value to people. In an effort to add beauty to their surroundings, many people spend hours gardening, and city workers plant trees, shrubs, and flowers in parks and on boulevards. On a larger scale, many people find the Canadian wilderness beautiful and would rather live in a world with wilderness than without it. Psychological, medical, and social benefits accrue from the aesthetic values of the environment. For example, research has shown that patients recover more quickly if their hospital room has a view of trees and natural landscapes (Krakauer, 1990). The value of natural sounds and areas as restorative environments (Hartig, Mang, & Evans, 1990) and of wilderness as sacred space (Graber, 1976) are examples of how important the environment's aesthetic values are.

A **moral justification** for conserving nature is that aspects or elements of the environment have a right to exist, independent of human desires, and it is our moral obligation to allow them to continue or to help them persist. An example of moral justification is the assertion that the Fraser River in British Columbia and the Red Deer River in Alberta (examples of the few remaining "wild" rivers in populated areas of Canada) have the right to exist as free-running waters. Similar moral arguments have been extended to many nonhuman organisms, such as trees and wildlife. For instance, in 1982 the United Nations General Assembly World Charter for Nature stated that species have a right to exist. From a human perspective, a strong moral claim for working toward ecological sustainability exists because humans have rights to

a healthy environment as well as rights to participate in environmental decision-making processes.

A new discipline, environmental ethics, analyzes these issues and the concerns about our moral obligations to future generations with respect to the environment. Environmental ethics is introduced briefly in the following section.

ENVIRONMENTAL ETHICS

During the 1970s, philosophers began to develop **environmental ethics,** a field that studies the value of the physical and biological environment. Because it is a large and complex academic subject, only a few aspects of the field are considered here.

The need for new environmental ethics has arisen because of the diverse changes that human activities and technology are bringing to the world. For instance, humans are having new effects on nature, are developing new knowledge of the environment, and are creating an expanded set of moral concerns. Environmental ethics indicates that an examination of the utilitarian, ecological, aesthetic, and moral consequences of these developments is necessary.

With regard to our new knowledge of nature, science and social science have been able to show us how we have changed our surroundings in ways that were not understood previously. For example, scientists have demonstrated that the burning of fossil fuels and the large-scale clearing of forests have changed the amount of carbon dioxide in the atmosphere, which is changing the global climate. This global perspective provides an impetus to examine new moral issues. Also, the extension of moral and legal rights to

Photo 2–14
The use of living animals in scientific experimentation is controversial. Is their use justifiable?

the moral responsibility to sustain nature for ourselves and for future generations. This philosophy has certain implications; for example, although the land ethic assigns rights to animals to survive as a species, it does not necessarily assign those same rights of survival to an individual member of a species (a deer or chicken, for example). This means we must distinguish between an ideal and a realistic land ethic. Another implication is that because the wilderness has intrinsic value, we, as morally responsible stewards, must maintain it for itself and because our own survival depends on it. Whether or not we agree with the land ethic, we need to consider whether ethical values should be extended to nonhuman biological communities. Our position will depend on our values and our understanding of natural systems and other environmental factors.

Given that human effects on today's environment have consequences for the future, any discussion of environmental ethics also involves the rights of future generations and what we owe them. This issue has become increasingly important because the impacts of technology have the potential to affect the environment for hundreds or thousands of years to come. Radioactive waste from nuclear plants, long-term climate changes resulting from land use changes and technology, extinction of large numbers of species as a result of human activities, and the direct effects of human population increases are among the issues of concern for the future. Depending on what we know about these issues, we will make value judgments about them, about the rights of future citizens, and about the idea of stewardship of the Earth. If we think it is important to consider the future in our decision making, then we are more likely to consider ourselves as merely the latest in a long line of humans who are the stewards of the Earth.

In response to the potentially major changes that these issues imply, some people have reacted by "hiding their heads in the sand," seeking a simpler life, and rejecting all science, technology, and progress. A more useful, longer-term response would be to use science and technology to the best of our abilities, keeping in mind our environmental ethics. Ernest Partridge (1981), a philosopher concerned with environmental ethics, has commented that scientific knowledge and discipline need to be augmented by a critical moral sense and passionate moral purpose if we are to ensure a better future.

Ultimately, there are many ways in which each of us can become involved in environmental ethics. Environmentalism encompasses a wide range of approaches, from the conservative to the radical, to making a difference in the world around us. In simple ways, every one of us can address environmental issues personally by adjusting our lifestyles and attitudes toward consumerism. By using the best available scientific instruments and methods, and being aware of the ethical implications of our actions, we can better understand and contribute to the appropriate management of our environment and its resources.

animals, trees, and objects such as rocks is seen as a natural expansion of civilization as it begins to incorporate the environment in ethics and politics.

Concern with environmental ethics involves discussion of the rights of animals and plants, of nonliving things, and of large systems that are important to our life support. One important statement of environmental ethics is Aldo Leopold's land ethic. In *A Sand County Almanac*, Leopold (1949) affirmed that all resources (plants, animals, and earth materials) have a right to exist, to continue to exist, and to continue to exist in a natural state in at least some locations. This land ethic indicates that humans are no longer conquerors of the land but are citizens and protectors of the environment. As citizens and protectors, humans should show love and reverence in their relationships with the land; land is not merely an economic commodity to be used up and discarded. Leopold's land ethic assumes that we are ethically responsible to other individuals and society, as well as to the larger environment of which we are a part (including plants, animals, soils, the atmosphere, and water). Note that such responsibility places some limits on the freedom of individuals and societies in their struggle for existence.

Leopold's land ethic suggests that each of us is a steward of our environment; our role as stewards includes

Photo 2-13
David Suzuki

David Suzuki may have retired from his position as full professor at the University of British Columbia in 2001, but he has not stopped working. An outspoken advocate for environmental sustainability, Suzuki used the skills he gained through 30 years in broadcasting to become Canada's best-known environmentalist, whose influence is widespread, from local communities to Parliament Hill. For instance, when former prime minister Jean Chrétien signed the Kyoto Accord, he credited Dr. Suzuki and the David Suzuki Foundation for raising public awareness of and support for measures to address climate change.

An internationally respected geneticist, Suzuki founded CBC Radio's *Quirks and Quarks* program and became the host of CBC's television series *The Nature of Things* in 1979. For decades, Suzuki has used his scientific expertise and credibility to bring attention to environmental issues, explaining complex scientific phenomena in a manner that is compelling and easily understood. He has received numerous awards for his work, including the UNESCO Science Prize, the United Nations Environment Programme Medal, and the Order of Canada. He has 18 honorary doctorates from universities in Canada and elsewhere, and for his work in support of First Nations people, he has been honoured with five names and formal adoption by two tribes. Author of 42 books, in 1990 he established the nonprofit David Suzuki Foundation (http://www.davidsuzuki.org/) to bring attention and find innovative solutions to environmental challenges.

The David Suzuki Foundation has worked to identify ways for society to live in balance with the natural world that sustains us, and has used science and education to promote solutions that conserve nature and help achieve sustainability. Focusing on four program areas—oceans and sustainable fishing, climate change and clean energy, sustainability, and the Nature Challenge—the Foundation aims to achieve sustainability within a generation. David Suzuki and those who work with him at the Foundation have helped provide Canadians with the knowledge, tools, and motivation they need to make simple changes in their everyday lives, changes that "make a difference" to "Our Environment."

We may think that our individual actions are inadequate, yet when combined, they can change the world—as the more than 360 000 Canadians who have joined the Foundation's Nature Challenge believe. The Nature Challenge provides an opportunity to lighten our footprint on the planet by making practical, science-based changes in the ways we consume energy, choose food, and travel. Reducing our consumption of resources, shifting to clean energy sources, protecting and conserving water, producing healthy food—such goals require significant shifts in government policies and a real commitment from governments, businesses, and ourselves to achieve sustainability in Canada.

By March 10, 2008, in partnership with the David Suzuki Foundation, over 500 members of the National Hockey League Players Association (NHLPA) were taking part in the NHLPA Carbon Neutral Challenge during the 2007–08 hockey season. Players from all 30 teams in the league purchased high-quality Gold Standard carbon credits to offset the travel emissions associated with playing professional hockey. Calculating that each player's travel generated 10 tonnes of greenhouse gas emissions, players who joined the challenge went carbon neutral, offsetting more than 5000 tonnes of carbon—the equivalent of taking 1000 cars off the road for one year.

David Suzuki has been described as passionate and even controversial. Yet, he has long challenged Canadians to consider the intersection of science, worldviews, and ethics as we identify pathways (and roadblocks) toward sustainability.

SOURCES: *Sustainability within a Generation: A New Vision for Canada*, D. R. Boyd, 2004, Vancouver: The David Suzuki Foundation; *Top Ten Great Canadians: David Suzuki*, Canadian Broadcasting Corporation, 2007, http://www.cbc.ca/greatest/top_ten/nominee/suzuki-david.html; *About David Suzuki*, David Suzuki Foundation, 2007, http://www.davidsuzuki.org/About_us/Dr_David_Suzuki/ ; "'Environmental Conscience' Urges Canadians to Tread Softly," C. Dean, 2005, *The New York Times*, http://www.nytimes.com/2005/10/18/science/earth/18prof.html?pagewanted=1&_r=1

Chapter Questions

1. Is the scientific method an appropriate guide to thinking effectively about environmental matters? Are there other approaches that might be valid?

2. Why is plant molecular farming so controversial? What are the ethical issues involved in PMF?

3. Can you identify one (or more than one) woman who might fit the label "mother of conservation" in Canada? What criteria would you use to justify your choice of this person?

4. Select a current environmental controversy in your locale and identify the social, economic, aesthetic, and ethical issues it raises. Which of these dimensions is most difficult to resolve? What steps might you take to resolve the controversy?

5. What are the most important environmental benefits and harmful conditions passed on to you by previous generations? What obligations, if any, do you have to future generations? For how many generations do your responsibilities extend?

6. Find an article from a newspaper about a controversial topic and make a list of any ambiguous or loaded words (words that convey an emotional reaction or value judgment) used in the article. In your opinion, is the article a systematic one or a personal opinion piece? Why or why not?

references

Bookchin, M. (1980). *Toward an ecological society.* Montreal: Black Rose Books.

Botkin, D. B., & Keller, E. A. (1995). *Environmental science: Earth as a living planet.* New York: John Wiley & Sons.

Devall, B., & Sessions, G. (1985). *Deep ecology: Living as if nature mattered.* Salt Lake City, UT: Peregrine Books.

Dunlap, R. E. (1987, July/August). Public opinion on the environment in the Reagan era. *Environment, 29,* 7–11, 32–37.

Environment Canada. (2007). *Funding technologies for the environment: A user's guide.* Ottawa: Environment Canada. www.bceia.com/documents/resources/8_Environment_Canada_FTE_WebSite.pdf

Graber, L. H. (1976). *Wilderness as sacred space.* Washington, DC: Association of American Geographers.

Hartig, T., Mang, M., & Evans, G. W. (1990). Perspectives on wilderness: Testing the theory of restorative environments. In A. T. Easley, J. F. Passineau, & B. L. Driver (Compilers), *The use of wilderness for personal growth, therapy and education* (pp. 86–95). Fort Collins, CO: U.S. Department of Agriculture, Rocky Mountain Forest and Range Experiment Station, General Technical Report RM-193.

Hays, S. (1959). *Conservation and the gospel of efficiency.* Cambridge, MA: Harvard University Press.

Hessing, M. (1993). Women and sustainability: Ecofeminist perspectives. *Alternatives, 19*(4), 14–21.

Horse Capture, G. P. (2006). Leave it to the School Children. In Smithsonian Institution, *Forces of change: A new view of nature* (pp. 144–157). Washington, DC: National Geographic Society.

Krakauer, J. (1990). Trees aren't mere niceties—they're necessities. *Smithsonian, 21,* 160–171.

Leopold, A. (1949). *A Sand County almanac.* New York: Oxford University Press.

Lovelock, J. (1988). *The ages of Gaia: A biography of our living Earth.* New York: Norton.

Mason, M. (1999). *Environmental democracy.* London: Earthscan.

Paehlke, R. (1992). Eco-history: Two waves in the evolution of environmentalism. *Alternatives, 19*(1), 18–23.

Partridge, E. (1981). *Responsibilities to future generations: Environmental ethics.* Buffalo, NY: Prometheus Books.

Prigogine, I., & Stengers, I. (1984). *Order out of chaos: Man's new dialogue with nature.* Toronto: Bantam Books.

Salleh, A. K. (1984). Deeper than deep ecology: The eco-feminist connection. *Environmental Ethics, 6*(4), 65–77.

Taylor, D. M. (1992). Disagreeing on the basics: Environmental debates reflect competing world views. *Alternatives, 18*(3), 26–33.

Yoon, C. K. (1996, August 28). Peregrine migration secrets unfold. *The Globe and Mail*, p. A6.

The Ecosphere We Live In

Earth's Life-Support Systems

"Insects pollinate crops for free, forests purify water, and the entire biosphere maintains a gigantic genetic library holding the codes for potential medicines, crops, fuels, and other valuable products. Nature, in its unobtrusive way, has been bankrolling human societies for millennia; it is time we included its contributions in our economic calculations and decision making."

Alan Cutler (2006, p. 20)

Chapter Contents

Chapter Objectives

After studying this chapter you should be able to

- identify and describe the Earth's major components

- outline the components and structure of ecosystems

- discuss ecosystem functions and their interconnections

- explain how ecosystem population dynamics work

- identify the major forces of change and adaptation affecting the Earth

- identify the key features of living systems that help humans learn to live sustainably

INTRODUCTION

The environmental problems and challenges we face have no simple solutions. However, improving our understanding of how the world works, and applying that knowledge, may help us make decisions that are directed toward sustainable environments and futures for ourselves, our communities, and the enveloping ecosystem of which everyone is a part. With that broad goal in mind, this chapter focuses on some fundamental features and vital interconnections of Earth's life-support systems.

MATTER AND ENERGY: BASIC BUILDING BLOCKS OF NATURE

MATTER

Matter is the material of which things are made, the stuff of life. Everything on Earth is composed of matter—everything that is solid, liquid, or gaseous, including our bodies, the air we breathe, oceans or lakes we fish or swim in, animals we see grazing, vegetables grown in our gardens or farmers' fields, and minerals extracted from the Earth. Matter is anything that has **mass** (weight) and takes up space. Essentially, the Earth is a **closed system** for matter. With the possible exception of meteors and meteorites that enter the Earth's atmosphere and add matter to the biosphere, most of the matter that will be incorporated into objects in future generations already is present and has been present since the planet came into being.

Scientists note that Earth's matter has two chemical forms: **elements** (the simplest building blocks of matter that make up all materials) and **compounds** (two or more different elements held together in fixed proportions by the attraction in the chemical bonds between their atoms). All matter is built from the 109 known chemical elements (92 naturally occurring and 17 synthetic; see Appendix A). While each element has its own unique atomic structure, elements can combine to form a seemingly boundless number of compounds. So far, chemists have identified more than 10 million compounds.

Scientists also tell us that all elements (and all matter) are composed of three types of building blocks: atoms, ions, and molecules. **Atoms** are the smallest particles that exhibit the unique characteristics of a particular element. In turn, atoms consist of subatomic, electrically charged particles known as **ions**. These ions are of three types: **protons** (which are positively charged), **neutrons** (uncharged or electrically neutral), and **electrons** (negatively charged) (see Figure 3–1a). A set number of protons

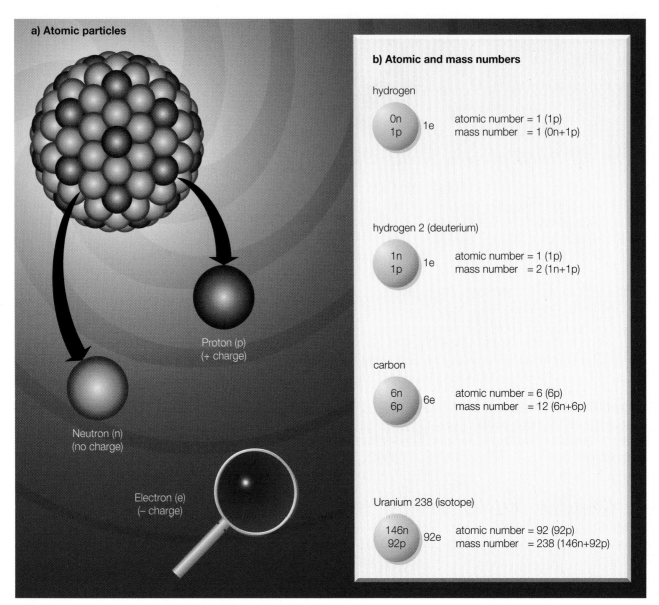

a) Atomic particles

Proton (p)
(+ charge)

Neutron (n)
(no charge)

Electron (e)
(– charge)

b) Atomic and mass numbers

hydrogen

| 0n 1p | 1e | atomic number = 1 (1p) |
| | | mass number   = 1 (0n+1p) |

hydrogen 2 (deuterium)

| 1n 1p | 1e | atomic number = 1 (1p) |
| | | mass number   = 2 (1n+1p) |

carbon

| 6n 6p | 6e | atomic number = 6 (6p) |
| | | mass number   = 12 (6n+6p) |

Uranium 238 (isotope)

| 146n 92p | 92e | atomic number = 92 (92p) |
| | | mass number   = 238 (146n+92p) |

Figure 3–1
Atomic structure

and neutrons, which have approximately the same mass, cluster in the centre of the atom and make up its nucleus. Electrons, which have little mass compared with protons and neutrons, continually and rapidly orbit the nucleus; they are held in orbit by attraction to the positive charge of the nucleus.

An atom of any given element, say hydrogen, is distinguished from that of other elements such as carbon or oxygen by the number of protons in that atom's nucleus (called its **atomic number**). Hydrogen, which is the simplest element, has only one proton in its nucleus and has an atomic number of 1. Carbon, in contrast, has six protons and an atomic number of 6. An even larger atom, uranium, has 92 protons and an atomic number of 92.

Scientists describe the mass of an atom in terms of its **mass number**, which is the number of neutrons (n)

plus the number of protons (p) in its nucleus. All atoms of a particular element have the same number of electrons and protons, but they may have different numbers of neutrons, which change the mass or weight of the atom (Figure 3–1b). These different forms of the same atom are called isotopes of that element, and they may exhibit different characteristics (such as radioactivity in the case of the isotopes of hydrogen and uranium).

Molecules are formed when two or more atoms of the same or different elements combine. In nature, some elements are found as molecules, including oxygen (O_2), nitrogen (N_2), and hydrogen (H_2). In chemical notations such as these, O alone would represent one atom of oxygen; 2O would represent two atoms of oxygen that had joined to form a molecule of oxygen. Molecules composed of two or more different elements are known as compounds. When we see the **chemical formula** H_2O, we know that this molecular compound, water, is formed of two hydrogen atoms chemically bonded to one oxygen atom. Similarly, glucose sugar, $C_6H_{12}O_6$, is a compound formed of 6 carbon atoms, 12 hydrogen atoms, and 6 oxygen atoms. An ionic compound such as sodium chloride (table salt) consists of oppositely charged ions (Na^+ and Cl^-) held together by the forces of attraction between opposite electrical charges.

As noted previously, most matter on Earth exists as compounds, both organic and inorganic. **Organic compounds** contain atoms of the element carbon and usually are combined with each other and with atoms of one or more other elements such as hydrogen, oxygen, nitrogen, sulphur, phosphorus, chlorine, and fluorine. Among the compounds that are important in our lifestyles are vitamins and aspirins, plastics and detergents, oil and natural gas, table sugar, and penicillin. Since carbon is organic, both CO and CO_2 are organic compounds.

Hydrocarbons, chlorinated hydrocarbons, chlorofluorocarbons (CFCs), and simple sugars are examples of different types of organic compounds. Hydrocarbons are compounds of carbon and hydrogen atoms. Methane (CH_4), for example, is the major component of natural gas. Chlorinated hydrocarbons are compounds of carbon, hydrogen, and chlorine. They are used in materials such as the insecticide DDT ($C_{14}H_9Cl_5$) and PCBs such as $C_{12}H_5Cl_5$, which have been used as insulation in electrical transformers. Freon-12 (CCl_2F_2), a coolant used in older refrigerators and air conditioners, is an example of a chlorofluorocarbon, a compound of carbon, chlorine, and fluorine atoms. Simple sugars such as glucose ($C_6H_{12}O_6$) are also organic compounds that most plants and animals break down in their cells to obtain energy.

All other compounds, including water (H_2O) and sodium chloride (NaCl), are **inorganic compounds**. Examples of inorganic compounds you will encounter in this book include ammonia (NH_3), carbon monoxide (CO), carbon dioxide (CO_2), nitric oxide (NO), nitrogen dioxide (NO_2), sulphur dioxide (SO_2), and sulphuric acid (H_2SO_4).

Matter Quality

The term *matter quality* reflects the relative value that humans place on the resources they use; this term does not reflect the value of the contribution that a resource makes to an ecosystem. Based on its availability and concentration, people classify matter as being of high or low quality. **High-quality matter** (such as coal and salt deposits) is usually found near the Earth's surface in an organized or concentrated form, so that its potential for use as a resource is great. **Low-quality matter** usually has little potential for use as a resource because it is dispersed or diluted (in the oceans or atmosphere) or hard to reach (deep underground). An aluminum can is a

more concentrated, higher-quality form of aluminum than the aluminum ore from which it was derived. That is why it is less costly in terms of energy, water, and money to recycle an aluminum can than to produce a new one from aluminum ore.

ENERGY

Energy, the ability or capacity to do work, is what enables us to move matter (such as our arms or legs or a basketball) from one place to another or to change matter from one form to another (such as to boil water to produce steam, or to cook food on a barbecue using natural gas). Forms of energy include light, heat, electricity, chemical energy in coal and sugar, moving water and air masses, and nuclear energy from isotopic nuclei. Among other things, we use energy to build, heat, and cool our homes and businesses, to process and transport food, and to keep our body's cells active and functioning properly.

Energy is either kinetic or potential. Matter has **kinetic energy** because it moves and has mass. Wind (a moving air mass), for example, has kinetic energy, as do flowing streams, moving cars, heat, and electricity. Forms of electromagnetic radiation such as visible light, microwaves, ultraviolet radiation, and cosmic rays also are types of kinetic energy. **Potential energy**, stored and potentially available for use, includes the chemical energy stored in gasoline molecules and food molecules, and in water stored behind a dam. Burning gasoline in a car engine changes the chemical bonds of its molecules into heat, light, and kinetic (or mechanical) energy that moves the car.

Energy Quality

Energy quality is a measure of energy's ability to perform useful work. **High-quality energy** derives from natural sources such as high-velocity wind and coal, or is generated by using other forms of high-quality energy. For example, energy is produced from concentrated sunlight, natural gas, gasoline, or nuclear fission (uranium). Such concentrated energy sources have great utility in industrial processes and in running electronic devices, lights, and electric motors. In contrast, **low-quality energy** is dispersed and has little ability to do useful work. For example, even though it contains more stored heat than all of Saudi Arabia's high-quality oil deposits, the Atlantic Ocean's energy is too widely dispersed to accomplish tasks such as moving vehicles or heating things to high temperatures (Miller, 1994). However, we can use low-quality energy from dispersed geothermal sources, for instance, to heat our homes and other buildings (to temperatures of 100°C or less) (see Enviro-Focus 11). If we match the quality of energy used to the specific task we need to perform, we will avoid wasting energy unnecessarily and save money, too.

CHAPTER 3: EARTH'S LIFE-SUPPORT SYSTEMS

Photo 3–1a
Dams provide hydroelectric power and flood protection.

Photo 3–1b
Wind farms generate power for electric grid systems.

PHYSICAL AND CHEMICAL CHANGES IN MATTER

When we melt snow to boil water for a cup of tea or hot chocolate during a winter camping trip, we do not alter the chemical composition of the H_2O molecules, but we change water from a solid to a liquid state. This **physical change** causes the water molecules to organize themselves differently in space. In lighting our camp stoves and burning the fuel, however, we initiate a **chemical change** or reaction between the carbon contained in the fuel and oxygen from the atmosphere. This chemical reaction produces carbon dioxide gas and energy ($C + O_2$ yields CO_2 + energy). In addition to showing that camp stove fuel is a high-quality, useful energy resource, this example demonstrates how burning carbon-containing compounds such as wood, coal, or natural gas adds carbon dioxide, a greenhouse gas, to the atmosphere.

The Law of Conservation of Matter

Under ordinary circumstances, matter is neither created nor destroyed, but is recycled repeatedly. Matter is transformed and combined in different ways, but it does not disappear—everything goes somewhere. That is why it is inaccurate to talk about consuming or using up resources, because we are using, discarding, reusing, or recycling the same atoms. We can physically rearrange the atoms into different spatial patterns or chemically combine them into different combinations, but we are not creating or destroying them. This is the **law of conservation of matter**, and, in affluent societies such as Canada's, it means that every disposable consumer good thrown away remains with us in one form or another. This is why we hear about the importance of waste reduction and pollution prevention.

First and Second Laws of Energy

The **first law of thermodynamics** (or the **first law of energy**) states that during a physical or chemical change energy is neither created nor destroyed. However, it may change form and it may be moved from place to place. When one form of energy is converted to another form in any physical or chemical change, energy input always equals energy output—we cannot get something for nothing in terms of energy quantity.

The **second law of thermodynamics** (or the **second law of energy**) indicates that with each change in form, some energy is degraded to a less useful form and given off to the surroundings, usually as low-quality heat. That is, in the process of doing work, high-quality energy is converted to more dispersed, disorganized, and lower-quality energy. If we used all of our camp stove fuel in making our cup of tea or hot chocolate, we would have lost energy quality (the amount of useful energy available for the future).

To consider how we lose energy quality, consider the incandescent light bulb. When electrical energy flows through the filament wires, it changes into about 5 percent useful light and 95 percent low-quality heat (see Box 3–1). This heat enters the environment and is dispersed by the random motion of air molecules (thus the suggestion that light bulbs really should be called heat bulbs). With each transfer of energy in these processes, heat is given off to the immediate surroundings and dissipates to the external environment and, eventually, through Earth's atmosphere to space. Effectively, the second law of energy means that we can never recycle or reuse high-quality energy to perform useful work.

Energy is constantly flowing from high-quality, concentrated, useful forms to low-quality, dispersed, and less useful forms. This tendency toward dispersal or disorganization is called **entropy**. Entropy is a measure

Photo 3–2

Typical compact fluorescent light bulb

Thomas Edison's incandescent light bulb, the one most of us have used for most of our lives, was invented in 1879 and remains a highly inefficient energy user. Since lighting uses about 14 percent of the energy consumed in our homes, increasing the efficiency of light bulbs will reduce not only energy consumption but also greenhouse gas emissions. The compact fluorescent light bulb (CFL) uses about 75 percent less energy to produce the same amount of light as an incandescent bulb. Replacing one 60-watt incandescent bulb with one 15-watt CFL would save about $16 over four years (if energy were priced at $0.07/kWh), and greenhouse gas emissions would be reduced by about 251 kilograms. The Canadian government announced in 2007 that it was committed to setting performance standards for all lighting and would be phasing out inefficient incandescent light bulbs by 2012. (See Chapter 11 for additional information.)

SOURCES: City of Calgary (2003). *The Compact Fluorescent Bulb—a Bright Idea for Your Home and the Environment,* City of Calgary, 2003, http://www.calgary.ca/docgallery/BU/environmental_management/ Climate_Change_and_You/Lightbulb.pdf; *Save Energy: Questions and Answers,* Natural Resources Canada, 2007, http://www .nrcan-rncan.gc.ca/media/newsreleases/2007/200704c_e.htm

of disorder: high-quality energy has a low entropy in contrast to low-quality energy, which has a high entropy. Entropy is increasing continuously in the universe (and at some point, billions of years from now, all energy will be uniformly distributed as low-quality heat). The second law of thermodynamics indicates that entropy (disorder) in a system tends to increase over time; the more energy we use (and waste) the more entropy (disorder) we create in the environment.

The apparent ability of living things to maintain a high degree of organization as they grow and develop conceals the fact that living organisms maintain that degree of order over time only with the constant input of energy. This is why animals must eat and plants must photosynthesize. Inevitably, plants and animals die and the system tends toward entropy.

EARTH'S LIFE-SUPPORT SYSTEMS

EARTH'S MAJOR COMPONENTS

The Earth's environment consists of four interconnected environmental spheres or layers. Surrounding the inner (solid) and outer (molten) cores and the mantle of the Earth are the lithosphere, hydrosphere, atmosphere, and biosphere or ecosphere (see Figure 3–2).

Although knowledge of the interior of the Earth is incomplete and imperfect, the **lithosphere** generally is said to consist of the upper zone of the Earth's mantle (to a depth of about 40 to 50 kilometres beneath the crust), as well as the inorganic mixture of rocks and mineral matter contained in the Earth's crust.

On the crust of the Earth lies the **hydrosphere**, the Earth's supply of moisture in all its forms—liquid (both fresh and saltwater), frozen, and gaseous. The hydrosphere includes the surface waters in oceans, lakes, rivers, and swamps; underground water wherever it is located; frozen water in the form of ice, snow, and high cloud crystals; water vapour in the atmosphere; and the moisture that is stored temporarily in the tissues and organs of all living organisms. The hydrosphere impinges on and overlaps significantly with the other spheres.

The **atmosphere** completely surrounds the solid and liquid Earth. Relative to Earth's radius, the atmosphere is a very thin layer of gases consisting mostly of nitrogen (78 percent) and oxygen (21 percent) plus small quantities of water vapour and argon, and minute amounts of other gases such as carbon dioxide and ozone (see Table 3–1).

Due to the forces of gravity and compressibility of gases, the two lowest layers of the atmosphere—the troposphere and stratosphere—together make up about 99 percent of the atmosphere's mass. The **troposphere** (containing about 80 percent of the atmospheric mass) is the lowest layer of the atmosphere and the zone in which most weather events occur. Its height above sea level varies from an average of about 6 kilometres at the poles to about 18 kilometres over the equator, and it also varies seasonally, being higher in summer than in winter. The next layer, the **stratosphere**, contains about 19 percent of the atmospheric mass and extends to about 50 kilometres above the Earth's surface.

The stratosphere and troposphere have very similar compositions, except that in the stratosphere the volume of water vapour is about 1000 times lower, and ozone is nearly 1000 times higher, than in the troposphere. Stratospheric ozone protects life on Earth's surface by absorbing most incoming solar ultraviolet radiation. If the **ozone layer** were a band of pure gas surrounding the globe at sea-level pressure and temperature, it would be no more than 3 millimetres thick, or about the thickness of three Canadian dimes (Government of Canada, 1991).

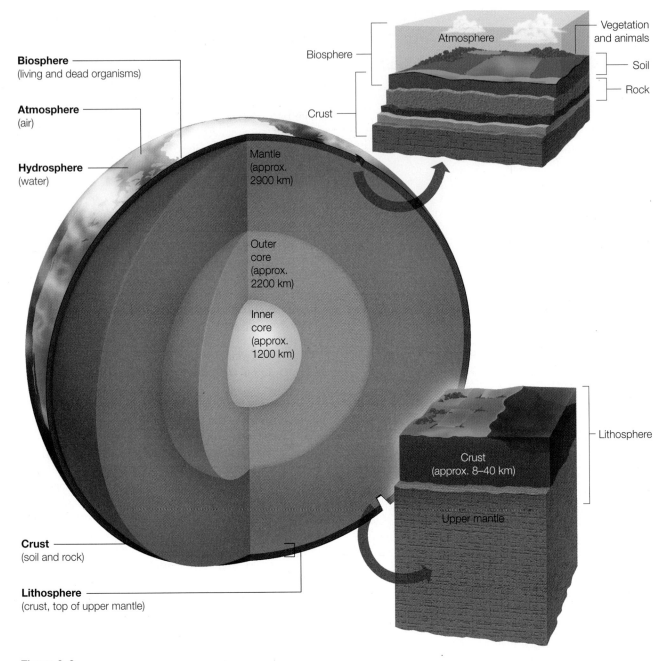

Biosphere
(living and dead organisms)

Atmosphere
(air)

Hydrosphere
(water)

Mantle
(approx.
2900 km)

Outer
core
(approx.
2200 km)

Inner
core
(approx.
1200 km)

Crust
(soil and rock)

Lithosphere
(crust, top of upper mantle)

Biosphere

Atmosphere

Vegetation
and animals

Soil

Rock

Crust

Lithosphere

Crust
(approx. 8–40 km)

Upper mantle

Figure 3–2
The general structure of the Earth

The **biosphere** (ecosphere) consists of the incredibly diverse plant and animal organisms that inhabit the Earth and their interactions with each other and with the atmosphere, hydrosphere, and lithosphere. While most living things inhabit the interface between atmosphere and lithosphere (a zone about 5 kilometres thick), some live largely or entirely within either the hydrosphere or the atmosphere, while many others move freely from one sphere to another. The ecosphere extends vertically about 32 kilometres from the ocean floors to above the tops of the highest mountains. Yet, if the Earth were an apple, the web of life within which we live would be no thicker than the apple's skin (Miller,

1994). The field of ecology tries to determine how this thin skin of air, water, soil, and organisms interacts.

Connections on Earth

Life on Earth depends on three pervasive and interconnected factors: energy flow, matter cycling, and gravity. In particular, it is the one-way flow of high-quality energy from the sun through the materials and living things of the ecosphere, and then into the environment as low-quality energy (and eventually back out into space) that is the ultimate source of energy in most ecosystems. In addition,

TABLE 3-1
PRINCIPAL GASES OF EARTH'S ATMOSPHERE

Component	Symbol or Formula	Percent of Volume of Dry Air	Concentration (in parts per million of air)
Uniform Gases[1]			
molecular nitrogen	N_2	78.08	
molecular oxygen	O_2	20.94	
argon	Ar	0.934	
neon	Ne	0.00182	18.2
helium	He	0.00052	5.2
methane	CH_4	0.00015	1.5
krypton	Kr	0.00011	1.1
molecular hydrogen	H_2	0.00005	0.5
Important Variable Gases[1]			
water vapour	H_2O	0–4	
carbon dioxide	CO_2	0.03	353.0
carbon monoxide	CO		100.0
ozone	O_3		2.0
sulphur dioxide	SO_2		1.0
nitrogen dioxide	NO_2		0.2

[1] The chemical composition of pure, dry air at lower elevations is unvarying through time, and its components are identified in the uniform gases section of this table. A number of minor gases, however, vary markedly according to location and time, as does the amount of moisture in the air. These are identified as variable gases in this table.

SOURCES: *Environmental Science: A Global Concern* (3rd ed.), W. P. Cunningham & B. W. Saigo, 1995, Dubuque, IA: Brown, p. 353; *Physical Geography: A Landscape Appreciation* (3rd ed.), T. McKnight, 1990, Englewood Cliffs, NJ: Prentice Hall, p. 53.

living organisms require the cycling of critical elements such as carbon, phosphorus, nitrogen, water, and oxygen through the ecosphere. Gravity is important in that it keeps the planet's atmospheric gases from escaping into space and it draws chemicals downward in the matter cycles.

Energy reaches the Earth continuously as sunlight, but less than 0.023 percent of the total energy reaching the atmosphere each day actually is captured by living things (through **photosynthesis**) (Kaufman & Franz, 1993). The remainder of the energy is reflected by cloud cover and does not reach the surface, or is radiated by the Earth's surface back into space as heat (see Figure 3–3 on page 70). The Earth is an **open system** for energy, continuously receiving and using energy from the sun and radiating waste heat into space.

ECOLOGY

Basic ecological knowledge is an important foundation of environmental awareness and is a basis for using and managing Earth's resources in an environmentally sound and sustainable manner. Part of such ecological knowledge is knowing how the biosphere works and how natural systems function and respond to change.

Ecology, from the Greek words *oikos* (house, or place to live) and *logos* (study of), is defined as the study of the interactions of living (biotic) organisms with one another and with their nonliving (abiotic) environment of matter and energy. As part of determining how Earth's living systems maintain the integrity of the ecosphere, ecologists may study individual species as well as the structure and function of natural systems at the population, community, and ecosystem levels. Other scientists and social scientists such as geologists, earth scientists, and geographers focus on understanding the patterns and distributions of living and nonliving elements of the environment and on the interrelationships of people, other organisms, and their environments.

One of the characteristics of life on Earth is its high degree of organization (see Figure 3–4). Starting at the simplest level, atoms are organized into molecules, which in turn are organized into cells. In multicelled organisms,

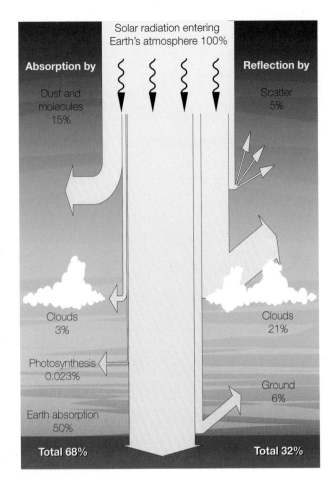

Figure 3–3

Schematic diagram of energy balance on the Earth

SOURCE: Adapted from *Human Geography: Landscapes of Human Activities,* J. Fellman, A. Getis, & J. Getis, 1995, Dubuque, IA: Brown, p. 454.

Photo 3–3
Because they occupy aquatic and terrestrial habitats, amphibians are sensitive indicators of environmental health.

cells are organized into tissues, tissues into organs (such as the brain or liver), organs into organ or body systems (such as the nervous system or digestive system), and organ systems into individual multicellular **organisms** (such as bears, whales, humans, orchids, and cacti).

An individual organism is a single member of a **species**, defined as a group of organisms that resemble one another in appearance, behaviour, chemical makeup and processes, and genetic structure and that produce fertile offspring under natural conditions. While estimates as to the number of species on Earth vary between 5 and 100 million (mostly insects, microscopic organisms, and small sea creatures), most of the world's species remain unknown. Only about 1.8 million species have been discovered and described (Environmental Literacy Council, 2007), and for the great majority of these species little is known about their roles and interactions.

Canola in a prairie field, brook trout in a particular stream, or people in Canada—a group of individuals of the same species living and interacting in the same geographic area at the same time—is called a **population**. Although all members of the same population share

common structural, functional, and behavioural traits, individuals in a population vary slightly in their genetic makeup and thus exhibit slightly different behaviours and appearances. This is known as **genetic diversity**. The place where the organism or population lives— whether oceans, forests, streams, or soils—is its **habitat**. Populations of different species interact, making up a biological **community**, such as an alpine meadow community or a prairie community.

A community and its members interact with each other and with their nonliving environment of matter and energy, making up an **ecosystem**. Wetlands, estuaries, and the Great Lakes are examples of aquatic (water) ecosystems, while grasslands, high mountain deserts, and Carolinian forests are examples of terrestrial (land) ecosystems. A broad, regional type of ecosystem characterized by distinctive climate and soil conditions and distinctive communities of plants, animals, and microorganisms adapted to those conditions is referred to as a **biome**. The geography of the biosphere—that is, of global terrestrial ecosystems or world biomes—is illustrated in Figure 3–5 on page 72. Canada has five terrestrial biomes (tundra, boreal forest, temperate deciduous and rain forest, grassland, mountain complexes) and both aquatic biomes (freshwater and marine). In Canada, these major biomes have been subdivided into more specific "ecozones" (15 terrestrial and 5 marine) that reflect Canadian ecological conditions, including dominant landforms, soils, climate, natural ecosystems and species (see Figure 3–6, p. 73). Finally, the highest level of organization is the biosphere, or ecosphere, which consists of all communities of living things on Earth, of all Earth's ecosystems together.

Generally the biosphere is not studied as a single large system; instead, the smaller but still globally interrelated ecological systems frequently are the focus of investigation. Ecosystems vary in size and location, but all are dynamic entities, always changing as a result of changes

Figure 3–4

Levels of biological organization

Photo 3–4
These zebras are visually similar, but each individual is genetically different.

Photo 3–5
Mixed-grass prairie in Grasslands National Park, in southern Saskatchewan.

in their external environments. These changes may be natural, as in grassland fires or changes in precipitation levels in a forest, or they may be human induced, such as by spraying a field or forest with an insecticide. Unless the change is one that exceeds the threshold (tolerance) limits of the individual ecosystem or the biosphere, ecosystems can usually compensate for the stresses of external changes without incurring permanent change. However, the buildup of greenhouse gases, stratospheric ozone depletion, and the rapid loss of biological diversity are examples of potentially serious and permanent changes to the ecosphere.

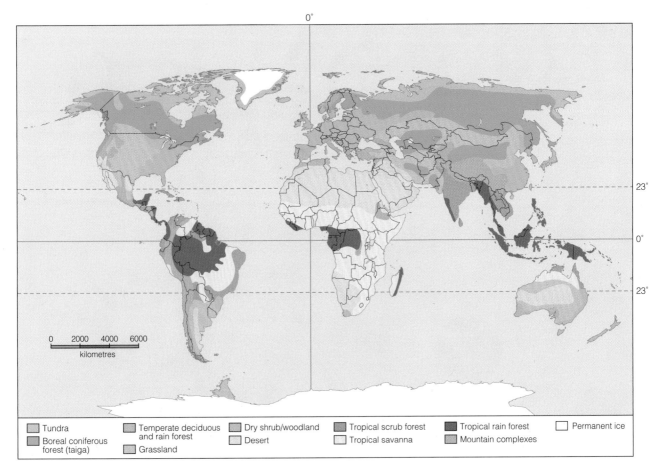

Tundra

Boreal coniferous forest (taiga)

Temperate deciduous and rain forest

Grassland

Dry shrub/woodland

Desert

Tropical scrub forest

Tropical savanna

Tropical rain forest

Mountain complexes

Permanent ice

Figure 3–5
Earth's major biomes

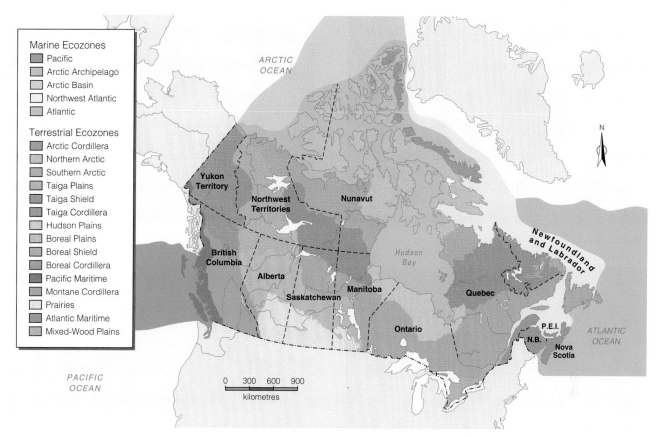

Figure 3–6

Ecozones of Canada

SOURCE: *The State of Canada's Environment—1996,* © Her Majesty the Queen in Right of Canada, Environment Canada, 1996. Reprinted with permission of the Minister of Public Works and Government Services Canada, 2008.

BIODIVERSITY

Biological diversity, or biodiversity, involves three different concepts: genetic diversity, species diversity, and ecological diversity. Genetic diversity, as noted previously, is the variation in genetic makeup among individuals within a single species. **Species diversity** refers to the number of different species (that is, species richness) and their relative abundance in different habitats on Earth. **Ecological diversity**, sometimes called habitat diversity, is the variety of biological communities—oceans, lakes, streams, wetlands, forests, grasslands, deserts—that interact with one another and with their physical and chemical (nonliving) environments. Every currently living species not only represents a form of life best suited to survive present conditions but also contains stored genetic information relating to its adaptation to Earth's changing environmental conditions through time (plus the raw material for future adaptations). Given these characteristics, biodiversity provides nature's insurance against ecological disasters.

In addition to generating billions of dollars annually for the global economy, Earth's abundant variety of genes, species, and ecosystems provides humans with food and medicinal products, energy, fibres, raw materials, and industrial chemicals. We depend on this **biocapital** (or natural capital—see Box 1–1 on page 11) for life forms and ecosystems, as well as for recycling, purification, and natural pest-control services.

Human cultural diversity is sometimes included as part of Earth's biodiversity. In the same manner as genetic material contained within other living species provides for future adaptability, so might the variety of human cultures represent our adaptability and survival options in the face of changing conditions.

TYPES OF ORGANISMS

For hundreds of years, biologists categorized living things into two broad categories: plants and animals. When microscopes revealed that many organisms did not fit well into either category at the cellular level, a five-kingdom classification system was devised. This system, while not perfect, consists of Prokaryotae, Protista, Fungi, Plantae, and Animalia. Bacteria are neither plants nor animals; they are **prokaryotic**, meaning they lack a nuclear envelope and other internal cell membranes. They have their own kingdom, Prokaryotae (see Figure 3–7 on page 75).

Photo 3–6a

Photo 3–6b

Photo 3–6c

Photo 3–6d

Diversity within genus and species is illustrated in these photos. All four bears belong to the genus *Ursus:* black bear (*Ursus americanus*) (3–6a), polar bear (*Ursus maritimus*) (3–6b), grizzly bear (*Ursus arctos horribilis*) (3–6c), and Kodiak brown bear (*Ursus arctos middendorffi*) (3–6d). The latter two are subspecies of the brown bear, whose coastal and island populations (the Kodiak browns) are genetically distinct from the interior and Arctic populations (the grizzlies).

The four remaining kingdoms are composed of organisms with a **eukaryotic** cell structure. **Eukaryotic** cells have a high degree of internal organization: a nucleus (genetic material surrounded by a membrane) and several other internal parts enclosed by membranes.

These organisms differ from one another in several ways, including their nutrition. Members of the Fungi kingdom (such as mushrooms and yeasts) secrete digestive enzymes into their food and then absorb the predigested nutrients, while members of the Plantae kingdom (such as ferns, conifers, and flowering plants) use radiant energy to manufacture food molecules by photosynthesis. Members of the Animalia kingdom ingest their food and digest it inside their bodies. Most members of the Animalia kingdom are **invertebrates** (they have no backbone, such as jellyfish, worms, insects, and spiders). Animals with backbones, the **vertebrates**, include fish (shark, tuna), amphibians (frogs, salamanders), reptiles (turtles, alligators), birds (eagles, robins, puffins), and mammals (elephants, whales, bats, and humans).

COMPONENTS AND STRUCTURE OF ECOSYSTEMS

The ecosphere and its ecosystems can be divided into two parts: the living or **biotic** components, such as plants and animals, and the nonliving or **abiotic** components, such as water, air, solar energy, and nutrients necessary to support life. Living organisms in ecosystems are usually classified as producers, consumers, or decomposers, depending on their nutritional needs and feeding type (see Figure 3–8 on page 76).

Sunlight is the source of energy that powers almost all life processes on Earth, and **producers** or **autotrophs** (self-feeders) are self-nourishing organisms that perform photosynthesis. Using **solar energy**, autotrophs convert relatively simple inorganic substances such as water, carbon dioxide, and nutrients into complex chemicals such as carbohydrates (sugars and starches), lipids (oils, waxes), and proteins. Hundreds of chemical changes take place sequentially during photosynthesis; in most

Kingdom

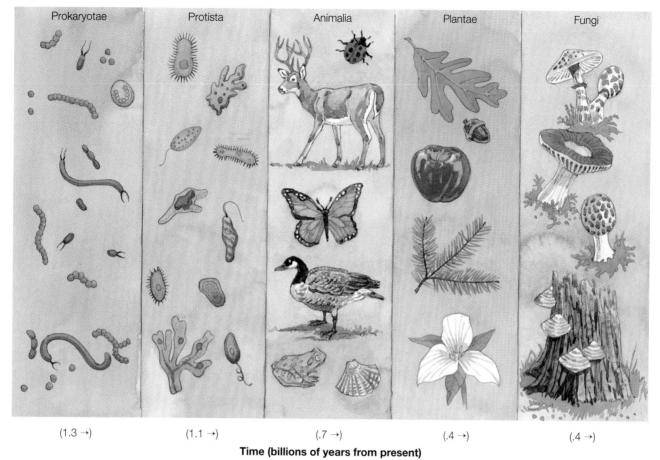

Prokaryotae	Protista	Animalia	Plantae	Fungi
(1.3 →)	(1.1 →)	(.7 →)	(.4 →)	(.4 →)

Time (billions of years from present)

Figure 3–7

The five-kingdom system of classification. Prokaryotes were the first organisms to appear; fungi are the most recent.

temperate-zone plants, photosynthesis can be summarized in the following way: $6H_2O + 6CO_2$ + solar energy yields $C_6H_{12}O_6$ (sugar) $+ 6O_2$. By incorporating the chemicals they produce into their own bodies, producers become potential food resources for other organisms. On land, green plants are the most significant producers; in aquatic ecosystems, algae and certain types of bacteria are important producers. Producers are the foundation of ecological productivity and ecosystem function.

A special group of bacteria (**chemotrophs**) converts the energy found in inorganic chemical compounds in aquatic and other environments into energy without sunlight. In the pitch-black thermal vent areas of deep oceanic trenches, for instance, nonphotosynthetic bacteria use the heat energy (generated by decay of radioactive elements deep in the Earth's core) from the vents to convert dissolved hydrogen sulphide (H_2S) and carbon dioxide (CO_2) into more complex nutrient molecules. Through **chemosynthesis**, these bacteria produce food energy for their nutritional needs and for other consumers in this special ecosystem (Lutz, 2000).

All other organisms in ecosystems are **consumers**, or **heterotrophs**, eating the cells, tissues, or waste products of other organisms. Heterotrophic organisms obtain the food energy and body-building materials they need either directly or indirectly from autotrophs and thus indirectly from the sun. Unable to manufacture their own food, heterotrophs live at the expense of other plants and animals. They are categorized broadly as macroconsumers or microconsumers.

Macroconsumers, who feed by ingesting or engulfing particles, parts, or entire bodies of other organisms (living or dead), include herbivores, carnivores, omnivores, scavengers, and detrivores. **Herbivores** (plant eaters), or **primary consumers**, such as deer, eat green plants directly. **Carnivores** (meat eaters), or **secondary consumers**, such as bobcats and certain snakes, feed indirectly on plants by eating herbivores. Most carnivores are animals, but the Venus flytrap is an example of a plant that traps and consumes insects. **Omnivores**, or consumers that eat both plants and animals, include black bears, pigs, and humans. **Tertiary consumers** are carnivores such as hawks that eat secondary (other carnivorous) consumers.

Many heterotrophs consume dead organic material. Those that consume the entire dead organism, such as vultures and hyenas, are known as **scavengers**.

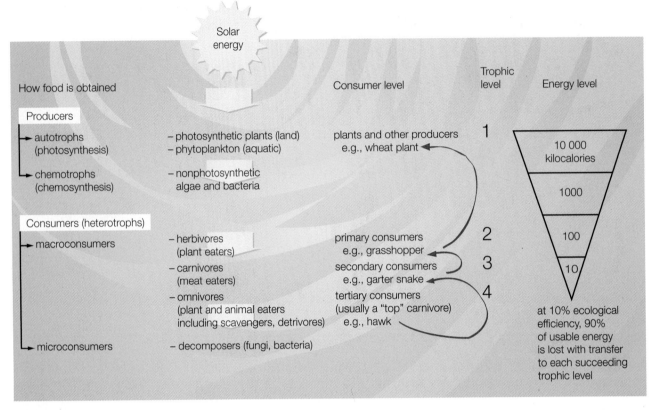

Figure 3–8

Classification of organisms and trophic levels in ecosystems

Consumers that ingest fragments of dead or decaying tissues or organic wastes are called **detrivores**, or **detritus feeders**. Examples are earthworms, shrimp, dung beetles, and maggots. **Microconsumers** or **decomposer** organisms such as fungi and bacteria live on or within their food source, completing the final breakdown and recycling of the complex molecules in detritus into simpler compounds (which we call rot or decay). Decomposers play the major role in returning nutrients to the physical environment, providing an important source of food for worms and insects in the soil and water.

Awareness of the crucial importance of decomposers to the continuation of life in ecosystems has developed relatively recently. As understanding of their performance and function has improved, so has appreciation of the vital link that decomposers play in the cycle that returns chemical nutrients to the physical environment in a form that can be used by producers. Given that organisms constantly remove necessary chemicals from the environment, it is not difficult to imagine how quickly nutrients in the soil would be depleted if decomposers did not recycle nutrients continually after the death of producers and consumers. The Earth would quickly be covered in plant litter, dead animal bodies, animal wastes, and garbage if decomposers did not act on them.

Both producers and consumers use chemical energy stored in glucose and other nutrients to drive their life processes. This energy is released by **aerobic respiration**, which uses oxygen to convert nutrients such as glucose back into carbon dioxide and water. A complex process, the net chemical change for aerobic respiration ($C_6H_{12}O_6$ + $6O_2$ yields $6H_2O$ + $6CO_2$ + released energy) is the reverse of photosynthesis.

Any individual organism depends on the flow of matter and energy through its body, while the community of organisms in an ecosystem survives by a combination of

Photo 3–7

Decomposers, including these fungi, play an important role in the process of returning nutrients to ecosystems.

PART 2: THE ECOSPHERE WE LIVE IN

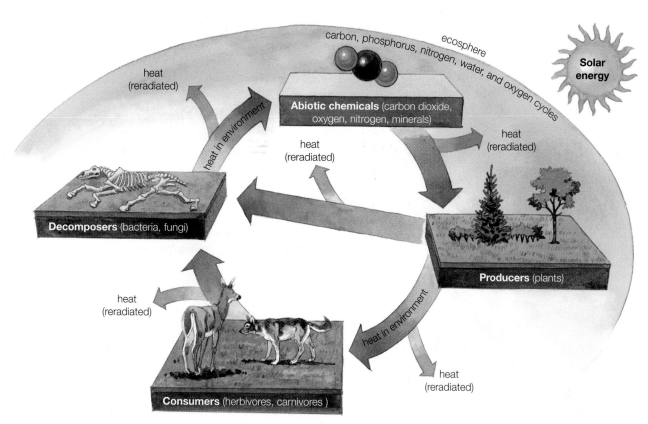

Figure 3–9

Energy flows and matter recycling connect energy, chemicals, and organisms in an ecosystem.

matter recycling and one-way energy flow. Energy, chemicals, and organisms are the main structural components of an ecosystem and are linked by energy flow and matter recycling (see Figure 3–9).

Tolerance Ranges of Species

Every population in an ecosystem exhibits a range of tolerance to variations in its physical and chemical environment. While a speckled trout population may do best at water temperatures between 14°C and 19°C, for example, a few individual trout can survive temperatures as high as 24°C or 25°C for short periods of time because of small differences in their genetic makeup, health, and age (Kaufman & Franz, 1993). Beyond the range of tolerance, however, no trout will survive. The **law of tolerance** notes that the presence, number, and distribution of a species in an ecosystem are determined by whether the levels of one or more physical or chemical factors fall within the range tolerated by the species.

Some organisms have wide ranges of tolerance to some factors and narrow ranges of tolerance to other factors. Generally, the least tolerance is exhibited during the juvenile or reproductive stages of an organism's life cycle. Highly tolerant species can live in a range of habitats with different conditions, and other species can adjust their tolerance to physical factors such as temperature, if change

is gradual. This adjustment to slowly changing conditions, **acclimation**, is a protective device, but it has limits. Each adjustment brings a species closer to its absolute limit until, without warning, the next small change triggers a **threshold effect**. This is a harmful or even fatal reaction to exceeding the tolerance limit (similar to adding the straw that broke the camel's back). This threshold effect explains why many environmental problems seem to arise so suddenly. Maple trees in Quebec and Ontario may suddenly seem to have begun dying in droves, but part of the cause may be decades-long exposure to numerous air pollutants, including acid precipitation. The concern about exceeding thresholds also explains why efforts must be made to prevent pollution and to ensure that biodiversity is maintained.

Limiting Factors in Ecosystems

An ecological principle related to the law of tolerance is the **limiting factor principle**. This principle asserts that too much or too little of any abiotic factor can limit or prevent growth of a population even if all other factors are at or near the optimum range of tolerance. Limiting factors in land ecosystems include precipitation, humidity, wind, temperature, light and shade, fire, salinity, available space, and soil nutrients. If you were to plant corn in soil that was lacking in phosphorus, even though all other factors were at optimum levels, the corn would not grow once it

CHAPTER 3: EARTH'S LIFE-SUPPORT SYSTEMS

Photo 3–8
In contrast to other trees in the region, these Ontario sugar maples have not been damaged noticeably by air pollution.

ROLES OF SPECIES IN ECOSYSTEMS

TYPES OF SPECIES IN ECOSYSTEMS

From a human perspective, the species in an ecosystem may be categorized into four types: native (or endemic), immigrant (or exotic), indicator (or bellwether), and keystone species. In a particular ecosystem, a given species may be more than one of these types. **Endemic species** are those that normally live and thrive in a particular ecosystem, while **immigrant** or **exotic species** are those that migrate into or are introduced into an ecosystem, deliberately or accidentally, by humans. Despite the benefits bestowed on humans by intentionally introduced species, many of them have negative effects on native species or native ecosystems because they lack natural predators in their new habitat. **Indicator species** such as lichens (see Box 3–2), neotropical migratory songbirds, and amphibians may provide early warnings of environmental damage to communities or ecosystems. The current decline in numbers of neotropical songbirds in North America indicates that both their summer habitats here and their winter habitats in Latin American and Caribbean

had used up the available phosphorus. Just as phosphorus levels determine how much corn will grow in a field, growth can be limited by an excess of an abiotic factor such as too much water or too much fertilizer. A limiting factor in aquatic ecosystems is *salinity* (the amounts of various salts dissolved in a given volume of water). So, too, is the **dissolved oxygen content** (the amount of oxygen gas dissolved in a given volume of water at a particular temperature and pressure), and availability of nutrients.

BOX 3–2
LICHENS AS INDICATORS OF ENVIRONMENTAL CHANGE: AIR QUALITY

Lichens have been recognized as bio-indicators of air pollution for over 140 years. Environment Canada's Ecological Monitoring and Assessment Network (EMAN) includes a lichen-monitoring method that citizens can use to determine whether their neighbourhoods have air quality problems. Different species of lichens that grow on tree bark have varying levels of tolerance to sulphur dioxide and other air pollutants such as nitrogen oxides, particulate matter, and ground-level ozone. By examining which of the 15 to 20 easily identifiable lichens are growing on trees near their homes, and the amount of bark that they cover, residents can gain a relative measure of local air quality. Lichens intolerant of air pollution, such as *Usnea* species, are seldom found in urban areas, while tolerant lichens, such as *Parmelia* and *Physcia* species (the grey lichen shown in Photo 3–9), are often found growing in great abundance in urban areas.

In 2004, a group of Brock University students and their professor tested the EMAN protocol in Hamilton, Ontario. They found a higher diversity and abundance of lichens on trees near the periphery of the city, suggesting that air quality improves with increasing distance from the downtown core. This study identified some

Photo 3–9
The grey lichens growing on a tree trunk near a four-lane roadway in Calgary are of the *Physcia* species.

"lichen deserts" (areas of low lichen density) that seemed to correspond with areas of high asthma incidences following summer smog episodes. This finding generated a follow-up study of the air chemistry around the lichen deserts and also prompted the City of Hamilton, EMAN, and Environment Hamilton (an environmental nongovernmental organization, or ENGO) to expand the lichen-monitoring program across the region.

SOURCES: *Monitoring Arboreal Lichens as Indicators of Air Quality,* Ecological Monitoring and Assessment Network, 2007, http://www.eman-rese.ca/eman/ecotools/protocols/terrestrial/lichens/intro.html; "Citizen Monitoring," *The Green Lane,* Environment Canada, 2006, http://www.ec.gc.ca/cleanair-airpur/default.asp?lang+En&n=536C69AA-1; "Lichens Used to Measure Air Quality," September 10, 2004, *EnviroZine, 46,* http://www.ec.gc.ca/EnviroZine/english/ossies/46/feature2_e.cfm

Photo 3–10
Introduction of the exotic zebra mussel to some North American aquatic environments has had devastating effects on crayfish endemic to the Great Lakes.

Pacific sea otter

other shellfish

kelp

sea urchin

Figure 3–10
Pacific Ocean sea otters: a keystone role

tropical forests are disappearing. In a similar way, many of the world's amphibians (frogs, toads, and salamanders) are declining, possibly due to increased ultraviolet radiation, chemical contamination, and other causes (see Chapter 12).

While all species play important roles in maintaining the structure and function of their ecosystems, some scientists consider the roles of certain species to be more important than their abundance or biomass would suggest. Bees, bats, and hummingbirds have been labelled **keystone species** because they play crucial roles in tropical forests by pollinating flowering plants, dispersing seeds, or both. Top predators, such as alligators, wolves, and giant anteaters, are designated as keystone species because they exert a stabilizing influence on their ecosystems by feeding on and regulating the populations of certain other species. Sea otters of the Pacific Ocean feed on sea urchins and other shellfish, helping to reduce the sea urchins' destruction of kelp beds, thereby providing a larger habitat for many other species and indirectly increasing species diversity (see Figure 3–10). Given that the long-term resilience of an ecosystem is linked to the activities of this species, if the sea otter is removed or its keystone role within the ecosystem changes, the basic nature of the community changes (with more sea urchins there is less kelp and fewer species). On the Canadian prairies, the ground squirrel also is considered a keystone species (see Box 3–3 on page 80). Population crashes and extinctions of other species that depend on the keystone species can send ripple effects through the entire ecosystem.

Ecological Niche

Each species meets the challenge of survival in its own unique fashion. The way an organism interacts with other living things and with its physical environment defines that organism's **ecological niche**, or role

within the structure and functions of an ecosystem. An ecological niche includes all the environmental (physical, chemical, and biological) conditions an organism or species needs to live, interact, reproduce, and adapt in an ecosystem. **Specialist species** have narrow niches, meaning a species may be able to live only in one type of habitat, eat a few types of food only, or tolerate a narrow range of climatic or other environmental conditions (see Enviro-Focus 3 on page 81).

In tropical and Canadian temperate rain forests (see Chapter 9), diverse plant and animal species occupy specialized ecological niches within the distinct layers of the forest. These specialized niches enable species to minimize or avoid competition for resources with other species, thus preserving species diversity. Canadian examples include salamanders, which depend on habitat found in old-growth forests, and the insectivorous pitcher and sundew plants found only in sphagnum moss/peat bogs. **Generalist species** have broad niches and are able to live in many different places while tolerating a wide range of environmental conditions. Humans are considered a generalist species, as are flies, mice, raccoons, and whitetail deer.

Interactions among Species

Different species in an ecosystem often interact and develop close associations with one another. The major types of species interactions are competition, predation, and three forms of symbiosis (parasitism, mutualism, and commensalism).

If commonly used resources are abundant, different species are able to share them and to come closer to occupying their fundamental niches. A **fundamental niche** is

CHAPTER 3: EARTH'S LIFE-SUPPORT SYSTEMS

BOX 3–3
IN DEFENCE OF "GOPHERS" (RICHARDSON'S GROUND SQUIRRELS)

The golden rodent with the impressive name—*Spermophilus richardsonii*—is a keystone species in the Canadian prairies. "Eliminating gophers would wipe out a whole suite of wildlife on the prairies," says biologist Cliff Wallis (Barnett, 1996, p. A4). A long list of species depends on the Richardson's ground squirrel (sometimes called gopher) for survival, from wild tomatoes that grow on ground squirrel mounds to salamanders that use ground squirrel burrows as shady shelters on their treks between wetlands. Without these ground squirrels, many birds of prey and mammals such as swift foxes and badgers would disappear for lack of food. According to Alberta provincial biologist Steve Brechtel, rare ferruginous hawks depend on Richardson's ground squirrels for 90 percent of their diet and eat up to 480 annually when raising their young. He suggests that prairie falcons and endangered burrowing owls (which use ground squirrel burrows for their homes) are in decline in part because the ground squirrel population is in decline (Barnett, 1996).

Richardson's ground squirrels have long been targets of eradication efforts by prairie farmers who claim the rodents cause millions of dollars in damage to their fields, grain, and other crops. Highly toxic strychnine is the poison of choice: it takes a mere 0.7 milligrams to kill a ground squirrel, the equivalent of a couple of grains of sand. Once the ground squirrel dies, the poison remains active and kills animals that eat the ground squirrel carcass. Since 1994, the federal government has restricted the amount of strychnine used to kill ground squirrels because of fears of contaminating groundwater and poisoning other animals.

Cliff Wallis points out that poor land management practices are a major contributor to farmers' problems with ground squirrels. People allow overgrazing to occur, clear all the trees that provide nesting sites for birds of prey, and cultivate right to the edges of fields so there is no room for coyote dens (ground squirrels are a staple of coyote diets). Clearly, many of the problems with ground squirrels have their origin in human actions.

University of Lethbridge biologist Gail Michener notes that Richardson's ground squirrels have survived for tens of thousands of years, far longer than humans have been commercially

cultivating the prairies. They are "definitely part of the prairies" and will not be driven easily from their homeland (Dempster, 1996, p. A4). Nor should ground squirrels be eradicated, because, in addition to providing food to predators, ground squirrels "balance the grazing pressure by eating species of plants that cows are less interested in" (Holyrood, cited in Barnett, 1996, p. A4). Given the principle of connectedness and the unknown or unanticipated effects people encounter when they simplify ecosystems, Richardson's ground squirrels deserve greater respect for their role as a keystone prairie species.

Photo 3–11
Richardson's ground squirrel: *Spermophilus richardsonii.*

In part, education about Richardson's ground squirrels will help to improve understanding and contribute to that greater respect. While a graduate student in geography at the University of Lethbridge, Adela Kincaid conducted survey research on rural and urban area residents' knowledge and attitudes toward ground squirrels. She found that urban people had a more positive attitude than did rural people. Rural people, who had greater knowledge about Richardson's ground squirrels, perceived problems caused by the rodents to be more serious than their urban neighbours did and supported more lethal management practices than urbanites. Urban residents "more often supported alternative management practices such as capture and relocation or the introduction of predators" (Kincaid, 2003, vi). Results from such research may help decision makers develop suitable public educational programs.

SOURCES: "Biologist Rises to Defence of Gopher," V. Barnett, April 27, 1996, *Calgary Herald*, p. A4; "Gopher Guru Says Critters Here to Stay," L. Dempster, April 17, 1996, *Calgary Herald*, p. A4; *A Study of Attitudes Pertaining to the Richardson's Ground Squirrel*, A. Kincaid, 2003, unpublished master's thesis, University of Lethbridge; "Richardson's Ground Squirrels," G. Michener, (n.d.), University of Lethbridge website: http://people.uleth.ca/~michener/

the full range of physical, chemical, and biological factors each species could use if there were no competition from other species. In most ecosystems, however, each species faces competition from other species for one or more of the same limited resources of food, sunlight, water, soil nutrients, or space. This is **interspecific competition**, in which parts of the fundamental niches of different species overlap significantly. Since no two species can occupy the same niche in the same community indefinitely, one species may occupy more of its fundamental niche than the other species as a result of competition between them. This **competitive exclusion principle**

means that one of the competing species must migrate to another area if possible, shift its feeding habits or behaviour, suffer a sharp decline in population numbers, or become extinct. **Intraspecific competition** occurs when individuals of the same species try to gain access to the same resources.

The degree of fundamental niche overlap may be reduced by **resource partitioning**. Dividing up of scarce resources occurs in order that species with similar requirements can use the resources in different ways, in different places, and at different times. Resource partitioning occurs between owls and hawks that feed

Pacific Yew: Trash Tree Coveted as Cancer Treatment

Photo 3–12

Pacific yew bark: one person's cancer treatment requires the bark from 6 to 100 trees.

For decades, the Pacific yew (a small shrub-like tree) was considered worthless in comparison to the highly profitable Douglas fir with which it co-existed in forested areas in western North America. To accommodate clear-cutting of Douglas fir, massive cutting and burning of the Pacific yew took place. Impacts on Pacific yew populations as a whole were particularly severe during the 1970s and 1980s when Douglas fir timber production was high. Although paclitaxel (an active anticancer chemical) was first extracted from the bark of the Pacific yew in the 1960s, it was not until human trials on women with previously incurable ovarian cancer were conducted from 1983 to 1989 that the Pacific yew became a product valued by society.

Taxol (the pharmaceutical name given to paclitaxel) is a successful cancer-fighting agent and is particularly useful in treating ovarian cancer. Since the Pacific yew initially was the only known source of paclitaxel, harvesting of the species became widespread. While this harvesting pressure was expected to decline as synthetic sources of taxol were developed, careful management and harvesting of the species was essential because the Pacific yew grows very slowly. Even in undisturbed populations, these trees change little in size and structure over several decades, suggesting that disturbed populations may require centuries to recover the population size and structure characteristic of old-growth forest stands (Busing & Spies, 1995). Conservation of Pacific yew required such actions as establishing genetic reserves for yew, replanting after harvest, and retaining some live yew trees in harvesting areas.

To help overcome the shortage of Pacific yew bark (the demand for paclitaxel was greater than the supply), all yew species were investigated as potential paclitaxel sources. In this process, the Canada yew was identified as a good source of paclitaxel, as well as two other taxanes that may be used to synthesize paclitaxel. Taxol has been synthesized chemically, and semi-synthetic versions have been developed using the needles and twigs from other yew species grown as agricultural products. In Ontario, for instance, the commercial harvest of Canada yew began in 2003, when about 5000 kilograms of foliage was harvested. Harvests increased to 320 000 kilograms of foliage from trees on private land in 2004, and to about 400 000 kilograms from public land in 2005 (Ontario Ministry of Natural Resources, 2007). Companies harvesting yew on public land are encouraged to comply with the Canada yew sustainable harvesting guidelines developed in 2002 by a partnership of the Canadian Forest Service and Prince Edward Island's Department of Agriculture and Forestry (see www.gov.pe.ca/photos/original/af_hemlock0402.pdf).

Given the challenges of harvesting Canada yew from the wild (remoteness of known locations of yew, difficulty in finding a reliable workforce to work in remote locations, and rising fuel costs to cover the large distances between wild yew sources and yew-processing facilities), the Ontario Forest Research Institute is attempting to develop Canada yew as a shrub crop for Ontario farmers and nurseries. This research may lead to establishment of Canada yew plantations in Ontario and eastern Canada. While the pressure on natural stands of Pacific yew has been reduced by development of alternative and synthetic sources of paclitaxel, its bark is still being used for taxol production.

(continued)

Although the Pacific yew is but one of the millions of species sharing planet Earth, its transition from trash tree to valued resource underscores the need to preserve and protect even the most seemingly insignificant species. Its use for medicinal purposes also raises an important ethical dilemma about the extent to which harvesting species to protect human health is a sustainable option.

SOURCES: *Modeling the Population Dynamics of the Pacific Yew,* R. T. Busing & T. A. Spies, 1995, United States Department of Agriculture, Forest Service. Research Note PNW-RN-515; *The Taxol Story—an Overview,* Natural Resources Canada, 2007, http:/scf.rncan.gc.ca/sbsite/yew/taxol; *The Current State of Canada Yew in Ontario,* Ontario Ministry of Natural Resources, 2007, http://mnr,gov.on.ca/MNR/sorr/yew_status.html

on similar prey; owls hunt at night while hawks hunt during the day. Similarly, some species of warblers hunt for insects in different parts of the same coniferous tree (Figure 3–11). Sharing the wealth among competing species results in each species occupying a **realized niche** (that portion of the fundamental niche actually occupied by a species).

Predation, in which members of a **predator** species feed on parts or all of an organism of a **prey** species, is the most obvious form of species interaction. A turtle eating a fish in a freshwater pond ecosystem, a fox feeding on a rabbit in a field ecosystem, and a killer whale culling a sick seal in a marine ecosystem are all examples of **predator–prey relationships**. Another type of predator–prey interaction is **parasitism**, a symbiotic relationship in which the parasite benefits by obtaining nourishment from the host and the host is weakened or perhaps killed by the parasite preying on it. Parasites such as ticks, mosquitoes, and mistletoe plants live outside the host's body, while other parasites such as tapeworms and disease-causing organisms (pathogens) live within the host.

Symbiosis is any intimate relationship between individuals of two or more different species. Sometimes symbiosis can take an extreme form. In the case of three-toed sloths, their fur is often occupied by green algae and pyralid moths that feed on the algae, as well as by house mites, a number of beetle species, and several other kinds of arthropods. A single sloth can be home to over 900 beetles (Perry, 1986).

Mutualism is a symbiotic relationship in which interacting species, such as honeybees and certain flowers, both benefit. In the process of feeding on a flower's nectar, honeybees also pick up pollen and pollinate the female flowers. Sometimes, mutualistic partners can be completely dependent on one another. In the case of the yucca plant and the yucca moth, for instance, the

Figure 3–11

Resource partitioning and niches among *Dendroica* species (wood warblers). Each species spends most of its feeding time in a distinct portion of the trees it frequents. The shaded regions identify where each species spends at least half its foraging time.

moth transfers pollen between plants and the plants provide both food and a safe habitat for the moth larvae, which hatch from eggs laid inside the flower. Without the specialist species of yucca moth, pollination (successful reproduction) would not occur in the yucca, and without the yucca plant, the moth would be unable to reproduce successfully because it lays its eggs only inside yucca flowers. Lichens are an obligate mutualism between a fungus and either an alga or a blue-green bacterium (the two species cannot live apart in nature). The fungus benefits from the photosynthesis of its algal partner, while the alga gains a moist microhabitat and better access to inorganic nutrients. Mycorrhiza is another mutualism between fungi and the roots of most vascular plants, whereby the plant benefits through better access to nutrients such as phosphate, and the fungus benefits from nutrients exuded from the plant roots (see Chapter 9).

Another type of symbiotic species interaction, **commensalism**, occurs when one species benefits while the other is neither helped nor harmed. On land, a good example of commensalism is the relationship between a tropical tree and its **epiphytes** (air plants) that live attached to the bark of the tree's branches. Epiphytes do not obtain nutrients or water directly from the tree to which they are anchored, but their position on the tree allows them to receive adequate light, water (by rainfall dripping down the branches), and minerals (washed out of the tree's leaves by rainfall). The epiphytes benefit from the association while the tree remains generally unaffected.

Research in old-growth forest canopies of the Pacific Northwest has revealed that epiphytes (lichens, mosses, and liverworts) contribute to the creation of treetop soil (from decaying remains of leaves, epiphytes, and needles). Since soils in temperate rain forests tend to be nutrient poor because of leaching by heavy rains, tree roots actually tap the soil up in their own canopies. When they are wet, nitrogen-fixing lichens are particularly important in canopies because they release excess nitrogen that may be absorbed by other epiphytes or the tree itself. The mutualism that yields this critical source of forest nutrition is declining as logging of old-growth forests (colonized most heavily by nitrogen-fixing lichens) is causing these lichens to decline (Moffett, 1997).

In a marine environment, commensalism occurs between various species of clownfish and sea anemones. The stinging tentacles of the anemones paralyze most fish that touch them, but clownfish gain protection by living unharmed among the tentacles and feeding on the detritus left from the meals of their host anemones. The sea anemones seem neither to be harmed by this relationship nor to benefit from it. A similar relationship occurs between manta rays and remora fish.

ENERGY FLOW IN ECOSYSTEMS

FOOD CHAINS AND FOOD WEBS

One way in which individuals in a community interact is by feeding on one another. Through feeding, energy, chemical elements, and some compounds are transferred from organism to organism along **food chains** (the sequence of who feeds on or decomposes whom in an ecosystem). Ecologists have assigned every organism in an ecosystem to a feeding or **trophic level**, depending on whether it is a producer or a consumer and what it eats or decomposes (refer to Figure 3–8 on page 76).

The first trophic level, and the basic provider of food for the rest of the food web, consists of producers, the plants that start the food chain by capturing the sun's energy through photosynthesis. Primary consumers (and omnivores) eat the plants and make up the second trophic level; secondary consumers (and omnivores) eat the herbivores and form the third trophic level; and tertiary consumers (and omnivores) belong to the fourth trophic level. Detrivores, or decomposers, process detritus from all trophic levels.

Simple food chains such as described above occur rarely in nature because few organisms eat just one other kind of organism. Typically, the flow of energy and materials through terrestrial, aquatic, and oceanic ecosystems occurs

Photo 3–13
The meeting of two links in the food chain.

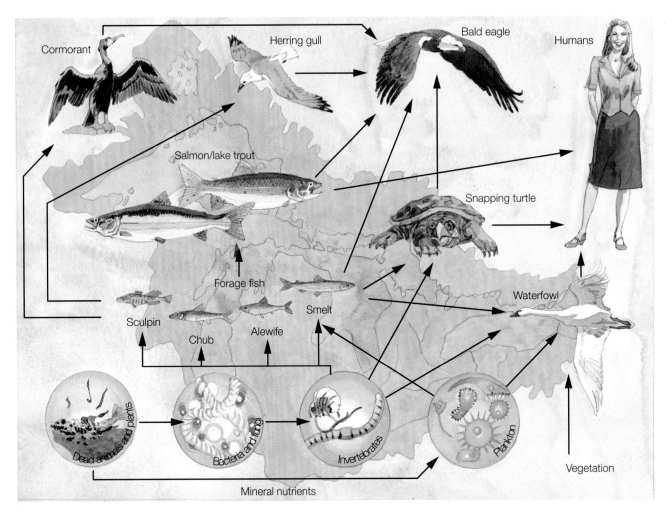

Figure 3–12

A simplified Great Lakes food web

SOURCE: *The State of Canada's Environment—1996,* © Her Majesty the Queen in Right of Canada, Environment Canada 1996. Reprinted with permission of the Minister of Public Works and Government Services Canada, 2008.

on the basis of a range of food choices on the part of each organism involved. These organisms form a complex network of feeding relationships called a **food web**. In a simplified Great Lakes example, the food web shows relationships between some of the better known species including lake trout, salmon, herring gulls, bald eagles, and humans (see Figure 3–12).

An important feature of energy flow in ecosystems is that it is one-way. Energy can move along the food chain until it is used; at that point, it is unavailable for use by any other organism in the ecosystem. Depending on the types of species and ecosystem involved, there can be up to a 90 percent energy loss with each transfer from one trophic level to the next (see Figure 3–8 on page 76). The greater the number of trophic levels or steps that exist in a food chain or web, the greater the cumulative loss of usable energy. (Reductions in energy are the result of the second law of thermodynamics.)

The large energy loss in moving to each successive trophic level explains why most food chains and webs rarely have more than four consecutive links or energy transfers. Energy flows also demonstrate why the eating habits of people can influence how many humans planet Earth can support. If people eat at lower trophic levels by directly consuming grains such as rice, rather than eating grain eaters such as beef cattle, they will be located on a shorter food chain and obtain more energy than meat eaters do from the same amount of plant material.

PRODUCTIVITY OF PRODUCERS

The rate at which producers in an ecosystem capture and store chemical energy as **biomass** (the amount of living or organic matter contained in living organisms) is that ecosystem's **gross primary productivity**. Since plants must respire to provide energy for their life processes, and respiration uses up some biomass, energy that remains after respiration occurs is known as net primary productivity. Essentially, **net primary productivity** represents the rate at which organic matter is incorporated into plant bodies so as to produce growth. Expressed simply, net primary productivity (or plant growth) equals gross primary productivity (total photosynthesis) minus plant respiration. Net primary productivity usually is reported in terms of kilocalories (of energy fixed by photosynthesis) per square metre per year, or in terms of dry weight (grams of carbon incorporated into tissue) per square metre per year.

In different parts of the Earth, net primary productivity varies greatly. Terrestrial communities are generally more productive than aquatic communities, partly because of the greater availability of light for photosynthesis and partly because of higher concentrations of available mineral nutrients. On land, estuaries, swamps and marshes, and tropical rain forests are most productive, while Arctic and alpine tundra and desert scrub ecosystems are least productive. Water surrounding aquatic ecosystems moderates temperatures, but the productivity of these systems is limited by scarce mineral nutrients and low light intensity.

It has been estimated that humans have destroyed outright about 12 percent of the terrestrial net primary productivity and currently use an additional 27 percent. Humans have appropriated nearly 40 percent of the terrestrial food supply, leaving only 60 percent for the millions of Earth's other land-based plants and animals (Postel, 1996). Keeping in mind that humans have taken the 40 percent that was most easily acquired, and that human populations continue to grow, concern arises about the planet's carrying capacity and the sustainability of human actions with regard to productivity in ecosystems.

Matter Cycling in Ecosystems

NUTRIENT CYCLES

If an organism such as a plant is to live, grow, and reproduce, it must take in variable amounts of different **nutrients**. Nine **macronutrients**—carbon, oxygen, hydrogen, nitrogen, phosphorus, potassium, calcium, magnesium, and sulphur—are the major constituents of the complex organic compounds found in all living organisms. Macronutrients are required in large amounts by most forms of life to make proteins, fats, and carbohydrates. Many organisms also require trace amounts of numerous **micronutrients** such as boron, copper, iron, zinc, molybdenum, chlorine, and manganese.

Multidirectional **nutrient cycles**, or **biogeochemical cycles**, are the means by which these nutrient elements and their compounds cycle continually through the Earth's atmosphere, hydrosphere, lithosphere, and biosphere,

connecting past, present, and future life. Unfortunately, toxins can also circulate through these same cycles (see Box 3–4). The five main cycles, driven directly or indirectly by incoming solar energy and gravity, are the carbon, oxygen, nitrogen, phosphorus, and hydrologic (water) cycles. While much research remains to be done before we fully understand major biogeochemical cycles, aspects of these cycles are discussed briefly below.

Carbon and Oxygen Cycles

Proteins, carbohydrates, and other molecules essential to life contain carbon; living organisms must have carbon available to them. Carbon dioxide gas, which makes up about 0.03 percent of the volume of the troposphere and also is dissolved in water, is the basis of the carbon cycle. Producers remove CO_2 from the atmosphere or water and, using photosynthesis, convert it into complex chemical compounds such as glucose ($C_6H_{12}O_6$). In doing so, they produce oxygen (O_2) and release it to the environment (see Figure 3–13 on page 87). Simultaneously, the compounds are used as fuel for aerobic cell respiration in producers, consumers, and decomposers. Respiration breaks down the glucose and other nutrient compounds and converts the carbon back to CO_2 in the atmosphere or water, where producers can reuse it.

Sometimes the carbon in biological molecules is not recycled back to the abiotic environment for a long time—the carbon stored (sequestered) in the wood of trees, for instance, may remain there for several hundred years. Both forests and oceans are major carbon sinks (carbon storage sites) and are important elements in the Kyoto Protocol (see Chapter 5). Generally, carbon circulates in the ecosphere as a result of the linkage between photosynthesis in producers and aerobic respiration in producers and consumers. Oxygen and hydrogen, which together with carbon form the compounds of life, cycle almost in step with carbon.

Oscillations in the balance of O_2 and CO_2 in the atmosphere have occurred throughout Earth's history. However, human activities that have disturbed the balance of the carbon cycle, in ways that add more carbon dioxide to the atmosphere than oceans and plants can remove, have increased markedly since the 1950s. People have cleared extensive areas of forests and brush, leaving less vegetation available to absorb CO_2, and people also may have exceeded threshold limits by burning increasing amounts of fossil fuels and woods, releasing CO_2 into the atmosphere at a rate greater than the natural carbon cycle can handle. (Discussion of the impacts of rising CO_2 in the atmosphere is found in Chapter 5.)

Nitrogen Cycle

One of the most significant macronutrients, nitrogen is crucial for all living things because it is an essential part

BOX 3-4
TOXINS AND THE GREAT LAKES ECOSYSTEM

In 1971, a biologist at Scotch Bonnet Island in Lake Ontario found only 12 herring gull chicks where there should have been 100. That disturbing discovery of the reproductive problems of the ubiquitous herring gull became a symbol of the problems afflicting wildlife in the Great Lakes ecosystem.

In the early 1970s, a program designed to monitor persistent toxic chemicals in the eggs of herring gulls soon showed that water birds in the Great Lakes were among the most heavily contaminated in the world. High levels of chlorinated organic contaminants in the gulls' eggs coincided with high embryonic mortality and behavioural changes in adults (such as inattentiveness) that resulted in lower hatching success and physiological abnormalities in embryos and chicks.

Contaminants in herring gull eggs declined through the 1970s as a result of regulations implemented to control use and production of chlorinated organic compounds. However, in 1981 and 1982, levels increased briefly again, indicating that persistent contaminants continued to cycle through the ecosystem. The less easily controlled sources of these contaminants included leaching from landfill sites, disturbance of lake sediments, and deposition from the atmosphere. As herring gulls are sensitive to the presence of biologically significant concentrations of chemicals in the Great Lakes, monitoring of contaminant levels in herring gull eggs continues and is now the longest-running annual wildlife contaminants monitoring program in the world. Recently, a newly discovered family of chemicals, polybrominated diphenyl ethers (PBDEs), has increased dramatically in Great Lakes gulls and has been added to the approximately 100 compounds analyzed in the monitoring program.

An indicator species, bald eagles are extremely sensitive monitors of ecosystem quality. The fact that nesting pairs reintroduced to both the north and south shores of Lake Erie continue to survive confirms that ecosystem quality in those parts of the Great Lakes has improved. The fact that many of their eggs are fertile also is evidence of improvements in environmental quality. In 1991, however, 8 of 12 hatchlings died of wasting by the age of four weeks—wasting is a syndrome linked with persistent toxic substances. In 1993, bald eagles were hatched with twisted beaks and deformed talons, a problem caused by persistent toxic substances. These events indicate that efforts made since the late 1970s to reduce some contaminant levels have made substantial progress, but not

Photo 3–14
Eaglet hatched with twisted beak.

sufficient progress to restore the viability of bald eagle chicks in the populations of bald eagles nesting near the shoreline of the Great Lakes. By implication, there is potential danger to the dense human population around the Great Lakes.

Although the issues of eggshell thinning, reproductive failure, and congenital deformities have been reduced in severity, contaminant effects of continuing concern include endocrine disruption (feminization of male reproductive tissues), suppressed immune function (increased susceptibility to infectious diseases), and genotoxicity (DNA mutations). Since it is not yet possible to retrieve or remove completely a persistent toxic substance once it has entered the environment, the focus must be on preventing the generation of such substances in the first place, rather than on trying to control their use, release, and disposal after they are produced. For those substances that persist and bioaccumulate in the environment, there is no safe level. The challenge is to implement the goal of zero discharge for persistent toxic substances—that is, to stop their generation, use, and release into the environment.

SOURCES: "Thirty Years of Monitoring Great Lakes Herring Gulls," Environment Canada, 2004, *EnviroZine, 43;* "Table 2: Summary of Some Contaminant-Related Effects Observed in Herring Gulls and Other Fish-Eating Waterbirds Inhabiting the Great Lakes," *The Green Lane,* Environment Canada, 2005, http://www.on.ec.gc.ca/wildlife/factsheets/fs_herring_gulls_table2_e.html; *The State of Canada's Environment—1991,* Government of Canada, 1991, Ottawa: Supply and Services Canada, p. 18-16; *Sixth Biennial Report under the Great Lakes Water Quality Agreement of 1978 to the Governments of the United States and Canada and the State and Provincial Governments of the Great Lakes Basin, International Joint Commission,* 1992, Ottawa: Author; "Keeping the Zero in Zero Discharge," P. Muldoon & J. Jackson, 1994, *Alternatives, 20*(4), 14–20.

of amino acids, which make up proteins (important structural components of cells) and nitric acids (which store genetic information). Although Earth's atmosphere is about 78 percent nitrogen gas (N_2), nitrogen gas is comparatively unreactive, so most plants and animals cannot use nitrogen gas directly from the atmosphere. The nitrogen must be "fixed" (that is, combined with oxygen or

hydrogen) to provide compounds that plant roots are able to use. The five steps in the nitrogen cycle, whereby bacteria convert nitrogen gas into water-soluble compounds containing nitrogen, are illustrated in Figure 3–14.

The complex nitrogen cycle starts with **nitrogen fixation**, a process that converts atmospheric nitrogen (N_2) into ammonia (NH_3). This conversion is done mostly

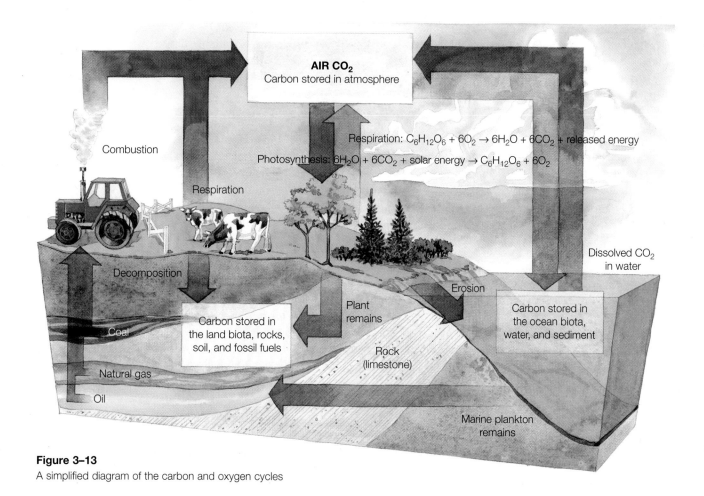

Figure 3–13

A simplified diagram of the carbon and oxygen cycles

Combustion

Respiration

Respiration: $C_6H_{12}O_6 + 6O_2 \rightarrow 6H_2O + 6CO_2$ + released energy

Photosynthesis: $6H_2O + 6CO_2$ + solar energy $\rightarrow C_6H_{12}O_6 + 6O_2$

AIR CO_2
Carbon stored in atmosphere

Decomposition

Coal

Natural gas

Oil

Carbon stored in the land biota, rocks, soil, and fossil fuels

Plant remains

Erosion

Rock (limestone)

Dissolved CO_2 in water

Carbon stored in the ocean biota, water, and sediment

Marine plankton remains

by nitrogen-fixing bacteria such as cyanobacteria (a type of photosynthetic bacterium) in soil and aquatic environments, and by the important *Rhizobium* bacteria, which live in special nodules or swellings on the roots of legumes such as beans, peas, and alfalfa. Ammonia also is found in organic nitrogen contained in plant and animal tissue. The most important pathway for plants to acquire nitrogen is through the cycling of organic nitrogen from dead plant matter into mineralized nitrogen. Thus, ammonia must be converted from organic to mineralized nitrogen.

In the second phase of the nitrogen cycle, called ammonification, ammonia is converted to ammonium ions (NH_4^+). In the third step of the cycle, nitrification, ammonium ions are oxidized into nitrate and nitrite ions. Ammonium, nitrite, and nitrate ions are deposited in the soil solution and bound to soil particles, from which

Atmospheric Nitrogen

1. Nitrogen fixation
2. Ammonification
3. Nitrification
4. Assimilation
5. Denitrification

NH_3 in soil

NH_3 NH_4^+

$NH_4^+ \rightarrow NO_3^-$ and NO_2^-

Figure 3–14

A simplified diagram of the nitrogen cycle

SOURCES: *Terrestrial Ecofunctions* (2nd ed.), J. Aber & J. Melillo, 2001, San Diego: Harcourt, pp. 256–260; *The Nature and Property of Soils* (12th ed.), N. C. Brady & R. R. Weil, 1999, Upper Saddle River, NJ: Prentice Hall, pp. 495–496.

CHAPTER 3: EARTH'S LIFE-SUPPORT SYSTEMS

they easily are taken up to plants in the fourth step, assimilation. Increasingly, as a result of human activities, atmospheric ammonium and nitrate ions are deposited in soils through precipitation. Finally, unused mineralized nitrogen compounds are released as gases in the fifth stage of the cycle, denitrification.

Humans have intervened in the nitrogen cycle in several ways. One important intervention occurs when burning fuels release large quantities of nitric oxide (NO) into the atmosphere. When nitric oxide combines with oxygen to form nitrogen dioxide (NO_2) gas, it can then react with water vapour to form nitric acid (HNO_3), a component of acid deposition (acid rain) that can damage trees and aquatic systems. Water pollution is another significant impact of human intervention in the nitrogen cycle, particularly as it relates to the use of nitrogen fertilizers. Overuse of commercial fertilizers on land can lead to excess nitrogen compounds in agricultural runoff and in the discharge of municipal sewage. Nitrogen-based fertilizers stimulate the growth of algae and aquatic plants that, when they subsequently decompose, deplete the water of dissolved oxygen and cause other aquatic organ-isms, including fish, to die of suffocation. Nitrates from fertilizers also can leach or filter down through the soil and contaminate groundwater, causing concern about the quality of drinking water.

Phosphorus Cycle

Phosphorus, one of the essential elements for life and a major constituent of agricultural fertilizers, does not exist in a gaseous state and does not circulate in the atmosphere. Instead, via the long-term geologic processes of the rock cycle, phosphorus slowly cycles from phosphate deposits on land to shallow sediments in the oceans to living organisms and then back to the land and oceans (see Figure 3–15). Although the Earth's crust contains a large amount of phosphorus, only a small fraction is available through conventional mining techniques. As a result, phosphorus is often a limiting nutrient for plant growth.

As water runs over rocks containing phosphorus, inorganic phosphate molecules are released into the soil, where they are taken up by plant roots. Phosphorus moves through the food chain in the same way as carbon and nitrogen do,

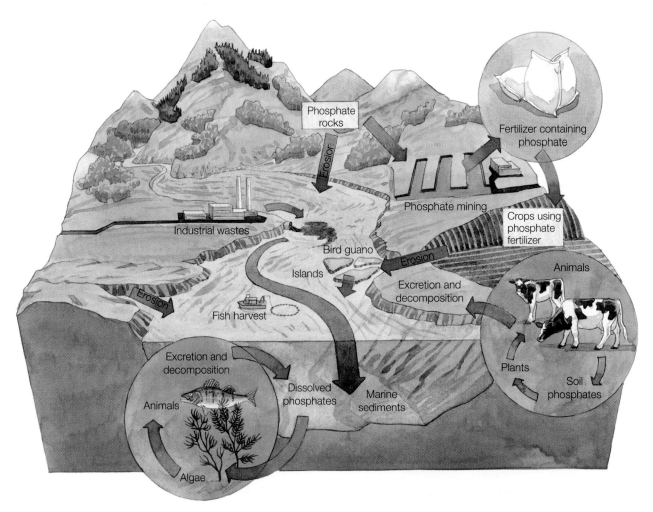

Figure 3–15

A simplified diagram of the phosphorus cycle in terrestrial and aquatic environments

when one organism consumes another. Eventually, decomposers release phosphorus, which becomes part of the inorganic phosphate in the soil that can be reused by plants. A similar process occurs in aquatic communities.

Human influences on the phosphorus cycle derive from activities that accelerate long-term losses of phosphorus from the land, including agricultural crop production that absorbs phosphates from the soil, removal of vegetation and clear-cutting of timber that leads to soil erosion, and mining phosphate rock to produce detergents and commercial fertilizers (to compensate for the steady loss of phosphate from farmers' fields). Other human activities that affect the phosphorus cycle are the addition of excess phosphorus to aquatic ecosystems through runoff of animal wastes from feedlots, from runoff of commercial phosphate fertilizers from cropland, and from discharge of municipal sewage.

Most freshwater lakes and streams contain little phosphorus. When excess phosphorus compounds (phosphates) are added to such aquatic systems, the increased phosphorus concentration stimulates plant growth and algal blooms: **eutrophication**. Eventually, when these plants and algae die, they sink to the bottom and decompose, using up much of the dissolved oxygen (anoxic conditions) and limiting the growth of many aquatic species. Massive fish kills can occur in extreme cases of eutrophication.

Hydrologic Cycle

The supply of water to the earth is constantly moving. In the hydrologic (or water) cycle, Earth's fixed supply of water circulates continuously from the oceans to the atmosphere to the land and back to the oceans, providing a renewable supply of purified water on land (see Figure 3–16 and Figure 7–3). The water cycle, driven by solar energy, involves seven main recycling and purifying processes: evaporation, transpiration, condensation, precipitation, infiltration, percolation, and runoff. Clouds form in the atmosphere when water evaporates from the oceans, soil, streams, rivers, and lakes, and transpires from land plants. After water vapour has condensed into liquid water droplets, water moves from the atmosphere to the land and oceans in the form of precipitation (rain, snow, hail).

Once on land, water can infiltrate the soil and percolate down through the soil and permeable rock formations

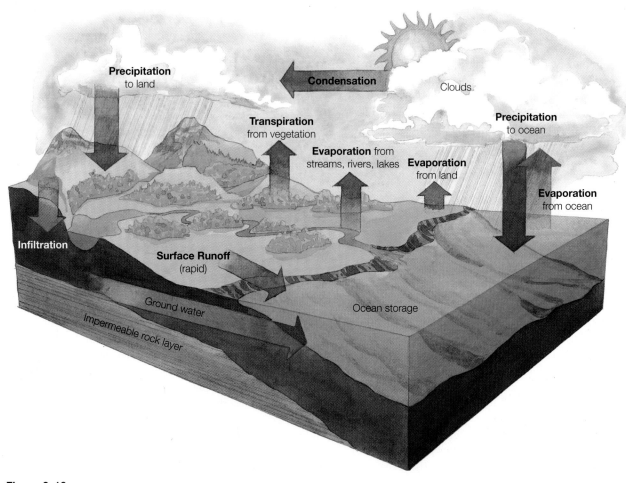

Figure 3–16
A simplified diagram of the hydrologic cycle

to groundwater storage areas, or it can run off in rivers and streams to coastal estuaries and back into the sea to begin the cycle again. Regardless of its physical form or its length of storage time in oceans, streams, reservoirs, or glaciers, every water molecule eventually moves through the hydrologic cycle. Great quantities of water—on the order of about 400 000 cubic kilometres—are cycled annually between Earth and its atmosphere.

TERRESTRIAL AND AQUATIC ECOSYSTEMS

THE GEOGRAPHY OF LIFE

For centuries, people have been fascinated by geographic variations in the kinds and numbers of species found in various parts of the world. Unless they are in zoos, polar bears do not inhabit southwestern British Columbia, nor do arbutus trees grow in the Northwest Territories. Geographic variations occur, in part, because the distributions of plant and animal species are governed by the ability of each species to tolerate the environmental conditions of its surroundings. On a global scale, distribution patterns of species have been recognized for centuries; in each major kind of climate a distinctive type of vegetation develops, and certain animals and other kinds of organisms are associated with each major type of vegetation. Similarly, certain aquatic organisms assemble in each of the Earth's major aquatic ecosystems.

LIFE ON LAND: MAJOR TERRESTRIAL BIOMES

A biome is a kind of ecosystem—a large, relatively distinct region such as a desert, tropical rain forest, tundra, or grassland characterized by certain climatic conditions, soil characteristics, and plant and animal inhabitants regardless of where on Earth it occurs. More than any other factor, the climate—particularly differences in average temperature and average precipitation—influences the boundaries of Earth's major biomes (refer to Figure 3–5, p. 72) and Canada's ecozones (refer to Figure 3–6, p. 73).

Precipitation generally determines whether a land area is forest, grassland, or desert. For instance, we find generally that forest areas receive more than 100 centimetres of precipitation per year, grasslands receive 25 to 75 centimetres, and desert areas receive less than 25 centimetres annually. When temperature and precipitation factors are combined, we find hot areas that receive 100 or more centimetres of rainfall per year sustain tropical savannas, whereas temperate areas with the same amount

of precipitation support deciduous forests. If temperate forest soil types are added as a limiting factor, we find that maples and beeches are more successful on high-nutrient soils while oaks and hickories are more successful on low-nutrient soils. Acting together, then, average annual precipitation and temperature along with soil type lead to deserts, grasslands, and forests (and associated vegetative and animal species) in tropical, temperate, and polar areas.

Although maps show the divisions between Earth's major biomes as sharp boundaries (refer to Figure 3–5), in reality, biomes blend into each other (see Figure 3–17). While various experts identify different numbers of classes of biomes, typically, terrestrial biomes are named for their dominant plant species (such as coniferous forest or grasslands), for the dominant shapes and forms (physiognomy) of the dominant plants (forest versus shrub land), or for the dominant climatic conditions (cold desert versus warm desert). Aquatic biomes usually are identified on the basis of their dominant animals.

Although the relationship between climate and vegetation is complex, over the long term, differences in average precipitation and temperature establish the type and amount of natural vegetation (biomes) that would grow in any particular area if human activities were not present.

Tundra, the northernmost biome, occurs under harsh polar climates characterized by low rainfall and low average temperature. The dominant vegetation of both *Arctic tundra* (occurs at high latitudes) and *alpine tundra* (occurs at high elevations) includes grasses, sedges, mosses, lichens, flowering dwarf shrubs, and mat-forming plants. All are adapted to extreme cold and a very short growing season. The dominant animal species differ, however, with the large land areas of Arctic tundra supporting important large mammals such as caribou as well as small mammals, birds, and insects. Small rodents and insects dominate the alpine tundra, which occurs in small, isolated areas. Parts of the tundra are characterized by **permafrost** (a permanently frozen layer of subsoil). Ecologically fragile, these areas may be changed permanently by human developments such as mines, roads, and recreational trails.

The *boreal forest,* or *taiga,* is found south of the tundra and is dominated by dense stands of relatively small (under 30 metres high) coniferous trees. Spruce, fir, larch, and certain pines that are adapted to the cold, dry, subpolar winters and short but warm growing seasons of high latitudes and high altitudes are dominant, but aspen, poplar, and birch are important flowering trees within the boreal forest. Although they cover a very large area in North America, boreal forests contain only about 20 major tree species that are the source of much lumber and pulp and paper (see Chapter 9). Dominant animals of boreal forests include some large mammals such as moose, deer, wolves, and bears; small rodents such as squirrels and rabbits; many insects; and

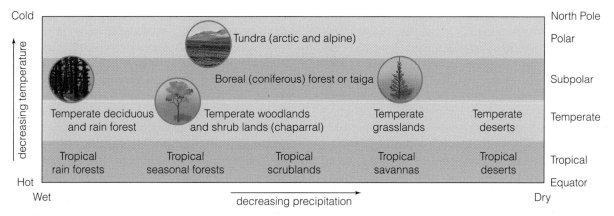

Figure 3–17
Simplified climatic effects on natural vegetation

Photo 3–15
Arctic tundra, northern Baffin Island, Nunavut.

migratory birds. Fires, windstorms, and insect infestations are common disturbances in boreal forests.

Temperate deciduous and rain forests occur where precipitation is relatively high and temperatures are slightly warmer than those of the boreal forests. Dominant tree species in the deciduous forests—important economically for hardwood production and products such as furniture—include tall maples, beeches, oaks, hickories, and chestnuts. Although deer are present, in temperate deciduous forests the low density of large mammals results partly from the deep shade of the forest interior (less food for ground-dwelling mammals). Small mammals such as squirrels and mice, as well as birds and insects, are abundant.

Rare *temperate rain forests,* such as those found on the northwest coast of North America, produce giant (over 70 metres tall), long-lived (over 400 years) conifer trees including redwood, Douglas fir, and western cedar. These trees grow in moderate temperature regimes where the rainfall exceeds 250 centimetres per year. The species diversity of plants and animals in temperate rain forests is low, partly because the climatic conditions favour specialized species and partly because the abundant growth of

the dominant vegetation produces a very deep shade in which few other plants can grow (limited food for herbivores). This biome is important economically as the large tree species continue to be a major timber source.

Temperate woodlands and shrub lands are located in areas with slightly drier climates than those found in temperate deciduous forest areas. Small trees such as piñon junipers, evergreen oaks, and pines characterize temperate woodlands. Fire is a common disturbance in these open, dry woodlands that frequently are used for recreational activities.

Temperate shrub lands, such as the dense chaparrals that occur along the coast of California, in Chile, South Africa, and the Mediterranean, are located in dry Mediterranean climates with low rainfall concentrated in the cool season. Important for watersheds and erosion control, these rapidly regenerating thickets of trees and small-leafed shrubs are adapted to fires. Much of the vegetation, including sage, is aromatic. Although few large mammals exist here, reptiles and small mammals are common. Humans find this climatic regime attractive, and housing developments are expanding rapidly into chaparral lands.

In areas of moderate temperature and 25 to 60 centimetres of seasonal precipitation (too dry for forests and too moist for deserts), *temperate grasslands* thrive on deep, mineral-rich soil. The dominant species in temperate grasslands, located in the prairies of North America, the pampas of South America, the steppes of Eurasia, and the plains of eastern and southern Africa, are grasses and other flowering plants (many are perennials with extensive root systems). Grasslands support the greatest diversity and highest abundance of large mammals, including the wild horses and antelopes of Eurasia, the huge herds of bison that used to roam the North American prairies, the kangaroos of Australia, and the antelopes of Africa.

Tropical biomes occur when the average annual temperature exceeds 18°C. *Tropical rain forests* grow in the wettest climates and in areas where copious, almost daily rainfall occurs. Even though soils are mineral-poor (nutrients are held in the living vegetation), tree species diversity is high—hundreds of species may be found within a few square kilometres in lightly disturbed rain forests of Central and South America, Indonesia, the Philippines, Borneo, parts of Malaysia, northeastern Australia, and Hawaii. Generally, tropical rain forests support at least three storeys of forest foliage, including many epiphytes. Animal species also are abundant; mammals frequently live in the trees, although some are ground dwellers. Insects and other invertebrates show great diversity. Many undiscovered species live in these relatively unknown tropical rain forests.

Tropical seasonal forests and *tropical savannas* occur where rainfall is high (up to 120 centimetres) and a pronounced dry season occurs, such as in India, Southeast Asia, Africa, and South and Central America. *Tropical savannas* (grasslands with scattered trees) in Africa exhibit the greatest abundance of large mammals remaining in the world, and plant species diversity is high also. Fire and grazing are common sources of disturbance.

Deserts occur in both temperate and tropical areas where there is little precipitation (less than 50 centimetres per year) and high evaporation. North Africa's Sahara Desert and deserts of the southwestern United States, Mexico, and Australia occur at low elevations. Cold deserts occur in areas such as the high country in Nevada

and Utah and in parts of western Asia. Communities and organisms in deserts, including invertebrate and vertebrate animals, possess specialized water-conserving adaptations. Nonmammalian vertebrates such as snakes and reptiles are the dominant animal species; desert mammals are usually small, such as the kangaroo mouse in North American deserts. Desert soils frequently lack organic matter but have abundant nutrients, needing only water to be highly productive. Common disturbances come in the form of occasional fires, occasional cold weather, and infrequent but sudden, intense rains that cause flooding.

Climate and vegetation vary with latitude (distance from the equator) and altitude (height above sea level). If we were to travel from the equator to the North or South poles or from low to high altitudes, we would see parallel changes in vegetation (see Figure 3–18). That is, changes in the type and distribution of vegetation we would see while hiking up a mountain (gaining altitude) would be similar to the changes in vegetation seen while travelling toward the North Pole (increasing latitude). Hiking some of the trails in the Canadian Rockies, for example, we would be able to see the temperate deciduous forest at the base of the mountains give way to subalpine coniferous species that, with increasing elevation gain, would give way to alpine tundra below the permanent ice and snow of the peaks.

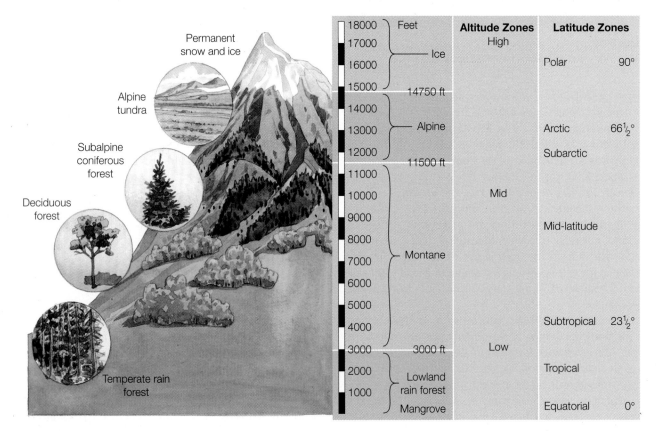

Figure 3–18
Generalized effects of altitude and latitude on climate and biomes

LIFE ON EARTH: MAJOR AQUATIC BIOMES

Oceans

Oceans cover about 71 percent of the Earth's surface, serving as a huge reservoir for carbon dioxide, helping to regulate the temperature of the troposphere, and providing habitats for about 250 000 species of marine animals and plants (many of which are eaten by humans and other organisms). Oceans contain many valuable resources, including sand and gravel, oil and natural gas, iron, phosphates, and magnesium. As long as their tolerance limits are not exceeded, their size and currents enable oceans to mix and dilute many human-produced wastes that flow or are dumped into them, rendering the wastes less harmful or even harmless (see Enviro-Focus 8).

The coastal zone and the open sea are the two major life zones of the oceans. Constituting less than 10 percent of the ocean's area, the **coastal zone** contains about 90 percent of all marine species and is where most of the large commercial marine fisheries are located. The coastal zone is the nutrient-rich, relatively warm shallow water that extends from the high-tide mark on land to the gently sloping, relatively shallow edge of the continental shelf at a depth of about 200 metres.

Coastal zones are among the most densely populated and most intensely used and polluted ecosystems on Earth. Coral reefs, estuaries, coastal wetlands, and barrier islands are among the most highly productive ecosystems within the coastal zone. Their high net primary productivity per unit of area is due to the ample sunlight and the nutrients deposited from land and stirred up by wind and ocean currents.

Found in warm tropical and subtropical oceans, slow-growing **coral reefs** are as rich in species as tropical rain forests; a single reef may contain more than 3000 species of

Photo 3–16
Rivers carry nutrients to the ocean, where the nutrients support many coastal and marine species. Fertile deltas also support human agriculture.

corals, fish, and shellfish. Not only do almost one-third of all the world's fish live on coral reefs, providing critical fishing grounds for many countries, but coral reefs also reduce the energy of incoming waves, thus protecting about 15 percent of the world's shorelines from storms. In spite of their importance, coral reef formations are being degraded and destroyed by pollution, siltation from clear-cutting operations inland, land-reclamation efforts, tourism, and mining of coral formations for building materials.

As bodies of coastal water partly surrounded by land, **estuaries** have access to the open sea and a large supply of fresh water from rivers. A combination of several factors—nutrients from the land transported into the estuary by rivers and streams, ocean current action that rapidly circulates the nutrients and filters out waste products, and the presence of many plants whose roots and stems mechanically trap food material—provides important nursery conditions for the larval stages of most commercially important shellfish and fin fish species.

Coastal wetlands and **mangrove swamps** also are breeding grounds and habitats for marine organisms (oysters, crabs), waterfowl, shore birds, and other wildlife. Here, too, human ignorance has caused the loss of estuarine environments as people have used coastal wetlands and tidal marshes as dumps or have filled them with dredged material to form artificial land for residential and industrial developments. Mangrove swamps often are destroyed to provide firewood and agricultural land.

Barrier islands, the long, low, narrow offshore islands of sediment that run parallel to much of North America's Atlantic and Gulf coasts, help protect coastal wetlands, lagoons, estuaries, and the mainland from storm damage by dispersing wave energy. These islands also come under stress from human recreational and developmental activities.

The second major life zone of the oceans, the open sea, has two main divisions: the **benthic environment** (ocean floor) and the **pelagic environment** (ocean water). The pelagic environment has three vertical zones—the euphotic, bathyl, and abyssal zones—that are based chiefly on the penetration of sunlight (see Figure 3–19 on page 94). The euphotic region (the upper 100 to 200 metres of ocean water beyond the continental shelf) allows enough sunlight to penetrate for photosynthesis to take place. Here, large populations of producers (microscopic cyanobacteria and protists) known as phytoplankton are eaten by slightly larger primary consumers (zooplankton) that are then eaten by other consumers such as baleen whales, herring, sardines, and other small fish. In turn, larger predators such as tuna, mackerel, seals, and orcas eat these small fish. Dead and decaying organisms fall to the ocean floor to feed microscopic decomposers and scavengers such as crabs and sea urchins.

The bathyl zone (from a depth of 200 to about 2000 metres) is lit dimly, much like twilight. Many species of large animals are found here, but at low density. Beyond

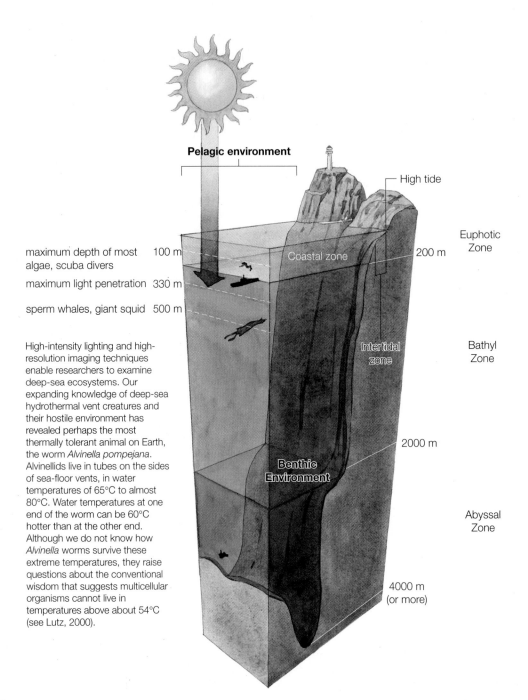

Pelagic environment

High tide

Euphotic Zone

maximum depth of most algae, scuba divers — 100 m

Coastal zone — 200 m

maximum light penetration — 330 m

sperm whales, giant squid — 500 m

Interidal zone

Bathyl Zone

High-intensity lighting and high-resolution imaging techniques enable researchers to examine deep-sea ecosystems. Our expanding knowledge of deep-sea hydrothermal vent creatures and their hostile environment has revealed perhaps the most thermally tolerant animal on Earth, the worm *Alvinella pompejana*. Alvinellids live in tubes on the sides of sea-floor vents, in water temperatures of 65°C to almost 80°C. Water temperatures at one end of the worm can be 60°C hotter than at the other end. Although we do not know how *Alvinella* worms survive these extreme temperatures, they raise questions about the conventional wisdom that suggests multicellular organisms cannot live in temperatures above about 54°C (see Lutz, 2000).

Benthic Environment

2000 m

Abyssal Zone

4000 m (or more)

Figure 3–19
Zonation in the marine environment

about 2000 metres, into the abyssal zone, very little light penetrates; the few organisms living in this zone are adapted to darkness and scarcity of food. For example, chemosynthetic bacteria surrounding hydrothermal vents (that release hydrogen sulphide) provide support for giant clams, worms, and other unusual life forms. Except at upwellings, where the upward flow of water brings nutrients to the surface (particularly in the Arctic and Antarctic—see Chapter 8), the productivity of the open sea is quite low, principally due to the lack of sunlight and the fairly low levels of nutrients such as nitrogen and phosphorus.

Freshwater Systems

Freshwater ecosystems include the standing water in lakes and ponds, the flowing water in rivers and streams, and freshwater wetlands (marshes and swamps). Lakes are large bodies of standing water formed when precipitation, overland runoff, or groundwater flowing from springs fills depressions on the Earth's surface. Typically, the water in large lakes has three basic life zones—littoral, limnetic, and profundal—while small lakes lack a profundal zone. Just as in marine environments, each zone provides habitats and niches for different species.

Part 2: The Ecosphere We Live In

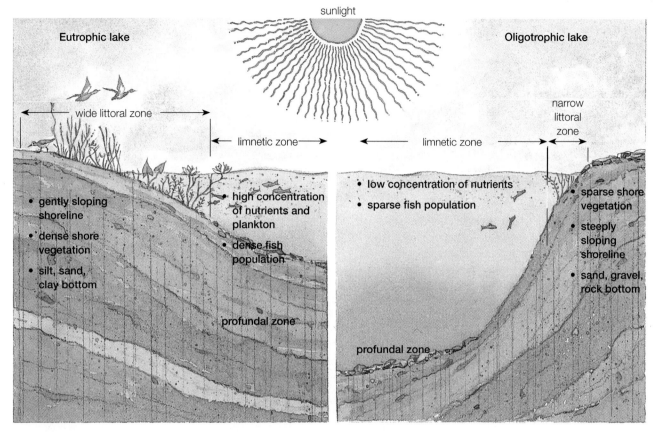

sunlight

Eutrophic lake

Oligotrophic lake

wide littoral zone

limnetic zone

limnetic zone

narrow littoral zone

- gently sloping shoreline
- dense shore vegetation
- silt, sand, clay bottom

- high concentration of nutrients and plankton
- dense fish population

profundal zone

- low concentration of nutrients
- sparse fish population

- sparse shore vegetation
- steeply sloping shoreline
- sand, gravel, rock bottom

profundal zone

Figure 3–20
Basic life zones in eutrophic and oligotrophic lakes

The **littoral zone** is the shallow-water and vegetated area along the shore of a lake or pond (see Figure 3–20). Because nutrient availability and photosynthesis are greatest here, this is the most productive zone of the lake. Frogs and tadpoles, turtles, worms, crustaceans, insect larvae, and many fish, as well as insects, are found in this zone. Extending downward as far as sunlight penetrates, the **limnetic zone** is the open-water area away from the shore. Here the main organisms are phytoplankton (photosynthetic cyanobacteria and algae) and zooplankton (non-photosynthetic organisms including protozoa—animal-like protists—and small animals, including the larval stages of many animals that are large as adults). Larger fish spend most of their time in the limnetic zone, although they may feed and breed in the littoral zone. Due to its depth, the limnetic zone has less vegetation.

The deepest zone of a lake is its **profundal zone**, where lack of light means that no producers live there. Considerable food drifts into the profundal zone from the other two zones and decay bacteria decompose the dead plants and animals, freeing the minerals from their bodies. With no producers to absorb and incorporate these minerals into the food chain, however, the profundal zone habitat is rich in minerals and anaerobic, and few organisms live there.

Normal lakes that have minimal levels of nutrients are unenriched or **oligotrophic**, whereas a lake that is enriched (with nitrates and phosphates) in excess of what producers need is termed **eutrophic**. Many lakes fall somewhere between the two extremes of nutrient enrichment and are called **mesotrophic** lakes.

Photo 3–17
Aquatic vegetation provides cover and nursery conditions for fish and shellfish.

Freshwater Rivers and Streams Movement of water from the mountains to the seas gives rise to different environmental conditions throughout a river system and from stream to stream. Headwater streams (the sources of a river) usually are shallow, swiftly flowing, highly oxygenated, and cold. Organisms here frequently exhibit adaptations such as suckers to avoid being swept away by the current, or flattened bodies to slip under or between rocks. Farther from its headwaters, the river usually widens and becomes deeper, slower-flowing, less oxygenated, and not as cold. Although their shapes are streamlined to reduce resistance when moving through water, organisms in these larger, slow-moving water bodies do not need the same adaptations as those in faster waters. In fact, where the current is slow, plants and animals characteristic of lakes and ponds replace those of the headwaters.

Flowing-water ecosystems are different from freshwater ecosystems not only because of water currents but also in their dependence on the land for much of their energy. Up to 99 percent of the energy input in headwater streams comes from leaves and other detritus (dead organic matter) carried by wind or surface runoff into the stream. Farther downstream, rivers have more producers and are less dependent on detritus as an energy source.

Water moving downhill is associated with landform creation: over the years, the friction from sediment-laden waters can level mountains and cut deep canyons into the landscape. Rocks and sediments removed by the water are deposited in low-lying areas, contributing to (salt) marshes and building up deltas and other landforms.

Inland Wetlands Transitional between aquatic and terrestrial ecosystems, **wetlands** are usually covered with fresh water at least part of the year and have characteristic soils and water-tolerant vegetation. Inland wetlands include marshes, dominated by grass-like plants; swamps, dominated by woody plants; bogs, including peat moss bogs; prairie potholes; mud flats; floodplains; fens; wet meadows; and the wet Arctic tundra in summer. While some wetlands are covered with water year-round, others are seasonal, including prairie potholes (small shallow ponds formed when glacial ice melted at the end of the last ice age) and floodplain wetlands.

Inland wetlands provide habitat for game fish, migratory waterfowl, beaver, otters, muskrats, and other wildlife, and they improve water quality by acting as a sink to filter, dilute, and degrade sediments and pollutants as water flows through them. Wetlands help control flooding by storing excess water during periods of heavy rainfall, or when rivers flood their banks, by slowly releasing the water back into the rivers. Not only do wetlands help to provide a steady flow of water throughout the year, they also reduce riverbank erosion and flood damage. Through infiltration, wetlands serve an important function as groundwater recharge areas. Freshwater wetlands produce many commercially important products such as wild

Photo 3–18
A flowing-water ecosystem in Banff National Park.

rice, cranberries, and peat moss. Many people also enjoy fishing, hunting, boating, photography, and nature study in wetland areas.

In spite of the ecological importance of permanent and seasonal wetlands, they are threatened increasingly by their conversion to cropland and by pollution, dredging

Photo 3–19
Cranberry fields are one example of the agricultural use of wetlands.

and mining, engineering (dams and highways), and urban development.

RESPONSES TO ENVIRONMENTAL STRESS

THE CONSTANCY OF CHANGE

The "balance of nature" is a misnomer—the key thing happening in nature is constant change, caused by both natural and human-related forces and adjustments to environmental stresses. When we talk about sustainability as a concept in the environmental sciences, we include the idea that populations, communities, ecosystems, and human systems all have the capacity to adapt to new and changing conditions. In the following sections, we consider the kinds of changes that have been going on and continue to go on in the world around us.

Changes in Population Size

Changes in human population sizes are governed by four variables: births, deaths, immigration, and emigration. Births and immigration contribute to gains in a population, while deaths and emigration lead to declines in population numbers. A simple formula describes this relationship:

Population change = (births + immigration) − (deaths + emigration).

Clearly, the influence of these variables is affected by changes in resource availability or other environmental changes.

Populations have a variable capacity for growth. Under ideal conditions—that is, when there are no limits on its growth—the **biotic potential** of a population is the maximum rate (r_{max}) at which it can increase. Under ideal conditions, populations of all organisms will increase **exponentially**. If any organism's biotic potential is plotted against time, a characteristic J curve will emerge (see Figure 3–21). In animal species, however, different biotic potentials exist because of variations in their reproductive span (when reproduction starts and stops), frequency of reproduction, litter size, and the number of offspring that survive to reproductive age. Generally, larger organisms such as elephants and whales have lower biotic potentials, whereas microorganisms have the greatest biotic potentials. The limiting factor principle asserts that in nature there are always limits to growth, and no population can continue to grow indefinitely at its biotic potential. Instead, a population will reach a size limit imposed by a shortage of one or more of the limiting factors of light, water, space, and nutrients. Essentially, the number of organisms in a population is controlled by the ability of the environment to support that population.

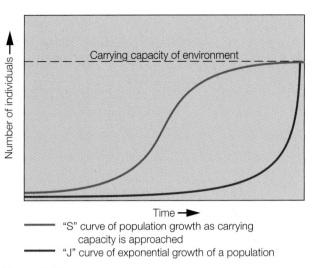

Figure 3–21
S and J curves of population growth

The limits set by the environment that prevent organisms from reproducing indefinitely at an exponential rate are known collectively as **environmental resistance**. **Carrying capacity** represents the highest population that can be maintained for an indefinite period of time by a particular environment as characterized by its particular limiting factors. Many factors determine carrying capacity, including predation, competition among species, migration, and climate. As well, seasonal or abnormal changes in the weather or food supplies, water, nesting or calving sites, and other crucial environmental resources can alter the carrying capacity for a population. If tracked over long periods of time, the rate of population growth for most organisms decreases to about zero; this levelling out occurs at or near the limit of the environment's ability to support a population. The curve on a graph of population numbers plotted against time has a characteristic S shape that also shows the population's initial exponential increase (note the J shape at the start), followed by a levelling out as the carrying capacity of the environment is approached (see Figure 3–21).

Sometimes, because of a reproductive time lag (the time required for the birth rate to fall and the death rate to rise in response to environmental resource limits), a population temporarily will overshoot the carrying capacity (see Figure 3–22a on page 98). Unless large numbers of individuals can avoid local environmental degradation by moving to an area with more favourable conditions, the population will crash. Often such a population will fall back to a lower level that fluctuates around the area's carrying capacity. Also during the overshoot period, if degradation and destruction of local environmental resources occur, the area's carrying capacity may be lowered.

In nature, three general types of population change curves may be observed: relatively stable, irruptive, and cyclic (Figure 3–22b on page 98). If we were to examine many of the species found in undisturbed tropical rain

CHAPTER 3: EARTH'S LIFE-SUPPORT SYSTEMS

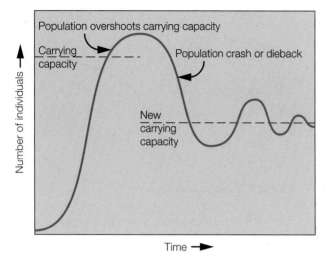

a) A reproductive time lag and population crash

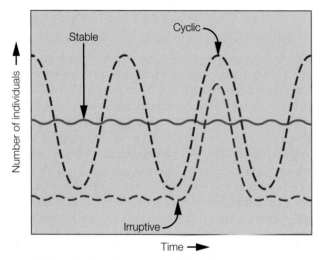

b) Three idealized types of population change curves

Figure 3–22
Selected population change dynamics

forest habitats, we would find their population sizes fluctuate slightly above and below their carrying capacities. If we assume no significant changes in those capacities, these species would be exhibiting relatively stable population sizes. If we considered a species such as the raccoon, which normally has a fairly stable population, we would observe an occasional explosion or irruption of the population to a high peak, followed by a crash to a relatively stable lower level. The population explodes in response to factors (such as better weather, more food, or fewer predators) that temporarily increase carrying capacity for the population. In some other instances, species undergo sharp increases and periodic crashes in their numbers; the actual causes of these boom and bust cycles are not well understood, although predators sometimes are blamed.

Species reproduction strategies vary widely. Some, such as algae, bacteria, rodents, many fish, most insects, and annual plants, produce a great many offspring early in their life cycle. The offspring usually are small, mature rapidly, and have short life spans, many dying before they can reproduce. Such species are opportunistic and reproduce rapidly when favourable conditions exist or when a new habitat or a new niche becomes available (a newly plowed field, a recently cleared forest). If environmental conditions are not favourable, however, such populations will tend to go through boom and bust cycles.

At the other end of the reproductive strategy spectrum are species such as humans, elephants, whales, sharks, birds of prey, and long-lived plants, whose offspring are few in number, fairly large, and often nurtured for lengthy periods to ensure that most reach reproductive age. Populations of these species exhibit an S-shaped curve, as their numbers are maintained near the carrying capacity of their fairly stable habitats.

Human populations, too, are affected by population biology dynamics. If we look back to events such as the 1845 destruction of the Irish potato crop (by a fungus infection), we can see a human population crash in which about 1 million people died and 3 million people emigrated. Today, changes in technology, society, and culture appear to have extended Earth's carrying capacity for the human species—we seem to have controlled many diseases, increased food production, and used energy and matter resources at rapid rates in order to make habitable and usable many formerly uninhabitable and unusable parts of the Earth. On a planet that has finite resources and space, a critical question is how long we will be able to keep extending this carrying capacity.

Biosphere II was a US$30 million experiment that attempted to develop a self-sustaining ecological system (effectively extending carrying capacity). Occupying more than 3 acres near Tucson, Arizona, the area was completely enclosed in glass and steel and its occupants were sealed off from the Earth. Powered by solar energy, and theoretically containing everything required to sustain life, Biosphere II housed more than 3800 species of macroscopic plants and animals, including eight human researchers, who spent two years (1991–93) living inside this artificial environment. The simulated Earth environments contained within Biosphere II were intended to provide food and the means to recycle water and wastes and to purify air and water.

Scientists and other observers criticized the project for having a secretly installed carbon dioxide recovery system (to augment Biosphere II's air recycling system), for letting outside air in, and for having a large supply of food hidden inside. While the creators of Biosphere II denied the charges, the experience showed how difficult it is to maintain natural cycles and species diversity even in such a simplified biosphere. This lesson should cause us to pause and think about how well complex natural ecosystems work and how appropriate our efforts to manage them better really are.

Biological Evolution, Adaptation, and Natural Selection

Understanding biological diversity is important if we are to meet the challenges for our sustainable future. In this context, it is important to appreciate that **biological evolution** (change in inherited characteristics of a population from generation to generation) is touted as the driving force of adaptation to environmental change. According to the theory of evolution, it is the evolution of populations from earlier forms that explains the diversity of life on Earth today. While this theory conflicts with the creation accounts of most religions, most biologists explain the changes in life on Earth based on evolutionary principles.

The theory of biological evolution indicates that the processes that lead to evolution involve the interplay of genetic variation and changes in environmental conditions. The first step is the development of genetic variability in a population. **Genes** (segments of various deoxyribonucleic acid [DNA] molecules found in chromosomes) impart certain inheritable traits to organisms. A population's **gene pool** is the sum of all genes possessed by the individuals of a population, but individuals within the population of a particular species do not share exactly the same genes. **Mutations**, the random and unpredictable changes in DNA molecules that can be transmitted to offspring, bring about this variability. Every time a cell divides, the DNA is reproduced so that each new cell gets a copy, but sometimes the copying is inaccurate, resulting in a change in the DNA and a subsequent change in inherited characteristics. External environmental agents such as radiation (X-rays, ultraviolet light) or certain toxic organic chemicals also may come in contact with the DNA and alter the molecule. The result of millions of random changes in the DNA molecules of individuals in a population is genetic variability.

Offspring with a mutation frequently fail to survive, but in other cases mutations result in new genetic traits that give individuals and their offspring improved chances for survival and reproduction. Any genetically controlled characteristic—structural, physiological, or behavioural—that enhances the chance for members of a population to survive and reproduce in its environment is called an **adaptation**.

Structural adaptations include coloration (which enables individuals to hide from predators or to sneak up on prey), mimicry (which allows individuals to look like a dangerous or poisonous species), protective cover (shell or thick skin, bark, thorns), and gripping mechanisms (hands with opposable thumbs). Physiological adaptations include the ability to poison predators, to give off chemicals that repel prey, and to hibernate during cold weather. The ability to fly to a warmer climate during winter is an example of behavioural adaptation, as are resource partitioning and species interactions such as parasitism, mutualism, and commensalism.

Individuals with one or more adaptations that enable them to survive under changed environmental conditions are more likely to produce more offspring with the same favourable adaptations than are individuals without such adaptations; this is known as **differential reproduction**. **Natural selection** is the process by which organisms whose biological characteristics (beneficial genes) better fit them to the environment are better represented by descendants in future generations than are those organisms whose characteristics are less fit for the environment. Natural selection has four major characteristics that over time demonstrate the combination of factors leading to evolution: genetic variability (inheritance of traits in succeeding generations, with some variation in those traits); environmental variability; differential reproduction that varies with the environment; and the influence of the environment on survival and reproduction.

Limits to adaptation exist in nature. Human lungs and livers, for example, do not quickly become more capable of dealing with air pollutants and other toxins to which we are exposed. Human skin cannot evolve sufficiently rapidly to be more resistant to the harmful effects of ultraviolet radiation. The reasons for our inability to adapt quickly relate chiefly to our reproductive capacity. Unlike mosquitoes, rats, and species of weeds, humans and other large species such as sharks, elephants, and tigers cannot produce large numbers of offspring rapidly, so our ability to adapt quickly to particular environmental changes through natural selection is very limited. In addition, since a population can adapt only for traits that are present in its gene pool, even if a favourable gene were present, most members of the population would have to die or become sterile so that individuals with the trait could become dominant and pass on the trait. This is hardly a desirable solution! We must remember, also, that species adaptations develop in the context of their ecological situation (relationships with other organisms and the environment) and that our knowledge of this complexity is incomplete.

Speciation and Extinction

Two other processes, speciation and extinction, are believed to have affected the millions of species on Earth. **Speciation** is the formation of two or more species from one as the result of divergent natural selection in response to changes in environmental conditions.

One mechanism that generates speciation is geographic isolation, a situation in which populations of species become separated for a long time in areas with different environmental conditions. This may occur naturally (as when part of a group migrates for food) or through human-related activities. Highway construction, for example, may quickly separate a small group of individuals from a larger population. If these groups remain geographically separated for a long time and do not interbreed, they may begin to diverge in their genetic makeup because of different selection pressures. Continued reproductive isolation may mean that members of the separated populations become so different that they cannot interbreed and produce fertile offspring. If this occurs, one species becomes two, as perhaps occurred with Arctic and grey foxes. It is thought that these two species were once one but separated into northern and southern populations that adapted to different environmental conditions (the Arctic fox with its white, heavy fur and short ears, legs, and nose adapted to cold conditions, and the grey fox with its lightweight fur and long ears, legs, and nose adapted to heat).

Extinction is the second process affecting Earth's species. A species is eliminated from existence when it cannot adapt genetically and reproduce successfully under new environmental conditions. The continuous, low-level extinction of species that has occurred throughout much of the history of life is termed **background extinction**. **Mass extinction**, in contrast, is the disappearance of numerous species over a relatively short period of geological time. Fossil and other geological evidence points to catastrophic global events that eliminated major groups of species simultaneously. While extinction is a crisis for the affected species, extinction provides an opportunity for other species to evolve to fill new or vacant ecological niches in changed environments (a process called adaptive radiation). Species biodiversity, one of the Earth's most important resources, may be expressed in an equation:

Species biodiversity = number of species + speciation − extinction.

Ecological Succession

A community of organisms does not spring into full-blown existence but develops gradually through a series of stages until it reaches maturity. The process of community development over time, during which the composition and function of communities and ecosystems change, is called **succession**. Ecological succession is a normal process in nature, and is in constant flux as a community or ecosystem responds to natural or human disturbance. A landscape that includes several successional stages represents maximum habitat for the greatest number of species.

Succession is usually described in terms of the species composition of the vegetation of an area, although each successional stage also has its own characteristic animal life. Ecologists recognize primary and secondary types of ecological succession, depending on conditions at a particular site at the outset of the process. **Primary succession** involves the development of biotic communities in a previously uninhabited and barren habitat with no or little soil. A bare rock surface recently formed by volcanic lava or scraped clean by glacial action, a new sandbar deposited by shifting ocean currents, and a surface-mined area from which all overburden (soil) has been removed are examples of conditions under which primary succession begins. Usually the first signs of life are the hardy pioneer species such as microbes, lichens, and mosses that are quick to establish large populations in a new area. However, it may take lichen 100 years to grow to be the size of a dinner plate. Depending on the climate in an area, primary succession may take several hundred to several thousand years.

Secondary succession begins in an area where the natural vegetation has been removed or destroyed but where soil is present. Burned or cut forests and abandoned farm fields are common sites where secondary succession occurs. The presence of soil permits new vegetation to spring up quickly, often in a matter of weeks, and subsequent successional stages to develop over the next 100 or more years.

Ecological succession is not necessarily an orderly process, with each successional stage leading inevitably to the next more stable stage until the area is occupied by a mature or **climax community**. The exact sequence of species and community types that appear during the course of succession in a given area can be highly variable. Even the climax community is not permanent; fires, floods, landslides, and extreme weather events all present opportunities for new species to colonize altered space, once again illustrating the constancy of change in nature.

HUMAN IMPACTS ON ECOSYSTEMS

Over the past century, human activities have simplified natural ecosystems. Subsequent to plowing native prairie grasses, clear-cutting forests, and filling in wetlands, we replaced the complexity of thousands of plant and animal interrelationships in these ecosystems with monocultures of wheat, canola, or commercially valuable trees, or with highways, parking lots, and buildings.

Humans spend a lot of money defending such monocultures from invasion by pioneer species because weeds (plants), pests (insects or other animals), and pathogens (fungi, viruses, or disease-causing bacteria) can destroy an entire monoculture crop unless it is protected by pesticides or some form of biological control. Given that fast-breeding insect species undergo natural selection and develop genetic resistance to pesticides, people end up using stronger doses or switching to new pesticides. Ultimately, natural selection in the pests increases to the point that these chemicals are ineffective. This danger is seen in the comeback of malaria, principally because of mutant forms of the mosquito-borne microbe that are becoming increasingly resistant to drugs (Nichols, 1997).

These processes highlight the important point that when humans intrude into nature, we can never affect just one thing; instead, we cause multiple effects, many of which are unpredictable in their outcomes. The **principle of connectedness** specifies that everything is connected to and intermingled with everything else—we are all in this together. The multiple effects of human activities result from our limited understanding of how nature works and our inability to identify which connections are strongest and most important in the sustainability and adaptability of ecosystems.

Cultivating monocultures is not the only way people simplify ecosystems. Many Canadian ranchers continue to poison ground squirrels that compete with livestock for grass and damage crops and fields, inadvertently eradicating species such as the burrowing owl and swift fox (refer to Box 3–3 on page 80). Ranchers frequently shoot wolves, coyotes, bears, and other predators that occasionally kill livestock. During the winter of 1995, some Saskatchewan sheep ranchers put out insecticide-laced meat to try to kill coyotes; at least 15 bald eagles were killed instead. One rancher was fined only $430, less than the cost of one guard dog (Dambrofsky, 1996).

Nomadic herders and ranchers around the world have permitted livestock to overgraze grasslands to the point where erosion turns these ecosystems into less productive deserts or wastelands. Furthermore, the cutting of large tracts of tropical and temperate rain forests has destroyed part of the Earth's biodiversity, and people have fished and hunted some species to extinction or near extinction; all of these activities simplify ecosystems. Even burning fossil fuels in our vehicles, homes, and industrial plants simplifies forest and aquatic ecosystems by creating air pollutants that not only degrade the atmosphere but also kill or weaken trees and fish.

Maintaining a balance between simplified human ecosystems and the more complex natural ecosystems that surround us is a challenge, particularly given the rate at which we have been altering nature for human purposes.

WORKING WITH NATURE

Living systems have six key features—interdependence, diversity, resilience, adaptability, unpredictability, and limits—that suggest humans could learn to live sustainably if they understood and mimicked how nature perpetuates itself. Learning to live sustainably begins with recognizing the following: humans are a part of, and not separate from, the dynamic web of life on Earth; human economies, lifestyles, and ultimate survival depend totally on the sun and the Earth; and everything is connected to everything else, although some connections are stronger and more important than others.

The law of conservation of matter and the second law of energy tell us that as we use resources, we add some waste heat and matter to the environment. In recent decades, the rapid economic growth and rising standard of living in Canada and other industrialized countries have been supported by accelerated resource consumption and increased use of Earth's materials and energy. Our attempts to maximize short-term economic gain have generated a legacy of degraded water, air, soil, forests, and biological diversity. "As the world becomes ecologically over-loaded, conventional economic development actually becomes self-destructive and impoverishing. Many scholars believe that continuing on this historical path might even put our very survival at risk" (Wackernagel & Rees, 1996, pp. 2–3).

One of the first things we must do is acknowledge and accept the reality of ecological limits and the resultant changes that such acceptance will bring to our socioeconomic systems. Even if we were to recycle more materials so that economic growth could continue without depleting resources and without producing large volumes of pollutants, we need to remember that recycling matter resources requires high-quality energy, which cannot be recycled. If we were to become a recycling society as an interim stage in moving toward achieving a sustainable society, we would need not only an inexhaustible supply of affordable high-quality energy, but also an environment with an infinite capacity to absorb, disperse, dilute, and degrade heat and waste. Since such efforts can be temporary solutions at best, the scientific principles and ecological functioning identified in this chapter help show us that human society, including the human economy, is a subsystem of the ecosphere. If we are to achieve sustainability, we must shift our emphasis "from 'managing resources' to managing ourselves" and "learn to live as part of nature." Such a shift in emphasis would mean that "economics … becomes human ecology" (Wackernagel & Rees, 1996, p. 4).

Such a shift would require us to undertake a range of actions to achieve sustainability, including reduction in use of matter and energy resources through more efficient and appropriate use of energy, a shift to renewable energy sources, less waste of renewable and nonrenewable resources of all types, and an emphasis on pollution prevention and waste reduction. Achieving a sustainable future will require that all Earth's citizens learn to work with nature.

CHAPTER 3: EARTH'S LIFE-SUPPORT SYSTEMS

Crawford "Buzz" Holling grew up in northern Ontario in the 1930s. He nurtured his love of nature as a member of the Royal Ontario Museum's Toronto Junior Field Naturalists. After receiving his postsecondary education at the universities of Toronto and British Columbia, he worked for several years in the Canadian Department of Forestry in Sault Ste. Marie, Ontario, before becoming an academic scholar. His 1973 paper "Resilience and Stability of Ecological Systems" is still considered a landmark, particularly in the field of systems ecology. Trained as an entomologist, he attempted to understand the responses of forest insects to food availability in his early work. This work is still important to understanding predator–prey relations. In this period, he also began to promote the idea that ecosystems do not follow a predictable path toward a single climax community. His ideas about the inherent unpredictability and instability of nature were novel and shaped his thinking about how we seek to manage our interactions with the environment.

Photo 3–20
Buzz Holling

Holling then began to consider "ecological–social interactions" or approaches to management more directly. In the early 1970s, he spearheaded the idea of adaptive management, a structured approach to developing policy and management strategies to learn from interventions and, if necessary, adapt to changing conditions. He argued that we need to consider management policies and practices as social experiments from which scientists, managers, and members of the public can learn.

Dr. Holling pioneered ideas about resilience in ecological and social systems and was the founding director of the Resilience Alliance, an international group of scholars and practitioners that attempts to understand the properties of adaptive ecosystems and institutions. He also served as the founding editor-in-chief of the open-access online journal *Conservation Ecology*, now renamed *Ecology and Society*. His ideas about ecology spearheaded a major shift in thinking, from studying not only individual populations but also the larger-scale communities and processes that affect them. He pursued many ideas about how nature responds to human interventions, considering how to determine if ecosystems are resistant, vulnerable, or resilient to external stresses, the role of humans within ecosystems, and adaptive approaches to environmental management. His most recent focus is on "panarchy," a term based on the Greek god Pan, which he and fellow scientists composed to reflect an understanding of the playfulness and unpredictability of nature while situated within a set of hierarchical systems. Through this concept, he has considered a range of human interventions within ecological systems and how they may affect resilience of those systems.

Dr. Holling's ideas have shaped our contemporary thinking about ecosystems and the multiple ways that humans affect them. He has received many awards for his work, including the Eminent Ecologist Award for outstanding contributions to the science of ecology in 1999. He also has been recognized as a Fellow of the Royal Society of Canada.

SOURCES: "Resilience and Stability of Ecological Systems," C. S. Holling, 1973, *Annual Review of Ecology and Systematics, 4,* 1–23; "The 2000 Kenneth Boulding Memorial Award," D. J. Rapport, 2001, *Ecological Economics, 36*(2): 361–364; "People," Resilience Alliance, 2007, http://www.resalliance.org/561.php

Chapter Questions

1. Using the second law of energy, explain why some people may choose to become vegetarians.

2. What are some of the reasons that aquatic food webs frequently have more trophic levels than terrestrial food webs?

3. Discuss the importance of bacteria to the nitrogen cycle.

4. Explain how people intervene in the Earth's phosphorus cycle, and how our activities have increased the natural rate of phosphorus release into the environment. Is this a problem?

5. Using the second law of energy, explain why there is such a sharp decrease in usable energy as energy flows through a food chain or web. Does the energy loss at each step violate the first law of energy?

6. Why do farmers often need to fertilize their crops with nitrogen and phosphorus, but not carbon?

7. Why is an understanding of biogeochemical cycles important in environmental science? Use one or two examples to justify your answer.

8. If all the producers (or, if all the decomposers and detritus feeders) were eliminated from an ecosystem, what would happen to that ecosystem?

9. If someone said to you that we should not worry about the loss of biodiversity because naturally occurring extinctions reduce biodiversity, how would you respond?

10. Why are coral reefs and coastal and inland wetlands such important ecosystems? Why have human activities destroyed so many of these vital ecosystems?

11. Is the human species a keystone species? Explain.

12. Why are natural ecosystems less vulnerable to harm from insects, plant diseases, and fungi than human-modified ecosystems?

references

Cutler, A. (2006). New frontiers, new explorations. In D. Botkin et al., *Forces of change: A new view of nature*. Washington, DC: Smithsonian Institution.

Dambrofsky, G. (1996, April 8). Ranchers bothered by killer coyotes. *Calgary Herald*, p. A3.

Environmental Literacy Council. (2007). How many species are there? http://www.enviroliteracy.org/article.php/58.html

Government of Canada. (1991). *The state of Canada's environment—1991*. Ottawa: Supply and Services Canada.

Kaufman, D. G., & Franz, C. M. (1993). *Biosphere 2000: Protecting our global environment*. New York: HarperCollins.

Lutz, R. A. (2000). Deep sea vents. *National Geographic, 198*(4), 116–127.

Miller, G. T. (1994). *Sustaining the Earth: An integrated approach*. Belmont, CA: Wadsworth.

Moffett, M. W. (1997). Climbing an ecological frontier: Tree giants of North America. *National Geographic, 191*(1), 44–61.

Nichols, M. (1997, May 19). Malaria's comeback. *Maclean's,* 57.

Perry, D. (1986). *Life above the jungle floor*. New York: Simon & Schuster.

Postel, S. (1996). Carrying capacity: Earth's bottom line. In J. L. Allen (Ed.), *Environment 96/97* (pp. 28–36). Guilford, CT: Dushkin Publishing Group/Brown and Benchmark.

Wackernagel, M., & Rees, W. (1996). *Our ecological footprint: Reducing human impact on the Earth*. Gabriola Island, BC: New Society.

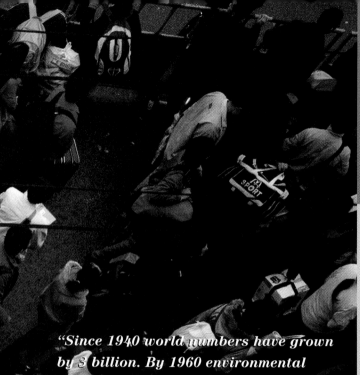

"Since 1940 world numbers have grown by 3 billion. By 1960 environmental stresses were already showing: severe soil erosion, spreading deserts, and shrinking forests. By 1970 there were added the problems of gross-scale pollution and, by 1980, acid rain and mass extinction of species, plus suspicion of the greenhouse effect and ozone-layer depletion. Today it is plain there is biospheric breakdown of multiple sorts. If present trends continue until 2025, will we be looking out on a biosphere needing centuries or millennia to repair?"

Norman Myers (1990, p. 39)

"The contentious issue of population growth and 'overpopulation' looms large in our collective imagination. Since Malthus, and more insistently in the last four decades, we have been barraged with strident claims that proclaim 'over population' is at the root of all our problems.... 'They' are the problem. 'We' are absolved of all responsibility."

Jael Silliman (1999, p. viii)

Chapter Contents

Chapter Objectives

After studying this chapter you should be able to

- discuss different aspects of the debate about human population, environment, and development

- describe dynamics that affect population size, including rates of birth, death, fertility, migration, and cultural factors

- debate the relative merits of different strategies for reducing population growth

- identify and describe alternative measures of human development

- consider how population, environment, and development issues apply in Canada with reference to the structure of the resource economy and the roles of Aboriginal peoples

INTRODUCTION

Many people have observed that human population growth and environmental damage have coincided. This link has led to claims by some scientists that the human population issue is *the* environmental issue. Indeed, scientific concern for this issue is frequently traced back to the writings of Thomas Malthus, an English clergyman, historian, and political economist who argued in 1798 that the human ability to multiply far exceeded our ability to increase food production (Box 4–1). His pessimistic conclusion was that unless people found a more humane solution to stabilizing their populations, famine, disease, and warfare would be inevitable because they would act to curb population growth.

His conclusions are highly contentious, even today. Karl Marx, who has inspired some social scientists for more than a century, argued that Malthus did not consider the socioeconomic conditions that placed people— particularly poor people—out of synch with the means of economic production. Furthermore, the predictions of Malthus have not come true. Since the early 19th century, the human population has increased almost sevenfold. About 70 percent of this increase has taken place since 1960. Technology has enabled humans to live at increasing densities, and thus far, humans have avoided a Malthusian fate. Karl Marx argued that distribution of economic resources—particularly access to property and other forms of capital—is at least as important in explaining the resource-population equation as overall population numbers.

Contemporary writers (like Jael Silliman, quoted at the beginning of the chapter), argue that the link between human population and environmental degradation is too simplistic. Continued emphasis on human population numbers has allowed industrialized countries to blame developing countries while failing to examine their own actions and contributions to environmental degradation. Nevertheless, even though Malthus did not anticipate the enormous growth in human populations in the 20th century or the capability of technological advances and human ingenuity, we are now receiving several environmental signals that suggest we are approaching a limit to the impacts that humans can make to the planet before its critical functions fail.

The tremendous increase in human numbers is testament to the biological success of humans as a species. But when we combine our biological success with our great technological power to cause environmental change, we realize that humans are using up, depleting, and degrading Earth's limited resources, threatening not only our own sustainability but that of other plant and animal species that share this planet. There is no doubt that we live on a human-dominated planet (Vitousek et al., 1997). Pollution

Long before most scholars were concerned about overpopulation, Thomas Malthus was writing his warning about it. Born in Surrey, England, Malthus studied theology at Cambridge and became an ordained minister. While still a minister, he began writing *An Essay on the Principle of Population,* which was published in 1798 and read by Darwin and Marx, among many others. In 1805 he was appointed a professor of modern history and political economy at Laileybury College; he held this position until his death.

Photo 4–1
Thomas Robert Malthus (1766–1834)

In his essay, Malthus clearly noted the potential of geometric growth in the human population to outstrip the arithmetical increase in food supply. To prevent this, Malthus felt population control was necessary. If people failed to control their own numbers, Malthus believed that "natural controls" of warfare, famine, and disease would solve the problem.

The premises on which Malthus based his arguments are included in the following excerpts from his essay:

> I think I may fairly make two postulata.
>
> First, that food is necessary to the existence of man.
>
> Secondly, that the passion between the sexes is necessary, and will remain nearly in its present state.... Assuming, then, my postulata as granted, I say, that the power of population is indefinitely greater than the power in the earth to produce subsistence for man.
>
> Population, when unchecked, increases in a geometrical ratio. Subsistence only increases in an arithmetical ratio. A slight acquaintance with numbers will show the immensity of the first power in comparison of the second.
>
> By that law of our nature which makes food necessary to the life of Man, the effects of these two unequal powers must be kept equal.
>
> This implies a strong and constantly operating check on population....

Photo 4–2
Karl Marx (1818–83)

[The power of population growth is so great] that premature death must in some shape or other visit the human race. The vices of mankind are active and able ministers of depopulation. They are the precursors in the great army of destruction; and often finish the dreadful work themselves. But should they fail in this war of extermination, sickly seasons, epidemics, pestilence and plague, advance in terrible array, and sweep off their thousands and ten thousands. Should success still be incomplete, inevitable famine stalks in the rear, and with one mighty blow, levels the population with the food of the world. (Malthus, 1798, 1803/1909, pp. 44–45)

In contrast, Karl Marx was a philosopher who founded the political economy field of study during the mid-19th century. He argued that society created the conditions of overpopulation. Specifically, he contended that accumulation and production processes associated with capitalism created a surplus of labour over jobs, thereby leading to increased unemployment, cheap labour, and poverty. "Relative surplus population" was not due to the abstract numerical ratio relation proposed by Mathus, but rather was the result of capitalist accumulation and the incessant drive to increase profitability by putting the squeeze on labour. His contemporary, Fredrick Engels, agreed, and in scathing critique of Malthus's assumptions, noted that "since it is precisely the poor who are the surplus, nothing should be done for them except to make their dying of starvation as easy as possible, and to convince them that it cannot be helped and that there is no other salvation for their whole class than keeping propagation down to the absolute minimum" (Marx & Engels, 1975, p. 437). These arguments sound resoundingly similar to those presented in the epitaphs at the beginning of this chapter.

SOURCES: *The Human Mosaic: A Thematic Introduction to Cultural Geography,* T. G. Jordan & L. Rowntree, 1990, New York: Harper & Row, p. 43; *Parallel Chapters from the First and Second Editions of an Essay on the Principle of Population,* T. R. Malthus, 1798, 1803, W. J. Ashley, ed., 1909, New York: MacMillan, pp. 44–45; *Collected Works, Vol. 3: Marx and Engels 1843–1844,* K. Marx & F. Engels, 1975, Moscow, Progress Publishers.

of natural environments, depleted energy reserves, reduced biodiversity, and wildlife extinctions are serious problems. Do these arise from the growth of human populations, or do they arise because of the ways human populations use their environments? This is a subtle, yet significant, distinc-tion. We suggest that development practices may degrade, maintain, or enhance environmental attributes. Debates over the relative influence of human numbers, technology, and consumption and the ways in which they advance or detract from sustainability are longstanding. As individuals, communities, and nation-states, we make choices about the location, timing, and use of environmental resources that are key to understanding and securing sustainability.

This chapter examines fundamental concepts about human population and factors affecting population changes globally and in Canada. We examine the debate about population, environment, and development, making links among several factors that influence human impacts on the Earth's resources. We also briefly examine development debates as well as measures of human well-being that suggest that there are multiple causes and effects of the ways in which we use Earth's resources. Finally, we examine these issues in Canada with specific reference to the nature of the resource economy and the role of Aboriginal peoples.

THE POPULATION–DEVELOPMENT DEBATE

If you are the typical age of most first-year university or college students, you probably were born after 1990. In 1980, the world contained close to 4.5 billion people. By 2006, the world's population reached 6.5 billion people, and it is possible—if the annual growth rate remains at about 1.2 percent—that during your lifetime human numbers will grow to about 8.9 billion. At that rate, about 78 million people are added to the Earth's population each year, more than twice the entire population in Canada. About 90 percent of these 78 million people are born in the developing nations of Africa, Asia, and Latin America (see Box 4–2). From 1995 to 2000, the average annual population growth rate in these developing regions was about 1.4 percent, while in developed nations such as Canada, the United States, Japan, and those of Western Europe, the growth rate was about 0.25 percent (U.S. Census Bureau, Population Division, 2006).

Yet, in terms of consumption, these figures are reversed. Canada, the United States, Japan, and the countries of Western Europe are by far the greatest consumers of the world's resources, using about two-thirds of the world's energy resources. Africa, for example, with about 14 percent of the world's population, uses only 3 percent of the world's energy resources. Some have estimated that "the annual commute by car into New York City alone uses more oil than the whole of Africa (excluding South Africa) in one year" (Elliott 1999, p. 40). In 1987, the World Commission on Environment and Development estimated that to achieve sustainable development, we had to increase the standard of living of developing countries, which would require a fourfold increase in output of product and services. Calculations of our ecological footprint suggest that if all people consumed as much as "average Canadians," we would require several more worlds to meet our demands (see Chapters 1 and 13). How can we achieve stable human population and stable consumption in aid of sustainable development? To address this question, we begin by discussing how population dynamics are understood.

FACTORS AFFECTING HUMAN POPULATION CHANGE

Historical growth of the human population is often described in terms of four major periods or stages (see Table 4–1). Stage 1 represents the early period of hunters

BOX 4–2
DISTINGUISHING BETWEEN DEVELOPED AND DEVELOPING COUNTRIES

Countries can be classified into two groups—developed and developing—based on a number of factors.

Developed countries (also known as postindustrial, highly developed countries [HDCs] or, in some cases, overdeveloped countries) have low rates of population growth and the longest **doubling times** (the length of time required for a population to double), are highly industrialized, and have high per capita incomes relative to the rest of the world. Countries such as Canada, the United States, Japan, Sweden, Australia, and Germany are HDCs; as noted, they are the largest resource consumers, particularly regarding fossil fuels. Developed countries have the lowest birth rates in the world, and in some, such as Germany, birth rates are just below those needed to sustain their populations and thus their populations are declining slightly. HDCs also have very low infant mortality rates.

Developing countries can be categorized as either moderately developed countries (MDCs) or less developed countries (LDCs). Moderately developed countries include Mexico, Thailand, and most South American nations. In these countries, birth rates and infant mortality rates are higher than those of highly developed countries, their level of industrialization is moderate, and their average per capita incomes are lower than those of highly developed nations.

Less developed countries include Bangladesh, Ethiopia, Laos, and Niger; these countries have the highest birth rates, the shortest doubling times, the highest infant mortality rates, the shortest life expectancies, and the lowest average per capita incomes in the world.

and gatherers, when total world population, population density, and average rate of growth were very low. Stage 2, beginning about the time of agricultural settlement, was characterized by the first major increase in the total world population and a much greater density of people. Stage 3 began about the time of the Industrial Revolution and saw a rapid increase in the human population resulting from improvements in health care and food supplies. Stage 4 represents today's increasingly urbanized world, in which the rate of population growth has declined in wealthy, industrialized nations but has continued to rise rapidly (until recently) in poorer, developing countries.

Although the total human population has increased with each succeeding stage, the modern era is unprecedented in terms of population growth (see Table 4–2).

The total human population has increased dramatically since 1950, with developing regions contributing the most to that growth. Although there was little or no change in the maximum length of a human lifetime during the second and third stages in the history of human population growth, there were changes in birth, death, and population growth rates, in age structure, and in average life expectancy. To ensure we understand these changes in population sizes and the causes of these changes, we now consider population dynamics.

POPULATION DYNAMICS

Understanding human population dynamics is the task of demographers. **Demography** is the scientific study

TABLE 4–1
A BRIEF HISTORICAL OVERVIEW OF HUMAN POPULATION GROWTH STAGES

Stage	Population Time Period	Total Human Density	Population	Average Rate of Growth
1. **Hunters and gatherers**	• From first human on Earth to beginning of agriculture	• About 1 person per 130–260 km² in the most habitable areas.	• As low as 250 000 to less than a few million	• At this time, the average annual rate of increase over the entire history of human population was less than 0.00011% per year.
2. **Early, preindustrial agriculture**	• Beginning between 9000 and 6000 B.C. and lasting until about the 16th century A.D.	• Domestication of plants and animals and the rise of settled villages increased human population density to 1 or 2 people per km².	• About 100 million by A.D. 1 and 500 million by A.D. 1600	• The growth rate was about 0.03%, large enough to increase the human population from 5 million in 10 000 B.C. to about 100 million in A.D. 1 (the Roman Empire accounted for about 54 million). • From A.D. 1 to A.D. 1000, the population increased to between 200 and 300 million.
3. **The machine age (Industrial Revolution)**	• Beginning about 1600 with the Renaissance in Europe and continuing until the 1950s	• The transition from agricultural to literate societies took place; better medical care and sanitation reduced the death rate; urban densities continued to increase.	• About 900 million in 1800, almost doubling in the next century, and doubling again to about 3 billion by 1960	• By 1600, the growth rate was about 0.1% per year, increasing about 0.01% every 50 years until 1950. • Growth resulted from discovery of causes of diseases, invention of vaccines, sanitation improvements, and medical and health advances; improvements in agriculture led to a rapid increase in production of food, clothing, and shelter.
4. **The modern era**	• From the 1950s onward	• Increasing urbanization of population.	• Estimated 6.2 billion in 2002	• The growth rate reached 2.1% between 1965 and 1970, declining slightly to between 1.7 and 1.8% in the 1980s and 1990s. • The HIV/AIDS pandemic threatens health in all regions.

SOURCE: Adapted from *Environmental Science: Earth as a Living Planet*, D. B. Botkin & E. A. Keller, 1995, New York: John Wiley & Sons, p. 87. Copyright © 1995. Reprinted by permission of John Wiley & Sons, Inc.

TABLE 4–2
WORLD POPULATION MILESTONES AND VITAL EVENTS

World Population Milestones Reached and Predicted World Population			World Vital Population Events			
			Time Unit	*Births*	*Deaths*	*Natural Increase*
1 billion in	1804		Year	131 144 457	53 930 540	79 213 917
2 billion in	1927	(123 years later)	Month	11 095 371	4 494 212	6 601 160
3 billion in	1960	(33 years later)	Day	364 779	147 755	217 024
4 billion in	1974	(14 years later)	Hour	15 199	6 156	9 043
5 billion in	1987	(13 years later)	Minute	253	103	151
6 billion in	1999	(12 years later)	Second	4.2	1.7	2.5
7 billion in	2013	(14 years later)				
8 billion in	2028	(15 years later)				
9 billion in	2054	(26 years later)				

SOURCE: *2002 World Population Datasheet,* Population Reference Bureau, 2003, p. 3. Used with permission. http://www.prb.org/pdf/WorldPopulationDS02_Eng.pdf

of the characteristics and changes in the size and structure of human populations. Demographers use a variety of tools, terms, and concepts to understand important population dynamics, including the national census (See Box 4–3). We consider some of these concepts later in this section.

As discussed in Chapter 3, changes in population sizes occur through births, deaths, immigration (arrivals from elsewhere), and emigration (individuals leaving to go elsewhere). How rapidly a population grows depends on the difference between the **crude birth rate (CBR)** and the **crude death rate (CDR)**. This difference is known as the **crude growth rate (CGR)**, and may be expressed as

$$CGR = CBR - CDR$$

In this simple equation, the crude birth rate (or, more simply, the birth rate) is the annual number of live births per 1000 population. It is a "crude" measure because it relates births to the total population without regard to the age or sex composition of that population. This means we cannot make accurate predictions about the future dynamics of the population based on such data.

BOX 4–3
NATIONAL CENSUSES

A census is an official count of the number of people in a country, including information about their age, gender, and livelihood. In Western civilization, the first estimates of population were conducted in the Roman era (particularly for taxation purposes), and there were occasional efforts to estimate numbers of people during the Middle Ages and the Renaissance. The first modern census was taken in 1655 in the Canadian colonies by the French and English.

Sweden began to undertake the first series of regular censuses in 1750, and the United States began in 1790 to undertake a census every ten years. However, many countries do not take censuses or conduct them only irregularly. For example, in much of the developing world, census coverage has been sporadic or inaccurate. Reasons for this include insufficient funds; lack of trained census personnel; high rates of illiteracy; isolated populations; poor transportation; and widespread suspicion of

government, which limits the kinds of questions census takers are able to ask.

Even in countries like Canada, census information may contain gaps and biases because of differences in collecting and analyzing data or because of changes in definitions over time. For example, historical and contemporary censuses have underreported the number of Aboriginal people in Canada. Many Aboriginal reserves and settlements are not completely enumerated, and the questions related to Aboriginal people have changed over time. While the overall impact on our understanding of the Canadian population as a whole may be small, the missing data may be significant for understanding smaller areas or patterns of change.

It is wise to remember that the limitations noted above cause various types of errors, omissions, or limitations when using census data. When relying on census data, one should acknowledge such potential for error or identify its limitations.

A measure of the rate of population increase (the annual growth rate) is

$$\frac{\Delta N}{N} \times 100$$

where ΔN is population change in one year.

The change in the population over the total number of people in one year, times 100 percent, will yield the change in population over one year. Using the formula above, a country with a population of 4 million and with 80 000 births per year would grow at a rate of 2 percent per year.

The crude death rate, also called the mortality or death rate, is calculated the same way as the crude birth rate: the annual number of deaths per 1000 population. The crude growth rate of a population is the net change, or simply the difference between the crude birth rate and the crude death rate.

Death rates can be calculated for specific age groups. For instance, the **infant mortality rate** is the ratio of deaths of infants under 12 months of age per 1000 live births. The 2006 infant mortality rate in the developing world was estimated at 57 per 1000 live births; in contrast, in the developed countries, the estimate was 6 per 1000 (Population Reference Bureau, 2007). Even though infant mortality worldwide has fallen significantly since 1970, in 1998, 7.7 million infants died before reaching their first birthday. This represents 14 percent of all deaths in that year (U.S. Census Bureau, 1999). These overall figures also hide enormous regional variations. Canada's infant mortality rate in 2006 was 5.3 per 1000, while that of Sierra Leone was 163 per 1000. In addition, in those world areas most affected by the HIV/AIDS epidemic (sub-Saharan Africa, India, and Southeast Asia), child mortality rates may double by 2010, reversing the hard-won improvements in child survival achieved through immunization and public health campaigns (Gelbard, Haub, & Kent, 1999).

National birth and death rates vary widely. In 2006, for instance, Niger recorded 43 births per 1000 population, while Italy and Canada recorded 10 and 11 births per 1000, respectively (Population Reference Bureau, 2007). In 2006, the infant mortality rates for all of Africa was 84 per 1000, but the rate was almost double in Sierra Leone (Population Reference Bureau, 2007). Even within nations, there can be variations in these rates. Infant mortality rates in Canada, the United States, and Western European nations ranged from 4 to 6.7. Note that low rates may obscure locally higher rates of infant deaths due, for example, to prenatal exposure to mercury, lead, or dioxins from industrial pollution, such as may have occurred in the Peace River health region of Alberta (Pederson, 1997). In the mid-1990s, the infant mortality rates for Aboriginal people were twice as high as for the rest of the Canadian population.

DEMOGRAPHIC TRANSITION

Based on their observations of what happened to the birth and death rates of the European population as it urbanized and industrialized during the 19th century, demographers developed a model of population change (see Figure 4–1). Although initially created as a four-stage model (and depicted this way in the figure), a fifth stage is sometimes introduced. Since all of the highly developed nations with advanced economies have gone through this **demographic transition**, demographers have suggested that this model is a key to understanding how human populations stabilize.

In the preindustrial stage, harsh living conditions gave rise to a high birth rate (to compensate for high infant mortality) and a high death rate; there was little population growth. Although no countries are in the first stage today, Finland in the late 1700s would have been in the first demographic stage. As a result of more reliable food and water supplies as well as improved health care, the second or transitional stage is characterized by a decline in the death rate. However, because the birth rate is still high, the population grows rapidly (by about 2.5 to 3 percent per year). By the mid-1800s, Finland was in the second stage of the demographic transition, as are much of Latin America, Asia, and Africa today. Much of Europe "solved" the problem of rapid population growth by encouraging emigration to other parts of the world.

Some developing countries seem to be caught in a **demographic trap**, unable to break out of the second stage. Partly, this is due to the very rapid changes in medical practices. In Europe, it took 150 years to move through the demographic transition, whereas many African countries began this process only in the last 60 years. Furthermore, different challenges, such as HIV/AIDS, have meant that the transition is not a smooth one; its trajectory may have unexpected peaks and valleys. Whether some of these nations will be able to achieve a lower birth rate before reaching disastrously high population levels remains unknown.

The third or industrial demographic stage is characterized by a declining birth rate that eventually approaches the newer, lower death rate. As it declines, population growth may fluctuate depending on economic conditions. The relatively low death rate, combined with a lower birth rate, slows population growth in the third stage. Reasons for the decline in births include better access to birth control, declines in infant mortality, improved educational and job opportunities for women, and the high cost of raising children. These reasons represent a cultural shift in social norms and values that take time to change. By the early 1900s, Finland had reached this stage.

In the fourth or postindustrial phase of the demographic transition, birth rates decline further to equal (or fall below) the low death rates. In some cases, this stage is

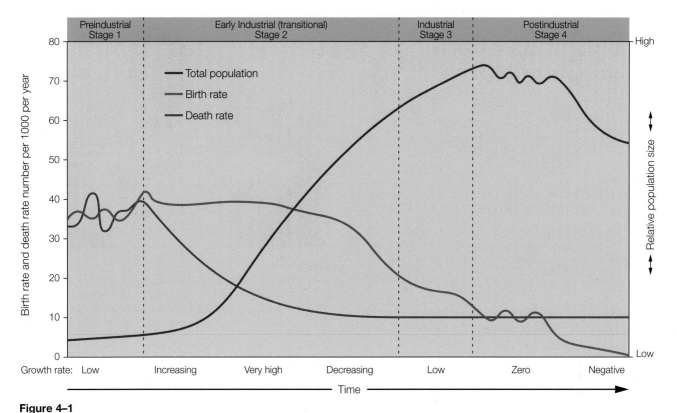

Figure 4–1

Demographic transition

This generalized model of the demographic transition illustrates how variations in birth and death rates over time result in changes in population size.

subdivided into a fifth stage to represent those countries that have moved beyond manufacturing-based industries into service- and information-based industries in a process called deindustrialization. Zero population growth (or even population decrease) is achieved because contemporary couples of childbearing age are reproducing in such low numbers that there will not be sufficient people of the next generation to replace them. In theory, it is at this point that emphasis can shift from unsustainable to sustainable forms of economic development. Ironically, countries having passed through these stages have the highest rates of consumption of the world's resources. As birth and death rates drop and become synchronized at a lower level, typically living standards and economic expectations rise. The paradox is that pressure on local environments may be displaced by countries as they can afford to import resources to meet demands for exotic foods, consumer goods, and fossil fuels. This observation is the core of the ecological footprint introduced in Chapter 1.

DISEASES AND DEATH

One of the key reasons why economically developed societies have been able to complete the demographic transition is that modern medicine has greatly reduced the number of deaths due to epidemic diseases. Typically, when an epidemic disease occurs in a population, a large percentage of people are affected by it—consider the number of people who contract cholera, measles, mumps, or influenza during an outbreak. In part, the spread of resistant forms of diseases such as tuberculosis, malaria, and cholera reflects the high density of populations of poor people (see Enviro-Focus 4 on page 113).

Human Immunodeficiency Virus (HIV) and Acquired Immune Deficiency Syndrome (AIDS) are also factors in the increasing incidence of deaths due to epidemics (because individuals with HIV/AIDS lack resistance to diseases). Worldwide, by 2006, about 23 million people had died from HIV/AIDS, and an additional 39.5 million people were infected with the virus (United Nations, 2006b). Two-thirds of the most affected countries are located in sub-Saharan Africa; in Swaziland, the country with the highest HIV/AIDS prevalence, more than one out of every three adults is HIV-positive (UNAIDS, 2006). The United Nations estimates that 90 percent of children now infected with HIV/AIDS were born in Africa. In Zimbabwe, where 20 percent of adults are infected, life expectancy at birth was estimated at 41 years in 1995–2000. This figure is 25 years lower than it might have been without HIV/AIDS, and life expectancy declined to 37 years in 2006 (Population Reference Bureau, 2007). It is estimated that by 2050, Zimbabwe's population will be 61 percent lower than its without-HIV/AIDS projection (United Nations

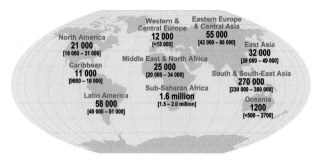

Figure 4–2

Estimated adult and child deaths from HIV/AIDS in 2007. A total of 2.1 (1.9–2.4) million people died of HIV/AIDS during 2007.

SOURCE: Slides and graphics: global summary of the AIDS epidemic 2007, UNAIDS. Available at http://data.unaids.org/pub/EPISlides/2007/071118_epicore2007_slides_en.pdf. Reproduced by kind permission of UNAIDS. HYPERLINK "http://www.unaids.org" www.unaids.org

Population Division, 2003). The global imbalance in the death rate by HIV/AIDS is illustrated in Figure 4–2.

AGE STRUCTURE

Analysis of the age structure of a population provides information about current and future social and economic status, patterns of resource use, and that population's likely impact on the environment. For any population, the number of males and the number of females at each age, from birth to death, can be represented in a generalized age structure (or population pyramid) diagram (see Figure 4–3 on p. 114). The diagram is divided vertically in half; typically the right side represents the females in a population, and the left side represents the males. The bottom one-third of the diagram represents prereproductive humans (from birth to 14 years of age); the middle one-third represents humans in their reproductive years (15 to 44), and

Photo 4–3

In postindustrial nations the aging of the population is evident.

Photo 4–4

HIV/AIDS educator Aderonke A. is wearing a Tshirt bearing the logo of the support organization she founded, called Potter Cares. She is one of the few openly HIV/AIDS-positive people in Nigeria, where HIV prevalence has soared to over 5% of the adult population.

the top one-third represents postreproductive humans (45 years and older). The width of each of these segments is proportional to the population size, so that the greater the width, the larger the population.

We can use **population age structure** diagrams to predict how a population will change over time. The overall shape of the diagram reveals whether the population is expanding, stable, or declining. The age structure diagram of a country with a very high growth rate, such as Kenya or Nigeria, is shaped like a pyramid. In contrast, the age structure diagrams of countries with stable or declining populations, such as Italy and Germany, have narrower bases (see Figure 4–4 on page 115).

In countries that have rapidly expanding populations, the largest proportion of the population is in the prereproductive age group. It is estimated that about one-third of the population worldwide is under 15 years of age. This means that the probability of future population growth is great; when all these children mature, they will become the parents of the next generation. Even if the birth rate does not increase and these parents have only two children, the population growth rate will continue to increase simply because there are more people reproducing.

In contrast, the narrower bases of the age structure diagrams of countries with stable or declining populations indicate that a smaller proportion of children will become the parents of the next generation. The age structure diagrams of countries with stable populations (neither growing nor shrinking) illustrate that the numbers of people at prereproductive and reproductive ages are approximately the same. In stable populations, also, a larger percentage of the population is in the postreproductive age group than in countries with rapidly increasing populations. Many nations in Europe have stable populations. Other European nations, such

"The Cell from Hell" and Other Epidemics

"The Cell from Hell"

Toxic dinoflagellates (*Pfiesteria piscicida*) have been keeping humans company from ancient times. Unicellular parasites belonging to both animal and plant kingdoms, and able to live in both salt and fresh water—the more polluted the better—dinoflagellates have been responsible for red tides (algal blooms) since biblical times. Since the early 1990s, dinoflagellates have killed billions of fish on the eastern seaboard of the United States, and afflicted hundreds of divers, fishers, sailors, and swimmers with festering skin sores, faulty memories, immune failure, and even personality changes. Able to take on 24 different shapes (from hibernating cyst to two-tailed flagellates that stun prey with neurotoxins), the airborne vapours from dinoflagellates have caused scientists studying them to lose consciousness. Dinoflagellates deserve their biohazard level-three status!

As much as they seem to be the latest science fiction threat, dinoflagellates appear to be emerging off the coast of North Carolina in response to nutrient-rich human and animal wastes that have been spilled into coastal rivers and flowed to the sea. North Carolina's booming hog industry (15 million pigs concentrated on clay-based soils) produces more waste than the people of New York City. When nitrogen-rich pig manure escapes into water courses (through leaching, or following collapse of a holding pond wall, for example), it becomes food for plankton, which in turn attract the voracious fish-flesh-eating dinoflagellates.

In spite of warnings from scientists about the unpleasant microbial consequences of, and need to clean up the waste created by, corporate pig-farming practices, North Carolina's health department denied there were any water quality problems and dismissed the toxic hangovers of fishers as hearsay. In what appeared to be an effort to protect the billion-dollar pig industry and other polluters, government officials regularly denigrated scientific findings. Human arrogance, poor government, and irresponsible economics are the chief reasons why dinoflagellates are flourishing in the ocean off North Carolina's coast (Barker, 1997).

Malaria

Endemic in sub-Saharan Africa, where often more than 50 percent of the population in rural areas is infected, malaria puts about 40 percent of the world's population at risk. Of the estimated 1 million people who die annually from malaria, about 800 000 are children under five years of age. In spite of massive efforts to eradicate it, malaria is making a comeback. There seems to be an upward trend in the number of cases in the Americas and some Asian countries. The increase is due partly to the growing resistance of malaria-carrying mosquitoes to insecticides and of the *Plasmodium* parasites to antimalarial drugs (World Resources Institute, 1992).

A growing number of Canadian travellers are bringing malaria home with them; in 1995, 637 cases of malaria were reported in Canada (Nichols, 1997). Infectious-disease specialists are alarmed that too many travellers are going into malaria-infected regions of Africa, Asia, and Latin America without accurate information or proper antimalarial medication. Chloroquine is the least costly and most widely used drug against malaria. Very effective when used in conjunction with a good primary health-care system, chloroquine administered outside of health-care systems has actually contributed to the resurgence of malaria. People who unknowingly were affected by malaria and stopped taking their antimalarial drugs too soon had low doses of the drugs in their system. This condition provided an ideal breeding ground for the development of mutations. Mefloquine, one of the main

Photo 4–5
Family members attend to a malaria victim.

(continued)

replacements for chloroquine, is more costly and may have side effects.

Cholera

In other parts of the world, the threats to human health posed by environmental deterioration were evident in early 1991, when for the first time in the 20th century a cholera epidemic struck six Latin American countries. More than 300 000 cases of cholera and 3200 deaths were reported by September 1991, mostly in Peru, but also in Ecuador, Colombia, Mexico, Guatemala, and Brazil. In 2005 the number of cholera cases reported to the World Health Organization was almost 132 000, including 2272 deaths (World Health Organization, 2006). Between June and September of that year, 43 638 cases, including 759 deaths, were reported in West Africa alone.

Cholera is an acute intestinal infection caused by the *Vibrio cholerae* bacterium and transmitted principally through contaminated water and food, particularly raw vegetables and seafood. Children are highly susceptible to this disease, which spreads rapidly in overpopulated communities with poor sanitation and unsafe drinking water. The outbreak in Peru appeared almost simultaneously in communities along a 1200-kilometre stretch of coastline. Cholera was felt to be a side effect of the rapid urbanization of that country. The growth of crowded slums and the lack of safe water and sanitation facilities, along with heavy rains in some cases, were key factors in these outbreaks. While cholera is treatable with rehydration salts, the ultimate solution requires improvements in water, sanitation, health and education, and food safety (World Resources Institute, 1992).

SOURCES: And the Waters Turned to Blood: The Ultimate Biological Threat, R. Barker, 1997, New York: Simon & Schuster; "Malaria's Comeback," M. Nichols, May 19, 1997, Maclean's, p. 57; The Fourth Horseman: A Short History of Plagues, Emerging Viruses and Other Scourges, A. Nikiforuk, 1991, Toronto: Viking; Weekly Epidemiological Report, World Health Organization, 2006, http://www.who.int/wer/2006/wer8131.pdf; World Resources 1992–93, World Resources Institute, 1992, New York: Oxford University Press.

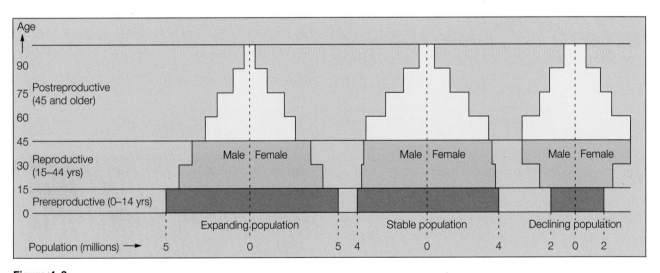

Figure 4–3

Generalized age structure diagrams for expanding, stable, and declining populations

as Germany and Hungary, have populations that are shrinking in size. In these countries, the prereproductive age group is smaller than either the reproductive or postreproductive age groups.

As is evident in Figure 4–4, most of the worldwide population increase since 1950 has occurred in the developing countries, reflecting the younger age structure as well as the higher-than-replacement-level fertility rates

of their populations. (Fertility rates are considered in a later section.) In 1950, about 66.8 percent of the world's population was found in developing countries in Africa, Asia (excluding Japan), and Latin America; the remaining 33.2 percent was in developed nations in Europe, the former Soviet Union, Japan, Australia, and North America. Since 1950, the world's population more than doubled, and the number of people in developing countries rose

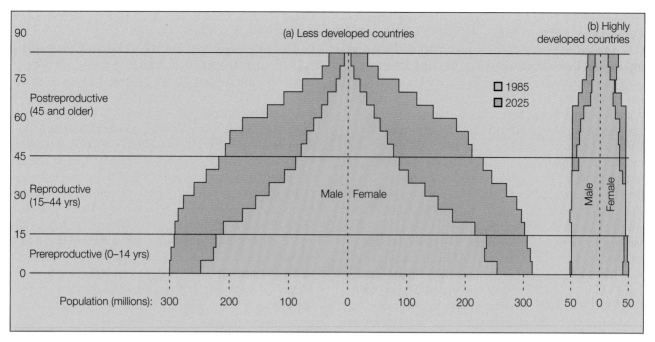

Figure 4–4

Age structure diagrams for less developed and highly developed countries

NOTE: The green region represents the actual age distribution in 1985. The orange region represents the projected increase in population and age distribution in 2025. Clearly there is a much higher percentage of young people in less developed countries than in highly developed countries. A much greater population growth is projected for less developed countries when their large numbers of young people enter their reproductive years.

to 81 percent of the worldwide population in 2006 (U.S. Census Bureau, Population Division, 2006). By 2006, world population was growing at a rate of 1.2 percent annually, implying a net addition of 78 million people per year. Seven countries account for half of that increase: India, 21.9 percent; China, 9.8 percent; Nigeria, 4.4 percent; and Pakistan, the United States, Indonesia, and Bangladesh, 3.5 percent each (United Nations, 2007b). In its *World Population Prospects: The 2002 Revision*, the United Nations estimated for the first time that by 2050, three out of every four countries in less developed regions will experience a below-replacement (2.1) fertility rate. The impact of HIV/AIDS in the most affected countries is anticipated to be more serious and prolonged than previously estimated (United Nations Population Division, 2003).

The proportion of a country's population in each age group strongly influences the demand for certain types of goods and services within that national economy. For instance, a country with a high proportion of young people has a high demand for educational facilities and certain types of health delivery services, whereas a population with a high percentage of elderly people requires medical goods and services specific to that age group. In Canada, we have an overall age structure that suggests we are an industrialized nation with a declining population. However, the population of Aboriginal people is growing more rapidly than the overall Canadian average, particularly in the Yukon and Northwest Territories, Nunavut, and northern regions of many provinces. The details and implications of

this pattern for environment and resource development are discussed later in this chapter.

FERTILITY RATES AND TIME-LAG EFFECTS

Fertility rates and time-lag effects also affect human population growth overall. In general, measures of fertility, or the actual bearing of offspring, are reasonably accurate indicators of the potential for future population growth. The **general fertility rate** is the number of live births per 1000 women of childbearing age per year. Ages 15 to 44 are commonly cited as the childbearing years. This indicator, however, is not commonly employed. A more helpful indicator, from the perspective of predicting potential future population growth, is the **age-specific fertility rate**, the number of live births per 1000 women of a specific age group per year.

Changes in the growth of human populations can be delayed by time-lag effects. One of the most important lag effects is the **total fertility rate (TFR)**, which is the average number of children expected to be born to a woman during her lifetime (TFR is based on the current age-specific fertility rate and assumes that current birth rates remain constant throughout the woman's lifetime). A TFR of 2.1 births per woman enables each woman to replace herself and her mate and allows for the death of some female children before they reach their reproductive years. However, from the day that a population achieves **replacement fertility**, that population will continue to grow for several generations—a phenomenon known as **population momentum** or **population lag effect**.

Population momentum occurs because a population that has had very high fertility in the years before reaching replacement level will have a much younger age structure than a population that has had lower fertility before reaching the replacement threshold. In a population that is approaching replacement-level fertility, the proportion of young people is important because the size of the largest recently born generation as well as the size of the parent generation determine the ultimate size of the total population when births and deaths finally are balanced. Even after reaching replacement-level fertility, as long as the generation that is producing children is disproportionately larger than the older generation (where most deaths occur), births will continue to outstrip deaths, and the population will continue to grow. Clearly, this time lag is important to human populations, as it has significant implications for resource use, environmental impacts, and sustainability.

In many less developed countries, the average replacement fertility is 2.5 or more, reflecting the greater risk of death faced by children in those countries. Figure 4–5 illustrates TFRs for a number of developing and developed nations. In 2006, for example, the total fertility rate in Afghanistan was 6.8; this means that a woman in her childbearing years would be expected to have about 7 children by the time she reached 49 years of age. If Afghanistan were to maintain a TFR of 6.8, its population would be expected to grow very rapidly, whereas if Canada maintained its TFR of 1.5 over a long time, the population

would decline. Populations in Europe are expected to decline in the 21st century.

A comparison of developed and developing nations suggests that the TFR declines as income increases. In countries such as Bangladesh, Nigeria, and Nepal, where the average income per person is a few hundred dollars per year, total fertility rates are high. In developed nations such as Canada, Japan, and Denmark, where per capita annual incomes are above US$10 000, total fertility rates are at or below replacement level. Since about 1950 there has been a downward trend in the world's TFR; this has been reflected in declining rates of population growth worldwide (although the world's population is still growing). Figure 4–6 illustrates the current and projected future decline in the world's total fertility rate from 1950 to 2020 as the world's population increases. As shown in Figure 4–6, by the year 2020, a woman would have about two children during her lifetime, a major decline from an average of greater than three in the 1990s (Kent & Crews, 1990).

MIGRATION

In the past, migration was an important way by which people could escape degradation of their local environment. In Western Europe, emigration in the 19th century reduced the pressures of rapidly growing populations on newly industrializing nations. For example, the potato famine in Ireland brought migrants to many places around the world, including Canada. Between 1846 and 1932, approximately 50 million Europeans left for the Americas and Australasia (Hall, 1995). Between 1881 and 1910,

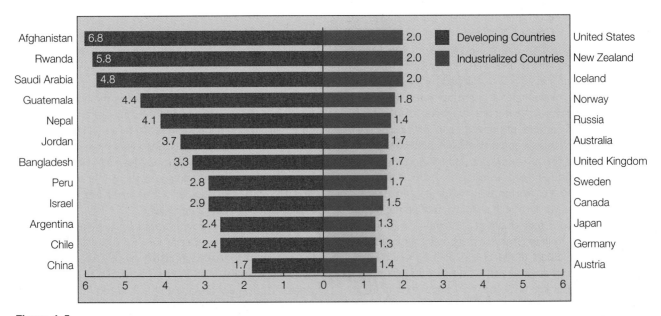

Figure 4–5

Total fertility rates (TFR) for selected countries, 2004

SOURCE: *2004 World Population Datasheet,* Population Reference Bureau, 2004. Reprinted with permission of the Population Reference Bureau. http://www.prb. org/pdf04/04WorldDataSheet_Eng.pdf

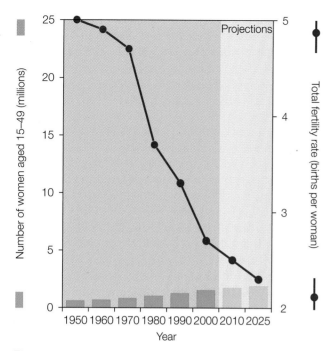

Figure 4–6

World decline in total fertility rate, 1950–2025

SOURCE: United Nations Population Division. 2006. World Population Prospects: The 2006 Revisions Population Database. http://esa.un.org/unpp/p2k0data.asp

about 20 percent of Europe's population increase emigrated to the "New World." Today, few countries are as welcoming of new residents. Many immigrants to Canada are now highly skilled. Despite the need for immigrants, new residents typically have more difficulty finding jobs that are suitable to their skills, have lower incomes than native-born Canadians, and often experience alienation (Statistics Canada, 2007b). Nevertheless, migrants will play an increasingly important role in Canadian and international population change in the next century (Gelbard et al., 1999). Migrants are increasing in number and in diversity, moving from and to more countries and for more varied reasons than ever before. For instance, in some countries, family reunification has surpassed employment as a leading reason for immigration.

In Canada, we are not replacing our current population through natural increase. Our population increased by 1.6 million people between 2001 and 2006. About 1.2 million of this increase, or about 240 000 per year, was due to immigration. This sounds like a lot of people. However, Canada, like many other industrialized countries, is facing serious labour shortages. These shortages will become greater as the current population of baby boomers begins to retire.

From an environmental perspective, one of the challenges of immigration is that the location of settlement is uneven and concentrated in a small number of places. Two-thirds of Canada's recent population increase took place in Alberta and Ontario, while most of the remainder took place in British Columbia and Quebec. Already 25 million people, or more than four-fifths of our population, live in urban areas, and nearly one-half live in the three largest urban areas: Greater Montreal, Greater Vancouver, and the "Greater Golden Horseshoe," a region of 100 municipalities along the western end of Lake Ontario. These three areas grew by 950 000 between 2001 and 2006, largely by immigration, and representing more than one-half of the country's population growth (Statistics Canada, 2007b). The concentration of new residents in the large metropolitan areas gives rise to more traffic congestion and higher pollution levels and places pressures on housing, education, and health services in those places.

By contrast, many midsize urban centres in interior locations and rural areas experienced very modest increases in population or declines. Increases in their populations may help to maintain facilities and services to their populations. However, Canadians' preference for living close to the border in large urban centres has created challenges for maintaining environmental quality and social well-being in these regions.

Other immigrants are refugees, people who are displaced because of environmental conditions in their home countries. There are concerns that changing climate conditions will cause or exacerbate changes such as rising sea levels, desertification, dry aquifers, and weather-induced flooding that will lead to a large number of displaced people. Environment-related migration has been most acute in sub-Saharan Africa, but migration also affects millions of people in Asia and India. Deteriorating soil and water conditions in North Africa and Latin America are now inducing people to leave these places. Since 1995, about 25 million people have been forced to move because their livelihoods became impossible due to drought, soil erosion, desertification, deforestation, and other environmental problems. In comparison, 27 million traditional refugees fled political upheavals; this number could easily double between 1990 and 2010 (Myers, 2005).

Immigrants challenge receiving nations in diverse ways, including the need to cope with expressions of anti-immigrant sentiment that may develop among residents, and demands to provide economic support for and extend political rights to immigrants. Refugees and involuntary migrants, cut off from traditional networks that provide socioeconomic support, are vulnerable to persecution and exploitation. Agencies such as the UN High Commission for Refugees need to address the issues faced by refugees and other displaced people around the world. Even in Canada, where immigration targets set by government have not been met, incidents related to illegal migration often bring out public sentiments that Canada is being overrun by newcomers. These challenges illustrate the need to pay greater attention to the range of services for all urban dwellers and to consider ways to encourage residents to look beyond the large metropolitan areas as places to call home.

Photo 4–6
Traditionally, large families have played an important social, cultural, and economic role in developing nations.

CULTURAL FACTORS

In the developed world, a decrease in family size is recognized as an important step toward reduction in the global population growth rate. Many cultures of the world, however, place a positive value on large families. Their reasoning is pragmatic: a large family provides such benefits as protection from enemies, a greater chance of leaving descendants, and a type of insurance for retirement. In societies without life and disability insurance and retirement programs, family members provide care for the elderly.

Other cultural arguments are offered for large families. In Africa, for example, cultural beliefs link men's virility with the number of offspring they produce. Additional reasons for large families in Africa include the formerly high rates of infant and childhood mortality, low education levels (particularly for women), young age at marriage, and lack of access to family planning services and safe, reliable means of birth control. Religious and moral arguments are also part of the discussion of why large families are considered valuable. The influence of these arguments is noted briefly in the following section, where we discuss strategies that have been used to reduce human population.

Addressing Global Health and Population Issues

INCREASING THE MARRIAGE AGE

One way to slow population growth is to delay the age of marriage and of first childbearing by women. This pattern tends to occur as more women enter the paid workforce and as education levels and standards of living increase. Sometimes, social pressures that lead to deferred marriage and childbearing are also effective in the medium to long term.

The average age at which women marry varies widely among all countries, but there is always a correlation between marriage age and a nation's fertility rate. The difference between Sri Lanka and Bangladesh, two developing nations in Asia, illustrates this relationship. In Sri Lanka, the average marriage age is 25 and the average number of children born per woman is 2.5. In Bangladesh, in contrast, the average age at marriage is 16, and the average number of children born per woman is 4.9. In 1950, China first set laws for minimum marriage ages; men could marry at 20 and women at 18. In 1980 these were revised upward so that the minimum marriage age was 22 for men and 20 for women. As a result of this and other population control programs that promoted a national goal of reaching zero population growth by the year 2000, China's birth rate dropped from 32 to 16 per 1000 people, and the fertility rate dropped from 5.7 to 1.8 children during the period 1972–98. Nevertheless, few countries would accept such regimes.

INCREASING EDUCATION LEVELS

In developing countries there is a strong correlation between the fertility rate and the amount of education a woman receives. Typically, women with more education tend to marry later and have fewer children. In Egypt, for example, 56 percent of women with no schooling become mothers in their teens, compared with just 5 percent of women who remained in school past the primary level (Brown, Renner, & Halweil, 2000). In part, education provides women with greater knowledge of ways to control their fertility and the means to improve the health of their families, thereby decreasing infant mortality. Education also opens doors to new careers and ways of attaining status for women besides motherhood. As family incomes of educated people have increased (because of their ability to earn more money), their standards of living also have increased and smaller family sizes have resulted.

FAMILY PLANNING IN DEVELOPING COUNTRIES

In the developing world, considerable emphasis is placed on family planning centres and their programs to provide birth control services. Both traditional methods (such as abstinence, breast-feeding, and induction of sterility with natural agents) and modern methods (including oral contraceptives, injectables and implants, surgical sterilization, mechanical devices, and medically provided abortions) have been used to decrease birth rates. Interestingly, the World Bank noted that traditional practices such as breast-feeding (because they delay the resumption of ovulation) sometimes have provided more protection against conception in developing countries than have family planning programs (Guz & Hobcraft, 1991). This outcome occurs because of cultural taboos against intercourse while women are breast-feeding and because breast-feeding is affordable to all segments of the population; in some cases, taboos are more culturally acceptable and more likely to be adopted than other means that rely on medical technology. Abortion is one of the most controversial methods of birth control from a moral perspective, even though it is widely used: around 45 million abortions are performed annually worldwide.

The use of contraceptives and contraceptive devices is widespread in many parts of the world. More than 60 percent of married women use these and additional family planning methods in Mexico, and more than 75 percent of people in Thailand use modern methods of contraception. However, only 8 percent of women in Mali use modern or traditional methods of contraception (Population Reference Bureau, 2007). This low rate of use results from cultural barriers to family planning, fear of adverse health effects from specific methods, and the low social status and educational levels of women, including the inability to afford contraceptives.

In many developing African countries, women and children grow the subsistence crops, graze animals, gather wood and water, use most of the household's energy in cooking, and care for the immediate environment of the household. Women are the primary resource and environmental managers in the household, and yet their health and education are often neglected compared with men. Women's education helps in improving the health of children and also enables women to plan their families and increase birth spacing (thus reducing maternal mortality risk).

Aside from the difficulty of achieving widespread social acceptance of the idea of fewer children and smaller families, many women need assurance that the children they do have will survive. The fact that Canadian infants are 30 times more likely to survive than those born in Sierra Leone is a telling example. Improved access to affordable family planning services is important in this context. In addition, in many male-dominated African societies, family planning centres provide information primarily to women. These centres might be more effective if both women and men were educated on birth control alternatives. Similarly, if unmarried adolescents could gain access to family planning services, and delay their first birth until they are in their twenties, the interval between generations would increase and help lower average fertility. By delaying marriage and childbearing, family planning education also helps reduce high-risk births to teenaged mothers.

Photo 4–7

Family planning education helps women to control family size and the interval between births. Men could benefit from such educational opportunities also.

A common problem in many male-dominated societies is that even if women do not want more children, they often do not use contraceptives because their husbands want more children, particularly sons. Many men in developing nations disapprove of family planning practices. Condom use is avoided (except with prostitutes, out of concern for HIV/AIDS) as it runs counter to cultural expressions of manhood and the desire to build up their ethnic group (Stock, 1995).

In various parts of the world, religion has an important influence on forms of birth control used. Many Catholics in developing countries consider natural family planning methods (including several cycle-based methods of family planning, such as the basal body temperature method and the ovulation method) the only acceptable forms of birth control. This has been publicly promoted by the Pope, the spiritual leader of the Catholic Church, and while these teachings apply to Catholics around the world, people living in more developed countries are more likely to choose other methods, such as sterilization and the pill. Political influences also are important; in 1984, for instance, when developing nations appeared ready to benefit from family planning, the U.S. administration under Ronald Reagan denied funding to the International Planned Parenthood Federation, one of the largest nongovernmental organizations providing family planning assistance to lesser developed countries. The U.S. prohibited funding for organizations involved in abortion-related activities or for countries where family planning activities were considered to be coercive (such as payment for undergoing sterilization). Ironically, while countries with ready access to the pill may be considered more "modern," the pill has, in recent years, been associated with an increase in human hormones found in wastewater entering our rivers and oceans which, in turn, affects the reproductive organs of fish (David Suzuki Foundation, 2007; see also Box 7–3). This unintended consequence illustrates how challenging it is to promote "development" while simultaneously protecting ecosystems and species.

NATIONAL BIRTH RATE REDUCTION PROGRAMS

Because the choice of population control methods involves social, moral, and religious beliefs, which vary widely among nations and individuals, it is difficult to generalize about a world approach to reduce birth rates. As early as 1974, however, representatives to the World Population Conference approved a plan that recognized the right of individuals to decide freely the number and spacing of their children, and their right of access to information to help them achieve their goals. The 1994 Program of Action of the United Nations International Conference on Population and Development (ICPD) reaffirmed these basic rights. The ICPD also directed attention to the need to increase people's—especially women's—access to information, education, skill development, employment, and high-quality health services. Empowerment of women, elimination of inequality between men and women, and education are three important factors in attaining sustainable futures throughout the world. The historic agreements reached at the ICPD were reaffirmed at subsequent UN conferences in the 1990s.

In 1978, recognizing that its rate of population growth had to decline or the quality of life for everyone in China would decrease, the Chinese government implemented a plan to push China into the third demographic stage (characterized by a decline in the birth rate and a relatively low death rate). Incentives to promote later marriages and one-child families were prominent in this aggressive plan, as were penalties (such

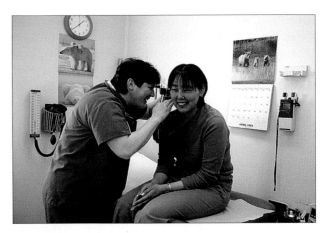

Photo 4–9
Access to good public health care for women may improve their control over their own fertility.

as fines, surrender of privileges) for the second and any succeeding child born in each family. Such drastic measures raise serious ethical questions, particularly as these measures may have greatest impacts on women.

While these measures compromised individual freedom of choice, they did bring about a drastic reduction in China's fertility from about 5.8 births per woman in 1970 to about 1.7 births per woman in 2006. In thousands of suspected cases, however, parents killed newborn baby girls in preference for male babies (keeping alive the tradition that sons provide old-age security for their parents). Even if these actions were not reported, evidence of the practice of female infanticide can be seen in demographic data. For example, during the 1960s and 1970s, the sex ratio at birth remained about 106 males per 100 females. In 1982 the ratio was 108.5, in 1987 it was 110.9, and in 1990 it was 111.3. In 2000 sex ratio at birth was reported at 116.9 males per 100 females, although by 2006, sex ratio at birth was reported to be 106 males per 100 females once more. Yet, in rural areas, the sex ratio continues to be uneven. In Hainan and Guangdong provinces in south China, these ratios were 135.6 males per 100 females and 130.3 males to 100 females, respectively. Although sex-selective abortion is strictly forbidden, it is still practised, particularly in rural areas. The result is millions of missing girls and women, a prospect that may result in future unrest.

From simple provision of information, to promotion and provision of some of the means of birth control, to offering rewards and implementing penalties, a wide variety of approaches has been used to reduce the rate of population increase in the developing world. Each approach has logistical, cultural, and ethical challenges that require careful consideration before they are introduced on a mass scale.

Photo 4–8
China's one-child policy is an example of an official government response to the need for population control.

THE POPULATION–
ENVIRONMENT–DEVELOPMENT
DEBATE

POPULATION, AFFLUENCE, AND TECHNOLOGY

The threats that humans pose to the sustainability of the environment depend, only in part, on the total number of people on Earth. It is also important to consider the impact each person has on the environment. In the past, when there were fewer people on Earth and when their technology was limited, human impact on the environment was small in scale and confined to local areas. If a local resource were overused, the effects were not large and were mainly of a physical nature. Long-term impacts were almost nonexistent. Now people have access to powerful technologies, chemical compounds, and artificial hormones (including medications) that have the potential to bring about large-scale and long-term environmental changes.

As early as 1971, Paul Ehrlich, a well-known American expert in population biology and ecology, suggested that the total environmental effect of the human population on the Earth's environment may be expressed as the product of the impact per individual times the total number of individuals. Ehrlich is known for developing the IPAT formula, where

$$\text{Impact} = \text{Population} + \text{Affluence} + \text{Technology}$$

According to this formula, either an increase in the total number of people or an increase in the individual impact each of us has on the environment results in an increase in the total human impact. Nevertheless, several scientists have emphasized population as the most important element in the equation. This approach to understanding population and environmental relationships has been criticized for oversimplifying the relationships among the variables. For example, Canada is a country with a small population, but Canadians are among the largest consumers of energy of any country. Box 4–4 poses the question, "Is Africa under- or overpopulated?" This question and the associated discussion highlight several ways in which we have made assumptions about development or have made errors in our understanding of landscape changes—errors that have led to inaccurate conclusions about the nature of population, environment, and development. Social science approaches to these issues highlight the social, cultural, institutional, and political

---

BOX 4–4
IS AFRICA UNDER- OR OVERPOPULATED? A SCHOLARLY DEBATE

"Africa is overpopulated now … its soils and forests are rapidly being depleted" (Ehrlich & Ehrlich, 1990, p. 39). The Ehrlichs promote a popular viewpoint: Africa is a continent in trouble. There is a simple logic in this claim made above. High rates of human population growth lead to environmental and social problems such as poverty and soil degradation. This is an assertion, however, it is not a fact. By contrast, the link between human population numbers and environmental degradation is a point of scholarly and practical debate.

There are at least two opposing views on population and local environmental change. One approach, which has long been advanced by Paul and Ann Ehrlich (1971, 1990) and Garret Hardin (1968, 1993), sees population growth leading to environmental decline. In this viewpoint, environmental degradation occurs because more people lead to increased use of land for farming and livestock rearing. As a result, greater pressures are placed on the land base, particularly as land is subjected to shorter fallow periods. In addition, people may add more cattle, overstocking their rangelands. In both cases, soil degradation begins, nutrients are exhausted or leach out, and soils become subject to erosion and, ultimately, to desertification. Incomes and food production fall, and poverty increases.

An alternative viewpoint is that population growth can have a positive influence on the productivity of environments. This viewpoint is associated with Ester Boserup (1965, 1981), who based this argument on observations from many countries and time periods. She agrees that as populations grow, demand for food and marketable crops increases and fallow periods shorten. But she suggests that there are many examples where these triggers spur the application of more labour and *complementary* inputs per unit of land. In developing countries, new, labour-intensive technologies are are applied to soils. These inputs are made to maintain and enhance yields, and the quality of land is improved. Thus, she suggests that population growth can lead to adaptation where there are resources, incentives, and opportunities to invest in the natural resource base. These incentives and practices may be most disrupted by poverty, war, and overexploitation arising from international economic markets or governmental policy.

These differences of opinion have encouraged scholars to determine what other factors aside from human population growth might be important in explaining environmental degradation and resource depletion. In fact, there are many variations on these themes. Geographers have pointed out that we need to identify where population growth rates are the greatest. They also suggest that we need to distinguish between changes that

(continued)

BOX 4-4
(CONTINUED)

are naturally occurring and changes that are human-induced, although given the dominance of human influence on the planet, this distinction is increasingly difficult to make (Vitousek et al., 1997).

There is no doubt that the current rates of population growth in Africa are among the highest in the world. However, these growth rates are very unevenly dispersed, concentrated on coasts, in cities, and in highland areas. For example, the mean national population density of Zambia is 13 people per square kilometre, with significant differences within the country as a result of the history of Portuguese colonialism and other human factors (Stock, 2004). As Africa is a large continent, it is important to look for specific evidence in specific locations.

There is evidence that global economic and political circumstances may exacerbate human use of the environment. For example, during the 1950s and 1960s in Nigeria and Senegal, international demand and favourable climatic conditions (wet years) led to increases in the cultivation and export of ground nuts. The wet decades were followed by a natural cycle of dry years. Soil that was broken during the wet decades was susceptible to erosion during drought periods that followed. While these cycles occur naturally, human intervention in these cycles resulted in heightened soil erosion and devastating economic impacts for residents of those countries. In the 21st century, farmers on the Canadian Prairies may be facing the vagaries of similar cycles. Settlements formed on the Prairies in the wet years of the early 20th century will be susceptible as the climate warms, although so far, some farmers have been somewhat shielded from these effects by technological inputs such as fertilizers and irrigation systems.

Today, many countries put more land into agricultural production to meet international demands and to provide economic exchange rather than to meet local food requirements. When international prices for commodities decline, there are greater pressures to put more land into production to gain some form of income. For example, coffee prices in the early part of the 21st century have reached all-time lows. As a result, Ethiopia, Cameroon, Burundi, Ivory Coast, and Tanzania, among others, earn less income from growing coffee than they receive in development aid or debt relief (Stuart & McAlpine, 2003). Falling prices place pressures on producers to cultivate more land in order to eke out a reasonable standard of living.

In the 1980s and 1990s, the World Bank and the International Monetary Fund introduced structural adjustment programs to developing countries with high debt loads. These programs were designed to help these countries restructure their econo-

mies, but they also required many countries to intensify production and to undertake cutbacks in health and education. These reductions had a dual effect, placing increased pressure on the land base and reducing the number of people with access to education and basic health care. Thus, public education programs that might lead to improving infant and child mortality rates and reducing fertility rates in the short term, as well as literacy and educational programs that might reduce population growth rates over the longer term, were made less accessible.

Although obtaining accurate and current data is difficult, the cost of preparing for and waging war in the 20th and 21st centuries has continued to increase. The value of arms production between 1950 and 1980, for example, increased by 3.3 percent per capita while population increased 1.7 percent. The financial burden per capita for arms doubled between 1950 and 1980. According to Hynes (1999, p. 49), estimates are that "military energy use can jump from 2 to 3 percent to 15 to 20 percent in wartime, estimates that do not include energy demand for weapons manufacture. Altogether the world's military may use as many petroleum products as Japan, the world's second-largest economy." About 20 percent of all global environmental degradation is due to military and related activities (Hynes, 1999). Monies spent on arms purchase are not available for health care, education, and other social programs that might address population issues. Furthermore, military use of land during wartime and peacetime also degrades land quality and introduces toxic chemicals. Thus, both the availability and the quality of land and soil resources for food production are significantly diminished.

A different kind of example suggests that sometimes we do not "read" the local landscape accurately. Europeans often view rain forests in Africa as "virgin" or "primary" forests that are key for maintaining biodiversity. However, many of Africa's tropical rain forests are secondary forests that have been cultivated for generations. Research in Guinea, using aerial photographs and anthropological field work, established that as human settlements became more concentrated, forest islands were planted by local people, who managed them as part of complex cultivation systems. As settlement in the country spread, more, rather than fewer, forest islands were created. Thus, human population and cultivation improved rather than destroyed soils and biodiversity (Fairhead & Leach, 1996).

As populations increase, will ecosystems collapse? Is Africa over- or underpopulated? Are environmental degradation and resource depletion due to increased numbers of people or other factors? You decide. But to make a convincing argument either way, you must make good use of evidence (see Box 2-1).

SOURCES: *The Conditions of Agricultural Growth: The Economics of Agrarian Change under Population Pressure,* E. Boserup, 1965, London: Allen & Unwin; *Population and Technological Change: A Study of Long-term Trends,* E. Boserup, 1981, Chicago: University of Chicago Press; *The Population Bomb* (Rev. ed.), P. Ehrlich, 1971, New York: Ballantine Books; *The Population Explosion,* P. Ehrlich & A. Ehrlich, 1990, London: Hutchinson; *Society and Ecology in a Forest Savanna Mosaic,* J. Fairhead & M. Leach, with research collaboration of D. Millimouno & M. Kamano, 1996, Cambridge and New York: Cambridge University Press; *Living within limits: Ecology, Economics and Population Taboos,* G. Hardin, 1993, New York: Oxford University Press; "The tragedy of the commons," G. Hardin, 1968, *Science, 162,* 1243–1248; "Taking Population Out of the Equation: Reformulating I=PAT," P. Hynes, 1999, in J. Silliman & Y. King (Eds.), *Dangerous Intersections: Feminist Perspectives on Population, Environment and Development* (pp. 39–73), 1999, Cambridge, MA: South End Press; *Africa South of the Sahara: A Geographical Interpretation* (2nd ed.), R. F. Stock, 2004, New York: Guilford Press; "Wake Up and Smell the Coffee," R. Stuart & S. McAlpine, June 12, 2003, *The Globe and Mail,* p. A17; "Human Domination of Earth's Ecosystems," P. M. Vitousek, H. A. Mooney, J. Lubchenco, & J. M. Melillo, 1997, *Science, 277*(5325), 494–499.

contexts in which population, environment, and development relationships occur. Today, scientists still struggle to measure and explain many of the basic relationships.

Increases in affluence (for some) and advances in technology have greatly increased the impacts people have on the environment. Whereas earlier peoples lived by hunting and gathering and used simple wooden or stone tools for crop production, today millions of car owners drive vehicles that use fossil fuels. Vehicle use generates significantly increased demands for oil and steel, and results in the release of air pollutants. Only many years after the invention of chlorofluorocarbons (CFCs) for use as a coolant in air conditioners and refrigerators and as a propellant in spray cans did we realize CFCs caused depletion of the ozone layer in the upper atmosphere. Immediately after the Second World War, dichlorodiphenyltrichloroethane (DDT) was used widely for agricultural and commercial applications to combat insect-borne diseases such as malaria. DDT was used heavily in North America until it was banned in Canada (1969) and in the United States (1972) because of its deadly and long-lasting effects on other plant and animal species, including humans. Some DDT continues to be used, principally in LDCs, although the implementation of environmental legislation and application of best practices procedures is helping to reduce the volumes applied. Clearly, the combination of rapid increases in both population and technology has increased human effects on the environment.

The addition of each new individual in the population of a developed or industrialized country results in a greater effect on the environment than it does in a developing nation. Canadians often express their concerns about the environmental impacts of developing nations whose populations continue to grow so rapidly compared with the Canadian population. However, we need to be aware that Canadians and residents of other industrialized nations have larger per capita effects on the environment because of our higher standards of living and greater use of technology and resources. Countries such as the United States, Japan, and those of the European Union, which have large populations and high levels of technology use, cause even more environmental effects. For example, the military is an intensive user of contemporary technology. In the United States, 20 000 military sites are considered the most polluted hazardous waste sites in the country. The Pentagon is the largest polluter in the United States, generating a tonne of toxic waste per minute, more toxic waste than the five largest U.S. chemical companies combined. This figure does not include the Department of Environment's nuclear weapons plants and the Pentagon's civilian contractors (Hynes, 1999).

The location and timing of human populations are also factors in their environmental impact. Some environments are more susceptible to degradation from human activities than others. In southwestern Saskatchewan,

Photo 4–10a

Photo 4–10b

Photo 4–10c

Population concentration and congestion are visible in the development of Canadian cities. Ste. Catherine Street, Montreal, is shown in 1901 (Photo 4–10a), 1952 (4–10b), and 2000 (4–10c).

CHAPTER 4: HUMAN POPULATION, ENVIRONMENT, AND DEVELOPMENT

for example, European settlers began to establish homesteads in the first decade of the 20th century. Unknown to these people, these were unusually wet years. In subsequent years, rainfall declined dramatically, and land that had been tilled for agriculture required large amounts of irrigation to be productive. Lands without irrigation were not highly productive. In short, dry lands were unable to sustain the population that had moved into the region to farm. When the droughts of the 1930s came, many farms failed and people left the region in search of employment elsewhere. They caused massive losses of native biodiversity as a result of turning the soil and replacing indigenous species with introduced crops and livestock.

The population–affluence–technology debate for developing countries raises a dilemma. Various aid agencies commonly strive to achieve two fundamental objectives: an improvement in the standard of living and a decline in overall human population growth. Supporting efforts to improve standards of living could contribute to an overall increase in environmental impacts, a result that is counterproductive to the environmental benefits of a reduction in population growth. Yet, developing countries rightly have pointed out in international forums that it is not reasonable for industrialized countries, with their massive wealth and record of resource consumption, to dictate to developing countries that they should not strive to improve their standard of living because of potential environmental impacts. This dilemma does not mean we should not support international aid, but it does indicate a need to better understand the dynamics of human population growth so that our aid efforts are effective and so that they do not contribute to overall environmental losses or increasing social inequalities.

MEASURING HUMAN DEVELOPMENT

While the 20th century was a time of unprecedented increases in material wealth and prosperity for some people across the world, these increases have been very uneven. Mass poverty, gross income inequalities, environmental degradation, and lack of political empowerment also characterize the life choices of much of the world's population. These situations did not arise simply because more people were living in developing countries. Rather, economic and political forces have placed these nations at a distinct disadvantage within the global political economy. One way to address such disadvantage is to adopt a means to measure and to illustrate inequalities, thereby focusing on elements that may be key in promoting sustainable human development.

The dominant measure of "development" has been the gross domestic product (GDP). This index is a measure of the market value of goods and services that circulate throughout an economy. Despite its popularity, GDP was never intended to measure development because it omits important elements of human development. By counting only monetary transactions as economic activity, the GDP omits much of what people value and activities that serve basic needs. The GDP does not distinguish, for example, the negative cost of providing hospital services from the positive value associated with being healthy. The GDP also ignores the value of leisure time spent in recreation and relaxation, or with family and friends (Cobb, Goodman, & Wackernagel, 1999), and it does not address the issue of distribution of wealth. Importantly, the overall value of GDP is not reduced when the production of goods and services degrades the quality of the environment or the ability of the environment to produce those services over time. Consequently, despite its pervasiveness, GDP is a poor measure of human well-being and environmental sustainability, and so other kinds of measures have been proposed.

Measures of human well-being can help to focus on the multiple causes and consequences of disparities between rich and poor, "haves" and "have nots." These variable measures reveal that wealth and well-being are not correlated automatically, particularly if we consider both the social and environmental dimensions of sustainability (see also Chapter 13).

The Human Development Index

Since 1990, the United Nations has published a human development index (HDI) that seeks to measure well-being in a way that is broader than GDP. The HDI is a composite measure that incorporates three dimensions: life span (measured by life expectancy), education (measured by adult literacy and enrolment in primary, secondary, and tertiary education), and standard of living (measured by purchasing power parity [PPP] income).

Between 1992 and 1999, Canada was the top-ranked country of the 194 nations included in HDI calculations. By 2004 (as reported in 2006), Canada's ranking had slipped to sixth place. This change does not reveal a decline in Canada's overall value (which in 2004 was .950), but rather slightly higher levels of wealth and investments in education and health services by countries such as Norway, Sweden, and Australia (see Table 4–3). Countries with an index of 0.8 or more represent high levels of human development.

Table 4–3 reveals some interesting contrasts. The United States, with the highest per capita income, ranks only eighth in terms of human development. Cuba, whose national income is less than 15 percent of that of the United States, has achieved a slightly higher life expectancy. Other data from the United Nations (2007a) reveal that at 36 percent, Cuba ranks above Canada and the United States in the proportion of seats held by women in national government. This is approximately the same proportion as Norway (38.2), Finland (37.5), and Denmark (36.9), and higher than Canada (24.3) and the United States (15).

TABLE 4–3

HUMAN DEVELOPMENT INDEX: SELECTED STATISTICS AND COUNTRIES, 2004

Rank	Country	HDI	Life Expectancy at Birth (Years)	Infant Mortality Rate (per 1000) (%)	Adult Literacy	Combined Gross Enrolment Rate for Primary, Secondary, and Tertiary Schools	GDP Per Capita
1	Norway	0.965	79.6	4	99[a]	100[b]	38 454
3	Australia	0.957	80.5	5	99[a]	113[b]	30 331
5	Sweden	0.951	80.3	3	99[a]	96	29 541
6	Canada	0.950	80.2	5	99[a]	93[c, d]	31 263
8	United States	0.948	77.5	7	99[a]	93	39 676
50	Cuba	0.826	77.6	6	99.8	80[d]	5700[e]

[a] For purposes of calculating the HDI, a value of 99.0% was applied.

[b] For purposes of calculating the HDI, a value of 100% was applied.

[c] This is a preliminary estimate, subject to further revision.

[d] Data refer to a year other than that specified.

[e] A preliminary estimate of $5700 (PPP US$) was used.

SOURCE: *Human Development Report 2006, Beyond Scarcity: Power, poverty and the global water crisis,* United Nations Development Programme, 2006, New York: Author.

Cuba is an interesting case; during the 1990s, its economy nearly collapsed when the Soviet Union—a major supplier of oil and importer of Cuban goods—dissolved and the United States tightened its embargo on Cuban goods. At that time, imports and exports fell by 80 percent, GDP declined by one-third, agricultural production dropped, and, according to one report, the average Cuban lost 30 pounds (Cameron, 2006). New forms of agriculture, such as permaculture and organic agriculture, were introduced. Havana became a major producing region, growing 50 percent of its food within the city. Bicycles were imported on a massive scale, solar power was provided to remote villages, and universities began to deliver courses across 50 satellite campuses. Today, Cuba's infant mortality rate and literacy rates rival those of more "developed" economies. All this was achieved with a per capita GDP estimated to be 14 to 19 percent of the GDP of other countries ranked at the top of the HDI. Even more surprising, Cuba's ecological footprint is now about 1.5 hectares (Canada's footprint is 7.6 hectares). Cuba is the only country in the world to have achieved such a high level of human development with such a small ecological footprint.

The Millennium Development Goals

In September 2000, the largest gathering of world leaders in history adopted the United Nations Millennium Declaration, committing their nations to work together to reduce extreme poverty, hunger, disease, lack of shelter, and exclusion from the benefits of development (such as education and services) while promoting gender equality, education, and environmental sustainability. These basic needs were considered part of each person's fundamental human rights to health, education, shelter, and security. These rights were translated into eight goals that became known as the Millennium Development Goals (see Table 4–4 on the next page). In addition, 18 targets (with time-dependent milestones) and 48 technical indicators were adopted by consensus through the United Nations and the International Monetary Fund. While progress has been made in several areas, it has not been uniform. For example, sub-Saharan Africa continues to have the highest numbers of people living in extreme poverty, the highest child and maternal mortality rates, and the largest numbers of people living in slums. Nevertheless, the goals are useful because they provide the means to make nation-states accountable for international commitments they have made to alleviate the plight of the world's poorest and least secure.

The Genuine Progress Indicator

In the United States and Canada, the genuine progress indicator (GPI) has been proposed as a measure of well-being. The GPI adds up a nation's expenses (GDP) and factors in sectors that are usually excluded from the market economy, such as housework and volunteering, and then subtracts social ills: crime, natural resource

Goal	Target	Progress
1. Eradicate extreme poverty and hunger	Halve, between 1990 and 2015, the proportion of people whose income is less than $1 a day.	In 1990, more than 1.2 billion people, constituting 28% of the developing world's population, lived on less than $1 a day. In 2002 this proportion of the population decreased to 19.4%. Most progress was made in Asia.
	Halve, between 1990 and 2015, the proportion of people who suffer from hunger.	The proportion of people lacking the food to meet daily needs declined, but not fast enough to decrease the number of people going hungry. In 2003, 824 million people in the developing world suffered from chronic hunger.
2. Achieve universal primary education	Ensure that, by 2015, children everywhere, boys and girls alike, will be able to complete a full course of primary schooling	Net enrolment ratios of primary schooling in the developing world increased from 79% in 1991 to 86% in 2004. Enrolment ranges from 95% in Latin America and the Caribbean to 64% in sub-Saharan Africa; in many countries of sub-Saharan Africa, such as Mali, Ethiopia, and Niger, fewer than half of primary-aged children attend school. Most improvement was made in South Asia, with an increase from 73% in 1991 to 89% in 2004.
3. Promote gender equality and empower women	Eliminate gender disparity in primary and secondary education, preferably by 2005, and in all levels of education no later than 2015	The percentage of women obtaining wage employment increased only slightly, from 43% in 1990 to 46% in 2004. The greatest improvement was in Oceania,[1] where the rise was from 28% to 37%, while some areas such as Northern Africa made no gains.
		Throughout the world, women's participation in national governments increased from 12% in 1990 to 17% in 2006. In Latin America and the Caribbean, 20% of government seats are held by women, while in Oceania only 3% of women are in government.
4. Reduce child mortality	Reduce by two-thirds, between 1990 and 2015, the under-five mortality rate	Infant survival has increased since 1990, yet, in 2004, 10.5 million children died before their fifth birthday. Most of these deaths occurred in sub-Saharan Africa, where the infant mortality rate remained high at 101 deaths out of 1000 births between 2002 and 2004. Factors such as the mother's education and family wealth influence infant mortality within countries. Vaccination of children for measles contributes to increased survival; although three-quarters of the world's children have been vaccinated, 454 000 died of measles in 2004.
5. Improve maternal health	Reduce by three-quarters, between 1990 and 2015, the maternal mortality ratio	Ratios of maternal mortality have changed little in the past 20 years; most deaths occur in sub-Saharan Africa and South Asia. Key to improving the situation are reproductive health services and family planning, yet the 200 million women who want to limit their childbearing have no access to contraception.
6. Combat HIV/AIDS, malaria, and other diseases	Have halted by 2015 and begun to reverse the spread of HIV/AIDS	Several countries have reduced HIV/AIDS infection rates, but overall number of people with HIV had continued to increase in most parts of the developing world. The number of people living with HIV/AIDS increased from 36.2 million in 2003 to 38.6 million in 2005. In sub-Saharan Africa, 64% of adults and 90% of children are infected. About 59% of HIV-positive adults living in sub-Saharan Africa are women.
	Have halted by 2015 and begun to reverse the incidence of malaria and other major diseases	Greater attention has been paid to controlling malaria through increased distribution of insecticide-treated mosquito nets within sub-Saharan Africa. Urban dwellers are six times more likely to use the nets than rural inhabitants.
		The incidence of tuberculosis is increasing 1% per year, particularly in sub-Saharan Africa. Of the 9 million cases of tuberculosis in 2004, 741 000 of these people also were living with HIV/AIDS.

Goal	Target	Progress
7. Ensure environmental sustainability	Integrate the principles of sustainable development into country policies and programs and reverse the loss of environmental resources	Thirteen million hectares per year are converted to agricultural land. The only region that has increased its forest area (from 17% to 20%) is East Asia. One sustainable improvement has been the 10% global decrease in energy use. Emissions of CO_2 continue to rise with population and economic growth.
	Halve, by 2015, the proportion of people without sustainable access to safe drinking water and basic sanitation	The proportion of people in the developing world with access to basic sanitation improved from 35% in 1990 to 50% in 2004. Although 1.2 billion people sanitation gained access to sanitation, reaching the 2015 target requires service to 300 million more people. Access to improved drinking water has continued to increase from 71% in 1990 to 80% in 2004.
	By 2020, achieve a significant improvement in the lives of at least 100 million slum-dwellers	Much of the urban growth in developing regions occurs in slums. Of the 4.6% annual growth of urban areas in sub-Saharan Africa, all but 0.1% is slum growth. Most urban growth in West and South Asia is slum growth. Only the North African region has decreased slum growth (0.15% annual decrease).
8. Develop a global partnership for development	Address the special needs of the least developed countries, landlocked countries, and small island developing states	Aid to developing countries reached $106 billion by 2005 (75% is used for debt relief). The UN aid target of 0.7% of gross national income directed to aid has been met only by Denmark, Luxembourg, Sweden, Norway, and the Netherlands, with 11 more European nations scheduled to meet the target by 2015.
	Develop further an open, rule-based, predictable, nondiscriminatory trading and financial system	In the past decade, developing countries gained better access to world markets. In 2004, 75% of their exports entered the developed world duty-free; this figure was higher for LCDs, at 79%. Barriers remain, including taxes for essentials such as clothing and farm products. The World Trade Organization has worked to reduce these barriers, and developed countries have committed to duty-free and quota-free imports from the developing world.
	Deal comprehensively with developing countries' debt	Debt payments have decreased by $59 billion since 1998; debt service constitutes 7% of export earnings. Some countries, however, still cannot afford to pay back this debt. In 2005, leaders of the Group of Eight (G8) industrialized nations promised to cancel the debt of heavily indebted countries that met certain criteria; thus 19 countries will have their debt cancelled while 11 others remain eligible for debt relief.
	In cooperation with developing countries, develop and implement strategies for decent and productive work for youth	Worldwide since 1995, the population of youth has grown by 135 million. The 85.7 million unemployed youth represent almost half of the 192 million unemployed people in the world.
	In cooperation with pharmaceutical companies, provide access to affordable essential drugs in developing countries	The number of people with access to antiretroviral drugs has increased in the developing world, with a substantial increase in sub-Saharan Africa (from 100 000 in 2003 to 810 000 in 2005). Even with this large increase, only one in five people globally has access to these drugs.
	In cooperation with the private sector, make available the benefits of new technologies, especially information and communications	Access to information and communication technologies has risen steadily; numbers of telephones increased from 530 million in 1990 to almost 3 billion in 2004. The largest growth was in mobile phones, because they provide access in areas with limited fixed lines. In 2004 alone, Africans purchased 15 million new mobile phones. By the end of 2004, 14% of the world's population was using the Internet; over 50% of the population in developed regions had access to the Internet, while only 7% had access in developing regions.

[1] The United Nations defines Oceania as the countries of Australia and New Zealand, Melanesia, Micronesia, and Polynesia.

Source: *The Millennium Development Goals Report 2007,* United Nations, 2007, New York: Author. http://www.un.org/millenniumgoals/pdf/mdg2007.pdf

depletion, and loss of leisure time (Baker, 1999). "We want people to rethink what progress is all about," says Mathis Wackernagel, director of Indicator Programs at Redefining Progress, the San Francisco–based policy organization that developed GPI and other social progress indicators. Because the GDP makes no distinction between transactions that contribute to or diminish well-being, it operates like a business income statement that adds expenses to income instead of subtracting them. GPI, on the other hand, differentiates between what most people perceive as positive and negative economic transactions, and between the costs of producing economic benefits and the benefits themselves. It adds up the value of products and services consumed in the economy—whether or not money changes hands" (Cobb et al., 1999, pp. 3–4).

In Nova Scotia, GPI Atlantic, a nonprofit research agency, was formed in 1997 to construct an index of sustainable development for that province. The Nova Scotia GPI consists of 22 social, economic, and environmental components under categories of time use, natural capital, environmental quality, socioeconomic indicators, and social capital.

The Canadian Index of Wellbeing

A made-in-Canada index for understanding national well-being is currently under construction. The Canadian Index of Wellbeing (CIW) is an attempt to document health, social, environmental, and economic factors into an understanding of Canadian well-being. The index distinguishes between positive attributes such as health and clean air and negative attributes such as sickness and pollution. It gives value to volunteer work and unpaid care-giving work and views overwork and stress as social deficits. It places value on educational achievement, early childhood learning, economic and personal security, a clean environment, and social and health equity. Initially, the calculation will establish national accounts that can be disaggregated regionally and provincially to capture geographic and social differences in well-being trends. Over time, a single composite index, like the one for HDI, will be established. Seven quality of life categories, or domains, will form the basis of the CIW, as listed in Table 4–5. These domains illustrate that achieving sustainability requires efforts to address environmental, social, and economic priorities.

POPULATION, ENVIRONMENT, AND DEVELOPMENT IN CANADA

The discussion of the ecological footprint in Chapter 1 and in other chapters illustrates how population numbers and environmental impacts of human activities are related in complex ways. In Canada, with a small population and an abundance of land, water, and other environmental resources, many environmental problems arise

TABLE 4–5
PROPOSED DOMAINS AND AREAS TARGETED FOR THE CANADIAN INDEX OF WELLBEING

Domain	Areas Targeted
Living standards	Secure and meaningful employment, adequate income, low-income rates, gap between rich and poor, food security, and affordable housing
Time allocation	Balance between paid work, unpaid work, and free time; the capacity to make choices about the use of time; and the stress of overload
Healthy populations	Self-rate health; disability-adjusted life expectancy (includes cancer, cardiovascular disease); physical health conditions such as low birth weight, asthma, obesity, and diabetes; rates of depression; functional health (injuries); smoking; physical activity; and overall satisfaction with health-care services
Ecosystem health	Good air and water quality, healthy forests, soils, marine environment, greenhouse gas emissions, waste diversion, and environmental sustainability
Educated populace	Literacy, numeracy, indicators of educational attainment, and quality of formal and informal learning
Community vitality	Safe communities, cohesion, trust in people, sense of belonging and identity, social networks and social participation, diversity and inclusion, community stability, and access to community resources and services
Civic engagement	Individual and collective actions designed to identify and address issues of public concern, and involvement in extrafamilial activities to improve the quality of life

Source: *Canadian Index of Wellbeing: Measuring What Matters,* Atkinson Charitable Foundation, March 2007, www.ciw.ca.

Geographer Alex Clapp stated that "forests and fish stocks may be renewable, but not sustainable" (1998, p. 137). This claim appears to be more fitting for minerals, which are nonrenewable or stock resources than for forests or fish, which can be regenerated. However, communities that have been built on resource extraction activities have experienced periods of rapid economic growth followed by periods of rapid economic decline ("boom" and "bust"), regardless of whether their economies have been based on fish, agricultural products, trees, or minerals. Resource towns that rely primarily on a single commodity that is either renewable or nonrenewable have experienced a series of boom and bust cycles. Part of the explanation for this is that resources are both natural and social. While natural resources are extracted from nature, their actual use and value to society is determined by human perceptions and cultural norms, technology, and prices that are set in a market economy. Thus, the availability of resources depends only partly on their physical supply. How much is extracted over what time period is also influenced by consumer demand, technological capability, and willingness or ability to pay for resources in a global marketplace. Under these circumstances, both nonrenewable and renewable resources are subject to overuse and exhaustion.

Social scientists (such as economists, geographers, and sociologists) have used the idea of the resource cycle to understand why, how, when, and where resources are exploited. According to the resource cycle, resources extracted for commercial purposes follow through a characteristic and predictable pattern of use that leads to overexploitation and collapse of the associated industry and communities. Typically, the resource cycle involves three stages:

Stage 1: A boom period that comprises exploration, discovery, and initial production of the resource

Stage 2: A profitable operational period in which capacity continues to expand and the industry becomes more capital (and often technology) intensive

Stage 3: Depletion of the resource where the resource becomes increasingly scarce, its price may rise, and alternatives may be developed. Allocation of the resource to different groups or uses (e.g., industry, wilderness, communities) becomes increasingly contentious and finally, the resource is exhausted or abandoned

The precise length of each stage may vary depending on the resource, the technology used to extract and process it, and the regulations established about its development, use, and trade. This pattern of boom and bust has been repeated over and over again in communities in Canada and around the world.

There is also a geography to these stages. The highest-quality and most easily accessible resources are extracted first (Stage 1). In forestry, these would likely be the largest and most easily accessible trees in valley bottoms. The revenues from these efforts go into purchasing more technology (e.g., equipment) or labour to intensify production and gain more profits. This allows for expansion of the region where extraction takes place (Stage 2). As profitable operations near their peak, they need to justify capital expenditures. Sometimes this is done by reducing the size of the labour force, or by extending the reach of the technology (e.g., logging up higher slopes, fishing in deeper waters, using new technology to obtain oil from oil sands). Once these measures are taken, firms typically withdraw from the resource operation (Stage 3). This pattern is true for renewable resources as much as for nonrenewable resources.

Ironically, perhaps, nonrenewable resources are rarely abandoned at the point of physical exhaustion. Rather, they are abandoned when they become too expensive to exploit or when alternatives become available. For example, in Canada, the rate and volume of coal mining dropped dramatically when natural gas became readily available. In contrast, renewable resources are more likely to be abandoned when both their physical and economic potential are exhausted. This happens when the resources have been harvested beyond the ability of the original population to reproduce sufficiently to recover and establish a healthy and sustaining population, as with the cod in Newfoundland (see Chapter 8). Unfortunately, while we frequently can find substitutes for nonrenewable resources (e.g., coal), we have discovered very few substitutes for many renewable resources (e.g., clean water). It is a result of this pattern of exploration, exploitation, and abandonment that Alex Clapp argued that resources such as fish and trees may be renewable, but their pattern of development in Canada has not been sustainable.

SOURCE: "The Resource Cycle in Fishing and Forestry," R. A. Clapp, 1998, *The Canadian Geographer, 43*(3), 327–330.

from resource extraction and development activities that take place many kilometres away from the major centres of human population. Canada has built its economy on the abundance of its natural resources—from fish and timber to fossil fuels and water (via hydroelectricity). But the environmental and development problems we face are due not to the numbers of people who live in the country, but rather to the ways we have configured our economies and communities to take advantage of our large natural endowment. Our resource economy has created cycles of resource exploitation that do not always provide for

sustainable ecosystems or sustainable communities (see Box 4–5).

Renewability and sustainability of our resources is an important distinction, as Box 4–5 reveals. Indeed, our reliance on natural resources—both nonrenewable and renewable—has generated patterns of expansion and depletion (sometimes only in the economic sense) that have not given resources or communities long-term sustainability. These patterns are reviewed when considering individual resources (such as timber, fish, and minerals) in subsequent chapters.

GOVERNMENT RESPONSIBILITY FOR RESOURCE DEVELOPMENT AND ENVIRONMENTAL PROTECTION

Canada's federal system of government grants federal and provincial governments powers of resource use and environmental protection based on the division of authority set out in the constitution. The Constitution Act, 1982, reproduced most of the provisions that had previously been established at Confederation under the British North America Act, 1867. Lands owned by the government are called Crown lands. In simple terms, provinces have the right to exploit all resources that are contained within their borders (e.g., trees, minerals), while the federal government has the right to regulate for all activities and resources that cross borders (e.g., birds, fish, navigable waters). The exception to this is agriculture, which was granted joint jurisdiction at the time of Confederation. However, a quick review of the basic powers of each level of jurisdiction reveals that this "simple" allocation is not so simple in practice (see Box 4–6). As many environmental or resource problems (e.g., air pollution, oil and gas development) were not anticipated at the time of the original signing, governments have continued to ask the courts to clarify the meaning of the Constitution for new challenges that arise from the split in jurisdiction between the provincial, territorial, and federal governments.

Although these powers may appear clearly specified, many "grey areas" remain. Provincial governments have fiercely defended their rights to exploit natural resources, and the federal government has been reluctant to exert its authority for environmental protection in areas where provincial governments also have authority.

For example, the federal government has responsibility for fisheries in Canada and can pass laws (under the Fisheries Act) to protect and manage fish, including habitat protection. The federal government may regulate activities that alter the flow or the quality of water if these activities affect fish or their habitat. The Fisheries Act is one of the most powerful pieces of environmental protection legislation in Canada, and the federal government has used this act to regulate and control pollution in aquatic marine, and riparian (water adjacent to land) environments. This power sometimes places the federal Department of Fisheries and Oceans in direct conflict with landowners—individuals or provinces—and requires the federal government either to impose its regulations or to negotiate a mutually agreeable solution. Tensions have arisen where federal fisheries management affect oil and gas development and hydroelectric power generation.

The 1982 amendment to the Constitution Act specifies that provincial governments have jurisdiction over

---

BOX 4–6
POWERS OF FEDERAL AND PROVINCIAL GOVERNMENTS

Federal Government

The federal government has broad powers to manage, including

- spending power;

- declaratory power: can take control over physical facilities associated with a particular resource (e.g., wheat marketing);

- peace, order, and good government: controls matters with national dimensions (e.g., emergencies, scarcities), though these national matters must be interpreted through time and are not necessarily fixed;

- trade and commerce, providing substantial control over interprovincial and export trading;

- indirect and direct taxation;

- sea coast and inland fisheries, including fishery management and pollution control regulations; the federal government has delegated many of the administrative duties for inland fisheries and aquaculture to the provinces but cannot delegate responsibility;

- shipping and navigation (can establish regulations for pollution);

- Aboriginal lands over all of the country;

- agriculture (shared with provinces).

Under the Constitution Act, the federal parliament may make laws relating to nonrenewable resources and energy, and federal laws are supreme in event of conflict. These powers have not been tested (e.g., the extent to which electricity-generating works are subject to federal powers).

Provincial Government

Generally, those resources that can be measured as stocks and are physically contained within provincial boundaries are regulated by provincial governments. Provincial governments are responsible for

- public lands;

- local works and undertakings;

- property rights;

- exploration for nonrenewable resources;

- development, conservation, and management of nonrenewable natural resources and forestry resources;

- agriculture (joint with federal government).

Municipal Government

Municipal governments have responsibilities delegated to them by provincial governments (such as provision of water and waste disposal for urban residents) but have no authority under the Constitution.

electricity-generating works. The extent to which such projects are subject to constraints under federal powers to regulate navigable waters and fisheries remains unclear. Typically, any hydroelectric power development will affect both provincial and federal areas of jurisdiction, and environmental assessments of projects are jointly undertaken.

Oil and gas development also has caused considerable tension between federal and provincial governments. Both the revenues from, and the environmental effects of, resource exploitation have been subject to heated debates. Environmental organizations have pointed out that the federal government has not taken strong action to protect the environments where oil and gas development takes place, despite having clear jurisdiction to do so (e.g., the oil sands in Alberta, offshore oil and gas development in Newfoundland and Labrador). Yet, as we note in Chapter 14, increased federal intervention in areas where provinces also have jurisdiction could risk years of court battles and national disunity. Thus, the constitutional division of powers is an important key to understanding the roles and responsibilities of different parties, as well as the reasons behind the tensions among different levels of government when it comes to environmental protection and resource development.

ABORIGINAL PEOPLE AND CANADA'S RESOURCE DEVELOPMENT

In the 2001 Census of Canada, 1 172 785 respondents identified themselves as Aboriginal. This represents about 3.8 percent of Canada's population. About one-half of these people live in urban areas, while the other half lives in rural or resource towns, primarily outside of agricultural communities. In Canada, issues associated with population, environment, and development are intertwined with commitments to and shared responsibilities with all residents, and especially Aboriginal peoples (see Box 4–7). There are two main reasons why **Aboriginal peoples**—First Nations, Métis, and Inuit—have become increasingly important players in Canadian debates about the development of our

natural resources. First, there is statutory recognition of the rights of Aboriginal peoples in relation to environment and resource entitlements. Aboriginal peoples have asserted sovereignty over lands and resources in areas of traditional territories and use. New interpretations of historical treaties signed at the time of European settlement and new treaties signed in the 20th century give credence to these assertions and require governments to respond accordingly. Second, most of the extraction of nonagricultural resources in Canada takes place in regions where Aboriginal people form a significant minority and often a majority of the local population. Consequently, they bear many of the environmental and social consequences of resource development. Aboriginal people will continue to be affected by resource developments and likely will want to participate as employees and decision makers to ensure that developments do not preclude their traditional land uses. The implications of these factors are described briefly below.

Recognizing Aboriginal Rights and Title

Aboriginal people of Canada are not homogeneous. Speaking many different languages, they engage in different cultural practices, pursue economic well-being in diverse ways, and enjoy a variety of governing systems. Historically, they have shared many characteristics and conditions of life, such as their relationships with the land and resources. Aboriginal peoples in Canada established cultural institutions for allocating resource uses and responsibilities that differed from those of Europeans who settled in Canada. These relationships and institutions were poorly understood by European settlers. Like other cultures, Aboriginal cultures are dynamic; some traditional practices have been retained and others modified, while still other traditions have been reduced in importance. For example, commercial hunting and trapping is not as prevalent as it was two or three centuries ago; nevertheless, those who engage in hunting and trapping activity likely incorporate contemporary technologies into their traditional practices.

BOX 4–7
WHO IS AN ABORIGINAL PERSON?

The Indigenous or Aboriginal people of Canada have been subjected to a complex series of classifications that have had direct effects on their life choices and chances. Today, the Census of Canada describes a person of Aboriginal identity as one who reports identifying with at least one Aboriginal group, who reports him- or herself as a Registered or Treaty Indian, or who is a member of a band or First Nation. Three Aboriginal groups typically are considered in Canada. First Nations refers to those who are Registered or Treaty Indians (registered under

the Indian Act and can prove descent from a band that signed a treaty) and a member of a band or a First Nation. Métis people are those who are descended from First Nations and European settlers with ancestral origins that include Scottish, Irish, French, Ojibway, and Cree and who identify with a culture that is distinct from either European or other First Nations cultures. Inuit are Aboriginal people located in northern Canada (north of the tree line) in the Northwest Territories, Nunavut, and northern Quebec and Labrador (also referred to as Nunavik).

CHAPTER 4: HUMAN POPULATION, ENVIRONMENT, AND DEVELOPMENT

Historically, the property rights of Aboriginal people were based in collective rights that involved complex family and community institutions for the transfer of property, rather than the market.

Representatives of both French and English colonial powers signed treaties with Aboriginal peoples. These treaties are significant because colonial governments believed they had to negotiate with the sovereign people of the region to extinguish their claims, so that resettlement could take place. Today, Aboriginal people contest the notion that treaties extinguished their claims, as European forms of property allocation were unfamiliar to their ancestors at the time of settlement. Some Aboriginal organizations have declared that they agreed to share their lands and resources in a treaty relationship that would respect their agreement to coexist as separate nations linked in a partnership with the Crown.

Regardless of whether treaties were signed, promises to protect the rights of Aboriginal people have not been fulfilled. Instead, land and resources were granted from federal and provincial governments to third parties for resource development. Consequently, lands for traditional activities have been reduced, degraded, or converted to other uses, precluding Aboriginal people from engaging in traditional practices or from participating in a contemporary economy of their own making.

Recent court decisions, including decisions made by the Supreme Court of Canada, have upheld Aboriginal title and rights established by the Royal Proclamation of 1763. These decisions have determined that Aboriginal people have legal entitlements to natural resources and that governments and commercial industry have a "duty to consult" Aboriginal people if any resource development has the potential to infringe on their resource use. The rights of Aboriginal people to use renewable resources are to be secondary only to specific conservation measures of government. Aboriginal rights are to be placed in priority over and above those held by commercial and recreational user groups (Bird, 2003). The *Sparrow* decision of 1990

was pivotal in this regard (see Boxes 4–8 and 8–6). The final decision, while directed to fisheries on Canada's West Coast, has shaped new resource management procedures across all jurisdictions and resource uses.

While historical practices have allowed commercial users (e.g., forestry and mining companies) to access resources without reference to their impact on Aboriginal rights, these practices are changing. Aboriginal peoples are gaining influence in decisions about resource allocation and management. New opportunities for Aboriginal participation are varied and include participation in joint ventures or resource partnerships, such as in forestry throughout Saskatchewan and parts of British Columbia; signatories to impact-benefit agreements, such as for diamond mining in northern Canada; advisory status over matters under the jurisdiction of another government, including some environmental assessment procedures in the Northwest Territories or the Aboriginal Fisheries Strategy of the Department of Fisheries and Oceans; equal participation in co-management, such as for several wildlife boards that operate in the northern portions of provinces or the territories or co-management arrangements with Parks Canada; and areas of self-government and exclusive jurisdiction, for example, the Sechelt Nation and the Nisga'a Nation in British Columbia.

Demographic Characteristics of Canada's Aboriginal Population

Some people may question the need for a heightened role for Aboriginal people, given that they constitute a relatively small proportion of the Canadian population. Yet, regional differences within provinces and territories reveal another picture. For example, Aboriginal people make up 15.44 percent of Saskatchewan's population. The median age for Aboriginal people is 21.7, 16.5 years lower than the median age of the province's non-Aboriginal population. In 2006, Aboriginal children made up about 27 percent of the total children (up to age 14) in

---

BOX 4-8
KEY ELEMENTS OF THE *SPARROW* DECISION IN 1990

In 1990, the Supreme Court of Canada indicated that

- Section 35 of the Constitution Act provides "a strong measure of protection" for Aboriginal rights;
- Aboriginal and treaty rights can evolve over time and must be interpreted in a generous and liberal manner;
- governments may regulate *existing* Aboriginal rights only for a compelling and substantial objective such as conservation;
- after conservation goals are met, Aboriginal people must be given priority to fish for food over other user groups;

- fishery regulations (of the federal or provincial governments) cannot interfere with Aboriginal rights to fish for food unless government can justify the interference;
- the onus of proving interference and that an existing right applies lies with Aboriginal people;
- regulating the fishery "in the public interest" that may interfere with Aboriginal rights is not acceptable. To justify interference, government must show that it is pursuing a valid government objective andupholding the honour of the Crown–trust relationship, and that conservation and safety are valid objectives.

TABLE 4-6

	Total Aboriginal	First Nations	Métis	Inuit	Total Non-Aboriginal
Total population	1 172 785[a]	698 025	389 780	50 480	30 068 240
Percent of total Canadian population	3.8	1.3	1.2	0.2	96.2
Predominant locations		Winnipeg, Vancouver, Edmonton, Toronto, Saskatoon, Northwest Territories, Yukon	Alberta, Manitoba, Ontario	Nunavut, northern Quebec, Newfoundland and Labrador, Northwest Territories	Toronto, Montreal, Vancouver regions
Median age[b]	n/a	24.9	29.5	21.5	39.7

[a] The total number of Aboriginal people is higher than the number who identify with each of the three groups.

[b] Exactly 50% of the population is above this age and 50% of the population is below this age.

SOURCE: *Aboriginal Identity Population by Age Groups, Median Age and Sex, 2006 Counts, for Canada, Provinces and Territories—20% Sample Data,* Statistics Canada, 2008, Cat. no. 97-558-XWE2006002, http://www.12.statcan.ca/english/census06/data/highlights/Aboriginal/index.cfm?Lang=E

the province, suggesting that the number and proportion of Aboriginal people will grow over time. Furthermore, approximately 83 percent of the population in northern Saskatchewan is Aboriginal, and many northern communities have few employment opportunities outside of the resource and service sectors (Northlands College, the Northern Labour Market Committee, and Saskatchewan Advanced Education and Employment, 2006). Elsewhere in Canada, First Nations, Métis, and Inuit people make up higher proportions of the population in the northern parts of the provinces and in the territories (see Table 4–6). These are the regions where much of Canada's resource extraction takes place, and Aboriginal people are the first to feel the effects of resource development. In this sense, Aboriginal people are both stakeholders and rightholders in relation to resource use and development.

In Canada, demographic change has combined with political change to give Aboriginal people a stronger role in environment and development debates. During the 20th century, the population of people who identified with Aboriginal ancestry increased tenfold, while the population of Canada rose by a factor of six. During the first half of the 20th century, Canada's population more than doubled, while the Aboriginal population grew much more slowly, but in the latter half, the population of Aboriginal people grew sevenfold, while the Canadian population only doubled (Statistics Canada, 2007a). Some of the increase is due to the drop in infant death rates, beginning in the 1960s. The fertility rate of Aboriginal people remains 1.5 times higher than the Canadian average, although this is a significant drop from four times the Canadian rate in the 1960s (Statistics Canada, 2007a). Life expectancy

increased in the latter part of the 20th century also. It appears that the Aboriginal population is moving from the second to the third stage of demographic transition. However, during this period, population will still expand until birth rates and death rates are re-established at a new, lower equilibrium.

Figure 4–7 illustrates that in 2006, Aboriginal "baby boomers" were about 10 years younger than their non-Aboriginal counterparts, and that there are relatively few Aboriginal people over the age of 65. The Aboriginal pyramid also has a wider base than the Canadian pyramid, suggesting that a larger proportion of the population is in a preproductive stage and set to grow rapidly in the near to mid-future. The noticeable increase in the Aboriginal population is partly due to demographic factors, but increased awareness of Aboriginal issues, constitutional discussions, and better enumeration of Aboriginal communities have also contributed to the increase in the number of people identifying as Aboriginal.

As Aboriginal people become more involved in environmental and resource management decisions, it is imperative that they have access to high levels of environmental security, health, and education so that they are in a strong position to take leadership roles. Unfortunately, Canada's recent history has placed these people at a disadvantage; where decisions about environmental and resource use have been made in the absence of Aboriginal involvement, they have frequently been to the detriment of the health and well-being of Aboriginal people. In Part 3 of this textbook, you will be able to identify several examples of these experiences, including heightened exposure to risks of uranium mining, insecure water quality, and disruptions in traditional ways of life as a result of logging and hydroelectric power generation.

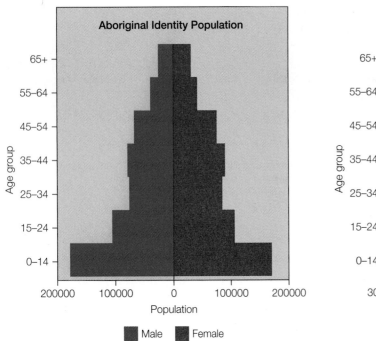

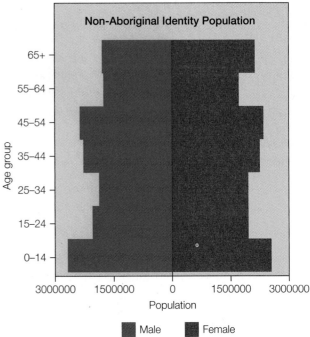

Figure 4–7

Population pyramids for Aboriginal and non-Aboriginal people in Canada, 2006

The scale for the horizontal line of each figure is different, because the overall population sizes of Aboriginal and non-Aboriginal people in Canada are different.

SOURCE: *Aboriginal Identity Population by Age Groups, Median Age and Sex, 2006 Counts, for Canada, Provinces and Territories—20% Sample Data,* Statistics Canada, 2008, Cat. no. 97-558-XWE2006002, http://www.12.statcan.ca/english/census06/data/highlights/Aboriginal/index.cfm?Lang=E

FUTURE CHALLENGES

GLOBAL POPULATION TRENDS

The human population has reached a turning point; although our numbers continue to increase, the global rate of population growth has declined during the past few decades and is predicted to continue to decline. Even if replacement fertility is reached rapidly on a global basis, it will take many years for the world population to stabilize (because of the momentum of the world's present age structure). Demographic experts at the United Nations have noted that with the continuation of fertility decline and increase in life expectancy, the population of the world will age much faster in the next 50 years. Three trends characterize this aging:

1. The median age of the world's population is increasing (from 23.5 years in 1950, to 28 years in 2005, to a projected 38 years by 2050).

2. The proportion of children under 15 years old is declining (from 34 percent in 1950, to 29 percent in 2006, to 15 percent in 2050).

3. The proportion of older persons (60 or over) has increased from 8 to 10 percent between 1950 and 2006 (United Nations, 2007b).

Europe will remain the world area most affected by aging of its population. In 1998, for instance, Italy was the oldest country in the world, with 1.6 persons aged 60 or above for each person below 15 years of age. In Africa, the youngest population region of the world in 1998, children made up 43 percent of the population while older persons constituted 5 percent. By 2050, Africa is projected to have twice as many children as elderly persons, although the effects of HIV/AIDS on life expectancy may alter this projection.

It is often difficult to separate the rate of growth in numbers of the human species inhabiting Earth from issues relating to food supply, land and soil resources, water resources, and the net primary production of the world's lands and oceans (such as forests and plankton). If population growth is slowed, and resource consumption per person is decreased, the world will be in a better position to tackle many of its most serious environmental problems. However, experience suggests that where population growth has slowed, consumption has increased. Some scholars have placed emphasis on slowing the rate of population growth to provide more time to address environmental problems. Others have emphasized other factors such as improving access to land and resources for those in developing countries, opposing militarism and war, and decreasing consumption as ways to address the population/resource consumption imbalance.

On May 25, 1984, Ron Sparrow, Jr., a member of the Musqueam Band, fished in the Fraser River using a net that was 45 fathoms long, 20 fathoms longer than was permitted under the band's food-fishing licence. Sparrow's defence was that he was exercising an Aboriginal right to fish, as guaranteed by the Constitution, and that the net restriction was invalid.

Photo 4–11
Ron Sparrow, Jr., in 1992.

The traditional territory of the Musqueam Band encompasses land now occupied by the City of Vancouver and surrounding areas. The salmon fishery in the Fraser River has been an integral part of Musqueam life, but has been subject to pressures from commercial fisheries that have developed on the Fraser. Ongoing disputes between Aboriginal people and commercial fishers raised tensions about which groups would gain access to the resource. (Some commercial fishers are Aboriginal; however, some Aboriginal people also fish for food and ceremonial purposes.)

The question of Aboriginal participation in fisheries is based on an interpretation of section 35 of the Canadian Constitution. This section of the Constitution "recognizes and affirms 'the existing Aboriginal and treaty rights of the Aboriginal peoples of Canada.'" After several court challenges, the Supreme Court finally decided that if government is to infringe on the rights identified in section 35(1), government must at least demonstrate a valid legislative objective. Acting in the general public interest was not sufficient. Thus, the Supreme Court's ruling, handed down on May 3, 1990, favoured Ron Sparrow and the Musqueam Band.

The Supreme Court decided that Aboriginal rights must be respected and that government departments could regulate for conservation purposes, but they could not do so with the justification that regulation was in the public interest. The court determined that Aboriginal rights superseded provincial and federal rights in this regard. This decision was significant in Canadian history because it set out specific requirements for the involvement of Aboriginal people in managing environmental resources. As a consequence of this decision, new developments that have an impact on environment and resources must be considered in relation to their effect on Aboriginal title and rights. This requirement applies to many resource sectors, including fishing and hunting, forestry, mining, and other land uses, and has created challenges to government agencies that seek to respect Aboriginal rights while considering commercial and other interests in environment and resources. From the perspective of "human population, environment and development" (the focus of this chapter), the court's decision illustrates the importance of Aboriginal people in land and resource development and management as it is understood in the Canadian Constitution.

SOURCE: "Sparrow (1990)," Musqueam Indian Band, 2003, http://www.musqueam.bc.ca/Sparrow.html

CANADA'S CHALLENGES

Canada faces particular challenges in relation to population, environment, and development. Environmental resource extraction and development has generated enormous wealth at a national scale, but the economic, social, and environmental impacts of development are uneven over time and across space. Canadians must soon come to grips with the ecological costs of large-scale resource exploitation if we are to maintain our status as a country of high income, human development, and environmental quality. Aboriginal people seek opportunities to participate in traditional activities, the wage economy, and associated decision-making processes. To ensure that Aboriginal people are full partners in Canada's development, we need to ensure that they have access to education and health services, along with basic environmental needs such as shelter and clean water. The same applies to other cultural groups in Canada as well.

As we see in Part 3 of this book, human demands on resources are numerous and multifaceted. If Canadians and other inhabitants of this planet are to experience a reasonable quality of life, we need to take steps to protect human and environmental health, to prevent resource abuse through conservation, and to preserve living systems. While it may seem an impossible task, many agree that it is a worthwhile goal to provide all people, whatever the size of the global population, with the opportunity for a life of quality and dignity.

The following chapters outline what is happening to natural resources in Canada, how Canadians can influence resource use and environmental change, what is being done (or has been done) about the various issues, and what needs to be done to ensure sustainability of Canada's part of the global environment.

Chapter Questions

1. How do the crude birth rate and the fertility rate differ? Which measure is a more accurate statement of the amount of reproduction occurring in a population?

2. A census is a simple count of a country's population. Discuss reasons why a census may not provide an accurate count of the number of people and demographic characteristics of a country's population. Do any of these reasons apply to Canada?

3. Why is it important to consider the age structure of a human population? What differences can you observe in the age structures of Aboriginal people and non-Aboriginal people in Canada?

4. What is meant by the demographic transition? When would one expect replacement fertility to be achieved—before, during, or after the demographic transition?

5. Debate the following statements: "Canada must increase immigration in order to avoid a collapse in our population." "Based on consumption patterns, Canada is overpopulated."

6. Many LDCs are very reluctant to introduce measures to reduce population growth in their countries. Why is this the case?

7. If all population growth were halted tomorrow, pressure on resources might still increase. Why?

8. Why should Aboriginal people, who form about 3.8 percent of Canada's population, play a key role in decisions about environment and resource development?

9. What did Alex Clapp mean when he said that fish and trees may be renewable, but they are not sustainable? Do you agree?

references

Baker, L. (May–June 1999). Real wealth: The Genuine Progress Indicator could provide an environmental measure of the planet's health. *E Magazine*, 37–41.

Bird, D. W. (2003). First Nations claim equal rights to manage national parks. In R. Anderson & R. Bone, R. (Eds.), *Natural resources and Aboriginal people in Canada: Readings, cases, and commentary.* Concord, ON: Captus Press.

Brown, L. R., Renner, M., & Halweil, B. (2000). *Vital signs 2000: The environmental trends that are shaping our future.* New York: Norton.

Cameron, S. D. (2006). Economic crisis forced Cuba to reduce ecological footprint. *Halifax Chronicle Herald.*

Cobb, C. W., Goodman, G. S., & Wackernagel, M. (1999, November). *Why bigger isn't better: The Genuine Progress Indicator—1999 update.* San Francisco: Redefining Progress. http://www.rprogress. org/publications/1999/gpi1999.pdf

David Suzuki Foundation. (2007). *Human hormones mess with male fish.* http://www.davidsuzuki.org/about_us/Dr_David_Suzuki/ Article_Archives/weekly10190701.asp

Ehrlich, P. (1971). *The population bomb* (Rev. ed.). New York: Ballantine Books.

Ehrlich, P., & Ehrlich, A. (1990). *The population explosion.* London: Hutchinson.

Elliott, J. (1999). *An introduction to sustainable development* (2nd ed.). London and New York: Routledge.

Gelbard, A., Haub, C., & Kent, M. M. (1999). World population beyond six billion. *Population Bulletin, 54.* http://www.prb.org/pubs/ bulletin/bu54-1.htm

Guz, D., & Hobcraft, J. (1991). Breastfeeding and fertility: A comparative analysis. *Population Studies, 45,* 91–108.

Hall, R. (1995). Stabilizing population growth: The European experience. In P. Sarre & J. Blunden (Eds.), *An overcrowded world? Population resources and the environment* (pp. 109–160). Oxford: Oxford University Press in association with The Open University.

Hardin, G. (1968). The tragedy of the commons. *Science, 162,* 1243–1248.

Hardin, G. (1993). *Living within limits: Ecology, economics and population taboos.* New York: Oxford University Press.

Hynes, P. (1999). Taking population out of the equation: Reformulating I=PAT. In J. Silliman & Y. King (Eds.), *Dangerous intersections: Feminist perspectives on population, environment and development* (pp. 39–73). Cambridge, MA: South End Press.

Kent, M. M., & Crews, K. A. (1990). *World population: Fundamentals of growth.* Washington, DC: Population Reference Bureau.

Malthus, T. R. (1909). *Parallel chapters from the first and second editions of an essay on the principle of population.* W. J. Ashley (Ed.). New York: MacMillan. (Original work published 1798 and 1803)

Myers, N. (1990). *The Gaia atlas of future worlds: Challenge and opportunity in an age of change.* London: Gaia Books.

Myers, N. (2005). Environmental refugees: An emerging security issue. Paper presented at the 13th Economic Forum, May 23–27, 2005, Session III: Environment and Migration, Prague.

Northlands College, The Northern Labour Market Committee, and Saskatchewan Advanced Education and Employment. (2006). *Northern Saskatchewan Regional Training Assessment Report, 2006–2007.* La Ronge, SK: Author.

Pedersen, R. (1997, July 14). High birth defects probed. *Calgary Herald,* p. A1.

Population Reference Bureau. (2007). *2006 world population datasheet.* http://www.prb.org/pdf06/06WorldDataSheet.pdf

Silliman, J. (1999). Introduction. In J. Silliman & Y. King, *Dangerous intersections: Feminist perspectives on population, environment and development* (pp. viii–xxiv). Cambridge, MA: South End Press.

Statistics Canada. (2006). *Population by sex and age group 2006.* http://www40.statcan.ca/l01/cst01/demo10a.htm

Statistics Canada. (2007a). Aboriginal peoples of Canada. http://www12.statcan.ca/english/census01/Products/Analytic/companion/abor/canada.cfm#5

Statistics Canada. (2007b). Longitudinal survey of immigrants to Canada. *The Daily.* http://www.statcan.ca/Daily/English/070430/d0704306.htm

Stock, R. (1995). *Africa south of the Sahara.* New York: Guilford Press.

UNAIDS. (2006). *Report on the global AIDS epidemic 2006.* http://www.unaids.org/en/HIV_data/2006GlobalReport/default.asp

United Nations. (2006a). *The Millennium Development Goals report.* New York: Author.

United Nations. (2006b). *2006 AIDS epidemic update.* http://data.unaids.org/pub/EpiReport/2006/04-Sub_Saharan_Africa_2006_EpiUpdate_eng.pdf

United Nations. (2007a). *UN Millennium Development Goals indicators.* http://millenniumindicators.un.org/unsd/mdg/SeriesDetail.aspx?srid=557&crid=

United Nations. (2007b). *World population prospects: The 2006 revision.* http://www.un.org/esa/population/publications/wpp2006/wpp2006_highlights.pdf

United Nations Population Division. (2003). *World population prospects: The 2002 revision.* http://www.un.org/esa/population/publications/wpp2002

U.S. Census Bureau. (1999). *World population profile: 1998 highlights.* http://www.census.gov/ipc/www/wp98001.html

U.S. Census Bureau, Population Division. (2006). *Tables by region: Aggregation options.* http://www.census.gov/ipc/www/idb/idbahelp.html#AGGOPT

Vitousek, P. M., Mooney, H. A., Lubchenco, J., & Melillo, J. M. (1997). Human domination of Earth's ecosystems. *Science, 277*(5325), 494–499.

WHO (World Health Organization). (2006). *Weekly epidemiological report.* http://www.who.int/wer/2006/wer8131.pdf

Photo 4–12

An outhouse perched over a pond serves as the only plumbing in this Bangladeshi slum. For a community to enjoy health, sanitary sewage disposal and clean water are essentials. Adequate sanitation levels in Canada and other countries are ranked in Table C/W-7 of the Canada and the World section.

Photo 4–13

Human population and development have considerable environmental effects at national and global levels. For information about how Canada's commitments to environmental protection and sustainability compare to those of other nations, see the Canada and the World section at the end of the book.

Photo 4–14

Children between the ages of one and four are particularly sensitive to environmental health stresses. To learn how Canada's child mortality rate compares to that of some other countries, see Table C/W-4 in the Canada and the World section.

Photo 4–15

A Bishnoi woman cooks over a dung fire in Rajasthan, India, creating indoor air pollution, a leading cause of environmentally related death and disease. See the Canada and the World section for more information about the countries most affected by this global problem.

Resources for Canada's Future

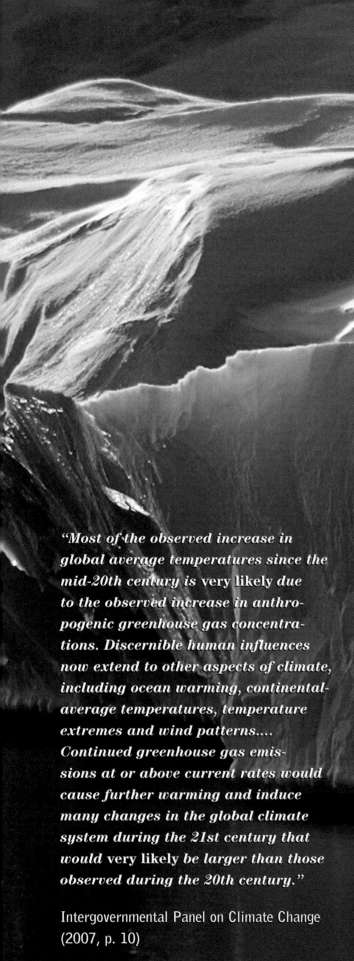

Our Changing Atmosphere

"Most of the observed increase in global average temperatures since the mid-20th century is very likely due to the observed increase in anthropogenic greenhouse gas concentrations. Discernible human influences now extend to other aspects of climate, including ocean warming, continental-average temperatures, temperature extremes and wind patterns.... Continued greenhouse gas emissions at or above current rates would cause further warming and induce many changes in the global climate system during the 21st century that would very likely be larger than those observed during the 20th century."

Intergovernmental Panel on Climate Change (2007, p. 10)

Chapter Contents

Chapter Objectives

After studying this chapter you should be able to

- understand the main issues and concerns relating to Canada's atmosphere

- identify a range of human uses of the atmosphere

- describe the impacts of human activities on the atmosphere around us

- appreciate the complexity and interrelatedness of issues concerning the atmosphere

- outline Canadian and international responses to the need to protect the atmosphere

- discuss challenges to a sustainable future for the atmosphere

INTRODUCTION

As far as we know, Earth's atmosphere is unique in its ability to provide all inhabitants of the ecosphere with the range of gases crucial to sustaining life's biological processes. In addition to providing oxygen for respiration, carbon dioxide for plant photosynthesis, nitrogen for nitrogen-fixing bacteria and ammonia-manufacturing plants, and other trace gases (noted in Chapter 3), the atmosphere protects all of Earth's inhabitants from the harmful effects of cosmic rays from outer space and ultraviolet (UV) radiation from the sun. As a fundamental part of the hydrologic cycle, the atmosphere transports water from the oceans to land. Another service atmospheric gases perform is regulating the Earth's surface temperatures, in part so that liquid water is available for living organisms. Each of these free ecosystem services of the atmosphere is crucial to the Earth's climate, and to life on the planet.

Human-induced changes began to occur in the composition of the thin film of gases that make up our atmosphere when energy from fossil fuels helped to ignite the Industrial Revolution, beginning about 1750. Subsequent growth in human productivity and technological creativity, as well as an unprecedented growth in the human population, resulted in the increasing use of the atmosphere as a dumping ground for many pollutants that, in turn, augmented the natural geological and biological forces of atmospheric change. The complexity of issues related to atmospheric pollution is staggering. At one time, the multiple effects of pollution were addressed by separate disciplines. Today, researchers understand that these multiple effects can be attributed to one pollutant. The consequences of such an interrelationship mean, for example, that a scientist cannot study climate change without accounting for photochemical smog, ozone depletion, and acidic deposition. Although atmospheric issues are treated separately in this text, the reader is cautioned that, in practice, impacts associated with atmospheric pollution cannot be isolated into exclusive categories but are multi-disciplinary and overlapping.

A variety of human activities, including industrial mining, smelting, electricity and heat generation, deforestation, and agricultural and transportation practices, have induced changes in the composition of the Earth's atmosphere. Each of these activities has contributed to major atmospheric effects, including increased acidity in the atmosphere, production of pollutant oxidants (such as photochemical smog) in localized areas of the lower troposphere, heightened levels of infrared-absorbing greenhouse gases (GHGs), and threats to the ultraviolet-filtering ozone layer in the stratosphere.

TABLE 5-1
CANADA'S CRITERIA AIR CONTAMINANTS

Criteria Air Contaminant	CAC Characteristics and Sources	Health and Ecosystem Concerns
Total particulate matter (TPM)	• A range of small solids or liquids of varying size and chemical composition. TPM refers to all particles with a diameter less than 100 microns.	• TPM affects human health and contributes to air pollution problems such as smog, acid rain, and poor visibility.
Particulate matter ≤ 10 microns (PM_{10})	• A subset of TPM; consists of particles that are 10 microns or less in diameter. Sources: blowing soil, road dust, industrial activities	• Particles may travel into the lungs and be captured by lung tissue.
Particulate matter ≤ 2.5 microns ($PM_{2.5}$)	• A subset of (PM_{10}); consists of particles that are 2.5 microns or less in diameter. Sources: particles form through chemical transformation of gases released from motor vehicles, gas plants, and forest fires	• Thought to be more dangerous than PM_{10} because particles of ≤ 2.5 microns can travel deeper into the lungs.
Carbon monoxide (CO)	• Toxic, colourless, odourless gas. Sources: generated primarily from incomplete combustion of fossil fuels	• CO displaces oxygen in red blood cells, reducing the amount of oxygen available for respiration. Can slow human responses and perceptions; prolonged exposure to low levels, or brief exposure to high concentrations, can cause unconsciousness or death.
Nitrogen oxides (NO_x)	• Consist primarily of gaseous nitric oxide (NO) and nitrogen dioxide (NO_2). Sources: produced when nitrogen (N_2) and oxygen (O_2) react in air at high temperatures, such as in internal combustion engines and furnaces	• NO_x contribute to the formation of ozone as well as the production of particulate matter and acid deposition, including acid rain.
Sulphur oxides (SO_x)	• Gaseous oxides of sulphur, mainly SO_2; a colourless gas with a pungent odour. Sources: produced by combustion of fossil fuels and by natural sources such as volcanoes	• Cause irritation of the upper respiratory tract in humans, and lead to acid rain.
Volatile organic compounds (VOCs)	• Photochemically reactive hydrocarbon compounds with a high tendency to pass from solid or liquid states to a vapour state when exposed to sunlight.	• VOCs are involved in a range of processes that lead to atmospheric pollution, including the formation of ground-level ozone (component of smog).

SOURCE: Statistics Canada. (2006). Human activity and the environment: annual statistics 2006. Ottawa: Ministry of Industry. Page 15. http://www.statcan.ca/english/freepub/16-201-XIE/16-201-XIE2006000.pdf

Transportation activities, for instance, are among the activities contributing significantly to Canada's criteria air contaminants (CACs). CACs are the major air pollutants—of concern because of their potential effects on human health and ecosystems—that the National Air Pollution Surveillance Network monitors at 150 stations in 55 cities across Canada. In 2004, transportation contributed 190 megatonnes of GHG emissions (28 percent of Canada's emissions growth from 1990 to 2004) and accounted for almost 75 percent of CO, more than 50 percent of NO_x, and more than 25 percent of the **volatile organic compounds (VOCs)** emitted (Statistics Canada, 2006). Table 5–1 identifies the seven criteria air contaminants and reasons for concern about them.

Since climate is the major factor influencing the planet's biodiversity, as well as the locations where humans can live, grow food, and have adequate water, climate change is a key threat to continued effective functioning of the biosphere. In the sections that follow, we explore some of the forces of change associated with Earth's climate, including increases in concentrations of greenhouse gases and thinning of the ozone layer. As well, we briefly discuss selected issues of ambient air pollution and long-distance transportation of pollutants in order to understand the ways in which human activities have caused atmospheric change and the implications of such changes. We also consider international and Canadian actions undertaken to reduce emissions and some challenges that occur in ensuring atmospheric quality.

RECENT CAUSES OF CLIMATE CHANGE

During the past century, several processes external to Earth's climate system have influenced trends in global climate. Five major processes appear to be involved: changes in solar intensity, changes in concentrations of stratospheric aerosols, increases in concentrations of greenhouse gases, increases in concentrations of tropospheric aerosols, and thinning of the ozone layer. Table 5–2 (p. 144) briefly summarizes the nature and effects of each of these causes of climate change (called *climate forcings*).

Developing policy regarding climate change is difficult, as each of the forces of change (listed above) evolves differently and has a unique effect, in time and space, on Earth's climate system. As you can see in Table 5–2, some activities warm the Earth, while others cool it. Such variation in effect and scale poses significant challenges to modelling and predicting climate change. At first glance, modellers' predictions appear contradictory: while temperatures will continue to increase globally, some local regions may encounter warmer climates, still others may become cooler. These apparent contradictions are explored in this chapter. Although research continues, we still have a lot to learn about the various influences on climate and climate change and about our ability to adapt to and reduce our vulnerability to changing climatic conditions.

EARTH'S NATURAL CLIMATE SYSTEM

Life forms on Earth are intimately connected with Earth's climate, and both work in conjunction to maintain environmental conditions suitable for life on the planet. A basic understanding of the Earth's natural climate system and the natural greenhouse effect is fundamental to appreciating human-induced changes in the atmosphere and the enhanced greenhouse effect. Our understanding of changes in the Earth's natural climate system is increased through such activities as evaluating the geological record, monitoring, and mathematical modelling.

THE GLOBAL CLIMATE SYSTEM

The global climate system is a complex matrix of interactions among the dynamic atmosphere, the circulating ocean, and the changing processes that affect the surface of the Earth (see Figure 5–1, p. 145). While many factors influence our global climate, scientists have determined that human activities are responsible for most of the observed warming during the past 50 years. Anthropogenic climate change has resulted largely from changes in the amounts of greenhouse gases in the atmosphere, changes in aerosols (small particles), and changes in land use, among other factors. As our climate changes, the probabilities of various weather events change: for instance, as Earth's average temperature has increased, heat waves and heavy downpours have become more frequent and intense, but extreme cold events have decreased in frequency (Intergovernmental Panel on Climate Change [IPCC], 2007).

Natural Greenhouse Effect

As part of the Earth's energy balance system, the atmosphere insulates the Earth's surface from the loss of heat to space through a process popularly known as the *greenhouse effect*. The role played by trace or greenhouse gases—the most important being water vapour, carbon dioxide (CO_2), methane (CH_4), ozone (O_3), and nitrous oxide (N_2O)—in this energy exchange is a critical one. The stratosphere is heated from the top down (intense ultraviolet radiation is absorbed by O_2 and O_3), while the troposphere is heated from the bottom up. When

TABLE 5–2
RECENT CLIMATIC INFLUENCES

Source of Change	Nature of Change
Changes in solar intensity	• Solar intensity fluctuates slightly from decade to decade and may have important effects on climate. • Researchers suggest that an increase in solar intensity over the past 300 years has increased the amount of energy flowing into the lower atmosphere by about 0.2 watts/m^2 over the past century.
Changes in concentrations of stratospheric aerosols	• Large explosive volcanic eruptions (such as Mt. Pinatubo, 1991) inject sufficient highly reflective sulphur-based aerosols directly into the stratosphere (10 to 50 km above Earth's surface) to cause temporary net surface cooling (until aerosols settle out of the atmosphere in 3 to 5 years). • Lower than average volcanic activity between 1920 and 1960 allowed more sunlight to reach the Earth's surface, perhaps contributing to slight surface warming.
Increase in concentrations of greenhouse gases	• An increase in radiative forcings (believed to be the result of a global increase in the concentrations of long-lived, well-mixed greenhouse and other trace gases) has amplified heat energy globally by about 2.5 watts/m^2 during the past century. • Additional increases in heat energy, of between 2 and 8 watts/m^2, are predicted if GHG concentrations continue to increase (see statistics cited in "Changes in Atmospheric Composition").
Increases in tropospheric aerosols	• During the past 50 years, concentrations of anthropogenic sulphate-based aerosols and other particulate matter found in the troposphere (0 to 10 km above Earth's surface) have increased substantially, particularly in the largely industrialized northern hemisphere. • Tropospheric aerosols are relatively short-lived and reflect solar energy away from the Earth's surface; they also induce changes in cloud properties that have additional effects on climate. Estimates indicate these aerosols have reduced solar energy at the Earth's surface by 0 to 1.5 watts/m^2; this effect likely will be compounded by increasing emissions from developing countries.
Thinning of the ozone layer	• Thinning of the stratospheric ozone layer, exacerbated by anthropogenic sources of persistent chlorine-based ozone-destroying substances (ODSs), has resulted in two notable, seemingly contradictory, effects: (1) an increase in UV rays reaching Earth's surface, boosting solar radiation that reaches Earth's surface (see "Thinning of the Ozone Layer"); and (2) a reduction, estimated at 0.2 watts/m^2, in the net amount of heat energy retained by the climate system. • Research suggests this trend may reverse with the elimination of ODSs under the Montreal Protocol.

SOURCES: *Meteorology Today* (5th ed.), D. C. Ahrens, 1994, St. Paul, MN: West; *Projections for Canada's Climate Future: A Discussion of Recent Simulations with the Canadian Global Climate Model*, H. G. Hengeveld, 2000, Ottawa: Minister of Public Works and Government Services; *Climate Change 2001: The Scientific Basis*, J. T. Houghton, T. Ding, D. J. Griggs, M. Noguer, P. J. van der Linden, X. Dai, K. Maskell, & C.A. Johnson, eds., 2001, Cambridge: Cambridge University Press.

solar radiation from the sun reaches the Earth's surface, it degrades into infrared (longer wavelength) radiation and then interacts with greenhouse gases in the troposphere. The even longer wave-length infrared radiation that results from this interaction, in turn, interacts with air molecules and increases their kinetic energy, warming both the troposphere and the surface of the Earth. Greenhouse gases retard the loss of heat from Earth to space, raising the temperature of the Earth's surface and surrounding air. By keeping the planet's mean surface temperature at about 15°C (about 33°C warmer than it would be otherwise), this natural greenhouse effect is crucial to life as we know it on this planet (see Figure 5–2).

Greenhouse gases enter the atmosphere through several natural processes. Water vapour, for example, enters the atmosphere via evaporation and transpiration processes. Ozone is produced through various chemical reactions within the atmosphere, and carbon dioxide comes mainly from plant and animal respiration, combustion, and the decay of organic matter in soils. Most of the naturally occurring methane is produced from the decay of organic matter in wetlands, while most naturally produced nitrous oxide enters the atmosphere from chemical reactions in soil.

Eventually, natural processes also remove greenhouse gases from the atmosphere. When carbon dioxide is absorbed into the oceans, or when forests and agricultural crops remove carbon dioxide as they grow, or when water vapour returns to the Earth as precipitation, these gases are said to have reached their destinations, or "sinks." When sources and sinks are in balance, atmospheric concentrations of greenhouse gases remain stable, but if the balance is upset, concentrations will change until a new balance is reached.

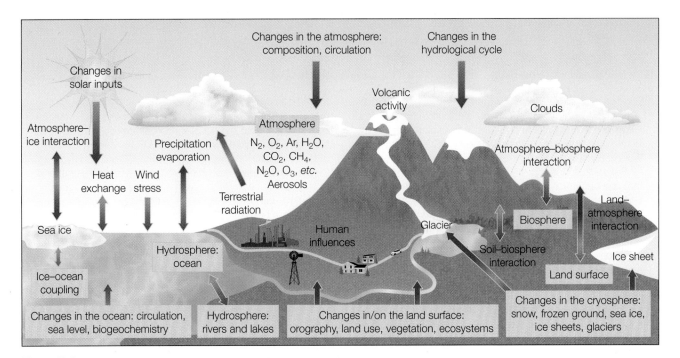

Figure 5–1

Components of Earth's climate system: processes and interactions

SOURCE: IPCC, 2007: *Climate Change 2007: The Physical Science Basis. Contribution of Working Group I to the Fourth Assessment Report of the Intergovernmental Panel on Climate Change* [Solomon, S., D. Qin, M. Manning, Z. Chen, M. Marquis, K. B. Averyt, M. Tignor and H. L. Miller (eds.)]. Cambridge University Press, Cambridge, United Kingdom and New York, NY, USA. p. 96.

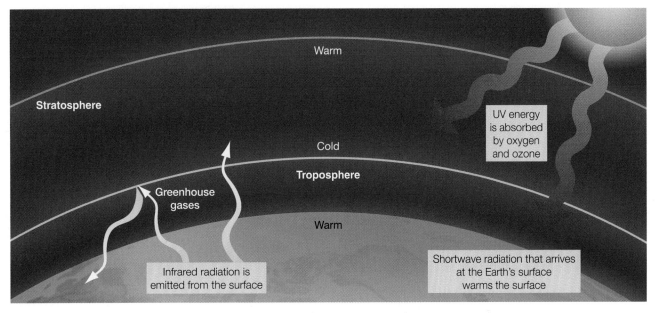

Figure 5–2

Natural greenhouse effect (Earth's mean energy balance)

SOURCE: From *Ozone Depletion and Climate Change,* Angus Fergusson, © Environment Canada. Reproduced with the permission of the Minister of Public Works and Government Services Canada, 2008.

Assuming all other factors remain constant, when greenhouse gas concentrations change, temperatures at the Earth's surface also change. Studies of the Earth's past climate—through proxy indicators of climate (including tree rings, corals, and fossilized air bubbles trapped in ancient ice)—show that concentrations of greenhouse gases were lower during glacial periods and higher during interglacial periods such as today. This finding reinforces the concept that concentrations of greenhouse gases are linked clearly to the type of climate we can expect

For decades, climatologists have expressed concern that the rate of change in climatic conditions is not within historic global norms and that this rate of change is a result of human-induced increases in greenhouse gases, particularly CO_2. What proof is there of rising atmospheric CO_2 concentrations?

Researchers use proxy indicators of climate to show that concentrations of GHGs were lower during glacial periods and higher during interglacial periods such as today. Instrument-collected global surface temperature data recorded since 1850 coincide very well with proxy data that, when extended back, indicate that the 20th century was the warmest on record, and 11 of the 12 years from 1995 to 2006 were among the 12 warmest years on record. The close alignment between proxy data and recorded temperature data provides the basis for climate change models (see Box 5–12). Of particular importance is the fossil record held in polar ice sheets. Fossilized air bubbles provide evidence of historic atmospheric chemical composition.

In 1998, a team of climate change scientists from Russia, the United States, and France withdrew an ice core from the Vostok, Antarctica, ice sheet (the core was drilled to a depth of 3623 metres, the deepest ever recorded). The air bubbles in this ice core contained evidence of atmospheric conditions through four climate cycles dating back more than 400 000 years before present (B.P.). Analysis of the air bubbles found within the ice core indicated that the concentration of atmospheric CO_2 had been very stable from 250 to 10 000 B.P. but had increased by 37 percent since 1750 (when the Industrial Revolution began).

Scientists know the source of CO_2 increase is anthropogenic through evidence from isotopic markers. Isotopes of the same atom have the same number of protons and electrons, but a different number of neutrons. They have similar *chemical properties* but slightly different *physical properties*. Carbon in methane and carbon dioxide from fossil fuel combustion are examples of a $\delta^{13/12}$ carbon; CO_2 from plant and animal respiration is an example of a $\Delta^{14}C$. Scientists compare isotopic CO_2 from present-day natural and human-induced sources to each other and with the fossil records to determine relative contributions from each source. This type of comparison enables climatologists to conclude that while concentrations from natural sources of CO_2 have remained fairly constant over time (present-day natural-source emissions are similar to those held in the ice record), those contributed by human actions have increased substantially. Climate change scientists conclude that human-generated GHGs are the source of the increase in atmospheric GHGs we currently are experiencing.

SOURCES: "Historical CO2 Record from the Vostok Ice Core," J.-M. Barnola, D. Raymond, C. Lorius, & N. I. Barkov, 2003, in *Trends: A Compendium of Data on Global Change*, Oak Ridge, TN: Carbon Dioxide Information Analysis Center, Oak Ridge National Laboratory, U.S. Department of Energy; "Estimates of Monthly Emissions and Associated 13C/12C Values from Fossil-Fuel Consumption in the USA," by T. J. Blasing, C. T. Broniak, & G. Marland, 2003, in *Trends: A Compendium of Data on Global Change*; *Basic Chemistry* (7th ed.), G. W. Daub & W. S. Seese, 1996, Upper Saddle River, NJ: Prentice-Hall; *Frequently Asked Questions about Climate Change*, H. G. Hengeveld, E. Bush, & P. Edwards, 2002, Ottawa: Environment Canada; "δ14 CO2 Records from Schauinsland," I. Levin & B. Kromer, 1997, in *Trends: A Compendium of Data on Global Change*, http://cdiac.esd.ornl.gov/trends/co2/cent-scha.html

on Earth (IPCC, 1995, 2007). Data from polar ice cores indicate that during the past 10 000 years (the current interglacial period), concentrations of carbon dioxide and methane have been remarkably stable—or they were, until about 200 years ago (see Box 5–2). By that time, following the start of the Industrial Revolution, humans unwittingly had begun an "experiment" with Earth's life support systems, known now by such terms as the enhanced greenhouse effect, global warming, and climate change.

Excluding water vapour and particulates, the atmosphere still consists of 99.9 percent nitrogen, oxygen, and argon, but the remaining 0.1 percent of atmospheric trace gases that are being altered by human activities is of great concern. Since the concentrations of these gases in the atmosphere are so low, it is possible for anthropogenic emissions to have a significant effect on them. Serious consequences for the stability of ecosystems and the well-being of human societies can arise from even small changes in the atmospheric concentrations of greenhouse gases. And because climate is a result of the exchanges of energy and moisture within the Earth–ocean–atmosphere system, anything that alters the distribution of energy within the system or the amount of energy entering or leaving the Earth's atmosphere inevitably changes the planet's climate. The reality is that atmospheric changes have enormous potential consequences for life and life-support systems on Earth (Hare, 1995; Hengeveld, 2000). This is why climate change issues demand our immediate attention and action.

HUMAN ACTIVITIES AND CHANGES IN ATMOSPHERIC COMPOSITION

In this part of the chapter we examine two major changes in atmospheric composition, specifically the enhanced greenhouse effect and thinning of the ozone layer. Changes in both greenhouse gases and the ozone layer are noted, as are selected effects of enhanced greenhouse gases and ozone depletion.

ENHANCED GREENHOUSE EFFECT

Since about 1800, atmospheric concentrations of greenhouse gases—carbon dioxide, methane, and nitrous oxide—have increased remarkably and now exceed any past levels detectable in the fossilized air bubbles of ice cores over at least the past 420 000 years. Also, the *rate* of increase is unprecedented in the last 20 000 years (Albritton, Filho et al., 2001; IPCC, 2001). Taking into account the uncertainties associated with the magnitude of climatic feedback from the terrestrial biosphere, climate projections suggest that, within the next 100 years, CO_2 concentrations almost certainly will double and may triple or quadruple those of preindustrial levels (from 0.03 percent today to between 0.05 and 0.12 percent). These values translate to increases in CO_2 levels of between 75 and 350 percent above 1750 values (Hengeveld, 2000; IPCC, 2001; McBean & Hengeveld, 1998). This is known as the *enhanced greenhouse effect.*

To scientists studying them, the sources of these increases clearly are human. In 2007, the Intergovernmental Panel on Climate Change (see Box 5–3) noted that "warming of the climate system is unequivocal, as is now evident from observations of increases in global average air and ocean temperatures, widespread melting of snow and ice, and rising global average sea level" (p. 5).

Primary sources of carbon dioxide include the combustion of fossil fuels for energy and the clearing of forests for agriculture and other uses. Sources of methane and nitrous oxide include biological processes associated with agriculture and various industrial sources. In addition, particularly since the 1970s, small doses of very potent, long-lasting synthetic greenhouse gases such as **halocarbons** have been added to the atmosphere for the first time. We do not fully understand all the interactions among these gases, and, when we add to the greenhouse experiment the interactions of other human experiments (such as those causing ozone depletion, acid precipitation, and smog), additional complications arise. Most alarming, perhaps, is that we know so little about how our experiments will turn out and how we will be affected (McBean & Hengeveld, 1998). Uncertainty, however, is not a reason to delay personal and political action on global climate change (Dotto, 2000).

Before we reflect on climate change projections for the future, we consider some characteristics of changes in greenhouse gases so that we can appreciate the effects human activities have on them and, in turn, how greenhouse gases affect climate change (see Box 5–2).

Changes in Natural and Synthetic Greenhouse Gases

Carbon Dioxide In 2004, it was estimated that Canadians contributed 758 megatonnes (Mt) of carbon dioxide equivalent (CO_2eq) to the atmosphere (see Box 5–4). This estimate represented a 0.6 percent increase over 2003 levels, a 26.6 percent increase over

---

BOX 5–3
THE INTERGOVERNMENTAL PANEL ON CLIMATE CHANGE (IPCC)

Made up of a group of leading, government-appointed scientists from over 30 countries, the IPCC was organized jointly by the World Meteorological Organization and the United Nations Environment Programme in 1988 to study global climate change. The IPCC's role lies in assessing peer-reviewed and published scientific and technical literature. Through consultation, negotiation, and evidence testing, the IPCC scientists provide consensus-based policy advice and scientific review. The IPCC is considered to be the authoritative voice for climate change information at the international level.

In presenting their climate change reports to the world, the IPCC uses a likelihood scale to indicate the probability of a defined outcome having occurred or occurring in the future. The categories identified below should be considered as having "fuzzy" boundaries.

BOX TABLE 5–1
TREATMENT OF UNCERTAINTIES IN IPCC ASSESSMENTS

Terminology	Degree of Confidence in Being Correct
Very high confidence	At least 9 out of 10 chance of being correct
High confidence	About 8 out of 10 chance
Medium confidence	About 5 out of 10 chance
Low confidence	About 2 out of 10 chance
Very low confidence	Less than 1 out of 10 chance
Very unlikely	< 10% probability
Exceptionally unlikely	< 1% probability

SOURCE: "Guidance notes for lead authors" Intergovernmental Panel on Climate Change. (2007). *Climate Change 2007: The Physical Science Basis. Contribution of Working Group I to the Fourth Assessment Report of the Intergovernmental Panel on Climate Change.* New York: Cambridge University Press. Page 3 and 4.

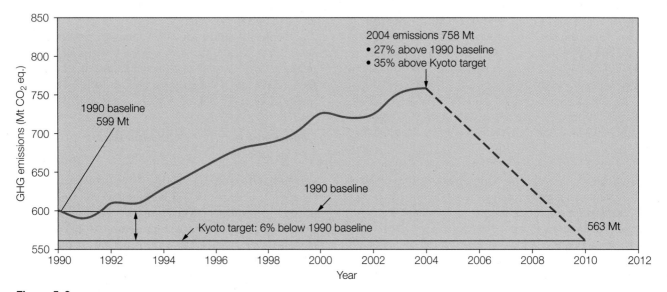

Figure 5–3

Canada's GHG emission trend and the Kyoto target

SOURCE: Government of Canada (2006). *Canada's Fourth National Report on Climate Change: Actions to Meet Commitments under the United Nations Framework Convention on Climate Change,* Environment Canada, 2006, p. 34, Figure 3.3.1. Reproduced with the permission of the Minister of Public Works and Government Services Canada, 2008.

the 1990 total of 599 Mt, and 34.6 percent above the Kyoto target of 563 Mt (see Figure 5–3). Carbon dioxide contributed 78 percent of total emissions, CH_4 accounted for 15 percent, while N_2O accounted for 6 percent of 2004 emissions. Synthetic GHGs, including PFCs, sulphur hexafluoride (SF_6), and HFCs, made up the remaining 1 percent. In 2004, about 82 percent of total GHG emissions in Canada originated in the energy sector, and about 7 percent of GHG emissions came from each of the industrial processes and agricultural sectors (Government of Canada, 2006) (see Figure 5–4 and Table 5–3).

Total human emissions of carbon dioxide into the Earth's atmosphere represent about 5 percent of the average natural flow of CO_2 into the atmosphere through plant and soil respiration and venting from surface waters of the oceans (see Figure 3–13, p. 87) (Hengeveld, 1998). Natural emissions of CO_2 are offset by their absorption by plants for photosynthesis and by direct uptake by the oceans. Just like a bank account, the "balance" of the global

carbon budget reflects changes in the amount of CO_2 in the atmosphere that are determined by the size of the average imbalance between inflow (sources) and outflow (sinks), not by the magnitude of the flows themselves.

Data from monitoring stations around the world indicated that by 2005, average atmospheric concentrations of CO_2 had reached 379 parts per million by volume (ppmv), up from a preindustrial level of about 280 ppm. Ice core records provide clear evidence that for at least 1000 years prior to the Industrial Revolution, the atmospheric concentration of CO_2 varied by only a few percentage points from an average value of 280 parts per million. This means that, generally, the natural carbon budget was well balanced (inflow equalled outflow) during that time period. According to the IPCC (2007), the annual CO_2 concentration growth rate was larger during the 10-year period 1995 to 2005 (at an average of 1.9 ppm per year) than it had been since continuous direct atmospheric measurements began in 1960 (the 1960 to 2005 average was 1.4 ppm per year).

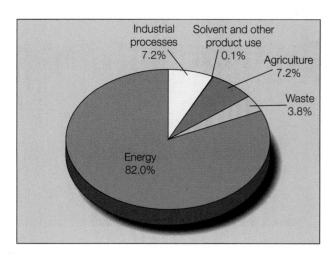

Figure 5–4
Canada's greenhouse gas emissions, by sector, 2004[1]

[1] Canada's inventory of GHGs uses an internationally agreed-upon United Nations Framework Convention on Climate Change reporting format. This format groups GHG estimates into six sectors, five of which appear above. The land use, land-use change, and forestry sector is not included in Canada's inventory totals, but in 2004 GHG emissions from this sector amounted to 81 000 kilotonnes.

SOURCE: *Canada's Fourth National Report on Climate Change: Actions to Meet Commitments under the United Nations Framework Convention on Climate Change,* Environment Canada, 2006, p. 33, Figure 3.2.1. Reproduced with the permission of the Ministry of Public Works and Government Services, Canada, 2008.

The major source of the increased concentration of CO_2 was growth in fossil fuel use as well as land use changes. For instance, deforestation and certain agricultural land management practices added between 2 and 9 gigatonnes (Gt) of carbon annually (Hengeveld, Bush, & Edwards, 2002). Although these amounts may seem small when compared with the 150 Gt of carbon released to and removed from the atmosphere each year by the carbon cycle, they have been sufficient to disrupt the natural balance between carbon sources and carbon sinks.

Part of the evidence supporting the human origin of increased atmospheric concentrations of CO_2 is the timing of the increase—about 60 percent of the increase in CO_2 has occurred since 1958, when fossil fuels powered a rapid growth in the postwar global economy. In addition to ice core data, other evidence comes from carbon isotopes in the atmosphere. Changes in their relative mix point to an increase in carbon isotopes that originate from burning fossil fuels and forests (IPCC, 1995). Since burning 1 kilogram (kg) of pure carbon releases 3.6 kg of CO_2, it is not difficult to appreciate why CO_2 levels have increased rapidly. All these changes in greenhouse gas concentrations also show that humans, in effect, have moved some gases from the uniform category to the variable category (see Table 3–1 on page 69).

Methane   Research based on high-resolution ice core data (see Box 5–2) has indicated that the atmospheric concentration of methane in 2005 greatly exceeded the natural range of 320 to 790 parts per billion (ppb) evident over the past 650 000 years. From a preindustrial value of about 715 ppb, methane concentrations rose to 1732 ppb in the early 1990s and were measured at 1774 ppb in 2005 (IPCC, 2007). While the growth rates have declined since the early 1990s (because total emissions from both anthropogenic and natural sources remained virtually constant), the IPCC (2007) noted that it was very likely that the observed increase in methane concentrations is due to human activities, chiefly agriculture and fossil fuel use.

Through a combination of measurement techniques, including aircraft and tethered balloon data, natural sources of CH_4 emissions (such as wetlands, termites, and oceans) are estimated to discharge 160 Mt/yr. Among the largest anthropogenic sources of methane are cultivated rice paddies (CH_4 is released by anaerobic activity in flooded rice lands), livestock-related enteric fermentation (which occurs in the digestive tracts of cattle and sheep), cooking fires, and **biomass burning**. Canadian estimates suggest that manure slurries annually release almost 1 million tonnes of CH_4, a significantly higher volume than had been estimated previously (Kaharabata, Schuepp, & Desjardins, 1998). This finding highlights a difficulty in methane research, namely gaining an understanding of the complex microbial processes that generate methane.

Nitrous Oxide   As is the case with other greenhouse gases, global atmospheric concentrations of nitrous oxide have increased. In 2005, N_2O reached 319 ppb; the preindustrial level was about 270 ppb (IPCC, 2007). More than one-third of N_2O emissions are related to human food production activities and vary depending on such agricultural factors as soil conditions, temperature, field management techniques, timing of fertilizer applications, and fertilizer type. For example, plowing of grasslands dramatically increases N_2O emissions from soils for several years after the disturbance. Rice paddy flooding methods also affect N_2O emissions.

While more research remains to be done regarding nitrous oxide, studies have shown that forest landscapes, soils, and oceans are natural sources of N_2O. When cleared by burning, forests generate a sustained pulse of emissions that continues at sustained high levels for extended periods after the burn. Through the nitrogen cycle, soils contribute about 60 percent of natural source N_2O. Oceans also are a large natural source of N_2O that respond quite rapidly to climate influences. Through isotopic studies, we are learning that several previously unknown processes may be involved in explaining these responses (Albritton, Filho et al., 2001; Hengeveld & Edwards, 2000).

Chlorofluorocarbons and Halons   Human-made chlorofluorocarbons (CFCs), also known by their trademark name, Freons, are compounds that contain chlorine (Cl) and fluorine (F) bonded to carbon (C). The most

Photo 5–1a

Photo 5–1b

Rice paddies and livestock are major human-related sources of methane gas emissions. Canada is the source of about 1 percent of the world's methane contributions to global warming.

widely manufactured chlorofluorocarbons include CCl_3F (CFC-11) and CCl_2F_2 (CFC-12). Bromine-containing compounds, called **halons**, are related to CFCs and used mostly in fire extinguishers.

Given that they are synthetic and their production is well documented, estimates of chlorofluorocarbons (CFCs) and halon emissions are reasonably precise. While these chemicals will continue to enter the atmosphere for some time after their production has stopped, some CFC emissions are peaking or declining because of production phase-outs established through the 1987 Montreal Protocol on Substances that Deplete the Ozone Layer (and later amendments). Concentrations of CFC replacements, while currently low, are increasing rapidly.

Some fluorine compounds, known as perfluorocarbons (PFCs), are byproducts of aluminum and magnesium smelting. These gases are present in the atmosphere at concentrations in the low parts per trillion, but because they absorb radiation in a highly efficient manner, and have molecular lifetimes of thousands and even tens of thousands of years, they contribute to the additional warming created by increased concentrations of greenhouse gases. (Additional information regarding chlorofluorocarbons and halons is found later in this chapter in the discussion of the thinning ozone layer.)

Aerosols Atmospheric aerosols are solid or liquid particles smaller than 100 micrometres (μm) in diameter that are suspended in the air. They consist of a variety of materials of natural origin, such as sea salt nuclei, wind-blown soil dust, and fog, as well as anthropogenic materials, such as cement dust, pulverized coal, and sulphuric acid mist. As noted in Table 5–2, aerosols affect both the stratosphere and the troposphere. Anthropogenic aerosols add to the complexity of atmospheric sciences; they contribute to photochemical smog, acidic deposition, and climate change, and they also have negative effects on human health and the environment. Given that they

exhibit negative radiative forcings (i.e., cooling effects), anthropogenic aerosols offset the positive radiative forces of GHGs associated with global warming. Concentrations of anthropogenic aerosols are expected to decrease over time, and although it is anticipated that their negative effects on human health and the environment will decrease, their ability to mitigate global warming will decrease as well. The lack of certainty regarding the effects of atmospheric aerosols on future climate trends is a major reason for the uncertainty associated with long-term climate prediction models (see Tables 5–2 and 5–3) (Ajavon et al., 2002).

Natural sources of aerosols, such as episodic volcanic eruptions (e.g., Mt. Pinatubo in 1991), significantly influence the regional formation of polar stratospheric clouds (see the section "Antarctic Ozone Depletion" later in this chapter). Analysis of polar ice cores suggests that large volcanic eruptions, such as Krakatoa in 1883, have had effects

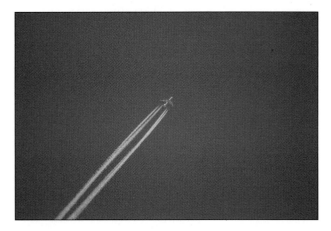

Photo 5–2

Aerosols from aircraft emissions may be becoming more important in both the troposphere and stratosphere. Although our understanding of linear contrails is low, they have a radiative forcing value of about 0.01 watts/m² (IPCC, 2007).

on climate in the past. Human sources, such as direct aircraft emissions, also have been implicated in the long-term trend toward higher stratospheric aerosol loading.

Sulphate aerosols can mask the regional effects of increased greenhouse gas concentrations (Hengeveld, 1999). Particularly in conjunction with fine aerosols from the burning of forests, one of the direct effects of sulphates is to produce a cooling effect that may moderate the warming from greenhouse gases (Taylor & Penner, 1994). Sulphate aerosols may promote cooler surface temperatures by providing condensation surfaces to aid cloud formation, thereby increasing reflection of solar radiation back to space, but this process is complex and not understood fully (see also the section "Effects of Ozone Depletion" later in this chapter).

Using human-produced aerosols to counteract increased greenhouse gas concentrations is not a practical solution because the complexity of the effects and influences of these aerosols are not well understood. Aerosols do not simply offset the much more uniform effects of greenhouse gases (Hengeveld, 1997). Also, aerosols are not a solution to greenhouse warming because of air quality impacts from burning fossil fuels and the costly effects that acid deposition incurs.

Generated principally in the industrialized regions of North America and Europe, and more recently in China and India, sulphur emissions also are of concern because of their contribution to acid precipitation (see the section "Acidic Deposition" later in this chapter). Presently, about 35 percent of aerosol emissions, principally in the northern hemisphere, are sulphates. In China, the world's leading producer and consumer of coal, acid precipitation (resulting from sulphur dioxide emissions from industrial and domestic use of coal) destroys hundreds of millions of dollars worth of crops and forest annually (Schoof, 1996). While industrialized North American and European emitters continue to reduce their sulphur emissions, it is possible their reductions will be offset by increases in sulphur emissions from developing countries such as China and India, which rely on their large reserves of coal to meet their increasing energy demands.

Satellite systems are becoming important contributors to our improved understanding of the complex and highly variable global distribution of aerosols and their effects on climate. When satellite and ice core data are compared, for instance, measurements suggest that ice core data underestimate past emissions. Such information can help in building more accurate climate projection models (see Box 5–12).

Radiative and Residence Characteristics of Greenhouse Gases

The ultimate effect on climate of higher concentrations of greenhouse gases depends on the radiative characteristics of these gases (that is, the types and amounts of energy they absorb, or their absorptive capacity) and their residence time in the atmosphere.

Photo 5–3

As the world's top producer and consumer of coal, China experiences high levels of acid precipitation, smog, and particulate pollution.

Carbon dioxide, the least efficient absorber of infrared radiation, has had the greatest climatic impact of all the human-related greenhouse gases, not only because emission volumes of CO_2 are much greater than those of other gases, but also because additional quantities of CO_2 may take from 50 to 200 years to return to sinks in the oceans and forests.

In contrast, methane absorbs 15 to 27 times as much infrared radiation over a 100-year time frame as does CO_2, but methane's direct impact on global warming is much smaller. This is because methane emissions are about 20 times smaller than CO_2 emissions and methane remains in the atmosphere for between 9 and 15 years only. Nitrous oxide emissions are about 1000 times lower than carbon dioxide emissions, but nitrous oxide absorbs 310 times as much infrared radiation as an equal mass of CO_2 over a 100-year time frame and remains in the atmosphere for 120 years (Government of Canada, 1996). CFCs and PFCs are the most powerful greenhouse gases: over a 100-year time frame, one tonne of CFC-12 (with an estimated atmospheric lifetime of 102 years) would absorb 8500 times as much infrared radiation as one tonne of CO_2.

Table 5–3, on the next page, illustrates the effect over 100 years of emissions of greenhouse gases relative to carbon dioxide. Although CO_2 is the least effective greenhouse gas per kilogram emitted, its contribution to global warming, which depends on the product of the GWP and the amount of gas emitted, is largest. Given a number of difficulties in devising and calculating the values of GWPs, including inadequate inclusion of feedbacks such as changing atmospheric composition, these values should be considered estimates and subject to change. The GWPs, however, help us understand more about the significance of each greenhouse gas and where to direct remedial actions.

EFFECTS OF ANTHROPOGENIC GREENHOUSE GAS EMISSIONS (2001)

Greenhouse Gas	Atmospheric Lifetime (years)	100-Year Global Warming Potential (GWP)	Radiative Forcing, 2000 (W/m^2)	Emissions, 2001 (Kt)[1]	Relative Contribution over 100 Years[2] (%)
Carbon dioxide	50–200	1	1.50	566 000	64.0
Methane	12 ± 3	21	0.49	93 000	19.0
Nitrous oxide	120	310	0.15	51 000	6.0
Hydrofluorocarbons	1.50–264	140–11 700	0.002	900	11.0
e.g., HCFC-22		1500			0.5
Perfluorocarbons	3200–50 000	6500–9200	0.002	6000	n.a.
Sulphur hexafluoride	3200	23 900	0.003	2000	n.a.

[1] Kt: kilotonne = 1000 tonnes.

[2] 2001 data do not total 100% due to rounding.

SOURCES: *2001 Greenhouse Gas Emissions Summary for Canada,* Environment Canada, 2003, http://www.ec.gc.ca/pdb/ghg/query/index_e.cfm; *European Environmental Agency Multilingual Environmental Glossary,* European Environmental Agency, 2003, http://glossary.eea.eu.int/EEAGlossary/searchGlossary; *Climate Change 2001: The Scientific Basis,* J. T. Houghton et al., eds., 2001, Cambridge: Cambridge University Press; "Greenhouse and Global Warming Potential Values," excerpt from the *Inventory of U.S. Greenhouse Gas Emissions and Sinks: 1990–2000,* United States Environmental Protection Agency, 2002, http://yosemite.epa.gov/OAR/globalwarming.nsf/UniqueKeyLookup/SHSU5BUM9T/$File/ghg_gwp.pdf

When we take absorptive capacity, atmospheric lifetime, and other factors into consideration, carbon dioxide has been estimated to account for 64 percent of the additional greenhouse warming that has occurred since preindustrial times, methane for 19 percent, nitrous oxide for 6 percent, and CFCs and halons for 11 percent (Shine et al., 1995). We may discover, as we attempt to reduce CO_2 emissions and find substitutes for other greenhouse gases, that rates of increase of emissions other than CO_2 may change too, requiring different responses and adaptations.

Clearly, future levels of greenhouse gas emissions will reflect the influence and interplay of factors such as population growth, economic growth, and deforestation rates on the one hand, and higher energy prices, improvements in energy efficiency, the availability of practical alternatives to fossil fuels, the development of policies and controls for regulating greenhouse gas emissions, and preserving reservoirs of carbon on the other hand (Government of Canada, 1996). Even if it were possible to hold carbon dioxide emissions at 1990 levels (i.e., Kyoto target), given current trends, atmospheric concentrations would continue to rise to a level about 60 percent higher than preindustrial levels (450 ppmv) by 2050, and about 85 percent higher (520 ppmv) by 2100 (IPCC, 1995).

These trends suggest that without significant progress in controlling emissions from fossil fuel use and burning or destruction of forests, a doubled carbon dioxide atmosphere appears inevitable by the end of the 21st century. With about 90 million people being added to the world population every year, and potential growth in the economies of India and China (fuelled largely by coal), the world community must be vigilant in controlling the upward pressure on greenhouse gas emissions. At the same time, full and careful consideration of the social, economic, and environmental dimensions of this issue is required. As well, uncertainties exist regarding the future size and behaviour of some of the natural sinks that remove greenhouse gases from the atmosphere. There are concerns about the ability of oceans and terrestrial ecosystems to continue to absorb nearly half the carbon dioxide emitted by human activities. Climate change could be affected by unexpected feedbacks as well. For instance, polar regions are estimated to have very large quantities of methane locked away in frozen hydrates. If large areas of permafrost were to thaw, some of this gas would be released and could result in a marked intensification of the greenhouse effect (Bubier, Moore, & Bellisario, 1995; Government of Canada, 1996).

EFFECTS OF ENHANCED GREENHOUSE GASES

Scientists are continuing to conduct research and make observations regarding the changes that an enhanced greenhouse effect is bringing about in the Earth's climate. With increased amounts of data available for the atmosphere, oceans, and cryosphere, with new analytical techniques through which to examine that data, and with more sophisticated climate modelling capabilities, our understanding of climate change has broadened. Through advances in simulations and models, projections of future climate changes have improved and confidence has grown in their results (although remaining uncertainties are recognized clearly—see Box 5–3, and Box 5–6).

The IPCC's Fourth Assessment Report (2007) notes a number of key observations regarding the nature of climate change; selected examples of these observations are highlighted in Box 5–5. Keep in mind the climate observations and changes identified in Box 5–5 as you review Figure 5–5, a summary presentation of the range of possible impacts of an enhanced greenhouse effect in Canada. For example, as climate models predicted, warming has been stronger in the middle and high latitudes than in the tropics, and strongest in the continental interiors of the northern hemisphere. In Canada, temperature records show the northwestern interior has warmed by as much as 1.8°C, while the eastern Arctic has cooled over the past 50 years (Government of Canada, 1996). What do these changes mean to those who call the Arctic their home, or whose livelihood is based on northern resources?

Long-term temperature data are scarce for deep ocean waters, but a cooling of over 1°C in the Labrador Sea between the early 1970s and 1990 has been observed

BOX 5–5
DIRECT OBSERVATIONS OF RECENT CLIMATE CHANGE

The Intergovernmental Panel on Climate Change publishes regular, comprehensive assessment reports detailing current knowledge and future projections of climate change. Previous reports were published in 1990, 1995, and 2001. Teams of authors who are nominated by governments and international organizations (including universities, research centres, and business and environmental associations) work together to produce these reports. The IPCC's Fourth Assessment Report—which involved over 150 contributing authors from over 30 countries—consists of four volumes released in the course of 2007. Working Group I's report (the physical science basis) provided the following (selected) scientific observations of climate change. Temperature changes in the atmosphere and ocean, changes in wind patterns, and sea-level rise are among the climate change observations. These observed climate changes portend potentially significant effects on humans, their activities, their health, and the plant and animal species on which they depend for their livelihoods.

- Of the 12 years from 1995 to 2006, 11 ranked among the 12 warmest years in the instrumental record of global surface temperature (since 1850). The 100-year (1906 to 2005) linear warming trend over the last 50 years (average of 0.13°C per decade) is almost twice that for the last 100 years. (See Box Figure 5–1a.)

- Observations since 1961 show that the average temperature of the global ocean has increased to depths of at least 3000 metres—the ocean has been absorbing more than 80 percent of the heat added to the climate system. This warming causes sea water to expand and contribute to sea-level rise. Global average sea level rose at an average rate of 1.8 millimetres per year between 1961 and 2003, but at a rate of about 3.1 millimetres per year between 1993 and 2003. (See Box Figure 5–1b.)

- Mountain glaciers and snow cover have declined on average in both northern and southern hemispheres. Decreases in glaciers and ice caps have contributed to sea-level rise. (See Box Figure 5–1c.)

- Average Arctic temperatures increased at almost twice the global average rate in the past 100 years.

- Satellite data since 1978 show that annual average Arctic sea ice extent has shrunk by 2.7 percent per decade (with summer decreases of 7.4 percent per decade).

- Temperatures at the top of the Arctic permafrost layer generally have increased by up to 3°C since the 1980s. The maximum area covered by seasonally frozen ground has decreased by about 7 percent in the northern hemisphere since 1900 (and decreases in spring are up to 15 percent).

- Long-term trends (1900 to 2005) have been observed in precipitation amounts over large regions. Significantly increased precipitation has been observed in eastern parts of North and South America, northern Europe, and northern and central Asia. Conversely, drying has been observed in the Sahel, the Mediterranean, southern Africa, and parts of southern Asia.

- Changes in precipitation and evaporation over the oceans are suggested by freshening of mid- and high-latitude waters, along with increased salinity in low-latitude waters.

- Mid-latitude westerly winds have strengthened in both hemispheres since the 1960s.

- More intense, longer droughts have been observed over wider areas since the 1970s, particularly in the tropics and subtropics. These changes in drought characteristics link increased drying with higher temperatures and decreased precipitation. Changes in sea surface temperatures and wind patterns, and decreased snowpack and snow cover also have been linked to droughts.

- The frequency of heavy precipitation events has increased over most land areas, consistent with warming and observed increases of atmospheric water vapour (warmer air can hold the extra water vapour).

- Evidence of an increase in intense tropical cyclone activity in the North Atlantic (since about 1970) is correlated with increases of tropical sea surface temperatures (but there is no clear trend in the annual numbers of tropical cyclones).

- Changes in extreme temperatures have been observed during the past 50 years; cold days, cold nights, and frost have become less frequent, while hot days, hot nights, and heat waves have become more frequent.

(continued)

BOX 5–5
(CONTINUED)

Changes in temperature, sea level, and northern hemisphere snow cover

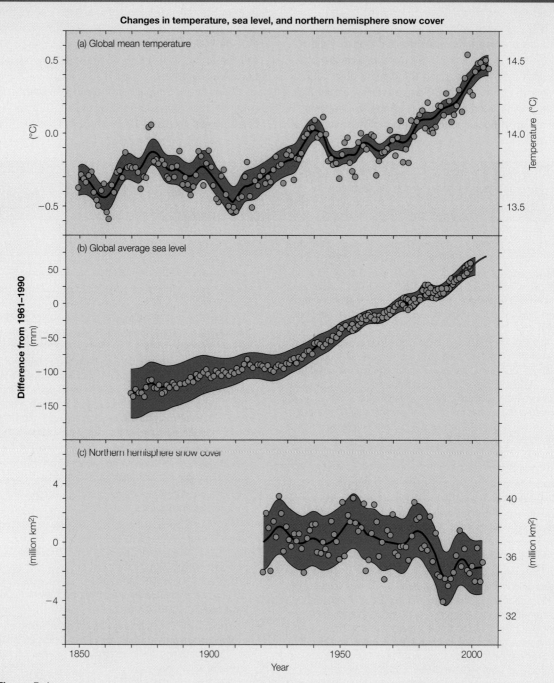

Box Figure 5–1

Changes in temperature, sea level, and northern hemisphere snow cover

NOTE: Observed changes in (a) global average surface temperature, (b) global average sea level from tide gauge (blue) and satellite (red) data, and (c) northern hemisphere snow cover for March–April. All changes are relative to corresponding averages for the period 1961–90. Smoothed curves represent decadal average values, green circles show yearly values. The blue shaded areas are the uncertainty intervals estimated from a comprehensive analysis of known uncertainties (a and b) and from the time series (c).

SOURCE: IPCC, 2007: Summary for Policymakers. In: *Climate Change 2007: The Physical Science Basis. Contribution of Working Group I to the Fourth Assessment Report of the Intergovernmental Panel on Climate Change* [Solomon, S., D. Qin, M. Manning, Z. Chen, M. Marquis, K. B. Averyt, M. Tignor and H. L. Miller (eds.)]. Cambridge, UK: Cambridge University Press, page 17.

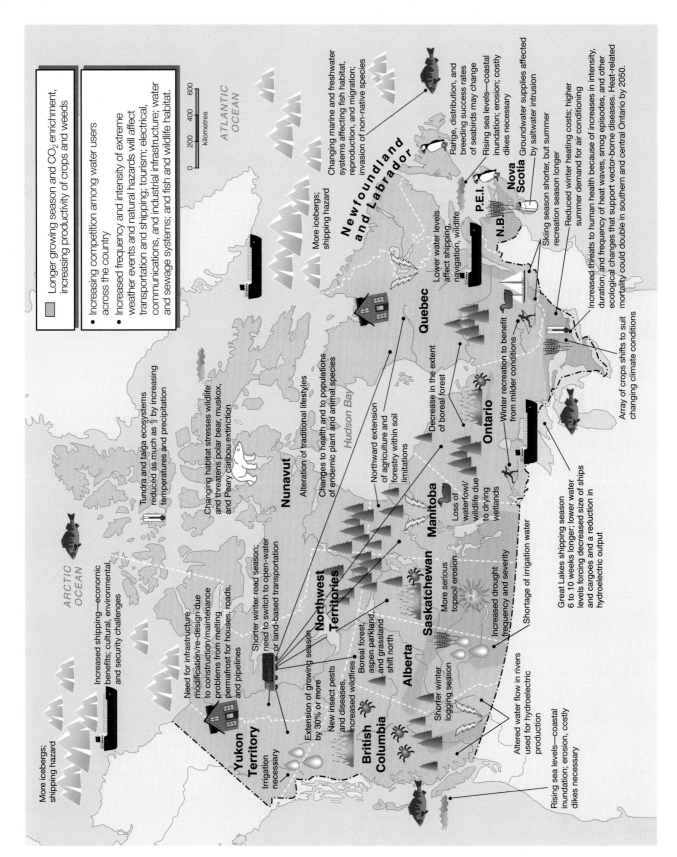

Figure 5–5

Potential effects of climate change across Canada

SOURCES: Data from Environment Canada. 2005. *Climate Change Overview.* http://www.ec.gc.ca/climate/overview_canada-e.html; Government of Canada. 2008. *From Impacts to Adaptation: Canada in a Changing Climate 2007.* http://adaptation.nrcan.gc.ca/assess/2007/index_e.php

(Lazier, 1996). While this may seem to be a small change, it is important to note that the top three metres of the ocean store as much heat as the entire atmosphere. Small changes in heat storage in the oceans can significantly affect both global climate and ecosystems. (See the section "Other Atmospheric Changes" later in this chapter.)

Although many Canadians might relish the prospect of a warmer climate in this high-latitude country—especially warmer winters—the kinds of climate changes predicted by global circulation models might not be positive ones. For instance, average global temperatures would be higher than at any time during the past 100 000 years (most computer models predict a global warming of at least 3.0°C over a period of just a few decades), and climatic changes could occur very quickly, providing ecosystems with little time to adapt to the new conditions and humans with little time to develop measures to counter such changes. This is an important issue because decision makers need reliable information at the local and regional levels in order to develop mitigation and adaptation policies. Despite concerns about the uncertainties associated with them, regional climate change scenarios are an important part of regional climate change planning and policy. The IPCC's (2007) statement, that there is now higher confidence in projected patterns of warming and other regional-scale features (e.g., changes in wind patterns, precipitation, and some aspects of extremes and ice), is significant for continued adaptive planning efforts (see Box 5–6).

BOX 5-6
REPORTING ON CANADA'S GREENHOUSE GAS EMISSIONS

International agreements to address climate change require all signatories to report annually on direct and indirect greenhouse gases (GHGs). These reports are necessary, for example, to generate indicators to compare signatories' performance, establish base-line comparison data, assess the accuracy of predictive climate change models, track emissions levels, and evaluate the effectiveness of GHG emissions reduction programs. In Canada, the Greenhouse Gas Division of Environment Canada is charged with the monitoring and reporting of our GHG emissions. The most current (2005) inventory reported a 0.3 percent increase in total GHG emissions compared to 2003 levels. What are these inventories based on? Are they accurate? How are they verified? Are they useful?

Canada's GHG inventory is based on international reporting methods developed by the United Nations Framework Convention on Climate Change (UNFCCC). *The Revised 1996 Intergovernmental Panel on Climate Change (IPCC) Guidelines of National Greenhouse Gas Inventories* details the reporting methodology. The IPCC seeks to report all human-induced direct and indirect GHG emissions (by source) and removals (by sink). The IPCC holds regular meetings to refine reporting methods in order to increase both the accuracy and verification of GHG data (IPCC, 1997).

The annual GHG reporting format is based on six emissions sources:

- Energy
- Solvent and other product use
- Industrial processes
- Agriculture
- Land-use change and forestry
- Waste

The reporting mechanisms used to complete Canada's inventory requirements are diverse and complex and vary from source to source. The example provided here is based on GHG inventories in Canada's energy sector; energy-related activities emit more than 80 percent of Canada's GHGs (Environment Canada, 2002b).

Of the six direct GHGs inventoried in Canada, three are associated with the energy sector, namely: carbon dioxide (CO_2), methane (CH_4), and nitrous oxide (N_2O). To avoid double counting, the four indirect GHGs associated with the energy sector (specifically, suphur dioxide (SO_2), nitrogen oxides (NO_x), carbon monoxide (CO), and nonmethane volatile organic compounds (NMVOCs) are reported as Criteria Air Contaminants and are not included in the energy sector (Environment Canada, 2002b, chap. 2, App. A) (see Table 5–1).

In energy sector accounting, emissions and removal estimates may be derived using the following methods: direct measurement, mass balance, technology-specific emission factor calculations, and average emission factor calculations. The general equation used to calculate emissions from fuel combustion activities (energy, manufacturing, construction, transportation, and all work and heat-generating combustion activities) is specified below (Environment Canada, 2002b).

Quantity of fuel combusted × Emission factor
per physical unit of fuel = Emissions

In this equation,

- the *quantity of fuel combusted* is based largely on quarterly reports from Statistics Canada. These reports estimate our energy supply and demand by balancing data about fuel production with data concerning fuel use (such as import/export, residential, and industrial energy use); and

- the *emission factor* is the relationship between the amount of pollution produced and the quantity of fuel processed or burned. Emission factors have been developed from studies conducted by national and international agencies, including Environment Canada and the U.S. Environmental Protection Agency. The emission factor for CO_2, for example, is based on the amount of fuel consumed, average carbon content of the fuel, and the portion of the fuel that is oxidized (Environment Canada, 2002a, chap. 2, App. A).

As GHG reporting is a relatively new requirement, published emissions totals are neither quantitatively exact nor completely accurate. In its guidelines document, the IPCC predicted

BOX 5-6
(CONTINUED)

there would be initial problems with accuracy in data reporting (because of the newness of the methodology). The IPCC also predicted that accuracy would improve over time as methods were adjusted. Initial problems were acknowledged in Canada's inventory reports; for instance, very few of the values reported were from direct measurement (most were estimates or calculated values). Under stipulations of the National Pollution Release Inventory, Canada has legally binding and direct reporting requirements for the four indirect GHGs emitted by the energy sector, but no reporting is required for any of the direct GHGs. The emission factors for many subsectors that are critical for emissions calculations were lacking or were based on incomplete data. Some categories required by the IPCC are not reported because the data do not exist. For example, waste gas and flaring emissions from petroleum refining are not reported because data are lacking.

Verification of emissions estimates occurs internally. The IPCC reporting guidelines suggest methods should be well documented, reproducible, and measured against other estimation methods. The IPCC guidelines also suggest that estimates derived from various methodologies be compared to measured data and other peer-reviewed estimates. The Greenhouse Gas Division of Environment Canada has a verification centre that is taking steps to develop consistent GHG standards, protocols, and methodologies for calculating, measuring, and verifying GHG emissions.

Despite their shortcomings, the value of GHG inventories should not be discounted. One of the most valuable outcomes relates to what is learned from conducting the inventories themselves. Data collection using consistent methodologies allows those collecting and analyzing data to assess the effectiveness of current methodologies and to make adjustments accordingly. In turn, this provides decision makers with more precise annual emissions and removal information. Data application is apparent already. By 2005, 15 years of tracking emissions data provided evidence of definitive trends that enabled the Greenhouse Gas Division to determine what additional steps were necessary to meet Canada's Kyoto commitments. GHG inventories also provided information about which subsectors to target for reduction efforts. Electricity and steam generation, vehicle emissions, and petroleum industries were responsible for almost 65 percent of the increase in GHGs during that same period (Environment Canada, 2005). If Canada is to meet its international GHG reduction commitments, inventory data are vital in determining where to best place our reduction efforts in order to meet the challenges in GHG reduction.

SOURCES: *Canada's Greenhouse Gas Inventory 1990–2000,* Environment Canada, 2002, wyswig://26/http://www.ec.gc.ca/pdb/ghg/1990_00_report/appal_e.cfm; *Canada's 2005 Greenhouse Gas Inventory: A Summary of Trends,* Environment Canada, 2005, http://www.ec.gc.ca/pdb/ghg/inventory_report/2005/2005summary_{e.cfm; http://www.ec.gc.ca/pdb/npri/documents/Final_CAC_Handout_e.pdf; *The Revised 1996 IPCC Guidelines of National Greenhouse Gas Inventories,* IPCC, 1997, http://www.ipcc-nggip.iges.or.jp/public/gl/invs4.htm

The effects that an enhanced greenhouse effect would have on human societies and natural ecosystems depend on how regional climates and affected societies respond. In turn, regional climate responses will depend not only on how local factors such as evaporation and soil moisture change, but also on how the circulation patterns of the oceans and the atmosphere evolve. Changing oceanic and atmospheric circulation patterns would cause some regions to warm dramatically, others to warm only moderately, and still others (possibly the North Atlantic region off the coast of Labrador) to cool. As storm tracks could shift at the same time, some areas would receive more precipitation and others less.

With an enhanced greenhouse effect, changes in the size or frequency of extreme events such as heat waves, droughts, hurricanes, and thunderstorms could occur. Small changes in climate variability can produce large changes in the frequency of extreme events. For example, a general warming would tend to lead to an increase in the number of days with extremely high temperatures during summer and a decrease in the number of days with extremely low temperatures in winter. One study suggests the frequency of intense five-day heat spells will become eight times more common in Toronto (Colombo,

Etkin, & Karney, 1999). This has important implications for direct heat stress, space cooling power demands, and air quality.

Some climate models suggest that precipitation will increase in intensity in some areas, leading to the possibility of more extreme precipitation events, including flooding, while other areas could experience more frequent or severe drought (IPCC, 2001). The risk of flooding in Canada would be expected to increase as a result of a warmer climate, mostly through rainstorm floods, and with heavier rainfall from more (and possibly more severe) thunderstorms and from fewer but larger rainstorms associated with large-scale weather systems (Francis & Hengeveld, 1998).

Research has revealed a tendency toward more extreme precipitation in the northern hemisphere; in particular, heavy rainfalls have increased in the United States, Japan, the former Soviet Union, China, and countries around the North Atlantic rim. Canadian records show heavier precipitation, mostly in the north, since 1940 (Francis & Hengeveld, 1998). Drought has become more common since 1970 in parts of Africa as well as along the coasts of Chile and Peru and in northeastern Australia. Most Canadians are aware of the devastating drought on the Prairies in the 1930s, but the worst drought on Canadian record occurred in 1961, the only year on record outside the range of climatic variability expected on the Prairies. Regional drought is part of the normal long-term climate regime of prairie ecosystems and imposes real hardship on prairie farmers. According to Agriculture and Agri-Food Canada (2003), years that qualify as displaying true drought conditions are 1936, 1937, 1961, 1984, 1988, 2001, and 2002.

Severe winter storms have become more frequent in the Pacific Ocean and, since the 1970s, there also has been an increase in the number and destructiveness of storms along the eastern coast of North America. In the past half-century, seven of the eight most destructive storms experienced in this region have occurred within the past 25 years (Francis & Hengeveld, 1998). In part, the magnitude of destruction reflects growing affluence, a demand for land, and building construction (often in vulnerable areas) that, together, increase the value of property at risk.

Absolute proof of climate change does not exist, although the international scientific consensus is that there is "*very high confidence* that the global average net effect of human activities since 1750 has been one of warming" and that "most of the observed increase in global average temperatures since the mid-20th century is *very likely* due to the observed increase in anthropogenic greenhouse gas concentrations" (IPCC, 2007, pp. 3, 10). While some scientists continue to challenge the climate change hypothesis, application of the precautionary principle indicates that action should be taken to prevent atmospheric deterioration. Later in the chapter we review some international and national efforts taken to deal with atmospheric issues.

Photo 5–4a

Photo 5–4b

It is predicted that global warming will cause greater climatic variability, damaging crops through more severe droughts (top) and more intensive precipitation (bottom).

Photo 5–5a   **Photo 5–5b**

Global warming has resulted in the retreat of Angel Glacier in Jasper National Park. Compare the 1935 photo (left) with the 2006 photo and notice how much the "wings" and "trunk" of the glacier have melted.

THINNING OF THE OZONE LAYER

In the following sections, we explore both the nature of the ozone layer and the changes occurring within it due to anthropogenic and natural ozone-depleting substances. In turn, the effects of reductions in the ozone layer on increasing ultraviolet (UV) radiation, and UV's effects on humans and the Earth's ecosystems, are identified. Links between ozone depletion and climate change also are noted.

The Ozone Layer

By absorbing harmful ultraviolet radiation in the stratosphere and serving as a radiation shield for living things on Earth, **ozone** (O_3) serves an essential protective function (Figure 5–6). Produced by a photochemical reaction, ozone is found throughout the atmosphere, although about 90 percent of it occurs in the stratosphere at altitudes of 18 to 35 kilometres (Figure 5–7). The maximum ozone concentration within this band or ozone layer occurs between 20 and 25 kilometres above the Earth's surface (World Meteorological Organization, 1994). Even here, ozone molecules are scattered so thinly (about 300 parts per billion at peak concentrations) that if compressed to ground-level pressure, they would form a band of pure ozone only 3 millimetres thick at sea level. This is equivalent to 300 **Dobson units** (DU), the unit usually used to measure the thickness of the ozone layer in the atmosphere (see Box 5–6).

Ozone is produced in largest quantities near the equator, where sunlight is most direct and intense.

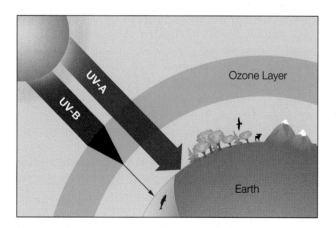

Figure 5–6

UV protection by the ozone layer

While UV-A (315–400 nanometre wavelength) and other solar radiation are not strongly absorbed by the ozone layer, UV-B radiation (280–315 nanometre wavelength) is partially absorbed and the amount of UV-B radiation reaching the Earth's surface is reduced greatly.

SOURCE: *Twenty Questions and Anwers about the Ozone Layer: 2006 Update*, D. W. Fahey, 2006, http://ozone.unep.org/Assessment_Panels/SAP/Scientific_Assessment_2006/Twenty_Questions.pdf

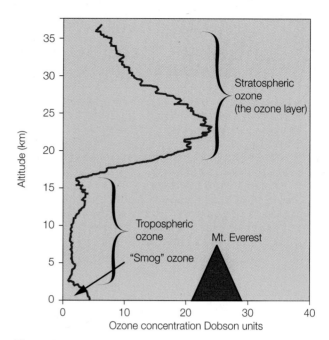

Figure 5–7

Distribution of ozone in the atmosphere

SOURCE: *The State of Canada's Environment—1996*, © Her Majesty the Queen in Right of Canada, Environment Canada, 1996. Reprinted with the permission of the Minister of Public Works and Government Services Canada, 2008.

However, varying stratospheric pressures and stratospheric winds cause ozone to move toward the poles, with the result that ozone may be 50 percent thicker at mid- and higher latitudes than in the tropics. Ozone thickness also varies seasonally. Arctic ozone levels are highly variable but generally are highest in late winter or early spring (February or March) and lowest in autumn. Antarctic levels are more predictable and are lowest in the Antarctic spring (October). Most poleward transport of ozone occurs in winter. With little or no ozone-destroying sunlight available at that time of year, stratospheric ozone increases over the winter and peaks near the end of the cold season (February in the northern hemisphere). As sunshine intensifies with the coming of spring, ozone depletion resumes and continues through the summer. In Canada this means lowest ozone thicknesses usually are recorded in the summer and fall, which coincide with lowest annual global levels (Newman, Pyle et al., 2002). In the tropics, where solar energy input is more constant over the seasons, ozone variations are much smaller.

Changes in the Ozone Layer

The human role in ozone layer depletion has been suspected since the late 1960s, when it was argued that water vapour and oxides of nitrogen from proposed subsonic and supersonic aircraft might deplete stratospheric ozone. Although effects of aircraft (and later, space shuttles) were thought to be negligible, the issue of chemical

Canada is recognized as a world leader among countries involved in research and development of new or improved environmental technologies, including those related to atmospheric science.

The Brewer Ozone Spectrophotometer, a ground-based ozone-monitoring instrument that was patented in 1991 by Environment Canada's Atmospheric Environment Service (now part of ARQX, the Experimental Studies Unit of Environment Canada), is a case in point. Considered to be the world's most accurate ozone-measuring device, the "Brewer" is produced in Canada and is used daily to collect and process data from the 12 Canadian sites established for the stratospheric ozone and UV monitoring program. The Brewer measures total ozone and spectral UV irradiation (290–325 nanometres) every 10 to 20 minutes during the daytime. These instruments also can measure ozone using the light of a full moon when the sky is clear; this is useful in the Arctic winter. The information derived from the Brewer network is used for ozone and UV index forecasting, trend analysis, and ongoing scientific research. Brewers can be adapted to measure other components of the atmosphere, such as nitrogen dioxide and aerosols. About 80 units were in use in more than 40 countries around the world in 2005.

contamination from our industrialized society began to be investigated.

In 1974, two American scientists, Drs. F. S. Rowland and M. Molina, hypothesized that chlorofluorocarbons (CFCs) could persist in the atmosphere long enough to diffuse upward into the stratosphere, be broken up by intense solar radiation, and release active chlorine atoms that, in turn, would destroy ozone. Initially people treated this theory with skepticism. However, growing evidence and discovery of the "ozone hole" over Antarctica in 1985 focused attention on CFCs and other synthetic compounds.

Humans appear to have increased tropospheric ozone by as much as 66 percent near Earth's surface, and about 20 percent in the upper troposphere (Hengeveld, 1999). In the northern hemisphere (outside of the tropics) principal sources of tropospheric ozone are industrial activities and, in the southern hemisphere, biomass burning. In the lower stratosphere, ozone concentrations over Canada

Photo 5–6

The box-like apparatus in the foreground is a Brewer Spectrophotometer, shown at the Bratt Lake Observatory. Consisting of a weatherproof spectrophotometer, azimuth tracker, and stand, this device provides near-simultaneous observations of the total ozone column, SO_2, and UV spectra. The solar trackers in the background measure diffuse solar radiation.

and Europe have declined by about 5 to 10 percent per decade since 1973 (Hengeveld, 1999).

Anthropogenic Ozone-Depleting Substances Chemicals known as industrial halocarbons emit halogen and bromine source gases that, ultimately, lead to stratospheric ozone depletion. Chlorofluorocarbon source gases, including carbon tetrachloride and methyl chloroform, are the most important chlorine-containing gases that destroy stratospheric ozone. Their use is widespread: CFC-11 (used in plastic foam blowing) and CFC-12 (used in vehicle air conditioners and refrigerator coolant) account for about half of the ozone-depleting chlorine entering the stratosphere (Environment Canada, 1999; Fahey, 2006). Bromine source gases include halons 1211 and 1301 (used originally in fire extinguishers, now in large computers and military hardware) and methyl bromide. Natural sources of chlorine and bromine emissions include terrestrial and oceanic ecosystems; methyl chloride is the most important natural source of chlorine. The partitioned columns in Figure 5–8 show how the major chlorine and bromine source gases contribute to the total amounts of chlorine and bromine in the stratosphere.

The most widely used of all the *ozone-depleting substances* (ODSs), CFCs were researched intensively in the early 1930s as a safe and efficient refrigerant to replace toxic ammonia. The characteristics of CFCs—nontoxic, odourless, nonflammable, noncorrosive, and chemically stable—quickly made them the prime choice as refrigerants. From the late 1950s to the late 1960s, the uses of CFCs multiplied: they were used as blowing agents in plastic foam production (for cushioning, insulation, packaging), as propellants in aerosol spray cans, and as solvents to clean electronic equipment and microchips. Today, CFCs continue to be used widely as coolants in refrigeration and air conditioning, as solvents in degreasers and cleaners, as a blowing agent in foam production, and as an ingredient in sterilant gas mixtures. Canada's 20 million household refrigerators alone contain

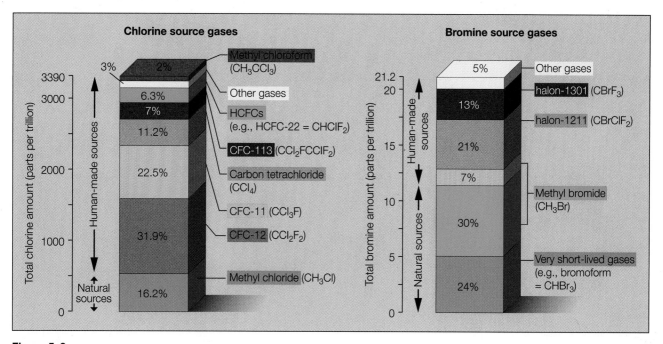

Figure 5–8

Stratospheric source gases, 2004

NOTE: The large differences in the vertical scales are significant: total chlorine in the stratosphere is 160 times more abundant than total bromine.

SOURCE: *Twenty Questions and Anwers about the Ozone Layer: 2006 Update*, D. W. Fahey, 2006, http://ozone.unep.org/Assessment_Panels/SAP/Scientific_Assessment_2006/Twenty_Questions.pdf

about 5 million kilograms of CFC-12 (each compressor contains an average charge of 0.25 kilograms of CFC-12). As is often the case, in trying to fix one problem (in this case, toxic ammonia), we inadvertently created or magnified the intensity of another (ODSs).

Their chemical stability allows CFCs to survive in the atmosphere for several decades to a few centuries (refer to Table 5–3). During this period, they diffuse gradually from the troposphere into the stratosphere, where they eventually are broken down by intense UV radiation. This process—which is more complex than described here—releases chlorine atoms that react easily with ozone, producing chlorine monoxide and oxygen (Figure 5–9, p. 162). In turn, the chlorine monoxide breaks down quickly, freeing its chlorine atom to combine again with another molecule of ozone. This property (actually a catalytic chain reaction) enables a single atom of chlorine to destroy approximately 100 000 ozone molecules over a one- to two-year period before it forms a more stable combination with another substance (Rowland, 1989). During the past 100 years, the abundance of chlorine in the stratosphere increased from a natural background level of about 0.6 parts per billion to about 3.6 parts per billion in 1994. If chlorine concentrations in the stratosphere decline, ozone concentrations in the mid- to low latitudes will recover slowly. But over the next few decades, increased stratospheric cooling is expected to keep stratospheric ozone at low concentrations during polar spring seasons.

One of only four countries to place an early (1980) ban on major propellant uses of CFCs, Canada had prohibited almost all aerosol uses of CFCs by 1990. By 2000, total chlorine from CFCs was no longer increasing, CFC-11 and CFC-13 had peaked (in 1994) and continued to decline slowly, and the rate of increase in levels of CFC-12 had slowed. In the stratosphere, however, CFCs are expected to persist for up to 50 years.

Other industrial halogens contribute to ozone depletion also. Methyl chloroform (CH_3CCl_3), introduced in the 1950s, is an all-purpose industrial solvent used to clean metal and electronic parts. A substitute for toxic carbon tetrachloride (CCl_4), methyl chloroform is used in large quantities as an industrial solvent, and much of it is vented directly to the atmosphere during metal cleaning. It was recognized as an important ODS in 1989, and since the mid-1990s, the atmospheric concentration of methyl chloroform had declined by approximately 20 percent; it was the first restricted halocarbon to show a decrease in atmospheric concentration (Ajavon et al., 2002; Environment Canada, 1999).

Hydrochlorofluorocarbons (HCFCs) contain chlorine, but because they contain hydrogen also, they break down in the lower atmosphere and result in a lower ozone-depletion effect. Used as substitutes for CFCs, HCFCs are known as transitional chemicals because they represent an interim step between strong ODSs and ozone-friendly replacement chemicals. By 2015, it is expected that HCFC use in Canada will have been reduced by 90 percent.

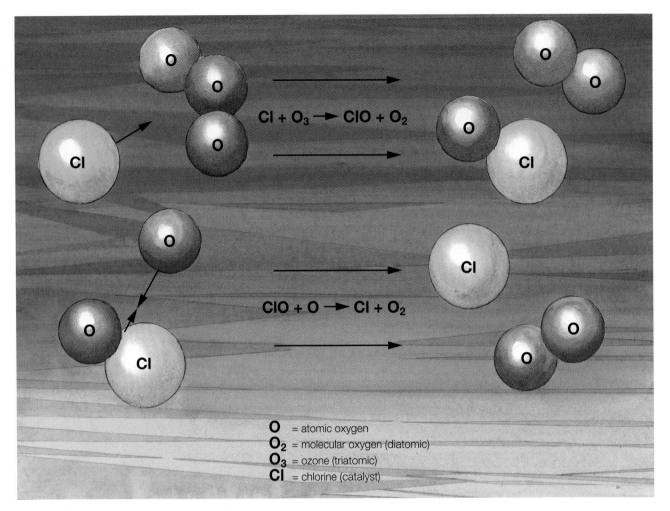

Figure 5–9

How ozone-depleting substances destroy stratospheric ozone

NOTE: Chemical reactions in the stratosphere are considerably more complex than the two equations shown here. However, these equations demonstrate the basic form of a chemical change reaction as occurs in depletion of ozone in the stratosphere.

SOURCE: Adapted from *Understanding Atmospheric Change: A Survey of the Background Science and Implications of Climate Change and Ozone Depletion* (2nd ed.), H. Hengeveld, 1995, SOE Report No. 95–2, Ottawa: Environment Canada. Reproduced with the permission of the Ministry of Public Works and Government Services Canada, 2008.

Worldwide, however, HCFCs are still used extensively and emissions continue to increase (Ajavon et al., 2002).

Halons are used primarily as fire suppressants for delicate equipment, computer and electronic equipment facilities, museums, ships, and tanks, and they are in general use in industries, homes, and offices. Halons were produced in large quantities in the 1980s. Levels in the atmosphere have not risen rapidly because most halons have not been vented yet, but remain stored in fire extinguishers. Halons contribute to about 3 percent of global ozone depletion, although their concentrations are increasing (along with concerns for future impacts of these long-lived ODSs).

Methyl bromide has been used as a pesticide since the 1960s but has been recognized as an important ODS only since 1991. Farmers use it to sterilize soil in fields and greenhouses, and to kill pests on fruit, vegetables, and grain before export. Approximately 90 percent of the methyl bromide use in Canada occurs in Ontario and Quebec. Scientists estimate that human sources of methyl bromide are responsible for 5 to 10 percent of global ozone depletion. Although it has a relatively short lifetime, bromine removes ozone very effectively; consequently, methyl bromide is considered a significant contributor to ozone depletion. This short lifetime characteristic suggests that an immediate reduction in consumption of methyl bromide could have a more immediate effect on reducing ozone depletion than would a reduction in consumption of longer-lived substances (but at the same time, this does not imply we should act on the longer-lived ODSs). In 2005, Canada acted to restrict use of methyl bromide (Health Canada, 2004).

Our use of industrial halocarbons, including CFCs, will continue to have far-reaching effects on the atmosphere.

While the chemical interactions and effects of these substances are extremely complex and not yet fully understood, we do know that they portend potentially severe atmospheric changes.

Natural Ozone-Depleting Substances Natural factors relating to changes in ozone levels include the 11-year sunspot cycle (Ram, Stolz, & Koenig, 1997), periodic reversals in wind direction over the equator, and volcanic eruptions. Volcanoes can erupt with sufficient force to inject dust particles and gases into the stratosphere. If that happens, volcanic particles (aerosols) can affect ozone levels because they speed up the chemical reactions that destroy ozone directly. They can also block incoming UV radiation and affect weather patterns that indirectly influence ozone formation and destruction. For the first six months following the eruption of Mt. Pinatubo in the Philippines in June 1991, local stratospheric ozone concentrations were as much as 20 percent below previous levels (Environment Canada, 2002a). The severe Antarctic ozone depletion in 1993 has been attributed partly to the presence of aerosols from this eruption (Manney et al., 1994). However, the impact of volcanic particles is short-lived: in a few years, particulates settle out of the atmosphere, thus posing a reduced threat to the ozone layer.

Spatial Variations in Ozone Depletion

Antarctic Ozone Depletion The British Antarctic Survey began measuring stratospheric ozone in 1957. In 1985 members of the survey published data showing clearly that ozone concentrations remained at about 300 Dobson units (DU) from 1957 to 1970, but after 1970 there was a sharp drop to about 200 DU by 1984 (Farman, Gardiner, & Shanklin, 1985). Since then, ozone concentrations have been quite variable, hitting a high of about 250 DU in 1988 and a low of about 91 DU in 1993. Since 1993, the minimum total ozone has remained at about 100 DU. Chemistry climate models project springtime Antarctic ozone levels will increase by 2010 because halogen levels are expected to have declined by then (Hamill & Toon, 1991; Newman, Pyle et al., 2002). Satellite data on ozone concentrations before 1985 confirmed the British Antarctic Survey findings, and the depletion in ozone was dubbed the ozone hole. Note that there is no actual hole in the ozone shield around the Earth, but there is a decrease in the concentration of ozone that occurs during the Antarctic spring—September to November—each year.

The most dramatic depletion of the ozone layer occurs over the Antarctic during the southern spring. Two events that occur in the southern polar region during winter are important to the severity of this ozone depletion. One event, known as the **polar vortex**, occurs during the polar winter (night), when the Antarctic air mass is partially isolated from the rest of the atmosphere and circulates around the pole. The second event is the formation of **polar stratospheric clouds** (PSCs); these form in the extremely low temperatures (below –78°C) that develop within the polar vortex as it matures, cools (in the absence of heating by sunlight or by the influx of warmer air from lower latitudes), and descends. Ice crystals in these clouds provide the medium for a complex variety of chemical reactions that lead to rapid depletion of ozone when sunlight returns in the spring (Toon & Turco, 1991) (see Photo 5–8 on page 165).

Antarctic ozone depletion has become more pronounced over time. In 1989, the area of serious depletion (where total ozone thickness was less than 220 DU) covered about 7.5 percent of the southern hemisphere. In October 1993, ozone thicknesses of 91 DU were recorded, and in 1993–94 the area of reduced ozone thickness covered about 10.7 percent of the southern hemisphere (an area about the size of North America). Since then, ozone losses often have started earlier and the affected areas have expanded more rapidly than previously, even extending beyond the tip of South America (see Photo 5–7). Every year, it seems, the ozone hole gets larger. In 1996, the ozone hole reached 26.0 million square kilometres in area; that record was broken in 1998 when the hole encompassed 27.3 million square kilometres, and again in 2000 when the hole was more than 30 million square kilometres in area (Environment Canada, 1999). In contrast, the 2002 ozone hole was very small (approximately 20 million square kilometres) and broke up earlier than in previous years (Wood & Bodeker, 2003). In 2003, ozone loss again was near record levels, dispelling hopeful predictions that ODS impacts had maximized.

New research highlights the interrelationships among atmospheric issues. Cooling of the Antarctic polar vortex, caused by ozone depletion and warmer temperatures

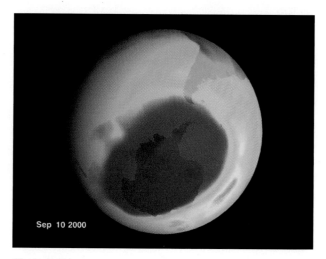

Photo 5–7

The Antarctic ozone hole in September 2000, at that time, its largest extent, and for the first time, extending over sizeable settled areas in southern South America.

elsewhere, has increased the speed of the polar vortex spin and could exacerbate climate changes. Climatologists in the southern hemisphere are concerned this dynamic could result in a permanent drought in southwestern Australia, where rainfall has been declining for the last 50 years (Byrnes, 2003).

Tropical and Mid-Latitude Ozone Depletion
Because the natural replenishment rate of ozone at low latitudes is high, ozone-depleting chemicals have had the least effect on tropical ozone levels. However, ice particles do occur in the stratosphere over the tropics, and at times there is an abundance of aerosols in the stratosphere from volcanic eruptions. As yet, however, there is no substantial evidence to support the theory that these particles cause ozone depletion in the tropics.

Satellite measurements show that average ozone concentrations over the mid-latitudes of the northern hemisphere have declined by about 7 percent from 1978 to 1994 (Figure 5–10). Mid-latitude ozone in both hemispheres continues to be depleted, 3 percent below 1980 levels in the northern hemisphere and 6 percent lower in the southern hemisphere. The tropics remain unaffected (Avajon et al., 2002).

Arctic Ozone Depletion
In 2000, UNEP's Ozone Secretariat highlighted the pronounced variability in the annual patterns of ozone loss between the North and South poles—ozone depletion in the Antarctic is much more consistent in amount, timing, and pattern of loss than is ozone depletion in the Arctic, largely due to greater variation in Arctic winter temperatures. In 1996–97, when

Arctic ozone levels increased, it was hoped that ozone losses had peaked. However, research indicated that higher ozone levels were associated with warmer Arctic winter temperatures and were not a reflection of the direct effects of current regulations regarding ODSs. Persistent low temperatures in the upper atmosphere are associated with greater ozone loss; because the Arctic has experienced comparatively mild winters recently, there has been a reduction in ozone loss (Ajavon et al., 2002; Newman, Pyle et al., 2002).

Since the Arctic vortex is much less stable than the southern polar vortex and breaks up sooner, and because the Arctic stratosphere is slightly warmer and less conducive to PSC formation, it is anticipated that ozone depletion on the scale experienced in the Antarctic will not occur in the Arctic. Nevertheless, if an enhanced greenhouse effect were to cool the upper atmosphere as predicted, the conditions for PSC would improve and increase the possibility of more pronounced Arctic ozone depletion. We need to appreciate that ozone depletion remains a global concern, from the poles to the tropics.

EFFECTS OF OZONE DEPLETION

When ozone depletion occurs in the stratosphere as a result of the use of CFCs and other industrial halons, that area of the upper atmosphere is cooled. Normally, when ozone absorbs incoming UV radiation, it warms the surrounding atmosphere. But as ozone levels decline as a result of ODSs, the stratosphere cools. In addition, carbon

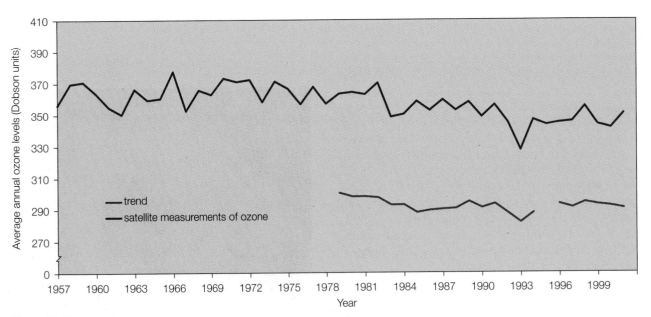

Figure 5–10

Average annual stratospheric ozone levels over Canada and globally

SOURCE: Data from Meterological Service of Canada, Environment Canada; National Aeronautics and Space Administration, U.S.A., State of the Environment Infobase, Technical Supplement 1, Indicator Profiles: Stratospheric ozone-average annual ozone levels. Environment Canada. 2005. Available at http://www.ec.gc.ca/soer-ree/English/indicator_series/techs.cfm?tech_id=21&issue_id=5&supp=1#techs.

Photo 5–8

Polar stratospheric clouds photographed over Sweden during winter 2000. These clouds support chemical reactions that change stable bromine and other chlorine compounds into more active, ozone-destroying substances, particularly ClO. PSC clouds often are seen with the human eye when the sun is near the horizon.

dioxide in the atmosphere (which is on the rise because of burning of fossil fuels) may contribute indirectly to stratospheric cooling and could accelerate the onset of Arctic ozone depletion.

Ozone depletion also may affect global climate indirectly through the loss of phytoplankton (a carbon sink; see Chapter 3). Threatened by increased levels of UV radiation, the productivity of oceanic phytoplankton—the basis of the ocean's food chain—may be reduced. If their productivity is reduced, their ability to store approximately 80 percent of the CO_2 released into the atmosphere by human activities will decrease. That means atmospheric concentrations of CO_2 may rise, enhancing the greenhouse effect and changing global climate. Phytoplankton also produce dimethyl sulphoxide, a chemical important in the creation of clouds above the oceans. Phytoplankton losses may affect cloud patterns and thereby affect global climate.

As increased levels of UV radiation reach the lower atmosphere, it is anticipated that the reactivity of chemicals such as ground-level ozone, hydrogen peroxide, and acids will increase. Such changes could exacerbate human health problems and could mean more difficulty and expense in achieving current air pollution reduction goals (United Nations Environment Programme, 1998). Ozone depletion will affect plants, including food crops. Ozone depletion also results in an increase in UV radiation reaching the Earth: this is the subject of the following section.

Increased Ultraviolet Radiation

Due to the release of ozone-depleting substances, the ozone layer over Canada is 5 to 10 percent thinner than it was before 1980. This is of concern because, when it is sufficiently intense, UV radiation can break stable chemical bonds and damage deoxyribonucleic acid (DNA), the genetic coding material that all living things carry in their cells. Of the three wavelength regions of UV radiation, the longest and least powerful wavelengths are known as UV-A (between 320 and 400 nanometres; 1 nanometre is 1 millionth of a millimetre). These wavelengths pass

CHAPTER 5: OUR CHANGING ATMOSPHERE

through the atmosphere almost as easily as visible light and are relatively harmless to most organisms within the normal range of intensity. In contrast, UV-C rays are the shortest (between 200 and 280 nanometres) and most biologically harmful, but they are absorbed almost completely in the upper atmosphere and do not reach the Earth's surface.

A small proportion of the powerful middle wavelengths (UV-B, between 280 and 320 nanometres) reaches the Earth's surface and may cause biological damage to people, plants, and animals (see Figure 5–6). Note that UV-B radiation has always affected people, but, as Canadians increasingly spend more time outdoors (and expose more of their skin while doing so), the effects on human health have become more prevalent. And as more UV-B reaches the Earth as a result of ozone depletion, it may compound the effects of our "sun-worshipping" habits.

How much UV radiation reaches the Earth's surface depends on the angle of the sun, the presence of atmospheric aerosols, the amount and type of cloud, and the thickness of the ozone layer. Ozone, because it absorbs almost all of the most harmful UV-C and most UV-B radiation, is one of the most important determinants of how much UV-B radiation reaches the Earth. It has been calculated that, under clear skies in the mid-latitudes, every 1 percent decrease in the thickness of the stratospheric ozone layer results in an increase in UV-B radiation of about 1.1 to 1.4 percent (McElroy et al., 1994).

Anticipated UV-B radiation increases during the next decade (at least) will continue to affect public health and will have impacts on terrestrial, freshwater, and marine plants; animals; agricultural crops and livestock; forests; freshwater resources; fisheries; and building materials. While there are widely varying responses from species to species and within different varieties of a single species, many plants will show reduced photosynthesis and growth. For instance, important global food supply crops such as wheat, rice, barley, peas, oats, sweet corn, and soybeans are particularly sensitive to UV-B radiation, as are tomatoes, cucumbers, broccoli, cauliflower, and carrots.

For every 1 percent increase in UV-B radiation reaching the Earth, food production could drop by 1 percent (Environment Canada, 1997). Vegetable production regions in both British Columbia and Ontario could be affected, as UV-B disrupts the way plants use nitrogen. Some livestock species would require protective shelters to avoid reduction in their productivity; other livestock, such as free-range species, would require more land to compensate for the reduced productivity of the plants on which they graze.

While only a few species of Canadian trees have been tested for UV-B sensitivity, increased radiation adversely affected over 45 percent of them, particularly young seedlings. This has important implications for the ability of sensitive replacement species to survive in clear-cut logged areas; if young trees fail to survive, forest sector

productivity will decline. Practices such as selective cutting (see Chapter 9) could help reduce potential losses.

Since more than 30 percent of the world's animal protein for human consumption comes from the sea, possible losses caused by ozone depletion would further stress many commercial fish species. Phytoplankton losses, described below, could disrupt fresh- and saltwater food chains and lead to a species shift in Canadian waters. In turn, loss of biodiversity could result in reduced fish yields for sport and commercial fisheries. Even farmed fish raised in shallow ponds with no shade provided could suffer cataracts and lesions (Environment Canada, 1997).

Organisms such as phytoplankton and zooplankton, living in the surface layers of lakes and oceans, may provide clear evidence of UV radiation damage related to ozone depletion because of their relatively direct exposure to the sun. The blooms of Antarctic phytoplankton, for instance, begin to develop just as ozone thinning is occurring; a 1990 estimate suggested that phytoplankton productivity was 6 to 12 percent lower within the zone of ozone depletion than beyond it (Prézelin, Boucher, & Schofield, 1994). Increased UV-B intensity also may be contributing to global declines in frog and toad populations (see Chapter 12).

Photo 5–9
Excessive exposure to the sun and ultraviolet radiation damages skin and may result in serious problems such as skin cancer.

These examples illustrate the complexity of determining increased UV radiation impacts on natural populations, and of predicting its effects on different ecosystems.

In terms of the public health effects of increased UV radiation, most people realize that too much sun (UV radiation) is dangerous for their skin and health. But how do we know when we should be cautious about being in the sun? Sunburned skin is damaged skin, but how long does it take our skin to burn when exposed? Does it make a difference if we are at the beach or in the mountains?

One tool to help us make decisions about our exposure to UV radiation is the UV Index (UVI). The UVI was a Canadian first; in 1992, Canadian scientists devised a method to predict the strength of the sun's UV rays, based on daily changes in the ozone layer. That same year, they developed the UVI and Canada became the first nation in the world to issue countrywide daily forecasts of the next day's UV levels. Environment Canada's UVI is produced for at least 48 locations across Canada, as well as holiday destinations, and is available on radio and TV, in the newspaper, through local weather offices, and on Environment Canada's Weather Forecast website.

Canada's original UVI was designed so the maximum value in southern Canada was 10 at midday in the summer and about 1 at midday during winter. Canadians learned that the higher the index value, the greater the potential for skin damage and the less exposure time it took for harm to occur. In February 2004, Canada's UVI was adjusted to conform to the standards set out by the World Health Organization (WHO). The main visible changes were the new exposure categories and appropriate health warnings (see Table 5–4). Since the international UVI values were higher than what Canadians were used to, Environment Canada anticipated that people might be more likely to pay attention to UV radiation when they normally did not think about it—in late winter and spring when it was still cold outside—and develop a better understanding of how UV radiation could affect them.

Depending on where you live in Canada, your exposure to UV rays will vary. In summer, you would receive roughly three times more UV radiation if you lived in southern Canada than if you lived in the Northwest Territories (Mills & Jackson, 1995). UV radiation also varies with altitude; the international index is adjusted to take elevation into account (increasing 3 percent per 1000 feet). The UVI also reflects the presence of snow on the ground (5 to 20 percent increase), and takes into account the reduction of UV radiation due to cloud cover.

The UVI helps us make informed choices and plan outdoor activities so we can prevent overexposure to the sun's rays. Not only can excessive sun exposure result in painful sunburn, it can lead to other serious health problems including melanoma, a life-threatening form of skin cancer. Excessive UV exposure also can lead to premature aging of the skin, cataracts, nonmelanoma skin cancers, and immune system suppression. Because skin cancer takes between 10 and 20 years to develop, and the incidence of skin cancers in Canada has increased rapidly during the past two decades, the full impact of post-1980 ozone depletion on Canadian skin cancer rates may be becoming evident (see Box 5–8). In addition, it is expected that a sustained 10 percent thinning of the ozone layer globally will result in nearly two million new cases of cataracts per year and a 26 percent increase in the incidence of nonmelanoma skin cancer (Environment Canada, 2002a). The Australian slogan "Slip, Slap, Slop" ("Slip on a T-shirt, slap on a hat, and slop on the sunscreen") is good advice for Canadians, too!

LINKING CLIMATE CHANGE AND OZONE DEPLETION

The likelihood that CFCs and other ODSs affected the climate system was first identified in the 1970s. As Figure 5–11 (p. 170) illustrates, we know that HCFCs, CFCs, and halons contribute to ozone depletion in the stratosphere and to climate change, while hydrofluorocarbons and perfluorocarbons contribute only to climate change. This knowledge is particularly important with respect to understanding how replacement options for ODSs could affect global warming. Phasing out ODSs and reducing greenhouse gas emissions can be achieved through such measures as improved containment of substances during their production and transport; reduced charges of the substances in equipment; reduced amounts of substances in existing equipment, chemical stockpiles, foams, and other products not yet released to the atmosphere; end-of-life recovery and recycling or destruction of substances; increased use of alternative or replacement substances with a lower or negligible global warming potential (GWP); and use of not-in-kind technologies (that do not use halocarbons but still achieve the product objective, such as stick or spray pump deodorants to replace CFC-12 aerosol deodorants).

OTHER ATMOSPHERIC CHANGES

Constantly interacting as they circulate, oceans and the atmosphere are closely linked in our efforts to understand long-term climate changes (see Figure 5–1). The cyclical nature of various atmosphere–ocean systems, how they overlap, and the uncertainty of how anthropogenic effects on the atmosphere will influence those systems add to the complexity of understanding system interactions and predicting how they might be influenced by the variables referred to in this chapter. Slight changes in the temperatures of ocean currents can influence air temperatures and weather patterns worldwide. Perhaps the best-known example of this is El Niño, but oceanographers

TABLE 5–4
THE INTERNATIONAL UV INDEX

UVI	Description	Sun Protection Actions
0–2	Low	• *Minimal sun protection* is required for normal activity. • Wear sunglasses on bright days. If outside for more than one hour, cover up and use sunscreen. • Reflection off snow can nearly double UV strength. Wear sunglasses and apply sunscreen.
3–5	Moderate	• *Take precautions*—cover up, wear a hat, sunglasses, and sunscreen, especially if you will be outside for 30 minutes or more. • Look for shade near midday when the sun is strongest.
6–7	High	• *Protection is required*—UV damages the skin and can cause sunburn. • Reduce time in the sun between 11 a.m. and 4 p.m. and take full precautions—seek shade, cover up, wear a hat, sunglasses, and sunscreen.
8–10	Very high	• *Extra precautions required*—unprotected skin will be damaged and can burn quickly. • Avoid the sun between 11 a.m. and 4 p.m. and take full precautions—seek shade, cover up, wear a hat, sunglasses, and sunscreen.
11+	Extreme	• *Take full precautions*—unprotected skin will be damaged and can burn in minutes. Avoid the sun between 11 a.m. and 4 p.m. and take full precautions—seek shade, cover up, wear a hat, sunglasses, and sunscreen. • Values of 11 or more are very rare in Canada. However, the UV Index can reach 14 or more in the tropics and southern United States. • White sand and other bright surfaces reflect UV and increase UV exposure.

NOTES:
- When visiting warmer climates, remember that UV radiation is more intense there; sun protection is particularly important.
- There is no such thing as a healthy tan; UV radiation from sun and tanning lamps is a major contributor to skin cancer.
- Wear tightly woven, loose-fitting clothing to cover your arms and legs; wear a hat with a wide brim to shade your face and neck; wear sunglasses that absorb or block 99 to 100 percent of UV radiation.
- Use sunscreen in conjunction with shade, clothing, hats, and sunglasses, not instead of them (and reapply every two hours); sunscreens are not intended to increase length of time spent in the sun but to reduce exposure and provide some protection from sunburn when people need to be in the sun; use a sunscreen with sun protection factor (SPF) of 15 or higher.

SOURCE: *UV Index and Sun Protection*, © Her Majesty the Queen in Right of Canada, Environment Canada, 2002, Reproduced with the permission of the Minister of Public Works and Government Services Canada, 2008. http://www.msc-smc.ec.gc.ca/education/uvindex/who_newstd2_e.html; www.msc-smc.ec.gc.ca/education/uvindex/protecting_yourself_e.html

have identified other, more subtle climatic effects resulting from currents, as well as effects on ocean circulation due to global warming. In the sections that follow, we briefly consider atmospheric changes associated with El Niño and the Southern Oscillation (ENSO), the Pacific Decadal Oscillation (PDO), acidic deposition, and airborne contaminants.

ENSO AND THE PDO

Global climate patterns can be disrupted by the ocean–atmosphere system called El Niño–Southern Oscillation (ENSO). The El Niño is an invasion of warm surface water from the western equatorial Pacific to the eastern equatorial

BOX 5–8
UV RADIATION AND SKIN CANCER IN CANADA

Did you realize that UV radiation from the sun is a human carcinogen? Did you know that tanning beds and lamps also emit UV radiation and are considered carcinogenic? According to the Canadian Cancer Society (2005), overexposure to UV radiation is a common, and preventable, risk factor for all kinds of skin cancer.

Skin cancer, the most commonly occurring cancer in Canada, accounts for about one-third of all newly diagnosed cancers. Fortunately, the most common forms of skin

cancer—basal cell carcinoma and squamous cell carcinoma—are nonlethal, and the most serious form, melanoma, is the least common skin cancer, so the incidence of death from skin cancer is low. Left untreated, however, skin cancers can cause extensive disfigurement. Overexposure to the sun's UV rays (sunburn is one indicator) during childhood and adolescence can lead to skin cancer in later years; even one or two blistering sunburns during childhood may double the risk of melanoma later in life.

BOX 5-8
(CONTINUED)

Since most skin cancers are related to overexposure to the sun, it should be possible to substantially reduce the number of new skin cancer cases simply by reducing exposure to UV radiation. While women are more likely than men to adopt sun safety measures (see Table 5–4), and sun safety efforts increase with age, people 15 to 24 years old spend the most time in the sun and rarely practise sun protection measures (Canadian Cancer Society, 2005). Educational programs such as the sun sensitivity tests and "spot check" described here may help people make healthy choices regarding their UV exoposure.

Yes	No	
☐	☐	I have red or blond hair.
☐	☐	I have light-coloured eyes—blue, green, or grey.
☐	☐	I always burn before I tan.
☐	☐	I freckle easily.
☐	☐	I had two or more blistering sunburns before I turned 18.
☐	☐	I lived or had long vacations in a tropical climate as a child.
☐	☐	My family has a history of skin cancer.
☐	☐	I work outdoors.
☐	☐	I spend a lot of time in outdoor activities.
☐	☐	I am an indoor worker, but I like to get out in the sun as much as possible when I am able.

- Score yourself 10 points for each "YES."
- Add an additional 10 points if you use tanning devices, tanning booths, or sun lamps.

(80–100) You are in the high-risk zone. Read on to find out how you can protect your skin from the sun.
(40–70) You are at risk. Take all precautions possible.
(10–30) You're still at risk. Carry on being careful.

A Sun Sensitivity Test and "Spot Check"

Your risk of skin cancer is related to your skin type and the amount of time you spend in the sun. How vulnerable are you? Try the Canadian Dermatology Association's Sun Sensitivity Test to determine your chances of getting skin cancer and whether you need to act differently with regard to UV exposure.

The Canadian Dermatology Association's "Spot Check" is a quick reference guide to moles and pigmented spots on the skin (see sidebar). Checking your moles and spots for changes could help catch skin cancer early when it is most easily treated. The Department of Dermatology and Skin Science at the University of British Columbia hosts a website designed to help people increase their awareness of changes in skin moles that might become malignant melanomas (see http://www.dermweb.org/molemelanoma/introduction.html).

For further information, contact the Canadian Dermatology Association.

SOURCE: Canadian Dermatology Association. Reproduced with permission.

spot check

Normal mole: Round or oval, even colour.
Many moles–*increased* risk of melanoma skin cancer.

Atypical mole: Mix of browns, smudged border, often bigger than 5 mm. *Increased* risk of melanoma skin cancer.

Melanoma skin cancer: Potentially deadly.
Look for *changes* in colour: new colour, black, brown, red, blue, or white.

Shape: Irregular, border scalloped but well defined.

Size: Enlarges.

Acinic Keratoses: Not skin cancer. Indicates excess sun exposure over many years. Red, rough, scaly spots, may itch or sting. *Increased* risk of skin cancer.

Basal cell skin cancer: Can cause disfigurement. Flesh-coloured, red, or black round bump with a pearly border, develops into ulcerating sore.

Squamous cell skin cancer: Can be life threatening. Thickened, red, scaly bump or wart-like growth, develops into a raised, crusted sore.

Common skin cancers usually appear on sun-exposed areas.

See your dermatologist if you note any of the above.

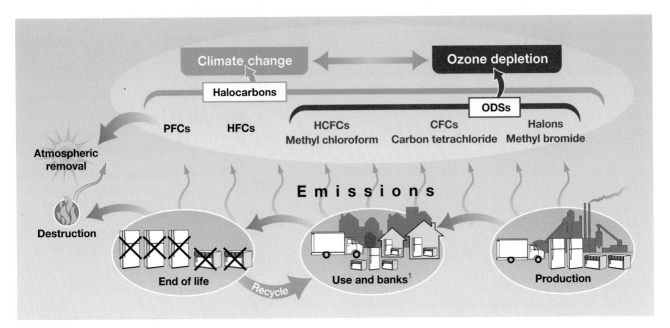

Figure 5–11

Linking climate change and ozone depletion

NOTES:

1. The term "banks" refers to the total amount of substances contained in existing equipment, chemical stockpiles, foams, and other products not yet released to the atmosphere.

2. Red denotes gases included under the Montreal Protocol and its amendments and adjustments, while green denotes those included under the UNFCCC and its Kyoto Protocol.

SOURCE: IPCC/TEAP Special Report (n.d.): *Safeguarding the Ozone Layer and the Global Climate System: Issues Related to Hydfrofluorocarbons and Perfluorocarbons: Summary for Policymakers*, p. 3, http://www.ipcc.ch/pdf/special-reports/sroc/sroc_spm.pdf

region and along the coasts of Peru, Ecuador, and northern Chile. Normally, the cold Peruvian current moves northward along these coasts, and southerly winds blowing offshore promote the upwelling of cold, nutrient-rich water that supports large populations of fish, particularly anchovies.

Each year, around Christmas time, a warm current of nutrient-poor tropical water moves south, displacing the cold water. In most years, El Niño is not very warm and lasts perhaps as long as a month. However, about every three to seven years, this phenomenon becomes very strong, persisting for several months. The Japanese Meteorological Agency considers an ENSO to be underway when the tropical Pacific Ocean is a minimum 0.5°C above normal for at least six consecutive months (Nkemdirim & Budikova, 1996). The 1997–98 El Niño was exceptionally strong and disrupted climate around the world.

El Niño changes the sea surface temperature and causes air pressure and wind patterns to change and perhaps reverse. That is, air pressure and wind at opposite ends of the South Pacific oscillate with El Niño; El Niño affects the atmosphere and global temperature by pumping heat energy into the atmosphere. What is strictly a local South American phenomenon is turned into an event with global implications.

Major El Niños cause high mortality in fish and marine plant populations along the Peruvian coast. In the tropics, ENSO events disrupt every aspect of the weather

and impact physical and human environments through monsoons and droughts; crops fail, forests burn, and terrestrial and marine habitats are compromised. In western North America and southern Canada, the northward extension of warm tropical waters provides greater than normal water vapour, which is associated with flooding in the west and midwest and unseasonably warm, dry winters in the foothills of the Rockies and western Prairies. Floods and droughts both negatively affect agricultural production. Continued research on ENSO events is important to improve our understanding of their potential perturbations that affect global climate.

Satellites and floating sensors are among the arsenal of instruments scientists presently use to help map the circulation of surface and deep currents in the oceans and to improve understanding of ocean–atmospheric interactions and links with climate change. In so doing, researchers have identified major elements of the ocean's circulation. In addition to El Niño–Southern Oscillation, observable shifts in sea surface temperatures affect local weather and may affect global climate patterns. The effects of these temperature shifts—the Pacific Decadal Oscillation (PDO), the Arctic Circumpolar Wave, the North Atlantic Oscillation, and Tropical Atlantic variability—on our society's use of natural resources illustrate the importance of understanding the behaviour of these phenomena (scientists continue to study them).

Any climatic temperature change has implications for the ways in which people manage their resources. In British Columbia, for example, melting mountain snowpacks provide drinking water and supply hydroelectric power plants. In warm phases of the PDO, when less snow accumulates in the mountains, new sources of fresh water and hydro power must be located. Also, the choice of which seedlings to grow in newly reforested areas is determined by temperature; foresters may see growth of seedlings slowed (or the young trees may be killed) by abrupt temperature changes caused by the different phases of PDO. Salmon stocks, too, are affected by the PDO. During a warm phase, phytoplankton and zooplankton at the base of the food chain decrease, ultimately lowering numbers of top-level predators such as salmon. PDO temperature changes are likely behind historical shifts in salmon runs. For instance, during the 1997 PDO, salmon runs off British Columbia collapsed while the Alaskan runs increased by over 200 percent. See also Box 5–9.

ACIDIC DEPOSITION

Acid precipitation is a global issue of concern in North America, parts of Europe (particularly Scandinavia), and, more recently, China and other industrialized areas of Asia. Numerous human activities—including the burning of fossil fuels for transportation, heat, and other energy needs; smelting and refining of metals; pulp and paper processing; and pesticide and fertilizer applications in agricultural operations—introduce both gaseous and particulate contaminants into the air, affecting local air quality. Whether they are common or more exotic substances, the atmosphere also can transport these contaminants long distances from their place of origin—no part of Canada is immune to atmospheric contamination.

In the late 1970s and during the 1980s, "acid rain" became a worrisome environmental issue for a great many Canadians. As early as the 1950s, scientists had detected abnormal acidity in precipitation and in the waters of Nova Scotia lakes. In the 1960s, severe losses among fish populations in acidified lakes southwest of Sudbury, Ontario,

were noted. In 1976, prompted by Canadian and international research findings, Environment Canada established a scientific program to study the occurrence and effects of long-range transport of airborne pollutants (LRTAP).

Scientists reported that meteorological conditions in Canada were conducive to long-distance transport of acidic pollutants and that sensitive soils, waters, fish, and forests were susceptible to damage. These meteorological conditions included prevailing winds that moved air masses containing acid-forming gases and other pollutants across the U.S. border from the Ohio Valley and the Cleveland and Detroit areas to Ontario and Quebec. Similarly, air masses containing emissions from central Canada and the United States drifted northeastward to southern New Brunswick and Nova Scotia.

Long-term research by David Schindler and other scientists at the Experimental Lakes Area in northwestern Ontario was instrumental in demonstrating convincingly that acid rain killed trout at acidic levels that U.S. politicians had said were harmless. The immediacy of the issue, and the realization that acid rain could affect everyone, helped ensure that scientists, the media, legislators, environmentalists, and the general public made acid rain a major focus of attention.

While the acid rain problem was first identified in the 1950s and 1960s, it was not until the late 1970s that governments funded research to determine the extent of the problem, and it was not until the 1980s that governments began to take action on acid precipitation. Since then, considerable effort has been expended to control the sources of acidifying pollution, but the problem remains unresolved—even after full implementation of current Canadian and American control programs, acid precipitation will continue to damage sensitive ecosystems (Environment Canada, 2005).

What Is "Acid Rain"?

Acid rain occurs when pollutants such as sulphur dioxide (SO_2) and nitrogen oxides (NO_x) are converted chemically to sulphuric acid and nitric acid in the atmosphere, transported, and eventually deposited. Since diluted forms of

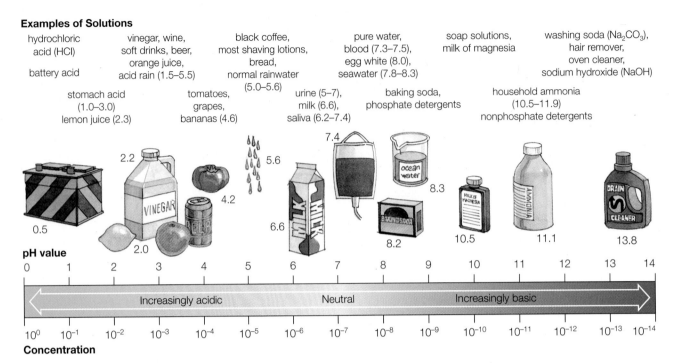

Examples of Solutions

hydrochloric acid (HCl)

battery acid

vinegar, wine, soft drinks, beer, orange juice, acid rain (1.5–5.5)

black coffee, most shaving lotions, bread, normal rainwater (5.0–5.6)

pure water, blood (7.3–7.5), egg white (8.0), seawater (7.8–8.3)

soap solutions, milk of magnesia

washing soda (Na_2CO_3), hair remover, oven cleaner, sodium hydroxide (NaOH)

stomach acid (1.0–3.0) lemon juice (2.3)

tomatoes, grapes, bananas (4.6)

urine (5–7), milk (6.6), saliva (6.2–7.4)

baking soda, phosphate detergents

household ammonia (10.5–11.9) nonphosphate detergents

2.2   4.2   5.6   7.4   8.3   6.6   8.2   10.5   11.1   13.8

0.5   2.0

pH value
0   1   2   3   4   5   6   7   8   9   10   11   12   13   14

Increasingly acidic   Neutral   Increasingly basic

10^0 10^{-1} 10^{-2} 10^{-3} 10^{-4} 10^{-5} 10^{-6} 10^{-7} 10^{-8} 10^{-9} 10^{-10} 10^{-11} 10^{-12} 10^{-13} 10^{-14}

Concentration

Figure 5–12

The pH scale

NOTE: Values shown are approximate.

these acids fall to Earth as rain, hail, drizzle, freezing rain, or snow (wet deposition), or are deposited as acid gas or dust (dry deposition), they are referred to as acidic deposition.

The strength of an acid is described by means of the logarithmic pH scale, where 0 is highly acidic, 7 is neutral, and 14 is basic or alkaline (see Figure 5–12). On this scale, normal rain has a pH value between 5.6 and 5.0, and acid rain has a pH below 5.0. Because the pH scale is logarithmic, a pH value of 3 is 10 times more acidic than a pH value of 4, and 100 times more acidic than a pH value of 5. Much of the precipitation that has fallen over eastern North America and Europe has been 10 to 100 times more acidic than natural rainfall.

Acidic Pollutants

As public concern and media attention about acid rain increased through the 1960s and 1970s—and governments responded with new emission standards—power plants, smelters, and industries began using smokestacks up to 300 metres high. These stacks enabled users to reduce local concentrations of air pollutants and to meet government standards without adding expensive air pollution control devices. Once released into the atmosphere, however, acidic pollutants could be carried up to 1000 kilometres by prevailing wind and weather systems, across national and international borders, before being deposited. Downwind of these tall stacks, regional pollution levels began to rise; effectively, the acid rain and other pollutants became "someone else's problem." Throughout this period,

environmental groups did a great deal to educate the media and the public about acid rain (and other pollution issues) and to encourage politicians to act against it.

The sulphur dioxide (SO_2) and nitrogen oxides (NO_x) emissions occurring in North America result mostly from electric power generation, nonferrous mining and smelting, upstream oil and gas operations, and transportation. In 2000, Canada generated 2.4 million tonnes of SO_2 emissions (68 percent from industrial sources, 27 percent from electrical utilities), while U.S. SO_2 emissions were measured at 14.8 million tonnes (about 67 percent from electrical generation stations). In 2000, about 60 percent of Canada's total 2.5 million tonnes of NO_x pollutants were formed during the burning of fossil fuels for transportation; U.S. NO_x emissions were 21 million tonnes that same year (Environment Canada, 2005). See Figures 5–13 and 5–14 for the distribution of SO_2 and NO_x emissions in Canada for 2000.

Between 1980 and 2001, as a result of the 1985 Eastern Canada Acid Rain Program and the 1998 Canada-wide Acid Rain Strategy for Post-2000, Canada-wide emissions of SO_2 declined by approximately 50 percent to 2.38 million tonnes, and emissions in eastern Canada declined by about 63 percent. In 2000, as part of the Ozone Annex to the 1991 Canada–U.S. Air Quality Agreement, Canada committed to annual caps on NO_x emissions from fossil-fuel power plants in central and southern Ontario (39 000 tonnes) and in southern Quebec (5000 tonnes). Canada also committed to stringent emission reduction standards for vehicles, fuels, and industrial boilers that

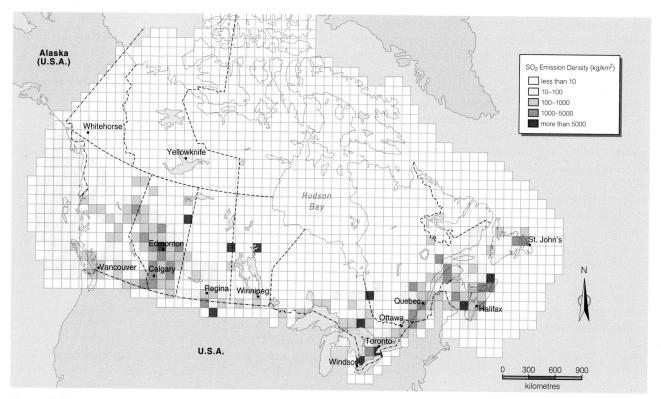

Figure 5–13

Distribution of SO₂ emissions in Canada, 2000

SOURCE: *Canadian Acid Deposition Science Assessment 2004*, Environment Canada, 2004. p. 14–15. Reproduced with permission from the Ministry of Public Works and Government Services Canada, 2008. http://www.msc-smc.ec.gc.ca/saib/acid/assessment2004/assessment_2004_e.pdf

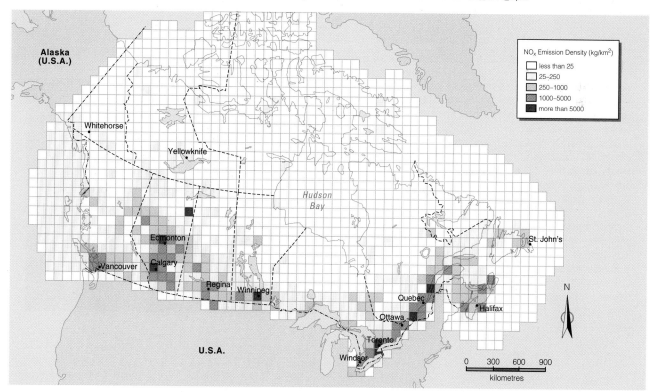

Figure 5–14

Distribution of NOₓ emissions in Canada, 2000

SOURCE: *Canadian Acid Deposition Science Assessment 2004*, Environment Canada, 2004. p. 14–15. Reproduced with permission from the Ministry of Public Works and Government Services Canada, 2008. http://www.msc-smc.ec.gc.ca/saib/acid/assessment2004/assessment_2004_e.pdf

were expected to reduce annual NO_x emissions from central and southern Ontario and southern Quebec (the transboundary region) by approximately 39 percent from 1990 by 2010 (Environment Canada, 2005).

Clearly, Canada cannot solve the acid precipitation problem alone. Between 30 and 90 percent of eastern Canada continues to receive acid deposition in excess of *critical loads* (the amount of acid deposition that a particular region can receive without being affected adversely) because of the transboundary flows of air pollutants from the United States (following the prevailing winds from west to east). Much of western Canada's geology is sensitive to acid deposition, but we lack data on both the levels of deposition and the assimilative capacity of the ecosystems to determine definitively the effects of acid deposition. Canadian–U.S. negotiation and cooperation on reducing acidic emissions and the cross-border flow of pollutants must continue if the additional 75 percent reduction in SO_2 emissions beyond 2010 required to protect eastern Canadian ecosystems from damage by acid deposition is to be achieved (Environment Canada, 2005; Statistics Canada, 2006).

Effects of Acidic Deposition

In addition to exposure to emissions from thermal generating stations in the United States, areas in the southern Canadian Shield, southern Nova Scotia and New Brunswick, and much of Newfoundland have been exposed to acidic deposition from smelters in Manitoba, Ontario, and Quebec. Because much of the region has little ability to buffer or neutralize acidic pollutants (due to thin, coarsely textured soils and granitic bedrock), many of the hundreds of thousands of small lakes are expected to continue to lose populations of fish and other freshwater species, resulting in a decline in species richness. The more than 170 000 small wetlands and lakes in the Ontario portion of the Canadian Shield, for example, are particularly vulnerable to the effects of acid rain, receiving over 10 kilograms per hectare per year of wet sulphate deposition (exceeding the critical load). This vulnerability is of concern because these water bodies (and their food chains) are important habitats for wildlife, including water-dependent birds (ducks, loons), fish species, and invertebrates (Environment Canada, 2005) (see Box 5–10). Development of Alberta's oil sands means the effects of acidic deposition may not be confined to eastern Canada; atmospheric emissions from production of oil may cause acidification of lakes and other water bodies in northern Saskatchewan because, like other parts of the Shield, soils in this area have a low capacity to buffer acidic deposition.

Acidic deposition affects some soils by removing essential nutrients through leaching; loss of calcium,

---

BOX 5-10
THE CANADIAN LAKES LOON SURVEY

Common loons are an excellent indicator of how lakes may be recovering, or not, from acid precipitation—because acid rain causes significant declines in the fish on which the loons feed. Two adult loons require more than 180 kilograms of fish during summer to raise one chick; on acidified lakes, chicks may starve from lack of food, and breeding success is reduced. Acid rain leaches toxic metals such as mercury from soils and sediments, and those metals may bioaccumulate in the food chain, also affecting reproduction.

Since about 1981, volunteers in Ontario administered by Bird Studies Canada (http://www.bsc-eoc.org/) have monitored the breeding success of loons on up to 800 lakes. Results of their work show that the proportion of loons breeding successfully in Ontario has declined, with the highest rate of decline on lakes with high acid levels. Larger lakes, even if acidified, are more likely to support loon pairs and their broods than are smaller or more acidic lakes. However, there are some encouraging signs of improvement. In some lakes near smelters (including Sudbury), emissions have been reduced dramatically and chemical recovery has occurred—increasing pH and/or alkalinity has allowed re-establishment of fish populations. The presence of fish directly influences nesting habitat suitability for fish-eating waterbirds such as the common loon.

Based on this and other research, the Canadian Wildlife Service predicts that once steady-state conditions are achieved

following the 2010 reduction in emission levels, 73 percent of eastern Canadian lakes will see no change in habitat suitability, except for improvements in central Ontario and Quebec near Sudbury and Rouyn-Noranda.

SOURCE: *The Canadian Wildlife Service Acid Rain Program*, Environment Canada, 2005, http://www.on.ec.gc.ca/wildlife/acidrain/ar3-e.html

magnesium and potassium nutrients negatively affects the health and growth of trees and depletes soil capacity to neutralize future loadings of acid deposition. In eastern Canadian areas where the critical load for soil was exceeded, lower growth of Ontario sugar maple trees, and a 30 percent lower growth rate in Quebec hardwood and coniferous stands were observed. Estimates suggest that current levels of deposition cause losses of more than one-half million cubic metres of wood, and hundreds of millions of dollars per year from forests in Atlantic Canada (Environment Canada, 2004). Studies of northern forests, where soils already are slightly acidic, indicate that anthropogenically acidified soils will take hundreds of years to recover, despite compliance with current emission reductions (Elvingson, 1999; Environment Canada, 2007b). Other soils, such as prairie chernozems, contain high amounts of calcium carbonate, an important buffer material that helps reduce adverse effects of acid precipitation, gas, and dust.

Other effects of acidic deposition include declines in numbers of fish in lakes and rivers in eastern Canada; this affects commercial fishing activities, particularly for Atlantic salmon, as well as recreational fishing expenditures (of billions of dollars annually). In addition to greatly increasing repair frequency, acid deposition on electrical transmission lines may reduce their life expectancy by 50 percent. Some of Canada's heritage buildings, including the Parliament Buildings, are damaged by acid precipitation. And, a variety of human health effects, involving susceptible groups such as the elderly, children, and people suffering from cardio-respiratory conditions such as bronchitis and asthma, place a high cost on the medical system (Environment Canada, 2004). Reduction of SO_2 emissions by an additional 50 percent would prevent 5000 premature deaths and provide between \$0.5 and \$5 billion annually in total health benefits (Environment Canada, 2007b).

SMOG AND GROUND-LEVEL OZONE POLLUTION

A highly recognizable air quality problem in Canada, smog, photochemical smog, and ground-level ozone pollution are derived principally from fossil fuel combustion in motor vehicles, power plants, and industrial processes. Considerable evidence of significant human and environmental effects of smog—including over 5900 deaths annually from stroke and cardiac and lung disease, and billions of dollars in health care costs—prompted the federal government to develop plans to minimize risks associated with particulate matter and ozone. In particular, efforts were undertaken to establish and apply Canada-wide standards (CWS) for particulate matter and ozone.

Five years into their program to achieve the standards, a federal progress assessment noted that millions of

Photo 5–10

Acid precipitation damages both natural and human environments, including important heritage structures such as statues and buildings.

Canadians, mostly in Ontario and Quebec, were exposed to levels of particulate matter and ozone above the ambient CWS targets. While some progress had been made in reducing emissions from both transportation and transboundary sources of air pollution, Environment Canada recognized that additional efforts (including promulgation of the Clean Air Act) were required to improve air quality sufficiently to meet the Canada-wide standards (Environment Canada, 2006b). We revisit federal efforts later in this chapter.

What Is Smog?

Smog is a noxious mixture of gases and particles that often appears as a haze in the air we breathe. The major components of smog are inhalable particulate matter (PM_{10}), fine particles ($PM_{2.5}$), and ozone. Sources of these pollutants include direct emissions from vehicles, factories, and wood burning. Smog also forms in the air from precursor gases such as NO_x, VOCs, SO_2, and ammonia (NH_3) (see Figure 5–15). A secondary pollutant, ground-level ozone is formed in sunlight from precursor gases such as NO_x and VOCs. As NO_2 absorbs sunlight, it splits into nitric oxide (NO) and an unstable form of O that immediately merges with oxygen (O_2) to form ozone (O_3).

Although many sources of air pollution are located outside cities (refineries, pulp mills, forest fires), there is a concentration of many different pollution sources in cities. In 2000, for example, air emissions in the Greater Vancouver Regional District (GVRD) totalled 525 000 tonnes, including 300 000 tonnes of carbon monoxide (CO), 75 000 tonnes of VOCs, 54 000 tonnes of NO_x,

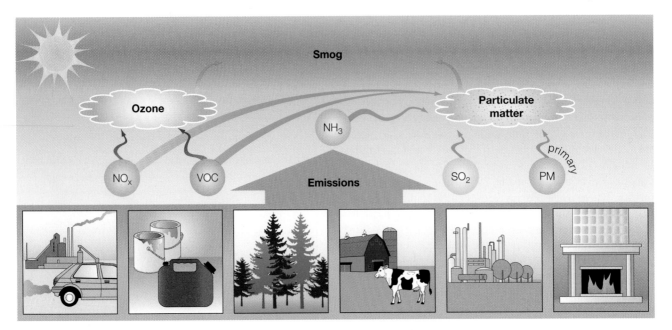

Figure 5–15

Formation of smog

SOURCE: *Government of Canada Five-Year Progress Report: Canada-wide Standards for Particulate Matter and Ozone:* iv. (January 2007), page 2. http://www. ec.gc.ca/cleanair-airpur/278E367A-B4E0-4342-9AC8-A2C2AD926488/Federal_CWS_Report_Jan_31_EN.pdf

8500 tonnes of SO_x, 88 000 tonnes of particulate matter, and many other hazardous air pollutants such as benzene and lead (City of Vancouver, 2002). Almost 80 percent of this pollution was produced by motor vehicles. One of the challenges facing policymakers is that even though motor vehicles are less polluting than they were a decade or two ago, more vehicles are on the road due to local population increases, more vehicles are being used on a per capita basis, and more of those vehicles are SUVs, pickups, and vans. Classified as light trucks, SUVs, pickups, and vans were responsible for 22 percent of transportation VOCs and 31 percent of transportation CO in Canada during 2004 (Statistics Canada, 2006).

Winds cannot always disperse the pollutants produced in the Greater Vancouver area; the result is **photochemical smog** that can stretch more than 50 kilometres out to Abbotsford and beyond. This smog can have serious health effects on humans, wildlife, and livestock, and can damage crops, natural vegetation, and buildings (see Box 5–11). Asthmatic attacks can worsen, risk of contracting respiratory diseases such as bronchitis can increase, and the danger of developing certain types of cancer can increase as well (Greater Vancouver Regional District, 1994). Although there is the immediate benefit of convenience when we hop into a car and drive wherever we want to go (rather than face the inconvenience of waiting for the bus), it is apparent that the results of our personal choices have diffuse and sometimes hidden environmental costs (e.g., diseases related to air pollution).

Canada's National Air Pollution Surveillance (NAPS) Network, a joint federal, provincial, territorial, and municipal program, measures atmospheric levels of five common pollutants in cities. These pollutants are SO_2, suspended particles, ground-level ozone, CO, and NO_2. Atmospheric pollutant data from NAPS are compared with the National Ambient Air Quality Objectives (NAAQOs) set out in the Canadian Environmental Protection Act.

The first NAAQOs developed in the mid-1970s consisted of a three-tiered approach (maximum desirable, acceptable and tolerable levels); these levels identified ranges of air quality with specific levels of effects, but were difficult to defend scientifically. Starting in 2000, a new, two-level NAAQOs framework was introduced. These levels are based on an extensive review of relevant scientific evidence, and are labeled as a Reference level (above which

Photo 5–11

Photochemical smog over the lower Fraser Valley.

BOX 5-11
AIR QUALITY AND YOUR HEALTH

Poor air quality affects us all.

Knowledge is growing about the wide range of negative effects that atmospheric contamination has on personal health and community well-being. However, many people seem unwilling to make changes that may require some personal inconvenience in order to reduce atmospheric pollution—not only for their own benefit but also for the well-being of future generations and the environment. Regardless of the future long-term negative effects of atmospheric contamination, many Canadians appear to be ignoring a very real, present, and personal reason for taking steps to improve air quality: the risk it presents to their health. Atmospheric contaminants cause death and chronic illness on a daily basis in Canada. Despite the fact that thousands of premature deaths and annual emergency room visits are attributed to poor air quality, the health industry generally has not been involved actively in promoting reductions in atmospheric pollutants.

Acid air pollution, smog, and ground-level ozone—alone or in combination—can be major human health hazards in both urban and rural areas. Major health effects of various forms of air pollution are related to impacts on the human respiratory system. For instance, research indicates that ground-level ozone increases the susceptibility of asthmatics to common allergens such as dust mites and moulds that thrive in ordinary buildings. Similarly, people with respiratory problems may suffer more symptoms during periods of high ozone levels. In Ontario, more people are admitted to hospitals for respiratory problems when elevated levels of ozone and/or sulphates occur (however, it is not clear that these pollutants are the only ones responsible for higher hospital admissions; particulates and climate also may play a role).

Research is continuing into the effects of low-level, long-term exposure to ground-level ozone and the decreased ability of people's lungs to ward off disease, particularly if the inhaled ozone has penetrated deeply into the lungs and damaged some of the alveoli (individual air sacs in the lungs where the exchange of oxygen and carbon dioxide takes place). After years of exposure, these small lesions in the lungs of experimental animals have been shown to result in connective tissue damage (scar tissue formation deep in the lungs); the implications of this accelerated aging of lung tissue for humans are being investigated.

While the impacts of acid deposition on the environment have been discussed widely, the effects of acid air pollution on human health have tended to receive less recognition. The suspended acidic particles of compounds such as sulphuric and nitric acids are small enough to penetrate deeply into our lungs when we breathe. There they may cause such effects as coughing, congestion, and constriction of the airways; increased mucus production in the respiratory system; and reduced ability to clear foreign matter from the lungs. Recent studies show that more people are hospitalized with respiratory problems on days when acid air pollution is relatively high.

Health Canada has compared children living in Portage la Prairie, Manitoba, where acid air pollution is low, with children in Tillsonburg, Ontario, where the pollution level is relatively high. On average, the Ontario children had a 2 percent lower lung function and more chest colds, coughs, allergies, and stuffy noses than their Prairie counterparts. While not dramatic, this measurable difference was followed up in studies of five Saskatchewan and five Ontario communities, where virtually the same results were found.

Other health problems derive from motor vehicle exhaust and combustion processes. Eye irritation, for example, is a result of two pollutants, peroxyacetyl nitrate and aldehydes. Particulates, originating from diesel exhaust and industrial activities, are of concern for human health for two reasons: they are small enough to be inhaled deeply into the lungs, and they act as a transport medium for compounds such as acids or metals that may adhere to them. Particulates and what is attached to them are known to cause short-term respiratory irritation.

People who exercise in a smoggy environment, such as running along a main thoroughfare during rush hour, may find a decrease in their performance due to carbon monoxide. Emitted from all motor vehicle exhaust, carbon monoxide binds with red blood cells much more readily than oxygen does. In this way, if some red blood cells bind with carbon monoxide, less oxygen may be available to the body's muscles and organs during the exposure to air pollution. Other groups at risk are pregnant women, infants, and people with cardiovascular or respiratory disease, including chronic angina. Smokers may be at particular risk because they have higher levels of carbon monoxide from smoking.

Indoor air quality can be affected as a result of energy conservation measures (more tightly sealed houses), and may present even greater health risks than does exposure to outdoor air pollution in our largest cities. As a result, attention has been given to the design and construction of "healthy houses" that substantially reduce human exposure to a wide range of indoor air pollutants. Healthy-house construction involves planning to achieve energy efficiency and healthy indoor air quality through insulation, specialized windows, and landscaping that captures natural energy. Construction materials are recycled, environmentally benign, and nonallergenic where possible. Although tightly sealed for energy efficiency, a healthy house is well ventilated through efficient air-exchange systems.

In the work environment, a variety of illnesses are attributed to "sick buildings." People report such maladies as minor eye irritation and tearing, nasal congestion and headaches, lethargy, sore throats, and coughs. Often these symptoms may be associated with building renovations, including painting, plastering, and carpeting; when combined with inadequate ventilation, the emissions associated with these activities frequently have an adverse impact on employees and workers.

Little is known about how much pollution we actually are exposed to, and how much really affects our health. Increasingly, researchers have people carry pollution-measuring devices so that "personal exposure monitoring" can be undertaken and relationships between regional air pollution monitoring data and personal exposure levels established. Such data are expected to help in assessing and developing air quality guidelines to protect human health.

effects on human health and/or the environment are demonstrated) and an Air Quality Objective (a concentration that reflects a specified level of protection for the general population and environment, and which considers aspects of technical feasibility) (Environment Canada, 2007).

Environment Canada indicated that, from 2003 to 2005, at least 30 percent (10 million) of Canadians lived in communities with PM$_{2.5}$ levels above the CWS, and at least 40 percent (13 million) lived in communities with ozone levels above the CWS. Most of these communities were in Ontario and Quebec, and a few in British Columbia. Many other communities across Canada were within 10 percent of the level of the standards. Over the 15 years of ozone data collection, national and regional average ozone levels have remained basically unchanged; this also suggests there is a corresponding "no improvement" in Canadians' health risk associated with ambient ozone levels (Government of Canada, 2006). Figure 5–16

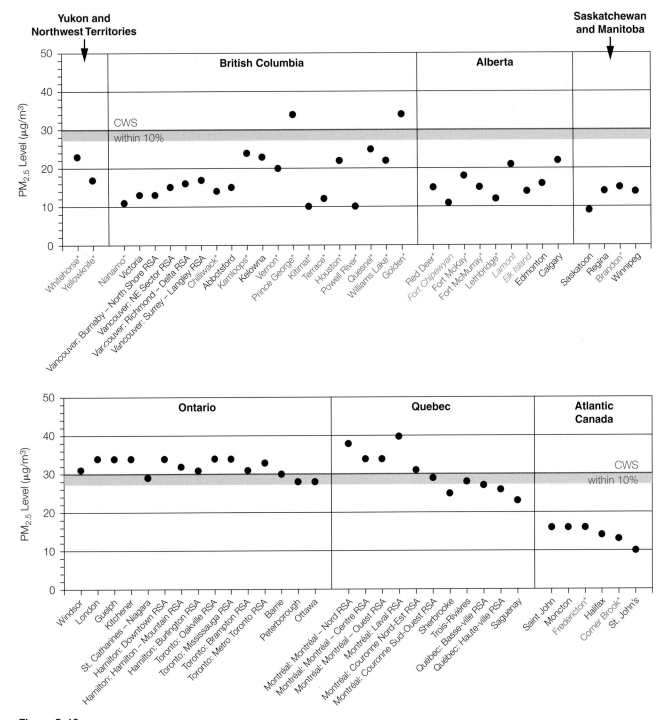

Figure 5–16a

PM$_{2.5}$ levels in Canadian cities, 2003 to 2005

PART 3: RESOURCES FOR CANADA'S FUTURE

NEL

illustrates both the reported $PM_{2.5}$ and O_3 levels in Canadian cities and subareas that are part of the monitoring network.

While very small airborne particles may be cause for concern about human health—because they are thought to contain unburned pieces of carbon originating from fossil

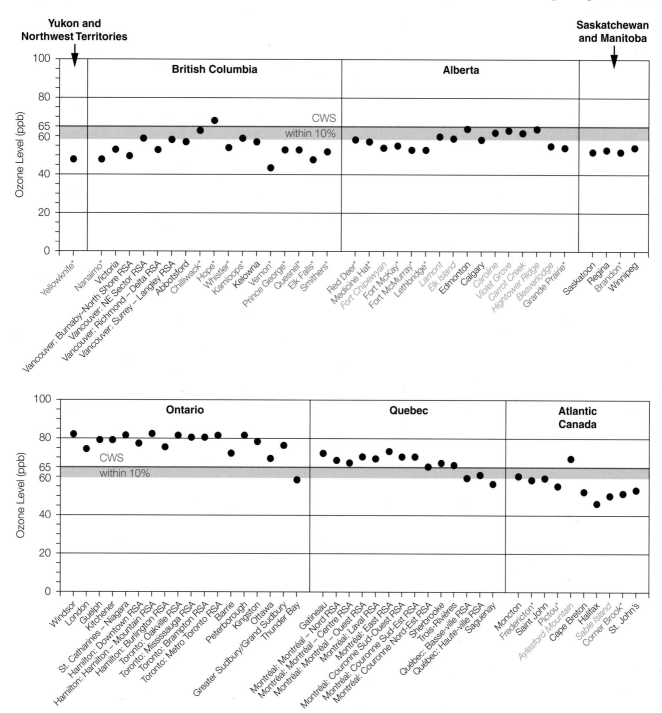

Figure 5–16b

Ozone levels in Canadian cities, 2003 to 2005

NOTES: As noted by the Government of Canada, the $PM_{2.5}$ levels shown are the "values of the 3-year average of the annual 98th percentiles of the daily 24-hour $PM_{2.5}$ based on the procedures in GDAD" (Guidance Document on Achievement Determination). Ozone values shown are "the 3-year average of the annual 4th highest daily maximum 8-hour average ozone, based on the procedures in GDAD." The yellow band represents levels within 10 percent of the CWS that are, specifically, the range 27 to 30 µg/m³ for $PM_{2.5}$, and 59 to 65 ppb for ozone. In terms of the $PM_{2.5}$ data, Kitchener and Guelph values are based on two years of data only. Community names in blue have populations of 100 000 or less, reported on a voluntary basis. Community names in green are nonurban monitoring stations.

SOURCE: *Government of Canada. Five-Year Progress Report: Canada-Wide Standards for Particulate Matter and Ozone: iv.* (January 2007) pages 26 & 29.
http://www.ec.gc.ca/cleanair-airpur/278E367A-B4E0-4342-9AC8-A2C2AD926488/Federal_CWS_Report_Jan_31_EN.pdf

fuel combustion in vehicles and heating of buildings—ground-level ozone (a colourless and highly irritating gas) arguably is Canada's most serious urban air pollution problem. The severity of the problem varies regionally across the country, depending on each city's land use, industrial base, commuting patterns, topography, season and weather conditions, prevailing winds, and location relative to other sources of ozone. Given these factors, settled rural areas downwind from large cities generally experience higher average annual ozone levels than do urban areas themselves.

Not all air pollution in every Canadian city is derived entirely from activities taking place within the city. Air quality in some Canadian cities is affected by the long-range transport of pollutants from other areas, principally the United States. The lower Fraser Valley (affected by Vancouver-area ozone), the Windsor–Quebec corridor (affected by local and U.S. Great Lakes and Midwest sources), and the Fundy region of southern New Brunswick and western Nova Scotia (affected by sources in the northeastern United States) are the three ozone problem areas in Canada (Canadian Council of Ministers of the Environment, 1990).

In December 2000, the United States and Canada committed to vigorous reductions in transboundary NO_x emissions as part of the Ozone Annex of the Canada–United States Air Quality Agreement. In 2003, the Canadian and American governments began to develop a Border Air Quality Strategy to reduce transboundary air pollution. But as long as car ownership and use continue to rise and traffic congestion continues to grow (at a pace that outstrips per vehicle reductions in energy use and airborne emissions), it is unlikely that overall levels of air pollution will continue to decline as rapidly as they have during the past decade.

PREDICTING CLIMATE CHANGE

In their efforts to analyze the climatic effects of increasing concentrations of greenhouse and other gases in our atmosphere, scientists use computer models to predict climate change and future climates. These models are based on the physical laws that govern behaviour of the earth–ocean–atmosphere system. Scientists use mathematical equations describing these laws to conduct experiments on the climate system that would be impossible (or unwise) to carry out in the real world. For instance, much of our understanding of potential climatic impacts of greenhouse warming comes from experiments on (1) greenhouse gases and aerosols (GHG + A), and (2) CO_2 concentrations doubled from 1980 levels at 1 percent per year compounded annually (Hengeveld, 2000).

The most elaborate of these models in the late 1980s were the general circulation models (GCMs), also known as global climate models. In three dimensions and over time, these models simulated the workings and interactions of the sun, atmosphere, oceans, land surfaces, soils, vegetation, and ice. Scientists used these GCMs to explore *equilibrium climate change*—the changes in climate that would be manifested after the climate system had stabilized in response to a given change, such as a doubling in greenhouse gas concentrations. Like any model, these GCMs had their strengths and limitations (see Box 5–12); they could represent some physical processes with precision but others with much less accuracy. For example, these models were unable to predict realistically the effects of global changes in climate on the subcontinental and regional characteristics of future climate and weather (Hengeveld, 1997).

In part due to a lack of computing power and limited knowledge of ocean processes, these 1980s GCMs could not simulate *transient climate change*—the behaviour of the climate system while it is changing (not after it has changed). Into the 1990s, however, a third generation of climate models known as coupled atmospheric–ocean general circulation models (AOGCMs) or, simply, coupled climate models, was developed. Canada's first coupled climate model, known as CGCMI, was developed by the Canadian Centre for Climate Modelling and Analysis in the mid-1990s. This model has been used internationally and was recognized as one of the leaders in simulation of climate systems (Hengeveld, 2000). Current AOGCM models incorporate all of the previously mentioned variables plus aerosols (AOGCM + A). Remembering that aerosols have negative radiative forcings that offset the warming influences of well-mixed GHGs, we can understand that the incorporation of associated aerosol variables is crucial for accurate modelling projections. Scientific consensus is that these AOGCMs model global climate changes with a confidence level of between 66 and 90 percent, but regional projections are less certain (see Box 5–12).

RESPONSES TO ATMOSPHERIC CHANGES

INTERNATIONAL ACTIONS

The transboundary nature of many atmospheric changes highlights the necessity for truly international action to control greenhouse gas emissions, to protect the ozone layer, to reduce acidic deposition, and to deal with other air pollutants. Although progress continues to be made in each of these areas, as noted below, a number of challenges remain to be overcome if international actions are to result in adequate protection of the Earth's atmosphere. International and national actions often are

BOX 5-12
MODELLING CLIMATE CHANGE

By Lawrence Nkemdirim, PhD, Intergovernmental Panel on Climate Change delegate (Canada)

Global average surface air temperature increased by about 0.6°C, give or take 0.2°C, since the last decade of the 19th century. The 1990s were the warmest decade; 1998 the warmest year. Most of the increase occurred in two separate periods; 1910–1945 and 1976–present but with a difference. The 1910–1945 warming was patchy, and regional; the present event is global. The largest increases have occurred in the mid- and high latitudes of northern hemisphere continents, where average warming rates have increased from 0.1°C to 2°C per decade.

These figures are in line with model projections of temperature change, due in part to a future doubling of atmospheric carbon dioxide concentration or its equivalent. Based on ensemble of climate models, the Intergovernmental Panel on Climate Change (IPCC), the international body especially created to report on climate change, estimates that average surface air temperature will rise between 1.5° and 4.5°C by the end of the 21st century (2070–2100).

What are climate models? How are they used to project future climates? Can they successfully attribute the present warming trend to the anthropogenically driven growth in atmospheric greenhouse gases (GHGs)? What are their shortcomings?

Climate Models

Climate models are physically based mathematical formulations of the various quantities, forces, and processes that determine climate and its variability over time and space. If a model successfully replicates present climate and its regional patterns and tests well against major features of past climates, it bolsters confidence in its use for projecting the climate of the future.

The climate system comprises land-, ocean-, and atmospheric-based quantities. Land quantities include the surface itself, the terrestrial biosphere and the **cryosphere** (ice sheets, seasonal snow, glaciers, and permafrost). Because the climate resulting from interactions among land, ocean, and the atmosphere does not impact the sun, the latter is not considered part of the climate system. Yet solar radiation is the most important external drive of the system.

Given the number of the variables involved and their space-time distribution, climate models are highly complex even for modest objectives. Climate models are hierarchical, ranging from the simplest one-dimensional models (latitude and height, for example), to complex three-dimensional ones involving latitudes, longitudes, and height on land and ocean. Modelling can be performed separately for the land-atmosphere system (Atmospheric General Circulation Model—AGCM) or the ocean (OGCM). In the most complex models the AGCM and OGCM are linked to produce a coupled Atmospheric Ocean General Circulation Model (AOGCM). Some AOGCMs treat only the ocean within the thermohaline, the zone where circulation, upwelling, and subsidence occur, while others include the entire depth.

Model Types

Simple models (1-D and 2-D) are useful tools for exploring relationships among the major climatic drivers. They provide insights into the consequences of change in one or more variables upon other variables and help answer questions concerning climate response to perturbation on a *global scale*. Broad latitudinal response may also be indicated. However, they are not powerful enough to simulate the impact of key processes on climate sensitivity (defined below), nor are they suited to the assessment of delays due to oceanic response and slow feedbacks. 3-D models perform those tasks. In addition, they provide transient (time-dependent) data useful for trending change from inception through to *equilibrium* (stability) as well as data suitable for regional analysis. 3-D models are expensive to run. They may require data not available at many locations, which leads to considerable parameterization (formulations representing possible system-wide impact of variables and processes observed at sub-grid level) and perhaps cumulative errors. Because their resolution is coarse, they do not capture regional patterns well.

Modelling the Impact of GHGs on Climate

General circulation models (GCMs) use data and scenarios (assumptions of patterns of future change in GHGs) to calculate how long it will take for the greenhouse gases combined to reach a level equivalent to double, triple, or quadruple the preindustrial concentration of carbon dioxide. The impact of the new concentration on climate is then assessed using the model. Key calculations include (a) the change in *net radiation* (difference between all incoming and all outgoing radiation fluxes), called *radiative forcing* and (b) *climate sensitivity*, which refers to the impact of long-term change in mean global temperatures following a doubling of atmospheric CO_2 or its equivalent. The term arises because any initial warming will impact several areas of the climate system, resulting in either the amplification of the original warming (positive feedback) or its damping (negative feedback).

Model Runs

Coupled Ocean Mixed layer—AGCM is run with the "present" GHG concentration until its response settles into a stable climate (Run 1). If the present climate is adequately captured, the model is run a second time with a suddenly increased CO_2 concentration (doubling is normal), stopping at the stage when a new equilibrium (statistically constant climate) is reached (Run 2). The difference in climate response between Runs 1 and 2 indicates the change due to CO_2 forcing. A slight modification of this procedure entails the continuation of Run 1 through the same period covered by the Run 2 but without any increase in CO_2 (Run 3). Run 3 is seen as a "control" run capable of capturing any non-GHG related climate perturbation during the time period covered by Run 2. If the coupled mixed-layer AGCM is further coupled with an OGCM representing the full depth of the ocean, a much longer time period will be required to achieve equilibrium because of ocean damping.

Model Validation

The latest generation of AOGCMs generally replicates annual and decadal temperature variability well. A comparison of the

(continued)

BOX 5-12
(CONTINUED)

results of the Canadian GCM2 against observed average global temperature data and projections by the Intergovernmental Panel on Climate Change showed that the new results are not in marked departure from earlier ones (GCM1 versus GCM2) especially with respect to trend. This appears to validate the predictive quality of the models. Similar agreement is shown by other models including GFDL (USA), HadCM (UK), and Ham3L (Germany). The small disagreements that occur among model response reflect minor differences in approaches to matters such as flux adjustment, aerosol parameterization, scaling up of small climate system processes, and representation of oceanic behaviour and its time lines. Given the convergence among several models, confidence in temperature prediction for the future at the global scale is high.

Attribution

The IPCC defines attribution as the process of establishing cause and effect with some defined level of confidence, including the assessment of competing hypotheses. In light of the close agreement between model response and observed data, can science attribute the current warming trend and its future to GHGs? To what degree can the current warming trend be attributed to GHG forcing, since it may not be exclusively free from natural ones, including external drives such as solar radiation and volcanic aerosols? Scientists have looked for answers

in what may be termed the balance of evidence. Such a balance may be sought from data in which surface air temperature is reconstructed from proxy records (coral, ice cores, tree rings, and historical documents) and matched against instrumental data. In a millennial northern hemisphere temperature reconstruction, the IPCC (2001) used instrumental data from 1000 to 1999 A.D. along with proxy records and found there is good agreement between the proxy data and the instrumental ones during the period when both series overlap. Hence the confidence that the temperature series are compatibly drawn. Second, until recently, temperature fluctuation was well within the 95 percent confidence band. This is interpreted as representing a system that is operating within the bounds of natural variability. However, in the last decade of the 20th century, temperature change has broken through that confidence band, indicating that it is unlikely to be part of the natural variability of the climate system. Third, the rate of temperature rise over the last decade and a half is unprecedented for a millennium that saw several significant trends over extended periods. Based on physical principles and model simulation, the IPCC concluded that natural forcing alone is unlikely to have produced the recent warming. On the other hand, both quantitative and qualitative consistencies between observed changes in climate and model response suggest that anthropogenic forcing is likely the lead factor in global warming.

SOURCES: The Second-Generation Coupled General Circulation Model (CGCM2), Canadian Meteorological Service, 2003, http://www.cccma.bc.ec. gc.ca/models/cgcm2.shtml; *Variations of Cloudiness, Precipitable Water, and Relative Humidity over the United States: 1973–1993*, W. P. Elliott and J. K. Angell, 1997, *Geophysical Research Letters, 24*, 41–44; "Relationships between Tropospheric Water Vapour and Surface Temperature as Observed by Radiosonde," D. J. Gaffen, 1994, *Geophysical Research Letters, 19*, 1839–1842; *Climate Change 2001—The Scientific Basis*, IPCC, 2001, Cambridge, UK: Cambridge University Press; *Increases in Middle Atmospheric Water Vapor as Observed by Halogen Occultation Experiment and Ground Based Water Vapor Millimeter-wave Spectrometer from 1991 to 1997*, G. E. Nedoluha, Bevilacqua et al., 1998, *Journal of Geophysical Research, 103*, 3531–3543.

---

interconnected and integrated in the search for efficient, effective, and equitable solutions to the problems of global warming and climate change.

Controlling Greenhouse Gas Emissions

The world community has recognized that anthropogenic greenhouse gases signify a real risk of climate change. At the 1992 Earth Summit, more than 150 nations (including Canada) signed the United Nations Framework Convention on Climate Change (UNFCCC). Although it did not set any specific goals for achieving its objectives, the UNFCCC called for nations to stabilize greenhouse gas concentrations in the atmosphere at a level that would prevent anthropogenic interference with the climate system. To prevent threats to food production and to enable economic development to proceed in a sustainable manner, the UNFCCC suggested that action should occur within a time frame that would allow ecosystems to adapt naturally to climate change. Given the rapidity with which

climate change may impact various ecosystems, the practicality of this goal is doubtful.

As a first step toward achieving these broad objectives, most industrialized nations committed to stabilize net greenhouse gas emissions (other than those covered by the Montreal Protocol) at 1990 levels by the year 2000. A variety of measures were considered, but many countries emphasized moderation of energy demand through increased efficiency of energy use. Also, replacement of high-carbon fuels such as coal and gasoline with alternatives such as propane, natural gas, and gasohol (or ethanol- or methanol-blended gasoline) was encouraged. France and Japan planned to increase their reliance on nuclear energy, while Germany and Denmark intended to increase use of renewable, wind-generated, and solar power sources. Some countries have used economic incentives or carbon taxes to influence consumer behaviour, and there have been calls for international emissions-trading agreements. The Earth Summit +5 meetings in 1997 reviewed international progress toward greenhouse gas reduction, and led up to the Kyoto meetings held in late 1997. At the Earth Summit +10, held in Johannesburg, South Africa, in September 2002, Canada's federal government promised to ratify the Kyoto Protocol and did so in December 2002.

In 2007, 15 years since the Rio Earth Summit was held, the executive secretaries of the Convention on Biological Diversity and the United Nations Convention on Climate Change stated that climate change "is recognised as an issue of extreme global importance" (Djoghlaf & de Boer, 2007). With the release of the IPCC's 2007 report proclaiming virtual certainty of the human role in global warming, Ahmed Djoghlaf and Yvo de Boer noted there had been a recent "sea change in international public and political awareness and resolve to take action" (Djoghlaf & de Boer, 2007). They believed that 2007 was a pivotal year in terms of moving the nations who were party to the UNFCCC toward the next phase of the international climate change abatement process. Of particular importance was the need to ensure a strong framework was established by 2010 to ensure continuity between the end of the Kyoto Protocol's first commitment period in 2012 and the coming into force of a future framework. Several key international meetings, including the 27th session of the IPCC in November 2007, and the United Nations Climate Change Conference in December 2007, were held to discuss long-term cooperative action to address climate change, mitigation measures, potentials, and policies.

The Kyoto Protocol on Climate Change

In December 1997, the legally binding Kyoto Protocol was established at a meeting in Japan of officials from 160 countries who had signed the UNFCCC. Under the Kyoto agreement, industrialized countries were required to reduce their collective emissions of greenhouse gases by 5.2 percent by the period 2008–12 (although there was no mechanism to deal with lack of compliance). When officials signed the Kyoto Protocol in April 1998, different countries agreed to different reduction targets relative to their 1990 levels; Canada's reduction was set at 6 percent below our 1990 level of greenhouse gases. Since emissions in most countries have increased since 1990, the effort required to get below the 1990s levels means that actual reductions will have to be in the range of 25 to 30 percent or more for Canada and 15 percent for the United States (Dotto, 1999; Environment Canada, 2007a). Furthermore, the IPCC has estimated that stabilizing atmospheric concentrations of greenhouse gases at 1990 levels would require reducing global emissions about 50 to 70 percent. This is well beyond any climate change goal yet contemplated by even the most aggressive, pro-environmental governments (Dotto, 1999).

Developing countries did not adopt specific emission reduction commitments in Kyoto, but an agreement was reached on a Clean Development Mechanism (CDM) that would allow industrialized countries to invest in projects that reduce greenhouse gas emissions in developing countries. Developed countries can then credit those emission reductions against their own Kyoto commitments because, regardless of the location where they occur, greenhouse gas reductions have the same long-term impact (United Nations Framework Convention on Climate Change, 2003).

After the meetings in Kyoto, Canada's provincial and territorial ministers of environment and energy met in Toronto to (1) approve a process to examine the impacts, costs, and benefits of implementing the Kyoto Protocol; (2) establish a credit for early action to reduce greenhouse gas emissions; and (3) strengthen voluntary action. The ministers agreed that no region of the country should be asked to bear an unreasonable burden as Canada acted to reduce greenhouse gas emissions (Environment Canada, 1998a). In February 1998, Prime Minister Chrétien established a Climate Change Secretariat, whose objectives included the responsibility to (1) develop the federal government's domestic policy on climate change; (2) develop a National Implementation Strategy to enable Canada to meet the Kyoto greenhouse gas emission reduction targets; and (3) manage a three-year, $150 million Climate Change Action Fund (CCAF) (Environment Canada, 1998a).

Signatories to the UNFCCC are obligated to report on their climate change status to the Secretariat; Canada's three reports were submitted in 1993, 1997, and 2001. Canada's *Fourth National Report on Climate Change* (2006) to the UNFCCC described Canada's policies and measures to address climate change as of December 31, 2005. However, the federal election in January 2006 resulted in a change in government and a new environmental agenda. The 2006 budget indicated that $1.3 billion would be invested in public transit infrastructure, including tax credits for public transit users. A commitment was made also to a 5 percent average renewable content in Canadian motor fuels by 2010.

In October 2006, Prime Minister Harper's government announced the introduction of Canada's Clean Air Act. This document promised intensity-based GHG reduction targets and committed the government to achieving reductions in GHG emissions between 45 and 65 percent from 2003 levels by 2050. Intense criticism from the opposition parties and environmental groups followed. Among other items, they pointed out the lack of fixed caps on GHGs until 2050 as well as the lack of reference to the Kyoto Protocol. The criticisms drove Harper's minority government to counter with an eco-ACTION plan, and to make significant changes to the Clean Air Act. Effectively a "forced" policy shift, the revised Act included "hard" rather than "flexible" intensity targets for emission reductions and severe penalties for noncompliance.

In indicating that Canada could not meet its Kyoto Protocol targets without precipitating an economic recession, and in ignoring the legally binding Kyoto targets in favour of a made-in-Canada solution to GHG emissions, has Harper exposed Canada to potential international sanctions? The Green Party, for one, challenged the government's assumptions, charging they were "economic fiction" and pointing out that "a sensible climate plan will not bring about economic ruin" (cited in Pole, 2007, p. 949). If Canada does fail to meet its Kyoto emissions targets, there are provisions for penalties. For instance, if Canada failed to meet its targets by 2012 (the first commitment period), Canada would be required to make up the difference plus a penalty of 30 percent during the second commitment period, and our ability to sell credits under emissions trading would be suspended (CBC News, 2007). We can only wait and see what will transpire during the next five years!

Protecting the Ozone Layer

Since the early 1980s, Canada has been a world leader in strongly supporting the need for international controls on ozone-depleting substances (ODSs) and in meeting and surpassing its ODS reduction commitments. On June 4, 1986, Canada became the first country to sign the Vienna Convention, a framework for controls on the production and consumption of ODSs. Canada played a leading role in developing the Montreal Protocol on Substances That Deplete the Ozone Layer, signed by 24 nations on September 16, 1987. The Montreal Protocol was the first truly international effort to cooperate on protecting the environment, and was the first international mechanism designed to address a rising global environmental problem (Environment Canada, 2002a). The protocol was the result of unprecedented cooperation between all levels of government, the scientific community, industry, and the Canadian public (Environment Canada, 1996).

The complex Montreal Protocol came into effect on January 1, 1989, and required each party to the agreement to freeze its production and consumption of CFCs at 1986 levels by July 1, 1989, to reduce them by 20 percent by 1993, and to further reduce them to 50 percent of 1986 levels by 1998. Also, each nation was required to limit its production and consumption of halons to 1986 levels by 1992. Recognizing that developing nations would need more than the specified time to control their emissions of ODSs, the Montreal Protocol permitted these countries a 10-year grace period in which to comply, and established a fund to provide them with financial and technological support. Canada contributes about $5 million per year to this fund and has provided technical assistance to Chile, China, Brazil, India, and Venezuela (Environment Canada, 2002a).

In 1996, an important milestone was reached when all developed countries (signatory to the protocol) eliminated the production and banned the importation of most new supplies of the most damaging ODSs, such as CFCs.

In recognition, the United Nations designated September 16 as the International Day for the Preservation of the Ozone Layer (Environment Canada, 1996).

The 10th anniversary of the Montreal Protocol was celebrated in September 1997, when the annual meeting of the parties was held in Montreal. At that meeting, Environment Canada released an independent economic analysis of the benefits and costs of the protocol. This study was undertaken to answer the question of whether the benefits from the protocol's global efforts outweighed their costs. The answer was an unequivocal "yes." In their efforts to prevent continued deterioration of the ozone layer from 1987 to 2060, nations are expected to avoid harmful impacts on human health, fisheries, agriculture, and building materials. In terms of health, for instance, it is expected that there will be more than 19 million avoided cases of nonmelanoma skin cancer worldwide by 2060, about 1.5 million avoided cases of melanoma skin cancer, and 333 500 avoided skin cancer deaths; about 129 million avoided cases of cataracts; and a significant reduction in illnesses and deaths from infectious diseases. The benefits from reduced UV radiation damage to fisheries, agriculture, and building materials were estimated at $459 billion. The net benefit of the protocol, shared by all nations, was $224 billion plus health benefits (not quantified) (Environment Canada, 1998b). In addition, technological innovation driven by the protocol is expected to contribute additional economic and environmental benefits.

In 2007, the Montreal Protocol had 191 signatories, and when the 20th anniversary meeting of the parties to the protocol was held in September 2007, delegates were part of one of the most successful international environmental treaties. So far, the production and consumption of over 95 percent of ODSs has been phased out, worldwide. While there has been progress in fighting ozone depletion, the battle is far from over. Reductions in ODSs take years to be reflected in the stratosphere and, because we still use some ozone-depleting chemicals, ODSs are continuing to build up. Even if all nations meet their international commitments to phase out ODSs, the ozone layer is not expected to return to normal (that is, to pre-1980 levels) until at least the year 2050—but it is expected to recover (Ajavon et al., 2002).

The relevance of international agreements to reduce air pollution was mentioned previously. Since the largest external impact on Canadian air quality comes from the United States, Canada and the United States developed specific agreements to address ozone depletion. These agreements include the Ozone Annex of the Canada–United States Air Quality Agreement and the Joint Plan of Action on Transboundary Air Pollution. Signed in 2000, the Ozone Annex was designed to reduce the transboundary flow of ground-level ozone between Canada and the United States. This agreement recognized ground-level ozone as an important contributor to smog and air pollution, and a key element in over 5000 premature deaths in Canada's cities each year (Environment Canada, 2000). The primary goal of the Ozone Annex was, and is, to obtain substantial improvements in Canada's air quality, as well as the associated public health benefits, such as fewer hospital admissions and doctor and emergency room visits. Attaining these goals requires a reciprocal arrangement between Canada and the United States (because the United States is the source of between 30 and 90 percent of the ground-level ozone problem in eastern Canada, and Canada is responsible for pollution flowing from Ontario and Quebec to the northeastern United States).

Other efforts to address transboundary air quality issues have involved establishment of a Border Air Quality Strategy, and participation in the North American Air Working Group of the Commission for Environmental Cooperation (CEC). Scientific and technical cooperation and research also occurs; for instance, collaborative research into the health effects of particulate matter has been undertaken in the Great Lakes Basin airshed, and in the Georgia Basin–Puget Sound international airshed. The Harper government has indicated that it will discuss with the Americans the potential of a cross-border SO_x and NO_x emissions-trading system as well as an annex to the Canada–United States Air Quality Agreement to reduce the transboundary flow of particulate matter.

Controlling Acidic Deposition

Canada and the United States have a history of air quality agreements dating back to 1985. Key agreements include the Canada-Wide Acid Rain Strategy for Post-2000, Canada–United States Air Quality Agreement, Eastern Canada Acid Rain Program, and Border Air Quality Agreement. The reduction of acidic deposition has focused on emissions of the two primary causal agents: sulphur dioxide and nitrogen oxides. Early agreements emphasized a reduction in sulphur dioxide. Canada–U.S. agreements that addressed the required reductions were the 1991 Canada–United States Air Quality Agreement and the Eastern Canada Acid Rain Program, a national agreement signed by all provinces from Manitoba eastward that worked in conjunction with the U.S. Acid Rain Program to cap sulphur dioxide emissions. In 1997, Canada and the United States developed a Joint Plan of Action on Transboundary Air Pollution, and in 1998, the Canada-Wide Acid Rain Strategy for Post-2000 was signed, emphasizing NO reductions as well as increased SO_2 reductions.

Current efforts to mitigate the acid precipitation problem in eastern Canada continue through the Canada-Wide Acid Rain Strategy Post-2000 and the Eastern Canada Acid Rain Program. The need to identify environment-specific critical loads poses difficulties for decision makers because they cannot implement across-the-board reduction policies (e.g., for SO_x emissions). Environment-specific critical loads are more labour intensive and take longer and are more costly to develop and implement. However, if the negative effects of acidic deposition are to be addressed successfully, researchers are convinced that critical load capabilities must be honoured. Environment Canada states that despite the more than 50 percent reductions in SO_x emissions in the United States and Canada, if further reductions do not occur, almost 800 000 square kilometres within Canada will continue to be damaged by acidic deposition (Environment Canada, 2002b). The Harper government has indicated that it will discuss with the United States the potential of a cross-border SO_x and NO_x emissions-trading system.

While the acidic precipitation issue appears to have declined in prominence compared to the current emphasis on climate change issues, it is clear that Canada continues to face significant air quality issues. We see this particularly in northern Canada, where residents and ecosystems are among the victims of long-range transport of air pollutants, suffering from the effects of air pollution without having generated the pollutants (see Enviro-Focus 5 on the next page). The importance of developing and complying with international agreements designed to reduce the effects of highly mobile atmospheric pollutants cannot be overemphasized. Developing, implementing, and enforcing effective legislation and regulations to protect Canada's air quality is equally important, and is the focus of the following section.

CANADIAN LAW, POLICY, AND PRACTICE

Election of the Harper government in January 2006 dramatically changed Canada's climate change policy. Where the previous government under Paul Martin had presented their "Moving Forward on Climate Change: A Plan for Honouring Our Kyoto Commitment" and pledged to spend $10 billion over seven years to effect specified cuts in average GHG emissions between 2008 and 2012, Prime Minister Harper's 2006 budget contained no mention of the Kyoto Protocol. Instead, the focus was on a made-in-Canada climate change plan, but no specific details were provided. CBC reported that 40 percent of Environment Canada's and Natural Resources Canada's budgets were cut, as were the One Tonne Challenge, a high-profile public education campaign on climate change, and the popular EnerGuide Retrofit Incentive program of grants to help Canadian homeowners improve the energy efficiency of their homes (Munroe, 2006).

The Clean Air Act, as proposed, outlined intensity targets that allowed major polluting industries, such as Alberta's oil sands, to continue to grow and continue to pollute while remaining under the government-imposed limitations. Following substantial criticism (as noted previously), environment minister John Baird's ecoAction plan mandated an industry target of 20 percent GHG reduction

Climate Change and Canada's Arctic

"My father taught me to read the weather when I was young. The same methods do not work today because the weather has changed, and I cannot teach my son."

These words poignantly capture the vulnerability of the Canadian North—its people and its environment—to climate change. Less reliable sea ice (for travelling, hunting, and fishing); stress on polar bears, seals, and caribou; and more exposed coastal infrastructure from diminishing sea ice are among the effects of climate change already being experienced in Canada's Arctic. In a time when the geopolitical and economic importance of the Canadian Arctic has increased, and the knowledge that the region is extremely vulnerable to current and projected climate change has grown, the resilience and adaptive capacity of all Arctic residents will be challenged as they respond to these changes.

Authors of the 2007 IPCC report stated that "the Arctic is in the early stages of a manifestation of a human-induced greenhouse signature" (p. 656). By late this century, annual warming in the Arctic is likely to be more than 5°C and greatest in winter at high latitudes. Warming will continue to decrease the length of time that snow remains on the ground, reducing its insulating effectiveness and leading to thawing of the permafrost

Photo 5–12

Displayed on a wall in the health centre at Pond Inlet, Nunavut, in 2006, this poster highlights climate-related constraints on the lifestyles and economic activities faced by many Arctic communities.

and subsequent damage to infrastructure built on it. Ice-rich permafrost was used as a design element in landfills and other holding facilities, and thus thawing of such areas could severely contaminate hydrological resources and incur large clean-up costs.

Sea ice is retreating as well, increasing coastal vulnerability to storms and affecting subsistence harvests. Earlier breakup of river and lake ice is evident, as are changes in vegetation (especially a transition from grasses to shrubs), identifiable on satellite imagery. Vegetation changes are consistent with a longer growing season and with changes in atmospheric CO_2 concentrations. Arctic glaciers will continue to melt, affecting global sea level and contributing to a freshening of ocean surface waters. Most Arctic residents now live in permanent communities, but many of these, particularly coastal Inuit communities, are located in low-lying coastal areas, making them vulnerable to sea-level changes.

Wildlife also is being affected by global warming. Many polar species are extremely vulnerable to climate change because they have specialized adaptations for harsh conditions or require specific winter snow cover or a particular timing of food availability. Both terrestrial and marine ecosystems are vulnerable because species richness generally is low; loss of a keystone species, such as lemmings, could have cascading effects on entire ecosystems. Alterations in sea-ice cover and water column properties and processes are ongoing, causing shifts in marine ecosystems. For example, seasonal cycles of micro-organisms and invertebrates are changing and leading to "out-of-step" predator–prey activities, and bottom-feeding birds and marine mammals are being replaced by pelagic fish in certain parts of the Arctic. Distribution of crustaceans, adapted for life at the sea-ice edge, and of fish such as Arctic cod that prey on them (see Figure 8–2), will shift with climate change and their abundance will diminish, seriously affecting other predators such as seals, sea birds, and polar bears. In communities where residents follow traditional and subsistence lifestyles, such changes in Arctic ecosystems have important (negative) dietary and economic effects. Consumption of country (wild) foods in Nunavut, for instance, accounts for 6 to 40 percent of total energy intake (106 to 440 grams per day) and 7 to 10 percent of the total household income (IPCC, 2007, p. 668). Adaptations are occurring already, for instance, through wildlife management regimes and through individuals' shifts in the timing and locations of their hunting and food-gathering activities. (Download a copy of the Arctic Climate Impact Assessment Scientific

Report from http://www.acia.uaf.edu/pages/scientific.html for more information.)

Species that migrate seasonally to Arctic regions rely on specific polar habitats (e.g., ponds, wetlands); if those habitats are compromised through climate change (as well as land use changes and hunting regulations), effects will be felt in local communities and in food webs beyond the Arctic. During the next 100 years, rapid rates of change are likely to exceed the ability of freshwater biota and their ecosystems to adapt to climate effects. Changes in the snow/ice/water budget, aquatic geochemistry, availability and quality of habitat, and biodiversity will challenge the ways humans traditionally have used the Arctic landscape. Necessary adaptations may include shifting from the traditional construction of ice roads to more open-water transportation and land-based travel to avoid hazardous ice conditions, altering harvesting techniques, and taking flood protection measures. New methods of access to drinking water may be needed; while considered a traditional practice, direct consumption of untreated surface water from lakes, rivers, and multiyear sea ice poses health risks of transmission of water-borne diseases to humans. In coastal communities, rising sea levels may contaminate groundwater resources.

Some Inuit people consider the adoption of climate change adaptation strategies to be unacceptable, as these types of responses affect critical aspects of culture and tradition. For instance, under the auspices of the Inuit Circumpolar Conference, and in her appearance before a U.S. Senate committee, Sheila Watt-Cloutier (2004) presented climate change as a human rights issue because many Inuit people felt climate change restricted their access to basic human needs that would lead to cultural and identity losses.

Climate change is one of several interconnected challenges facing the sustainability of Arctic communities and livelihoods today. While most impacts of climate change are perceived to be negative, there may be opportunities to increase ecotourism and cruise tourism activities, particularly as they might assist in protection of important environmental areas, including parks. As loss of summer ice may improve the navigability of Arctic waters, including the fabled Northwest Passage, cruise shipping may increase and provide new economic

Photo 5–13
Climate change may permit increased numbers of cruise ships to visit Arctic communities, such as the *Hanseatic* shown here, preparing to leave Pond Inlet in August 2006.

prospects for community members. However, as a warming climate alters the character and distribution of sea ice, cruise ships and other vessels increasingly are likely to encounter dense, hull-penetrating, multiyear ice in parts of the Arctic, including the Northwest Passage (Stewart et al., 2007). The ice-strengthened *Explorer*, the first ship designed specifically for the transit of passengers in polar regions, and the first to take visitors through the Northwest Passage, was also the first cruise ship to sink in polar waters, off the coast of the Antarctic Peninsula in November 2007. The sinking of the *Explorer* highlights additional implications of climate change, including how to minimize risks to cruise ships and tourists visiting the Arctic, and determining appropriate safety, emergency response measures, and environmental protection standards in the region.

Clearly, given the uncertainties of accurately predicting all aspects of climate change, and the difficulties inherent in identifying how politically, culturally, and economically diverse communities will interact with their environment as it changes, working toward sustainability within the Artic requires much more research. The Canadian government's investment in funding research for the International Polar Year, 2007–9, represents a good start to increasing our knowledge of climate change impacts and adaptation of northern Canadians.

SOURCES: "Polar Regions (Arctic and Antarctic)," O. A. Anisimov, D. G. Vaughan et al., in *Climate Change 2007: Impacts, Adaptation and Vulnerability*. Contribution of Working Group II to the Fourth Assessment Report of the Intergovernmental Panel on Climate Change, M. L. Parry et al., eds., 2007, Cambridge, UK: Cambridge University Press, 653–685; "North America," C. B. Field, L. D. Mortsch et al., in *Climate Change 2007*, 617–652; "Sea Ice in Canada's Arctic: Implications for Cruise Tourism," E. J. Stewart, S. E. L. Howell, D. Draper, J. Yackel, and A. Tivy, 2007, *Arctic, 60*(4), 370–380. "Presentation to the Senate Commmittee on Commerce, Science and Transportation," Inuit Circumpolar Conference, S. Watt-Cloutier, Sept. 15, 2004, Washington, DC.

by 2020 that would reduce annual GHG emissions by 150 megatonnes, and required that industrial emissions be cut in half by 2015. In addition, beginning with the 2011 model year, the government intended to regulate the fuel efficiency of cars and light trucks and also strengthen the energy efficiency standards for some energy-using products such as light bulbs. Indoor air quality standards also were to be established. Caps were to be set for NO_x, SO_x, VOCs and particulates, to be effective in the 2012–15 timeframe. The NO_x cap, for instance, was expected to be 600 kilotonnes, a 40 percent reduction from 2006 levels. Companies would be granted some flexibility to select the most cost-effective approach, ranging from in-house emissions cuts, to contributing to a technology development fund, to trading domestic emissions credits, and to accessing the Kyoto Protocol's Clean Development Mechanism.

Baird claimed that "Canada now has one of the most aggressive plans to tackle greenhouse gases and air pollution in the world" (cited in Pole, 2007, p. 956). The *Regulatory Framework for Air Emissions* document outlines the Clean Air Regulatory Agenda, "the cornerstone of the government's broader efforts to address the challenges of climate change and air pollution" (Government of Canada, 2007, p. iii). Given that reversing the progressive increase of total GHG emissions could not occur immediately, the government initially focused on short-term targets to stabilize emissions and intends to follow with efforts to reduce overall emissions from industry. Every five years, starting in 2012, the regulations regarding industrial air emission will be reviewed for their progress toward attaining the specified medium- and long-term emission reduction objectives.

In February 2007, the federal government announced it was establishing a $1.5 billion capital source (Canada ecoTrust Fund) that would be distributed equitably among all provinces and territories to assist with their clean air and climate change initiatives. From February through May 2007, the government delivered 13 announcements regarding their support of clean air and energy-efficient projects in all provinces and territories. In his March 2007 speech in Edmonton, announcing ecoTrust funding for Alberta, Harper also announced the establishment of a joint task force (between the federal and Alberta governments) to investigate new carbon capture and storage technology. The task force was given eight months to report on the economic, technical, and regulatory hurdles to large-scale implementation of carbon capture and storage.

On issues as complex as climate change, provincial interests vary. In terms of total Canadian CO_2 production, our emissions intensity per capita is the second highest in the world, and, within Canada, Alberta is the highest emitter of CO_2, largely because of its energy production industries (Government of Canada, 2006). The Alberta government has viewed reductions in CO_2 and other GHG emissions as disproportionately affecting the province's economy, particularly the energy (oil) industry. The province has argued for voluntary industrial initiatives that it believes could achieve real greenhouse gas reductions at a lower cost than legislated actions. To date, however, reliance on voluntary industry initiatives has failed to achieve the intended targets, and is unlikely to achieve the Kyoto objective of reducing emissions to 6 percent less than 1990 levels (Pembina Institute, 2000; Rainham, 1999).

In 2007, Alberta became the first North American jurisdiction to mandate GHG reductions for large industrial facilities. Accounting for about 70 percent of Alberta's industrial GHG emissions, the 100 affected facilities (that each emit more than 100 000 tonnes of GHGs per year) were required to reduce their emissions intensity by 12 percent by July 1, 2007. Not only were there objections from industry regarding the lack of time to undertake necessary technological changes, but also the proposed legislation (Bill 3, the Climate Change and Emissions Management Amendment Act) was criticized for allowing emissions to increase. The Pembina Institute, for instance, noted that intensity targets for industrial emitters would permit oil sands producers to be in compliance with legislation while more than doubling their real emissions over 2003 levels. Alberta's emissions could rise to 72 percent above 1990 levels by 2020, a significant departure from the deep reductions required to combat climate change (Ray, 2007).

In an effort to help clarify roles and responsibilities, and to ensure a standard approach to environmental protection across the country, the federal, provincial (except Quebec), and territorial governments have partnered under the framework of the Canadian Council of Ministers of the Environment (CCME) (see Box 5–13). Their intergovernmental cooperation through the Harmonization Accord is intended to attain improvements in effectiveness, accountability, predictability, and clarity of environmental management—the level of government that is best situated to act most effectively on a specific issue is assigned that issue. Each level of government retains and can exercise its legal authority within these arrangements (Environment Canada, 2006a).

The Canada-wide Standards Sub-Agreement enables the CCME to use a cooperative approach in developing and implementing consistent environmental policies, standards, objectives, legislation, and regulations in all jurisdictions. For instance, the CCME was able to develop ambient air quality standards for benzene, mercury, particulate matter, ground-level ozone, and dioxins and furans, because of the willingness of federal, provincial, and territorial governments to cooperate. Although Quebec did not sign the agreement that led to these standards, it remains committed to act within its area of jurisdiction in a manner consistent with them (Environment Canada, 2006a).

At the federal level, Environment Canada has lead responsibility for air pollution matters, but Health Canada (through the Canadian Environmental Protection Act),

Transport Canada, and Natural Resources Canada play important roles also.

Both federal and provincial governments recognize the important roles of municipalities in taking actions to improve air quality, such as developing smog management plans, investing in public transit, planning land use, and "greening" municipal fleets. Federal funds—from programs such as New Deal for Cities and Green Municipal Funds, which are managed at arm's length by the Federation of Canadian Municipalities—help stimulate innovation in environmental infrastructure projects and practices. While Montreal and Vancouver (Greater Vancouver Regional District) have received specific authority from their provincial governments to take direct pollution control actions, other municipalities (Kelowna, Calgary, Guelph, Hamilton, Kingston, Mississauga, Ottawa, Sudbury, Toronto, Waterloo, Winnipeg, and Halifax) have developed their own air quality plans (Environment Canada, 2006c). Many municipalities take part in a range of government programs, such as the Commuter Challenge, designed to increase awareness of air quality issues.

The Commuter Challenge, a national program aimed at increasing Canadians' awareness of the benefits of sustainable commuting by encouraging people to walk, cycle, take transit, carpool, or tele-work instead of driving alone to work, takes place during Environment Week each year. People in communities and workplaces across Canada compete to have the highest percentage of participation in the national event. When participants register online, they can see the contribution their participation made—for example, in terms of the amount of GHGs they prevented from entering the atmosphere by cycling, and in terms of the distance of their sustainable commute. In 2007, more than 42 000 people participated, and Calgary

ranked first in participation in the population category of 1 million or more. Other population category winners were Winnipeg (500 000 to 999 999), Central Okanagan, including Kelowna (100 000 to 499 999), Victoria (50 000 to 99 999), Whitehorse (10 000 to 49 999), and Indian Head, Saskatchewan (under 10 000). Events such as this promote thinking not only about air quality issues but also about how individuals can make a difference in their environment.

Canadian Partnerships and Local Actions

Information transfer and education programs have been part of Canada's efforts to deal with air quality and climate change issues. For instance, in partnership with

Photo 5–14
Planting seedlings for new forests is one way to help remove carbon dioxide from the atmosphere.

the Knowledge of the Environment for Youth (KEY) Foundation, Environment Canada undertook an education initiative to develop and implement curriculum materials for schools across Canada on protection of the ozone layer. In order to make environmentally responsible decisions, people need to know the purpose and function of the ozone layer and understand how human activities contribute to the ozone-depletion problem. This initiative recognized the important role that education plays in encouraging appropriate actions and discouraging damaging behaviours. The KEY Foundation—itself an educational partnership among people who work in environment, school system, government, and industry sectors—has been recognized as a credible source of accurate, balanced, and current education resources on the environment.

Training programs also have an important role to play, for instance in the recovery and recycling of ODSs in servicing refrigerator and air conditioning units. As part of a previous National Action Plan for the Recovery, Recycling and Reclamation of CFCs, more than 95 000 people were trained in the recovery and recycling of ODSs in servicing refrigerator and air conditioning units. Industry cooperation was critical in the success of these ventures, achieving reductions specified under the Montreal Protocol faster than required.

Clean Air Day, proclaimed by the federal government in 1999 in response to requests from community-based environmental, health, and transportation groups, provides a focal point for information and action on clean air and climate change issues. Celebrated each year during Environment Week, Clean Air Day focuses on local, grassroots ideas and events that promote taking action on clean air, including the Commuter Challenge noted previously. Environment Canada works with many organizations and community groups to support and deliver Clean Air Day; the partners have created their own web site (www.cleanairday.com) that provides information on reduction of air pollutants and GHGs.

Clean Air Online (CAOL) is an Environment Canada–led project that takes advantage of the Internet to help create an informed and active Canadian community. Specifically, CAOL's national website provides locally relevant, timely, action-oriented information, tools, and resources focused on air quality issues. The project links to a pilot project in the greater Toronto area, but coordinates and shares information from different sources to illustrate the links between air quality and our activities, and to support individual actions to improve air quality and protect health. While the general public is the intended audience, information on the website is suitable for students, researchers, decision makers, and industry members (see http://www.ec.gc.ca/cleanair-airpur/).

Community-level actions regarding air quality are numerous and varied, but perhaps one of the most successful has been implemented by the City of Calgary. By 1996, Calgary had a climate change action plan in place. The city took the position that even a small reduction in greenhouse gases by its municipal services operations would be one step toward the larger goal of benefiting the global community. In 2002, Calgary formally committed to reducing its corporate greenhouse gas emissions to 6 percent below the 1990 level by 2012. Only four years into the program, emissions were reduced by 4 percent, an excellent achievement given Calgary's unprecedented growth during the last several years. Recently, the city set a new target to reduce corporate GHG emissions by 50 percent from 1990 levels by 2012; when it accomplishes this goal, Calgary will become the first major city in North America to do so. Among the six key areas on which Calgary is focusing its efforts to reduce its GHGs are (1) increasing use of green power, (2) capturing methane from landfills for energy use, (3) greening the city's vehicle fleet, and (4) improving the energy efficiency of buildings and facilities.

The main contributor to Calgary's Target 50 action plan is the city's Green Power Initiative, an agreement with ENMAX Energy Corporation to increase Calgary's "green electricity" to 75 percent of its total use by January 1, 2007 (City of Calgary, 2006). The city's commitment will enable ENMAX to develop a 37-turbine wind farm in southern Alberta. This action would reduce Calgary's overall corporate GHG emissions by about 40 percent.

Calgary's action on climate change is part of its overall commitment to achieve environmental excellence in all aspects of its operations. Other dimensions of Calgary's climate change activities include a "green fleet" initiative that involves an idling reduction policy for city fleet vehicles, an ecofuel biodiesel project, and increased use of hybrid gasoline/electric vehicles. With 77 vehicles powered by biodiesel, Calgary's pilot initiative is one of the largest in western Canada. The city uses a B5 blend during the colder months to avoid gelling, and a B20 blend during warmer months. By April 30, 2006, the city had used nearly 1 million litres of biodiesel, reducing GHG emissions by approximately 16 percent per litre compared to exclusive use of petroleum diesel (City of Calgary, 2007).

Calgary's wastewater treatment operations produce methane, which the Bonnybrook Wastewater Treatment Plant captures, producing about 11 million kilowatt hours per year of green power to run the plant. Using this green power avoids the emission of over 10 000 tonnes of GHGs from other fuel sources. Another element in GHG reduction is Calgary Transit's "Ride the Wind" program that made the light rail transit system the first wind-powered public transit system in North America. The city's purchase of zero-emissions wind energy has helped financially support development of 12 windmills in southern Alberta and has avoided the production of 26 000 tonnes of GHGs (City of Calgary, 2007).

Calgary's climate change program continues to be recognized as one of the leading municipal climate change mitigation efforts in Canada. For instance, in 2006, the Target 50 City of Calgary Climate Change Action Plan was awarded the Federation of Canadian Municipalities–CH2M HILL

Photo 5–15
Traffic lanes reserved for buses, car pool vehicles, and cyclists are becoming more common in Canadian cities.

Sustainable Community award in the energy/renewable energy category, and in 2005, Calgary became Canada's first city to reach the highest milestone in the Partners for Climate Protection program aimed at helping municipalities reduce GHG emissions. City employees, particularly those in Environmental Management, who have worked with their colleagues to implement new ways of thinking and new ways of operating with respect to environmental sustainability, are justifiably proud of their accomplishments. You might like to find out what action your community has taken regarding climate change and air quality.

FUTURE CHALLENGES

In light of the potential that changes in the composition of Earth's atmosphere have to jeopardize the planet's life-support systems, the level of international cooperation that has developed to control greenhouse gases, ozone-destroying substances, and other pollutants has been a major success. Even though our understanding of atmospheric changes is incomplete (but improving), actions to stabilize and reduce greenhouse gases and ozone depletion have become more scientifically based.

However, the social and economic challenges involved in controlling and reducing greenhouse gas and other emissions appear to be formidable. Although the use of CFCs and other ODSs affects only a small part of the global economy, their elimination has been difficult despite the availability of practical alternatives. Greenhouse gases derive principally from fossil fuels; fossil fuel energy is the basis of our industrial economy. As a result, "reducing greenhouse gas emissions to the level necessary to stabilize their atmospheric concentrations will require a massive reorientation of the world's energy use away from carbon-based fuels and towards more benign alternatives and greater energy efficiency" (Government of Canada, 1996). Such adjustments could have enormous political, social, and economic costs if they are undertaken too quickly, particularly since economically practical fossil fuel alternatives are not yet "mainstream." At the same time, without decisive action, GHG concentrations could rise to levels that pose serious consequences for human societies as well as the natural world.

One approach to shifting our orientation has been proposed by Ralph Torrie (1999), one of Canada's foremost experts in sustainable energy. His vision of a low-carbon future suggests Canadians can cut greenhouse gas emissions by 50 percent of current levels over the next 30 years by using existing energy-efficient technologies and techniques. Take personal transportation, for example. Canadians travel on average about 20 000 kilometres per year, mostly in personal vehicles. If nothing is done to reduce carbon emissions in this sector, we will have pumped 140 megatonnes of GHGs into the atmosphere by the year 2030, 90 percent of it coming from personal vehicles and the remainder from airplanes. Five factors influence how much greenhouse gas we emit from our travels: the number of trips, the length of the trips, the mode of travel (walking, cycling, driving an automobile, or taking transit), the fuel efficiency of the vehicle, and the type of fuel used in the vehicle.

In Torrie's low-carbon scenario, changes in each of these factors can lead to reductions in greenhouse gas emissions. Torrie identifies three practical ways to reduce energy consumption: (1) reduce demand, (2) triple fuel efficiency, and (3) expand transit use. Easing demand for fuel can occur when people gain access to what they need and want with fewer and shorter trips. Not only can the Internet help achieve this, so can the design of new neighbourhoods (and the redesign of old ones) to reduce dependency on our vehicles (see Chapter 13). Secondly, in a low-carbon future, vehicle efficiency and the use of alternative fuels are among the factors that will lead to reduced GHG emissions from personal transportation. By 2030, fuel efficiency is expected to be two to three times higher than it is today; a new generation of vehicles will

"Our emotional, spiritual and cultural well-being and health depend on protecting the land…. We cannot find our way with band-aid solutions. For Inuit, the environment is everything." These words from Sheila Watt-Cloutier form part of the citation for the lifetime achievement award granted to her by the Royal Canadian Geographical Society in 2006. Born in Kuujjuaq, Quebec in 1953, Sheila Watt-Cloutier says she

Photo 5–16
Sheila Watt-Cloutier

travelled only by dogsled for the first 10 years of her life. The life that she led as a child was formative and she became a strong defender of Inuit traditions.

Watt-Cloutier has long been a spokesperson for the rights of the Inuit. She has worked on a range of issues, including education and health rights for her people, as well as economic development concerns. From 1995 to 1998, she helped oversee the administration of the Inuit claim under the James Bay and Northern Quebec Land Claims Agreement. She has been the president of the Inuit Circumpolar Council, which represents the Inuit people of Canada, Greenland, Alaska, and Chukotka (in Russia). Speaking for a coalition of northern Indigenous peoples in the international negotiations preceding the 2001 Stockholm Convention, she was instrumental in helping to ban the generation and use of persistent organic pollutants (POPs), which were contaminating the Arctic food web.

Watt-Cloutier then turned her attention to climate change and its adverse effects on Arctic ecosystems and ways of life. She placed her name as principal plantiff on a petition to the Inter-American Commission on Human Rights (located in Washington, DC) and requested relief from human rights violations due to climate change. This petition also was signed by 62 Inuit hunters and elders from communities across Canada and Alaska, alleging that unchecked emissions of greenhouse gases from the United States violated Inuit cultural and environmental human rights as guaranteed by the 1948 American Declaration of the Rights and Duties of Man. Although the petition was rejected by the Inter-American Commission, just two months later, the commission invited Watt-Cloutier to testify with her international legal team at a hearing on climate change and human rights on March 1, 2007.

Following years of political activism, her work has resulted in many prestigious awards: the Global Environment Award from the World Association of Non-Governmental Organizations, the Aboriginal Achievement Award for Environment, the United Nations Champion of the Earth Award, and the Canadian Environment Award Citation of Lifetime Achievement, to name a few. In 2006, Watt-Cloutier received the Order of Canada, our country's highest honour, and in 2007 she was chosen as the recipient of an international United Nations Award (Mahbub ul Haq Award) for outstanding contributions to human development. In 2007, she was nominated for the Nobel Peace Prize for her work on climate change.

SOURCES: "Sheila Watt-Cloutier: Citation of Lifetime Achievement, 2006," *Canadian Geographic*, 2006, http://www.canadiangeographic.ca/cea/archives/archives_lifetime.asp?id=159; "Speakers' Biographies. Panel 1: Enhancing Canadians' Quality of Life," *Networks of Centres of Excellence*, Government of Canada, 2006, http://www.nce.gc.ca/agm2006/swcloutierbio_e.htm

be powered by hybrid gasoline/electric engines, hydrogen fuel cells, biodiesel, ethanol, and perhaps other sources. If that hydrogen were made from natural gas, the fuel cycle efficiency would be about 75 percent, several times higher than efficiencies derived from present internal combustion engines. If the hydrogen were derived from hydro-electricity, an almost zero-emission vehicle would result. Biomass fuels could contribute significantly here also, provided sufficient attention would be paid to ensuring crops provide food as well as fuel.

Torrie's third source of increased fuel efficiency is based on a 10 to 20 percent growth in the number of people taking transit to work. Future transit systems would use highly efficient vehicles, running on alternative fuels, and provide a more diversified and customer-responsive transit system, with door-to-door, on-demand service.

On a personal level, several actions can help reduce the risk of climate change. Individually, for example, we can buy ozone-friendly products and ensure that the technicians who service our refrigerators or air conditioners recover and recycle the CFC coolants. Collectively, we will need to re-examine our attitudes toward the automobile and public transit. If communities can be designed with sustainability in mind, walking and bicycling could reduce reliance on vehicles and fossil fuels. Sustainable agricultural methods (see Chapter 6) as well as energy-efficient housing and transportation alternatives (see Chapter 13) are part of the suite of actions required if greenhouse gas emissions are to be reduced significantly and the ozone layer is to recover fully.

In addition, improved communication between the scientific community and the public is necessary. If research findings are to be applied to reduce the risks of atmospheric change, awareness and understanding must be increased. One way to accomplish this is to restore, maintain, and enhance both national and local state-of-the-environment monitoring and reporting operations. As well, it will be important to disseminate more broadly the findings of these operations. Wider exposure of results from monitoring studies, presented through school, college, and university curricula and in the media, will be important in ensuring that all members of Canadian society are aware of the environmental choices facing them and the substantial amount of work that is needed if the rate of atmospheric change is to be influenced by individual actions.

Knowledge building has been ongoing for decades in the scientific communities associated with atmospheric change, but there is a need for clear and effective translation of scientific information into laypersons' terms. Just as the international community rallied to undertake significant measures to stop the depletion of the ozone layer once they understood the implications of ozone depletion, so too might more members of Canadian society act in more environmentally responsible and sustainable ways if they possessed a better understanding of how their actions affect the environment in which they live.

TORONTO Bike Month

Photo 5–17
Toronto's Bike Week campaign includes almost 150 events that promote cycling as good for your health and the environment.

Chapter Questions

1. Why is acidic deposition a problem of continuing importance to Canadians? In what ways is your region affected by acidic deposition? What efforts have been made to overcome the problem?

2. Discuss the major causes and effects of ozone depletion (both for the world and for Canada).

3. Discuss the different anthropogenic greenhouse gases in terms of their contributions to global warming.

4. What consumption patterns and other lifestyle choices do you make that directly and indirectly add greenhouse gases to the atmosphere? What actions might you take to reduce your contribution to this problem?

5. What do you think are the most important initiatives to combat ozone depletion and greenhouse gas emissions on an international scale? Within Canada? Justify your choices.

6. In highly technological societies, is 100 percent clean air possible? Is it a feasible air quality standard? Why or why not?

Agriculture and Agri-Food Canada. (2003). *Historical perspective of droughts on the Canadian Prairies.* http://www.agr.gc.ca/pfra/drought/drhist_e.htm

Ajavon, A. L., Albritton, D., Mégie, G., & Watson, R. (2002). Executive summary, final, UNEP/WMO "Scientific assessment of ozone depletion: 2002." http://www.unep.org/ozone/pdfs/execsumm-sap2002.pdf

Albritton, D. L., Filho, L. G. M., et al. (2001). *Technical summary of the Working Group I Report. Climate change 2001: The scientific basis.* Intergovernmental Panel on Climate Change. http://www.grida.no/climate/ipcc_tar/wg1/

Bubier, J. L., Moore, T. R., & Bellisario, L. (1995). Ecological controls on methane emissions from a northern peatland complex in the zone of discontinuous permafrost, Manitoba, Canada. *Global Biogeochemical Cycles, 9,* 455–470.

Byrnes, M. (2003, September 23). Scientists see Antarctic Vortex as drought maker. Reuters. http://asia.reuters.com

Canadian Broadcasting Corporation (CBC). (2007, February 14). *Kyoto and beyond: Kyoto Protocol FAQs.* http://www.cbc.ca/news/background/Kyoto/#s7

Canadian Cancer Society/National Cancer Institute of Canada. (2005). *Canadian cancer statistics 2005.* Toronto: National Cancer Institute and Canadian Cancer Society.

Canadian Council of Ministers of the Environment. (1990). *Management plan for nitrogen oxides (NO_x) and volatile organic compounds (VOCs). Phase 1.* Winnipeg: Author.

City of Calgary. (2006). *Climate change.* http://www.calgary.ca/portal/server.pt/gateway/PTARGS_0_0_104_0_0_35/http%3B/content.calgary.ca/CCA/City+Hall/Business+Units/Environmental+Management/Climate+Change/Climate+Change.htm

City of Calgary. (2007). *Environmental Management: Major accomplishments to date.* http://www.calgary.ca/portal/server.pt/gateway/PTARGS_0_0_104_0_0_35/http%3B/content.calgary.ca/CCA/City+Hall/Business+Units/Environmental+Management/Climate+Change/What+The+City+is+Doing+about+Climate+Change/Major+City+Accomplishments+to+Date.htm

City of Vancouver. (2002). *Environmental trends: State of the air.* www.city.vancouver.bc.ca/commsvcs/licandinsp/inspections/environment/trends/air.htm

Colombo, A. F., Etkin, D., & Karney, B. W. (1999). Climate variability and the frequency of extreme temperature events for nine sites across Canada: Implications for power usage. *Journal of Climate, 12,* 2490–2502.

Djoghlaf, A., & de Boer, Y. (2007). 15 years after the Rio Summit, practical action is needed. *Inter Press Service News Agency.* http://ipsnews.net/columns.asp?idnews=37982

Dotto, L. (1999). *Storm warning: Gambling with the climate of our planet.* Toronto: Doubleday.

Dotto, L. (2000). Proof or consequences. *Alternatives Journal, 26*(2), 8–14.

Elvingson, P. (1999). What hopes for recovery? *Acid News, 2,* 13–14.

Environment Canada. (1996). *International day for the preservation of the ozone layer: Recognizing human achievement.* http://www.ec.gc.ca/minister/speeches/ozone_s_e.htm

Environment Canada. (1997). *Stratospheric ozone.* http://www.ec.gc.ca/ozone/

Environment Canada. (1998a). *Addressing climate change.* http://www.ecoaction.gc.ca/index-eng.cfm

Environment Canada. (1998b). *Global benefits and costs of the Montreal Protocol: A summary of study results.* http://www.ec.gc.ca/press/protocol_b_e.htm

Environment Canada. (1999). Stratospheric ozone depletion. *SOE Bulletin, 99*(2) (Summer). http://www.ec.gc.ca/soer-ree/english/Indicators/Issues/Ozone/default.cfm

Environment Canada. (2000). *The Ozone Annex to the Canada–United States Air Quality Agreement, 1991.* http://www.ec.gc.ca/press/000519i_f_e.htm

Environment Canada. (2002a). *A primer on ozone depletion.*

Environment Canada. (2002b). 2001 *Annual progress report on the Canada-wide acid rain strategy for post-2000.* Ottawa: Author.

Environment Canada. (2004). *2004 Canadian acid deposition science assessment.* Ottawa: Author.

Environment Canada. (2005). *Acid rain and the facts.* http://www.ec.gc.ca/acidrain/acidfact.html

Environment Canada. (2006a). *Canadian governments action on clean air.* http://www.ec.gc.ca/cleanair-airpur/default.asp?lang=En&n=3067CF5B-1

Environment Canada. (2006b). *Government of Canada five-year progress report: Canada-wide standards for particulate matter and ozone.* Ottawa: Author. http://www.ec.gc.ca/cleanair-airpur/caol/pollution_issues/cws/s4_e.cfm

Environment Canada. (2006c). *Municipal governments action on clean air.* http://www.ec.gc.ca/cleanair-airpur/default.asp?lang=En&n=8E4CBD90-1

Environment Canada. (2007). *National Air Pollution Surveillance (NAPS) Network: Annual Data Summary for 2004.* http://www.etc-cte.ec.gc.ca/publications/naps/naps2004_annual.pdf

Environment Canada. (2007a). *Climate change overview: What is the Kyoto Protocol?* http://www.ec.gc.ca/climate/Kyoto-e.html

Environment Canada. (2007b). *National Inventory Report, 1990-2005: Greenhouse gas sources and sinks in Canada.* http://www.ec.gc.ca/pdb/ghg/inventory-report/2005_report/all_eng.chm

Fahey, D. W. (2006). *Twenty questions and answers about the ozone layer: 2006 update.* http://ozone.unep.org/Frequently_Asked_Questions/

Farman, J. C., Gardiner, B. G., & Shanklin, J. D. (1985). Large losses of total ozone in Antarctica reveal seasonal ClO_x/NO_x interactions. *Nature, 315,* 207–210.

Francis, D., & Hengeveld, H. (1998). *Extreme weather and climate change.* Ottawa: Minister of Supply and Services.

Government of Canada. (1996). *The state of Canada's environment—1996.* Ottawa: Supply and Services Canada.

Government of Canada. (2006). *Canada's fourth national report on climate change: Actions to meet commitments under the United Nations Framework convention on Climate Change.* Ottawa: Environment Canada.

Government of Canada. (2007). *Regulatory framework for air emissions.* http://www.ecoaction.gc.ca/news-nouvelles/20070426-1-eng.cfm

Greater Vancouver Regional District. (1994). *Let's clear the air: Draft air quality management plan—Summary document.* Vancouver:Author.

Hamill, P., & Toon, O. (1991). Polar stratospheric clouds and the ozone hole. *Physics Today, 44*(12), 34–42.

Hare, F. K. (1995). Contemporary climatic change. In B. Mitchell (Ed.), *Resource and environmental management in Canada* (pp. 10–28). Toronto: Oxford University Press.

Health Canada. (2004). *Re-evaluation of methyl bromide.* http://www.pmra-arla.gc.ca/english/pdf/rrd/rrd2004-01-e.pdf

Hengeveld, H. G. (1997). 1994–95 in review: An assessment of new developments relevant to the science of climate change. *CO_2/Climate Report,* 97-1, 52 pp.

Hengeveld, H. G. (1998). Frequently asked questions about the science of climate change. *CO₂/Climate Report,* 98-2, 9 pp.

Hengeveld, H. G. (1999). 1997 in review: An assessment of new research developments relevant to the science of climate change. *CO₂/Climate Report,* 99-1, 46 pp.

Hengeveld, H. G. (2000). *Projections for Canada's climate future: A discussion of recent simulations with the Canadian Global Climate Model.* Ottawa: Minister of Public Works and Government Services.

Hengeveld, H. G., Bush, E., & Edwards, P. (2002). *Frequently asked questions about climate change science.* Ottawa: Minister of Supply and Services.

Hengeveld, H. G., & Edwards, P. (2000). 1998 in review: An assessment of new research developments relevant to the science of climate change. *CO₂/Climate Report,* Spring 2000, 65 pp.

Intergovernmental Panel on Climate Change. (1995). Climate change 1995. Summary for policymakers: Radiative forcing of climate change. In J. T. Houghton et al. (Eds.), *Climate change 1994— Radiative forcing of climate change and an evaluation of the IPCC 1992 emission scenarios* (pp. 7–34). Cambridge, UK: Cambridge University Press.

Intergovernmental Panel on Climate Change. (2001). *Summary for policymakers. Climate change 2001: Synthesis report.* Geneva: World Meteorological Organization and United Nations Environment Programme.

Intergovernmental Panel on Climate Change. (2007). *Climate Change 2007: the physical science basis. Contribution of Working Group I to the Fourth Assessment Report of the Intergovernmental Panel on Climate Change.* New York: Cambridge University Press.

Kaharabata, S. K., Schuepp, P. H., & Desjardins, R. L. (1998). Methane emissions from aboveground open manure slurry tanks. *Global Biogeochemical Cycles, 12,* 545–554.

Lazier, J. R. N. (1996). The salinity decrease in the Labrador Sea over the past thirty years. In D. G. Martinson et al. (Eds.), *Natural climate variability on decade to century time scales.* Washington, DC: National Research Council, National Academy Press.

Manney, G. L., Zurek, R. W., Gelman, M. E., Miller, A. J., & Nagatani, R. (1994). The anomalous Arctic lower stratosphere polar vortex of 1992–1993. *Geophysical Research Letters, 21,* 2405–2408.

McBean, G. A., & Hengeveld, H. G. (1998). The science of climate change. *The Climate Network, 3*(3), 4–7.

McElroy, C. T., Kerr, J. B., McArthur, L. J. B., & Wardle, D. I. (1994). Ground-based monitoring of UV-B radiation in Canada. In R. H. Biggs & M. E. B. Joyner (Eds.), *Stratospheric ozone depletion/UV-B radiation in the biosphere* (pp. 271–282). Berlin: Springer-Verlag.

Mills, C., & Jackson, S. (1995). Workshop report: Public education messages for reducing health risks from UV radiation. *Chronic Diseases in Canada, 16*(1). http://www.phac-aspc.gc.ca/publicat/cdic-mcc/16-1/d_e.html

Munroe, S. (2006). *The Kyoto Protocol Issue in Canada.* http://canadaonline.about.com/od/environment/i/kyotoprotocol.htm

Newman, P. A., Pyle, J. A., et al. (2002). Polar stratospheric zone: Past and future. In A. L. Ajavon, D. Albritton, G. Mégie, and R. Watson, Executive Summary, Final, UNEP/WMO "Scientific Assessment of Ozone Depletion: 2002." Geneva: UNEP/WMO.

Nkemdirim, L., & Budikova, D. (1996). The El Niño–Southern Oscillation has a truly global impact: A preliminary report on the ENSO Project of the Commission on Climatology. *International Geographical Union Bulletin, 46,* 27–37.

Pembina Institute. (2000). *Five years of failure: Federal and provincial government inaction on climate change during a period of rising industrial emissions.* Drayton Valley, AB: Author.

Pole, K. (2007). Baird introduces proposed ecoAction plan. *Environment Policy and Law, 18*(1), 949, 956.

Prézelin, B. B., Boucher, N. P., & Schofield, O. (1994). Evaluation of field studies of UV-B radiation effects on Antarctic marine primary productivity. In R. H. Biggs & M. E. B. Joyner (Eds.), *Stratospheric ozone depletion/UV-B radiation in the biosphere* (pp. 181–194). Berlin: Springer-Verlag.

Rainham, D. (1999). Global climate change: Is global warming a health warning? *Encompass, 4*(2), 15–17.

Ram, M., Stolz, M., & Koenig, G. (1997). Eleven year cycle of dust concentration variability observed in the dust profile of the GISP2 ice core from central Greenland: Possible solar cycle connection. *Geophysical Research Letters, 24,* 2359–2362.

Ray, R. (2007). Alberta introduces GHG emissions intensity bill. *Environment Policy and Law, 17*(11), 937–938.

Rowland, F. S. (1989). Chlorofluorocarbons and the depletion of stratospheric ozone. *American Scientist, 77,* 36–45.

Schoof, R. (1996, November 4). "A sea of coal": Chinese struggle to wipe out throat-stinging smog. *Victoria Times Colonist,* p. D10.

Shine, K. P., Fouquart, Y., Ramaswamy, V., Solomon, S., & Srinivasan, J. (1995). Radiative forcing. In J. T. Houghton et al. (Eds.), *Climate change 1994—Radiative forcing of climate change and an evaluation of the IPCC 1992 emission scenarios* (pp. 163–203). Cambridge, UK: Cambridge University Press.

Statistics Canada. (2006). *Human activity and the environment: Annual statistics 2006.* Ottawa: Minister of Industry.

Taylor, K. E., & Penner, J. E. (1994). Response of the climate system to atmospheric aerosols and greenhouse gases. *Nature, 369,* 734–737.

Toon, O. B., & Turco, R. P. (1991). Polar stratospheric clouds and ozone depletion. *Scientific American, 264*(6), 68–74.

Torrie, R. (1999). *Powershift: Cool solutions to global warming.* Vancouver: David Suzuki Foundation.

United Nations Environment Programme. (1998). *Environmental effects of ozone depletion: 1998 assessment.* Nairobi: Secretariat for the Vienna Convention for the Protection of the Ozone Layer and the Montreal Protocol on Substances That Deplete the Ozone Layer.

United Nations Framework Convention on Climate Change. (2003). *Proposed new methodologies submitted to the Executive Board.* http://cdm.unfccc.int/EB/Panels/meth/PNM_Recommendations/index.html

Wood, S., & Bodeker, G. (2003, September 22). Antarctic ozone hole—near record levels. National Institute of Water and Atmospheric Research, New Zealand, news release. http://www.niwa.cri.nz/news/mr/2003/2003-09-22-1

World Meteorological Organization. (1994). *Scientific assessment of ozone depletion 1994.* WMO Global Ozone Research and Monitoring Project, Report No. 37. Geneva: Author.

CHAPTER 6

Agroecosystems and Land Resources

Chapter Contents

"In the last decade there has been much discussion on creating a more stable, more sustainable agricultural industry ... that would be less polluting, would maintain (even enhance) our healthy and attractive landscape, and would be less stressful on farm operators ... even a brief scan should convince anyone that 'sustainable agriculture' ... is quite different from the present pattern, and that even moving in the direction of achieving [sustainability] objectives requires major changes in much of our present society."

I. McQuarrie (1997, pp. 54–55)

Chapter Objectives

After studying this chapter you should be able to

- understand the main issues and concerns relating to Canada's land resources and their agricultural use

- identify a range of agricultural and competing uses of our land resources, and appreciate the importance of protecting agricultural land for food production

- describe a range of effects of agricultural activities on land and associated water resources, and understand why alternative forms of agriculture such as organic farming are growing

- appreciate the complexity and interrelatedness of issues relating to land and agroecosystems, including biofuels and diseases

- outline a range of responses to the need for sustainable agriculture and agroecosystems

- discuss challenges to a sustainable future for land resources, agroecosystems, and agriculture

INTRODUCTION

Historically, Canada has depended on natural resource consumption (agriculture, fisheries, forestry, mining, energy) for its economic well-being. Since the 1960s, however, there has been a shift away from resource-based to service-based industries in Canada. From 1961 to 2000, agricultural, forest, and mineral products industries dropped from 21 percent to 11.5 percent of Canada's GDP (gross domestic product), while personal and business service industries increased their share of GDP from 8 to 14.5 percent (Statistics Canada, 2005a). Employment in the agricultural, forest, and mineral products industries dropped from 23 percent in 1961 to 9 percent in 2002, while employment in the business and personal services industries grew from 11 percent to 29 percent during the same time period. Additionally, the agricultural sector experienced a 60 percent drop in the number of farms between 1951 and 2001, and another 7 percent decline between 2001 and 2006 (Statistics Canada, 2005a, 2006b).

Despite the drop in number of farms, in 2003, the value of Canada's agri-food exports was $24.3 billion; in 2004 that export value rose to $26.5 billion, and dropped to $26.2 billion in 2005 due to effects of drought and lower grain prices. In 2006, however, the exports increased by 6.2 percent above the 2005 value to $27.9 billion. During 2006, wheat exports accounted for $3.6 billion ($2.7 billion in 2005), canola seed amounted to $1.6 billion ($1.2 billion in 2005), and exports of fresh and frozen beef and pork products totalled $4.0 billion ($4.2 billion in 2005) (Agriculture and Agri-Food Canada, 2005b, 2006b).

Beyond the significance of Canada's agricultural lands to our economy, their diversity and quality provide attractive green space and scenic qualities; offer important wildlife habitat, watershed, and carbon sequestration functions; and are linked closely to our sense of national identity.

In this chapter, the main focus is on agricultural uses of land resources and on the impacts that food (and some non-food) production activities have on sustainability of land and affected water resources. When agriculture is carried out in a sustainable manner, the natural resource base (land) is protected; degradation of soil, water, and air quality are reduced or prevented; the economic and social well-being of Canadians is enhanced; a safe and high-quality supply of agricultural products is assured; and the livelihoods and well-being of agricultural workers and their families are safeguarded (Agriculture and Agri-Food Canada, 1997a).

As the environmental archaeology of many ancient societies demonstrates, civilizations depend on the ecological viability of their agricultural base (Taylor, 1994). While many Canadians take our reasonably inexpensive and safe food for granted, and pay little attention to the environmental implications of farming (McKenzie, 2002), neglect of the physical and biological resource on which agriculture depends will jeopardize our economic sustainability (Science Council of Canada, 1992). We examine the nature of these concerns and consider actions undertaken and efforts required to move toward environmental as well as economic sustainability of Canadian agricultural lands.

CONTEMPORARY CONDITIONS IN CANADIAN AGRICULTURE

CANADA'S AGRICULTURAL LAND BASE

With a total surface area (land plus fresh water) of almost 10 million square kilometres, Canada occupies 7 percent of the world's land mass and supports about 0.5 percent of the world's people. A wide range of landscapes and ecological zones across Canada (see Chapter 3) results in great diversity of climate, landform, vegetation, mineral, and hydrocarbon resources, and supports a variety of economic activities. Environmental concerns associated with agricultural activities include soil fertility, water quality, loss of wildlife habitat and wetlands, pesticide and herbicide use, and the effects of biotechnology on biodiversity. Other effects of industrialization of agriculture and agroecosystems relate to globalization of the food system and food security. (Some of these concerns are discussed in other chapters also.)

It is important to have reliable information about the quality and suitability of land resources for particular uses if we are to use and manage Canada's lands wisely and sustainably for agricultural production, as well as other activities. One of the largest land inventories undertaken in the world, the Canada Land Inventory (CLI) focused on information about our most productive lands, mostly in the southern, heavily populated portions of the country. Completed in the 1970s, the CLI provides information regarding the long-term capabilities of about 2.6 million square kilometres (km^2) of land to support agriculture, outdoor recreation, forestry, waterfowl, and ungulates.

The CLI categorized Canada's soil capability for agriculture into seven classes. The supply of soil capability classes 1 to 3, which provide Canada's dependable agricultural land base for crop production, is 492 727 km^2, or about 5 percent of our total land area. Saskatchewan and Alberta contain the largest areas of dependable land, with 190 105 km^2 and 106 462 km^2, respectively. Ontario follows, with 76 537 km^2. Far more limited than most Canadians realize, class 1 agricultural capability lands occupy less than 1 percent (49 048 km^2) of Canada's total land area. Of class 1 land in Canada, 56 percent (27 635 km^2) is located in southern Ontario. Saskatchewan (12 282 km^2) and Alberta (6 719 km^2) also contain significant class 1 land areas (Statistics Canada, 2005b). Another 2 percent of

land (although not as suitable as classes 1, 2, or 3 land) is used for agriculture in Canada (Hoffman, 2001). Figure 6–1 illustrates the location of agricultural areas within Canada, while the amount of dependable agricultural land (in CLI classes 1 to 3) in each province is identified in Table 6–1.

It is worth noting that Canada does not have any vast agricultural reserves; virtually all the land that is amenable to agricultural production and that has not been built on or paved over is in agricultural use. As Canadian cities and towns expanded between 1971 and 2001, urban uses such as suburbs and shopping centres occupied 31 087 km^2 of land and covered 14 300 km^2 (about 3 percent) of our dependable agricultural land. By 2001, 7.5 percent of Canada's best (CLI class 1) agricultural land was lost due to urbanization, including losses of more than 11 percent of Ontario's class 1 land, close to 7 percent of Alberta's, and more than 2 percent of Manitoba's (Statistics Canada, 2005b). In practical terms, land used for urban purposes is lost permanently to agriculture. This is partly because construction of houses and other buildings, installation of sewage systems, and paving land destroy the soil structure and make reclamation for agriculture too expensive.

Despite the impression given by the preceding statistics, there are limited data about how much land suitable for agriculture actually is being farmed, and there is no current national database identifying how much land really is available for agricultural use. This is an important gap in knowledge, given that expanding human needs and economic activities have put increasing pressures on land, and that achieving sustainable agricultural uses of land depends, in part, on reliable data.

Conflicting land uses have heightened many Canadians' awareness of the necessity of balancing competing demands on our limited land if we are to maintain both a healthy environment and a prosperous economy. The resulting challenge for sustainable agriculture is to maintain and enhance the quality of Canada's finite agricultural soils as well as the air, water, and biodiversity resources that are part of our agroecosystems.

Agroecosystems are communities of living organisms, together with the physical resources that sustain them, such as biotic and abiotic elements of the underlying soils and drainage networks, that are managed for the purpose of producing food, fibre, and other agricultural products. These are complex and dynamic ecological processes and systems, with many interrelationships; any action in one component of an agroecosystem affects other components and ecosystems. For example, a farmer's decision to use management practices such as fertilizers or pesticides is influenced by his or her access to technology, as well as by the economics of the marketplace and government policy. Such management practices affect the health of agroecosystems and, ultimately, the productivity and sustainability of agriculture in Canada.

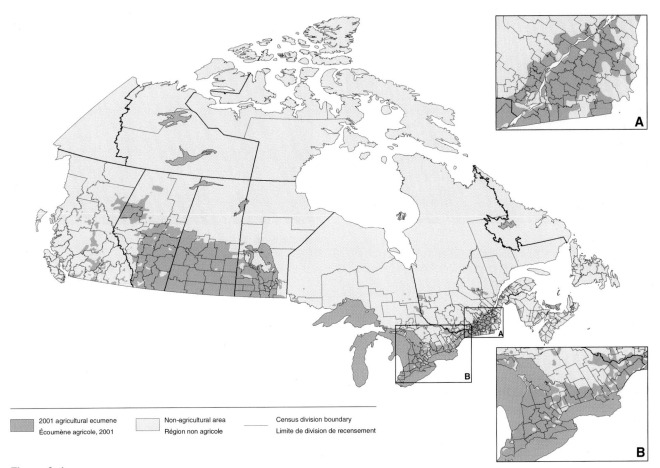

Figure 6–1

Canada's agricultural land, 2001

SOURCE: *Canadian Agriculture at a Glance*, Statistics Canada, 2004, Cat. no. 96-325-XPB, p. 15.

T A B L E   6 – 1

CANADA LAND INVENTORY: DEPENDABLE AGRICULTURAL LAND (KM², BY PROVINCE[1])

Agricultural Land Capability Class[2]	NF	PE	NS	NB	PQ	ON	MB	SK	AB	BC	Canada
1	0	0	0	0	223	27635	2111	12282	6719	78	49048
2	0	2626	1700	2056	10713	23335	29617	73341	38704	1574	183667
3	67	1422	10219	13823	13625	25567	24499	104482	61039	5270	260012
Total	67	4048	11920	15879	24560	76537	56228	190105	106462	6922	497727
(% of total)	(0.0)	(0.8)	(2.4)	(3.2)	(5.0)	(15.5)	(11.4)	(38.6)	(21.6)	(1.4)	(100)

NOTE: Figures may not add up due to rounding.

[1] The territories (Yukon Territory, Northwest Territories, and the Territory of Nunavut) are not covered by the CLI.

[2] Land capability classes 1, 2, and 3 are Canada's prime agricultural lands containing the best soils with the highest potential to produce varied crops now and in the future. Saskatchewan possesses the largest amount of these dependable agricultural lands, followed by Alberta, Ontario, and Manitoba. In general, dependable agricultural lands are located where climatic conditions are favourable for farming. Class 1 land is Canada's only land with no significant constraints (e.g., climate, soil quality) to crop production.

SOURCES: "The loss of dependable agricultural land in Canada," *Rural and Small Town Canada Analysis Bulletin, 6*(1) Statistics Canada, 2005, http://www.statcan.ca/english/freepub/21-006-XIE/21-006-XIE2005001.pdf

Photo 6–1a

Photo 6–1b

Canada depends on a small percentage of good-quality land to support agriculture such as in the Fraser River delta (Photo 6-1a) and the St. Lawrence River valley (Photo 6-1b). Balancing competing demands for land is a necessity if both a healthy environment and a prosperous economy are to exist.

THE CHANGING NATURE OF CANADIAN AGRICULTURE

Creating a sustainable agricultural industry in Canada requires an ability not only to identify and alleviate environmental challenges but also to understand and deal with technological and socioeconomic changes in the agricultural sector. Accordingly, before considering human activities and impacts on agricultural environments, we briefly identify the issues that characterize contemporary North American agriculture and review the nature of technological and socioeconomic changes encountered within Canadian agriculture.

Table 6–2 summarizes a range of economic, environmental, and social issues that characterize contemporary agriculture. The message of this table is that although we have achieved dramatic increases in short-term food production, conventional agricultural technologies have done so by increasing long-term social and environmental costs in soil degradation, loss of arable land, use of an increasingly controlled and select number of species, a greater reliance on chemicals, and increased financial debt (Alasia & Rothwell, 2003; Hoffman, 2001).

Since the 1960s, the total area of Canada's agricultural land has remained stable at about 676 000 km². However, changes in the social, economic, and technological conditions associated with the industrialization of agriculture in Canada have been reflected in a decrease in the number, and a growth in the size, of farms in Canada. As farmers have been squeezed by increasing costs and declining returns (on average, in 2005, farmers spent 86 cents in operating expenses for a return of one dollar in gross farm receipts), they have been challenged to increase their farm production in order to maintain a favourable expenses-to-receipts ratio. With expenses rising faster than revenues, both the number of farms and the number of farm operators in Canada continued their decades-long decline; another 17 550 farms were lost and over 19 000 people left farming between 2001 and 2006. Average farm size has increased from 50 hectares in 1901 to 295 hectares in 2006 (Statistics Canada, 2002c, 2006b). This situation reflects the influences that economic systems have on human behaviour and points to the potential of economic concerns to compromise environmental sustainability. For more data on the nature of Canadian farming in 2006, see Box 6–1 on pp. 202–203.

Blueberries have overtaken apples in terms of area devoted to fruit production; in 2006, apples were grown on 54 612 acres (a drop of 14.4 percent since 2001), while blueberries were grown on 126 745 acres (an increase of 16.7 percent since 2001). The area devoted to grapes rose 14.9 percent between 2001 and 2006; about 70 percent of the 30 059 acres are located in southern Ontario. British Columbia is home to about 27 percent of the vines, but grape areas also have spread into Quebec (2 percent) and Nova Scotia (1 percent). Wineries in both Ontario and British Columbia enjoy world-class reputations, and wine tourism (where vineyards have their own wineries to sell their products and offer tours and cooking classes) helps add value to the basic grape crop. British Columbia's cranberries, accounting for over 54 percent of Canada's crop in 2001, were grown on 7453 acres; Quebec's cranberry crop accounted for 35 percent of the Canadian total. Plantings of Saskatoon berries increased almost 80 percent between 1996 and 2001, to 2937 acres. The three Prairie provinces accounted for almost 95 percent of the Saskatoon berries used to make jams and jellies (Statistics Canada, 2002c, 2007b).

Eastern Canada has remained the key poultry and egg-producing region of Canada; in 2006, farmers reported

TABLE 6-2

ECONOMIC, ENVIRONMENTAL, AND SOCIAL ISSUES THAT CHARACTERIZE CONTEMPORARY NORTH AMERICAN AGRICULTURE

Economic	Environmental	Social
• Technologically efficient crop production • Increased crop specialization and reliance on monocultures • Increased dependence on fossil fuels, chemical fertilizers/pesticides, and borrowed capital • Reduced profitability; dramatic increases in input costs but low farm produce prices contribute to financial stress among farmers • Increasingly mechanized and industrialized approach to food production • Reliance on canola oil, durum wheat, and a few others as major export crops • Security of food supply and agricultural economy at risk • Export markets subject to foreign protectionism • Increased reliance on imports (often of foods that could be grown here) • Production of food almost totally dependent on oil and gas (to provide chemicals and machinery, and to process and distribute farm products)	• Decline in soil productivity • Growing dangers to animal and human health (chemical and biological risks such as Bovine Spongiform Encephalopathy) • Increased vulnerability of plants, especially monocultures, to climatic changes, increasing frequency of extreme weather events, and new diseases • Ongoing requirement by corporate-based seed banks to use custom-designed fertilizers and pesticides • Reduced long-term resilience due to decreased genetic diversity in plants • Increased use of biotechnology and genetically modified organisms • Surface and groundwater contamination by fertilizers, herbicides, and pesticides • Loss of wildlife habitat • Combined effects of soil erosion, acidification, compaction, salinization, and irrigation cost taxpayers over $1 billion per year • Use of farm chemicals and runoff resulting in sediment damage to inland lakes and waterways, loss of recreational fishing, increased water treatment, and dredging costs • Loss of land to urbanization	• Crushing debt burden • Income disparity between rural and urban dwellers increasingly favours urban populations • Rapid disappearance of family farm, rural life • Loss of agricultural land to encroaching urban development, transportation networks, airports, and industrial parks • Almost 50% of land converted to urban use was formerly prime agricultural land • Growing concern about pesticide safety and soil degradation • Concern about long-term effects of agricultural chemicals on human health and the environment (e.g., nitrates in groundwater) • Growth of alternative farming techniques, partly due to increase in public demand for organic products • Goal of long-term stewardship of land for future generations

SOURCES: "The Rural/Urban Divide Is Not Changing: Income Disparities Persist," A. Alasia & N. Rothwell, 2003, *Rural and Small Town Canada Analysis Bulletin, 4*(4), 1; *Environmental Politics in Canada: Managing the Commons into the Twenty-First Century,* J. I. McKenzie, 2002, Don Mills: Oxford University Press; *Farming Facts 2002,* Statistics Canada, 2003, Ottawa: Minister of Industry; *Off Course: Restoring Balance between Canadian Society and the Environment,* D. M. Taylor, 1994, Ottawa: International Development Research Centre.

raising 125.3 million hens and chickens. A record 15.8 million head of cattle were reported on Canadian farms in 2006, and 15 million hogs, another record high number. Alberta accounted for 34 percent of Canada's national beef herd and 14 percent of its sheep (Ontario has about 37 percent of Canada's 1.1 million sheep). The number of dairy cows in Canada declined by 6 percent between 2001 and 2006, but milk production remained reasonably steady because of improved genetics and better animal nutrition. Nontraditional livestock has become more popular, with goats (almost 183 000 of them) kept for meat and milk, and llamas for their meat and wool (Statistics Canada, 2002c). Also, following the outbreak of "mad cow" disease in Europe, bison were perceived as healthier choices by

markets in France, Belgium, Germany, and Britain. Bison numbers grew almost 35 percent to 195 728 between 2001 and 2006. For information on "mad cow" disease in Canada, see Box 6–2 on page 204.

As a result of technological and socioeconomic changes, the Canadian agriculture and *agri-food industry*—farmers, suppliers, processors, transporters, grocers, and restaurant workers—employed nearly 2.1 million people and generated about $95 billion in 2002 (Statistics Canada, 2003b). Canada's top agri-food exports in 2004 were nondurum wheat, fresh boneless beef, canola seed, frozen fries, fresh pork, frozen pork, durum wheat, biscuits and crackers, and food preparations. Agri-food has become one of the top five industries in Canada,

BOX 6-1

A SNAPSHOT OF AGRICULTURE IN CANADA IN 2006

In May 2007, Statistics Canada released new data from the 2006 Census of Agriculture. Conducted every five years, just like our population census, the agriculture census provides comprehensive information about farm operations and operators as well as national and provincial trends across Canada. Here is a snapshot of some key characteristics of Canadian agriculture in 2006 (with comparisons to 2001 as appropriate).

Canadian Farmers

The average age of farm operators increased from 49.9 to 52.0 years between 2001 and 2006. In 2006, women made up 27.8 percent Canadian farmers, an increase of 1.5 percent since 2001. Farmers increasingly used computers for their farm business, rising to 46.4 percent in 2006 from 39.4 percent in 2001. Over 75 percent of farmers used their computers to search the Internet for information to help them make decisions regarding their farm business.

Canadian Farm Operations

Canada has 16 tractors per 1000 hectares, the fewest tractors per thousand hectares among the G7 countries. The United States reports 27, France 69, Germany 80, the United Kingdom 87, Italy 200, and Japan 459 tractors per hectare (the world record). These numbers demonstrate the extensification (not intensification) of Canadian agriculture—our farms are relatively large with tractors that can farm more hectares per machine.

Canada had 5902 million-dollar farms in 2006; they accounted for 2.6 percent of all farms and 39.7 percent of total farm receipts. Yet overall, the number of farms in Canada decreased between 2001 and 2006, as Box Table 6-1 reveals.

BOX TABLE 6-1
NUMBER OF FARMS BY PROVINCE, 2001 AND 2006

Province	Number of Farms 2001	Number of Farms 2006	Percentage Change from 2001 to 2006
Newfoundland and Labrador	643	558	−13.2
Prince Edward Island	1 845	1 700	−7.9
Nova Scotia	3 923	3 795	−3.3
New Brunswick	3 034	2 776	−8.5
Quebec	32 139	30 675	−4.6
Ontario	59 728	57 211	−4.2
Manitoba	21 071	19 054	−9.6
Saskatchewan	50 598	44 329	−12.4
Alberta	53 652	49 431	−7.9
British Columbia	20 290	19 844	−2.2
Canada	246 923	229 373	−7.1

BOX TABLE 6-2
TYPES OF FARMS IN CANADA, 2001 AND 2006

Farm Type	Number of Farms 2001	Number of Farms 2006	Percentage of Total Farms 2001	Percentage of Total Farms 2006
Cattle ranching and farming	86 159	75 598	34.9	33.0
Hog and pig farming	7 388	6 040	3.0	2.6
Poultry and egg production	4 937	4 578	2.0	2.0
Sheep and goat farming	4 143	3 815	1.7	1.7
Other animal production	22 703	26 779	9.2	11.7
Oilseed and grain farming	69 671	61 667	28.2	26.9
Vegetable and melon farming	5 031	5 239	2.0	2.3
Fruit and tree-nut farming	7 743	8 329	3.1	3.6
Greenhouse, nursery, and floriculture production	8 889	8 754	3.6	3.8
Other crop farming	30 259	28 574	12.3	12.5
Total	246 923	229 373	100.0	100.0

Field crop farms made up the largest percentage of Canadian farms in 2006 (see Box Table 6-2). The top field crops, by area farmed (hectares), were wheat (9 852 200), hay (8 237 000), canola (5 027 200), and barley (3 689 900). The top fruits, by area farmed (hectares), were blueberries (110 069), apples (22 100), grapes (12 164), and strawberries (5204). Demand for year-round, high-quality products has boosted greenhouse production of vegetables—by 2006, operators (mostly in Ontario) were growing vegetables under plastic and glass on more than 22 million square metres, the equivalent of 2727 Canadian football fields.

Demand for corn (and prices) rose in late 2006 and early 2007, driven by the expanding corn-derived ethanol fuel sector in the United States. While most Canadian corn is grown in Ontario and Quebec, new plant varieties enabled farmers to expand the zones in which corn was produced in Manitoba, Nova Scotia, New Brunswick, and Saskatchewan. Potato farming, however, decreased in Canada. In 2003, after 15 years of continuous expansion in the world's appetite for French fries, the rising Canadian dollar caused American buyers to source more of their potatoes internally, in turn causing farmers in Prince Edward Island, Nova Scotia, Ontario, Saskatchewan, Alberta, and British Columbia to reduce the area planted with potatoes.

Honeybees and leafcutting bees are used for pollination of crops. Farmers kept 553 594 colonies of honeybees in 2006,

BOX 6-1
(CONTINUED)

BOX TABLE 6-3
LIVESTOCK AND POULTRY INVENTORIES, 2001 AND 2006

	2001	2006
Cattle	15 551 449	15 773 527
Sheep	1 262 448	1 142 877
Pigs	13 958 772	15 043 132
Chickens	126 159 529	125 314 793

BOX TABLE 6-4
ORGANIC FARMING IN CANADA, 2006

Certification Status	Number of Farms	Percentage of All Farms in Canada
Certified organic	3 555	1.5
Organic but not certified	11 937	5.2
Transitional	640	0.3

71.5 percent of which were located in the Prairies. Saskatchewan had 55.6 percent of Canada's leafcutting bees (used exclusively for pollination of alfalfa plants), but blueberry producers in eastern Canada also are using leafcutting bees to help increase fruit set, and leafcutter pollination is proving successful in some vegetable seed production (e.g., carrot and onion).

In terms of livestock production, chickens are most numerous (see Box Table 6–3); 25.9 million hens lay the 13 dozen eggs consumed annually by each Canadian.

Organic farming is a small segment of Canadian agricultural production, but one of the industry's goals is to increase its market share to 10 percent of the Canadian retail market by 2010. **Certified organic** products have been accredited officially as conforming to specified requirements (such as using natural fertilizers and raising animals in conditions that mimic nature as much as possible), and contain at least 95 percent organic ingredients. **Transitional** products come from producers who have not yet attained certified organic status, but who are establishing organic management practices in accordance with standards (see Box Table 6–4).

Land Management

Almost 77 percent of all cattle are in western Canada, where just over half (54.3 percent) of the solid manure produced from these operations is spread over 5.6 million acres of land. Hog and dairy operations typically spread liquid manure; in 2006, over 2.7 million acres of land received liquid application.

Spreading manure over larger areas helps improve nutrient management and enables operators to meet various provincial regulations.

Another land management measure is zero tillage (or no tillage), where crop residues are left on the soil surface to trap moisture, contribute to soil organic matter, protect against erosion, and thereby improve farmers' incomes (see Box Table 6–5 and Box 6–8).

Irrigated land in Alberta accounts for 63.5 percent of the national total. Ontario accounts for 45.3 percent of the total irrigated vegetable area, while British Columbia accounts for 52.8 percent of the total irrigated fruit area.

BOX TABLE 6-5
CHANGING TILLAGE TECHNIQUES, 1996, 2001, AND 2006

Type of Tillage	Percentage of Area Worked		
	1996	2001	2006
Conventional (plowing deep, wide furrows)	53	40	28
Conservation (midpoint between conventional and no-till)	31	30	26
No-till (thin slit in soil)	16	30	46

SOURCE: *Canadian Agriculture in 2005: A Tough Year in Review*, V. Mitura & M. Trant, 2006, Statistics Canada, Cat. no. 21-004-XIE; *Snapshot of Canadian Agriculture*, Statistics Canada, 2007, http://www.statcan.ca/english/agcensus2006/articles/snapshot.htm

accounting for about 8.1 percent of the gross domestic product (Agriculture and Agrifood Canada, 2006c). Farmers have seen net farm incomes increase from $2.461 billion in 2000 to $2.625 billion in 2005 (Statistics Canada, 2006). International trade agreements such as the North American Free Trade Agreement and the World Trade Organization Agreement also have important economic and environmental influences on Canadian agriculture (see Box 6–2).

Such changes have resulted in a move from mixed farming to specialized systems such as **monoculture** farming (cultivation of one species over a large area) and megafarms (consolidated farms). In terms of monoculture farming, Saskatchewan grows almost 51 percent of Canada's wheat (excluding durum). Western Canada (provinces west of Ontario) contains about 73 percent of the total hay area, while Eastern Canada (provinces east of Manitoba) accounts for about 98 percent of the soybean area and 96 percent of Canada's corn area (Statistics Canada, 2003a). One of the problems facing monoculture farming is that plants of a single species are highly susceptible to insects and diseases. Megafarms have brought another important change: in Canada, about 8 percent of farms occupy about 43 percent of all farmland, and although only 2.6 percent of farms had gross receipts of over $1 million in 2006, they accounted for nearly 40 percent of all agricultural receipts (Statistics Canada, 2003a, 2007c). These data mean that a small proportion of farmers actually determines whether sustainable practices are applied on almost half of Canada's finite agricultural lands (Government of Canada, 1996; Statistics Canada, 2000).

Since the 1960s some important changes in agricultural land use have occurred in Canada. For example, farmlands near urban centres frequently were converted to residential, commercial, and industrial uses; land that subsequently was brought into agricultural production tended to be of lower quality. Another important change is

that land uses have been changing. Farmers have reduced the amount of land on which they grow crops, from about 36.4 million hectares in 2001 to just over 35.9 million hectares in 2006. A third major change is that the area devoted to **summerfallow** (land not sown for at least one year to conserve soil moisture and to enhance nitrogen accumulation, chiefly a Prairie practice) has continued to decline (by 25.1 percent from 2001 to 2006). Farmers made this change partly on the basis of evidence that summerfallowing contributed to soil **salinization** (see the discussion of soil quality on pp. 214–215). The decline in summerfallow land also reflects technological changes and farmers' increasing use of no-till and other conservation seeding practices (these practices retain soil moisture but do not require the land to remain idle for a year). The economic need to keep arable land productive, in combination with diversified and extended crop rotations, improved seeding and tilling methods, and proper use of herbicides, also have contributed to reduced summerfallow land (Statistics Canada, 2007).

BOX 6–2
BOVINE SPONGIFORM ENCEPHALOPATHY (BSE) IN CANADA

Changes in the way we inhabit the planet have disrupted the equilibrium of the microbial world. Microbes proliferate rapidly, mutate frequently, and adapt with relative ease to new environments and hosts. They are quick to exploit new opportunities to change and spread. Numerous factors, including those linked to human activities, can accelerate and amplify these natural phenomena, as has happened in recent years. Trends contributing to renewed microbial threat include rapid population growth, rural-urban migration, international travel and trade, collapsing health systems, environmental manipulation, changing weather patterns, misuse of medicines, and altered agricultural and animal husbandry practices.

These changes have produced ideal conditions for human-to-human transmission of diseases, created new breeding sites for insects and other vectors that carry disease, and encouraged the emergence of antimicrobial resistance. They have also disrupted ecological systems in which pathogens and natural animal hosts have coexisted in equilibrium for centuries.

As a result, new diseases are emerging at an unprecedented rate. In the last decades of the 20th century, more than 30 new diseases—including HIV/AIDS and Ebola haemorrhagic fever—were detected for the first time in history. Bovine spongiform encephalopathy ... is one of these newly emerging diseases.

—World Health Organization, 2002

What Is BSE?

BSE ("mad cow disease") is a progressive, fatal disease of the nervous system of cattle and other ruminants[1], characterized by spongy degeneration of brain tissue. BSE belongs to the group of diseases known as transmissible spongiform encephalopathies (TSEs). Scrapie is a TSE that has affected sheep and goats for over 200 years, and chronic wasting disease (CWD), a relatively new TSE first identified in 1967 in deer in Colorado research facilities, affects cervids such as mule deer, whitetail deer, and elk. There are no tests to determine whether living animals are affected (diagnosis is confirmed by microscopic examination of an animal's brain after its death), and there are no treatments or vaccines for these diseases. The time between an animal's exposure to BSE and the onset of clinical signs (such as nervous or aggressive behaviour, abnormal posture, lack of coordination or difficulty in rising from a lying position, decreased milk production, and weight loss despite an increased appetite) usually is four to five years (World Health Organization, 2002).

While not considered contagious, BSE is linked to variant Creutzfeldt-Jakob disease (vCJD) in humans. A rare and fatal form of TSE that was first diagnosed in 1996 in people who lived in the United Kingdom and France, vCJD is thought to be linked to the consumption of meat products derived from BSE-infected cattle.

What Is the Origin of BSE?

Research indicates that the first probable infections of BSE in cows occurred in the 1970s, with two cases of BSE detected in

[1] *Ruminants* are animals such as cattle, sheep, goats, bison, elk, and deer whose stomachs have four compartments. These animals are efficient feeders because the bacteria in the rumen (one of the compartments) allows the animal to digest low-grade feed such as hay, straw, and corn silage.

England in 1986. BSE may have originated as a result of feeding scrapie-infected sheep products (meat-and-bone meal) to cattle. The outbreak was then amplified and spread throughout the cattle industry in the United Kingdom by feeding rendered[2], prion-infected, bovine meat-and-bone meal to young calves. It takes only a 1-gram piece of infected brain material, the size of a peppercorn, to cause infection in cattle. While the use of rendered material was banned by Great Britain in 1988, and the number of BSE cases has dropped progressively since 1992, scientific research is ongoing regarding other possible means of BSE transmission.

Although the origin of BSE remains unknown, currently the most widely accepted theory is that (for reasons that are not understood) the normal cellular prion protein (PrP) self-converts into an infectious, pathogenic, amyloid protein or prion. An unconventional protein with no nucleic acid, prions can change normally shaped cellular prion protein into abnormal shapes, causing changes in brain tissue (Corato, Ceroni, & Savoldi, 2000; Saborio, Permanne, & Soto, 2001; Travis & Miller, 2003; U.S. Centers for Disease Control and Prevention, 2007; World Health Organization, 2002). The presence of these abnormal proteins is used as a laboratory marker in the detection of BSE in both humans and animals.

BSE in the UK, North America, and Elsewhere

By January 1993, at the peak of the BSE epidemic in the UK, almost 1000 new cases of BSE per week were reported, and by the end of 2005 over 184 000 cases of BSE had been confirmed there. Since then, relatively small numbers of BSE cases have been reported in herds through much of the rest of Europe, particularly France, Germany, Ireland, Portugal, Spain, and Switzerland. By 2005, Japan had confirmed 20 cases of BSE.

In 1993, one eight-year-old cow from an Alberta farm tested positive for BSE. This animal had been imported from the UK in 1987. Canada's first case of BSE in a domestic animal was confirmed in May 2003, and the first BSE case in the United States was confirmed in December 2003. By May 2007, 14 cases of BSE had been identified in North America: 11 in Canada and three in the United States (see Box Figure 6–1). Most of the BSE cases in Canada have been linked to the same strain that caused the BSE outbreak in the UK, but this strain has not been identified in any American-born bovine cases of BSE.

Within hours of the announcement of Canada's first BSE case, the United States declared a ban on all imports of Canadian beef; Mexico and Japan (Canada's second and third most important export beef markets) followed shortly with similar actions. During 2002, over 80 percent of Canadian beef exports

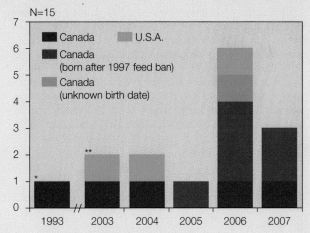

* Cow imported from U.K. into Canada
** Cow imported from Canada into U.S.A.

Box Figure 6–1

BSE cases in North America, by year and country of death, 1993–2007

SOURCE: is "BSE (Bovine Spongiform Encephalopathy, or Mad Cow Disease)," *Centers for Disease Control and Prevention*, 2007, http://www.cdc.gov/ncidod/dvrd/bse

(worth about $2 billion) had gone to the United States. When the U.S. border closed, Canada's beef producers lost an estimated $11 million per day, and 5000 jobs were lost in Canada. Federal and provincial governments implemented several short-term aid schemes to increase slaughterhouse capacity, expand foreign markets for Canadian beef, and provide about $2 billion in direct "mad cow relief" aid.

In April 2004, the United States lifted import restrictions on ground beef, bone-in cuts of beef, and offal from animals younger than 30 months; live animal imports and meat from older animals remained banned. It was not until July 2005 that the U.S. border partially reopened to young live Canadian cattle; in December 2005 Japan relaxed the ban on Canadian (and American) beef it had imposed two years previously, allowing cattle younger than 21 months to enter the country as long as high-risk materials such as heads and spinal cords were removed.

Canada's Efforts to Protect against BSE

To protect consumers from health risks associated with BSE, and to minimize the likelihood that cattle will be exposed to BSE and that the disease will grow and spread, Health Canada and

[2] *Rendering* means purifying or extracting something by melting it, such as heating solid fat slowly until as much liquid fat as possible has been extracted from it. The protein that is linked to BSE is resistant to normal inactivation procedures such as heat; this protein may not be destroyed completely in the rendering process and may remain active in the rendered material. Changes in the rendering process during the early 1980s, which eliminated the solvent-extraction process and second steam-heat treatment, may have been the reason the protein survived.

(continued)

BOX 6-2
(CONTINUED)

the Canadian Food Inspection Agency (CFIA) have developed a wide-ranging set of internationally recognized, science-based safeguards. CFIA's responsibility to implement animal health and disease control programs entails use of veterinary services, disease surveillance, laboratory-based diagnostic testing, domestic and import controls, animal biologics, and a livestock feed program (CFIA, 2007b). CFIA has legislative authority to impose quarantines and to require the destruction of animals that are suspected of being diseased; CFIA also operates the compensation program for owners of animals and animal products ordered destroyed.

Other actions that CFIA has undertaken include the following:

- 1990: BSE was made a reportable disease in Canada (any suspected case of BSE must be reported to a federal veterinarian).

- 1992: CFIA implemented a national BSE surveillance program to test the brains of high-risk cattle for BSE; by 2007, about 160 000 animals had been killed and tested for BSE.

- 1997: Canadian regulations banned the feeding of rendered protein products (brains, spinal cords, and other parts known as specified risk material, or SRM) from ruminant animals to other ruminants. However, cattle still can be fed the remains of chickens, hogs, and other animals, and cow blood is still used in cattle feed.

- 2000: CFIA suspended the importation of rendered animal material of any species from any country that Canada did not recognize as "BSE-free."

- 2001: A Canadian Cattle Identification Program was established for cattle and bison; this program ensured that an individual animal's movements from its herd of origin to its slaughter could be traced.

- 2007: An enhanced feed ban came into effect on July 12; this ban is expected to prevent more than 99 percent of potential BSE infection sources from entering the Canadian feed system by addressing any contamination that could occur as feed is manufactured, transported, or stored. The new feed regulations ban certain cattle tissues (SRM) from all animal feed, pet food, and fertilizer, not just from cattle feed. To help ensure the infrastructure for effective disposal of SRM is in place, the federal government indicated it would invest $80 million in provincial cost-shared disposal programs. The end goal of CFIA's actions is to eradicate BSE from the national herd. With the new regulations in place, eradication is expected by about 2017.

Photo 6–2
On September 1, 2003, more than 450 000 kilograms of beef were served free at community barbecues held across Canada in an effort to pull the beef industry out of the slump that followed the first case of BSE.

In May 2007, in recognition of the effectiveness of Canada's efforts to monitor, mitigate, and eradicate BSE, the World Organization for Animal Health (OIE) categorized Canada as a "controlled risk BSE country" (CFIA, 2007a). This status is important in relation to restoring international trade, signifying that appropriate scientific standards and BSE safeguards are in place.

SOURCES: *OIE Recognizes Canada's BSE Surveillance and Eradication Programs*, Canadian Food Inspection Agency, 2007a, http://www.inspection. gc.ca/english/corpaffr/newcom/2007/20070522e.shtml; *Transmissible Spongiform Encephalopathies (TSEs)*, Canadian Food Inspection Agency, 2007b, http://www.inpsection.gc.ca/english/anima/heasan/disemala/spong/e; "Prions and Risk for Human Health," M. Corato, M. Ceroni, & F. Savoldi, 2000, *Instituto Lombardo Accademia di Scienze e Lettere Rendiconti Scienze Chimiche e fisiche geologiche biologoche, 134*(102), 109–114; "Sensitive Detection of Pathological Prion Protein by Cyclic Amplification of Protein Misfolding," G. P. Saborio, B. Permanne, & C. Soto, 2001, June 14, Nature, 411, 810–814; "A Short Review of Transmissible Spongiform Encephalopathies and Guidelines for Managing Risks Associated with Chronic Wasting Disease in Captive Cervids in Zoos," D. Travis & M. Miller, 2003, Journal of Zoo and Wildlife Medicine, 34(2), 125–133; *Understanding the BSE Threat*," World Health Organization, 2002, http://www.who.int/csr/resources/publications/whocdscsreph20026/en; *BSE (Bovine Spongiform Encephalopathy, or Mad Cow Disease*, U.S. Centers for Disease Control and Prevention, 2007, http://www.cdc.gov/ncidod/dvrd/bse/

While factors such as declining farm incomes, low market prices for agricultural products, and natural disasters influence their decisions, farmers' range of choice regarding crops to plant has widened as improved crop breeding, seeding and tilling methods, and marketing skills have encouraged diversification. Spring wheat remained the dominant Prairie crop in 2006, but oilseeds (canola, soybeans) and pulse crops (dry field peas, lentils, and beans) increased and more land was used for less expensive perennial forage crops such as alfalfa, tame hay, and improved pasture rather than wheat and barley. Other factors, such as the efforts of the Canola Council of Canada to promote expansion of acreage devoted to canola for use in the biodiesel industry, also affect farmers' choices (see the following section). Although Ontario continues to produce almost two-thirds of Canada's grain corn (a high-energy source of animal feed), increases in grain corn crops in Quebec and Manitoba have been driven by the significant increase in hog production in those provinces. Grain corn also is used in the production of ethanol, a crop-derived alcohol that is added to gasoline to increase octane levels and to improve engine performance through cleaner-burning fuel. Prince Edward Island continues to farm about 24 percent of the total area (over 97 600 acres) devoted to Canada's potato crop. Vegetables such as sweet corn, green peas, beans, tomatoes, and carrots were grown on over 330 700 acres in 2001. In Alberta in particular, and in Saskatchewan, an increasingly large area is being devoted to culinary and medicinal herbs such as basil and echinacea (Statistics Canada, 2002c). For instance, Saskatchewan grows 90 percent of the mustard that is sent to France and processed as Dijon mustard.

Another change influencing Canadian agriculture is an apparent push toward production of biofuels such as ethanol and biodiesel. Biofuels may be made from various agricultural products, but significant amounts of cropland may be required to produce these fuels in commercial quantities in Canada. Converting land to produce energy rather than food clearly raises challenging questions about intergenerational equity, particularly regarding questions of food security and environmental costs, such as volume of water required to grow and process the biofuel crops. The benefits and challenges associated with biofuels in Canadian agriculture are the focus of the following section.

Canadian Agriculture and Biofuels

The use of vegetable oils for engine fuels may seem insignificant today, but such oils may become, in the course of time, as important as petroleum and the coal-tar products of the present time.

—Dr. Rudolf Diesel, 1912 (cited in Methanol Institute & International Fuel Quality Centre, 2006, p. 5)

Using vegetable oil as an engine fuel is not a new idea: in 1885, Dr. Rudolf Diesel's first engine was fueled by peanut oil, and Henry Ford's 1908 Model T was designed to run on ethanol ((S&T)[2] Consultants Inc. & Meyers Norris Penny LLP, 2004b). However, as petroleum refining expanded in the 1920s, and as the price of petroleum declined, the idea of crop-based commercial fuels faded away. It was not until the late 1980s and 1990s that biodiesel and ethanol received renewed attention as viable alternative fuels. Growing public awareness of environmental and sustainability issues; rising oil prices; increasing political efforts to achieve a reliable, self-sufficient energy source; liberalization of global trade and the concomitant need to find ways to support domestic agricultural production; technological breakthroughs; and the implementation of new incentive programs have stimulated growth in the biofuels industry.

What Are Biofuels and How Are they Made? **Biofuels** such as ethanol and biodiesel are made from agricultural products. **Ethanol** is a grain- or cellulose-based alcohol, while biodiesel is an *ester* (an organic, often fragrant compound formed in a reaction between an acid and an alcohol with the elimination of water) derived from vegetable oils and animal fats (see Table 6–3, p. 208). To date, North American fuel ethanol has been produced mostly from crops containing starch (e.g., corn), but elsewhere in the world ethanol is manufactured primarily through the fermentation of sugar (e.g., sugarcane). Most Canadian biodiesel companies use low-cost feedstocks (fish oil, animal fats, and recycled cooking oil), but, because of its wide availability, canola could become the feedstock of choice if our domestic biodiesel production capacity were to grow (Stiefelmeyer et al., 2006).

Biodiesel is made through a chemical process known as transesterification. Triglycerides, such as canola seeds, are crushed and the resulting oil is reacted with an alcohol (methanol) in the presence of a strong acid or base catalyst (sodium methylate), to produce a mixture of fatty acids, methyl esters (biodiesel), and glycerol. Approximately 90 percent of the product is biodiesel and 10 percent is glycerin (used in the pharmaceutical, food, and cosmetics industries). The meal resulting from seed crushing is a high-protein feed that provides good nutrition for Canadian dairy, beef, and sheep. This meal could help reduce annual imports of high-protein feed, worth about $200 million. The biodiesel produced can be used in any diesel engine with few or no modifications or blended with diesels at any level (for instance, a 20 percent biodiesel–petrodiesel blend is known as B20, and pure biodiesel is labelled B100).

The basic process to make ethanol involves enzymatic *hydrolysis*, a chemical reaction in which a compound reacts with water, causing decomposition and the production of two or more other compounds, such as when starch is converted to glucose. Ethanol production involves the

TABLE 6-3

SELECTED CHARACTERISTICS OF BIODIESEL AND ETHANOL

Characteristics	Biodiesel	Ethanol
Source material(s)	• Vegetable oils (soy, canola), recycled cooking oil, animal fats, tall oil (byproduct of pulp and paper operations), algae, slaughterhouse waste.	• Grains (wheat, barley), corn, potatoes, cellulose (straw, prairie grasses), forestry wastes (sawdust), municipal solid waste, recycled newsprint.
Production process	• Transesterification; typical products are methyl esters and glycerin.	• Enzymatic hydrolysis; typical products are anhydrous (pure) alcohol and distillers grain.
Potential environmental benefits relating to energy	• Biodiesel is 11 percent O_2 by mass, combusts better than conventional diesel (reduces unburned hydrocarbons by 93%, CO_2 by 78%, CO by 50%, sulphates and PM by 50%). • Is free of sulphur and PAHs. • Is renewable, biodegradable – and nontoxic. • Diverts waste products from landfill sites (reduces methane). • Derives about 60 percent of its energy from sunlight (via photosynthesis).	• Fuel-grade ethanol is about 99% pure alcohol with important properties that make it an excellent fuel additive. • Ethanol contains 35% O_2, which encourages more complete combustion of fuel. • Gasoline containing a 10% ethanol blend will reduce carbon monoxide emissions by 25 to 30%, particulate matter by 50%, and VOCs by 7%. • Can substitute for aromatic hydrocarbons such as benzene. • Is renewable, biodegradeable.
Economic benefits	• Every $1 invested in biodiesel infrastructure returns $2 of economic activity. • Using 1 million tonnes of canola seed to produce biodiesel would supply over 500 million litres of biodiesel that would produce $200+ million in additional gross farm revenue, create 500 new jobs, and bring capital expenditures of over $165 million.	• If ethanol were used in 50% of Canadian gasoline, 3000 to 6000 jobs would be created by 2020. • Over 70 percent of revenue from an ethanol plant is spent within 150 km of plant site. • In capital and operating costs, compares favourably with Hibernia and oil (sands) projects. • Renewable ethanol, produced using sustainable agricultural practices, could help stabilize farm income and reduce government support payments to agriculture.
Safety	• Nontoxic in its purest form; as a blend, still less toxic than regular diesel fuel. • Much less flammable than petroleum-based diesel; regular diesel burns at 50°C, pure biodiesel (B100) ignites at 150°C.	• Relatively corrosive. • Evaporates easily. • Absorbs water molecules so is difficult to transport.
Challenges	• Cold flow properties (at lower temperatures, biodiesel tends to lose viscosity). • Production and distribution costs. • Loss of agricultural land for food production. • Food security and intergenerational equity. • Water demands to grow and process biofuel crops.	• Transportation difficulties. • Need to find feedstocks that are less demanding to produce. • Loss of agricultural land for food production. • Food security and intergenerational equity. • Water demands to grow and process biofuel crops.

SOURCES: *Biodiesel in Chemcad: The Challenge—Biodiesel Production,* Chemstations, Inc., 2006, http://www.chemstations.net; *A Biodiesel Primer: Market and Public Policy Developments, Quality, Standards and Handling,* Methanol Institute & International Fuel Quality Centre, 2006, http://www.biodiesel.org/resources/reportsdatabase/reports/gen/20060401-GEN369.pdf; *Biodiesel Question and Answer Sheet,* Olds College School of Innovation, BioFuel Technology Centre, n.d., Olds, AB: Olds College School of Innovation; *Economic, Financial, Social Analysis and Public Policies for Biodiesel, Phase 1,* (S&T)² Consultants Inc. & Meyers Norris Penny LLP, 2004, http://www.greenfuels.org/biodiesel/pdf/OConnor-Report-Biodiesel2004.pdf; *Economic, Financial, Social Analysis and Public Policies for Fuel Ethanol, Phase 1,* (S&T)² Consultants Inc. & Meyers Norris Penny LLP, 2004, http://www.greenfuels.org/biodiesel/pdf/OConnor-Report-Ethanol2004.pdf; *The Economic Impact of Canadian Biodiesel Production on Canadian Grains, Oilseeds and Livestock Producers—Final Report,* K. Stiefelmeyer, A. Mussell, T. Moore, & D. Liu, 2006, http://www.georgemorris.org/GMC/Publications/DomesticandInternationalMarketing.aspx

hydrolosis of starch to sugars, and fermentation of sugars to ethanol via yeast; the resulting "mash" or "beer" is distilled and dried to produce anhydrous ethanol, suitable for blending with gasoline. Fuel ethanol is a high-octane, oxygenated (35 percent of content) fuel component, but most of the product is used in low-level blends (5 to 10 percent ethanol in gasoline). The use of newer source materials for ethanol production, such as crop residues (straw, corn stover), forestry wastes (sawdust), municipal solid waste, recycled newsprint, prairie grasses, and algae is being researched, as are newer production processes such as thermal depolymerization.

From an efficiency standpoint, biodiesel is a very efficient fuel: for every unit of fossil energy consumed in the production of biodiesel, 3.22 units of energy are released when biodiesel is burned. This is more than twice the energy efficiency of ethanol (1.34). However, the feedstock used to produce ethanol or biodiesel affects the energy yield of biofuels. For example:

- 1 hectare of sugarcane grown in Brazil produces almost twice as much ethanol as the same area of corn grown in Canada
- typically, 1 hectare of canola grown in Canada yields 1000 litres of biodiesel
- to run a car in Canada for one year on biofuel would require all the corn from 0.6 hectares or slightly less than 2 hectares of wheat; in Brazil, 0.3 hectares would provide sufficient biofuel for the same level of consumption

Canada would need to use 36 percent of its agricultural land to produce enough biofuels to replace 10 percent of the fuel used for transportation; in contrast, Brazil could obtain the same result by using only 3 percent of its farmland. It will take an estimated 4.6 million tonnes of corn, 2.3 million tonnes of wheat, and 0.56 million tonnes of canola for Canada to attain its biofuels target of 5 percent of fuel consumption by 2010. Grown domestically, these feedstocks would represent 48 to 52 percent of the total corn-seeded area, 11 to 12 percent of the wheat-seeded area, and about 8 percent of the total canola-seeded area (McKenna, 2007).

In many parts of the world, possibly including Canada, production of biofuels raises concern about allocating farmland to energy production rather than to food production. While national food security is a question Canadians may not have thought much about yet, it is possible that choices made now to allocate agricultural land to biofuel crops rather than food production will defer the food security issue to future generations. Large-scale production of corn as a biofuel source has the potential to exacerbate existing problems of groundwater depletion, soil erosion, algae blooms, and pesticide and fertilizer runoff (McKenna, 2007). If the corn-growing area for biofuels were expanded to include Saskatchewan and Manitoba, for instance, dryland farming systems would

require the construction of additional irrigation works to meet the major water demands of growing and processing this biofuel crop. Have decision makers given sufficient attention to the implications for agricultural sustainability of their decision to promote biofuels? Who decides what is sustainable—and who should decide? European Union sources already have identified the far-reaching social and environmental problems that increased production of agrofuels bring: destruction of various ecosystems, water scarcity, land conflicts, rural impoverishment and depopulation, human rights violations, food insecurity, and compromised food sovereignty. As well, the real climate benefits of biofuel crops increasingly are in doubt, particularly when land use change and displacement are taken into account (Gilbertson et al., 2007).

Clearly, such issues need to be assessed and understood fully, from economic, social, and environmental perspectives, in order to ensure that appropriate decisions are made regarding agriculture and biofuels and that anticipated benefits occur in all sectors. While efforts to reduce GHGs are necessary, is it appropriate to devote so much agricultural land to processes that support our vehicles? While there is need for careful reflection on these issues, it is important to realize how Canada's biofuels industry compares with other world regions and to question whether biofuels are sustainable.

How Does Canada Compare? Brazil and the United States produce about 70 percent (44.7 billion litres in 2005) of the world's ethanol. Canada's annual production of ethanol is about 600 million litres; this was expected to increase to 840 million litres in 2007, but we lag behind many parts of the world in "going renewable." With new incentives (see below), the Canadian government anticipates that ethanol production will grow to 2.74 billion litres by the end of 2010. In Canada, commercial production and use of ethanol as a blending component of gasoline began in Manitoba in 1981 (see Table 6–4, p. 210); now about 1400 service stations in six provinces offer either 5 or 10 percent blends of ethanol and gasoline.

The European Union leads the world in biodiesel production (3.6 billion litres in 2005), while the United States produced 288 million litres in 2005. Commercial production of biodiesel in Canada was almost nonexistent until 2005, when the first large-scale biodiesel production facility opened in Sudbury, Ontario. While most of Canada's biodiesel is exported to the United States, the public transit (biobus) systems in both Montreal and Saskatoon, and the fleet vehicles of Ontario Hydro, the city of Toronto, and Guelph Transit, use biodiesel (City of Saskatoon, n.d.; Natural Resources Canada, 2002; Toronto Hydro Corporation, 2005).

Biodiesel development is at a very early stage in Canada; while four companies have produced small quantities of biodiesel for transportation demonstration purposes, the only commercial biodiesel production has come

TABLE 6-4
ETHANOL PLANTS IN CANADA TO 2004[1]

Company	Location	Start-up Date	Feedstock	Capacity (million litres per year)
Mohawk Canada	Minnedosa, MB	1981	wheat	10
Commercial Alcohols	Tiverton, ON	1988	corn	20 (7 million for fuel)
Pound Maker Agventures	Lanigan, SK	1990	wheat	13.5
Commercial Alcohols	Chatham, ON	1997	corn	150 (120 million for fuel)
Permolex	Red Deer, AB	1998	wheat	26 million

[1] In 2003, the first round ($78 million) of a federal government Ethanol Expansion Program was announced, with the intention of reducing transportation-related greenhouse gas emissions. Allocations totalling 749 million litres of annual production were granted to one existing and six new companies.

SOURCE: Modified from *Economic, Financial, Social Analysis and Public Policies for Fuel Ethanol, Phase 1*, Natural Resources Canada, November 22, 2004. Table 2–1, p. 5. Reproduced with the permission of the Minister of Public Works and Government Services. Courtesy of Natural Resources Canada, 2008. http://www.greenfuels.org/ethanol/pdf/OConnor-Report-Ethanol-2004.pdf

TABLE 6-5
COMPARISON OF CANADIAN BIOFUELS AND GHG EMISSIONS ON A LIFE-CYCLE BASIS[1]

Blends of Biofuels with Petroleum Diesel	% Fewer GHGs Compared to Petroleum Diesel or Gasoline
100% biodiesel	64–92% less than petroleum diesel
20% blend	12–18% less than petroleum diesel
2% blend	1–2% less than petroleum diesel
E-10 (10% ethanol, 90% gasoline) from corn	3–4% less than gasoline
E-10 (from cellulosic materials)	6–8% less than gasoline
E-85 (85% ethanol, 15% gasoline)	75% less than gasoline

[1] A life-cycle basis for comparison includes analysis of GHG emissions from production of the organic materials to the use of the final product as a fuel.

SOURCE: *Biofuels—An Energy, Environmental or Agricultural Policy?* F. Forge, 2007, http://www.parl.gc.ca/information/library/PRBpubs/prb0637-e.htm

from Ocean Nutrition, a fish oil processor in Nova Scotia. This company has been processing about 1 million litres of fish oil to remove the high-value omega-3 fatty acids, and converting the remainder into biodiesel for power generation. Milligan Bio-Tech in Foam Lake, Saskatchewan, has produced some biodiesel for the Saskatoon Biobus project, as has the Rothsay, Quebec, plant for the Montreal Biobus project.

Can Biofuels Help the Environment? There are "mixed" environmental advantages of replacing fossil fuels with their biological counterparts. In terms of biodiesel, for instance, the life-cycle emissions of CO and particulate matter from 100 percent blend biodiesel (B100) are less than 70 percent of that from regular diesel, and sulphur can be reduced by about 92 percent and virtually eliminated from vehicle tailpipes. These differences help reduce smog and human health problems. The Canadian government has estimated that benefits to the environment through the use of renewable fuels will reduce GHG emissions by more than 4.2 megatonnes, the equivalent of taking more than 1 million cars off the road each year (Canola Council of Canada, n.d). Table 6–5 provides a comparison of Canadian biofuels and GHG emissions on a life-cycle basis; note that 100 percent biodiesel and E-85 are the only blends to achieve major GHG reductions. As noted previously, there are fundamental questions about the implications for food security and sustainable agriculture if land is converted from production of food crops to biofuels. As well, there are major concerns about water demands to grow and process biofuel crops that must be addressed.

Getting to the Future with Biofuels? The federal government has pledged to ensure that all gasoline in Canada will contain an average of 5 percent renewable fuel content by 2010, and that diesel fuel and heating oil will contain an average of 2 percent by 2012. To facilitate this, in December 2006, the government announced

Photo 6–3

The world's first canola biodiesel jet car, 2007 Corvette F/C. This jet car is powered by a J60 Pratt and Whitney engine that puts out 7500 hp. Equipped with a hand-built afterburner, the car burns 15 gallons of canola biodiesel per run. This car is used in communities to promote drug awareness and positive lifestyles.

For more information, see www.prairielandmotorsports.com

$345 million to help farmers raise the capital necessary to construct or expand biodiesel production facilities, not just supply grain. As part of this investment, in April 2007 the four-year, $200 million ecoAgriculture Biofuels Capital Initiative (ecoABC) was launched. The ecoABC project is expected to increase Canada's renewable fuel capacity by 1.5 billion litres and to be part of the renaissance of agriculture being generated by renewable fuels (Agriculture and Agri-Food Canada, 2006a).

In July 2007, a new federal ecoENERGY for Biofuels program was announced, with funding at $1.5 billion in operating incentives to Canadian producers of biofuels. Coupled with the requirement for 5 percent renewable fuels content in gasoline by 2010, the government expected this new ecoENERGY for Biofuels program would increase energy diversity in Canada, improve the environment by reducing GHGs, and revitalize farms and rural communities across our nation. Building on the wheat and canola grown by western farmers, and the corn and soybeans grown in eastern Canada, the federal government expects that 20 new world-class biofuels facilities will create over 14 000 new jobs in rural communities and provide a new market for over 200 million bushels of grains and oilseeds (Agriculture and Agri-Food Canada, 2006a; Canadian Renewable Fuels Association, 2007).

The Canadian Petroleum Products Institute (CPPI) has indicated that it supports the federal government's development of a renewable fuel policy for Canada. CPPI also supports a national policy to maximize the environmental benefits that may be achieved through use of renewable fuels. Some people in Canada today believe that biofuels are part of a global transition to new forms of energy—and that, for Canadians, the conversion starts on our farms. But is this the most appropriate direction to achieve agricultural sustainability?

HUMAN ACTIVITIES AND EFFECTS ON AGRICULTURAL LANDS

Agriculture and land management practices affect the environmental sustainability of agroecosystems. This section identifies some of these management practices and their effects on soil resources, water resources, and biodiversity. As well, greenhouse gases and energy use are considered.

EFFECTS ON SOIL RESOURCES

In an agricultural context, soil resource quality refers to the ability of the soil to support crop growth without resulting in soil degradation or other harm to the environment (Acton & Gregorich, 1995). Soil quality is affected by land use and by land management practices. Growing a single species over a large area (monoculture cropping), leaving the land fallow, intensive row cropping (where bare soil is exposed in the spaces between crop rows), and up-and-down slope cultivation contribute to the processes that reduce soil quality. These processes result in loss of organic matter; erosion by wind, water, and tillage; changes in soil structure; salinization; and chemical contamination. Each of these concerns is discussed briefly below.

Levels of Soil Organic Matter

Organic matter (plant, animal, or microorganism matter, either living or dead) is the source of key plant nutrients such as carbon, nitrogen, phosphorus, and sulphur (see Box 6–3 on the next page). Organic matter improves the physical and chemical properties of soil by storing and supplying plant nutrients, retaining carbon, helping water infiltrate into soil, stabilizing soil, and reducing the risk of crusting of the soil surface. Organic matter promotes movement of oxygen and carbon dioxide through the soil, enabling soil organisms such as algae, fungi, and cyanobacteria to thrive. The amount of organic matter in agricultural soils varies between 1 and 10 percent; how much is optimal depends on local climate, the amount of clay in the soil, and the intended use of the land.

Although there is a lack of comprehensive data regarding soil organic matter across Canada, it is known that levels of organic matter usually decline during the decade following crop cultivation on previously undisturbed forest or grassland soils. Research has shown that since initial cultivation, Canada's uneroded agricultural soils have lost between 15 and 30 percent of their organic matter. However, trends in some regions indicate that levels of organic matter have stabilized or are increasing because of improved management practices. In the Prairie provinces, for example, where frequent summerfallowing had cost farmers over $70 million per year in lost nitrogen alone, more farmers are replenishing organic matter taken out of the soil through cropping by adding crop residues, manure, and commercial fertilizers (note that chemical fertilizers do not replace carbon) (Agriculture and Agri-Food Canada, 2003b; Gregorich et al., 1995). Still other farmers are switching to more environmentally benign tillage types (see Boxes 6–1 and 6–8). In 2006, 72 percent of farmers were practising conservation and zero tillage, practices that help retain soil organic matter and reduce erosion (Statistics Canada, 2007). Still other farmers are using grasses or legumes in crop rotations to add organic matter to the soils, or are putting their fields under continuous cropping regimes to boost organic matter levels. More research is needed to answer fundamental questions, however, such as what levels of organic matter are ideal for crop growth.

Wind, Water, and Tillage Erosion

Erosion of soil by wind and water is the most widespread soil degradation problem in Canada; these natural processes are accelerated or minimized by the types of cropping and land management practices used (Larney et al., 1998). For instance, risks of wind and water erosion can be reduced through changes in land tillage practices, including reductions in summerfallow, changes in cropping patterns, and use of erosion control measures.

Tilling (plowing) the land, particularly on rolling or hummocky land where gravity moves soil downhill during plowing operations (i.e., *tillage erosion*), contributes to loss of topsoil. The topsoil is the soil layer best able to support life because it contains most of the soil's organic matter (the smallest, lightest soil particles contain the greatest proportion of plant nutrients and are highly susceptible to wind erosion). *Wind erosion* is more widespread than water erosion, even though wind erosion has a lower transport capacity. If topsoil is blown or washed away, carbon and nitrogen are lost, and the remaining soil has a reduced ability to provide the fertility required for crops, as well as a lowered capacity to accept and store water and support soil microorganisms. Also, if eroded topsoil is carried into water bodies, detrimental effects such as blocked waterways, buried vegetation, smothered fish, and increased costs of water treatment can occur.

Canada's agricultural lands have been classified in terms of their susceptibility to erosion. Almost all regions of the country are concerned about wind erosion, but the Prairies experience particularly extensive, damaging wind erosion. About 36 percent of cultivated land in the Prairies is subject to high to severe risk of wind erosion, particularly in parts of southern Manitoba and Alberta and in a large part of Saskatchewan (see Figure 6–2) (Wall et al., 1995). Soil losses to wind erosion not only lead to reduced productivity and loss of economic returns, but also cause abrasion damage to buildings, machinery, and vegetation. Airborne nutrients and pesticides eventually may degrade water quality and aggravate health problems in downwind areas. In response to such risks, many farmers in the Prairie provinces converted their annual crops planted in sandy areas to perennial forage crops. This soil conservation measure resulted in a 7 percent decrease in risk of wind erosion between 1981 and 1991 (Wall et al., 1995).

Soil erosion by water varies widely across Canada, with the most severe losses of soil occurring in the Peace River area and Fraser Valley of British Columbia, and parts of Saskatchewan, southwestern Ontario, the Eastern Townships of Quebec, and Prince Edward Island. All of Canada's agricultural regions are at risk of soil erosion by water, but the risk is greatest on land that is being cultivated intensively; overall, about 20 percent of Canada's agricultural areas have a moderate to high level risk of *water erosion*. While the Prairie provinces have a low inherent risk of soil erosion by water, the same is not true for other regions. Eighty percent of cultivated lands in the Maritimes, 75 percent of British Columbia lands, and 50 percent of lands in Ontario have been identified as having high to severe risk of soil erosion by water (see Figure 6–2) (Wall et al., 1995). In British Columbia's

Figure 6–2

Risk of wind and water erosion in Canada

SOURCE: *State of Canada's Environment—1996*. Environment Canada. Figures 11.9 and 11.10 © Her Majesty the Queen in Right of Canada, Environment Canada (1996). Reproduced with permission of the Minister of Public Works and Government Services Canada, 2008.

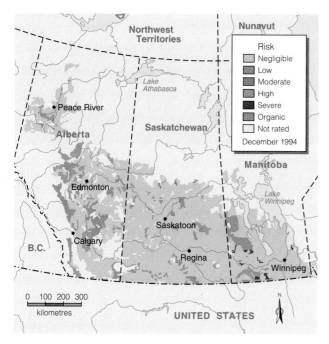

a) Risk of wind erosion in the Prairie provinces under 1991 management practices

NOTE: Management practices based on 1991 Census of Agriculture.

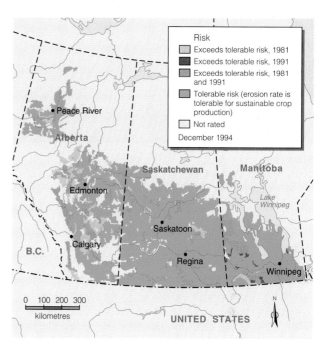

b) Risk of water erosion in the Prairie provinces, 1981 and 1991

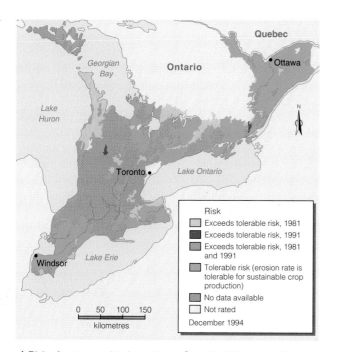

c) Risk of water erosion in southern Ontario, 1981 and 1991

NOTE: "Tolerable risk" refers to soils that are at risk of erosion at a rate that is tolerable for sustainable crop production under the most common management practices.

Peace River area, erosion on summerfallow lands has been as high as 14 tonnes per hectare per year, and in the Fraser Valley, erosion rates under row crops have been as high as 30 tonnes per hectare annually. Potato lands in Atlantic Canada experience major erosion problems; in Prince Edward Island, losses of up to 20 tonnes of soil per hectare per year have occurred in the past; serious long-term problems may result if annual soil losses exceed 5 to 10 tonnes per hectare. In 2003, Prince Edward Island identified soil erosion (and associated nutrient and pesticide runoff) as a major environmental problem. Heavy rain storms and spring runoff washed soils into estuaries and ponds, destroyed fish habitat, and contributed to fish kills (Kelly, 2003). In southwestern Ontario, water erosion may reduce yields by as much as 40 percent. Soil eroding from agricultural areas in the Great Lakes basin has transported pesticides, such as the no-longer-used insecticide DDT, to ground and surface waters.

Not only is soil loss by water erosion costly in terms of reduced crop productivity and higher production costs, but sediment damages occur as well. These damages include reductions in channel capacity; alteration and destruction of fish habitats; accelerated plant and algal growth from excess nutrients; buildup and transportation of heavy metals, pesticides, and other toxic substances; lower recreational values; and the increased costs of ensuring water is fit for human consumption.

Photo 6–4

Water erosion is a major factor in the decline of soil quality, particularly on land under intensive cultivation.

Photo 6–5

An example of soil salinization in an agricultural area of southern Alberta.

Soil Structure

Soils that are low in organic matter content, wet, and finely textured are most vulnerable to structural degradation, particularly if land management practices such as intensive tillage, row cropping, and short rotation periods are employed. One of the most recognized forms of structural degradation, **soil compaction** results mainly from repeated passes of heavy machinery over wet soil during tillage and harvesting, causing what was a well-aerated soil to restrict air and water movement, thus reducing the ability of plant roots to penetrate the soil and derive sufficient moisture and nutrients.

Certain crops, such as potatoes, corn, soybeans, and sugar beets, often are associated with compaction because they require long growing seasons—being planted in the early spring and harvested in the fall when the soil is frequently moist. Soil compaction not only reduces crop yields but also costs Canadian producers millions of dollars annually.

One study reported that economic losses due to soil compaction were greatest in Quebec, where it was estimated that 20 percent of the best farmland was compacted. In British Columbia, soil compaction was widespread and, in Ontario, 50 to 70 percent of clay soils were adversely affected by compaction. In Atlantic Canada, with its naturally compacted subsoils and *hardpans* (hardened soil layers with greatly reduced porosity), farming on moist soils causes additional compaction. Soil compaction is not a serious problem on the Prairies (Topp et al., 1995).

Soil Salinization

Salinization, an excess of salts in soils, is another factor that can reduce the capacity of soil to produce crops. Saline (salty) soils restrict the amount of water and nutrients plants can withdraw from the soil, thereby reducing crop production. Unlike soil erosion, which usually occurs on the surface, salinization generally affects soils at depth.

In dryland soils, such as those on the Prairies, salinization is a natural process that takes place when a high water table, high rate of evaporation, and soluble salts all occur together (Government of Canada, 1996). About 6 to 8 million hectares of land in western Canada contain soils that may be affected by salinization.

Prairie saline soils existed long before settlement and cultivation occurred, but land management processes that affect the soil–water balance (such as replacing natural vegetation with crops and summerfallow or applying irrigation water) may modify the extent of soil salinity. The precise role of summerfallow in soil salinization remains unclear, although it is known that, in areas of groundwater recharge, summerfallow can increase the risk of saline seep formation (where salty groundwater discharges) because there are no crops, especially deep-rooted plants such as alfalfa, to take up moisture from the soil. Similarly, since manure contains salt (originating from the salt in animal feed), overapplication of manure as a fertilizer may raise the level of salt in soil.

Water movement from areas of saline soils to streams, lakes, or underground aquifers carries salts that can degrade the quality of water available for domestic use, livestock, and irrigation. Salt water draining from saline soils may degrade the quality of neighbouring downslope areas also, suggesting that controls on drainage may help efforts to reclaim saline areas.

While soil salinity is a continuing problem in some Prairie soils, only about 2 percent of Prairie agricultural land has more than 15 percent of its area affected by salinity (Eilers et al., 1995). Most (62 percent) Prairie agricultural land has less than 1 percent of its area affected by salinity; nevertheless, more than 2 million hectares are affected. Losses to farmers because of soil salinity in southern and central regions of Alberta, Saskatchewan, and scattered parts of Manitoba were estimated to have ranged between $104 and $257 million per year during the 1980s (Government of Canada, 1991). Since then, the Prairie Farm Rehabilitation Administration (PFRA) has recognized the need for research into the causes and solutions of salinity (as well as other soil quality issues).

While it is recognized that conservation farming holds considerable potential to overcome many of Canada's soil problems, no coordinated campaign has been mounted against soil degradation. In contrast, in the U.S. Great Plains states, where soil problems are similar in nature and scale to those in the Canadian prairies, an organized and well-funded soil conservation program has existed since the 1940s. This is not to say that Canadian farmers have not tried to take action; more than 100 farmers in Alberta's Warner County organized to fight soil salinity and were given special assistance by the federal and Alberta governments (Agriculture and Agri-Food Canada, 2003b). Ignoring soil problems or masking their effects with new chemicals, fertilizers, and equipment is insufficient; a long-term commitment is required to respond effectively to soil conservation needs.

Chemical Contamination

Agricultural pesticides are human-made chemicals used to kill unwanted plants and animals and to control insects, weeds, and crop diseases. Fertilizers and pesticides (agrochemicals) simultaneously have helped increase food production and have had negative effects on soil and water quality and vegetation health. Some of the socioeconomic benefits of agrochemical use include a doubling of global food production since 1960, increased security of food supply, and employment opportunities in the agrochemical industry. However, use of pesticides that contain organochlorides (such as endrin, chlordane, heptachlor, mirex, and toxaphene) seriously threaten human and environmental health (see Box 6–4).

Over 73 percent of Canadian farmers applied pesticides (herbicides, insecticides, fungicides) to their crops

BOX 6 – 4
RISKS OF PESTICIDES

Although pesticides have been available on store shelves for many years and are put to a variety of uses, we know too little about the hazards they pose. While pesticides are not all equal, at the core of the calls for stronger pesticide regulation are health hazards; after all, synthetic pesticides are poisons selected for their ability to kill or repel living organisms. Are farmers and other populations exposed to pesticides at risk? How vulnerable are nontarget and beneficial insects (honeybees, ladybugs, dragonflies), birds, aquatic organisms, wildlife, and domestic animals to pesticide toxicity? Since we know that pesticides contaminate ground and surface water, as Rachel Carson described in 1962 in *Silent Spring*, as well as our indoor and outdoor air and our food, are the calls for bans on pesticide use appropriate?

Here are some of the health hazards pesticides pose:

- *Neurotoxicity*—Pesticides may cause nervous system damage, including acute poisoning, respiratory distress, seizures, and even death. An acute poisoning episode can cause lingering damage, as can chronic exposure, which may result in Parkinson's disease and other degenerative neurological illnesses. In both insects and humans, especially children under age six, organophosphates and carbamates inhibit an enzyme (cholinesterase) necessary for normal nervous system function.

- *Carcinogenicity*—The active ingredients of many pesticides are known or suspected carcinogens that research often associates directly with cancers such as multiple myeloma, breast cancer, non-Hodgkin's lymphoma, prostate cancer, leukemias, and pancreatic cancer. The incidence rates of childhood cancers and non-Hodgkin's lymphoma have risen significantly since the 1970s, in tandem with the proliferation of pesticide use.

- *Endocrine disruption*—Some pesticides (and other chemicals) may mimic, block, or spur increases in levels of naturally occurring hormones. Such disturbances in the body's endocrine system may explain the increase in hormone-sensitive cancers, such as breast cancer. Hormonal imbalances may affect development and growth, maturation, fertility, and reproduction.

- *Other adverse effects*—Research has associated pesticides with a variety of effects, including bronchospasm, a concern in light of the dramatic rise in prevalence of childhood asthma since the 1980s.

Industrial agriculture relies on synthetic chemicals for its success. Yet in the context of sustainable agriculture, deliberately spraying poisons on the food we consume makes no sense. Since insect pest populations can develop resistance to the products applied to eradicate them, they can rebound with more damaging effects than previously, requiring ever-greater dependence on chemical pesticides. Health issues associated with the use of pesticides on food, as well as health implications for farmers and farm workers who apply the chemicals, work in the fields or orchards (especially after spraying), and handle produce in the processing plants, are significant. It is not surprising that many Canadians have called for reductions in use of pesticides in municipal operations, or for bans on pesticide use altogether. In 2001, the Supreme Court of Canada ruled that all municipalities have the power to ban nonessential pesticide uses. To date, 22 Ontario municipalities have enacted bylaws preventing pesticide use. Do you know whether your municipality has placed a ban on cosmetic pesticide use?

SOURCES: "Why the Data Matter: The Risks of Pesticides," *The Toxic Treadmill*, Environmental Advocates & New York Public Interest Research Group, 2001, http://www.eany.org/reports/treadmill/data_matter.html; "Ontario Communities Have the Right to Ban Cosmetic Pesticide Use," D. Saxe, July 3, 2007, *Environmental Communication Options* news release, http://www.huffstrategy.com/MediaManager/release/Dianne-Saxe/3-7-07/Ontario-Communities-Have-the-Right-to-Ban-Cosmetic-Pesticide-Use/654.html

during 2001. The highest percentages of farms where pesticides were applied were in Saskatchewan (83 percent), Prince Edward Island (80 percent), and Ontario (79 percent). Only 48 percent of farmers in British Columbia and Nova Scotia applied pesticides to their crops (Korol, 2004). Other sources of chemical contamination that threaten soil and plant health include heavy metals associated with the livestock industry, and extensive use of nonrenewable fossil fuels to run agricultural equipment.

Given that Canadians are concerned about the impacts that farm practices can have on the environment and on human health, many provinces have established pesticide reduction programs. For example, Ontario's Food Systems program aimed to reduce pesticide use by 50 percent by 2002. In addition, farmers often attempt to identify and apply beneficial (or best) management practices (BMPs). BMPs in Canada vary depending on the different regional and ecological conditions farmers encounter, but all BMPs attempt to manage production systems to achieve environmental goals while maintaining acceptable levels of economic returns. Examples of BMPs include regular soil testing, manure runoff containment, and integrated pest management.

Integrated pest management (IPM) uses all suitable control measures to reduce pest-related losses to an acceptable level with the goal of respecting biodiversity and reducing risks to ecosystems and human health. The main components of IPM programs are (1) planning and managing production systems to prevent organisms from becoming pests, by controlling whether and how land is plowed, planting diverse crops, managing the kinds of crop rotation used, planning planting dates, and handling harvests to reduce presence of pests; (2) identifying potential pests; (3) monitoring populations of pests, beneficial organisms, and all other relevant ecological factors, which involves recognizing ecological communities and ecosystems as well as the effects one species may have on other species; (4) establishing economic, damage, and action thresholds that allow pests to exist at low, tolerable levels (because the goal is control, not extinction); (5) applying cultural, physical, biological, chemical, and behavioural control measures to maintain pest populations below threshold levels, which may include use of highly specific chemicals (used sparingly), genetically resistant stock, biological controls (natural enemies of pests including parasites, diseases such as *Bacillus thuringiensis*, and predators such as ladybugs and some species of wasps); and (6) evaluating the effects and efficiency of pest-control measures used. IPM reduces the release of toxic chemicals into the environment while enabling economically viable production of crops; the more IPM is employed, the better it is for the environment and for individual ecosystems (Government of Canada, 1996).

The suitability of soil for various uses, including food production, can be affected by **chemical contamination** from herbicides, insecticides, algicides, and fungicides. While some research shows that contamination of agricultural soils with pesticide and nonpesticide contaminants is not a serious problem, other studies show that Canadian agricultural soil is contaminated by heavy metals such as cadmium, lead, and zinc. These metals are persistent and affect the health of plants, animals, and humans (Webber & Singh, 1995). Heavy metals enter agricultural soils mostly through atmospheric deposition, as well as through fertilizers, animal manures, and sewage sludge that is applied to agricultural land as a source of organic matter and nutrients.

Acid precipitation (see Chapter 5) and the use of nitrogen fertilizers can augment the natural acidity of some soils. This *acidification* causes nutrient deficiencies and has reduced crop yields in the Maritimes and even in some Prairie areas where soils generally have a high pH because they are alkaline. Application of lime to reduce acidity has been a common practice among farmers.

Farmers' efforts to increase plant production through widespread, liberal application of fertilizers can result in excess potassium, nitrogen, and phosphorus in soils, water, and plant systems. This occurs when manure and/ or fertilizer, applied in excess of plant requirements, leads to a buildup of nutrients in the soil. When the capacity of the soil to retain these nutrients is surpassed, they will be lost to the atmosphere or to surface or groundwater (Chambers et al., 2001). In the lower Fraser Valley and southern Ontario, high nitrate levels and fecal coliform bacteria in wells used for drinking water have been traced to the application of fertilizers and manure to fields, as well as to leakage from septic tanks. The cumulative effects of septic systems also may result in widespread contamination of shallow groundwater. Given the large areas involved in agriculture, and the concentrations of dairy cattle, poultry, and other livestock in these areas, heavy applications of manure may exceed the assimilative capacities of the soils and lead to declines in water quality (see the discussion "Contamination from Livestock Production Activities," starting on page 219).

Desertification

Desertification is a biophysical process of land degradation that occurs (in arid, semi-arid, and dry subhumid areas of the world) as a result of complex interactions between unpredictable climatic variations and unsustainable land-use practices, often by people who, in struggling for survival, overexploit agricultural, forest, and water resources. Desertification is more than just desert encroachment; it refers to degradation of dry land to the point where it is difficult to restore its former level of productivity (partly because of the loss in biological diversity). Desertification occurs in all continents when accelerated soil erosion, driven by water, wind, and salinization, causes reductions in soil quality, effective rooting depth, vegetative cover, and biomass productivity. Research has demonstrated a strong link between the desertification that affects an estimated 5.8 million hectares of land per year and the release of CO_2 from soil and vegetation to the atmosphere (Lal, 2001; Larney et al., 1998).

Worldwide, desertification directly affects about 250 million people; nearly 1 billion people, most of whom live in the poorer regions of the world, are at risk from desertification (Food and Agriculture Organization, 2002). African nations are the most vulnerable and the least able to combat the problem without international assistance. During the 1970s and again in the 1980s, devastating droughts affected the West African Sahel, and thousands of people and millions of animals died. Satellite images clearly showed altered vegetation patterns, and people began to talk about expanding deserts and sand dunes on the march. Closer scientific examination revealed that much of the vegetation change reflected water shortage and not permanent loss of soil fertility or land degradation. However, the loss of soil productivity, crop failures, scarcity of fuel wood, and reduced availability of grazing lands for livestock forced many people to abandon their land and become environmental refugees (see Chapter 4).

The United Nations Convention to Combat Desertification (UNCCD), to which Canada is both a signatory and donor party, helps provide support to countries experiencing serious drought and desertification, particularly Africa. The Canadian International Development Agency (CIDA) and the International Development Research Centre (IDRC) were mandated to implement the convention for Canada.

While the West African Sahel is the most seriously affected region in the world, vast areas in Asia as well as North, Central, and South America also are affected by desertification (see Figure 6–3). With its dry lands in the Prairie provinces, Canada is technically an affected

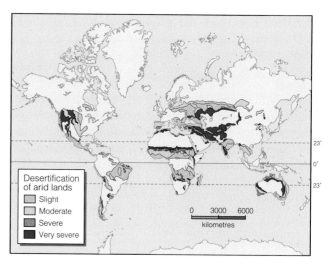

Figure 6–3

World drylands and desertification

SOURCE: *Risk of Human-Induced Desertification,* United States Department of Agriculture—National Resources Conservation Service, 1999, http://www.nrcs.usda.gov/technical/worldsoils/mapindex/dsrtrisk.html

country under UNCCD. Should climate changes occur as predicted, and currently dry regions become drier, Canada's partnership approaches to addressing land degradation and desertification will be vital in responding appropriately to the management challenges. Continued cooperation and collaboration among all levels of federal and provincial departments (e.g., agriculture, environment, natural resources, and forestry) will help ensure integration of a range of environmental, social, and economic concerns in decision making. Canadian universities, technology, and research centres will help in understanding and solving dryland farming issues through contributions relating to climate monitoring and research, soil organic matter, genetic diversity, tillage systems, livestock management, and other topics. Canadian civil society, too, will help combat desertification through the efforts of conservation groups to improve Canadians' awareness of such issues as land degradation and conservation farming techniques. Still other conservation groups can collaborate with industry, government, and NGOs to protect native grasslands and reclaim marginal lands. For example, Canadian Aboriginal communities are discussing with federal and provincial governments ways to adapt their traditional knowledge to dryland management on the Prairies. In Alberta, members of the Blood Tribe from the Blackfoot Nation are implementing the Blood Tribe Irrigation Project. This is a 12-year collaborative irrigation project designed to promote economic development through sustainable agriculture. Components of the project include training and information, construction, and farming and agri-business activities. Collaborative efforts such as these, as well as education, awareness, and research, are key to helping Canada combat land degradation at home and around the world.

Photo 6–6

Desertification is particularly problematic in Africa, where a combination of unsustainable land-use practices and climatic variations have resulted in overexploitation of the land.

EFFECTS ON WATER RESOURCES

Both surface water and groundwater resources can be affected directly by agricultural use of land. **Surface runoff** can carry sediment, nutrients, pesticides, and bacteria from agricultural lands and contaminate surface water bodies. Groundwater resources can be contaminated by nutrients or pesticides when rainwater, irrigation water, and snowmelt percolate through the soil. The discussion that follows highlights two major sources of water contamination, namely, crop and livestock production activities. Irrigation use and its effects also are considered.

Contamination from Crop Production Activities

The nutrients that plants need for growth are obtained from soil, water, and air. If a farmer is to attain economic yields and sustain soil fertility, it is often necessary to replace the nutrients removed when crops are harvested by adding extra nitrogen, phosphorus, and potassium in the form of manure or commercial fertilizers. Over 5 million tonnes of potash, phosphate, and nitrogen from commercial fertilizers were applied to Canadian farmlands in 2000 (Statistics Canada, 2002a). Depending on the type and intensity of crop and land management practices, soil characteristics, weather, and the type and amount of chemicals applied, that portion not used by crops or absorbed or retained in the soil can move into surface water or leach into groundwater.

Several **aquifers** in Canada show significant amounts of agrochemicals, mainly nitrates. For example, significant leaching of nitrates (which can make water unfit for human consumption) has been reported in an important aquifer near Osoyoos in the southern Okanagan Valley, British Columbia. Septic tank effluent and fertilizer use in orchards were the major suspected sources of nitrates. In the Fraser River Valley, also in British Columbia, the Abbotsford aquifer has been highly susceptible to contamination from extensive use of high-nitrogen poultry manure on raspberry and forage crops. Leaching occurs here, too, this time in combination with climatic (heavy winter rainfall) and soil conditions. Monitoring of nitrate concentrations since 1995 suggests not only that nitrates have increased annually at a rate of 0.7 milligrams per litre, but also that about 60 percent of the samples collected from a highly sensitive region of the aquifer exceed the Canadian Water Quality Guidelines safe limit of 10 milligrams per litre. Twelve different pesticides have been detected in the Abbotsford aquifer, four at levels exceeding the Canadian Freshwater Aquatic Guidelines, and four (for which there are no Canadian guidelines) that exceed Washington State water quality standards for groundwater. Studies of well-water contamination by nitrates, bacteria, and herbicides, conducted in Ontario, Quebec, New Brunswick, and Nova Scotia, have shown similar findings and concerns.

Other agrochemicals also cause concerns about water quality. If phosphorus enters surface-water bodies, for example, it can lead to accelerated eutrophication (nutrient pollution). Given that about 30 percent of Canadians (mainly rural residents) rely on groundwater for domestic purposes, and that more than 85 percent of livestock consume water from underground sources, protecting water resources from agricultural contamination is essential (Government of Canada, 1996; Reynolds et al., 1995).

Water quality surveys and monitoring efforts reveal that pesticides frequently are found in concentrations below the safe limits specified in the Canadian Water Quality Guidelines, while concentrations of nutrients and bacteriological contaminants sometimes exceed acceptable limits. In terms of groundwater, although there are insufficient long-term, detailed monitoring data to provide a comprehensive understanding of the current status and trends of agrochemicals entering Canada's groundwater, one of the main impacts of agricultural activities on water quality is contamination by nitrates (from fertilizers, the use of manure instead of chemical fertilizers, and feedlots).

From a human health perspective, widespread use of nitrate fertilizers increases the risk of well-water contamination in rural areas and heightens the risk of methemoglobinemia, a condition in which iron in the hemoglobin molecule (the red blood pigment) is defective, and thus the blood is unable to transport oxygen effectively to a person's tissues. Sometimes called "blue baby syndrome" because the skin and mucous membranes of individuals with this condition display a bluish discolouration, methemoglobinemia may be inherited or acquired through exposure to chemicals such as nitrates (NO_3), particularly in drinking water. Infants under four months of age are at specific risk of nitrate toxicity from contaminated water. Nitrates are a known reproductive toxin; most babies with congenital methemoglobinemia die in infancy, while others may suffer mental retardation, seizures, and other neurological problems (Medline Plus, 2007). Livestock, too, may experience nitrate poisoning and show symptoms such as staggering and difficulty standing up. While research assessing the effects of nitrate exposure on humans is ongoing, reports have provided mixed findings regarding nitrate in drinking water as a risk factor for cancer. It is clear, however, that people using private wells (which tend to be shallower and thus more susceptible to contamination) as well as those using municipal water supply systems should be aware of the need to ensure protection of their source water supplies (Weyer, 2001).

Pesticides sometimes are said to be less of a problem than they were 20 to 30 years ago because current pesticides are less persistent and more specialized. However, we cannot escape the fact that pesticides (particularly insecticides and herbicides) are an integral part of modern agricultural production. Public concerns remain about potential health hazards associated with water contamination, specifically persistence and bioaccumulation issues (see Chapter 7). Such concerns have encouraged increased use of nonchemical pest controls and decreased use of pesticides. For instance, mechanical and hand weeding are among the most common alternative methods of pest control, and are of particular interest to organic producers. Other methods of controlling pests include cultivating tolerant or resistant plants, seeding in fall, and using green manure—crops such as legumes grown specifically to be plowed into the soil (Korol, 2004). Public health and safety concerns are one reason why water quality has emerged as a key environmental issue facing agriculture in the 21st century.

Contamination from Livestock Production Activities

As noted previously, meat is a prime product of Canadian agriculture. Intensive livestock operations (ILOs), confined feeding operations (CFOs), or feedlots have become the dominant method of producing beef, hogs, and poultry in Canada. Feedlots enable livestock producers to increase their production to meet domestic and offshore demands for meat and poultry products. Feedlots also provide an ideal market for Canadian-produced grains; given the abundance of feed grains, western Canada can now produce bacon more profitably than any other region in the world (Nikiforuk, 2000). The apparent economic potential of ILO facilities has garnered government support and resulted in the rapid growth of feedlots throughout Canada, particularly on the Prairies, where, in 2006, Alberta accounted for 34 percent of the national beef herd (5.1 million cattle). Such expansion has generated conflict between proponents who see ILOs as positive economic operations, supporting a federal commitment to low food prices, and opponents who are concerned about contamination and health, environmental, and nuisance risks associated with feedlot facilities.

What is an ILO, and how does it generate contamination? Alberta Agriculture (2000) defines an intensive livestock operation as one where more than 300 *animal units* are confined in facilities at a density of 43 animal units per acre for more than 90 consecutive days, and where the producer has to manage the manure generated at the facilities. Alberta Agriculture defines animal units as the number of animals of a particular category of livestock that will excrete 73 kilograms of total nitrogen in a 12-month period. How many animals does it take to excrete this much nitrogen per year? Alberta Agriculture determined that one beef and one bison cow or bull would do so, but that it would take 1320 calves, 60 000 broiler chickens, and 1500 sows or boars (hogs) to produce that amount of nitrogen.

Most of the negative effects of feedlots result from the volume of manure produced at these operations.

Every day, one 454-kilogram feedlot steer produces about 27 kilograms of manure (9954 kilograms annually). In "Feedlot Alley," a small region north of Lethbridge, Alberta—Canada's largest concentration of livestock—about 500 000 cattle, 200 000 hogs, and 600 000 poultry generate a volume of manure equivalent to the waste that would be produced from a city of about 8 million. Even a single 500-sow farm producing 20 piglets per sow per year creates as much effluent as a town of 25 000 people, without a waste treatment system. Clearly, the growth of animal factories has created industrial-scale waste problems (Hasselback, 1997; Nikiforuk, 2000).

If properly applied to land, manure is an excellent slow-release fertilizer and source of organic matter. Manure application to land is particularly valuable in southern Alberta, where mineral soils (low organic content and high pH) are prevalent. However, the principal environmental hazard of ILOs is the possibility of surface and groundwater contamination from manure storage and application, including the leaching of nitrates and/or pesticides. Bacteria and parasites also contribute to contamination and to public health concerns regarding gastrointestinal illness. As residents of Walkerton, Ontario, discovered when heavy rain washed manure from farm fields into one of the wells that supplied their drinking water system, *E. coli* O157:H7 is a deadly pathogen (see discussion of the Walkerton case in Chapter 7).

Poultry CFOs generate another type of contamination. Typically, various heavy metals (such as arsenic, cobalt, copper, iron, manganese, selenium, and zinc) are added to poultry diets to improve weight gain and disease prevention. When poultry waste containing fairly high concentrations of heavy metals is dispersed repeatedly onto land, the runoff and leaching of heavy metals from the poultry waste–amended soil pose potential environmental risks to surface and groundwater (Han et al., 2000). A new composting process, designed to convert liquid hog, dairy, and poultry manure into dry organic fertilizer within a six- to eight-week period, has been tested on an Abbotsford farm by early 2006. The bio-drying process (heat energy within the manure is used to evaporate the moisture) removes much of the methane gas associated with manure storage, filters out ammonia, reduces GHGs such as nitrous oxide, and, because the waste is composted in containers rather than spread over land, helps producers who are facing encroaching urban development and have limited land on which to apply large volumes of manure. This project was part of the federal Greenhouse Gas Mitigation Program for Canadian Agriculture (Soil Conservation Council of Canada, 2005).

Air quality is a third concern associated with ILOs. Over 150 gaseous compounds may be emitted when manure is spread on land; people living in areas of dense livestock operations complain about the headaches and nausea caused by odours from these gases. Despite growing health concerns and residents' appeals against ILOs, the Alberta government plans included to doubly beef production and triply hog production. Research into the hog barn "neighbourhood effect" (the impact that large-scale hog operations have on people living close to them) indicates that residents in the vicinity of the Lethbridge hog barns face many of the same health and quality of life risks that hog barn workers do. Both barn workers and residents are exposed to volatile organic compounds (VOCs), ammonia, and other sulphur- and sulphide-containing compounds that may cause respiratory system ailments, mucous membrane syndrome, and organic dust toxic syndrome. The existence of the hog barn neighbourhood effect suggests that planning and development authorities must employ the precautionary principle when they consider permit applications for large-scale hog operations, even as they must attempt to balance the interests of producers, investors, and local residents (Johnston & Weibel, 2005–6).

On January 1, 2002, the Alberta government introduced a new provincial regulatory framework for its confined feeding operations. Based on the 2000 Code of Practice for Responsible Livestock Development and Manure Management, the new standards and regulations set the type and size of ILOs that must be approved, established new water protection buffer zones for operators applying manure, and identified who should be notified of a proposed or expanding ILO (Government of Alberta, 2001). While these regulations were designed to "ensure our $5-billion livestock industry can grow and expand" (Government of Alberta, 2001), grassroots activists remain concerned about the long-term health of rural communities and ecosystems. For additional information on feedlots, manure management, public health concerns, and actions taken to resolve these issues, see Box 6–5 on page 222.

Since some of Canada's largest livestock farms, with the highest density of animals per square kilometre, are near major cities, these are the areas where conflicts (e.g., odour issues) between nonfarming residents and farmers may occur. Very large livestock farms are located in western Canada near Vancouver, Lethbridge, Red Deer, and Winnipeg; in eastern Canada, in Ontario's Niagara region; and in Quebec, near Joliette, Granby, Drummondville and south of Montreal, Quebec City, and eastward down the St. Lawrence River valley (see Figure 6-4).

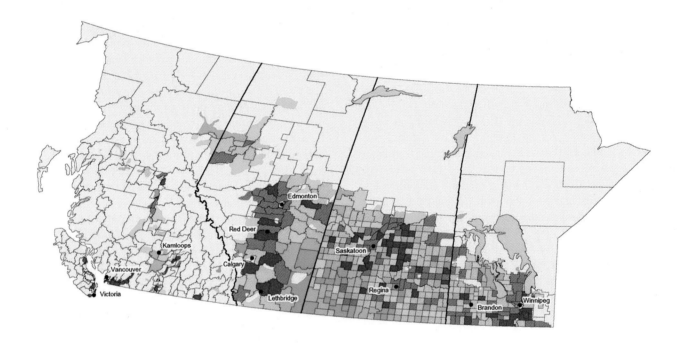

Animal units per km² of farmland on very large livestock operations, 2001

5.0 – 15.0	35.1 – 50.0	No very large livestock operations (300 or more animal units)
15.1 – 25.0	50.1 – 100.0	
25.1 – 35.0	> 100.0	Non-agricultural area

—— Census consolidated subdivision boundary

Very large livestock operations in Western Canada: 4,990

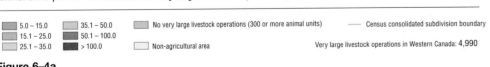

Figure 6–4a

Very large livestock operations, western Canada, 2001

SOURCE: "Living with the Farm Next Door," *Canadian Agriculture at a Glance*, Statistics Canada, 2004, page 147. Catalogue no. 96-325-XPB.

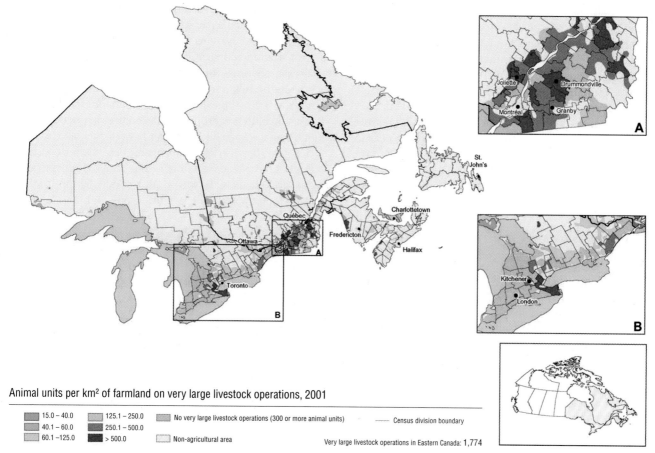

Animal units per km² of farmland on very large livestock operations, 2001

15.0 – 40.0	125.1 – 250.0	No very large livestock operations (300 or more animal units)
40.1 – 60.0	250.1 – 500.0	
60.1 –125.0	> 500.0	Non-agricultural area

—— Census division boundary

Very large livestock operations in Eastern Canada: 1,774

Figure 6–4b

Very large livestock operations, eastern Canada, 2001

SOURCE: "Living with the Farm Next Door," *Canadian Agriculture at a Glance*, Statistics Canada, 2004, page 148. Catalogue no. 96-325-XPB.

Irrigation Effects

Agriculture accounted for 9 percent of the total water withdrawals in Canada in 2001 (see Figure 7–5 on page 266). Of the 4098 million cubic metres of water taken up for agricultural uses, 85 percent was used for irrigation and

Photo 6–7

A farmer spreads manure on a field to replace nutrients lost through harvesting.

the remaining 15 percent for livestock watering (Statistics Canada, 2000). Agriculture (irrigation) is the highest consumer of water; because of the high rate of evaporation from agricultural fields, only about 25 percent of the water withdrawn for irrigation is returned to its source (Shrubsole & Draper, 2007).

In western Canada irrigation is used to increase the productive capacity of land for forage, cereal, and oilseed crops, while in eastern Canada irrigation traditionally has been applied to fruit, tobacco, and vegetable crops. Irrigated crops come with a price tag: reservoir construction floods scenic river valleys, destroys historically and culturally important sites, reduces or eliminates habitat for fish and wildlife, and alters the flow and water quality of a river, often disadvantaging downstream users. Sediments accumulate in reservoirs, reducing their capacity, and below a dam there may be streambed erosion. These impacts associated with major infrastructure for irrigation can change flooding patterns to the detriment of some adapted species such as cottonwood trees, reduce water quality, harm fish populations, and, because of water fluctuations from reservoir operation, destroy waterfowl nests and homes of water-dwelling mammals such as beaver and muskrat.

CHAPTER 6: AGROECOSYSTEMS AND LAND RESOURCES

Traditional irrigation techniques have included flooding of fields and use of overhead sprinklers (see Photos 6–9a–c on page 225), but these approaches often result in high rates of evaporation, runoff, and deep percolation. Precision irrigation techniques are becoming increasingly important in sustainable agriculture. The idea of precision irrigation is that water is applied (dripped, sprayed, sprinkled, bubbled, or misted at low pressure) through small devices onto the soil surface very near the plant or below the soil surface directly into the plant root zone (see Photos 6–9d–e). Also known as micro-irrigation systems, these devices are very popular in regions where water supplies are limited, or where water is expensive, because precision irrigation techniques minimize the use of water and fertilizer (water + fertilizer = fertigation). These smaller systems also require less power to operate than traditional irrigation equipment, reduce weeds and disease (because of the limited wetted area), and can operate on hilly terrain with no runoff and without wind interference. Typical applications of micro-irrigation systems include row crops such as onions, peppers, squash, and tomatoes; small fruits and berries such as strawberries, blackberries, and raspberries; new shelter belt trees around farmsteads; and high-value fruit trees, vineyards, and greenhouses. However, all relevant factors such as land topography, soil, water, crop, and agro-climatic

BOX 6-5
FEEDLOTS, MANURE MANAGEMENT, AND PUBLIC HEALTH CONCERNS

Intensive livestock operations raise a number of environmental and community health issues, most associated with the safe, nontoxic disposal and recycling of manure. We examine these issues more closely in the following sections.

Feedlot Operation

A typical feedlot operation consists of an enclosed animal area, a slurry pond or lagoon to catch the feedlot runoff, manure storage facilities, and surrounding agricultural land. In consuming feed or silage, livestock extract nitrogen and other elements; in turn, the majority of the nitrogen consumed is excreted either as urine or feces. The 9954 kilograms of manure produced annually by a single steer includes 1410 kilograms of solids, 56 kilograms of nitrogen, and 18 kilograms of phosphorus (Gregorash, 1997). The excreta are collected in the slurry pond, lagoon, storage tank, or trench, or removed by scraping the feedlot. The manure is then stored in piles either outside or within storage buildings and, after decomposing for six to eight months, is distributed onto fields as fertilizer for feed crops such as corn or barley. In some places, the feed grown is harvested and consumed by local livestock.

Manure Storage and Application

Storing manure (in facilities with impervious bases) allows operators to apply it to the land when the crop uptake of nutrients is most rapid and runoff from fields is least likely. Knowing when and how much manure to apply is a complex task that involves understanding soil characteristics, crop requirements, characteristics of the manure (moisture, salt, nutrients), nutrient releasing rates, geology, and slope of the land. Manure may be spread on any given piece of land once every three to six years. Most larger feedlot operations cannot grow all the feed grain required and must import it from other provinces or areas where the price is right. Since hauling manure beyond 18 kilometres is uneconomical, nutrients in the manure seldom go back to the fields where the feed grain was produced (Gregorash, 1997). To avoid overloading the soil on their own land, feedlot operators make arrangements to spread manure on neighbouring fields. Since feedlots are concentrated spatially, concern has been expressed regarding increasing manure concentrations in soil.

Photo 6–8
Sows in a holding pen on a hog farm.

Pollution and Human Health Problems

As the size and density of livestock feeding operations increase, so does the potential for adverse effects on soil and water quality: runoff from feeding areas, feedlots, manure storage facilities, or manured fields may contaminate surface waters with sediments, nutrients, organic matter, and bacteria. If more manure has been applied to the land than the crops can use, nitrogen, phosphorus, and salts may accumulate in the soil, and groundwater may become contaminated with nitrates. Excessive phosphate and nitrogen in water bodies promote algae, weed growth, and eutrophication.

Health researchers classify public health concerns associated with ILOs into three types: air quality, surface-water quality, and groundwater problems. Each health concern is considered briefly here.

Air Quality Problems

The public's major air quality complaint about feedlots is the smell (often considered a nuisance effect). Manure-spreading operations release gaseous compounds such as hydrogen sulphide, ammonia, carbon dioxide, and methane (Hasselback, 1997). People downwind of the manure application may complain about a variety of effects, including headaches, nausea, and aggravated asthma and respiratory problems. Air quality monitoring by Alberta Environment (2000) near livestock feeding operations in the Lethbridge area from September 1998 to July 1999 revealed that, with the exception of hydrogen sulphide, all substances detected were at levels within Alberta's ambient air quality guidelines.

The concentrations of substances in our ambient air vary from second to second because of turbulence in the atmosphere. To enable their practical use, these concentrations are expressed as averages over specified time periods. The monitoring of air quality parameters that took place in Lethbridge was based on measuring concentrations, in parts per million by volume (ppmv), of a number of substances, for one-hour annual averaging periods. For instance, the guideline for concentrations of hydrogen sulphide was 10 ppmv, for ammonia was 2000 ppmv, and for nitrogen dioxide was 212 ppmv. The basis for these one-hour averages was odour perception. In 2000, only hydrogen sulphide concentrations were above the guideline; with the expansion in livestock feeding operations since then, would concentrations have increased also? (Current Alberta ambient air quality objectives may be found at: http://environment.alberta.ca/645.html.)

The health implications of inhaling the mixture of gases and odours are unclear, although it is known that airborne dust (from manure spreading) can carry diseases and transmit *E. coli* (Tessier, 2001). In the Lower Fraser Valley, British Columbia, ammonia from manure is known to volatize (change from a liquid or solid to a vapour) into the atmosphere and react with particles of urban smog (industrial pollutants and vehicle emissions). When this happens, a thick band of white haze forms over the intensive poultry farming area of Abbotsford. Scientists indicate that this white haze is a rural version of urban smog, specifically associated with emissions from intensive agricultural production of poultry and other livestock manures (Environment Canada, 1999). There are concerns that rural smog will result in similar respiratory effects caused by urban smog.

Surface-Water Quality Problems

Human health problems may arise when leaching, runoff, or overflows from manure lagoons deliver increased bacterial loadings to surface-water bodies, including irrigation canals, near livestock operations. Bacteria of concern include *E. coli* O157:H7, *Campylobacter*, and *Salmonella*. In Alberta, the province's highest rates of intestinal infections are found in Feedlot Alley, and many cases are associated with people in the livestock industry (Hasselback, 1997; Nikiforuk, 2000). The experience of residents of Walkerton, Ontario, in May 2000 confirms the epidemic level of sickness (and even deaths) that *E. coli* O157:H7 can inflict on humans when just one manure-contaminated well is connected to a drinking water supply system.

The diffusion of parasites that may be spread by cattle, such as *Cryptosporidium parvum* and *Giardia lamblia,* is a growing concern. *Cryptosporidium* has caused several large waterborne outbreaks of human disease in North America: recent outbreaks in Canada have occurred in Cranbrook and Kelowna, British Columbia, and Owen Sound, Ontario. The parasite is resistant to chlorination, but may be removed by filtration, although inadequate water treatment facilities may not remove parasite oocysts (eggs). This is of concern because spring thaw can result in the overland flow of billions of oocysts from stored manure and infected animals, and treatment facilities may have difficulty cleaning and filtering the water. Several communities in Alberta and elsewhere have been under orders to boil domestic water supplies because treatment facilities cannot guarantee parasite-free water.

Another concern is that pig manure can contain high concentrations of endocrine-disrupting chemicals, including natural estrogens. Scientists have shown that these chemicals have long-term, adverse effects on the growth, development, and reproduction of fish and wildlife (see Box 7–3 on page 279). Runoff from fields treated with pig manure quickly enters adjacent streams or other water bodies and results in eutrophication or acute toxicity (Environment Canada, 1998).

Groundwater Problems

Vertical movement of liquids in the hydrological cycle may carry chemicals, including nitrates, into underlying aquifers. While humans can tolerate low levels of nitrate, a level above 10 milligrams per litre renders water unfit for human consumption. "Blue baby syndrome" (methemoglobinemia) may affect infants who ingest high levels of nitrate (Pederson & Johnson, 1997). As a result of livestock operations and fertilization practices, nitrate contamination of shallow groundwater aquifers has occurred in many parts of North America. Generally, contamination decreases with increasing depth, but Walkerton's medical health officer has raised concerns regarding the safety of deep groundwater wells in the area. Preventing contamination of aquifers from agricultural or any other activities is vitally important because no effective technology exists to cleanse aquifers.

Community Stresses

In Alberta, stresses on long-term friend and family relationships have increased as a groundswell of concern has developed regarding ILOs and their expansion within the province. Citizen unrest, protests against feedlot expansion, and appeals regarding large-scale operations have gone largely unheeded by the Alberta government (Ahmed, 1999). Just west of Feedlot Alley, for example, the County Residents for Fair Taxation group brought attention to the subsidization of ILO operators by grain farmers and acreage owners. The County Residents group pointed out that a 65-hectare feedlot with 25 000 head of cattle paid the same annual property tax as a 65-hectare grain farm, even though the impact of the feedlot on water services and roads was up to 500 times that of the grain farm (Ahmed, 1999). Over 1200 people signed a petition urging the County of Lethbridge to introduce a business tax; the county implemented the tax in late 1998. Other local actions have met with limited or no success. It is unlikely, however, that citizens strongly opposed to unimpeded expansion of the livestock industry will cease their pressure for reform.

(continued)

Actions to Improve ILOs

In Alberta, a Code of Practice for the Safe and Economical Handling of Animal Manures has been in place since 1995. Grassroots activists note that the most important weakness of this code is that it is a guideline only and is unenforceable. Without enforceable regulations, they feel, improper management of ILOs will continue. Concerns about the process by which ILO expansion could take place, and about monitoring and enforcing the environmental sustainability of these operations, led Alberta Agriculture to propose (in 1999) a Regulatory Framework for Livestock Feeding Operations in the province. The new framework came into effect on January 1, 2002. Now all developments must comply with regulations and standards regarding manure management and protecting water from manure runoff.

Other actions to improve ILOs include efforts to reduce odour issues by altering nutritional strategies for cattle, particularly through manipulation of the type and quantity of protein in their feed (Lethbridge Research Centre, 1999). Best management practices can also be implemented to reduce the possibility of soil and water contamination from animal wastes. One example is the creation of a riparian buffer zone by lining manure lagoons with trees and vegetation. This action provides a rich source of soil microbes that degrade and consume nutrients such as nitrate and phosphorous found in manure. Cows and Fish, a successful program aimed at helping producers protect riparian habitat and decrease manure runoff into surface water, is discussed in Box 6–7 on page 229.

Other protective actions that can be taken include transporting manure to fields farther away from ILOs; testing receiving soils for nitrogen and phosphorus; and monitoring collection lagoons to prevent overflow and seepage. Even though these actions will increase operating costs, they will go a long way to preventing future pollution and public health problems.

SOURCES: "Grassroots Activism on the Prairies," A. Ahmed, 1999, *Encompass, 3*(4), 16–17; *From Conflict to Cooperation*, Alberta AFRD, 1999, http://www.agric.gov.ab.ca/c2c/index.html; *Air Quality Monitoring: Lethbridge Area—1998–99, Near Livestock Feeding Operations*, Alberta Environment, 2000, http://environment.gov.ab.ca/info/posting.asp?assetid=6390&categoryid=1; "Endocrine Disruptors and Hog Manure," Environment Canada, November–December, 1998, *Science and the Environment Bulletin, 4*; "Manure Causing White Haze," Environment Canada, May–June, 1999, *Science and the Environment Bulletin, 12*; "Feedlot Manure: An Issue That Doesn't Go Away," D. Gregorash, 1997, *Encompass, 2*(2), 19–20; "Intensive Livestock Operations and Health Problems," P. Hasselback, 1997, *Encompass, 2*(2), 4–5; *Scientists Target Air Quality in New Feedlot Manure Study*, Lethbridge Research Centre, 1999, http://res2.agr.ca/lethbridge/rep1999/adva0302.htm; "When Water Kills," A. Nikiforuk, June 12, 2000, *Online* Macleans, http://www.macleans.ca/pubdoc/2000/06/12/Cover/35699.shtml; *Animal Wastes as a Source of Drinking Water Contamination*, T. L. Pederson & B. T. Johnson, 1997, ExtoxNet, http://www.ace.orst.edu/info/extoxnet/faqs/safedrink/feed.htm; *Manure Handling Strategies for Minimizing Environmental Impacts*, S. Tessier, 2001, Manitoba Agriculture, Food and Rural Initiatives, http://www.gov.mb.ca/agriculture/livestock/pork/swine/bab10s08.html; "New Regulatory Framework: Striking a Balance," Alberta Agriculture and Rural Development, 2002, http://www1.agric.gov.ab.ca/$department/newslett.nsf/all/gm10196

conditions must be studied carefully to ensure an appropriate selection of micro-irrigation devices.

In parts of the Prairies where surface waters are scarce, not all impacts of water storage areas are negative. In addition to the water they provide for irrigation, water impoundments and canals can be used for recreation and fishing, and may provide new types of habitat for wildlife. In the past, the brush and weeds that grew beside canals and fence lines provided excellent cover for birds and small mammals. More recently, increased chemical control of brush and weeds and the attempts to reduce water losses through canal lining and use of water pipelines have diminished the positive effects of irrigation works on wildlife.

In the Prairie provinces, irrigation water is applied to over 635 000 hectares. While the area to be irrigated has not enlarged significantly during the past decade, there has been an increase in the amount of water applied per hectare since 1981. This trend, combined with regional climate-change scenarios that point to more frequent and prolonged droughts on the Prairies, with increased drying up of wetlands, suggests the need for improved efficiency in water use. With modern methods and technology, irrigation needs for extensive grain, oilseed, fruit and vegetable production may be reduced by 10 to 50 percent (Government of Canada, 1996).

Other environmental concerns related to irrigated land result from the increased use of pesticides and fertilizers compared with amounts farmers would usually employ under dryland conditions. When irrigation water runs off the fields, residues from these substances may enter streams or be leached into groundwater, contaminating those water bodies. Irrigation may exacerbate dryland salinization of soils by altering shallow groundwater conditions that, in turn, accelerate surface evaporation. Replacing natural vegetation with short-season cereal grains is one action that can trigger salinization. Salts also can leach from irrigated lands, sometimes as a result of unlined canals causing water tables to rise in areas where salts are present in the subsoil. About 6 to 8 million hectares of land in western Canada contain soils that may be affected by salinization.

EFFECTS ON BIODIVERSITY

Agricultural impacts on genetic, species, and ecosystem biodiversity of native wild species have become an important environmental issue. "Generally speaking, the quantity

Photo 6–9a

Photo 6–9b

Photo 6–9d

Photo 6–9c

Photo 6–9e

Irrigation water is applied to the land using a variety of methods, including centre pivot (6–9a), oscillating sprinklers (6–9b), irrigation canals (6–9c), micro-sprinklers (6–9d), and drip hoses (6–9e).

and quality of wildlife habitat in Canada have been degraded by settlement and agricultural development. Although farmlands and rangelands do provide enhanced habitat for certain species ... others have declined as a direct result of agricultural expansion and production practices. Many species of native plants, amphibians, reptiles, fish, birds, and mammals are endangered or threatened as a consequence of habitat loss to agriculture" (Government of Canada, 1991, p. 9-9; Environment Canada, 2001).

Agricultural development has contributed to the *endangered status* (threatened with imminent extirpation or extinction) of birds such as the mountain plover, sage grouse (prairie), and sage thrasher; mammals such as the swift fox; vascular plants such as the cucumber tree (see Box 9–3, p. 380), American ginseng, and pink milkwort; and reptiles such as the blue racer snake (Statistics Canada, 2000).

Current agricultural land management practices have modified, and continue to modify, biodiversity in several ways. Biodiversity is reduced when agricultural production systems with little crop rotation (such as in monocultures) provide large areas of uniform habitat. Deforestation, the replacement of indigenous plants with other crops, the drying of wetlands, and the use of insecticides and herbicides have reduced the populations and areas of distribution of numerous species and also resulted in the introduction of new species. Aquatic biodiversity can be affected by water draining from agricultural fields, carrying nutrients, eroded sediments, and pesticides. Similarly, wild species composition and abundance can be affected through selective grazing of preferred forage plants that alters the vegetation composition (Government of Canada, 1996; Mineau et al., 1994).

On the prairies, much of the original habitat has been altered significantly, largely through agriculture. Less than 1 percent of the original tallgrass prairie remains, and less than 20 percent of each of the shortgrass prairie, mixed-grass prairie, and aspen parkland remain (Environment

Canada, 2001; Gauthier & Henry, 1989; Trottier, 1992). This level of modification of original ecosystems has led to a concern for their continued viability and for the survival of the species that inhabit these areas, on the prairies and beyond (Van Tighem, 1996). The following sections identify particular effects of agricultural activities on wetlands and grazing lands.

Wetland Loss and Conversion

Wetlands, along with their ecologically productive and purifying functions and their contributions to the socio-economic well-being of Canadians (see Figure 6–5), have been disappearing since settlement began. In the Great Lakes basin, for example, wetlands have been lost to agricultural and residential development at a rate of 8100 hectares per year. Despite the massive loss of wetlands, they continue to contribute billions of dollars annually to the Canadian economy through support of commercial and sports fishing, waterfowl hunting, trapping, recreation, peatland forestry, water purification, groundwater discharge, and flood peak modification.

There is potential danger to wetlands from the pesticides and nutrients used in intense agricultural activities as well. Shoreline wetlands on the Canadian side of Lake Erie are a case in point. From 1992 to 1994, researchers studying the problem showed that pesticides were transported in water and in sediments from streams and creeks surrounding the wetlands into the wetlands and downstream into Lake Erie. Alachlor, a carcinogenic and oncogenic (tumour-producing) pesticide banned in 1989, was detected at one of the sampling stations. The highest pesticide concentrations occurred between May and July, immediately after pesticides were applied to the fields and following spring precipitation. Research continues into the impacts and cumulative effects of chronic exposure of Lake Erie's marsh and lake biota to these concentrations of pesticides.

Conversion of wetlands to other uses has been significant in many regions of Canada. For instance, 70 percent of sloughs in the central prairie wetland area (including 59 percent of wetlands in the Red River Valley), 65 percent of Atlantic salt marshes, 70 percent of Pacific estuarine marshes, and 70 to 80 percent of southern Ontario and St. Lawrence Valley hardwood and shoreline swamps have been converted. Eighty-five percent of the decline in Canada's original wetland area is attributed to drainage for agriculture (Rubec, 1994). Severe effects such as this result in marked shifts in vegetation and animal species composition, including that of migratory species. Changes in habitat have direct effects on populations and life cycles of ducks, geese, swans, shorebirds, songbirds, and butterflies that inhabit North, Central, and parts of South America. The risk to biodiversity through habitat change is epitomized in the example of migratory songbirds and the shift from traditional shade-loving coffee plants to

Photo 6–10

The burrowing owl is just one prairie species whose existence has been endangered by the agricultural alteration of its habitat.

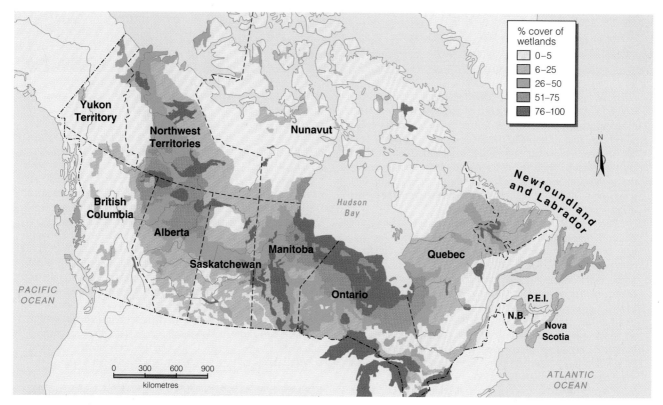

Figure 6–5

Distribution of wetlands in Canada, 1996

SOURCE: Adapted from *The State of Canada's Environment—1996,* Environment Canada, Figure 10.12. © Her Majesty the Queen in Right of Canada, Environment Canada, 1996. Reproduced with the permission of the Minister of Public Works and Government Services Canada, 2008.

high-yield, sun-loving plants in modern Latin American coffee plantations (see Box 6–6 on the next page).

In spite of their historical effects in Canada, certain agricultural practices can enhance wildlife habitat and promote biodiversity. Some farmers may strive to maintain populations of pollinator species, pest predators, and soil fauna, as well as to preserve wetland habitats (which also conserves groundwater and helps protect against drought). Planting shelter belts, instituting planned grazing systems, and planting forage crops on marginal croplands are other means by which farmers may provide habitat for many forms of wildlife. Taking steps to ensure that soil organic matter is retained (thereby providing habitat for microorganisms) and employing integrated pest management techniques can reduce the risks from pesticides to nontarget species. Furthermore, farmers can take part in habitat conservation programs such as the North America Wetlands Conservation Council (NAWCC). In partnership, the North American Waterfowl Management Plan and the NAWCC (see Chapters 7 and 12) jointly have administered over $500 million in joint-venture projects. These projects have secured and enhanced over 800 000 hectares of key habitat and restored waterfowl populations and habitat (North America Wetlands Conservation Council, 2002).

Rangeland Grazing

About 40 percent of the world's land surface is used for grazing (Cardy, 1997). Most grazing takes place in arid, semi-arid, and dry subhumid climates or on land that is unsuitable for cultivated crops (because of steep slopes, for instance). Throughout the world, both domestic and wild animals forage on grasses, forbs, and shrubs, and provide people with valuable commodities such as food, fibre, and draft animals. Grazing lands also provide intangible products or values such as open space, natural beauty, and the opportunity to study natural ecosystems. Often referred to as rangelands in Canada, the value of grazing lands for wildlife and ecosystem functions has not been calculated, although their economic importance is tremendous.

Rangeland ecosystems are based on disturbance from grazing animals, fire, and drought (Manzano & Navár, 2000; Trottier, 1992). In the past, natural disturbances such as bison grazing and fire were important in stimulating new plant growth and nurturing a healthy range. Bison impacts on the prairies and foothills ranges often were severe but short-lived, because the yearly cycle of bison migration between the plains and foothills provided effective rest and regeneration periods for grazed areas (Adams & Fitch, 1995). Today, however, fire is

CHAPTER 6: AGROECOSYSTEMS AND LAND RESOURCES

BOX 6-6
MIGRATORY SONGBIRDS, COFFEE PLANTATIONS, AND FAIR TRADE IN LATIN AMERICA

Attempts by coffee growers in Latin America to increase yields may be putting migratory songbird populations at risk in North America. Earlier studies of the decline of the songbird populations noted that widespread deforestation and fragmentation of habitat were the principal threat to the birds' survival. Research indicates that at least part of the cause of the decline may be the modernization of the coffee plantation, where the former emphasis on shade-loving coffee plants has shifted to high-yield dwarf varieties that require lots of sun.

When habitat for the migratory birds became scarce, they became increasingly dependent on the traditional coffee plantation, where coffee plants were raised under a shady canopy of native trees. With the conversion to sun-loving plants and the associated increase in inputs such as synthetic fertilizers, pesticides, herbicides, and fungicides, the birds have less habitat. Remaining habitat often has been contaminated by chemicals that can be detrimental to the birds' survival. Although there is no absolute proof that the switch to sun plantations has caused the decline in bird numbers, research in Guatemala, for instance, shows that the higher-yield plantations support about one-half the diversity of the shade plantations.

In response to the concern for the migratory bird population, Conservation International has instituted a bird-friendly coffee certification program that helps ensure the coffee purchased was grown on a shade plantation, using organic methods and with fair trade criteria. Starbucks, a major coffee company, has partnered with Conservation International in Chiapas, Mexico, to assist in preservation of small, traditional shade coffee farms in areas of high biodiversity and to help promote ecologically sound practices in tropical ecosystems.

TransFair is Canada's independent certification organization for fair trade in coffee, tea, cocoa, and sugar products. When fair trade logos appear on coffee products, for instance, consumers are guaranteed that their coffee beans were purchased from democratically organized, small groups of farmers who themselves are listed and monitored by the FairTrade Labelling Organizations International (FLO). TransFair's licensees must pay a set minimum price that covers the costs of production, advance payment or extend credit to producers to help them avoid debt while they finance the next year's production, and agree to longer-term trading relationships that provide producers with added security to plan for the future and promote sustainable production practices (TransFair Canada, 2001). Often, producers are paid premium prices to help improve social conditions in their communities and to support more environmentally sustainable agricultural techniques (often the traditional, small-scale, shade-grown, and chemical-free practices) that help cultivate healthy communities and habitats (TransFair Canada, 2001).

A pilot project in the United Kingdom initiated the suggestion that small-scale farmers in the northern hemisphere could cooperate and coordinate their marketing efforts and develop consumer demand for their products in ways similar to fair trade associations operating in Latin America. However, using a fair trade marketing approach in the north raises questions about equity: is it more appropriate to buy from local growers for environmental reasons or to keep the focus on fair trade in the southern hemisphere because it is more fragile economically? Provided consumers recognize the impacts of their purchases, and carefully select which producers and commodities they will support, social and environmental benefits should grow.

Photo 6-11
Consumers who buy local, organic produce at farmers' markets or stores contribute to the economic sustainability of small-scale farmers and help to reduce air pollution and GHGs because the produce travels shorter distances to markets.

SOURCES: "Birds Lose Out in Modern Coffee Plantations," 1997, *Encompass, 1*(2), 24; *Giving Back: A Guide to Starbucks in the Community,* Starbucks Coffee Company, 1999, Seattle; *Fair Trade Criteria,* TransFair Canada, 2001, http://www.transfair.ca; "Juan Valdez, meet Jane Walden," C. Berry, 2003, *Alternatives Journal, 29*(4), 26–27.

---

uncommon on the range and, because of fences and roads, livestock do not emulate the periodic foraging of bison (Bork, 2000). Cattle grazing is more regular and more concentrated.

Beginning in the latter half of the 19th century, as the number of livestock on the range grew, grazing pressure resulted in the overuse of favoured plants. Heavy and very heavy grazing levels resulted in loss of important forage species (that is, a reduction in biodiversity, with a concomitant reduction in animal productivity); decrease in the protection that plants contribute to soil stability; increased erosion of exposed soils; and decreased water infiltration on hard-packed ground (Bakker, 1998; Bork, 2000; Thurow, 2000). Changes in plant biodiversity not only affected habitat for native species, including birds (Dale, 2000), but also resulted in a loss of carbon sinks, an important element in climate change (Arnalds, 2000; Janzen, 2000). Globally, the United Nations has estimated that degradation of grazing lands due to overgrazing and other agricultural practices unsuited to dryland ecosystems has put the livelihoods of approximately 1 billion people at risk (Dowdeswell, 1997).

Livestock grazing also has been the major cause of **riparian** habitat disturbance, in which uncontrolled livestock break down stream banks, eat and trample shrubs that provide shade for stream dwellers and other wildlife, disturb stream beds, and contaminate water with fecal coliforms. For information about Cows and Fish, an Alberta initiative directed at ensuring sustainability of riparian habitats exposed to grazing livestock, see Box 6–7.

Although we tend to think of rangeland as grasslands, ecosystems used for grazing in Canada include tallgrass, mixed, and fescue prairie; forested rangelands; and wetland, sandhill, salt flats, and valley (coulee) *complexes* (Johnson, 1995). *Complexes* is the name given by ecologists to abrupt local changes in terrain that contain plant species adapted to local conditions; complexes are perhaps the most important wildlife habitat left on the prairies. Before European settlement, native rangelands supported hundreds of plant species, as well as grazing animals such as bison, elk, deer, and antelope. Rangelands also sustained a network of predators and scavengers

BOX 6–7
THE COWS AND FISH "EXPERIMENT"

By Lorne Fitch, Provincial Riparian Specialist, Alberta Cows and Fish Program

In the United States, the use and abuse of riparian landscapes by livestock grazing has been a focal point of nearly three decades of debate. Issues about riparian use began in Alberta with a focus on fish. In the 1970s, the impact of decades of unmanaged livestock use on several high-profile trout streams in west-central Alberta became apparent through biological surveys. Those baseline surveys provided the catalyst to galvanize restoration actions designed to improve habitat conditions for trout.

Initial efforts for recovery involved fencing programs to permanently exclude livestock from variable portions of riparian areas. Exclusion fencing can provide rapid recovery and help to demonstrate a site's biological potential, often quickly; this was the case for the initial riparian management program in west-central Alberta. However, as the program to use exclusion fencing as the prime riparian management tool expanded, some issues related to the narrow focus became apparent. Initial fencing costs are high and the associated maintenance of fences in close proximity to an area prone to flood damage often exceeds the original cost. Stream-bank fencing also was perceived as a loss of abundant forage and a limitation of the opportunity for livestock water. Additionally, and contrary to disturbance process theory in ecosystem dynamics, exclusion fencing conveyed the notion that riparian areas and cattle are incompatible. As well, streams, the adjoining riparian zone, and watersheds function as units and are inseparable; exclusion fencing does not allow the opportunity to find the solution to a riparian grazing problem in the adjacent uplands and to manage on a landscape basis.

The Alberta Cows and Fish initiative began as a recognition that resolution of the impasse over riparian areas and their management would be accomplished with a range of solutions, including, but not exclusively, stream-bank fencing. In 1992 six groups and agencies sat around a rancher's kitchen table and established what would become the Cows and Fish program. This partnership between the Alberta Cattle Commission, Trout Unlimited Canada, the Canadian Cattlemen's Association, (then) Alberta Environmental Protection, Alberta Agriculture, Food and Rural Development, and Fisheries and Oceans Canada

(and later PFRA) created a synergy of experience, perspective, background, and resources that broadened the approach to riparian issues.

The Cows and Fish program began (and continues) as a different way to engage with people, especially livestock producers, to move beyond suspicion, denial, and conflict to trust, acceptance, and cooperation. Engagement begins with ecological awareness, a nonthreatening, nonconfrontational extension effort to help people understand some of the ecological processes that shape the landscape they live on and make a living from. Part of that critical, initial message is that there are choices and alternatives to current management practices. As the antithesis of the top-down approach, Cows and Fish encourages the formation of local or community teams, composed of technical, producer, and other local interests, to engage with each other to "drive" the process.

The Cows and Fish program assists in the assemblage of technical advice and tools for management changes to provide alternatives to current practices. Information sources include those innovative, progressive, or practical solutions already being used by a limited and select group of landowners. Key tools, part of ecological "literacy," include demonstration sites and riparian health assessment. It is difficult to sell concepts or ideas without tangible products or examples. Demonstration sites are products, examples of changes in grazing management that people can see, review, and reflect on whether these management changes make sense for their own operations. Sites selected for demonstration purposes also represent research opportunities to test and measure riparian response to a particular grazing management option. Since many livestock producers are reluctant to experiment, at their own expense and risk, the development of demonstration sites using capital from elsewhere provides some of the first steps in a community to acceptance of other management ideas.

Riparian health assessment is a useful tool that allows people to critically observe, measure, and assess the status of ecological function on their own property or within their communities. The term "riparian health" is used to mean the ability of a riparian area to perform certain key ecological functions. These functions

(continued)

include sediment trapping, bank building, water storage, aquifer recharge, water filtration, flow energy dissipation, maintenance of biodiversity, and primary production. If these functions are impaired, so too will be the ability to sustain agricultural operations. Health assessment is not just an ecological "measuring stick"; it becomes a communication device to allow people with differing backgrounds and experience to "see" a riparian area and its status through the same set of eyes. Arguments about riparian condition are minimized and a much more productive discussion about how to restore damaged areas can begin. The current status of watersheds within a community can become a catalyst for action based on health assessments and forms a benchmark useful to chart progress, both on individual properties and within watersheds.

The Alberta Cows and Fish program assists in community-based conservation through a process of engagement that creates opportunity to move from conflict to cooperation. Stewardship opportunity is created through a four-stage "process" or "pathway." It begins with ecological awareness, a fundamental building block often skipped in other initiatives. The second step is assisting in the development of teams and partnerships. A network of resource professionals, landowners, and others who value riparian landscapes needs to form to solve issues and problems in a multidisciplinary fashion. Step three is the assemblage of technical advice and tools for management changes to provide options and alternatives to current practices. Part of this step includes the development and use of ecological measuring sticks

to assess riparian function or "health." Those measuring sticks allow an objective review of watershed condition, link ecological status to management, help galvanize community action, and provide a monitoring framework for landowners and others. Other tools help communities link biodiversity, economics, and water quality to management actions and alternatives.

The last step (although the process steps are often constantly repeated) is critical: it is the transfer of responsibility for action to the community, which is in the best position to make the changes and benefit from them. Riparian (and by association, watershed) actions need to be community based, locally driven, and largely voluntary. To help a community arrive at this point requires knowledge-building, motivation, acknowledgment of problems, and empowerment. The reasons for positive action may result from enhanced awareness, motivated self-interest, concern about legislation, marketing opportunity, or altruism. The net effect will be a return to a landscape that maintains critical ecological function and provides a greater measure of support for agricultural operations. Cows and Fish is about building a cumulative body of knowledge that we all should know, including how riparian systems function and link us, how watersheds work, the vital signs of landscape health, the essentials of how people need to work together, how solutions need to benefit us all, and the kinds of information that will enable us to restore or maintain natural systems and build ecologically resilient communities and economies.

NOTE: See the complete article at www.cowsandfish.org. Each year, in conjunction with Canadian Environment Week, individuals and organizations whose actions have a positive impact on Canada's most pressing environmental issues are eligible to receive awards in the following categories: Climate Change, Conservation, Environmental Health, and Environmental Learning. The "Cows and Fish" program won the Gold Award in the Environmental Learning category for 2003 (Canadian Environment Awards, 2003, http://www.canadiangeographic.ca/cea/archives/archives_year.asp?year=2003).

including grizzly bear, prairie wolf, coyote, swift fox, eagle, magpie, and crow. Today very little native grassland remains on the Canadian prairies, and the prognosis for survival of the remaining grasslands is poor. As a result, many rangeland management efforts have focused on grasslands conservation and rehabilitation (Johnson, 1995; Trottier, 1992).

The integrity of Canada's rangeland ecosystems (and associated levels of socioeconomic well-being) has been of concern since the early 1900s. Indeed, the United Nations Environment Programme classified Canadian prairie soils as low to moderately degraded (in terms of soil degradation, desertification, and damaged riparian habitat), with the potential for severe degradation because our climate is cold and dry and soil recovery processes are slow (Middleton & Thomas, 1997). Rangeland restoration and management efforts require a thorough understanding of how ecosystems function and how consumers (livestock, wildlife, and people) interact with producers and decomposers, sun, climate, water, and soil (see Chapter 3). Given the understanding that rangelands are in a constant

state of flux, and that an appropriate degree of disturbance provided by controlled grazing may be essential to maintaining that state, rangeland management efforts increasingly are directed toward ecosystem processes (Bakker, 1998; WallisdeVries, 1998).

In May 2004, in conjunction with the launch of the Nature Conservancy's Campaign for Conservation: Saving Canada's Natural Masterpieces, 50 plains bison were released into the Old Man on His Back Prairie and Heritage Conservation Area (OMB) in southwestern Saskatchewan. Intended as the start of a new herd of this species, designated threatened by the Committee on the Status of Endangered Wildlife in Canada (COSEWIC), as fewer than 1000 plains bison exist in Canada, the plains bison are an integral part of efforts to re-create a large prairie grassland ecosystem. The first of a new generation of plains bison at OMB, a female calf was born in November 2005 (normally calves are born in the spring) and survived the winter. Twenty new calves were born in the spring of 2007, helping to maintain and enhance biodiversity on this mixed-grass prairie area. By studying the effects of natural grazers such as bison on these grasslands, it may be possible to use this case as a model for other areas, not only in terms of large-scale conservation of grasslands, but also to demonstrate that a shift toward sustainable agriculture and ecotourism will provide new economic opportunities for prairie communities (Semmens, 2004).

Good stewardship of rangelands involves many considerations. Among the most important in managing disturbances are the use of *stocking rates* (the number of animal units grazed per area, depending on range quality) and grazing practices. The Society for Range Management (Holechek, 1993), for example, suggested that a conservative stocking rate of 30 to 40 percent of forage use would facilitate rangeland recovery, maintain adequate food and cover for wildlife, protect soil resources, and give the highest long-term economic returns with the least risk. Other grazing practices that permit rest periods for plant recovery include rotation grazing, even distribution of grazing, the use of plants at an appropriate time in their life cycles, and prescribed burning (Trottier, 1992). Rehabilitation of riparian habitats, however, requires the exclusion of grazing species. This has proved a difficult issue to resolve, since producers traditionally have relied on stream bed access to provide water to livestock. Restricting stream access, providing off-stream watering sites, and placing feed away from streams are measures that help protect riparian habitat (Adams & Fitch, 1995).

Balancing economic and social needs with threshold limits of rangeland ecosystems is a key challenge in rangeland sustainability. Extensive ecosystem knowledge is necessary to achieve this balance. Given the importance of rangeland health in Canada, many private individuals, ENGOs, universities, and government agencies have pooled their resources to fund the required research. Alberta's Cows and Fish program is one example; another is the Prairie Ecosystem Study (PECOS), which involved the universities of Saskatchewan and Regina, Environment Canada, and Agriculture Canada in studying regional sustainability from socioeconomic, health-risk, and land and biota health perspectives. Similarly, the International Institute for Sustainable Development's Great Plains Sustainability Study researched the relationships among economic development, societal needs, and the environment.

GREENHOUSE GASES

Given its dependence on weather and climate, agriculture will be among the sectors most affected by climate change (Manitoba Climate Change Task Force, 2001). Indeed, agriculture acts both as a sink and as a source for several atmospheric greenhouse gases thought to be responsible for climate change. Agricultural activities relate to GHG concentrations in four main ways: (1) soils are an important

Photo 6–12

Given the risks of wind and water erosion of prairie lands, many farmers employ conservation tillage practices, including the use of implements such as the seed wheel.

natural source of and reservoir for carbon; (2) methane is emitted from livestock and liquid manure; (3) nitrous oxide is released from nitrogen fertilizers; and (4) carbon dioxide is released from the burning of fossil fuels in farming activities. In combination, degradation and mismanagement of agricultural lands and deforestation have added between 2 and 9 gigatonnes of carbon to the atmosphere annually (Hengeveld, Bush, & Edwards, 2002).

In 2000, the agricultural sector's CO_2 equivalent greenhouse gas emissions totalled 60 megatonnes and contributed 8.3 percent of Canada's total GHGs. Agriculture accounted for 70 percent of Canada's total emissions of NO_2 (36 000 kilotonnes) and 25 percent of CH_4 emissions (24 000 kilotonnes). Carbon dioxide emissions from soils contributed 55 percent of agriculture's emissions (33.4 megatonnes), while enteric fermentation emissions from domestic animals accounted for 29 percent (17.7 megatonnes), and manure management contributed 16 percent (9.4 megatonnes) (Environment Canada, 2002).

Although fertilizer use has remained relatively constant since 1985, the amount of nitrogen (N) in the total fertilizer mix increased from about 10 percent in 1960 to about 30 percent in 1985 (Government of Canada, 1994). The reason for the increased proportion of N in fertilizers was to accommodate higher-yielding crops that required more N than was available in most Canadian soils, but research under the Greenhouse Gas Mitigation Program has found that optimal fertilizer application rates for corn farmers in Ontario are less than the standard recommended rates most producers use. Farmers may be able to reduce nitrogen rates and reduce the risk of surplus nitrogen leaching through soil or being lost to the atmosphere (Soil Conservation Council of Canada, 2006). In addition to emissions from use of nitrogen fertilizers, nitrous oxides are generated from nutrient cycling in agricultural soils. The issue of atmospheric N generated from agricultural activities is receiving considerable attention, in part because losses of N from manure and fertilizers not only impact the environment but also represent potentially serious sources of economic loss for farmers (Chambers et al., 2001).

Since cultivation began, estimates are that Canada has lost between 25 and 35 percent of its total agricultural soil carbon (Smith, Desjardins, & Grant, 2001). Even though it is believed that the carbon content of Canada's cultivated soil is at equilibrium (because losses during the first few years are most rapid), small fluxes of carbon into or out of soils can translate into large quantities of CO_2 when totalled across Canada (Smith et al., 2001).

Soil carbon fluxes influence the overall greenhouse gas balance for agriculture. This means that an individual farmer's actions to retain and increase levels of organic matter in soils can assist the soil to sequester carbon (because soil carbon is stored in soil organic matter) and offset CO_2 emissions from agriculture. Increasing conservation tillage and zero tillage are among the practices that are useful from the perspective of both climate change and soil quality (see Box 6–8). Additional agricultural practices that may help reduce greenhouse gas emissions include green manures, reduced summerfallow area, increased forage production, improved crop yields, reduced methane emissions from farm animals

(through improved feed additives and feeding technology), improved efficiency of manure use, decreased fossil fuel use, and increased use of renewable fuels such as ethanol and biodiesel.

In general, as the climate changes, and appropriate policy frameworks, economic incentives, and markets are established, there could be economic opportunities for Canadian farmers to plant alternative crops and to use their lands in ways that would benefit carbon sequestration. Agricultural practices such as zero tillage and agroforestry could enhance the absorption of CO_2 from the atmosphere into soils and forests, and help in development of related agro-industries such as ethanol production (Manitoba Climate Change Task Force, 2001).

ENERGY USE

Many of today's farmers have adopted an industrial approach to agriculture: high production levels are achieved through large inputs of industrial products, including energy (Boyd, 2003; McKenzie, 2002; Taylor, 1994). Agricultural activities consume energy directly through the processes of tilling, harvesting, heating, and ventilation. Fuels for transportation account for over 50 percent of the energy used in primary production on

---

BOX 6–8
CONSERVATION TILLAGE AND ZERO TILLAGE

During the past decade or so, producers, industry, and government have made concerted efforts to reduce the extent of wind and water erosion on Canada's agricultural lands through the use of soil conservation practices. An appropriate mixture of land management practices tailored to the conditions and needs of individual farms can provide multiple benefits for preserving soil health and productivity, minimizing water contamination, conserving wildlife habitat, and maintaining farm nutrient balances.

While not all farms require erosion control and some practices are applicable in some areas and not others, examples of management practices include growing forage crops in rotations or as permanent cover, growing winter cover crops, planting shelter belts, strip cropping, using buffer strips, and using conservation tillage techniques and contour cultivation.

As shown in Box Table 6–6, agricultural practices can have important effects on changes in soil carbon content.

BOX TABLE 6–6
ESTIMATED CHANGES IN SOIL CARBON ASSOCIATED WITH AGRICULTURAL PRACTICES IN CANADA

Parameter	Change in Carbon (C)
Convert arable land to permanent cover	Sequestration: + 0.62 mg/ha/yr
Include forages in crop rotations	Sequestration: + 0.44 mg/ha/yr
Convert from conventional to zero-tillage practices	Increase in soil C: 0.13 mg/ha/yr
Reduce summerfallow to 1 in 3 years (from 1 in 2 years)	Loss reduction: 0.03 mg/ha/yr
Improve fertilizer use efficiency (by 50 percent)	Sequestration: + 0.04 mg/ha/yr

SOURCE: "Estimated Changes in Soil Carbon Associated with Agricultural Practices in Canada," W. N. Smith, R. L. Desjardins, & B. Grant, 2001, *Canadian Journal of Soil Science, 81*, 221–227.

BOX 6-8
(CONTINUED)

In 1991, conservation tillage, including zero tillage, was used on 31 percent of the land seeded; by 2006, over 70 percent of farmers practised conservation and zero tillage. Zero tillage leaves a portion or all of the crop residue on the soil surface and special equipment sows seeds for the new crop through the standing stubble from the previous crop (see Photo 6–13). This practice provides protection against erosion, reduces soil crusting, helps retain moisture by trapping snow, allows rain and snowmelt water to soak directly into the ground, and increases soil organic matter content. In addition, continuous ground cover provides better habitat for ground-nesting birds and a wide array of other wildlife. Studies in Alberta and Manitoba demonstrated that using conservation farming practices improved farmers' incomes by $6.42 per hectare per year in Alberta and by $32.78 per hectare per year in Manitoba (note that this figure included several additional conservation practices). "These systems appear to be the most cost-effective soil practice for general use across the country" (Government of Canada, 1996, pp. 11–20).

- **Conventional tillage:** Most of the crop residue (plant material remaining after harvest) is incorporated into the soil.

- **Conservation tillage:** Most of the crop residue is left on the soil surface to provide protection against erosion, reduce soil crusting, and increase the organic matter content of soils; also known as mulch tillage, minimum tillage, and reduced tillage.

- **Zero tillage:** Any system where soil is not disturbed between harvesting one crop and planting the next; includes direct seeding into stubble or sod; also known as no tillage.

Since the 1970s, Ducks Unlimited, a private, nonprofit charitable organization dedicated to the conservation of wetlands for the benefits of North America's waterfowl, wildlife, and people, has worked in partnership with farmers to assist them in conserving their soil and water resources while improving the environment for wildlife and people. By 1995, Ducks Unlimited had invested $1.6 million in research on and demonstration of zero tillage. Increased funding through Prairie CARE (Conservation of Agriculture, Resources and Environment), a major component of the North American Waterfowl Management Plan, allowed Ducks Unlimited to expand its role in zero tillage in all three Prairie provinces as well as in Ontario and British Columbia.

One Saskatchewan farmer began to use zero tillage in 1985 because he saw the depletion of his soil resources and wanted his farm to remain viable for his children. "Zero till addresses the long-term sustainability of the land and my family, as well as providing a better home for wildlife" (Lyseng, 1995, p. 15). An important benefit of zero tillage is that fall-seeded crops are more likely to survive over winter with the protection of straw and crop residue. For example, this farmer would plant fall rye or winter wheat following a harvest and watch the new crop grow for a month or two until freeze-up. With the spring melt the

Photo 6–13
Ducks Unlimited agrologist Lee Moats, a zero-till farmer, inspects a winter wheat field he seeded in August. He displays viable plants ready to spring to life in April. The old straw cover and the new wheat plants provide good duck nesting cover.

crop would be waiting for returning ducks. The cover from fall-seeded crops means ground-nesting birds of all species have a better chance to avoid predation. The absence of spring field operations means nest successes are higher than they are when conventional farming methods are used (Lyseng, 1995). Fewer compaction problems result as well.

Caring for Canada's soil resources is an increasingly critical challenge, particularly in light of the loss of dependable agricultural land from competing uses such as urban development. Use of overlapping conservation farming techniques such as zero or minimum tillage, continuous cropping, crop rotations, and stubble mulching are necessary to achieve soil conservation.

SOURCES: *The State of Canada's Environment—1996,* Government of Canada, 1996, Ottawa: Supply and Services Canada; "Why Zero Till?" R. Lyseng, 1995, *Conservator, 16*(1), 14.

the farm, while a further 25 percent is accounted for by production and distribution of fertilizers. Approximately 3 percent of Canada's total energy consumption is used on farms to support primary agricultural production (Government of Canada, 1996).

A major environmental concern regarding energy use in agriculture is consumption of fossil fuels and the resultant emission of greenhouse gases. If production and use of biofuels could be expanded, environmental benefits could include lower net carbon dioxide emissions. Biodiesel, for instance, reduces emissions of CO_2 by 78 percent on a net life-cycle basis (see Table 6–3). Other practices, including reduced tillage, new herbicides with lower application rates, and genetic improvements in plants such as lower fertilizer needs, point the way toward reduction in energy use and increased sustainability of agroecosystems.

RESPONSES TO ENVIRONMENTAL IMPACTS AND CHANGE

Agricultural sustainability depends on the integration of economic, social, and environmental concerns. One way in which Agriculture and Agri-Food Canada has promoted sustainability has been through development of market opportunities for Canadian agricultural and agri-food products. World trade in unprocessed grains (such as wheat), oilseeds (mostly canola), meat and meat products, and live animals enabled the agriculture sector in Canada to reach $27.9 billion in exports during 2006. Sales to the United States made up 58 percent of this trade, followed by 8.5 percent to Japan, and 6.4 percent to the European Union (Agriculture and AgriFood Canada, 2006b).

Some people criticize this approach for its apparent emphasis on sustainable economic growth rather than environmental sustainability. This example highlights the different views people may bring to the quest to achieve sustainability of agricultural lands. Different perspectives often generate conflict; resolution of the conflict requires responses that incorporate understanding about the cultural, economic, and ecological roles of land. Research conducted by social scientists contributes significantly to our understanding of these issues and helps to provide a foundation to ensure that agriculture operates in a sustainable manner.

Throughout the world, many people believe that an efficient food production system involves growing crops where costs are lowest (often in developing countries) and shipping the food to markets around the world. The trend toward globalization means that food in our stores may travel an average of 2000 kilometres to get here (Olson, 1997). This model of food production is supported by international agreements such as the North American Free Trade Agreement (NAFTA) and the General Agreement on Tariffs and Trade (GATT). Some environmentalists have warned that GATT and similar negotiations regarding trade deregulation in agricultural products would spell the end of many of the world's small- and medium-scale farming operations that practise sustainable agriculture. Such a threat to sustainable agriculture highlights the growing awareness of the benefits of buying locally grown foodstuffs (see Boxes 6–6 and 6–9). Box 6–10 provides a brief background to international negotiations regarding subsidies and the reform of agricultural trade rules and agreements.

The drive for efficiency does not always consider social and environmental effects, especially in developing nations. For instance, when officials in developing countries emphasize **cash crops** (crops grown for export) over

---

BOX 6–9
THE "100-MILE DIET": EATING LOCALLY AND THINKING GLOBALLY

The "100-Mile Diet" is an interesting example of individuals' efforts to work toward regional food sustainability and to implement the idea of eating locally and thinking globally. Shocked when they realized the distance that typical ingredients of North American meals travelled before reaching their plates, Alisa Smith and James MacKinnon experimented with eating only food grown or produced within 100 miles of their home in Vancouver. From March 21, 2005, to March 21, 2006, as they discovered the challenges of eating locally, their appreciation grew for issues such as the family farm crisis, organic farming, and community gardening. In the book they wrote about their local "foodshed" experience, *The 100-Mile Diet: A Year of Local Eating*, they raised important questions regarding the effects of globalization, the oil economy, monoculture, and environmental

collapse; they also wrote about how this experience connected them to the people and places that sustained them.

In April 2006, Smith and MacKinnon founded the 100-Mile Society, tapping into the media attention they had garnered, and hoping to enable other people to reconnect to their food. Thousands of people from across North America joined the society as "100-Milers" and promised to eat "100-Mile meals." The 100-Mile Thanksgiving campaign in the fall of 2006 gained support from a variety of environmental groups as well as many "slow food" chapters. Even the city of Albany, New York, started its own local eating challenge! In July 2006, *Maclean's* magazine named Smith and MacKinnon to its 2006 honour roll.

Do you know where the food you eat comes from? How much of it is from within 100 miles of your home?

BOX 6–10
THE WORLD TRADE ORGANIZATION AND AGRICULTURAL REFORM

The General Agreement on Tariffs and Trade (GATT) was drawn up by 23 countries and came into force in January 1948 as an international forum to encourage free trade between member states through the regulation and reduction of tariffs on traded goods. Up to 1994, the contracting parties to the GATT struggled through eight "rounds" of negotiations in efforts to reduce tariffs and produce rules to govern international trade. Typically, however, as tariffs were reduced, other nontariff barriers to trade were established. This meant that, through export and import subsidies, more developed countries (MDCs) were able to provide a protectionist advantage to their agricultural sector at the expense of less developed countries (LDCs). Agricultural trade issues are critical for LDCs, since most of their GDP is connected with the agricultural sector, and the subsidies imposed by MDCs frequently prevent access to their markets by LDCs.

The most recent and most comprehensive round of negotiations, the Uruguay Round, lasted seven years (1986–94) and established the World Trade Organization (WTO) to replace the provisional GATT. The 1994 GATT agreements included an Agriculture Agreement that, with pressure from the Cairns Group (see sidebar), established agriculture as a sector requiring trade liberalization.

The Uruguay Round of negotiations established a schedule for subsidy reduction, as did the Doha Agreement, a declaration from the Fourth WTO Ministerial Conference held in Doha, Qatar, in November 2001. The Doha Agreement also included a mandate for negotiations on agricultural trade and was geared to help poor countries—the World Bank estimated that successful negotiations could raise global income by more than $500 billion per year by 2015, with 60 percent of that gain going to poor countries.

A major purpose of the Fifth WTO Ministerial Conference was to report on the progress of the Doha Agreement. Canada and its Cairns Group partners went to the September 2003 meetings in Cancun, Mexico, seeking ambitious reforms in agricultural trade (including cessation of subsidies such as the $300 billion provided by the United States and the European Union to their farmers). However, talks among the 148 members of the WTO collapsed on the fourth day of the Fifth Ministerial Conference. Agriculture appeared to be the critical, divisive issue: developing countries were seeking real market-opening concessions that would require developed nations to make significant adjustments (that is, incur domestic costs) in order to achieve a "greater good" for the global economic system. In seeking genuine free trade, developing nations pursued removal of wealthy nations' protectionist barriers for domestic agriculture (and other items

such as the pharmaceutical patent monopolies that result in "sky-high" prices for lifesaving medicines). As one commentator (Greider, 2003, p. 12) noted, "profiles in courage [were] not on the agenda at Cancun," and leaders from wealthier nations failed to offer compromises on which the trade talks depended. With the breakdown of talks at Cancun, reform of the agricultural trading system was delayed once again; rather than increasing their production, LDCs continue to face existing subsidies.

In the summer of 2006, five years of Doha Round negotiations ended without agreement; many observers question whether the WTO is relevant in the absence of trade concessions from rich developed nations.

The Cairns Group

The Cairns Group consists of 17 nations (including Canada) that together account for one-third of the world's agricultural exports. Formed in 1986, the group pushed for fair trade in agricultural exports and largely was responsible for reform in agricultural trade being established in the Uruguay Round (in the Agreement on Agriculture). By acting collectively, the Cairns Group has had more influence and impact on the WTO agriculture negotiations than any one individual country could have had by acting independently.

The group members seek three key reforms: (1) deep cuts to all tariffs and removal of tariff escalation, (2) elimination of all trade distortions caused by domestic subsidies, and (3) elimination of export subsidies. In addition, the Cairns Group supports the principle of special and differential treatment for developing countries. Cairns Group ministers want the WTO's framework for agricultural liberalization to support the economic and technical assistance needs of developing and small country members. The Cairns Group also is committed to achieving a fair and market-oriented agricultural trading system that places trade in agricultural goods on the same basis as trade in other goods.

Cairns member groups are Argentina, Australia, Bolivia, Brazil, Canada, Chile, Colombia, Costa Rica, Guatemala, Indonesia, Malaysia, New Zealand, Paraguay, the Philippines, South Africa, Thailand, and Uruguay.

SOURCE: *An Introduction,* Cairns Group, n.d., © Commonwealth of Australia reproduced with permission. http://www.cairnsgroup.org/introduction.html

SOURCES: "Minister Vanclief in Cancun to Fight for Canada's Agriculture Sector," Agriculture and Agri-Food Canada, September 9, 2003, http://www.agr.gc.ca/cb/index_e.php?s1=n&s2=2003&page=n30909a; "$600 Million in Federal Transition Funding to Be Delivered Directly to Producers," Agriculture and Agri-Foods Canada, September 19, 2003, http://www.agr.gc.ca/cb/ index_e.php?s1=n&s2=index&page=2003_09; *General Agreement on Tariffs and Trade,* CIESIN, n.d., Columbia University, http://www.economist.com/finance/PrinterFriendly.cfm?Story_ID=2071855; "The Real Cancun: WTO Heads Nowhere," W. Greider, September 22, 2003, *The Nation,* 11–17; *Trade and Investment—World Trade Organization,* International Institute for Sustainable Development, n.d., http://www.iisd.org/trade/wto/gatt.htm; "The World Trade Organization," Global Policy Forum, n.d., http://www.globalpolicy.org/socecon/bwi-wto/index.htm; "Overnight-Rich and Poor Square Off over Farm Trade in Cancun," A. Wheatley & R. Waddington, September 12, 2003, Agriculture Online, http://www.agriculture.com/worldwide/IDS/2003-09-12T063421Z_01; *Agricultural Trade: Backgrounder,* World Trade Organization, 2003a, http://www.wto.org/english/docs_e/legal_e/ursum_e.htm#aAgreement; *Negotiations, Implementation and Development: The Doha Agenda,* World Trade Organization, 2003b, http://www.wto.org/english/tratop_e/ dda_e/dda_e.htm

food production for local people, and when people do not have access to land to grow their own food or have enough money to buy it, one result is increasing migration to cities. Few jobs are available in the cities, so poverty increases and poor people continue to be exploited as cheap sources of labour. Also in the name of efficiency, pesticides that are banned in Canada (and elsewhere) may be used in developing nations. Other environmental degradation occurs due to nonexistent or weak legislation and regulations, and lack of enforcement.

Alternatives to the globalization of the current food system include **regional sustainability**. In this system, developing countries would be encouraged to grow food for themselves first and then crops for export. Such a shift, however, would require either debt reduction or debt forgiveness by the developed world (Olson, 1997). Canada already provides hundreds of millions of dollars worth of food annually to countries in need; a reduction in food aid would enable Canada to shift its emphasis toward debt reduction of developing countries. Reduced debt would enable developing nations to move toward regional sustainability and decrease their reliance on developed nations.

The following section briefly considers some examples of the international initiatives that have been taken toward agricultural sustainability.

INTERNATIONAL INITIATIVES

In 1992, Agenda 21 (see Box 1–2, p. 17) noted that world food production must more than double in the next 40 years to meet the needs of a growing population, more than 80 percent of whom will live in the developing world. A key challenge then, and now, is to increase agricultural production without further degrading the environment. In 2002, the Johannesburg Summit (Earth Summit +10) focused on the many practical steps necessary to address Earth's pressing problems of poverty and environmental degradation. Instead of producing only outcome documents (as in previous Earth Summits), delegates to the Johannesburg Summit launched over 300 voluntary partnerships among governments, NGOs, ENGOs, intergovernmental organizations, and the private sector. Tied to government responsibilities and commitments to improve implementation efforts, these partnerships are intended to ensure that established targets are met, including improving agricultural yields, expanding access to clean water and sanitation, and managing toxic chemicals (Food and Agriculture Organization, 2002; United Nations, 2002a, 2002b).

For many years, Canada's International Development Research Centre (IDRC) has promoted sustainable agriculture projects in various countries around the world. IDRC's projects have included research on indigenous knowledge systems and farming systems designed to maximize use of the marginal lands that many small-scale farmers in developing countries are obliged to cultivate, while doing the least environmental damage. IDRC has investigated the use of alternative farming practices such as integrated pest management, which reduces the need for costly chemical fertilizers, and agroforestry, which incorporates the use of trees for multiple purposes such as forage, firewood, windbreaks, and soil enrichment.

In many developing nations, women bear the major burden in agriculture and food production. They have extensive knowledge of local ecosystems and can help in conserving biodiversity and protecting the environment if given an opportunity to be involved equally in decision making relating to sustainable agriculture (Jowkar, 1994; Seck, 1994). The United Nations Environment Programme and International Fund for Agricultural Development documented and published hundreds of examples of African successes in halting environmental degradation, many of them as a result of women's indigenous knowledge and related activities.

The role of concerned and committed citizens from around the world in striving toward environmental sustainability has always been important, but the collaboration among citizens and scientists expressed through the activities of the Union of Concerned Scientists (UCS) provides evidence of the efficacy of partnerships in helping to improve environmental management. Box 6–11 highlights selected examples of the UCS's actions regarding sustainable agriculture.

CANADIAN EFFORTS TO ACHIEVE SUSTAINABLE AGRICULTURE

Chapter 10 of Agenda 21 presents an integrated approach to land planning and management designed to lead toward sustainability. Based on Agenda 21, Canada identified several priorities relevant to our domestic land issues. These priorities emphasized provincial land use functions, namely increased use of information systems; strengthening of federal, provincial, and territorial relations; consultations and partnerships; support of Aboriginal land use initiatives; coordinated state-of-the-environment monitoring; and application of an ecosystem approach to land use planning and management (Government of Canada, 1996).

In practice, achieving sustainable agricultural food production systems in developed countries such as Canada is a complicated process that involves a range of political, socioeconomic, and environmental challenges resulting from changes that industrialization and technology have brought to agriculture. Approaches to sustainable agriculture in Canada involve cooperative efforts of governments, industry, ENGOs, and farmers in developing new agricultural policies and practices. Nontraditional activities such as organic farming and game ranching also may help promote sustainability through "individual" actions. Discussion of these activities follows.

"Thoughtful action based on the best available science can help safeguard our future and the future of our planet"

—Union of Concerned Scientists, 2007b

The Union of Concerned Scientists (UCS) began in 1969 as a collaboration between students and faculty members at the Massachusetts Institute of Technology. Their science-based 1993 "Warning to Humanity" regarding human effects on the environment (see Enviro-Focus 1 on page 7) set them apart from other nonprofit organizations. Now more than 200 000 scientists and citizens, from all walks of life, combine independent scientific research and citizen action in efforts to solve problems and to secure changes in government and corporate policies and practices.

The UCS maintains that sustainable agriculture practices can protect the environment and produce high-quality, safe, and affordable food without undermining current productivity or the resources on which agricultural depends. Despite the strong scientific basis of sustainable agriculture, much remains to be learned about complex interactions among soil fertility, plant vigour, and the behaviour of both beneficial insects and pests, for example, and about agriculture as a system. And, the UCS indicates, focusing on sustainable rather than industrial agriculture means that different combinations of scientists and scientific information are required now. Rather than chemists developing pesticides, sustainable agriculture needs soil scientists to discern the mysteries of healthy soil. Similarly, sustainable agriculture needs weed ecologists to search for new ways of cultivating and using crops to control weeds, rather than molecular biologists developing crops that are tolerant to herbicides.

In promoting their goal of sustainable agricultural practices, the UCS has worked toward elimination of harmful "factory farming" methods and attempted to strengthen governmental management of genetically engineered food. To achieve these goals, the UCS mounted a series of public campaigns about food protection, sustainable food production, genetic engineering, and antibiotic resistance. Their position paper on pharmaceutical and industrial crops raises concerns about the new generation of food crops that are being modified—not for agronomic purposes such as to repel pests or to be compatible with chemical pesticides—but to produce pharmaceutical or industrial compounds such as drugs, vaccines, and plastics. The UCS believes that such genetically engineered crops pose a sufficient threat to the safety of the American food supply that, in order to take the "harm" out of "pharma" crops, they have requested the U.S. Department of Agriculture implement a (limited) ban on outdoor production of these crops. You can follow the UCS's progress on this and other campaigns on their website.

SOURCES: *Position Paper: Pharmaceutical and Industrial Crops*, Union of Concerned Scientists, 2006, Cambridge, MA: Author; *Protect Our Food*, Union of Concerned Scientists, 2007a, http://www.ucsusa.org/food_and_environment/; *What we do*, Union of Concerned Scientists, 2007b, http://www.ucsusa.org/ucs/about/

Nontraditional Agricultural Activities

In Canada, efforts to sustain agroecosystems have focused historically on stewardship of land and soil resources on individual farms. Individually, farmers have been searching for new ways to diversify and to achieve sustainability within their agroecosystems. Nontraditional agricultural activities have been gaining in popularity, including **organic farming** (reliance on a management system using natural soil-forming processes and crop rotation schemes rather than synthetic inputs), **alternative livestock production** (raising non-native species and domesticated native species), and **agroforestry** (combining production of trees, shrubs, agricultural plants, and/or animals in the same land area). Agricultural biotechnology efforts have resulted in biofertilizers, biofeeds, and plants with novel traits. Organic farming, game farming and ranching, and biotechnology activities are discussed briefly below.

Organic Farming   Founded in 1975, Canadian Organic Growers (COG) is a national information network for organic farmers, gardeners, and consumers. Their objectives include conducting research into alternatives to traditional chemical- and energy-intensive food production practices, and endorsing practices that promote and maintain long-term soil fertility, reduce fossil fuel use, reduce pollution, recycle waste, and conserve nonrenewable resources. In addition, COG assists in educational and demonstration projects to help people understand the value and integrity of organic foods.

Organic farming is one way to promote the goals of a decentralized, bioregionally based food system that sees food produced by local farmers and consumed by local people. Reducing transportation costs, bolstering local marketing systems and economies, and promoting greater regional food self-reliance are other benefits of consuming organic (and other) foods within the region where they are produced.

The 2006 Census of Agriculture revealed that 15 511 farms produced at least one category of certified organic agricultural products. About 5.2 percent (11 937) of all farms in Canada produced organic (but not certified organic) commodities in 2006, and 6380 of these farms reported animals or animal products as their major product. Most of the noncertified organic farms were located in British Columbia (1720) and Ontario (1545). Hay or field crops were the dominant certified organic commodity, reported by 2462 operations, 50 percent of which were located in Saskatchewan and 18.9 percent in Ontario. Only Prince Edward Island and Saskatchewan reported more certified field crop farms than noncertified farms. Transitional farms, en route to becoming certified organic, also reported field crops as their dominant product (almost 38 percent of them were located in Saskatchewan). Organic maple products, regardless of their certification status, came mostly from Quebec. British Columbia dominated in organic fruit and vegetable production.

In June 1999, the government of Canada unveiled a new National Standard of Canada for Organic Agriculture. This standard outlined principles for organic agriculture that endorsed production and management practices that would contribute to the quality and sustainability of the environment and ensure ethical treatment of livestock. Among its provisions, the standard (1) prohibited both the use of ionizing radiation in the preservation of food and the use of genetically engineered or modified organisms, (2) promoted maximum use of recycling, and

(3) encouraged maximum rotation of crops and promotion of biodiversity. This standard was designed to help Canadian producers of organic foods gain greater and easier access to international markets that demand these kinds of standards (Government of Canada, 1999).

On December 21, 2006, the revised Canada Organic Standard and Permitted Substances List was approved. This decision represented a great step forward because, although Canada's organic standard had been in place since 1999, it had not been codified in law. Certification of organic producers and handlers and accreditation of certifiers had been voluntary, except in Quebec. The Canadian organic community had wanted a mandatory regulatory system to make it possible to secure equivalency agreements with other countries. The Canada Organic Regime defines accredited certifiers, procedures for inspection and certification, a Canada Organic seal (see Photo 6–15 on page 241), surveillance and enforcement, and maintenance of the Canada Organic Standard and Permitted Substance List (Canadian Food Inspection Agency, 2008; Organic Trade Association, 2006a, 2006b).

ENVIRO-FOCUS 6

Agriculture in Canada's Metropolitan Areas

Would it surprise you to know that in 2006 there were more than 35 400 farms with their headquarters in Canada's largest urban areas? Although most of the best farmland in Canada is near major population centres, farms often seem to be overlooked as part of our urban landscapes.

Farmers who locate close to large metropolitan areas encounter both benefits and challenges. For instance, farmers have easily accessible markets for their perishable and other fresh farm products when they sell directly to urban consumers through farmers' markets, at U-pick fruit farms, and in greenhouses and nurseries. Vegetables can be harvested at their ripest and delivered quickly to city restaurants, and farmers who have large labour needs may find they can hire workers more easily because of their proximity to urban areas. Typically, urban centres provide good transportation networks as well as access to food processing facilities. Locating close to urban areas also enables farmers to augment their income with off-farm revenue.

Photo 6–14
Consumers have access to fresh, locally grown produce at seasonal farmers' markets in many urban areas in Canada.

Over 31 percent of farms in Canada's census metropolitan areas (CMAs)[1] are field crop farms, and almost 19 percent of farms involved animals such as goats, sheep, horses, bees, and rabbits. Horse operations generate some revenue from agri-tourism, although the agriculture census does not tally this. Beef farms accounted for close to 17 percent of urban farms, while fruit and vegetable farms made up almost 13 percent of metropolitan area farms. Greenhouse, nursery, and floriculture operations involved only 9.4 percent of urban farms, but they returned almost 25 percent of gross farm receipts among all urban farm operations. Almost half (47.5 percent) of the farms in urban areas have gross receipts under $25 000; however, there are many more million-dollar farms in urban areas (20.3 percent) than Canada-wide (2.6 percent).

In 2006, over 8 percent of all farms in urban areas produced certified, transitional, or uncertified organic products, another niche product area that is succeeding in metropolitan areas. The largest concentration of organic farms in metropolitan areas is in British Columbia; Victoria reported almost 31 percent of its farms produced organic products, Vancouver had almost 16 percent, and Kelowna reported just over 12 percent. Moncton, New Brunswick, reported 11.1 percent organic farms. As difficult as it might be to believe, given its more than 5 million people and status as Canada's largest CMA, Toronto had 2839 farms in 2006, 230 of them growing mainly organic products. Just like those in other urban areas, Toronto's farms focused mostly on fruit, vegetable, greenhouse, and nursery products, and horse farms were the dominant type of animal operation.

Among the challenges of operating a farm close to urban areas is the competition for land—farmland near cities often commands higher prices than elsewhere (see data presented here). Higher land prices near urban areas may persuade farmers to sell their property and move to where land is less expensive. When farmland is sold, development pressures related to urban growth become a concern. For instance, for every square kilometre of farmland converted to residential or commercial uses, the ability of farmers in Ontario's

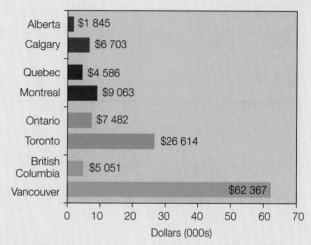

Box Figure 6–2

Value of farmland and buildings near cities (dollars per hectare), 2001

SOURCE: *Canadian Agriculture at a Glance*, Statistics Canada, 2001, Cat. no. 96-325-XPB, p. 20.

Niagara and B.C.'s Okanagan regions to grow specialty crops, such as tree fruits, grapes and nuts, is reduced. Since these crops require specific microclimates to flourish, loss of these agricultural lands could mean permanent loss of capacity to grow these crops. Challenges occur also when cities grow and encroach on land on their outskirts; farmers frequently face complaints from their new neighbours about odours and noises associated with normal farm practices.

In efforts to control the rate of conversion of agricultural land to urban uses, different provinces and municipalities use different methods, including preferential tax policies, right-to-farm legislation, and land use planning and zoning regulations. Regulations vary from voluntary, nonexclusive zoning to mandatory, exclusive agricultural zoning, such as was implemented during the 1970s in British Columbia. While stronger zoning regulations have helped reduce agricultural land conversion, they have been criticized because farmers lose the ability to profit from development of their

---

[1] A census metropolitan area (CMA) has a population of at least 100 000, with an urban core of at least 50 000. Canada's 33 CMAs are St. John's, Halifax, Moncton, Saint John, Saguenay, Quebec City, Sherbrooke, Trois-Rivières, Montreal, Ottawa-Gatineau, Kingston, Peterborough, Oshawa, Toronto, Hamilton, St. Catharines-Niagara, Kitchener, Brantford, Guelph, London, Windsor, Barrie, Greater Sudbury, Thunder Bay, Winnipeg, Regina, Saskatoon, Calgary, Edmonton, Kelowna, Abbotsford, Vancouver, and Victoria.

(continued)

land. We must remember, however, that in order to have productive farms in the future we need to focus on preserving the limited supply of our good-quality farmland today. To plow it, or to pave it? —that is the challenging question underlying the maps in Box Figure 6–3.

SOURCE: *Farming in Canada's CMAs*, Statistics Canada, 2006, http://www.statcan.gc.ca/english/agcensus2006/articles/CMA.htm

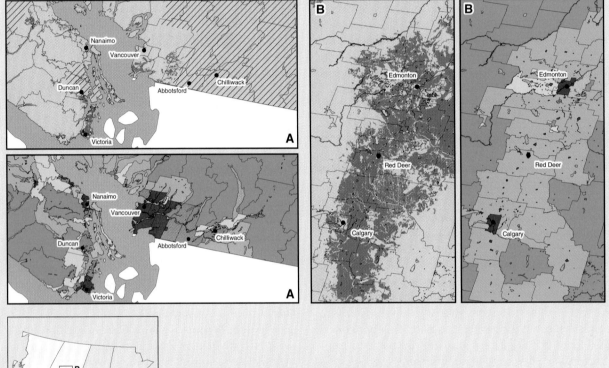

Canada Land Inventory agricultural land capability classification

Classes 1 – 3   Data not available

Other classes   Source: Canada Land Inventory, National Soil Database, Agriculture and Agri-Food Canada, 1998

Box Figure 6–3

a) Plow it, or pave it? Agricultural lands and population density in western Canada

NOTE: Canada Land Inventory agricultural land capability classification shows that in British Columbia, only 1 percent of land is prime agricultural land (Classes 1 to 3); this land is located mainly in the Okanagan Valley and Lower Mainland, home to over 2 million people. Urban sprawl often consumes agricultural land in the surrounding areas faster than population growth would suggest, largely because new developments have larger lot and house sizes than those in the city centre. In Alberta, there is growing concern about the residential developments in the corridor between Calgary and Edmonton; this growth raises the price of land beyond what farmers can afford and increases the likelihood that the land will be sold to developers for housing and other uses. In western Canada, much of the growth in urban and suburban land uses has occurred on agricultural land.

b) Plow it, or pave it? Agricultural lands and population density in eastern Canada

NOTE: Many provinces have experienced problems with cities expanding into farming areas. With more than half of Canada's Class 1 agricultural land, southern Ontario also contains the largest cities in the province and a large proportion of Canada's population. Extreme development pressures over the past few decades have resulted in the loss of much agricultural land, particularly land in the Niagara area, where tree fruits, nuts, and grapes are grown. Their loss may mean permanent loss of capacity to produce these crops.

SOURCE: *Canadian Agriculture at a Glance*, Cat. no. 96-325-XPB, Statistics Canada, 2006, pp. 24, 25, http://www.statcan.ca/english/research/96-328-MIE/96-328-MIE2004003.htm

Photo 6–15
Canada's organic logo is permitted to be used only on those food products certified as meeting the revised Canadian standard for organic production and that contain at least 95 percent organic ingredients. Questions remain about the composition of the materials in the allowable 5 percent nonorganic ingredients.

Photo 6–16
The opportunity to socialize with the farmer and other shareholders is just one of the benefits of community shared agriculture farming.

Canadian consumers could help the agricultural sector to achieve sustainability by buying organically grown or raised products. Just as in Europe, where demanding consumers increasingly have supported organic farmers and assisted in ensuring agriculture is both sustainable and competitive, Canadian consumers could help Agriculture and Agri-Food Canada to recognize organic agriculture as a viable and competitive approach to sustainable farming (Ecological Agriculture Projects, 1997).

Community shared agriculture (CSA) farms are a related development in which local people share with farmers the risk of organic food production by buying a share in the produce prior to the growing season. This enhances farmers' security in knowing that their entire harvest is sold ahead of time and reduces their debt load since they do not need a credit margin in the spring. CSA farmers also help ensure biological diversity, since most grow more than 30 varieties to satisfy the needs of their shareholders (Hunter, 1999). Sometimes, depending on the individual farmer, a share in the produce involves a commitment on the part of the shareholder to work in the CSA garden for a day or more. CSA farms promote local production and consumption with associated reduction in transportation needs, thus contributing in small ways toward reduced air quality problems. CSA farms also provide opportunities for urban residents to "get their hands dirty" and perhaps help people appreciate directly the value of agricultural land. (In Chapter 13 we consider urban agriculture in the context of community gardens and some of the benefits these gardens can bring to people and the planet.)

Game Farming and Ranching   One type of alternative livestock production is the raising of game species. Farmers and ranchers have discovered that the pleasant-tasting, low-fat meat of the North American elk, or wapiti, makes it an attractive ranching species. The elk's velvet (nonhardened antler) is an annual crop and is valued highly in the marketplace. Although elk have been part of the ranching scene for 30 to 40 years, the industry has grown greatly since the mid-1980s. In 1990, 35 prominent elk ranchers formed the North American Elk Breeders Association (NAEBA) to promote elk ranching as an agricultural pursuit. By 2006, Canada's 905 elk farms contained over 69 000 animals. Alberta, with 352 elk farms and almost 34 000 animals, and Saskatchewan, with 353 farms and almost 26 000 elk, were home to about 85 percent of elk farms.

Capturing elk from the wild is illegal, and reputable elk ranchers do not take part in these activities. However, the first captive elk herd in any area is based on wild animals. In Manitoba, in 1995, the province's natural resource officers used elk baiting, particularly around Riding Mountain National Park, to attract and then capture wild elk (Chambers, n.d.). These captured elk formed the basis of a new provincial game ranching industry.

Photo 6–17
Wild elk are the basis of initial herds for game ranching and captive breeding purposes.

Opposition was expressed about wild animals being kept in captivity, about the threat of the spread of disease among the unique subspecies of elk in the area, and about poaching. Like many other provinces, Manitoba already had difficulties with poaching and the trade in animal parts. Harvesting of antler velvet (called *velveting*) "to sell to the lucrative Asian folk medicine market" (Chambers, n.d.) was of great concern as a stimulus to increased poaching. According to the NAEBA, annual revenues from velveting just one mature bull elk were US$1495, and profits from velvet supplies typically would pay for feeding the entire herd year-round (Elk On Line, 1996). In Alberta in 2000, elk antlers and velvet supported a $52.5 million industry (Derworiz, 2000).

Chronic wasting disease (CWD) is a fatal degenerative disease of the brain that affects elk and deer. Following the importation of a diseased elk from South Dakota in 1989, elk have tested positive for CWD on 40 farms in Saskatchewan (Alberta Agriculture, 2006; Thomas, 2003). In 2002, one elk on an Alberta farm tested positive for CWD, and by May 2007, CWD had been found in a total of 29 wild deer since the first case was discovered in September 2005.

Canada's Health of Animals Act identifies CWD as a reportable disease that falls under the Canadian Food Inspection Agency (CFIA). Since the present federal policy is to eradicate CWD from Canada, affected farms are quarantined and the infected animal(s) as well as the remaining herd(s) are "depopulated." Since 1996, the CFIA has destroyed over 7500 animals from Saskatchewan and Alberta farms, and farmers have been compensated millions of dollars for the loss and costs of disposal of their elk. In 2003, four Saskatchewan elk farmers were prohibited from growing grain or raising livestock because their land might harbour CWD organisms. Available evidence suggests that transmission of CWD may occur when the animals congregate around human-made feed and water stations and contaminate their water and feed with saliva, urine, and feces. Until it can be proven that elk (or deer) will not become reinfected with CWD, the farmers cannot grow crops, and no compensation is available to them (Alberta Agriculture, 2006; Thomas, 2003).

Following discovery of CWD, prices for farmed elk and deer collapsed. South Korea halted imports of elk products from North America, and the United States stopped the sale of trophy deer and elk to American hunt farms. Saskatchewan banned imports of male deer and elk from Alberta to its hunt farms. In August 2002, to control or prevent the further spread of CWD in Alberta, the province announced a mandatory CWD Surveillance Program. Elk and deer farmers must submit the heads from all farmed animals over one year of age that die or are slaughtered, and the product from slaughtered animals must be held at abattoirs until CWD test results are available. While there is no scientific evidence that humans can be affected by CWD, Alberta's precautions appear to heed the World Health Organization's advice that no meat source possibly infected by prions should be allowed into the human food system (Alberta Agriculture, 2006). The CWD program has expanded to wild animals, and during the 2007–8 season, Alberta hunters were required to submit deer heads taken from animals killed in the high-risk areas along the Alberta–Saskatchewan border to Fish and Wildlife offices.

Agricultural Biotechnology The Canadian Environmental Protection Act (1999) defines **biotechnology** as the "application of science and engineering in the direct or indirect use of living organisms or parts or products of living organisms, in their natural or modified forms." Although it is not a new discipline, biotechnology is an umbrella term that covers a broad spectrum of scientific tools from agricultural, biological, chemical, and medical sources. Biotechnology takes advantage of living organisms, or their parts, to produce products; making yogurt, cheese, and bread are said to be traditional biotechnological activities. More advanced activities include the production of antibiotics, vaccines, and enzymes.

One new aspect of biotechnology is *genetic engineering* (GE), which involves removing or transferring specific characteristics or genetic information (DNA) from one organism to another, thus altering the characteristics of these organisms (see Figures 6–6 and 6–7). Biotechnological products are used extensively in agriculture, drug manufacturing, medical treatment, and pollution control. In Canada, the most prevalent biotechnology is **bioremediation**, used widely in resource-based industries such as oil wells, mining, and pulp and paper operations to break down or degrade hazardous substances into less hazardous or nontoxic substances (Statistics Canada, 2000).

Some of the benefits claimed for biotechnology in Canada are the production of newer and better products that may be lower in price than their traditional counterparts; more rapid diagnosis and treatment of certain diseases; and, in agriculture, the potential for superior food products and healthier agricultural plants and animals.

Proponents say that when it is combined with traditional techniques, biotechnology provides a way to develop plants, animals, and foods with novel attributes. For instance, researchers have taken a natural organic insecticide gene from a soil bacterium (*Bacillus thuringiensis*, abbreviated *Bt*) and inserted it (via a "gene gun" or viral vector) into corn, potatoes, and cotton to enhance the bug-killing capacity of these plants. The new gene lands in the genome of the plant and may disrupt its normal functioning in ways that are not predictable. This kind of genetic transfer does not occur in nature. The altered plants produce toxins continuously and throughout the plant so that the corn borer, Colorado potato beetle larvae, or cotton boll weevil will be killed by "natural" means when they bite into the GE plants. By 1999, Canadian approval had been granted for insect-resistant (i.e., genetically modified) corn, potatoes, and cotton and more than 40 other genetically altered crops (Boyens, 2000; Bueckert, 2000).

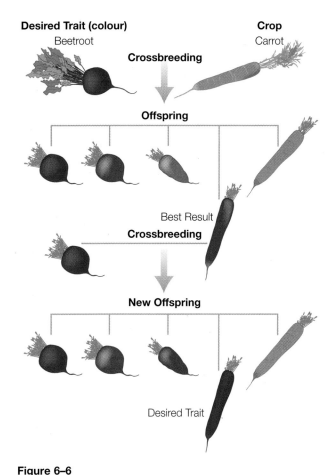

Desired Trait (colour)   **Crop**
Beetroot   Carrot

Crossbreeding

Offspring

Best Result

Crossbreeding

New Offspring

Desired Trait

Figure 6–6

Traditional crossbreeding of plants

SOURCE: Adapted from Miller/Hackett. Living in the Environment Cdn 1/e. page 100. © 2008 Nelson Education Ltd. Reproduced by permission. www.cengage.com/permissions.

Commercially prepared foods that contain *Bt* include cereals, pancake mixes, corn chips, and soy formulas (Canadian Alert in Genetic Engineering, 2000). Other crops engineered to produce pharmaceutical compounds include tobacco used to produce an antibody against tooth decay, canola grown commercially in Canada to produce a blood anticoagulant (leech protein), and soybeans used to produce a lubricant (Union of Concerned Scientists, 2006).

A number of potential environmental risks are associated with commercial genetically engineered agricultural products, however. These concerns relate to the potential for organisms such as plants to spread and transfer their genetically altered material (known as outcrossing) and increase harm to nontarget species from the release of modified plants or microorganisms (Agriculture and Agri-Food Canada, 1997b). This could disrupt the balance in natural ecosystems through the replacement of a few or large numbers of species.

Research suggests this concern may be valid. Cornell University researchers reported how *Bt* corn plants (spliced with a gene from *Bacillus thuringiensis*) might represent a risk because most hybrid corn releases the *Bt* toxin in pollen. When pollen from *Bt* corn was dusted on milkweed, only 56 percent of young monarch butterfly larvae survived, compared with 100 percent survival of larvae on leaves dusted with untransformed pollen or on leaves with no pollen (Losey, Rayor, & Carter, 1999). A common weed that often surrounds corn fields, milkweed is the exclusive source of food for these butterflies. This research suggested *Bt* corn pollen might be problematic for the conservation of monarch butterflies, particularly given that 50 percent of the summer monarch population is concentrated in the mid-western American "corn belt." Since the amount of *Bt* corn planted in the United States is projected to increase significantly over the next few years (suggesting that a substantial proportion of available milkweeds may be within range of corn pollen deposition), research must be conducted to evaluate the risks of this agrotechnology on the monarch butterfly. However, Prakash (2001, p. 13) reports that "the initial fear about the reported damage to monarch butterflies from *Bt* corn has not held up in additional studies." Clearly, conflicting research results suggest the need for continued investigation.

Just as some plants have been made insect-resistant, other plants have been made resistant to herbicides such as glyphosate or glufosinate ammonium, chemicals that are capable of killing not only weeds but all plant life. In 1995, field trials of genetically engineered crops took place around the world. In 1996, these trials resulted in commercial crops, including two herbicide-resistant canolas grown in Canada (Boyens, 2000). By 1998, about 6.5 million acres or 50 percent of the total area of transgenic canola grown in Canada was herbicide-tolerant (Kneen, 1999b) and, in 1999, 60 percent of Canada's canola crop was genetically engineered. As well, one in every three acres of corn, 25 percent of soybeans, and 20 percent of potatoes grown in Canada were genetically modified (Boyens, 2000).

Since 1996 about 20 000 Canadian farmers have paid Monsanto Canada about $15 per acre to buy herbicide-resistant canola seeds (called Roundup Ready). Herbicide resistance appeals to farmers because they can reduce their chemical spraying. Canola, for instance, normally requires several passes of herbicides (to kill foxtail, wild mustard, and other unwanted vegetation) at a cost of at least $40 per acre for the herbicides plus the labour involved in spraying. Herbicide-resistant canola requires one spraying of a herbicide such as Roundup at a cost of about $20 per acre. Multinational corporations such as Monsanto, DuPont, and Novartis claim they have created new crops that will reduce the need for agricultural chemicals. However, as critics note, these crops are designed to be used with matching herbicides manufactured by the same companies that created the crops, thus ensuring the sale of specific chemicals. There are concerns that agrotoxins eliminate biodiversity, "not only in the crop, but perhaps even more importantly, in the soil in which it is grown" (Kneen, 1999a,

Phase 1
Make Modified Gene

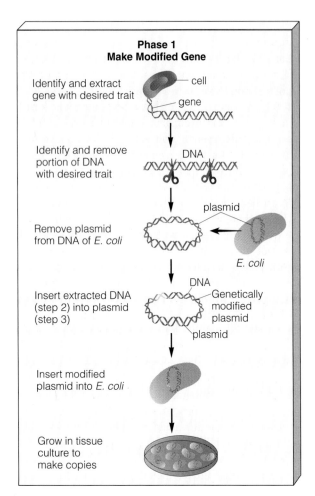

Identify and extract gene with desired trait

cell

gene

Identify and remove portion of DNA with desired trait

DNA

Remove plasmid from DNA of *E. coli*

plasmid

E. coli

Insert extracted DNA (step 2) into plasmid (step 3)

DNA

Genetically modified plasmid

plasmid

Insert modified plasmid into *E. coli*

Grow in tissue culture to make copies

Phase 2
Make Transgenic Cell

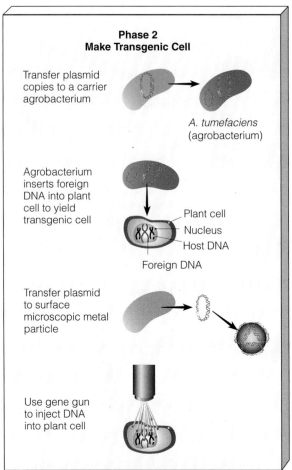

Transfer plasmid copies to a carrier agrobacterium

A. tumefaciens (agrobacterium)

Agrobacterium inserts foreign DNA into plant cell to yield transgenic cell

Plant cell

Nucleus

Host DNA

Foreign DNA

Transfer plasmid to surface microscopic metal particle

Use gene gun to inject DNA into plant cell

Phase 3
Grow Genetically Engineered Plant

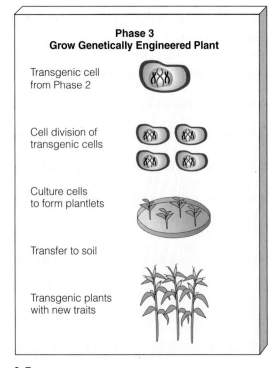

Transgenic cell from Phase 2

Cell division of transgenic cells

Culture cells to form plantlets

Transfer to soil

Transgenic plants with new traits

Figure 6–7

Genetic engineering of plants. Transgenic plants may look no different from their nonmodified counterparts.

SOURCE: Figure adapted from Miller/Hackett. *Living in the Environment* Cdn 1/e. page 101. © 2008 Nelson Education Ltd. Reproduced by permission. www.cengage.com/permissions.

p. 25; Agriculture and Agri-Food Canada, 1996). Concerns for human health as well as that of other species affected by genetically engineered crops have increased over time and are among the issues considered in Box 6–12 (p. 246).

Given such concerns, on April 1, 1997, the then new Canadian Food Inspection Agency (CFIA) took over responsibility for regulating agricultural products to see whether they are safe for humans, animals, and the environment. New regulatory requirements have been developed to address the safety of novel organisms in the environment. Before the agricultural products of biotechnology may be used, each undergoes a preregulatory review to determine if the new product is "substantially equivalent" to a product already approved (in which case it will be approved for release) or if a risk assessment will be required. If a risk assessment is necessary—say, for plants with unique traits—a series of guidelines outline the criteria that must be considered in assessing risk (Agriculture and Agri-Food Canada, 1997c).

Sometimes, potential risks can be managed by imposing conditions that reduce risks, such as limiting the release of a bioengineered product to a confined area. In the case of plants with novel traits, an environmental assessment is required for confined field trials, a second assessment is required for unconfined release, and if a plant is to be used as a food or feed, then it must undergo further safety assessments by Health Canada or CFIA before it is used in commercial production. The Union of Concerned Scientists is concerned about the risks to the environment from the outdoor production of food and nonfood pharmaceutical and industrial crops. While they have not called for a ban on all outdoor production of such food crops in the United States, they suggest that genetic engineers could shift to completely enclosed production systems because they pose little or no threat to human food supply and the environment.

Controversy associated with genetic engineering is compounded by the high financial stakes attached to the acceptance (or not) of these technologies. In 2006, the WTO ruled that a European Union (EU) moratorium on approvals of GMOs was illegal. The EU's regulatory system for GMOs uses the precautionary principle wherein the possibility of harm to human health or the environment, even in the absence of scientific certainty or probability of harm, is sufficient to justify precautionary measures. This WTO ruling suggests that science, rather than concern, will be the basis for trade restrictions—crop and food safety regulations must be based on science and not used to interfere with the trade of safe products. Some people feel that as the fourth-largest producer of GMO crops in the world (5.8 million acres in 2005, mostly of canola, maize, and soybeans), Canada may benefit from this decision and may see increased acreage and trade in GMOs. The WTO's decision "may be used as a precedent for the proposition that the precautionary principle is not a valid basis for measures relating to human and environ-ment health" (AWB Bio-Bulletin, 2006). Other people are greatly concerned that this challenge to the precautionary principle signifies that decisions will be made on incomplete and potentially inaccurate "science" in order to achieve financial, not environmental, benefits.

Partnerships

Environmental issues related to agricultural use of land can be national in scope or can exhibit regional distinctiveness. National agricultural issues pertaining to the environment include greenhouse gas emissions and climate change impacts, energy use, and genetic resources. Regional concerns include soil quality, water quality, and wildlife issues. Through the agricultural component of Canada's Green Plan (which ended March 31, 1997), a number of federal–provincial–territorial agreements were established to support activities aimed at ensuring long-term sustainability of the resources that agriculture depends on and shares with other users, as well as to assist the transition to more sustainable farming practices. Activities under the Green Plan also helped Canada meet national and international environmental commitments, such as the Conventions on Climate Change and on Biological Diversity.

With funding from the sustainable agriculture component of Canada's Green Plan, and building on the National Soil Conservation Program, Ontario farmers developed the idea of environmental farm planning. Each farmer assessed his or her own farm to highlight its environmental strengths, identify areas of concern, and set realistic goals to improve environmental conditions. In addition, many farmers voluntarily organized themselves into various associations and societies, such as the Ecological Farmer's Association of Ontario, aimed specifically at environmental objectives.

Canada's Agricultural Policy Framework

By 2003, all of Canada's ministers of agriculture had signed or initialled the comprehensive Federal-Provincial-Territorial Framework Agreement on Agricultural and Agri-Food Policy for the Twenty-First Century (APF). The national agricultural and agri-food policy has three main goals: (1) to foster confidence in Canada's food safety and quality systems and the environment, (2) to accelerate advances in science and technology, and (3) to help farmers become more profitable by providing them with risk management and other tools they need to improve their management and technical skills (Agriculture and Agri-Food Canada, 2003a).

The Framework Agreement also sets out common environmental outcome goals that include reduction of agricultural risks to water, soils, and atmosphere (including global warming) and that ensure improved stewardship through the adoption of environmentally beneficial practices. These outcomes include increased

BOX 6–12
GENETICALLY MODIFIED FOODS: ISSUES OF CONCERN

Dubbed "Frankenfoods" by the media, genetically modified foods (GMFs) usually are indistinguishable from nature's products. No labels help consumers identify these genetically engineered products, and no signs separate conventional from transgenic, or "novel," foods. How, then, are consumers to know if the gene-spliced foods on supermarket shelves are safe? We can't, at least not definitively, because very little research has been done on the effects of genetic engineering (GE) and GMFs on human health.

In Canada, and elsewhere, public opinion about the safety of GMFs varies widely. According to one nationwide poll, 61 percent of Canadians feel secure enough about the safety and benefits of biotechnology that they are willing to accept some long-term, unintended risks in exchange for potential health benefits (May, 2000). A 1999 poll conducted in 15 member states of the European Union indicated that only 41 percent of those polled felt biotechnology would improve their quality of life in the next 20 years. While the United States National Research Council declared that GMFs are safe (Macilwain, 2000), Britons are so concerned about the ill effects of biotechnology that a British court acquitted Greenpeace participants on a charge of destroying genetically modified, "contaminated" crops because they constituted a potential environmental threat (Chaundy, 2000). In May 1999, the 115 000-member British Medical Association called for a moratorium on GE foods and more independent research on its safety (Boyens, 2000). In 2002, the European Union determined to keep GM produce out of Europe's food system by requiring both honest labelling and a regulatory system to trace the origins of GM corn or soybeans from the supermarket back to the farm of origin (Greider, 2003).

Biotechnology applied to livestock and food crops to create GMFs has been touted as a method of securing food sources for the world's growing population (Coghlan, 2000; Wambugu, 2000). GMFs such as *Bt* plants have been created to provide potentially increased product yield; decreased pesticide use via bioinsecticides; greater resistance to bacterial, viral, and fungal plant diseases; and increased tolerance to cold, heat, and drought (Pearce, 2000; Wilkinson, 1998). From a human health perspective, edible vaccines (surgically implanted inside a food that needs no refrigeration) are being investigated to help alleviate enteric (intestinal) diseases in developing nations (Powell, 1999).

Potential negative consequences of GMFs also are widely acknowledged. Although reactions of humans to unfamiliar genetic material are uncertain, health concerns centre on the links of GMFs to toxicity, allergic reactions, antibiotic resistance, cancer, and immunosuppression, among others. Problems with unintended or secondary effects of genetic modification, such as transfer of the antibiotic resistance gene, have been raised, as have concerns about human error in creation of transgenetic material introduced into target organisms (Gasson, 1998; Powell, 1999).

Environmental concerns about GMFs focus on the unknown effects of GM crops, including the risk of a gene spreading from the transgenic organism to other organisms in the environment. This "gene escape" can occur when pollen from a transgenic

Photo 6–18
An anti-GMF display in Munich, Germany, 2002.

plant is carried by wind or insects to a wild, nontransgenic plant. If the pollen fertilizes the wild plant, the resulting hybrid will contain the transgene. If the hybrid plant survives and reproduces with other wild plants of the same species, the transgene may become firmly established in the wild plant population. While it is true that cross-pollination (outcrossing) has occurred with crop plants since the beginning of agriculture, the introduction of new genes may add new risks such as the development of "superweeds," the inadvertent production of toxins or allergens in new plants used as food, or an increased risk of resistant pests (Altieri, 2000; Arriola, 1998; Hails, 1998; Hill, 1998; Powell, 1999).

The industrialization of agriculture also has resulted in a reduction in plant and animal diversity. Of Canada's 220 livestock breeds, about 60 are rare or endangered. The greatest losses of farm animal biodiversity are occurring in the poultry and swine industries, where, for example, only three multinational companies own all of the "elite" genetic breeding stock lines to produce commercial turkeys for the world. The birds are all highly selected strains with very narrow genetic variability; because of genetic manipulation (to increase size and white breast meat), today's traditional Christmas turkeys can no longer breed naturally but are inseminated artificially. Even with high levels of disease risk with such a small gene pool, this system is considered a model for the future of other livestock industries (Chiperzak, 1999).

In evaluating GMFs, it is important to define what constitutes risk (and how much risk is acceptable) and what constitutes environmental harm (Hails, 1998). Will the impacts of GMFs be more or less harmful than existing methods of enhancing plant growth and productivity? Biotechnology holds the promise of enormous economic gain (mainly, it seems, for multinational corporations), but questions regarding environmental and social sustainability at a global scale have created heated debate among stakeholders. As governments and industry push toward acceptance of some scientific research to promote the biotechnology industry, citizens and environmental nongovernmental organizations look to other scientific documents and the precautionary principle to support

BOX 6-12
(CONTINUED)

their arguments. Opponents of GMFs, while not opposed to biotechnology per se, advocate caution and the need for decision makers to obtain more information before making irreversible decisions. Emerging from the debate is a call to science not to lose sight of the need to conduct transparent, repeatable studies to answer concerns related to the safety of GMFs.

It seems clear, however, that the future of genetic modification in agriculture will not be settled by good science and risk assessment calculations alone, but will be determined in the political and legal arenas and through regulatory regimes (Bueckert, 2000; Gray, 1998). For instance, on January 29, 2000, the United Nations Convention on Biological Diversity adopted the Cartagena Protocol (also known as the Biosafety Protocol), an international agreement regulating trade in genetically modified organisms. The Cartagena Protocol, signed by 75 countries, advocates a precautionary principle of environmental law and treats environmental issues as equal to trade-related issues. In January 2000, Canada committed to sign the Cartagena Protocol. In late September of that same year, a coalition of 80 groups, including the Council of Canadians and Greenpeace Canada, called on the federal government to honour this commitment. According to the coalition, Canada's failure to sign the protocol reinforced the view that government ranked trade objectives ahead of human health, the environment, and biodiversity (Bueckert, 2000).

In May 2000, the Sierra Legal Defence Fund filed a petition under the Auditor General Act concerning Canada's Federal Regulatory Framework for Biotechnology. In September 2000, the Auditor General's office responded by saying that Canada's system already provided the necessary regulatory, legal, and policy framework to evaluate the health and environmental impacts of biotechnology (Government of Canada, 2000). Nevertheless, Agriculture Canada announced a 12-year study to assess more thoroughly the impacts of GMFs on human health and the environment (Teel, 2000).

At the Codex Alimentarius Commission, work is ongoing in Canada and internationally to examine approaches to labelling genetically modified products. In Canada, three major consultative efforts revealed strong support for mandatory labelling of foods when significant nutritional or compositional changes were made, in comparison to foods already on the market, and in cases where safety concerns such as allergenicity were identified. These consultations also determined that a voluntary labelling approach by food manufacturers or distributors to identify these foods to consumers was acceptable provided the label statement was truthful and not misleading (Canadian General Standards Board, 2000).

Designer Genes at the Dinner Table, a 1999 citizens' conference on food biotechnology, emphasized the importance of giving ordinary Canadian citizens a direct part in decision-making processes regarding the future of food. Conducted in the context of the federal government's renewal of the Canadian Biotechnology Strategy, this citizens' conference demonstrated a promising method for addressing socially controversial issues such as food biotechnology. The first of its kind in Canada, this conference enabled citizens to consult with experts as they considered issues associated with food biotechnology. In making recommendations, such as the need for the Canadian Biotechnology Advisory Committee to resolve GE food labelling issues, citizens stressed that old models of decision making were no longer viable, particularly in light of rapidly changing technology (Citizens' Panel on Food Biotechnology, 1999). Similarly, the Royal Society of Canada's Expert Panel on the Future of Food Biotechnology (2001) recommended that regulation of new food biotechnology products be guided by prudence and a precautionary approach to the regulation of biotechnology that would pay special attention to protection of health and the environment. Such a regulatory stance appears to have been challenged successfully in Europe (see the last paragraph of the Agricultural Biotechnology section on page 245).

SOURCES: "Ten Reasons Why Biotechnology Will Not Ensure Food Security, Protect the Environment and Reduce Poverty in the Developing World," M. Altieri, 2000, SustainAbility Online, http://www.sustainability.com/cage/10reasons.html; "Are We Too Late?" P. Arriola, October 8, 1998, *Nature*, http://helix.nature.com/debates/gmfoods/gmfoods_3.html; *Unnatural Harvest: How Genetic Engineering Is Altering Our Food*, I. Boyens, 2000, Toronto: Doubleday Canada; "Government Pressed to Sign Biosafety Protocol," D. Bueckert, September 28, 2000, *Calgary Herald*, p. A12; *Standard for the Voluntary Labelling of Foods Obtained or Not Obtained through Genetic Modification*, Canadian General Standards Board, 2000, http://www.pwgsc.gc.ca/cgsb/032_025/intro_e.html; "Peter Melchett: Lord of the Greens," B. Chaundy, September 20, 2000, BBC News Online, http://news6.thdo.bbc.co.uk/hi/english/uk/newsid%5F934000/ 934110.stm; "Old MacDonald Had a Farm, Eee Eie Eee Eie Oh-oh," J. Chiperzak, 1999, *Alternatives Journal, 25*(1), 15; *Citizens' Panel Final Report: Designer Genes at the Dinner Table*, Citizens' Panel on Food Biotechnology, 1999, Calgary: University of Calgary; "Judging Gene Foods," A. Coghlan, April 15, 2000, *New Scientist*, p. 4; "Food and Drink," M. Gasson, October 8, 1998, *Nature*, http://helix.nature.com/debates/gmfoods/gmfoods_4.html; *Review of Federal Laws, Regulations, and Policies on Genetically Modified Organisms, Specifically Relating to Sustainable Development: Summary of the Response of Federal Departments to the Petition from the Sierra Legal Defence Fund*, Government of Canada, 2000, http://www.cfia-acia.agr.ca/english/ppc/biotech/enviro/sierrafse.shtml; "Be Careful What You Wish …," A. Gray, October 15, 1998, *Nature*, http://helix.nature.com/debates/gmfoods/gmfoods_5.html; "A High-Level Food Fight," W. Greider, November 3, 2003, *The Nation*, p. 16; "Relative Risk," R. Hails, October 1, 1998, *Nature*, http://helix.nature.com/debates/gmfoods/gmfoods_2.html; "Sceptically Speaking …," J. Hill, October 1, 1998, *Nature*, http://helix.nature.com/debates/gmfoods/gmfoods_1.html; "US Academy Study Finds GM Foods Are Safe," C. Macilwain, April 13, 2000, *Nature, 404*, 893; "Canadians Unafraid of Biotech," K. May, July 24, 2000, *Calgary Herald*, p. A5; "Feeding Africa," F. Pearce, May 27, 2000, *New Scientist*, 40–43; *Seminal Paper on Agricultural Biotechnology: A Summary of the Science*, D. P. Powell, 1999, Crop Protection Institute of Canada, www.plant.uguelph.ca/riskcomm/gmo/cpi/CPI-nov-99htm; *Expert Panel on the Future of Food Biotechnology: Summary Statement*, Royal Society of Canada, 2001, http://www.rsc.ca/index.php?page_id=119; "Study to Probe Altered Crops," G. Teel, August 31, 2000, *Calgary Herald*, p. A1; "Feeding Africa," F. Wambugu, May 27, 2000, *New Scientist*, 40–44; "Benefits and Risks of Genetic Modification in Agriculture," M. Wilkinson, October 1, 1998, *Nature*, http://www.nature.com/nature/debates/gmfoods/ gmfoods_contents.html

use of appropriate manure and fertilizer management practices as well as pest and pesticide management practices, increases in zero-till or conservation tillage, improved management of riparian areas, improved practices for management of odours and particulate emissions, and protection of biodiversity (Agriculture and Agri-Food Canada, 2003a). However, the APF continues Canada's focus on voluntary efforts rather than regulated standards to deal with environmental problems caused by agriculture (Boyd, 2003).

Sustainable agriculture policies and practices need to ensure that (1) environmental quality is maintained or enhanced; (2) individuals and companies engaged in food production are rewarded adequately, both economically and socially; and (3) an adequate, accessible, and safe food supply is assured. Additionally, the Canadian agricultural industry needs to ensure it can adapt to potential future climate changes. These elements are present, in various forms, in the programs and initiatives that are being implemented to achieve the national vision for agriculture outlined in Canada's current Agricultural Policy Framework.

Agriculture and Agri-Canada's current five-year (2003–8) Agricultural Policy Framework (APF) focused on stabilizing funding in order to achieve "common objectives in ... food safety and quality, the environment, renewal, science and innovation, and business risk management" (Agriculture and Agri-Food Canada, 2007). Constant changes in the agricultural context, both nationally and globally, give rise to new challenges and opportunities in planning for the future. Thus, in preparation for the next generation of agricultural policy (2008 iteration of the APF), federal, provincial, and territorial governments have been working with the industry and seeking input from interested Canadians. The objective is to "make Canada the world leader in food safety, innovation and environmentally-responsible production" (Agriculture and Agri-Food Canada, 2005a).

The environment programs of the Agricultural Policy Framework are intended to "help the agriculture and agri-food sector achieve environmental sustainability in the areas of soil, water, air and biodiversity" (Agriculture and Agri-Food Canada, 2005a, p. 11). One of these programs, the Environmental Farm Planning (EFP) program, encourages on-farm results by assisting producers to adopt beneficial management practices such as converting environmentally sensitive crop land to perennial cover, planting and maintaining shelter belts, and improving water supply capacity by improving their ability to deal with drought situations. Considerable effort has been expended to integrate federal and provincial environmental programs to achieve economic and environmental sustainability at the farm level (see Table 6–6). These types of partnerships have been effective and need to continue within the new APF.

Cooperative research into sustainability of agroecosystems also continues, some of it in partnership with industry.

Photo 6–19
The Prairie Care Project helps conserve and restore wetland habitat for waterfowl and other species.

Examples of these efforts include developing disease- and pest-resistant crop varieties; reducing pesticide use; developing integrated approaches to pest management; improving the efficiency of animals (through breeding and nutrition), resulting in less manure and better use of forage and grains; and developing more efficient fertilizer application technology and innovative approaches to manure management, especially because these affect water quality.

FUTURE CHALLENGES

Even though there has been progress toward managing agricultural lands in a sustainable manner, difficulties remain. Farming methods have not always encouraged agriculture to depend on the natural system's heterogeneous characteristics but rather have pushed farmers to standardize procedures and technology to achieve uniform results in mass quantities (industrial agriculture). Nevertheless, the call for alternative agricultural practices—ones that are sustainable and maintain agricultural resources as renewable resources—has grown. The realization that the status quo is not sustainable means that new and creative alternatives are required. Stewardship, protection, and monitoring, as well as knowledge-building, are part of the new alternatives. Since some of the most effective agricultural innovations have been undertaken by farmers, including developments in conservation farming techniques, the ability of farmers to respond to stewardship interests and economic changes, and to adopt new management systems and technologies, needs to be incorporated in approaches to sustainable agroecosystems. The Agricultural Policy Framework (APF) referred to previously attempts to involve all stakeholders in strengthening the agriculture and agri-food sector and has held public as well as private discussions on what is needed for the future development of this sector. The contributions of all

Environmental Farm Planning (EFP)

Objective:
- To help agriculture recognize its impact on the environment and to promote the continuous growth of the stewardship ethic within the agriculture industry by contributing to agricultural producers' adoption of environmentally beneficial management practices in managing land, water, air, and biodiversity

Implementation:
- Through provincially delivered EFP programs across Canada, producers are encouraged to develop environmental farm plans, implement action plans and beneficial management practices (BMPs), and continuously evaluate the environmental performance of their farming operations.

Integration:
- Producers who develop EFPs may be eligible for technical and financial assistance to implement their on-farm action plans through the National Farm Stewardship Program and the Greencover Canada Program.

National Farm Stewardship Program (NFSP) (supports EFP)

Objective:
- To accelerate adoption of BMPs on Canadian farms and agricultural landscapes. This outcome will be achieved through the provision of cost-shared incentives to producers for the implementation of BMPs that address on-farm risk where identified in producers' farm plans.

Implementation:
- A national list of BMP categories and associated practices has been developed to identify those BMPs eligible for assistance under the program. Provincial lists identify which BMPs from the national list are eligible for financial and technical assistance within each province.

Integration:
- Producers whose EFPs (or equivalent agri-environmental plans) have been completed and reviewed are eligible to apply for $50 000 in federal funding and technical assistance through the National Farm Stewardship Program and Greencover Canada.

Greencover Canada Program (GCP)

Objective:
- To maximize environmental benefits to Canadians by protecting land from wind and water erosion, improving water quality, enhancing biodiversity, and increasing carbon sequestration in the soil.

Implementation:
- Over five years, $110 million will be available to help producers improve grassland management practices, protect water quality, reduce greenhouse gas emissions, and enhance biodiversity and wildlife habitat.

Integration:
- Greencover Canada focuses on four components: converting environmentally sensitive land to perennial cover, managing agricultural land near water, providing technical assistance to help producers adopt BMPs, and planting shelterbelts.

SOURCE: *Agricultural Policy Framework*, Agriculture and Agri-Food Canada, 2005, http://www4.agr.gc.ca/AAFC-AAC/display-afficher. do?id=1173969168670&lang=e

sectors, including civil society, need to be considered seriously in moving toward sustainable agroecosystems.

At the same time, farmers across Canada continue to face a range of pressures—from the weather to grasshoppers, from low commodity prices to BSE, and from GMOs to biofuels—that have resulted in major financial challenges. Without financial health in Canada's agricultural industry and at the farm level, environmental improvements are difficult to effect. As noted earlier in this chapter, incomes have fallen and indebtedness has risen as farmers' costs for fertilizers, pesticides, and commercial feeds have risen and as stiffer competition has occurred in the global economy (MacRae & Cuddeford, 1999; Statistics Canada, 2002b). The economic climate continues to be a difficult one in which to promote environmental stewardship. Yet, the push for sustainable agriculture derives in part from its economic viability and in part from the practical solutions it provides to most of

●●● young
environmental professionals

NETWORKING ▪ CAREERS ▪ PROFESSIONAL DEVELOPMENT

Young Environmental Professionals (YEP) is a volunteer organization that provides opportunities for young professionals in the fields of environment and sustainability. Founded in late 1997 in Toronto, YEP now has over 2000 members and four additional chapters in Calgary (established in 2001), Vancouver (2002; called Connecting Environmental Professionals), the National Capital Region (2003) and Edmonton (2006). Guided by a National Steering Committee (with representatives from private, public, and voluntary sectors), the main focus of YEP is to provide career development and networking opportunities for its members by presenting speakers, hosting workshops, and providing a mentorship program.

To build capacity among its members, the YEP follows three principles:

1. *Education*: YEP helps educate its members by providing informal learning opportunities, including its website (http://www.yepcanada.ca/) as well as workshops and speaker sessions.

2. *Engagement*: YEP's monthly meetings provide mentoring and support for the active participation of members in a variety of community activities and projects.

3. *Employment*: At monthly meetings and other events, YEP may distribute job postings and bring together potential employers and employees.

In March 2008, YEP held a workshop for 18- to 30-year-olds, called the GLOBE Forum for Emerging Environmental Leaders; YEP's forum was a side event to the biennial trade fair and conference on business and the environment (GLOBE 2008) held in Vancouver. A partnership initiative of the Vancouver chapter of YEP, the GLOBE Foundation, the Delphi Group, and the University of Waterloo's Centre for Environment and Business, YEP's forum focused on engaging the next generation of community actors, business entrepreneurs, and policy thinkers—in other words, people like you, who will be the leaders in building the businesses and finding the solutions to 21st century environmental issues. Among other benefits, the forum offered professional networking opportunities for emerging environmental leaders, an executive mentorship program, and employment and community project ideas for the emerging leaders to implement when they returned to their communities, postsecondary institutions, or workplaces.

Beyond special events such as the forum, which bring new talent, ideas, and actions to YEP, the Vancouver chapter has hosted Dr. Bill Rees to speak about ecological footprint analysis, the Calgary chapter has heard from experts in nuclear energy and carbon markets, while the Toronto chapter has hosted workshops focusing on environmental issues in the Greater Toronto Area. YEP's Edmonton chapter has provided information about making everyday living more sustainable, and also publishes the biweekly EdeN (Edmonton Environmental e-Newsletter), a fun source of information that helps individuals identify personal and career growth, mentoring, and volunteer opportunities. The Ottawa chapter met with author Jeffrey Simpson about his book on meeting Canada's climate change challenges.

While most members of YEP work in environment and sustainability fields, this is not a requirement for membership. A $30 lifetime membership fee to join YEP is honoured by all chapters.

Photo 6–20

The environmental activities and accomplishments of the YEP Edmonton chapter begin when members meet to listen to speakers and share ideas.

SOURCES: "Welcome to YEP Canada.ca," Young Environmental Professionals, 2007, http://www.yepcanada.ca/; thanks to Robyn Jacobsen (YEP Edmonton), Santa Luangkam (YEP Toronto), and Cariad Garrett (Connecting Environmental Professionals, Vancouver) for providing information about YEP.

the erosion, contamination, and energy issues farmers face (MacRae & Cuddeford, 1999). Whether or not the APF will succeed in creating an environment within which research in the sciences and social sciences will bring new and sustainable opportunities and approaches to rural communities remains to be seen.

The health and productivity of agroecosystems clearly are fundamental necessities in sustainability of agricultural land resources. However, it is difficult to monitor trends or changes in agroecosystem quality without an adequate information base. This lack also makes it difficult to determine if public and private investments in sustainability activities, such as maintaining life-support systems, preserving biological diversity, and maintaining the productive capacity of species and ecosystems, are achieving the desired ends. The APF specifies that the Implementation Agreements with each province and territory will contain targets and indicators to be used in measuring and monitoring the progress made in achieving established environmental outcome and farm environmental management goals. Here, too, the utility and effectiveness of these targets and indicators need to be demonstrated.

Among the most promising tools to monitor agroecosystems and to enhance our knowledge and database are remote sensing and geographic information systems (GISs). GISs can link together Statistics Canada's Census of Agriculture, Agriculture and Agri-Food Canada's research station experimental data, and data from farmers to improve the baseline for assessing changes. Specifically, indicators of agroecosystem health may be manipulated within a GIS, including soil degradation, soil quality, crop yield, soil cover and management, conservation practices adopted, land conversions, and nutrient balance.

Progress has been made toward preserving biological diversity and maintaining the productive capacity of species and ecosystems through the increased use of sustainable land management practices. The challenge is to continue, as appropriate, to increase conservation tillage, to decrease summerfallow, to find alternatives to agrochemicals and to reduce use of herbicides and pesticides, to remove more marginal land from crop production into forage or other uses, and to continue to restore and enhance wildlife habitat. Stewardship remains an important impetus for continued protection of agroecosystems, given that wind and water erosion; salinization; soil compaction; organic matter loss; contamination of groundwater by nitrates, pesticides, and bacteria; and genetic engineering developments continue to occur.

Resolving these challenges to the sustainability of Canadian agroecosystems and land resources requires long-term commitment. Given appropriate care, the health of agricultural soils and agroecosystems can be maintained and even improved. As our understanding of environmental and other impacts on Canadian agriculture increases, and as sustainable and conservation methods continue to improve, it will become easier to avoid adverse impacts from farming operations. Achieving the goal of sustainable agriculture is a responsibility shared among farmers, the agri-food industry, government, and consumers. Cooperation and partnerships among these groups is key to ensuring the sustainability of both agriculture and the environment.

Chapter Questions

1. Identify and discuss the main ways in which soil quality of agricultural lands may be degraded. What are the sources and impacts of other human activities on agricultural lands?

2. Why should soil conservation and biodiversity of agroecosystems be a concern of every Canadian, not just farmers?

3. Why are integrated pest management approaches better for the environment than earlier approaches? How could you employ IPM principles in a small vegetable garden behind a house in a city or town?

4. Could farming lead to desertification in Canada? How might it be prevented?

5. In Canada, many farming activities illustrate that the link between population and environmental impact is not a direct one. What kinds of agricultural technology used in farming amplify the effects of human influence on the environment? What kinds of agricultural technology might reduce this effect?

6. Describe the various efforts Canada has made in attempting to achieve sustainable agriculture at international and national levels. Identify the range of efforts made (if any) by your provincial government.

7. What are some of the advantages and disadvantages of nontraditional agricultural activities (such as organic farming and biotechnology) in achieving economic and environmental sustainability of Canadian agricultural lands and plant and animal resources?

Acton, D. F., & Gregorich, L. J. (1995). Understanding soil health. In D. F. Acton & L. J. Gregorich (Eds.), *The health of our soils—Toward sustainable agriculture in Canada.* Ottawa: Agriculture and Agri-Food Canada. http://www.agr.gc.ca/nlwis_snite/index_e.cfm?s1=pub&s2=hs_ss&page=7

Adams, B., & Fitch, L. (1995). *Caring for the Green Zone: Riparian areas and grazing management.* Lethbridge, AB: Alberta Environmental Protection.

Agricultural biotechnology: Canada and the WTO ruling on genetically modified organisms. (November 1, 2006, Vol 1, Issue 3), *AWB Bio-Bulletin,* available at http://www.agwest.sk.ca/publications/Bio-Bulletin/BBNov06.pdf

Agriculture and Agri-Food Canada. (1996). *Biotechnology, agriculture and regulation.* http://www.aceis.agr.ca/fpi/agbiotec/geninfo.html

Agriculture and Agri-Food Canada. (1997a). *Agriculture in harmony with nature: Strategy for environmentally sustainable agriculture and agri-food development in Canada.* Ottawa: Author.

Agriculture and Agri-Food Canada. (1997b). *Information bulletin ... Biotechnology and environmental concerns: Outcrossing.* http://www.aceis.agr.ca/fpi/agbiotec/crosse.html

Agriculture and Agri-Food Canada. (1997c). *Information bulletin ... Regulating agricultural biotechnology in Canada: Environmental questions.* http://www.agr.ca/fpi/agbiotec/enviroe.html

Agriculture and Agri-Food Canada. (2003a). *Federal–Provincial–Territorial Framework Agreement on Agricultural and Agri-Food Policy for the Twenty-First Century.* http://www.agr.gc.ca/cb/apf/index_e.php?section=info&group=accord&page=accord

Agriculture and Agri-Food Canada. (2003b). *Prairie soils: The case for conservation.* http://www.agr.gc.ca/pfra/soil/prairiesoils.htm

Agriculture and Agri-Food Canada. (2005a). *Agricultural Policy Framework.* http://www4.agr.gc.ca/AAFC-AAC/display-afficher.do?id=1173969168670&lang=e

Agriculture and Agri-Food Canada. (2005b). *Exports—Agri-food for 2005.* http://atn-riae.agr.ca/stats/4000_e.pdf

Agriculture and Agri-Food Canada. (2006a). *Canada's new government launches ecoagriculture biofuels capital initiative.* http://www.agr.gc.ca/cb/index_{e.php?s1=n&s2=2007&page=n70423

Agriculture and Agri-Food Canada. (2006b). *Exports—Agri-food for 2006.* http://atn-riae.agr.ca/stats/4141_e.pdf

Agriculture and Agri-Food Canada. (2006c). *An overview of the Canadian agriculture and agri-food system.* http://www.agr.gc.ca/pol/index_e.php?s1=pub&s2=sys&page=intro

Agriculture and Agri-Food Canada. (2007). *Growing forward.* http://www.agr.gc.ca/pol/grow-croiss/pr-im_e.php?page=accord

Alasia, A., & Rothwell, N. (2003). The rural/urban divide is not changing: Income disparities persist. *Rural and Small Town Canada Analysis Bulletin, 4*(4), 1.

Alberta Agriculture, Food and Rural Development. (2000). *Livestock regulations stakeholder advisory group.* http://www.agric.gov.ab.ca/economic/policy/ilo/index.html

Alberta Agriculture, Food and Rural Development. (2006). *Chronic wasting disease (CWD) of elk and deer.* http://www1.agric.gov.ab.ca/$department/deptdocs.nsf/all/agdex3594?opendocument

Arnalds, A. (2000). Evolution of rangeland conservation strategies. In A. Arnalds & S. Archer (Eds.), *Rangeland desertification* (pp. 153–165). London: Kluwer Academic.

Bakker, J. P. (1998). The impact of grazing on plant communities. In M. F. WallisDeVries, J. P. Bakker, & S. E. VanWieren (Eds.), *Grazing and conservation management* (pp. 137–184). Dordrecht: Kluwer Academic.

Bork, E. (2000). Grazing can improve native plant diversity in range. *Lethbridge Research Centre.* http://www4.agr.gc.ca/AAFC-AAC/display-afficher.do?id=1180547946064&lang=e

Boyd, D. R. (2003). *Unnatural law: Rethinking Canadian environmental law and policy.* Vancouver: UBC Press.

Boyens, I. (2000). *Unnatural harvest: How genetic engineering is altering our food.* Toronto: Doubleday.

Bueckert, D. (2000, September 24). Government pressed to sign Biosafety Protocol. *Calgary Herald,* p. A12.

Canadian Alert in Genetic Engineering. (2000). *Biotechnology: Giving pollution a life of its own.* http://www.sustainability.com/cage/

Canadian Food Inspection Agency. (2008). *Canada Organic Regime: A certified choice.* http://www.inspection.gc.ca

Canadian Petroleum Products Institute. (2006). *Essential features of a national policy on renewable fuels.* http://www.cppi.ca/News_Releases.html

Canadian Renewable Fuels Association. 2007. *Prime Minister Harper builds on his biofuel promise.* http://www.greenfuels.org/news/2007-07-05.htm

Canola Council of Canada. (n.d.). *Canola-based biodiesel can help the environment* (brochure).

Cardy, W. F. G. (1997). Foreword. In N. Middleton & D. Thomas (Eds.), *World atlas of desertification* (2nd ed.) (p. vi). London: Arnold.

Chambers, A. (n.d.). Manitoba's elk—Just another farm animal? Sierra Club. http://www.sierraclub.ca/prairie/elk.html

Chambers, P. A., Guy, M., Roberts, E. S., Charlton, M. N., Kent, R., Gagnon, C., Grove, G., & Foster, N. (2001). *Nutrients and their impact on the Canadian environment.* Agriculture and Agri-Food Canada, Environment Canada, Fisheries and Oceans Canada, Health Canada, and Natural Resources Canada. http://www.durable.gc.ca/group/nutrients/report/index_e.phtml

Dale, B. (2000). Range management can help save prairie birds. *Lethbridge Research Centre.* http://www4.agr.gc.ca/AAFC-AAC/display-afficher.do?id=1180547946064&lang=e

Derworiz, C. (2000, August 12). Disease may wipe out elk industry. *Calgary Herald,* pp. B1, B2.

Dowdeswell, E. (1997). Preface. In N. Middleton & D. Thomas (Eds.), *World atlas of desertification* (2nd ed.) (p. iv). London: Arnold.

Ecological Agriculture Projects. (1997). *Agriculture and Agri-Food Canada's strategy for environmental sustainability.* http://eap.mcgill.ca/MagRack/EC/ec1_1_2.htm

Eilers, R. G., Eilers, W. D., Pettapiece, W. W., & Lelyk, G. (1995). Salinization of soil. In D. F. Acton & L. J. Gregorich (Eds.), *The health of our soils—Toward sustainable agriculture in Canada* (pp. 77–86). Ottawa: Agriculture and Agri-Food Canada.

Elk On Line. (1996). *Elk Breeders Home Page.* http://www.wapiti.net/

Environment Canada. (2001). *Effects of agriculture on biodiversity in Canada.* http://www.eman-rese.ca/eman/reports/publications/biodiv-sci-asses/biodivio.htm

Environment Canada. (2002). *Canada's greenhouse gas inventory 1990–2000. Factsheet overview.* http://www.ec.gc.ca/pdb/ghg/factsheet_e.cfm

Food and Agriculture Organization of the United Nations. (2002). *Challenges and opportunities for the World Summit on Sustainable Development: FAO's perspective.* Paper prepared for the World Summit on Sustainable Development, Johannesburg, August 26–September 4. http://www.fao.org/wssd/docs/ChallengesandOpportunityfinal.doc

Forge, F. (2007). *Biofuels—An energy, environmental or agricultural policy?* http://www.parl.gc.ca/information/library/PRBpubs/prb0637-e.htm

Gauthier, D. A., & Henry, J. D. (1989). Misunderstanding the prairies. In M. Hummel (Ed.), *Endangered spaces: The future for Canada's wilderness* (pp. 183–195). Toronto: Key Porter.

Gilbertson, T., Holland, N., Semino, S., & Smith, K. (2007). *Paving the way for agrofuels: EU policy, sustainability criteria and climate calculations*. Amsterdam: Transnational Institute, Corporate Europe Observatory, and Grupo de Reflexion Rural.

Government of Alberta. (2001, December 20). *Confined feeding operation regulations and standards balance industry growth with environmental and health protection*. http://www.gov.ab.ca/acn/200112/11733.html

Government of Canada. (1991). *The state of Canada's environment—1991*. Ottawa: Supply and Services Canada.

Government of Canada. (1994). *Canada's national report on climate change: Actions to meet commitments under the United Nations Framework Convention on Climate Change*. Ottawa: Supply and Services Canada.

Government of Canada. (1996). *The state of Canada's environment—1996*. Ottawa: Supply and Services Canada.

Government of Canada. (1999). *Canada introduces national standard for organic agriculture*. http://www.cfia-acia.agr.ca/ english/corpaffr/newsrelease/19990629e.shtml

Gregorich, E. G., Angers, D. A., Campbell, C. A., Carter, M. R., Drury, D. F., Ellert, B. H., et al. (1995). Changes in soil organic matter. In D. F. Acton & L. J. Gregorich (Eds.), *The health of our soils—Toward sustainable agriculture in Canada* (pp. 41–50). Ottawa: Agriculture and Agri-Food Canada.

Han, F. X., Kingery, W. L., Selim, H. M., & Gerard, P. D. (2000). Accumulation of heavy metals in a long-term poultry waste-amended soil. *Soil Science, 165*(3), 260–268.

Hasselback, P. (1997). Intensive livestock operations and health problems. *Encompass, 2*(2), 4–5.

Hengeveld, H. E., Bush, E., & Edwards, P. (2002). *Frequently asked questions about climate change science*. Downsview, ON: Environment Canada, Science Assessment and Policy Integration Branch.

Hoffman, N. (2001). Urban consumption of agricultural land. *Rural and Small Town Canada Analysis Bulletin, 3*(2), 1–11.

Holechek, J. L. (1993, July). Policy changes on federal rangelands. *Trail Boss News*, 1–2.

Hunter, E. (1999). Community agriculture rises in Quebec. *Alternatives Journal, 25*(1), 24.

Janzen, H. (2000). Managing range essential to maintaining soil carbon stores. *Lethbridge Research Centre*. http://www4.agr.gc.ca/AAFC-AAC/display-afficher.do?id=1180547946064&lang=e

Johnson, W. (Ed.). (1995). *Managing Saskatchewan rangeland* (rev. ed.). Regina: Economic Regional Development Agreement.

Johnston, T., & Weibel, A. (2005–2006). Industrial hog production and the hog-barn neighbourhood effect in Lethbridge County, Alberta. *Western Geography, 15/16*, 53–67.

Jowkar, F. (1994). Women bear the brunt. *Our Planet, 6*(5), 16–17.

Kelly, B. (2003). Prince Edward Island, Department of Fisheries, Aquaculture and Environment, response to questionnaire survey for *Our Environment: A Canadian Perspective*, Third Edition.

Kneen, B. (1999a). Death science creeps onto the farm. *Alternatives Journal, 25*(1), 10–11.

Kneen, B. (1999b). *Farmageddon: Food and the culture of biotechnology*. Gabriola Island, BC: New Society.

Korol, M. (2004). *Fertilizer and pesticide management in Canada, 1*(3). Ottawa: Minister of Industry.

Lal, R. (2001). Potential of desertification control to sequester carbon and mitigate the greenhouse effect. *Climatic Change, 51*(1), 35.

Larney, F. J, Bullock, M. S., Janzen, H. H., Ellert, B. H., & Olson, E. C. (1998). Wind erosion effects on nutrient redistribution and soil productivity. *Journal of Soil and Water Conservation, 53*(2), 133–138.

Losey, J. E., Rayor, L. S., & Carter, M. E. (1999, May 20). Transgenic pollen harms monarch larvae. *Nature, 399*, 214.

MacRae, R., & Cuddeford, V. (1999). *A green food and agriculture agenda for Ontario. The Environmental Agenda for Ontario Project*. http://www.cielap.org/infocent/research/agri.html

Manitoba Climate Change Task Force. (2001). *Manitoba and climate change: Investing in our future. Report of the Manitoba Climate Change Task Force*. Winnipeg: Author.

Manzano, M. G., & Navár, J. (2000). Processes of desertification by goats overgrazing in the Tamaulipan thornscrub (*matorral*) in north-eastern Mexico. *Journal of Arid Environments, 44*, 1–17.

McKenna, P. (2007, July 18). "Corn biofuels "dangerously oversold" as green energy." *NewScientist Environment*. http://environment.newscientist.com/article/dn12283-corn-biofuel-dangerously-oversold-as-green-energy.html

McKenzie, J. I. (2002). *Environmental politics in Canada: Managing the commons into the twenty-first century*. Don Mills: Oxford University Press.

McQuarrie, I. (1997). Agriculture and ecology. In T. Fleming (Ed.), *The environment and Canadian society* (pp. 54–55). Toronto: ITP Nelson.

Medline Plus, Medical Encyclopedia. (2007). Methemoglobinemia. http://www.nlm.nih.gov/medlineplus/ency/article/000562.htm

Methanol Institute and International Fuel Quality Center. (2006). *A biodiesel primer: market and public policy developments, quality, standards of handling*. www.biodiesel.org/resource/reportesdatabase/reports/gen/20060401-GEN369.pdf.

Middleton, N., & Thomas, D. (Eds.). (1997). *World atlas of desertification* (2nd ed.). London: Arnold.

Mineau, P., McLaughlin, A., Boutin, C., Evenden, M., Freemark, K., Kevan, P., McLeod, G., & Tomlin, A. (1994). Effects of agriculture on biodiversity in Canada. In Environment Canada, Biodiversity Science Assessment Team, *Biodiversity in Canada: A science assessment for Environment Canada* (pp. 59–113). Ottawa: Supply and Services Canada.

Natural Resources Canada. (2002). *Biobus Project: Biodiesel demonstration and impact assessment with the Société de Transport de Montréal (STM)*. http://www.nrcan-rncan.gc.ca/media/archives/newsreleases/2002/

Nikiforuk, A. (2000, June 12). When water kills. *Online Macleans*. http://www.macleans.ca/pubdoc/2000/06/12/Cover/35699.shtml

North America Wetlands Conservation Council. (2002). *NAWCC (Canada) celebrates a decade of influencing change*. http://www.terreshumidescanada.org/pubs.html

Olson, K. (1997). Agriculture and the environment. *Environment Views and Network News, 1*(1), 22.

Organic Trade Association. (2006a). *Canada organic standard and regulation*. http://www.ota.com/pp/canada.html

Organic Trade Association. (2006b). *Canada's organic products regulations*. http://www.ota.com/standards/canadian.html

Prakash, C. S. (2001). The genetically modified crop debate in the context of agricultural evolution. *Plant Physiology, 126*, 8–15.

Reynolds, W. D., Campbell, C. A., Chang, C., Cho, C. M., Ewanek, J., Kachanoski, R. G., et al. (1995). Agrochemical entry into groundwater. In D. F. Acton & L. J. Gregorich (Eds.), *The health of our soils—Toward sustainable agriculture in Canada* (pp. 97–109). Ottawa: Agriculture and Agri-Food Canada.

Rubec, C. D. A. (1994). Canada's federal policy on wetland conservation: A global model. In W. J. Mitsch (Ed.), *Global wetlands: Old world and new* (pp. 909–917). Amsterdam: Elsevier Science B.V.

Science Council of Canada. (1992). *Sustainable agriculture: The research challenge*. Report No. 43. Ottawa: Author.

Seck, M. (1994). Unearthing the impacts of tenure. *IDRC Reports, 22*(2), 11–12.

Semmens, G. (2004, May 15). Threatened status may aid plains bison. *Calgary Herald*, p. A3.

Shrubsole, D., & Draper, D. (2007). On guard for thee? Water (ab)uses and management in Canada. In K. Bakker (Ed.), *Eau Canada: The future of Canada's water* (pp. 37–54). Vancouver: UBC Press.

Smith, W. N., Desjardins, R. L., & Grant, B. (2001). Estimated changes in soil carbon associated with agricultural practices in Canada. *Canadian Journal of Soil Science, 81*, 221–227.

Soil Conservation Council of Canada. (2005). *New composting process beats the weather and avoids urban-sprawl conflicts.* http://www.soilcc.ca/ggmp/gg_news/a_LiqManure.html

Soil Conservation Council of Canada. (2006). Report to Canadian producers. http://www.soilcc.ca/

(S&T)² Consultants Inc. & Meyers Norris Penny LLP. (2004a). *Economic, financial, social analysis and public policies for biodiesel, phase 1.* http://www.greenfuels.org/biodiesel/pdf/OConnor-Report-Biodiesel2004.pdf

(S&T)² Consultants Inc. & Meyers Norris Penny LLP. (2004b). *Economic, financial, social analysis and public policies for fuel ethanol, phase 1.* http://www.greenfuels.org/biodiesel/pdf/OConnor-Report-Ethanol2004.pdf

Statistics Canada. (2000). *Human activity and the environment 2000.* Ottawa: Minister of Industry.

Statistics Canada. (2002a). *Human activity and the environment: Annual statistics 2002.* Ottawa: Minister of Industry.

Statistics Canada. (2002b). *2001 Agriculture Census: Total area of farms, land tenure and land in crops, provinces.* http://www.statcan.ca/english/Pgdb/econ124a.htm

Statistics Canada. (2002c). *2001 Census of Agriculture: Canadian farm operations in the 21st century.* http://www.statcan.ca/Daily/English/020515/td020515.htm

Statistics Canada. (2003a). *Farming facts 2002.* Ottawa: Minister of Industry.

Statistics Canada. (2003b). *Gross domestic product, income-based.* CANSIM table 380-0001. http://www.statcan.ca/english/Pgdb/econ03.htm

Statistics Canada. (2005a). *Human activity and the environment: Annual Statistics 2005.* Ottawa: Minister of Industry.

Statistics Canada. (2005b). The loss of dependable agricultural land in Canada. *Rural and Small Town Canada Analysis Bulletin, 6*(1), http://www.statcan.ca/english/freepub/21-006-XIE/21-006-XIE2005001.pdf

Statistics Canada. (2006). *2006 Agriculture Census: Total farm area, land tenure and land in crops.* http://www40.statcan.ca/101/cst01/agrc25a.htm?sdi=number%20farms

Statistics Canada. (2007). *Snapshot of Canadian agriculture.* http://www.statcan.ca/english/agcensus2006/articles/snapshot.htm

Stiefelmeyer, K., Mussell, A., Moore, T., & Liu, D. (2006). *The economic impact of Canadian biodiesel production on Canadian grains, oilseeds and livestock producers—Final report.* http://www.georgemorris.org/GMC/Publications/DomesticandInternationalMarketing.aspx

Taylor, D. M. (1994). *Off course: Restoring balance between Canadian society and the environment.* Ottawa: International Development Research Centre.

Thomas, D. (2003, January 14). Saskatchewan: Former Sask. elk ranchers hit with total farming ban. *Edmonton Journal.* http://www.cwdinfo.org/index.php/fuseaction/news.detail/ID/208bbf5c0efa86beb752b6a515439ff6

Thurow, T. L. (2000). Hydrologic effects on rangeland degradation and restoration processes. In A. Arnalds & S. Archer (Eds.), *Rangeland desertification* (pp. 53–67). Dordrecht: Kluwer Adademic.

Topp, G. C., Carter, M. R., Culley, J. L. B., Holmstrom, D. A., Kay, B. D., Lafond, G. P., et al. (1995). Changes in soil structure. In D. F. Acton & L. J. Gregorich (Eds.), *The health of our soils—Toward sustainable agriculture in Canada* (pp. 51–60). Ottawa: Agriculture and Agri-Food Canada.

Toronto Hydro Corporation. (2005). *Our green fleet.* http://www.torontohydro.com/corporate/initiatives/green_fleet/index

Trottier, G. C. (1992). *A landowner's guide: Conservation of Canada's prairie grassland.* Canadian Wildlife Service. http://www.pnr-rpn.ec.gc.ca/nature/whp/prgrass/df03s00.en.html

Union of Concerned Scientists. (2006). *Position paper: Pharmaceutical and industrial crops.* http://www.ucsusa.org/food_and_environment/genetic_engineering/ucs-position-paper.html

United Nations. (2002a). *Frequently asked questions about the Johannesburg Summit.* http://johannesburgsummit.org/html/basic_info/faqs.html

United Nations. (2002b). *Johannesburg Summit 2002.* http://johannesburgsummit.org/html/whats_new/feature_story41.html

Van Tighem, K. (1996). From wilds to weeds: Alberta's changing ecosystems. *Environment Views, 19*(5), 5–8.

Wall, G. J., Pringle, E. A., Padbury, G. A., Rees, H. W., Tajek, J., van Vliet, L. J. P., et al. (1995). Erosion. In D. F. Acton & L. J. Gregorich (Eds.), *The health of our soils—Toward sustainable agriculture in Canada.* Ottawa: Agriculture and Agri-Food Canada. http://res2.agr.gc.ca/publications/hs/index_e.htm.

WallisdeVries, M. F. (1998). Large herbivores as key factors for nature conservation. In M. F. WallisDeVries, J. P. Bakker, & S. E. VanWieren (Eds.), *Grazing and conservation management* (pp. 1–20). Dordrecht: Kluwer Academic.

Webber, M. D., & Singh, S. S. (1995). Contamination of agricultural soils. In D. F. Acton & L. J. Gregorich (Eds.), *The health of our soils—Toward sustainable agriculture in Canada* (pp. 86–96). Ottawa: Agriculture and Agri-Food Canada.

Weyer, P. (2001). *Nitrate concentrations and human health.* http://www.cheec.uiowa.edu/nitrate/health.html

Photo 6–21

Sustainable agricultural practices should not require government subsidies. How does Canada compare to its global neighbours in providing agricultural subsidies? Turn to the Canada and the World section to find out.

Photo 6–22

A young black bear sits on alert in the Rocky Mountain wilds. Wilderness protection is an important part of land resource management, and Canada's global performance in this area is revealed in Table C/W-12 of the Canada and the World section.

Chapter Contents

"Water is a precious and finite natural resource, one which is essential to all life and vital to ecological, economic and social well-being. Yet, water is often wasted and degraded. Therefore we face both individual and collective responsibilities to use and manage water resources wisely. This will only be accomplished as we recognize the intrinsic value of water and practice conscious and committed stewardship, recognizing that this precious heritage must be safeguarded for future generations."

Canadian Water Resources Association (1994)

"Canadians are profligate water users.... Canada ranks second highest in terms of per capita water consumption after the United States and is 65 percent above the OECD average."

Linda Nowlan (2005)

Chapter Objectives

After studying this chapter you should be able to

- understand the nature and distribution of Canada's freshwater resources and describe how scientists measure water availability

- illustrate the importance of water, including how it contributes to conflicts and hazardous events

- identify a range of human uses of freshwater resources and their impacts on freshwater environments

- discuss freshwater management strategies and challenges in Canada

INTRODUCTION

Water has sustained Canadians' high quality of life for centuries, and our lakes and rivers have provided a template for the settlement patterns of the country. First Nations people of southern Canada located their villages along riverbanks or coastal shorelines, as did subsequent European and other settlers. Indeed, all of our major cities have grown alongside these same water bodies. Water has played and continues to play an important role in contemporary culture, including our art and music. Fresh water is also the lifeblood of the ecosphere and continues to sustain many economic and recreational activities of Canadians.

At first glance, Canadians would appear to have little cause for concern about the supply and management of fresh water. In 2006, the needs of 33.1 million Canadians were served by a renewable supply that is the envy of many other countries. Canada ranks among the largest consumers of water—in 2004, our daily indoor household use averaged 329 litres per capita (Environment Canada, 2007b). In rural areas of Africa, Asia, and Latin America, in contrast, average water use is between 20 and 30 litres per capita per day (Jones, 1997). European countries consume on average 200 litres per capita in residential areas (World Water Council, 2006). Gleick (1996) suggests that 50 litres per capita per day would meet basic human domestic needs (see Figure 7–1 on the next page).

Around the world, more than 1.1 billion people do not have access to safe drinking water; pollution is rampant, and water supplies are drying up. As well, 2.6 billion people lack water for proper sanitation, which often leads to disease and high infant mortality rates. In situations of drought, developing nations often are prone to food shortages; in Canada, irrigation often supports agriculture in times of drought. Relative to people in other countries that belong to the Organization for Economic Cooperation and Development (OECD), Canadians use more water and pay relatively lower prices.

Despite an overall abundance of water, there is considerable geographic variation in its availability and quality. Shortages, contamination, and even tragedies also have been part of Canada's water supply. In this chapter, we examine the global water supply and illustrate how scientists estimate water availability. We consider Canada's water supply and distribution and highlight relevant issues related to its sustainability. Later in the chapter, Canadians' use of freshwater resources and some of the effects that our activities have on the quality of freshwater supply are discussed. Selected initiatives of governments, local groups, and private-public partnerships are considered also.

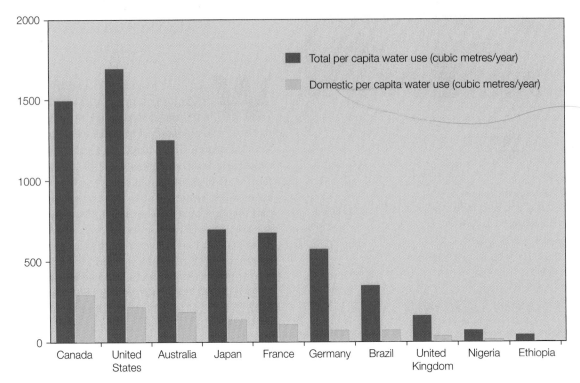

Figure 7–1

Annual and daily per capita freshwater use, selected countries, 2000

SOURCE: Adapted from *Water Reports 23—Review of World Water Resources by Country*, Food and Agricultural Organization of the United Nations, 2003, ftp://ftp.fao.org/agl/aglw/docs/wr23e.pdf

WATER SUPPLY AND DISTRIBUTION

EARTH'S FRESHWATER RESOURCES

The Earth's freshwater resources have remained virtually unchanged since the beginning of time. Fresh water constitutes less than 3 percent of Earth's water supply (see Figure 7–2). The remaining 97.24 percent is in the oceans and is too salty for drinking, irrigation, and most industrial applications. Of the 2.76 percent that is fresh water, most of it is in glaciers and ice caps. Only about 0.79 percent of the Earth's fresh water is located on land and available in inland seas, lakes, rivers, soil moisture, groundwater, and other sources. Even humans' many dams, reservoirs, and irrigation works store relatively little of the Earth's fresh water. To put freshwater resources into perspective, if we imagined the world's water supply filled a gallon jug (3.78 litres), the usable freshwater supply would amount to less than one-half teaspoon (2.5 millilitres). We have generally considered this to be a plentiful supply, as water is continuously renewed and purified through the **hydrologic cycle** (see Figures 3–16, p. 89, and 7–3, p. 260). However, our

Photo 7–1

Water quality is degraded by many human activities, including log storage and the discharge of chemicals from pulp and paper mills.

accelerated rates of consumption for industrial use and increased temperatures as a result of climate change place our initial assumptions at risk. For example, in 2003, Statistics Canada reported the rapid retreat of glaciers. Since 1850, about 1300 glaciers have lost between 25 and 75 percent of their mass, with most of this reduction occurring in the last 50 years (Statistics Canada, 2003). These figures give us pause to consider how we can best ensure long-term sustainable water use.

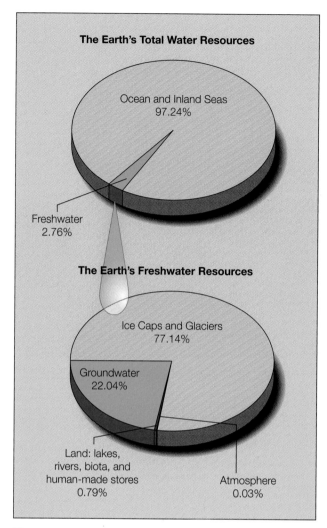

Figure 7–2

The Earth's water resources

SOURCE: U.S. Geological Survey, http://ga.water.usgs.gov/edu/
earthwherewater.htm

ESTIMATING SUPPLY: THE GLOBAL WATER BUDGET

As we discussed in Chapter 3, the global water supply on the surface of the Earth depends on several factors in the hydrologic cycle, including the amounts and rates of precipitation, evaporation, transpiration, stream flow, and subsurface flow. To estimate the water supply, scientists use a model called the **water budget**. The annual global freshwater budget is a balance among evaporation, atmospheric transport, precipitation, and storage. For continents, the balance of water can be described as

$$P = E + r$$

where P is precipitation, E is evapotranspiration, and r is runoff.

The major components of the global water cycle include evaporation from the land and ocean surfaces, precipitation onto the ocean and land surfaces, the transport of water from land areas to ocean via the atmosphere, and the return flow of water from the land into the ocean as runoff. In the ocean, the cycle also involves the mixing of fresh and salt water near the ocean surface, as well as transportation by ocean currents and sea ice. On land, the situation is more complex. The global water budget must include estimates of deposition of rain and snow on land; water flow as runoff; infiltration of water into the soil and groundwater; storage of water in soil, lakes, streams, groundwater, and polar and glacial ice; and use of water by vegetation and humans. These inputs, outputs, and storage places are illustrated in Figure 7–3 on the next page.

Figure 7–3 illustrates the values associated with the movement of water through the hydrologic cycle. The figure shows that precipitation over land is greater than evapotranspiration, meaning that a large amount of water evaporated from the oceans is carried by air currents and eventually falls on land and returns to the ocean by way of runoff through rivers.

The simplicity of the formula belies the complexity of obtaining an accurate picture of how water moves across the surface of the earth. The water balance has conventionally been estimated using observational data at the ground surface through instruments such as stream gauges. However, obtaining accurate measures across the Earth's surface is expensive, time-consuming, and frequently impractical. Many scientists are trying to determine if satellite or remote sensing might help in estimating evapotranspiration and precipitation over larger spatial scales.

The water budget requires information on precipitation (as snow or rain) temperature, latitude, soil water-holding capacity, and storage volumes in ice and snow to determine inputs. But several uncertainties exist. Different global data sets of temperature, precipitation, snow and ice volumes, and soil water-holding capacity may lead to varying estimates of water deficit and surplus. Different assumptions about how evapotranspiration works can affect the outcome of the model. As temperature is a key variable, different estimates of climate change may raise uncertainties as well. Data sets, compiled over large areas, may have missing data values in some locations or times, and the quality of the data sets may vary throughout regions of the world and various time periods. Errors within the data for small areas may become larger as data are aggregated across larger spatial scales. Thus, there are many uncertainties associated with the basic measurements necessary to estimate the global water budget. Scientists also need to gain a better understanding of the mechanisms involved in global water circulation and balance, and they need to integrate this understanding into climate and water budget models if they are to understand the overall availability of water and how this might be affected by climate change and human activities.

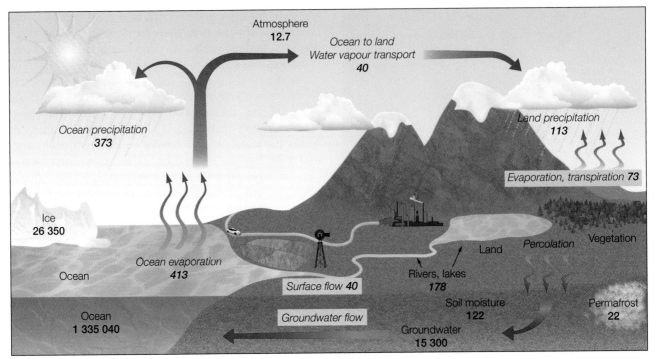

Note: Estimates of the main water reservoirs, given in plain font in 10^3 km^3, and the flow of moisture through the system, given in slant font $(10^3$ km^3 yr$^{-1})$, equivalent to Eg $(10^{18}$ g) yr^{-1}.

Figure 7–3

The hydrologic cycle with values for inputs, outputs, and storage (water budget)

NOTE: Units in this figure are 1000 cubic kilometres for storage and 1000 cubic kilometres per year for exchanges.

SOURCE: From *Estimates of the Global Water Budget and Its Annual Cycle Using Observational and Model Data*, Kevin E. Trenberth, Lesley Smith, Taotao Qian, Aiguo Dai, John Fasullo, *Journal of Hydrometeorology*, Volume 8, August 2007, p. 759. Used with permission of the American Meteorological Society.

CANADA'S FRESHWATER RESOURCES

Climate is the key factor in determining freshwater resources. Canada's average annual precipitation is about 600 millimetres, ranging from 100 millimetres in the High Arctic to over 3500 millimetres along the Pacific Coast. Over one-third of our precipitation falls as snow, most of which is released to runoff and river flow in spring (Pearse, Bertrand, & MacLaren, 1985). Given our northern environment, 100 000 glaciers alone are estimated to contain 1.5 times the volume of **surface waters** (Government of Canada, 1991).

Canada's **groundwater** resources (defined as all subsurface water) continue to be a largely hidden resource. Thirty percent of Canadians (8.9 million people) rely on groundwater for drinking water, as do more than half the world's population (UNESCO, 2002). In Canada, 90 percent of agricultural water relies on groundwater sources, generally found in aquifers (Environment Canada, 2004a).

Aquifers are rock formations (sands, gravels, or other materials) that provide reasonable flows and quantities of groundwater. Nationwide, we know that groundwater represents about 37 times the total amount of water contained in rivers and lakes in Canada (Government of

Canada, 1991), but we know very little about its precise location, extent, quantity, and quality. This ignorance reflects the complexity of surficial and bedrock geology.

Like surface water, groundwater is constantly in motion as part of the hydrological cycle. Aquifers are resupplied or recharged from surface water, mainly by infiltration of precipitation (rain or snow) in the soil. The rate of recharge varies according to factors such as soil type, vegetation cover, slope, and soil moisture content. Typically, water moves more slowly in the ground than on its surface. Although in some areas complete recharge of groundwater may take only a few days or a week, in others it may take over 10 000 years. In comparison, the average turnover (complete replacement) time of river water is about two weeks.

It is unclear how many aquifers are located in Canada, as their limits are not as well defined, topographically, as those of surface waters. There are many gaps in knowledge about the total quantity of groundwater, the ways groundwater interacts with surface water and aquatic ecosystems, aquifer recharge rates, and methods of evaluating groundwater flow. In many cases, groundwater levels and quality are not regularly monitored, hindering our understanding of its availability. For example, in

2001, 64 percent of Canadian farmers with their own wells did not have their water tested regularly, and only 16 percent had it tested once a year. This gap in knowledge is surprising given the fact that Agriculture and Agri-Food Canada (2000, p. 62) has stated that "nitrate contamination is agriculture's chief environmental effect on groundwater quality."

Wetlands, primarily located in Manitoba, the Northwest Territories, and Ontario, represent 14 percent of Canada's area. These act as the kidneys for many river systems because they filter and purify water. Wetlands also moderate stream flow during floods and droughts.

Lakes are valuable elements of Canada's water supply; they act as storage basins in regulating the flow of rivers to the sea, provide for water transport, and supply a rich habitat for natural life and human enjoyment. With about 9 percent of the country covered by fresh water in lakes and rivers, Canada contains more lakes and inland waters than any other country. For instance, Canada has 45 lakes with an area larger than 1000 square kilometres, and has (or shares with the United States) seven of the world's largest lakes. The largest lakes in Canada (some of which are shared across the border) are Huron, Great Bear, Superior, Great Slave, Winnipeg, Erie, and Ontario.

Rivers, too, are key sources of water for the country. The two largest are the Mackenzie River, which empties into the Arctic Ocean and drains a large part of northwestern Canada, and the St. Lawrence, which drains the Great Lakes and empties into the Gulf of St. Lawrence (see Figure 7–4 on the next page). With the largest volume at its mouth, the St. Lawrence River has long served as a seaway for commercial ships from the Great Lakes to the Atlantic Ocean. This important shipping route led to the industrial development of the St. Lawrence–Great Lakes region. The Mackenzie is Canada's longest river and is used for commercial navigation to a more limited degree. Canada also relies on its rivers to provide hydroelectric power, particularly those that drain into Hudson Bay from northern Manitoba and Quebec. The Fraser River, which drains into the Pacific Ocean, is well suited to power generation, but such development has been prohibited because of its value as a salmon-bearing river. Regional rivers, such as the South Saskatchewan River, also provide water for urban areas such as Saskatoon.

Annual runoff, the flow of water in rivers, is the best measure of a nation's water supply because this flow is renewed by the hydrologic cycle. In contrast, only a small portion of lakes and groundwater reservoirs is renewed annually. For instance, only 1 percent of the Great Lakes is renewed through precipitation—the remaining 99 percent of the water represents meltwater from the last ice age. This point suggests that proposals to divert water from the Great Lakes must consider the desirability and feasibility of tapping into this nonrenewable portion of the resource.

In Canada, runoff is estimated to be about 105 000 cubic metres per second (Laycock, 1987; Pearse et al., 1985). That's enough water to fill 210 million backyard swimming pools per day! With 9 percent of the world's flow, this volume of water places Canada third in the world in water endowment (following Brazil at 18 percent and the former Soviet Union at 13 percent). Canada has about 0.5 percent of the world's population. When runoff per capita is calculated, we have over twice the supply per capita of Brazil (see Table 7–1 on page 263). These data suggest that Canada is one of the "have" nations when it comes to an abundance of fresh water. However, there does not appear to be a direct relationship between economic growth and water availability. For instance, levels of economic development in Australia, France, and Israel are comparable to those in Canada, but availability of water is very different.

The supply of and demand for water are not evenly distributed over time and space. Average runoff rates vary across the country. About 60 percent of Canada's water drains north, while 90 percent of the population lives within 300 kilometres of the Canada–U.S. border. This means that many areas in the southern part of the country experience restricted water supplies. Five of the six water-deficient areas in the country are located in the more arid regions of Canada that, ironically, are dominated by agricultural land uses that rely on water (see Figure 7–4).

Water availability is a major concern even in the Great Lakes basin, the world's largest freshwater lake system, because demands for water are the highest there. Water demands of the almost 80 percent of Canadians who live in urban areas are substantial. Meeting their demands and treating their sewage wastes can be a particularly significant problem when we realize that 45 percent of Canadians live in urban centres of 1 million people or more, including Vancouver, Calgary, Edmonton, Toronto, Montreal, and Ottawa-Gatineau (Statistics Canada, 2007). Stormwater sewer and combined sewer (stormwater and wastewater) discharges, which can contain nutrients, biocides, fertilizers, and industrial wastes, also are urban-related water problems that add to these pressures.

Runoff rates also vary with time. During wet periods, lakes are renewed by river flow; river flow in turn is a function of the rainfall. During long droughts, little infiltration or percolation occurs to recharge groundwater storage, and there is little runoff to maintain river flows and lake levels. As a result, plants and trees become parched and water bodies may shrink in size. Conversely, during long periods of heavy rainfall, there is little absorption into saturated ground and runoff and sedimentation increase, sometimes causing lakes and rivers to flood. Major floods in June 1995 on the Oldman and South Saskatchewan rivers in southern Alberta, in July 1996 in the Saguenay River–Lac Saint-Jean area in Quebec, and in May 2008 in the St. John River in New Brunswick, have

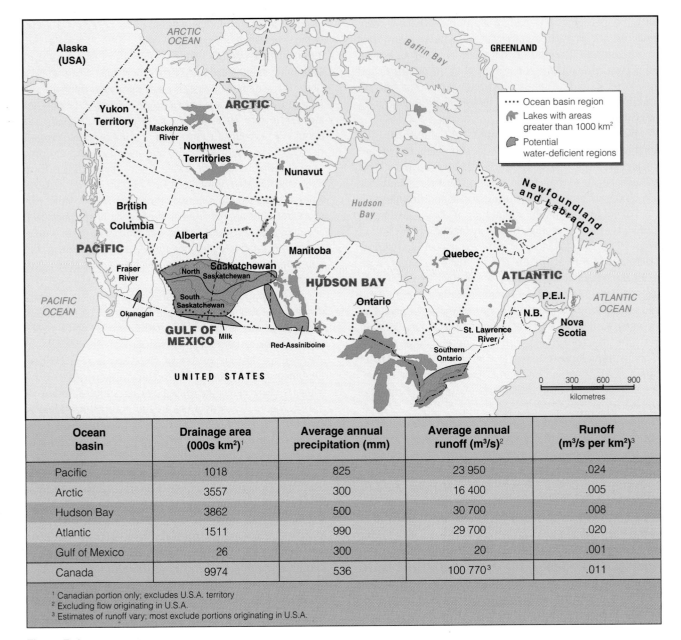

Ocean basin	Drainage area (000s km²)[1]	Average annual precipitation (mm)	Average annual runoff (m³/s)[2]	Runoff (m³/s per km²)[3]
Pacific	1018	825	23 950	.024
Arctic	3557	300	16 400	.005
Hudson Bay	3862	500	30 700	.008
Atlantic	1511	990	29 700	.020
Gulf of Mexico	26	300	20	.001
Canada	9974	536	100 770[3]	.011

[1] Canadian portion only; excludes U.S.A. territory
[2] Excluding flow originating in U.S.A.
[3] Estimates of runoff vary; most exclude portions originating in U.S.A.

Figure 7–4

Drainage regions and potential water deficiency regions in Canada

SOURCES: *Water: The Emerging Crisis in Canada,* H. A. Foster & W. R. D. Sewell, 1981, Toronto: James Lorimer, in association with the Canadian Institute for Economic Policy; *Water Is a Mainstream Issue,* Inquiry on Federal Water Policy, 1984, Ottawa: Environment Canada; *Currents of Change: Final Report, Inquiry on Federal Water Policy,* P. H. Pearse, F. Bertrand, & J. W. MacLaren, 1985, Ottawa: Environment Canada.

been attributed to intense rainfall. Higher than normal winter precipitation helped set the stage for the 1997 spring floods on the Red River in Manitoba.

In addition to variations in supply, water quality is a concern in different parts of Canada. Concentrations of naturally occurring impurities (minerals) such as calcium, magnesium, sodium, potassium, sulphate, and chloride can impair the use of surface water for drinking, swimming, or supporting diverse aquatic life. Groundwater quality can be affected too. In parts of the Prairie provinces, the Niagara Escarpment, New Brunswick, and Nova Scotia, the groundwater is so salty that most plant species are unable to tolerate it. In North Battleford, Saskatchewan, almost 6000 people became ill in April 2001 after drinking water contaminated with *Cryptosporidium.* Groundwater in other parts of Canada contains toxic chemical constituents (such as arsenic, fluoride, and uranium) derived from mineral deposits, while other substances (such as iron) create taste and colour problems. The quality of fish habitat can suffer as a

TABLE 7-1
WATER SUPPLY PER CAPITA FOR SELECTED COUNTRIES

Country	Supply ($10^3 m^3$/year/person)
Canada	120.00
Brazil	45.20
Australia	19.70
United States	11.50
France	3.19
China	2.23
India	1.90

SOURCE: "Appraisal and Assessment of World Water Resources," I. A. Shiklomanov, 2000, *Water International, 25*(1), 11–32. Reprinted by permission.

result of these chemical changes, as well as from low flow levels that reduce a river's capacity to dilute, dissolve, or absorb pollutants.

The global circulation of water on the Earth's surface provides for "free trade" of pollutants through land, air, and water. Essential nutrients as well as pollutants are transported through the cycle. This explains why levels of contamination in Arctic mammals and fish are so high (see Chapter 8) even though very few humans live there.

The Importance of Water

WATER AS A COMMON LINK

Water is a key component of the Canadian economy and the Canadian identity. Canadians have been demanding protection of their natural heritage, including water resources and aquatic ecosystems.

One of the ways in which rivers are being protected for future generations is through the Canadian Heritage Rivers System (CHRS). The goal is to establish a system of Canadian Heritage Rivers that reflects the diversity of Canada's river environments and celebrates the role of rivers in Canada's history and society. As well, the public is encouraged to learn about, enjoy, and appreciate Canada's rivers. On January 18, 1984, the Canadian Heritage Rivers Board was established to administer the Canadian Heritage Rivers System and to review river nominations for inclusion in the program. As a cooperative program of the federal, provincial, and territorial governments, CHRS objectives include ensuring long-term management that will conserve and protect the natural, historical, and recreational values of the best examples of Canada's river heritage (see Van Tighem, 1990). In 1996, the French River in Ontario was the first Canadian Heritage River to be named. Today, 40 heritage rivers across Canada have been designated for both natural and human heritage values, with management plans to address these values.

WATER AS A SOURCE OF CONFLICT

As fundamental as water is to life on Earth, climate change has the potential to disrupt water resources and water-dependent activities. Water has long been considered a commodity that has raised tensions between nation-states. In the global context, almost 150 of the world's 214 major river systems are shared between two countries, and another 50 are shared by three to ten nations. Many nations already have seen conflict over access to shared water resources, and the future is likely to bring more conflict, especially if global warming occurs as predicted and severe droughts become more frequent.

In the Middle East, the 1967 Arab–Israeli war was fought partly over access to water from the Jordan River basin. In the future, the issue of sharing water between countries will become even more contentious as demands grow in response to increasing population and continuing agricultural and industrial development. For example, Turkey's $20 billion Southeast Anatolian Project, "the biggest engineering feat in history," is used about 2 percent of the annual flow of the Euphrates River for irrigation and planned to use about one-third of the Euphrates' total flow. Unless the principal states of the Tigris–Euphrates basin (Turkey, Syria, and Iraq) cooperate in determining optimal use of water, a crisis is inevitable because all three countries' plans for irrigation and hydroelectric projects would consume about one-third more than the total flow of the Euphrates (Frederick, 1996; Pope, 1996).

More recently, "water terror" has been an effective weapon in civil wars around the world. During the Bosnian conflict, Serbs discovered how "to hit their enemies where it really hurt: in the water supply" (Serrill, 1997, p. 16). When Serbs shut off Sarajevo's electricity, and with it the city's water pumps, city residents, including dozens of Muslims, were forced to line up at wells, making the Muslims easy targets for snipers and mortar shells.

Changes in the availability of water resources also may affect Canada's relations with its neighbours. Since Canada shares many water bodies with the United States, there could be increased pressure to negotiate water management agreements that satisfy the needs and desires of both countries. Depending on the scarcity or abundance and distribution of water, the issue of large-scale water exports could be raised (see Box 7–1 on the next page).

Canada has been blessed with an abundant supply of water relative to its population. Around the world, water shortages are emerging. The United States, in particular, has demonstrated a strong interest in water from Canadian sources. At the heart of the issue is a controversy about whether water is an essential component of our life support systems and should be retained in its natural state or if water should be developed as a commodity for the economic benefit of those who exploit and export it. Bottled water is already a significant industry; however, shipping bulk quantities of fresh water poses a range of options of much greater magnitude.

Proposals for water export are wide ranging in their scope and ingenuity. During the last half of the 20th century, at least nine proposals were made for large-scale water diversions from Canada to Alaska. These included a $100 billion mega-project to pipe water from James Bay in northern Quebec to the western United States; a plan to dam dozens of rivers in British Columbia, the Yukon, and the Northwest Territories and use the Rocky Mountain trench as a massive storage reservoir; a scheme to use tugboats to tow icebergs to Mexico; and proposals to pump water into rafts the size of football fields to distribute to other parts of the world.

While many of these plans have received cool reception from Canadians, Canada already exports water in bulk to the United States via pipeline and truck. However, these current exports pale in comparison to the proposed megaprojects. When the North American Free Trade Agreement (NAFTA) was being negotiated, Canadians wanted bulk water exports exempted. NAFTA applies to all goods, and it is not clear if bulk water is considered such a good. Furthermore, the agreement contains no explicit mention of water in its natural state, and there is no specific exemption for water as there is for the export of raw logs and unprocessed fish.

If water exports are allowed, they are most likely to be undertaken by tanker. Volumes transported in this way are not even close to the volumes diverted to provide hydroelectricity for Canadians and for export. According to David Boyd (2003, p. 65), "Current proposals for bulk water export proposals would use up to one percent of the flow of affected rivers, while existing hydroelectric operations often divert more than 30 percent, and in some cases over 80 percent, of river flows." Despite the difference in these proportions, water in place also provides many intangible benefits such as habitat for aquatic species, recreational uses, and aesthetic services. We need to consider the full ranges of benefits and costs before determining the viability of water exports.

WATER AS A HAZARD

Sufficient water of appropriate quality is essential to a productive economy. As well, the presence of water has motivated individuals to locate their homes, cottages, and other facilities on the shores of Canada's many lakes, streams, and rivers. While communities and industries choose to locate on or close to water bodies for transportation, dangers associated with floods and storms may compromise the safety of people and their property, and damages may entail the loss of lives and property, as well as high cleanup and repair costs. In the Saguenay–Lac Saint-Jean region floods in Quebec in July 1996, about 12 000 people were evacuated from their homes as more than 50 towns and villages were inundated by flood waters that resulted from more than 270 millimetres of rain. Ten people died, 100 homes were washed away, about 1000 homes and 20 major bridges were heavily damaged, and $800 million in damages resulted. In addition, more than 100 tonnes of toxic waste and chemicals spilled into the Saguenay River when floods damaged or destroyed industrial facilities such as pulp and paper mills. Although chemicals such as phosphoric acid, urea, and ferric chloride were dispersed in the heavy river flow, there was concern for toxic hot spots in river sediments. A $450 million relief fund was established to compensate flood victims, and many Canadians contributed to the relief effort.

The 877-kilometre-long Red River regularly floods Manitoba's valley of silty loam left behind following the retreat of Lake Agassiz about 7700 years ago. In some years the floods are more severe than others. In terms of crest levels, the 1826 flood remains the worst—it reached 11.1 metres above the river bed when it crossed the forks of the Red and Assiniboine rivers in the heart of Winnipeg. Manitobans still measure the Red River floods relative to the 1826 flood (Pindera, 1997).

In 1948 and 1950 the river crest reached 9.2 metres; 80 000 people fled Winnipeg, 20 000 residents were evacuated from rural areas, 13 000 homes and farms were flooded, and damage estimates totalled $606 million in 1997 dollars. After those floods, a plan to "tame the Red" was implemented. Massive clay dikes and diversion dams were built in the Winnipeg area, and the $63 million Red River Floodway was opened in 1968. A 47-kilometre-long channel that diverts the Red River around Winnipeg, the floodway was one of many permanent structures erected to control the flow of flood water. By the 1970s, eight towns between the U.S. border and Winnipeg were protected with permanent dikes. In 1979, a flood similar to the 1950 flood tested these defence systems; most held back the flood waters and only 7000 people fled their homes.

The history of flooding in the Red River valley reveals that floods commonly occur when the winter

Photo 7–2
Some Manitoba communities were inundated by the 1997 Red River flood despite sandbagging.

snowpack in the southern headwaters of the river thaws before the northern Manitoba reaches of the river are free from ice. From November 1, 1996, to April 20, 1997, record levels of snow fell on ground that had been saturated through a wet autumn. Areas south and east of Winnipeg received winter precipitation amounts that were 175 percent of the annual average, and parts of the Red River **drainage basin** in North Dakota received precipitation amounts of more than 200 percent of the annual average. Just days after the runoff began in early April, a major storm dumped another 50 to 70 centimetres of snow and freezing rain on top of the near-record snowpack of 250 centimetres.

The 1997 spring flood extended over 205 000 hectares, or about 5 percent of Manitoba's farmland, creating a 2000-square-kilometre "Red Sea." Had the floodway, dams, and dikes not been built, it is estimated that the crest of the flood, the second-highest in Manitoba history, would have measured 10.4 metres. Instead, the floodway kept the water level at 7.5 metres. Still, 28 000 Manitobans were evacuated (6000 from Winnipeg), and 2500 properties between Winnipeg and the U.S. border were damaged. Even though 45 000 laying hens and 2000 cattle were moved to safety, dairy farmers' losses were estimated at $1.3 to $2 billion. Total damages tallied more than $500 million, mostly for repairs to roads, bridges, farms, and homes.

Given the importance of ecologically healthy water bodies for habitat and ecosystem support (for all flora and fauna), and our dependence on water for life support and economic and recreational activities, the principle of sustainability must apply to the full range of water uses. That is, the value of wetlands and estuaries, of aquifers and groundwater recharge areas, and of precipitation regimes must be accounted for in planning and managing water resources. Implementing these initiatives will require leadership at all levels of government.

WATER USES AND PRESSURES ON WATER QUALITY

WATER USES

Every day, at home and at work, we use water in so many situations—cooking, washing, bathing, watering lawns, carrying away the unwanted byproducts of our lives—that we are inclined to take it for granted. The two basic types of water use are instream uses and withdrawal uses. **Instream uses**, including hydroelectric power generation, transportation, waste disposal, fisheries, wildlife, heritage conservation, and recreation, occur "in the stream" (water remains in its natural setting). **Withdrawal uses**, such as municipal use, manufacturing, irrigation, mineral extraction, and thermal power generation, remove water from its natural setting by pipes or channels for a period of time and for a particular use. All, part, or none of the water withdrawn may be returned to its source. The quantity of water withdrawn or used is referred to as **intake**. **Discharge** refers to the amount returned to the source. The difference between intake and discharge is called *consumption*—the amount of water removed or "lost" from the system making it unavailable to downstream users.

Two other measures of withdrawal use are recirculation and gross water use. **Recirculation** refers to water that is used more than once in a specific process or distribution system, or used once and then recycled to another process. Most commonly, recirculation occurs in industries such as pulp and paper, petroleum refining, and steel making. **Gross water use** is the total amount of water used (intake + recirculation).

Aquatic environments may be altered, also, if the chemical, physical, or biological characteristics of the discharge are different from the characteristics of the receiving water body. Although many Canadians now understand that pollution issues are not solved by diluting wastes into rivers and lakes, many water bodies still receive discharges from a variety of point and nonpoint pollution sources. **Point sources** discharge substances from a clearly identifiable or discrete pathway, such as a pipe, ditch, channel, tunnel, or conduit from an industrial site, for example. **Nonpoint sources** discharge pollutants in an unconfined manner, for example, runoff from urban and agricultural areas.

From the perspective of supporting ecosystem species, functions, and processes, it is vital to know how much water is required to meet instream needs. In Canada, this knowledge has been growing but is still incomplete. We do, however, have a better understanding of how much water is needed for withdrawal than for instream uses.

Photo 7–3

On-farm and commercial feedlots, such as this one in Alberta, are potential nonpoint sources of water contamination.

Withdrawal Uses

Thermal power production constitutes the largest withdrawal use of water in Canada, followed by manufacturing, municipal, agricultural and mining withdrawals (see Figure 7–5). The thermal power industry, which includes both fossil fuel and nuclear electrical generating stations, was responsible for 64 percent of total water intake in 1996—almost five times more than the next biggest user, manufacturing (Environment Canada, 2007a). According to Statistics Canada (2000), generating 1 kilowatt of electricity—about enough to light a small house for one hour—requires 140 litres of water in a typical fossil fuel generating plant and 205 litres in a typical nuclear generating station. Most of this water is used for cooling purposes and is returned to its source at an elevated temperature. The manufacturing sector primarily uses water as a coolant, solvent, transport agent, and source of self-generated energy. Note that our use of thermal power has increased constantly since 1972. In contrast, the manufacturing and mining sectors have reduced their withdrawals through improved water technology efficiency. Increased recirculation of water reflects some of the declines in water use for these sectors.

In total, more than 45 billion cubic metres of water were withdrawn from Canadian sources in 1996, an 88 percent increase since 1972 (Environment Canada, 2007a). In 2004, Environment Canada estimated residential use at 329 litres per person per day. Urban water uses vary across the country, from a high of over 645 litres per day in the Yukon to about 113 litres per day in Nunavut (see Figure 7–6). Interestingly, residential per capita use varies with the size of municipality, from a low of 291 litres per day in municipalities with a population of

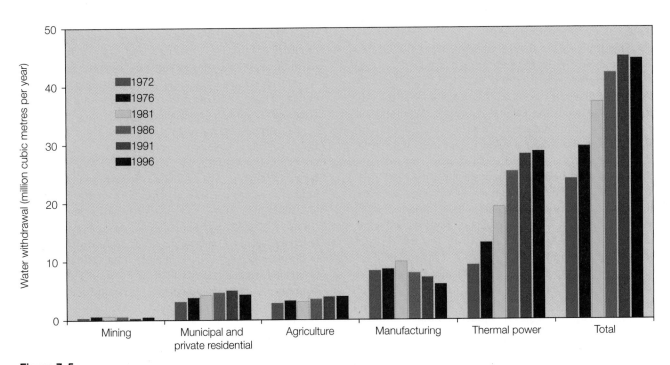

Figure 7–5

Water use in Canada, 1972–1996 (million cubic metres per year)

NOTE: Data for some sectors have been extrapolated and rounded.

SOURCE: *Water Use,* © Her Majesty the Queen in Right of Canada, Environment Canada, 2008, http://www.ec.gc.ca/water/en/manage/use/e_use.htm. Reprinted with permission of the Minister of Public Works and Government Services Canada, 2008.

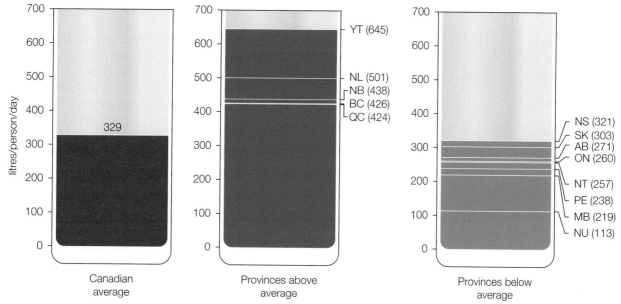

Figure 7–6

Average daily per capita residential water flow by province and territory (2004) (litres/person/day)

SOURCE: *Municipal Water Use, 2004 Statistics*, Environment Canada, 2004, http://www.ec.gc.ca/water/en/info/pubs/sss/e_mun2004.htm

at least 500 000 to 497 litres per day in municipalities with populations between 2000 and 5000 (Environment Canada, 2007a).

Aging infrastructure also accounts for high levels of water consumption, with some water never actually reaching water users. Actual losses vary. According to a survey of municipalities in 2004, reported system losses ranged from zero in the Yukon to a high of 20 percent of the water supply in Quebec municipalities (Environment Canada, 2007a). The average was 13 percent loss across the country (Environment Canada, 2007a).

A high intake of water produces a high volume of wastewater, which means the costs of supporting our municipal water infrastructure (water and wastewater treatment plants and pipes) are high. However, Canadian water rates are very low compared with those of other countries (see Figure 7–7, p. 268). Communities generally have not paid the full cost of providing water, partly because water costs were subsidized by property taxes and/or grants from provincial or federal governments, and partly because major investments in such infrastructure as water treatment plants, sewage plants, and pipes were postponed or not made at all. These factors influence the efficiency of water use and the effectiveness of treatment. While low water rates correspond closely with high use, they fail to reflect the true cost of supplying water to consumers and provide little incentive for people to curb water use.

Groundwater is the primary source of domestic supply for 8.9 million (30 percent of) Canadians (Rutherford, 2004), including more than 80 percent of rural residents. This total varies by region. For instance, 100 percent of

Prince Edward Island's population relies on groundwater, as does 60 percent of the population of New Brunswick (Environment Canada, 2004a). The biggest consumers of groundwater are the manufacturing, mining, thermal power generation, and aquaculture sectors, followed by the municipal and agricultural sectors, and the beverage industry. About 26 percent of municipalities with water supply systems reported water shortages from 1994 to 1999 because of droughts, infrastructure problems, and increased consumption. In a water use survey published by Environment Canada (2002b), municipalities that relied on municipal groundwater systems, particularly in southern Ontario, the Prairies, and the British Columbia interior reported water shortages more frequently than did municipalities that depended on surface waters.

Agriculture accounted for 9 percent of total 1996 withdrawals (Environment Canada, 2007a). This water was used mainly for irrigation (85 percent), but also for livestock watering (15 percent). High rates of evaporation from agricultural fields mean irrigation is the largest *consumer* of water in Canada. (Do not confuse this point with the fact that thermal power generation is the largest *withdrawal user* of water in Canada.)

Instream Uses

Instream water uses cannot be measured in the same manner as withdrawal uses since the water is not removed from lakes or streams. Instead, flow rates and water levels are the critical measurements.

In 2004, Canada obtained over 58 percent of its electricity from falling water (hydroelectricity);

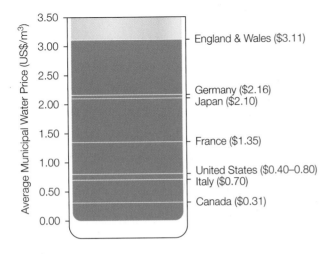

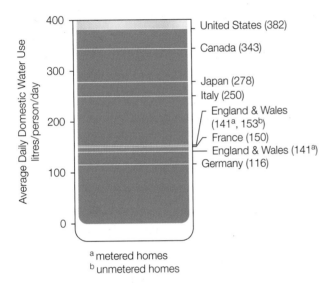

Figure 7–7

Estimated per capita residential water use and price for G7 countries in the 1990s

NOTE: Prices are calculated using a purchasing power parity method. Figures do not include the cost of waste treatment.

SOURCES: Adapted from *The Price of Water: Trends in OECD Countries,* Organization for Economic Cooperation and Development, 1999, Paris: Author.

Newfoundland, Quebec, Manitoba, and the Yukon produced almost 100 percent of their electricity in this manner. With some untapped hydroelectric sites still available in Quebec, Newfoundland, Manitoba, British Columbia, and the territories, and given Canadians' large appetite for energy (see Chapter 11), proposals for additional hydro dams may be expected in the future. However, these developments have adverse human and environmental effects, may conflict with withdrawal and other instream water uses, and likely will generate controversy (see "Hydroelectric Generation and Impacts" later in this chapter).

Water transport remains the most economical means of moving our important raw materials, such as wheat, pulp, lumber, fossil fuels, and minerals. The main transportation waterways are the St. Lawrence River, which allows passage of ocean-going ships from the Atlantic Ocean deep into the heart of North America; the Mackenzie River, which is a vital northern transportation link; and the lower Fraser River on the Pacific coast (refer to Figure 7–4). Since cargo in the hundreds of millions of tonnes is transported along these routes each year, it is important to have reliable and predictable lake and river levels.

In 2002, the Canadian commercial freshwater catch was valued at $76 million, up 6 percent from the previous year (Fisheries and Oceans Canada, 2003). An even more economically important instream use is sport fishing, with one in five Canadians participating in recreational fishing, or approximately 5 million in 2000 (900 000 visitors/tourists also come to Canada to fish). Sport fishers spent almost $4.8 billion on related goods and services. Swimming, boating, and camping are additional water-based recreational activities enjoyed by millions of Canadians each year.

Achieving an acceptable balance between withdrawal and instream uses is an ongoing challenge for water managers. Policies, legislation, regulations, and impact assessment procedures are some of the mechanisms frequently used to guide water and other resource management activities. Although water is becoming increasingly important as an international environmental issue and is of increasing importance to Canada's economic, social, and environmental agendas, both federal and provincial agencies received large cuts in budgets and staff during the 1990s (Bruce & Mitchell, 1995). However, the incidents at Walkerton and North Battleford spurred new investments during the 2000s in source water protection and improvements in infrastructure for drinking water.

PRESSURES ON WATER QUALITY

Water quality problems are seen most frequently at the local or regional level. Water managers must consider at least four aspects of water quality problems. The first aspect is the nature of the toxic or nontoxic substance, its position in the hydrologic cycle, and all the media (air, groundwater, surface water) that transport or store water. The second aspect of water quality concerns the source, amounts, types, and timing of substance releases. The third aspect concerns where the problem occurs, and focuses on a specific geographic region such as the Great Lakes or the Fraser River. Finally, managers must determine how to implement any protective or remediative action. A mix of research, monitoring and analysis, standard-setting, incentives, regulations, enforcement, and penalties can help achieve goals for water management. Examples that highlight some of these aspects of water quality management are described below.

Quality issues relating to municipal use of water include increased **biological oxygen demand (BOD)** and disease-causing bacteria in the discharge of (untreated) wastewater. Efforts to address wastewater quality are described in greater detail later in the chapter. Additionally, over the past 40 years, the volume of Canadian crop and livestock production has increased considerably. Often these gains were achieved through new technologies involving mechanization, genetics, biocides, fertilizers, and irrigation. The gains in production through the use of these technologies sometimes have come at the cost of degraded water quality. Agricultural uses raise many questions, including the public cost of irrigation works, potential environmental and health problems associated with fertilizer- and pesticide-laden runoff, and soil salinization and erosion problems. Since most crop irrigation takes place in the west, principally in Alberta, these issues are of particular importance there. In the South Saskatchewan River basin, for example, water returning to the rivers via irrigation channels and field runoff carries with it not only fertilizers, pesticides, salts, and sulphates in the form of suspended solids, but also dissolved solids at higher levels than what they were before irrigation. Additionally, water quality may also be affected by chemicals leached from small scale, unmonitored garbage dumps on rural properties (Rolfe, 2008, personal communication).

Clearly, such contaminants reduce the overall quality for the next surface or groundwater user as well as for aquatic life. Leaky drainage pipes, evaporation, and seepage from irrigation canals and ditches result in inefficient use of water. However, water from leaks and seepage is beneficial to local wildlife and vegetation (see Chapter 6); when economic efficiency and biodiversity values conflict, on what bases do we make decisions? In the Great Lakes–St. Lawrence region, most water withdrawals for agricultural purposes are used in stock watering.

Discharge of water used in mining (for cooling, drilling, and operating equipment) and in recovering oil from tar sands (for deep well injection) may degrade water quality by adding suspended solids, heavy metals, acids, and other dissolved substances. Tailings ponds may leak, discharging contaminated water into groundwater or surface bodies (see Box 7–4, p. 283, and Chapter 11). Arctic residents, for example, are concerned about water quality deterioration from abandoned metal mines, as well as from oil and gas developments. Polluted tailings ponds at abandoned uranium mines in Saskatchewan are highly toxic and pose serious risks to the Aboriginal peoples who live near them (see Box 11–6, p. 464).

Pollutants that are contained in the wastewater from the manufacturing sector range from biodegradable wastes to substances, such as PCBs and PAHs, that are toxic to fish, wildlife, and humans. Effluent from pulp and paper mills includes solid waste and chlorinated organic chemicals such as dioxins and furans, all of which may have detrimental effects on aquatic ecosystems. Residents in British Columbia, northern Alberta, northern Ontario, and the Atlantic provinces have expressed concerns about such discharges. Most thermoelectric plants use water as a coolant, returning water to the source in essentially the same quantity but at a higher temperature. This "heat pollution" can harm aquatic species, such as trout, that require cool water. Increased water temperature also can increase evaporation rates, which may raise salt concentrations to unacceptable levels (Government of Canada, 1991; Pearse et al., 1985).

Instream uses also affect water quality. Hydroelectric turbines do not consume water, but significant amounts evaporate from storage reservoirs. Damming rivers not only converts wild rivers into regulated ones but also results in loss of habitat for wildlife and fish, barriers to fish movement, and changes in downstream river flow regimes. Hydro dams have inundated valuable agricultural land in the Columbia, Kootenay, and Peace River valleys in British Columbia and have destroyed some salmon runs. In the dry Okanagan valley, irrigation sometimes has reduced tributary flows late in the season and affected fish propagation (Pearse et al., 1985).

Commercial navigation requires high water levels, which may cause bank erosion and threaten beaches, while dredging to maintain depth disturbs bottom sediments and degrades water quality. Relative to navigation and hydroelectrical generating interests, shore property owners in the Great Lakes–St. Lawrence basin prefer lower water levels because they minimize erosion and protect the owners' beaches, dock facilities, and other property. Shipping may facilitate the introduction of exotic species (such as the zebra mussel—see Box 7–2 on the next page—introduced into Lake St. Clair via the ballast water of a European ship) and cause pollution, including spills of hazardous materials that may pose threats to municipal water supplies and recreation. Icebreaking operations also pose a threat to fish and wildlife (Government of Canada, 1991; Pearse et al., 1985).

Discharging municipal and industrial wastes into water bodies has become increasingly less feasible. This is not only because growth in industrial production and population generates more wastes for discharge (often exceeding a water body's **assimilative capacity**, discussed in Chapter 3), but because industrial wastes in particular contain persistent and toxic contaminants that remain in the environment. These contaminants affect fish and wildlife and their particular habitat requirements: many species are highly sensitive to changes imposed by pollutants as well as by dams, diversions, and wetland drainage. In northern and coastal areas, fish and wildlife provide the major source of income and are valued as food, as integral to a way of life, and as recreational and aesthetic resources. Water-based recreational pursuits usually do not involve withdrawing or consuming water,

BOX 7 – 2
ZEBRA MUSSELS AND LAKE ERIE

Historically, pollution in the Lake Erie basin was moderated in a process by which the productive algae and fine soil particles from farmland erosion absorbed or adsorbed pollutants. As a result, Lake Erie organisms showed relatively low concentrations of toxic contaminants compared with the other Great Lakes. This may change, however, as eroded soil and nutrient levels decline and as zebra mussels deplete algal populations, thus increasing rates of bioaccumulation of contaminants.

The original aquatic community of Lake Erie was devastated by the almost total removal of native vegetation from the basin and by the exotic fish species that invaded after commercial fisheries severely exploited the native species. Along with carp, zebra mussels have impacted heavily on the recovering aquatic community. Voracious filter feeders, zebra mussels are not strongly affected by natural predators or diseases; the zebra mussel population has exploded and caused rapid changes in water quality and clarity as well as in the food web.

Zebra mussels consume large amounts of phytoplankton; their feeding caused a 77 percent increase in water transparency (clarity) between 1988 and 1991. Increased clarity of water permitted sunlight to penetrate deeper, in turn allowing rooted aquatic plants to spread into deeper water. Many organisms benefited ecologically from this change, but in some areas plant growth interfered with swimming and boating.

The mussels' eating habits, which both deplete the phytoplankton food source also used by other filter feeders and assimilate toxic contaminants, have affected the food web and may result in major changes in the future abundance of various species of fish. Mussels remove large amounts of particulates, which means that more contaminants remain in the water. The result could be higher contaminant concentrations in the remaining phytoplankton and zooplankton, as well as higher concentrations in fish and wildlife species feeding on the plankton or directly on the mussels and other bottom dwellers.

First introduced into lake St. Clair, a small lake adjacent to Lake Erie, zebra mussels also spread rapidly through aquatic ecosystems. In the United States, a dynamic map reveals the rapid movement of mussel populations throughout the Great Lakes and associated aquatic ecosystems. Box Figures 7–1a and 7–1b, maps from 1988 and 2005, reveal an ever-encroaching population.

When zebra mussels arrived, they created physical problems such as clogged intake pipes and jammed machinery. We now know, however, that the invasion by this exotic species has had far more complex effects. Chemical and biological methods have been proposed to control the mussels, but, mindful of other biocontrols that have proved disastrous, most of the scientific community is reluctant to take these measures. This situation highlights the point that restoring and protecting the Great Lakes ecosystem requires a commitment to achieving sustainability, fostering cooperation and coordination, and preventing pollution problems before they arise.

1988 Zebra Mussel populations

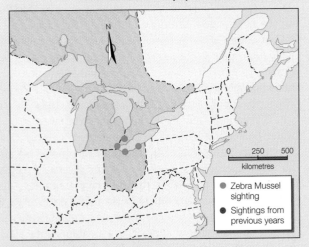

Box Figure 7–1a
Zebra mussel populations, 1988

2005 Zebra Mussel populations

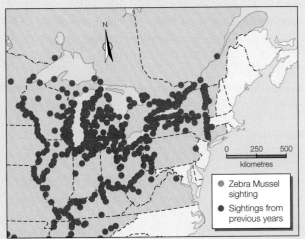

Box Figure 7–1b
Zebra mussel populations, 2005

SOURCE: National Atlas of the United States of America, 2007, www.nationalatlas.gov/

SOURCES: *State of the Great Lakes: 1995*, Governments of the United States of America and Canada, 1995, Ottawa: Supply and Services Canada; "Zebra Mussels: Holding Back the Tide," 1997, *Coastal Heritage, 11*(4), 10–12.

but are affected by water body features such as surface area, depth, rate of flow, quality, temperature, and accessibility.

Canadian cities often suffer water quality problems because they rely on aging infrastructure. Sanitary sewers transport wastewater from residences and businesses to treatment plants, while storm sewers capture rainwater or snowmelt and flow into nearby water courses, including natural streams, human-made channels, or pipes. Combined sewers carry both sanitary and storm drainage. During dry weather, combined sewers carry all contents to treatment plants. During wet weather, the volume of water may exceed the capacity of treatment plants. Consequently, this mix of water may flow untreated into natural water bodies (e.g., the Fraser River, Lake Erie, the Atlantic Ocean). Combined sewers were the standard until the Second World War and are still found in older parts of many Canadian cities, including Edmonton, Winnipeg, Toronto, Ottawa, Montreal, Quebec City, and Halifax (Environment Canada, 2002a).

Stormwater runoff can be a significant pollutant of municipal waterways. During wet weather, the rains flush pollutants from the streets, sometimes overloading the storm drains and flushing directly into waterways within urban ecosystems. In Vancouver, the occasional high loading of pollutants into the Fraser River from surface runoff can exceed that from sewage treatment plants. It is often difficult to trace the source of pollutants because there is no single "point source" that can be monitored and regulated. Stormwater can contain many kinds of pollutants, including trace metals that are part of gasoline, chemicals used in lawn and garden care, as well as chemicals used in commercial operations such as dry cleaners. These collect and drain into the sewage system during storms. Factors such as land use, rainfall intensity, buildup time, and traffic intensity affect the quality of stormwater runoff and the kinds of contaminants that can enter the municipal system. In the greater Vancouver region, residential areas and roads are the largest source of contaminants, followed by industrial areas. While industrial areas have higher concentrations of pollutants, residential areas in greater Vancouver occupy the largest geographic area. On a positive note, the switch to lead-free gasoline has helped to improve the quality of urban waterways.

On a national basis, Canadians withdraw only about 2 percent of our water resources from their natural settings. We *consume* less than 1 percent of that amount. This level of consumption might suggest that our instream resource needs are always being met. However, important regional and local problems exist in areas such as the Old Man River watershed in the southern Prairies, and individual tributary watersheds in the Great Lakes basin. Since all of these watersheds are linked to others through the hydrologic cycle, finding the right geographic scale to

Photo 7–4
The purpose of this image of a fish beside a sewer lid in Montreal is to remind urbanites that the underground network of pipes is linked to "natural" waterways that have flora and fauna we seek to sustain. Have you noticed fish drawn by the sewers in your community?

define and solve a water problem is crucial for successful management.

Most of Canada's serious water use problems are related to degraded water quality and to disrupted flow regimes, not to inadequate supply. First Nations people are among those whose traditional water-based activities have been most affected by deterioration from pollution and by water storage and diversion projects that manipulate lake levels and river flows. "There is hardly a major drainage system anywhere south of the Arctic which has not been affected by these pressures" (Pearse et al., 1985, p. 48). Furthermore, growing uncertainty about economic and social trends and about the impacts of human influences on climate, land use, and the distribution of water means that water management policies must support, protect, and promote a high-quality, sustainable water supply.

HUMAN ACTIVITIES AND IMPACTS ON FRESHWATER ENVIRONMENTS

As previously noted, human use of water resources—for domestic and urban, industrial, power generation, and recreational purposes—has a variety of impacts on fresh water and freshwater environments. This section covers in more detail examples of the kinds of impacts that result from each of these four types of water use.

DOMESTIC AND URBAN USES AND IMPACTS

Safe Drinking Water and Sanitation Facilities

On a global basis, one in six people lives without regular access to safe drinking water. Canada's drinking water is safer than that of many other nations. In developing countries, 80 percent of illnesses are water related; globally, researchers estimate that 5 million people die each year from diseases associated with unsafe drinking water or inadequate sanitation (Hunter et al., 2001). These statistics reflect the facts that more than 1 billion people lack safe drinking water supplies, about 4 billion have inadequate sanitation facilities, and developing nations and the global community are unable to protect their drinking water from several threats that Canadians rarely think about.

In Canada, where municipalities have the responsibility to provide their citizens with safe drinking water, there are four major approaches to ensuring high-quality tap water. These approaches are land use planning; drinking water quality guidelines and regulations; water treatment systems; and reporting of results. The role of guidelines, regulations, and treatment systems is discussed below.

Drinking Water Guidelines and Regulations
The Guidelines for Canadian Drinking Water Quality indicate that good-quality drinking water is free from disease-causing organisms, harmful substances, and radioactive material. Good-quality drinking water also tastes good, is aesthetically appealing, and is free from objectionable odour or colour. Although they are not legally binding, these guidelines specify limits for substances and describe conditions that affect drinking water quality in Canada. Under the Canadian Environmental Protection Act, these guidelines act as "environmental yardsticks" to help assess water quality issues and concerns, establish water quality objectives at specified sites, provide targets for control and remediation programs, and provide information for state-of-the-environment reporting.

Provinces also establish laws that specify standards for treatment-plant operating procedures and how testing results will be distributed. Traditionally, publicly owned utilities operating at the municipal level have provided Canadians with drinking water. There is no single approach that utility companies use to implement drinking water quality. For instance, British Columbia, New Brunswick, Ontario (since early 2001), Quebec, and the Yukon require all samples to be tested at labs that have been certified, while the Northwest Territories provides little control. (See Sierra Legal Defence Fund, 2001, for additional information on provincial approaches.)

Drinking Water Treatment Facilities
Treatment plants ensure the delivery of safe, clean water to the majority of Canadians. A typical water treatment process is described in Figure 7–8. The major goal of water treatment is to ensure, through a series of filters, that water is free of sediment, a problem frequently found in surface water sources. Filters may be so effective that waterborne pathogens such as *Giardia* are removed. Disinfectants, such as chlorine, are used effectively in most water treatment systems to kill waterborne microorganisms. However, there are concerns that the use of chlorine can produce trihalomethanes (THMs), specifically chloroform, which can cause cancers of the liver and kidneys. Newer technologies include ozone and ultraviolet light. The failure to provide treatment facilities to remove pathogens and microorganisms contributes to the high incidence of disease and death in the developing world.

Canadians are now seriously questioning the ability of drinking water plants to adequately treat water. In April 2001, the residents of North Battleford, Saskatchewan, learned that the parasite *Cryptosporidium*, which caused illnesses, had entered the city's water supply. An independent judicial inquiry to investigate why the system failed considered water facilities, the role of managers and regulators, as well as government regulations and policies. The tragic consequences of improper water treatment were also experienced in Walkerton, Ontario, where seven people died and 2300 more became ill as the result of contamination of the town's water system in May 2000. The source of the contamination was identified as *E. coli* (*Escherichia coli*) O157:H7, a lethal strain of the common, usually harmless, *E. coli* bacterium found in the intestinal tract of humans and animals. Given Canadian water regulations and treatment systems, a key question became: how did *E. coli* get in the drinking water? Independent evaluations of both localities found human error and ineffective government regulation to be key factors leading to these tragedies.

The inquiry into the cause of the Walkerton tragedy revealed the following:

- The contaminated groundwater well, constructed in 1978, had not been approved by the Ontario Ministry of the Environment (MOE), and nothing was done to rectify the situation.
- During 1996, the Ontario government closed MOE and Ministry of Health (MOH) water testing laboratories, actions taken without consideration of the capacity in the private sector, or among municipalities, to test municipal water supplies (Kreutzwiser, 1998).
- Private water testing laboratories were required only to report water testing results to municipalities that had requested the tests, rather than to the MOE or MOH, where water tests previously were conducted and through which MOE and medical officials could be alerted.
- *E. coli* had been present in the 1978 well prior to May 2000, and nothing had been done to rectify this.

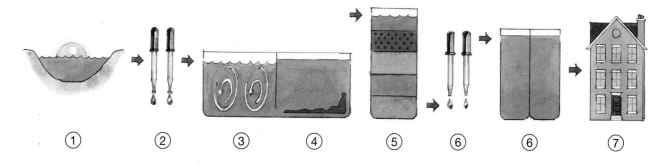

1. **Water intake pipe**

   The water intake pipe extends into the lake, river, or well that supplies water to the facility. In large lakes, these pipes may extend hundreds of metres from the facility. Where necessary, chlorine is used to keep zebra mussels from colonizing in the system.

2. **Chemical storage and feeding**

   Chlorine is added to the incoming water to kill microorganisms. Alum and lime may be added also. Alum concentrates suspended particles such as silt to aid their removal. Lime changes the pH level where required. The chemicals are mechanically mixed into the water before moving on to the flocculating basin.

3. **Flocculating basin**

   The flocculating basin stirs the water to concentrate suspended particles. The clumps of particulate that form are known as *floc*.

4. **Settling basin**

   Heavy flocs drop out of the water in the settling tank and collect along the bottom. The settled floc is removed by scrapers that move along the bottom. The cleanest water is left at the surface to be drawn off through spillways that lead to filtering basins.

5. **Rapid sand filters**

   The water is already quite clear by the time it reaches the stacked layers of fine sand, activated carbon, gravel, and rocks that form the rapid sand filters. The layer of sand removes fine bits of floc, algae, and silt from the water. The layer of activated carbon removes taste- and odour-producing chemicals.

6. **Pure water basin**

   The purified water goes into holding basins prior to distribution. Safe levels of chlorine are added to check the growth of algae and microorganisms. Lime may be added to control the pH level. A controlled pH level protects the metal components of the distribution system from corrosion.

7. The treated water is tested regularly to ensure quality. Large holding tanks store the water until it is needed in people's homes.

Figure 7–8

Typical municipal water treatment process

SOURCE: *Water and Wastewater Treatment,* Ontario Clean Water Agency, http://www.ocwa.com/frproces/htm. Reprinted with permission.

- Walkerton's water treatment plant manager and workers lacked adequate training to effectively operate the facility; they falsified labels and test samples, and claimed the water was clean even when it was contaminated with *E. coli*.
- In May 2000, a heavy spring rainfall caused higher than normal runoff, some of which was contaminated with *E. coli*–infected manure and entered the 1978 well.
- At this time Walkerton's chlorinator was inoperative.
- Lab reports identifying the presence of *E. coli* were not acted on by the Public Utilities Commission (which knew the lab results), delaying for four days the order to boil water.

A follow-up study suggested that water contamination resulted from many failures in a complex system involving workers, local governments, regulatory bodies, and provincial governments. Government cutbacks and lack of regulatory enforcement contributed to both the Walkerton incident and the contamination of water supplies in North

Battleford (Woo & Vincente, 2003). One analysis of the costs of Walkerton identified $64.5 million in hard costs and an additional $90.8 million in the less tangible costs of illnesses suffered and lives lost (Brubaker, 2002). While it is difficult to determine longer-term impacts, children under five years of age and elderly people may have other longer-lasting complications arising from the primary infection.

While tragic, such incidents are relatively rare. However, across Aboriginal communities, water quality problems are more common. A national assessment of water and wastewater systems specific to First Nations communities conducted by Indian and Northern Affairs Canada (INAC) in 2001 revealed that of the 740 community water systems assessed, 45 percent posed medium water quality risks, while 29 percent posed high risks (INAC, 2003). Reasons ranged from inadequate equipment, procedures, and training of operators to poor water sources and onsite treatment processes. The federal government initiated funding for water infrastructure on reserves in the 1990s and in 2003 introduced a multiyear, $600 million First Nations Water Management Strategy. Nevertheless, in late 2005, the public became aware of the long history of unsafe drinking water in Aboriginal communities when residents of the Kashechewan reserve in northern Ontario were evacuated because the water became unsafe to drink or use. Years of neglect of water quality issues on reserves suggest that the incident on the Kashechewan reserve is neither isolated nor easily fixed.

Some observers believe that the problems in Walkerton, North Battleford, and Kashechewan are no longer isolated incidents—increased development is depleting and degrading our water resources and putting our water supplies at risk. There is also concern about Canada's aging water and wastewater infrastructure and the need to provide significant funding to improve it. These concerns are given tangible form through the establishment of criteria and indicators that can track performance.

The Sierra Legal Defence Fund (2006), since renamed Ecojustice, compiled a report card on Canada's drinking water systems, grading each province and territory on such criteria as protection of drinking water sources, quality of water treatment and testing, and ability to inform the public (see Table 7–2). Ontario (after Walkerton), Quebec, and Alberta were given the best grades, while the Yukon, Prince Edward Island, Newfoundland, and New Brunswick received the lowest grades. Concerns were raised that no jurisdiction has developed and applied advanced standards and approaches similar to those used in the United States. In 2002, Ontario established the Nutrient Management Act, which set high standards for activities that might introduce pollutants into watercourses. How other governments across Canada will respond to crises such as Walkerton and North Battleford and to the Sierra Legal Defence Fund report remains to be seen.

Wastewater Treatment Facilities   Once municipal water has been used and goes down the sink or toilet, treatment of the wastewater is required. In urban centres, this takes place in sewage treatment plants (see Figure 7–9 on page 276). Municipalities may offer one of three levels of sewage treatment. **Primary treatment**, the lowest degree of treatment, is a mechanical process involving removal of large solids, sediment, and some organic matter (steps 1–4 in Figure 7–9). From that point, even though it contains many pathogens, the fluid may be discharged to a receiving water body (thus the danger of contamination) or may enter a secondary treatment process. The sludge is removed and taken to a digester for further processing.

Secondary treatment employs biological processes in which bacteria and other microorganisms degrade most of the dissolved organics. After treatment, about 30 percent of phosphates and about 50 percent of nitrates remain in the suspended solids (steps 5 and 6 in Figure 7–9).

In aeration tank digestion (activated sludge process), effluent from the primary process is mixed with a bacteria-rich slurry, air or oxygen is pumped through the mixture, and bacterial growth decomposes the organic matter. Water siphoned off the top of the tank typically is disinfected, usually by chlorination, before it is released into the environment. Sludge is removed from the bottom of the tank; some of it may be used to inoculate the incoming primary effluent, but because of its toxic content (metals, chemicals, pathogens), most of the sludge is dried and landfilled. In Calgary, sewage sludge is injected into farmers' fields as a soil conditioner. Applied at a maximum of once every six years, the injected fields are monitored carefully and consistently for contaminants such as heavy metals.

If a municipality has space, it may construct a sewage lagoon where exposure of the effluent to sunlight, algae, aquatic organisms, and air slowly degrades the organic matter (with lower energy costs). Natural or constructed wetlands also act effectively to absorb nutrients and other pollutants at low cost. Even in Canada's cold climate, wetlands are proving to be important components of municipal water treatment systems.

Tertiary treatment is a chemical process that removes phosphates, nitrates, and additional contaminants such as salts, acids, metals, and toxic organic and **organochlorine** compounds from the secondary effluent. Sand filters or carbon filters may also be used in advanced wastewater treatment. The treated effluent may be discharged into natural water bodies or used to irrigate agricultural lands and municipal properties such as parks and golf courses. Because tertiary treatment greatly reduces nutrients in the treated wastewater, algal blooms and eutrophication are reduced in receiving waters.

Wastewater treatment levels vary considerably across Canada, since it is the provinces that enact laws. While

TABLE 7-2

GRADING CANADA'S DRINKING WATER TREATMENT SYSTEMS, PROGRESS 2001–2006

Province	Grade 2001	Grade 2006	Comments
Alberta	B	B	Good: treatment standards; contaminant standards; accredited labs for water quality testing; operator certification. Needs improvement: testing. Lacking: public reporting.
British Columbia	D	C+	Good: accredited labs for water quality testing; operator certification. Needs improvement: treatment standards; contaminant standards; testing; public reporting.
Manitoba	C–	C+	Good: accredited labs for water quality testing; operator certification; public reporting (planned). Needs improvement: treatment standards; contaminant standards; testing.
New Brunswick	C–	D	Good: accredited for water quality testing. Needs improvement: treatment standards; testing. Lacking: contaminant standards; water treatment system design regulation; operator certification; public reporting.
Newfoundland	D	C–	Good: testing; government testing of water quality; public reporting. Needs improvement: treatment standards; contaminant standards. Lacking: operator certification.
Northwest Territories	C	C+	Good: contaminant standards; testing; accredited labs for water quality testing; public reporting. Needs improvement: treatment standards. Lacking: operator certification.
Nova Scotia	B–	B	Good: treatment standards; contaminant standards; testing; accredited labs for water quality testing; operator certification. Lacking: public reporting.
Nunavut	C	C	Good: contaminant standards; accredited labs for water quality testing. Needs improvement: treatment standards; testing. Lacking: operator certification; public reporting.
Ontario	B	A–	Good: treatment standards; contaminant standards; testing; accredited labs for water quality testing; operator certification; public reporting.
Prince Edward Island	F	C–	Good: testing; accredited labs for water quality testing; operator certification. Needs improvement: public reporting (but plans in works). Lacking: treatment standards; contaminant standards.
Quebec	B	B+	Good: treatment standards; contaminant standards; testing; accredited labs for water quality testing; operator certification. Needs improvement: public reporting (reports at the regional level only).
Saskatchewan	C	B–	Good: accredited labs for water quality testing; operator certification; public reporting. Needs improvement: treatment standards contaminant standards; testing.
Yukon	D–	C–	Good: contaminant standards; testing; accredited labs for water quality testing; operator certification. Needs improvement: treatment standards. Lacking: public reporting.
Federal Government	Not Graded	F	Needs improvement: evaluation and regulation of chemicals; formulation of standards for guidelines. Lacking: First Nations drinking water safety; binding minimum drinking water standards; recognition of a right to clean drinking water; tracking of national drinking water data; trends and best practices.

SOURCE: *Waterproof: Canada's Drinking Water Report .Card*, Sierra Legal Defence Fund, 2001, Vancouver: Author; *Waterproof 2: Canada's Drinking Water Report Card*, Vancouver: Author, http://www.ecojustice.ca/publications/reports/waterproof-2-canadas-drinking-water-report-card. Reprinted with permission from the Sierra Legal Defence Fund.

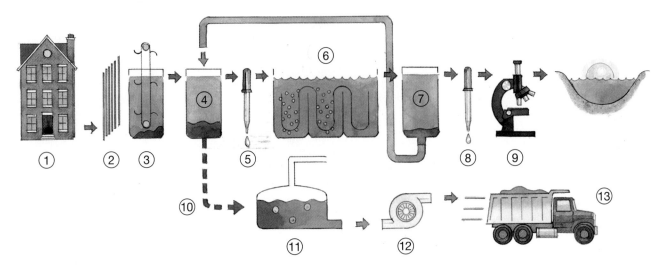

1. Plant influent
Waste enters the treatment facility through the municipal sewer system.

2. Coarse bar screen
Metal bars collect large debris such as rags, wood, plastics, and so on.

3. Grit removal
The wastewater flows through a channel, allowing dense inorganic material to settle on the bottom. Scrapers, hoppers, and clam buckets remove the collected grits.

4. Primary settling
The wastewater flows into large settling tanks, where suspended solids and organic material are allowed to sink to the bottom. The raw sludge that settles is removed through hoppers and sent through the digestion process.

5. Partially treated wastewater is drawn from the top of the settling tanks and chemicals are added to remove phosphorous.

6. Aeration tanks
Large aeration tanks mix the partially treated wastewater with oxygen to support bacteria, which devour organic waste. The bacteria levels are managed to provide the most efficient removal process.

7. Final settling
The cleanest wastewater is drawn from the top of the aeration tanks through spillways. By this point the water is already quite clear. Polymers may be added to concentrate any remaining material. Again, suspended particles settle to the bottom and are removed by scrapers or hoppers.

8. Disinfection
The cleanest water is drawn from the surface and disinfected with chlorine or ultraviolet light to kill bacteria.

9. The treated water is tested to ensure it meets provincial standards and is returned to the original water source.

10. Sludge from the aeration and final settling tanks is drawn from the bottom of the tanks and pumped to the primary settling tank. Not only does this sludge have a high water content, but it contains oxygen and bacteria that improve the efficiency of the treatment process.

11. Primary digest
Sludge removed throughout the process is pumped to digesters for processing. Anaerobic bacteria consume organic waste in the digesters. This process produces gases that are used to fuel plant boilers and heat facilities.

12. Dewatering process
Vacuum filter or centrifuge systems remove water from the processed sludge to thicken it. The water removed in the process is pumped to the primary settling tank to reenter the treatment process.

13. The concentrated sludge, or bio-solid waste, is taken away for incineration or conversion into fertilizer.

Figure 7–9

Typical sewage treatment process

SOURCE: Adapted from *The Water and Wastewater Treatment Process*, Ontario Clean Water Agency, n.d., http://www.ocwa.com/home/documents/62wattreat.pdf. Reprinted with permission.

Photo 7–5

This solar-powered sewage treatment plant in Woodbridge, Ontario, is a biological ecosystem that simulates a natural wetland for the purposes of treating domestic sewage.

almost all of the population received at least primary treatment and most received tertiary treatment of their wastewater, the highest levels of treatment exist in Ontario and the Prairie provinces. Nationwide, 6 percent of Canadians received no wastewater treatment; their wastewater was released straight into a receiving water body. In general, municipal wastewater treatment levels have been rising steadily in Canada. Although there are regional variations in treatment levels, between 1983 and 1996, the number of Canadians served with sewers who received some level of sewage treatment rose from 72 to 94 percent (Statistics Canada, 2000). During the same period, the number of people serviced by tertiary treatment rose from 28 to 41 percent.

The Sierra Legal Defence Fund confirmed these variations in sewage treatment quality when it reported on 22 systems across the country in 2004 (Table 7–3, p. 278). Victoria, Vancouver, Saint John, Montreal, Charlottetown, St. John's, Halifax, and Dawson City dumped a total of 3 billion litres of untreated or minimally treated sewage into watercourses daily, almost 40 000 litres per second. Of these cities, Victoria was the only city that discharged all of its raw sewage and had made no improvements to its wastewater treatment. In total, Victoria dumped 34 billion litres of raw sewage in the Strait of Juan de Fuca each year. By 2007, the Capital Regional District was working with the Province of British Columbia to plan new sewage treatment facilities (for more discussion, see Enviro-Focus 8, pp. 336–338). Some cities have made improvements since 1999, including Calgary, Edmonton, and Whistler, all of which treat 100 percent of their sewage with tertiary treatment. The value of this report is in providing simple, yet effective, ways to understand the options for water treatment and the relative success of waste treatment practices in communities across the country.

Water treated to a level that will protect human life may still stress aquatic ecosystems when discharged. This occurs because the lower the level of sewage treatment provided, the greater the biological oxygen demand of the effluent and the greater its impact on aquatic life. Also, unless wastewater receives secondary treatment, disease-causing bacteria may remain in the effluent. None of these levels of treatment has a proven ability to remove toxic substances, however, and persistent chemicals such as DDT, PCBs, or mirex are removed only by very advanced treatment such as that employing activated carbon. Endocrine disrupters have become a relatively recent concern in drinking water (see Box 7–3, p. 279). Drinking water supplies may be affected severely by inadequately treated municipal wastewater discharges, industrial and agricultural pollution of water bodies, and leaking landfill sites (see also Chapter 8).

DEMAND FOR WATER

Another water issue relates to domestic demand for water. At the same time as the safety and security of our water supplies are declining in some areas due to pollution, dropping water tables, and prolonged drought conditions, our demand for water is rising (Environment Canada, 1995). Because of increasing demand, municipal water supply is becoming one of the most critical water issues in Canada. Residential water use accounts for nearly one-half of all the water used in Canadian municipalities. Each Canadian uses approximately 329 litres of water per day inside the home (Environment Canada 2005); the ways we use that water are identified in Figure 7–10 on page 279.

Sometimes we do not realize how much water we consume in our everyday activities. For instance, 65 percent of all residential water use takes place in the bathroom; if your toilet is more than 10 years old, and you flush 4.5 times per day, over the course of one year you will have used about 30 000 litres of water to dispose of about 650 litres of body waste. If your toilet is one of the 25 percent that leaks after flushing, you could be losing up to 200 000 litres of water in one year. Laundry accounts for 20 percent of domestic water use. If you water your lawn in summer, it could need about 100 000 litres of water during the growing season.

In 2004, 72 out of 510 responding Canadian municipalities (14.1 percent) with water supply systems reported problems with water availability. About 12 percent of Canadians on municipal water systems rely exclusively on groundwater for drinking water and other domestic uses. Larger municipalities that depend exclusively on groundwater are highly susceptible to water availability problems, particularly if the population in the municipality is growing, if the municipality permits unrestricted use of water, and if water prices are low.

The price Canadians pay for water varies significantly across the country, yet Canadians still pay the lowest rate

TABLE 7–3

GRADING WASTEWATER TREATMENT SYSTEMS IN CANADA: PROGRESS, 1999–2004

City	Grade		Comments
	1999	**2004**	
Victoria	F–	Suspended	Preliminary screening, no treatment. More than 34 billion litres of raw sewage still discharged each year.
Vancouver	C–	D	Up to 22 billion litres of combined overflows each year. Upgrades to 100% secondary treatment won't be completed until 2030.
Edmonton	B+	A–	Upgraded to 100% tertiary treatment and UV disinfection.
Calgary	A	A+	UV disinfection added to 100% tertiary treatment. Additional upgrades in the works ($250 million).
Regina	B	B+	Enhanced secondary treatment with expanded UV disinfection. Extensive upgrades planned.
Saskatoon	C+	C+	100% secondary treatment. Minimal changes since 1999.
Brandon	D	B–	Implemented 100% secondary treatment and UV disinfection. Combined overflow of up to 2.8 million litres per year.
Winnipeg	C	B–	100% secondary treatment. Reduced number of combined sewers; still 1 billion litres of combined sewer overflow per year.
Hamilton	C–	C+	Upgraded to secondary and tertiary treatment. Discharges 5.9 billion litres of raw sewage each year. Only 88% of population had its waste treated before discharge.
Toronto	C/B	B–	Toughest sewer-use bylaw in country. Secondary treatment. Still discharges 9.9 billion litres of untreated sewage and runoff each year.
Ottawa	C	B–	Secondary treatment. Seasonal chlorine disinfection, no dechlorination. Overflow system controls installed.
Montreal	F+	F	Primary treatment only. No discernable progress made.
Quebec City	C	B	Secondary treatment with seasonal UV disinfection. Combined sewer overflow events reduced.
Saint John	E	D	Reduction in combined sewers. Primary and secondary treatment. Almost 40% of population still receives no waste treatment.
Fredericton	B	B	Secondary treatment with UV disinfection. No major improvements since 1999. Low percentage of combined sewer overflow events.
Charlottetown	E	E+	Primary treatment only. Volume of discharges not monitored. Plans to upgrade to secondary treatment.
Halifax	E–/C	D	More than 65 billion litres of raw sewage discharged each year. Regional plants provide secondary or tertiary treatment.
St. John's	F–	E	More than 33 billion litres of raw sewage discharged each year. Primary sewage treatment plant under construction.
Yellowknife	B+	B+	100% secondary treatment with natural UV disinfection. Only minor changes since 1999.
Whitehorse	B–	B–	Secondary treatment. Minimal progress since 1999. Efforts underway to reduce volumes of sewage. No raw sewage discharges.
Dawson City	F–	E	Still discharging 1 billion litres of raw sewage per year. Awaiting funding for upgrade to secondary treatment.
Whistler	not rated	A	100% tertiary treatment.

SOURCE: Adapted from *The National Sewage Report Card, Number Three,* Sierra Legal Defence Fund, 2004, http://www.ecojustice.ca/publications/reports/national-sewage-report-card-iii/. Reprinted by permission of the Sierra Legal Defence Fund.

for water among G8 nations (see Figure 7–7, p. 268). A survey of municipalities in 1999 indicated that Canadians pay about $1.14 for 1000 litres. This amount has increased from about $0.82 per 1000 litres in 1991, and now includes a waste treatment component of about 39 percent. Because meeting increasing water demands requires the construction of new (or expansion of existing) facilities, all of which consume land, energy, and financial resources, water conservation is an important factor in improving the quality and protecting the quantity of our water resources.

BOX 7–3
ENDOCRINE DISRUPTERS

Research is showing that many toxic substances are capable of disrupting the endocrine system of fish, birds, reptiles, amphibians, and mammals. The endocrine system is responsible for many vital functions, such as growth, development, reproduction, and the immune system. Natural hormones play a vital role in these functions. Endocrine-disrupting chemicals (EDCs), such as PCBs, dioxins, nonylphenols, lindane, dieldrin, and inorganic chemicals such as mercury and tin, mimic or inhibit hormones. These chemicals are produced and released by multiple sources, including municipal effluents, pulp and paper production, industrial processes, incineration, agricultural practices, and boat maintenance.

Exposure to EDCs can take place through direct contact with pesticides or other chemicals or through ingestion of contaminated water, food, or air. When released into the environment, EDCs lead to ecosystem impacts, including enlarged thyroid glands in salmon and herring gulls. Cross-bill deformities, super-normal clutching, and decreased hatching success have been observed in birds from the Great Lakes.

Human health also is threatened by exposure to persistent toxins from municipal sewage and industrial and agricultural chemicals. Chemicals may be those used in agriculture (e.g., insecticides, herbicides), in industry (e.g., detergents, resins, plasticizers), or in the home (e.g., plastics). Some studies have found that the type of plastic used for hospital intravenous bags as well as the practice of heating food in plastic containers may leach EDCs. Endocrine disrupters are persistent in the environment and accumulate in fat, so the greatest exposures may come from eating fatty foods and fish from contaminated water. A study of Michigan women who consumed more than 0.5 kilograms of Lake Michigan fish per month during their pregnancies found that their newborns showed a significantly higher percentage of decreased birth weight, head circumference, and neurobehavioural development. Psychological tests administered to these same children when they were four years old indicated they were suffering from learning deficits. Reproductive disorders and cancers have been reported in the female children of women who took certain types of estrogen while pregnant.

SOURCE: *Endocrine Disrupting Substances in the Environment,* Environment Canada, 1999, http://www.ec.gc.ca/eds/fact/broch_e.htm

Figure 7–10

Use of water in Canadian homes

- **5%** cleaning
- **10%** kitchen/drinking
- **20%** laundry
- **30%** toilets
- **35%** showers/baths

SOURCE: *Water: No Time to Waste: A Consumer's Guide to Water Conservation,* Environment Canada, 1995, Ottawa: Supply and Services Canada.

It is estimated that water metering reduces water consumption between 20 and 50 percent, and reduces the amount of wastewater requiring treatment by about 10 percent. For example, in 2004, Canadian households served by metered water systems used about 266 litres per person per day compared to 467 litres per day for households that paid flat rates for water (Environment Canada, 2004b). By 2004, 63 percent of Canadian municipalities used water meters, the greatest proportion of those being in Ontario, the Northwest Territories, Nova Scotia, and the Prairie provinces (Environment Canada, 2007b). Water conservation programs, including restricting residential consumption during peak summer demand, are also effective in reducing consumption.

There also is a need to address aging infrastructure. In 1996, it was estimated that over 50 percent of the urban water infrastructure was unacceptable due to leaks and other signs of wear and required an investment of $36 billion to correct the problem (Federation of Canadian Municipalities, 1996). Failure to make needed investments in water infrastructure can contribute to future water crises. In 2003, the federal budget allocated $3 billion to infrastructure improvements in Canadian cities. These funds were earmarked for all forms of infrastructure, including roads and water supply facilities, but critical water infrastructure needs in urban areas are not being met. Provincial governments are recognizing that maintenance of public infrastructure is a key concern for residents of Canadian cities and rural areas. Accordingly, in 2008, Saskatchewan allocated new funding for infrastructure needs.

Photo 7–6
Built to overcome a height difference of 99 metres between Lake Erie and Lake Ontario, the Welland Canal profoundly affected lake levels and flows.

THE GREAT LAKES AND ST. LAWRENCE RIVER BASIN: A CASE STUDY

Straddling the Canada–U.S. border, the Great Lakes–St. Lawrence River basin contains about 18 percent of the world's fresh surface water, accounts for about 4 percent of the total length of Canada's shoreline, and is home to 45 percent (about 15 million) of the Canadian population. About 30 million Americans also live in the Great Lakes basin. About one out of three Canadians and one out of seven U.S. residents depend on the Great Lakes for their drinking water. The Great Lakes also have played a major role in the development of both countries. The Great Lakes form part of the inland waterway for the shipment of goods into and out of the heart of the continent; are the site of industrial, commercial, agricultural, and urban development; and are a source of hydro, thermal, and nuclear energy as well as recreation.

Broad, long-standing issues affecting the Great Lakes–St. Lawrence River basin include deteriorating water quality through industrial and municipal uses, fluctuating water levels, flooding, and shoreline erosion. Acid precipitation, airborne toxins, depletion of wetland areas, the sale and diversion of water from the system, increased demand on shoreline recreational facilities, and climate change are among the concerns affecting the basin.

Since the early 20th century, significant changes in land use have occurred in the Great Lakes–St. Lawrence basin, including deforestation, drainage of wetlands, and urbanization. These changes have altered the runoff characteristics of the drainage basin, as have the navigational and other structures built to regulate the outflows of Lakes Superior and Ontario. Other human activities have affected lake levels and the lakes themselves: examples include the Long Lac and Ogoki diversions built to bring water into Lake Superior for hydropower generation and logging; the diversion at Chicago that takes water out of Lake Michigan to support domestic, navigation, hydroelectric, and sanitation uses; and the Welland ship canal, built to bypass Niagara Falls and to provide water for power generation (Environment Canada, 1990). Dredging and channel modifications have affected lake levels and flows as well.

Compared with natural factors, human effects on lake levels are small. Nevertheless, changing Great Lakes water levels are of great concern because of their impact on the multiple and often conflicting uses of the lakes. As noted earlier, from an erosion and flood perspective, shore property owners often prefer relatively lower lake levels because low levels mean less risk to their properties. In contrast, shipping and hydroelectric companies prefer relatively higher lake levels because they permit the transport of more cargo and the generation of more hydroelectricity (Sanderson, 1993). Depending on the lake and climate change scenario employed, predictions are that lake levels may drop by 0.5 to 2.5 metres. This is a significant threat, not only to shipping and other economic concerns but also to the ecology of the Great Lakes and the lower St. Lawrence, where increases in tidal effects and saltwater intrusion could occur (Government of Canada, 1996).

Since there is an annual cycle of levels on the Great Lakes (high in summer and low in winter), as well as periodic effects from the passage of storms (on Lake Erie, for example, a major storm can cause short-term water level changes of as much as 5 metres), damage due to wave action can be extensive (Environment Canada, 1990; Sanderson, 1993). Along the Canadian shore of the Great Lakes, flooding and erosion damages were particularly high during 1952, 1972–1973, and 1985–1987. However, for every 1 centimetre decline in Great Lakes water levels, 93 metric tonnes must be subtracted from the total load a Great Lakes boat can carry (Environment Canada, 1990). Balancing such competing interests, and improving shoreline management to achieve sustainability of water resources and related habitats, are among the challenging responsibilities of agencies such as the

International Joint Commission (IJC), provincial governments, and municipal planners.

Eutrophication and persistent toxic chemicals have been the focus of water quality issues in the Great Lakes basin for many years. By the late 1960s, scientists, policymakers, and the general public were aware that high levels of nutrients such as phosphorus and nitrogen were causing eutrophication of the Great Lakes. Lake Erie in particular was "dying" from uncontrolled growth of aquatic plants, lowered levels of oxygen, and conditions unfavourable to fish survival. During the same period, "the Cuyahoga River running through Cleveland was so clogged with oils and greases that it caught fire in 1969. The city had to build a fire wall and declare the river a fire hazard" (Royal Commission on the Future of the Toronto Waterfront [RCFTW], 1992). The United States/Canada Great Lakes Water Quality Agreement of 1972 initiated a program of activities that has now seen significant declines in the concentration of nutrients.

By the late 1970s, more complex problems relating to synthetic toxic chemicals were the focus of attention. Over 360 compounds have been found in Great Lakes waters, more than one-third of which have been shown to be toxic to humans and wildlife. By 1985, 11 compounds had been identified as critical pollutants in the Great Lakes basin ecosystem (see Table 7–4 on the next page) because of their **persistence**, recycling, wide dispersal, **bioaccumulation**, and **biomagnification** in the food web (International Joint Commission, 1992; RCFTW, 1992).

While levels of some critical contaminants in the Great Lakes ecosystem have been reduced, two factors combine to suggest that future improvement may be slow. The first factor is that contaminants are released continuously from sediments as the ecosystem slowly purges itself; the second factor is that the inputs of toxic substances continue. For example, although PCBs have been banned, PCB inputs continue because more than 50 percent of the PCBs that were produced are still in use, in storage, or at disposal sites. This means PCBs have the potential to enter the Great Lakes environment (International Joint Commission, 1992).

Of the many issues concerning the sustainability of the Great Lakes, pollutants remain one of the most difficult. The Canada–U.S. Strategy for the Virtual Elimination of Persistent Toxic Substances in the Great Lakes has revised deadlines and goals for many pesticides such as chlordane, aldrin, dieldrin, DDT, mirex, and toxaphene (see Table 7–4). These toxins and others are linked to the endocrine-disrupting chemicals (EDCs), discussed in Box 7–3.

According to the State of Great Lakes 1999 report, the results of efforts to improve environmental conditions have been mixed. On the positive side, the number of wildlife species in the Great Lakes region has increased, and 3000 hectares of wetlands and 200 kilometres of shoreline habitat have been rehabilitated. There also has been a large reduction in the levels of dioxins, furans, PCBs, and DDT. However, the report recognized that "an additional tenfold reduction may be needed to reach acceptable risk levels" (Environment Canada, 1999). Conditions in Hamilton Harbour are improving, as 12 new fish species have been observed there. Improved operations of sewage treatment plants have led to improved water quality.

While by most standards environmental quality has greatly improved in the Great Lakes area, there is consensus that the targets originally set failed to address adequately the damages that have resulted from practices of unsustainable human activities. On July 26, 2000, the IJC released its Tenth Biennial Report on Great Lakes Water Quality. The IJC stated pollution levels were still too high and called for measures to address the problem of persistent toxic substances by strengthening the Binational Toxins Strategy. The IJC (2000) also suggested that "failure to address the challenge of restoration during this time of economic prosperity will result in future generations of Great Lakes citizens inheriting the consequences of our inaction." There is also concern over the emergence of a non-native fish, the round goby.

Other water quality issues exist in various locations throughout the Great Lakes–St. Lawrence basin, and the rest of the country as well. One example is Ontario's Trent–Severn Waterway, between Lake Ontario and Georgian Bay. It was conceived as a military defence route in the 1780s, but built for commerce in the 1800s (and completed in 1920). Today, nearly 200 000 recreational boats use its locks and channels. Communities that once needed the waterway as a means of bringing logs to their lumber mills now depend on tourism dollars from the boaters and tourists who patronize their marinas, stores, hotels, and restaurants. Water quality problems are among the environmental challenges that face the waterway. Phosphate pollution from agricultural lands and from lawns is causing algae and weed problems, and the growing population of cottagers has led to increased pollution from septic tanks. If these are not well maintained, they can leak disease-causing bacteria into lakes and rivers and contaminate shallow groundwater supplies. Also, as the number of residents and cottagers has grown, development has encroached into wetlands, threatening some rare plant species (Cayer, 1996). These concerns highlight the importance of land use planning to help ensure water quality throughout Canada.

INDUSTRIAL USES AND IMPACTS

Industrial sites have been located near water bodies not only for the water they supply, but also for the transportation, heating, cooling, and effluent discharge roles they fulfill. Historically, ignorance about the cumulative impacts of industrial activities on the environment led to groundwater and soil contamination and other downstream effects. Today, there is greater awareness of the complexity and severity of cumulative impacts; however,

CHAPTER 7: FRESH WATER

TABLE 7-4
CRITICAL POLLUTANTS IN THE GREAT LAKES BASIN ECOSYSTEM, 1991 AND 2001

Pollutant	Use	Method of Entry into Great Lakes Basin
All polychlorinated biphenyls (PCBs)[a]	• Insulating fluid in electrical transformers and in production of hydraulic fluids, lubricants, and inks. • Previously used as a vehicle for pesticide dispersal. • Includes 209 related chemicals of varying toxicity.	• From air or in sediments.
DDT and its breakdown products (including DDE)[b]	• Insecticide. • Most uses stopped in Canada in 1970. • Still used heavily for mosquito control in tropical areas on other continents.	• From air or in sediments.
Dieldrin[b]	• Insecticide once used extensively on fruits. • Use no longer permitted for termite control in Canada.	• From air or in sediments.
Toxaphene[b]	• Insecticide developed as a substitute for DDT. • Used on cotton. • Canadian use virtually ceased in early 1980s.	• From air or in water or in sediments.
2,3,7,8-Tetra-chlorodibenzo-p-dioxin (TCDD) and	• Chemicals created in manufacture of herbicides used in agriculture and for prairie (range) and forest management. • Byproduct of burning fossil fuels with chlorinated additives, wastes containing chlorine, and in pulp and paper production processes that use chlorine bleach.	• From air or in water or in sediments.
2,3,7,8-Tetra-chlorodibenzofuran (TCDF)	• Created in production of pentachlorophenol (PCP). • Contaminant in Agent Orange herbicide used in the Vietnam War. • Most toxic of 75 forms of dioxin (polychlorinated dibenzodioxins).	
Mirex[c]	• Fire retardant. • Pesticide to control fire ants.	• From air or in sediments. • Residuals from manufacturing sites, spills, and landfills.
Mercury	• Used in metallurgy. • Byproduct of paint, chlor-alkali, and electrical equipment manufacturing processes.	• Occurs naturally in soils and sediments. • Releases into aquatic environment may be accelerated by acidic deposition.
Alkylated-lead	• Fuel additive. • Used in solder, pipes, and paint.	• Released when burning leaded fuel, waste, cigarettes, and from pipes, cans, and paint chips.
Benzo(a)pyrene	• Produced when fossil fuels, wood, wastes, and charcoal are burned, including in forest fires. • From automobile exhausts. • One of many forms of polycyclic aromatic hydrocarbons (PAHs).	• Product of incomplete combustion of fossil fuels and wood.
Hexachlorobenzene (HCB)	• Byproduct of burning fossil fuels and wastes that contain chlorinated additives. • Found in manufacturing processes using chlorine. • Contaminant in chlorinated pesticides.	• Byproduct of combustion of fuels and incineration of waste.

[a] Manufacture and new uses prohibited in Canada and United States.
[b] Use restricted in Canada and United States.
[c] Banned for use in Canada and United States.

SOURCES: Adapted from *The State of Canada's Environment—1991*, Government of Canada, 1991, Ottawa: Minister of Supply and Services Canada, p. 18-15; "Critical Pollutants in the Great Lakes," *Great Lakes Online*, University of Wisconsin Sea Grant Institute, 2001, http://www.seagrant.wisc.edu/communications/Publications/One-pagers/CriticalPollutants.html; *Regeneration: Toronto's Waterfront and the Sustainable City: Final Report*, Royal Commission on the Future of the Toronto Waterfront, 1992, Toronto: Supply and Services Canada and Queen's Printer of Ontario, p. 105.

measures to address these impacts are often elusive, and long-term effects arising from previous industrial activity are in some cases only beginning to be realized.

Industrial activities, including resource extraction, food processing, and manufacturing, rely on large amounts of clean water to produce their goods as well as water to carry away the waste and byproducts of these processes. While manufacturing withdraws the second-highest volume of water in the country (see Figure 7–5, p. 266), use of more efficient water technologies has enabled this sector to withdraw significantly less water since 1981. With continued emphasis on efficiency and conservation, further reductions in withdrawal rates (perhaps as much as 40 to 50 percent) are expected to continue, with no sacrifice of economic output or quality of life. Currently, the development of the oil sands in Alberta has raised many concerns with respect to its demands for water and its effect on water quality. Beyond concerns about the contribution of this industry to greenhouse gas emissions, social effects in northern Alberta communities, and the displacement of wildlife and destruction of habitat, the availability of water is now viewed as a potential limiting factor to the development of this resource (see Box 7–4).

BOX 7–4
THIRSTING FOR OIL MAY LEAVE US DRY

Oil sands are deposits of bitumen, a heavy black viscous form of crude oil that must be processed before it is refined to produce gasoline and diesel fuels (see also Chapter 11). Bitumen is so heavy that it will not flow unless it is heated or diluted with lighter hydrocarbons. Only 7 percent of bitumen can be reached by surface mining; the rest is obtained by drilling wells and injecting water, as steam, into the bitumen so that it can flow and be pumped to the surface (also called in situ methods). To produce 1 cubic metre of synthetic crude oil, a mining operation requires about 2 to 4.5 cubic metres of water.

The development of Alberta's oil sands deposits has been rapid and extensive. With increased production, the demand for water is large and rising. Mining of bitumen has major impacts on water, including draining of wetlands, removal of the overburden (the materials that lie above the bitumen), dewatering of the basal aquifer (the zone that underlies the bitumen), and storage of wastewater. Continued expansion will drain more peatlands, use more surface and groundwater, and create more waste.

The oil and gas sector in Alberta uses over 7 percent of all water allocations, including 37 percent of all groundwater

allocations. This percentage may seem relatively small, yet the geography of this allocation is important. In 2005, companies were allowed to divert 359 million cubic metres from the Athabasca River, or more than twice the volume of water required to meet the annual municipal needs of the City of Calgary. And, companies are licensed to divert more in the future—thus far, in 2007, up to 66 percent of the surface water from the Athabasca and its tributaries. Unlike municipalities that return water to rivers after use, less than 10 percent of the water used in oil sands extraction returns to the river. Despite recycling of water, much ends up in tailings ponds or evaporates from the ponds' surface.

For in situ operations, groundwater is also used to produce steam that is injected underground to extract bitumen. Deep saline aquifers are expected to supply about 40 percent of the water required for in situ operations over the next 20 years. In situ processes use much less water than mining; however, the use of fresh and saline water for in situ operations has increased fivefold since 1999, and the use of saline water also creates impacts associated with waste disposal and wastewater treatment processes.

Photo 7–7
Alberta oil sands mining.

Photo 7–8
Alberta oil sands tailings pond.

(continued)

Three basic issues related to water arise with the growth of the oil sands. Firstly, the rapid rate of growth has outstripped predictions and our ability to provide adequate investigation of impacts or alternative production technologies. For example, growth of the industry was so rapid that in 2004, the use of fresh water was three times higher than predicted by the Alberta government using 2001 data. The use of saline water was twice that predicted. It is not clear if withdrawals from aquifers will provide for sufficient recharge. Furthermore, we do not know the impacts that gaps left underground may have on groundwater, and we have insufficient monitoring to provide adequate baseline data and record changes. Despite the fact that water has been considered a limiting factor in future production, growth has been so rapid that new, less water-intensive measures have not been developed fully.

Secondly, related to the rapid production is concern over whether a sufficient quantity of water is available to support ongoing oil sands production, let alone other uses. Water supply has been identified as one of the top four challenges for mining operations in Alberta. Changes in the basal aquifer that underlies the deposits also are uncertain. For example, it is not clear how the use of groundwater will affect the quantity of surface water bodies, including wetlands that depend on groundwater recharge. In one mining project, the basal aquifer is predicted to be partially recharged from the Athabasca River, which is already being consumed for other mining operations. The impact of climate change on water availability is also a concern that has not been resolved. Thirdly, the impacts of these developments on water quality are many and largely unknown. Concerns include the effect of water withdrawals on the aquatic ecosystem, particularly fish habitat during the low flow period of the rivers in winter.

The use of water for in situ bitumen recovery operations has a number of potential and realized environmental impacts, including

- removal of fresh water from the watershed
- drawdown of fresh aquifers and changes in groundwater levels
- depressurization of geological formations by the removal of water, resulting in decreased aquifer pressure and increased rates of recharge of water
- removal of bitumen from production zones, which can result in significant changes in the storage and flow of water in and through these zones when the depleted bitumen reservoirs become groundwater aquifers
- availability of saline water
- waste disposal in deep saline aquifers
- landfilling of waste from waste treatment processes (Griffiths, Taylor and Waynillowicz, 2006, pp. 3–4).

Water quality also is affected by disposal of mature fine tailings. Land that was once boreal forest and wetlands is now covered by 50 square kilometres of toxic tailings ponds. About 6 cubic metres of tailings are created for every cubic metre of bitumen mined. The pollutants become concentrated in the tailings ponds where wastewaters are collected. The current practice of storing fluid, fine tailings in ponds presents challenges, including the possible migration of pollutants through the groundwater system and leaks into the surrounding soil and surface water. In theory, these ponds may be reclaimed over time. At minimum, it will be decades before the fine clay particles in the tailings ponds settle out and the waters can be reclaimed.

SOURCE: *Troubled Waters, Troubling Trends: Technology and Policy Options to Reduce Water Use in Oil and Oils Sands Development in Alberta.* Griffiths, M., Taylor, A. and Waynillowicz, D., 2006, Drayton Valley, Alta: Pembina Institute. http://pubs.pembina.org/reports/TroubledW_Full.pdf

Groundwater Contamination

Toxic industrial byproducts enter aquatic environments, including groundwater, as point sources of waste disposal or pollution. Point sources related to waste disposal sites for industrial chemicals include underground injection wells for industrial waste, waste rock and mill tailings in mining areas, and coal tar at old gasification sites. Point sources of pollution include leaks or spills from tanks or pipelines that often contain petroleum products, wood preservation facilities, and road salt storage areas. In terms of groundwater contamination, the pollution potential is greatest if disposal occurs in or near sand and gravel aquifers. Over many years in Ville Mercier, Quebec, industrial wastes had been placed in lagoons in an old gravel pit. Predictably, water supplies of thousands of residents in the region were rendered unusable, and a replacement supply had to be pumped from a well 16 kilometres away (Environment Canada, 1996b).

The overall extent of groundwater contamination from industrial sources in Canada is unknown, although hundreds of individual cases have been investigated. Such cases include contamination by the pesticide aldicarb in Prince Edward Island, industrial effluents in Elmira, Ontario, and various pesticides in the Prairies, as well as creosote contamination in Calgary and other communities, and industrial contamination in Vancouver. Frequently, recognition of the contamination occurs only after water users have been exposed to potential health risks and the cost of cleaning the water supply is extremely high (Environment Canada, 1996b). Cleanup often is impossible, and groundwater aquifers may remain contaminated for decades or longer.

In addition, contaminated groundwater migrates via the hydrologic cycle to nearby rivers and lakes, creating surface water pollution that can be as serious as contamination of groundwater supplies. Given that groundwater moves slowly, it may take decades before contamination is detected; scientists expect the discovery of additional contaminated groundwater aquifers and new contaminants during the coming decades. Experience suggests prevention of contamination in the first place is by far the most practical solution to this problem.

Among the wide variety of industrial chemicals in commercial use worldwide, dense nonaqueous phase liquids (DNAPLs) are particularly troublesome. DNAPLs include dry-cleaning solvents (such as trichloroethylene and tetrachloroethylene), wood preservatives, and chemicals used in asphalt operations, automobile production and repair, aviation equipment, munitions, and electrical equipment. DNAPLs can be generated and released in accidents such as during a major tire fire in Hagersville, Ontario. Heavier than water, DNAPLs sink quickly and deeply into the ground, where they dissolve very slowly and then may move with the groundwater flow. These sources of contamination are very difficult to find and almost impossible to clean up (Environment Canada, 1996a). Except in large cities, drinking water is rarely tested for these contaminants, yet in 1995 a study of more than 480 municipal and communal groundwater supplies determined that almost 12 percent of them contained detectable concentrations of either trichloroethylene or tetrachloroethylene (Government of Canada, 1996). Both of these **organohalides** are toxic and are known to affect the central nervous, respiratory, and lymph systems in humans. Tetrachloroethylene is probably a **carcinogen** to humans; trichloroethylene causes liver damage in experimental animals (Manahan, 1994). In 2003, the federal government introduced regulations for the use and disposal of tetrachloroethylene to ensure that they did not enter wastewater of industrial and commercial operations.

Leaking underground storage tanks and piping constitute another widespread impact of industrial activities on water resources. During the past two decades, there has been an increasing number of leaks of petroleum products because the 30- to 40-year-old tanks in which these products were stored had inadequate corrosion protection. (Before 1980, most tanks were made of steel and up to half of them leaked by the time they were 15 years old.) Most petroleum products have the potential to contaminate large quantities of water: for example, 1 litre of gasoline can contaminate 1 million litres of groundwater. In the Atlantic provinces, where groundwater usage is high, the problem of leaking underground storage tanks is particularly severe. Often the problem is detected only when people start smelling or tasting gasoline in their water (Environment Canada, 1996c).

Acidic Deposition

Atmospheric changes, some of which result from industrial activities, are affecting freshwater systems. Acidic deposition continues to be a severe stress on freshwater ecosystems in eastern Canada. Water chemistry models

predicted that up to 20 000 of the lakes in these areas would become acidic (pH under 5) under 1980 emissions levels (Jones et al., 1990). Sulphate deposition during the 1980s and 1990s declined from a high of 40 kilograms per hectare per year to an average of 10 to 15 kilograms per hectare per year. Since the critical value is thought to be less than 8 kilograms per hectare per year, the current reduction programs in Canada and the United States (targeted at an objective of 20 kilograms per hectare per year) mean that as many as 25 percent of Atlantic Canada's lakes likely will not recover, even if reduction programs are implemented fully and reduction targets are exceeded. However, many provincial monitoring programs in eastern Canada were closed during the 1990s and 2000s, making difficult to obtain accurate regional assessments (Environment Canada, 2006).

It is clear that in spite of improvements in industrial emissions and reduced deposition loads, many lakes are continuing to lose populations of fish and other freshwater species. The variable levels of improvement in lake acidity seen in monitoring studies of 202 lakes throughout southeastern Canada showed that in Ontario, 60 percent of lakes tested were improving, 7 percent were worse, the rest were stable; in Quebec, 11 percent were improving, 7 percent were worse, the rest were stable; and in the Atlantic region, 12 percent were improving, 9 percent were worse, the rest were stable (Government of Canada, 1996; Schindler & Bayley, 1991).

More recent research has suggested that the effects of acid rain, global warming, and ozone depletion are having **synergistic (or, multiplicative) effects**. These effects include (1) a series of reactions that reduce the likelihood that acidified lakes can ever fully recover, and (2) enhanced movement of organochlorine pollutants and mercury from warm regions to regions at high altitudes and latitudes. Scientists estimate that SO_2 emissions from the United States and Canada need to be reduced by 75 percent. However, limits for another significant airborne water pollutant, nitrous oxides (NO_x), have yet to be determined. The case of acid rain highlights the complexity of dealing with water issues. Although progress has been made in reducing sulphur emissions, synergistic effects are weakening the ability of lakes to recover, very significant reductions in sulphur are required, and there is no agreement on the amount of emissions from other substances that might have to be reduced.

Recognizing that Canada's environment must be viewed as an integrated system of ecosystems means that the 1991 Canada–United States Air Quality Agreement may be viewed partly as a response to human impacts on water. That is, because the atmosphere is an important medium for the exchange of matter and energy within and among ecosystems, actions affecting air quality are important in a water quality context also. In this instance, the focus of the Canada–United States Air Quality Agreement is on reducing emissions of SO_2 and

CHAPTER 7: FRESH WATER

NO_x. The link between air and water quality and acid deposition is clear. In trying to meet the need for reduced emissions, the federal government initiated a Canada-wide Acid Rain Strategy for Post-2000.

HYDROELECTRIC GENERATION AND IMPACTS

Historically, Canada has been one of the world's major builders of dams and diversions. By 1991, 650 major dams had been built or were under construction in Canada; over 80 percent of the dams are for electric power generation, and many of the diversions are used to concentrate flows for hydroelectric development. While substantial economic benefits result from damming and altering rivers, these activities also incur wide-ranging, long-term ecological consequences related to the effects of impounding water in reservoirs and of altering natural patterns of stream flow (see Table 7–5). Social disadvantages also occur, such as when communities are flooded out or people are forced to modify their traditional ways of life and livelihood.

From an ecological perspective, the Peace–Athabasca delta area in northern Alberta is an example of how the balance of an ecosystem that depends on flooding can be altered by construction of dams and reservoirs. The delta is a key staging and nesting area for waterfowl and is an important habitat for bison, moose, and various fish species. Since the late 1960s, when the Bennett Dam was constructed on the Peace River in British Columbia 1200 kilometres upstream from the delta, the dam has been lowering the annual flood peak levels of the Peace River. Effects on the ecosystem have been significant, particularly the successional trend from wetlands to less productive land habitats and decreased biodiversity (Environment Canada, 1993; Government of Canada, 1991, 1996). As a remedial effort, weir construction has been undertaken to try to offset the effects of the upstream river regulation and enhance water levels for wetlands.

Other wetlands in the Saskatchewan River delta and the Atlantic provinces have been affected by the

TABLE 7–5
SELECTED ECOLOGICAL AND SOCIAL IMPACTS OF DAMS AND DIVERSIONS

Activity	Process/Comment	Impacts

Impounding water in reservoir	• Reservoirs enlarge existing lakes or create new lakes in former terrestrial or wetland ecosystems.
	• In Canada, hydroelectric reservoirs cover an area of 20 000 km².
	• Dams can lead to local and regional problems, but alternatives have environmental consequences: e.g., coal-fired thermal power plants emit more greenhouse gases and toxic substances such as mercury.
		• Displaces people.
		• Disrupts wildlife habitat.
		• Influences local climate.
		• May cause small earthquakes.
		• Affects water quality and quantity.
		  – Increased evaporation, reduced flow downstream.
		  – Change in water temperatures.
		  – Decrease in dissolved oxygen level.
		  – Increase in nutrient loadings and eutrophication.
		  – Potential degradation or enhancement of fish habitat.
		• Converts organic matter flooded by reservoir to toxic methylmercury, which accumulates and magnifies in food webs, making fish unsafe for human consumption.
		• Causes shoreline problems due to fluctuating water levels: shoreline biological communities unable to establish; erosion and turbidity increase.

Altering natural stream-flow patterns	• Efforts to control flooding by building dikes, hardening shorelines, or regulating stream flow with dams and diversions must be balanced with the preservation of fish and wildlife habitats, ecosystem functioning, and the way of life of Aboriginal peoples and other local residents.	• Reduces natural flooding and annual flood peak levels. • Causes loss of waterfowl and wildlife habitat. • Causes successional trends from wetlands to less productive terrestrial habitats, with consequent reduction in biodiversity.
Interbasin diversions	• Diversions involve the transfer of water from one river basin to another.	• May result in transfer of fish, plants, parasites, bacteria, and viruses.

SOURCES: *The State of Canada's Environment*, 1996, © Her Majesty the Queen in Right of Canada, Environment Canada 1996. Reprinted with permission of the Minister of Public Works and Government Services Canada, 2008.

operation of upstream dams. Since the late 1960s, in Atlantic Canada, hydroelectric developments have eliminated or modified extensive areas of freshwater wetlands, flooded property and wildlife habitat, altered summer water temperatures, and reduced downstream water quality during low flow periods, a factor that is particularly important for watercourses receiving pollutants (Environment Canada, n.d.). Impassable dams on the Indian (Halifax County), Mersey, Sissiboo, and Meteghan rivers in Nova Scotia have rendered most Atlantic salmon habitat inaccessible, and inadequate flows for fish downstream of the Annapolis River dam presented serious problems in 1991.

In the late 1970s, the Smallwood Reservoir of the Churchill Falls hydroelectric project in Labrador experienced problems with high levels of methylmercury accumulation in fish downstream, but 16 years after the flooding, mercury levels dropped back to normal levels (Environment Canada, n.d.). Concerns about the transfer of foreign species from one basin to another halted the Garrison Diversion project in North Dakota. This project could have introduced biota from the Missouri River system into the Hudson Bay watershed (Government of Canada, 1996). Cancellation of Phase 2 of the James Bay hydro project reflected concern about the ecological, social, and economic aspects of the megaproject (see Enviro-Focus 7 on the next page).

It appears that the era of big dams and diversions slowed down after the 1970s in Canada. Between 1984 and 1991, only six large dams were constructed (e.g., Rafferty–Alameda, Oldman, and Laforge), some only after lengthy public discussions. Long-standing plans for the Kemano River (British Columbia), Conawapa–Nelson rivers (Manitoba), and Phase 2 of the James Bay project (Quebec) have been shelved indefinitely. Combined, the changes in economics, priorities, and political influence (particularly of Aboriginal people) have made the construction of large dams and diversions less desirable and feasible.

This same trend is not evident in the developing world, where dam construction is proceeding quickly. However, as the cancellation of the Arun River dam in Nepal points out, changes in public and political thinking about the value of water resources will help protect the natural, cultural, and recreational values of rivers in the future. On the other hand, the Three Gorges dam in China, constructed between 2000 and 2009, is the largest dam ever built both in terms of hydropower generation and the number of people requiring resettlement. Depending on the source of information, estimates suggest that between 1.2 and 1.9 million people will be moved; through its construction and resettlement plans, the dam has destroyed productive agricultural land and natural resources, and raised international protest (see Chapter 11) (see also Wu, 1999; Li, Waley and Rees, 2001; Block, 2003).

RECREATIONAL USES AND IMPACTS

Many Canadians enjoy water-based recreational activities. The effects of these activities, including engine discharges, contamination from fecal coliforms and artificial snow making, and nutrient enhancement through fertilizer and pesticide runoff, have various impacts on water resources. Second homes and seasonal residences also introduce developmental impacts such as faulty or poorly maintained septic tanks, construction of facilities on the foreshore, and higher peak demand for water.

Growing demands from ski resorts to tap nearby water bodies for snow-making purposes are likely to continue, and to increase if climate change occurs. Golf courses also require water for irrigation. In light of the potential for decreased snowfall and reduced stream flow under changing climatic conditions, the use of other sources of water increases in importance. One possibility, applied on a trial basis in ski resorts in Canada, turns ski resort or household effluent into snow. Golf course irrigation technology now employs state-of-the-art systems to control the timing and amount of water applied to greens and to apply only an appropriate amount of fertilizer or pesticide to help reduce nutrient-laden runoff.

Over the past two to three decades, popular recreational areas such as the Gulf Islands in British Columbia, Georgian Bay in Ontario, and Minnedosa in Manitoba have experienced increased population growth and related development of recreational housing and facilities. Where water is in high demand, relevant authorities in some instances have taken action to institute water restrictions during summer drought periods and to encourage water conservation by offering subsidized rates on low-flush toilets, for example. Water costs (prices) to consumers also have been increased to help pay for improved supply and treatment systems.

The impacts that recreational development can have on community water supply and treatment facilities are seen clearly in the town of Banff, located in Banff National Park, Alberta. With a resident population of about 7000, the town of Banff provides the water infrastructure to accommodate up to 25 000 visitors per night and about 4 million visitors per year. Obviously, there is a large difference in the nature and cost of facilities required to service 7000 residents versus 25 000 visitors. With federal assistance, the town bears the cost of operating and maintaining water facilities for its own and for visitors' use, and levies taxes on residents and businesses to help raise funds required to do so. Up to the year 2000, the town had not instituted a direct water service charge to visitors (such as a toilet tax included in the price of a hotel room). However, since water use is now metered, user pay charges have been implemented.

The resort town of Tofino, British Columbia, also has experienced water shortages. Tofino, located in one of the wettest regions in Canada, ran out of drinking water in

Hydroelectric Dams in Northern Quebec: Environmental and Human Issues

Photo 7–9a
La Grande Rivière dam.

Photo 7–9b
The land before dam construction.

On April 30, 1971, then Quebec premier Robert Bourassa unveiled plans created by Hydro-Québec to dam several rivers in the northern part of the province, thereby creating tens of thousands of jobs, a new export product (power), an enticement to investment in extractive industries, and an opportunity to increase the economic autonomy of the province. Two months later, construction of roads into the James Bay area began, though the feasibility study being conducted by Hydro-Québec had not been completed and the Cree and Inuit residents had not been informed of the plans to flood their territory. Daniel Coon Come, grand chief of the Cree, and others such as Billy Diamond, chief of the Rupert House Cree, organized quickly to protect their territory and way of life.

In May 1972, lawyers for the Indians of Quebec Association, through whom the Cree brought their protest, sought a court injunction to halt the project. On November 15, 1973, Judge Malouf granted the injunction, announcing his decision that work on the James Bay project should cease immediately because the development would damage the environment and destroy the Cree and Inuit ways of life.

The developers immediately appealed. One week later, on November 22, Judge Turgeon reversed Judge Malouf's decision, indicating that because of the investment in the development to date, the inconvenience to the James Bay Energy Corporation and the James Bay Development Corporation would be greater than the damage to the Cree if the project proceeded. Feeling powerless to stop the first phase of the James Bay project, the Cree entered into negotiations concerning Aboriginal rights, which culminated in the 1975 James Bay and Northern Quebec Agreement, giving the Cree millions of dollars in compensation and Quebec sovereign rights to the region. Ultimately, the completed Phase 1 of the James Bay project (the La Grande Rivière hydroelectric complex) flooded more than 10 000 square kilometres of land to generate more than 10 000 megawatts of power, and cost an estimated $16 billion. Work was scheduled to begin in 1992 on the addition of 5000 megawatts of power to the James Bay complex via Phase 2 in the Great Whale (La Grande Baleine) River area. This portion was expected to be completed in 1995.

The scale of Phase 2 of the James Bay project stimulated worldwide debate. Proponents of the development argued that Canadians and Americans needed large amounts of electricity for their homes and businesses, and that hydroelectric power was environmentally sound (as it was renewable and did not contribute to global warming). Opponents noted that the Great Whale project would flood over 5000 square kilometres in an area where 12 000 Cree and 5000 Inuit lived, and that caribou, snow geese, marten, beaver, black bear, polar bear, and elk were at risk of losing their habitat. Other concerns were raised about methylmercury accumulation and poisoning of the food supply for local inhabitants, and about disrupting the balance of an incompletely understood complex hydrological cycle in the area. More legal wrangling occurred, and in 1990 the National Energy Board granted Hydro-Québec a licence to export electricity to New York and Vermont, provided that there was no conflict with relevant environmental standards and that the federal government conducted an environmental impact assessment.

Groups began forming networks to lobby against Phase 2 of the project, including the James Bay Defence Coalition, the New England Energy Efficiency Coalition, coal-mining interests in the United States, and political and environmental activists such as the Sierra Club. More legal and political action followed. Activists in Maine and Vermont succeeded in convincing their state governments to refuse power from the Great Whale project. In 1992, the New York Power Authority cancelled a $12.6 billion contract with Hydro-Québec when the state legislature passed a law requiring the state to explore conservation and alternative energy sources before importing power. Several other states followed suit in response to pressure from environmental groups and because of a diminished need for electricity.

On August 31, 1993, Hydro-Québec released its 5000-page environmental impact statement (EIS) for the Great Whale project. This EIS indicated that the project would have impacts that were moderate and localized, that could be mitigated, and that would displace no Aboriginal communities. A joint panel of federal, provincial, and Aboriginal representatives reviewed the EIS, and on November 17, 1994, ordered Hydro-Québec to rework the study. The following day, Quebec premier Jacques Parizeau announced that the Great Whale project was no longer a priority of the provincial government and would not be constructed.

Nevertheless, this is a story that has not yet ended. In 2002, the James Bay Cree approved a new arrangement under the James Bay and Northern Quebec Agreement, called "la Paix des Braves". The new deal included a cash payment to the Cree of $24 million in 2002, $46 million the following year, and then $70 million per year for 48 years. The Cree also gained more control over logging and jobs with Hydro-Québec. In return, the Cree agreed to drop lawsuits against the government that totalled between $2.4 and $3.6 billion. The agreement allowed Hydro-Québec to build its planned $3.8 billion hydroelectric projects on the Rupert and Eastmain rivers, subject to environmental approval. However, under the agreement, Quebec discarded plans to construct 14 new dams and flood 8000 square kilometres of Cree land. The new agreement also established a joint Cree–Quebec Forestry Board to review forestry regulations and plans for the Cree territory and recommend forestry activities that are compatible with the Cree people's traditional uses of the region and environmental protection. The agreement gained support but also criticism from the Cree people and environmental organizations, over concerns that hunting, fishing, and trapping would be severely compromised and that promised jobs would not materialize. Supporters have suggested that the funding will provide for improved housing and community projects and new arrangements will make the Cree Nation a major player in the administration of the territory. Given the long and complex history of this megaproject, it will be important to monitor both social and environmental effects to determine the long-term impacts of this agreement.

SOURCES: "Community-Based Observations on Sustainable Development in Southern Hudson Bay," L. Arragitainaq & B. Fleming, 1991, *Alternatives, 18*(2), 9–11; *Hydro Quebec Released Their Environmental Impact Statement,* A. A. Bennett, 1993, http://bioc09.uthscsa.edu/natnet/archive/nl/9309/0001.html; *Background on Hydro-Québec in James Bay,* D. Deocampo, 1993, http://bioc09.uthscsa.edu/natnet/archive/nl/9303/0043.html; "Cree Referendum Approves New Agreement with Quebec," Environment News Service, Feb. 5, 2002, http://www.ens-newswire.com/ens/feb2002/2002-02-05-03.asp; "The Environmental and Human Issues Raised by Large Hydroelectric Dams in Northern Québec," P. Grégoire, R. Schetagne, & M. Laperle, 1995, *Technical Bureau Supplement to Water News, 14*(1); "Cree Vote Yes on Quebec Deal," R. Taylor, Feb. 8, 2002, *Indian Country Today,* http://www.indiancountry.com/content.cfm?id=1013186960; *James Bay Dam, Electricity and Impacts*, n.d., Trade and Environment Database, http://gurukul.ucc.american.edu/TED/JAMES.HTM; "Feature: Victory over Hydro-Québec at James Bay," A. Wilson, 1994, *The Planet,* http://www.sierraclub.org/planet/199412/ftr-canada.asp

RELATED SOURCE: For a summary of major environmental modifications brought about by the project, see "The James Bay Hydroelectric Project," F. Berkes, 1990, *Alternatives, 17*(3), 20.

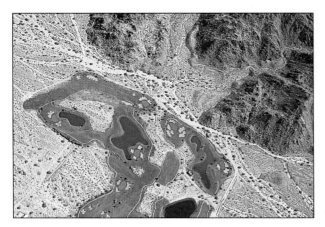

Photo 7–10
How much water is required to keep this desert golf course green?

Photo 7–11a

August 2006. Just prior to the Labour Day weekend—the busiest long weekend of the year—all lodging and food service businesses were shut down, other commercial water users were cut off, and the residents were required to ration their use on an emergency basis. To meet immediate needs, a local creek was diverted and residents were told to boil water. This situation arose, in part, because of rapid population growth and expansion of water use due to tourism. The town's water supply is reserved on nearby Meares Island. Residents were reluctant to expand the reservoir because expansion would require cutting down trees on an island that had been subject to previous public protests. However, after intermittent years of low water levels, and the complete shutdown in 2006, the town worked with federal and provincial governments to complete an expanded water system in 2007.

RESPONSES TO ENVIRONMENTAL IMPACTS AND CHANGE

Concerns for the long-term availability and quality of water highlight the importance of planning for a sustainable future, one that includes fresh water. As the examples in Table 7–6 demonstrate, international as well as individual and cooperative efforts make a difference when it comes to achieving sustainability of freshwater resources.

CANADIAN LAW, POLICY, AND PRACTICE

It is no longer sufficient to consider single aspects of the resource—quantity, quality, surface, or ground—in decision making. Now, water resource managers must collect, assess, blend, and synthesize data on the biotic and

Photo 7–11b
Two issues associated with water contamination are diseased fish, such as this walleye with lymphosarcoma (Photo 7–11a), and public health concerns (Photo 7–11b).

abiotic characteristics of water resources so that the health and productivity of entire aquatic ecosystems can be maintained. The following sections document some responses to considering water within a broader ecosystem perspective.

Water Legislation and Policy Responses

There is a considerable volume of Canadian legislation pertaining to water (see Table 7–7, p. 292). While the International Boundary Waters Treaty Act dates from the early 20th century, most of the water-related legislation dates from (or was revised during) the 1980s. The Canada Water Act (1970) provides for comprehensive and cooperative management of Canada's water resources, including water quality issues. In 1971 the Department of the Environment and the Inland Waters Directorate (now

TABLE 7-6
INTERNATIONAL INITIATIVES RELATED TO WATER IN CANADA

Initiative	Objectives
Agenda 21	Created by the United Nations Conference on Environment and Development (UNCED) to recognize international obligations to protect the quality and supply of freshwater resources and to manage them in an integrated fashion. Upon signing, Canada committed as well to help developing countries and local communities link the knowledge, people, and organizations that would enhance their decisions and policies about water.
	UN designation of 2005–2015 as the International Decade for Action: "Water for Life." Established in recognition that millions of people around the world face water shortages, children die every year from water-borne diseases, and drought regularly afflicts some of the world's poorest countries. The goal is to meet international targets for water and sanitation by 2015, including the Millennium Development Goals to reduce by half the proportion of people without access to safe drinking water by 2015 and to stop unsustainable exploitation of water resources. At the World Summit in Johannesburg in 2002, two other goals were adopted: to develop integrated water resource management and water efficiency plans by 2005 and to halve, by 2015, the proportion of people who do not have access to basic sanitation.
World Water Day	Established to draw attention to international water-related issues that affect people's health and security. In 2007, the theme was "Coping with Water Scarcity," which highlighted the significance of cooperation and the importance of an integrated approach to water resource management at both international and local levels.
Ramsar Convention	Adopted in 1971 to conserve and stem the loss of wetlands around the world. In 1981, Canada became a contracting party to the Convention on Wetlands of International Importance, an intergovernmental treaty that provides the framework for international cooperation for conservation of the world's wetland habitats. Through the Canadian Wildlife Service, Canada has designated over 13 million hectares of wetlands and associated uplands in its 33 Ramsar sites.
North American Waterfowl Management Plan (NAWMP)	Established by Canada, the United States, and Mexico in response to the rapid loss of wetlands and waterfowl populations after the Second World War. The plan emphasizes the importance of the long-term health of the land and uses massive cooperative funding of land conservation programs as a tool for restoring waterfowl and other wildlife habitat. Across North America, 32 regional habitat joint ventures are identified as priorities, the largest region including Canada's prairie potholes, which provide the breeding area for half of North America's waterfowl population. Most of the original grasslands in this area, as well as 40 to 70 percent of the original wetlands, have been lost to agricultural development. Ducks Unlimited, an NGO operating in Canada and the United States, has been an important partner in implementing NAWMP's continental conservation program.
Great Lakes Water Quality Agreements	In 1909, Canada and the United States signed the Boundary Waters Treaty to establish the International Joint Commission (IJC). The IJC was assigned three basic responsibilities: to arbitrate disputes related to boundary waters, to conduct feasibility studies for both federal governments, and to approve applications for water diversion projects that would affect flow on either side of the border.
	Although concerns about water quality were raised as early as 1912, the first Great Lakes Water Quality Agreement (GLWQA) was signed in 1972. In addition to setting common water quality objectives, the GLWQA established cooperative research programs and called for surveillance and monitoring to identify problems and to measure progress. Since then, new agreements have been signed that emphasize maintenance of the chemical, physical, and biological integrity of the Great Lakes ecosystem. The IJC monitors the implementation of these agreements.
Remedial Action Plans (RAP)	A strategy used in the Great Lakes region to identify the types of pollution present in a waterway, the geographic extent of the affected area, how water quality will be restored, and who will monitor restoration. RAPs in Canada are carried out under the 1994 Canada–Ontario Agreement Respecting the Great Lakes Basin Ecosystem. This agreement sets firm targets for environmental priorities in the Great Lakes and serves as a coordinating mechanism between the federal and Ontario governments. Where RAPS are established, local citizens are key to establishing priorities and implementing and monitoring results.

TABLE 7-7

SELECTED CANADIAN WATER LEGISLATION AND RELATED POLICIES, PROGRAMS, AND PLANS

Date	Water Legislation and Related Policies, Programs, and Plans
1909	International Boundary Waters Treaty Act (the International Joint Commission was established)
1970	Canada Water Act
1970	International Rivers Improvement Act
1971	Department of the Environment Act (Department of the Environment and Inland Waters Directorate were established)
1972	Great Lakes Water Quality Agreement
1978	Revised Great Lakes Water Quality Agreement of 1978
1979	Government Organization Act
1984–85	Inquiry on Federal Water Policy
1985	Arctic Waters Pollution Protection Act
1985	Canada Shipping Act
1985	Canada Wildlife Act
1985	Dominion Water Power Act
1985	Fisheries Act
1985	Navigable Waters Act
1987	Federal Water Policy
1987	Federal Wetlands Policy
1987	Great Lakes Health Effects Program
1987	Protocol to the Great Lakes Water Quality Agreement
1988	Canadian Environmental Protection Act
1988	St. Lawrence Action Plan
1988	Water 2020: Sustainable Use for Water in the 21st Century (Science Council of Canada)
1989	Great Lakes Action Plan (Preservation Program; Health Effects Program; Cleanup Fund)
1990	The Green Plan
1992	Canadian Environmental Assessment Act
1992	Northwest Territories Waters Act
1992	Yukon Waters Act
1993	National Roundtable on the Environment and the Economy Act
1993	St. Lawrence Vision 2000
1994	Department of Natural Resources Act
1994	Migratory Birds Convention Act
1994	Split Lake Cree First Nation Flooded Land Act
1998	Freshwater Water Strategy
1998	Mackenzie Valley Resource Management Act
2002	Nutrient Management Act (Ontario)
2003	First Nations Water Management Strategy (federal)
2003	Drinking Water Protection Act (British Columbia)

defunct) were established in recognition of the need for better environmental management in general and water resources in particular.

As the agency charged wholly with the responsibility of administering the Canada Water Act, Environment Canada tries to ensure that Canada's freshwater management is undertaken in the best national interest, and promotes a partnership approach among the various levels of government and private-sector interests that contribute to and benefit from sustainable water resources.

Shared Jurisdiction In Canada the division of responsibilities for water is complex and often is shared. Under the Constitution Act of Canada, provinces have primary responsibility for both surface and groundwater resources and legislate flow regulation and most areas of water use. The federal government has responsibility for the northern territories, national parks, First Nations reserves, navigation and fisheries, and in areas of trade, treaty relations, taxation, and statistics. The shared responsibilities are health, agriculture, significant national water issues, and interprovincial water issues (see chapter 4). Thus, when rivers or lakes cross provincial or national boundaries, both the federal and provincial governments get involved. In order to provide more efficient ways of managing the environment, federal and provincial governments are trying to "harmonize" their programs. Promoted through the Canadian Council of Ministers for the Environment in 1993, the goal is to ensure that the services provided by senior governments are not duplicated.

Ecological Monitoring and Assessment Network
The Ecological Monitoring and Assessment Network (EMAN) was established by Environment Canada in 1994 to improve communication and cooperation among scientists conducting ecological monitoring activities. EMAN is a national coordinating network that provides the means for these scientists to link with national hydrological, weather, wildlife, forest, and agricultural networks as well as other North American and global monitoring and research networks. In addition, EMAN promotes broad distribution of results in both scientific and popular literature.

CANADIAN PARTNERSHIPS AND LOCAL ACTION

Achieving sustainability in any resource context requires an integration of effort and cooperation among nations, organizations, and individuals. Canadians have been developing the means to achieve the necessary cooperation and partnerships; the following examples demonstrate a variety of forms that actions toward sustainability have taken.

Flood Damage Reduction Program

At the national level, the Canadian government and various provinces have signed agreements regarding flood damage reduction and flood risk mapping in an effort to discourage inappropriate development and reduce flood loss and damage in flood risk areas. (Flood risk areas consist of the floodway and floodplain: see Figure 7–11.) These agreements generally sought to identify, map, and designate flood risk areas in urban communities and, through public information programs, increase awareness of flood risk among the general public, industry, and government agencies.

This major policy initiative of the 1970s not only restricted building in the mapped floodplains, but also succeeded in reducing flood losses and in preserving many river valleys in high-population regions for wildlife and recreational activities. Since its development, flood damages paid by the federal government through its Disaster

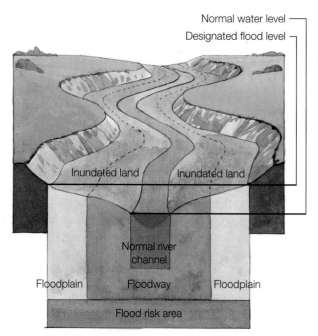

Figure 7–11
Schematic example of flood risk areas

SOURCE: Adapted from *Information Sheet: Calgary, Alberta,* Alberta Flood Damage Reduction Program, © Her Majesty the Queen in Right of Canada, Environment Canada, (n.d.). Reproduced with the permission of the Minister of Public Works and Government Services Canada, 2008.

Photo 7–12
In Collingwood, Ontario, Enviropark reflects cooperative efforts among industry, governments, and local groups.

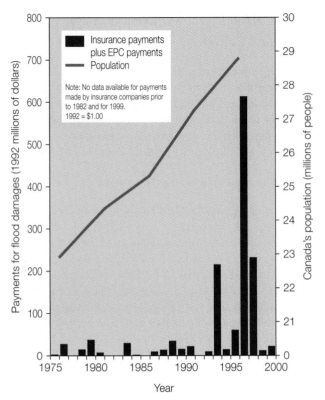

Figure 7–12

Flood damage payments in Canada, 1975–1999: Payments provided by Emergency Preparedness Canada (EPC) and the insurance industry

SOURCE: "The Cultures of Flood Management in Canada: Insights from the 1997 Red River Experience," D. Shrubsole, 2001, *Canadian Water Resources Journal, 26*(4), 461–480. Reprinted with permission.

Financial Assistance program and by insurance companies in Canada continue to rise (see Figure 7–12).

Watershed Planning

The planning and management of water and other resources on a **watershed** basis is an example of an ecosystem-based approach to achieving sustainability. In Ontario, Conservation Authorities have existed since the 1940s. The Conservation Authorities Act gives these agencies the power to study their watersheds in order to determine how the natural resources of the watershed may be conserved, restored, developed, and managed. Unfortunately, the act limits Conservation Authorities' powers to use water, to alter watercourses, and to fill and construct in floodplains (Mitchell & Shrubsole, 1992).

Planning for areas defined on an ecosystem basis, such as a watershed, historically has not been promoted in the provinces. However, watershed planning has become more important as a result of the water tragedies of Walkerton and North Battleford. Several provinces now pay attention to protecting source water and to improving wastewater quality. For example, the governments of Quebec and Saskatchewan introduced watershed-based

management intended to involve and integrate the needs of multiple users, demonstrate responsibility from source to sink, and improve the health of water sources, lakes, rivers, and associated ecosystems.

Making a Difference Locally

From coast to coast, there is a growing need to find ways to manage local waterways for sustainability. In each province, joint boards or groups such as the Meewasin Valley Authority (Saskatchewan), the Lake Winnipeg Stewardship Board (Manitoba), and the Fraser River Action Plan (British Columbia) work in partnerships with government agencies, the private sector, and civic organizations to protect a range of ecological, social, and economic values of water. The Swan Lake Christmas Hill Nature Sanctuary, located just a few minutes from downtown Victoria, British Columbia, provides one example of the importance of dedicated volunteers and the differences they make to the environmental health of a community and its water resources. While the issues and events described in Box 7–5 are specific to this nature sanctuary, they are repeated—with local differences—in many parts of Canada. The abundance and successes of these organizations demonstrate the significance of local stewardship in the movement toward environmental sustainability.

FUTURE CHALLENGES

Fresh water is essential to humanity and to all life. As the fundamental basis of aquatic and related ecosystems, sustainability of water is vital. Achieving sustainability of fresh water involves finding a proper balance in meeting all the competing needs for water—that is, in balancing human needs and the needs of natural ecosystems. Although Canada contains a wealth of fresh water underground and in its lakes, rivers, and wetlands, regional differences exist in the infrastructure and distribution of water, its quality, the human environments it supports, and the wildlife that depend on it.

In the Prairies and the interior of British Columbia, there is competition for limited water supplies between agricultural irrigation interests, growing urban demands, energy production, and the desire of residents to preserve natural ecosystems. In the most heavily populated and industrialized regions of the country, including the Windsor–Quebec corridor and parts of the Pacific and Atlantic coasts, water is plentiful, but impaired water quality and physical alterations to aquatic habitats are problematic. Persistent toxins such as PCBs in Great Lakes and St. Lawrence River sediments and the presence of DNAPLs and other contaminants in groundwater are among the unintended and poisonous byproducts of past industrial development.

In the north and other sparsely populated regions of the country, transport of contaminants (acid precipitation,

The transformation of Swan Lake, British Columbia, from a smelly, murky, polluted pond to a quiet nature sanctuary bordered by walking and cycling trails is a tribute to community vision and cooperation and many hours of work by local volunteers. While this story reflects events in one location, there are countless other examples of Canadians' dedication to improving local water bodies and environmental quality in general.

By the mid-1850s, the area surrounding what is now the Swan Lake Christmas Hill Nature Sanctuary had been cleared of most trees and native vegetation for agriculture. In about 1860, the area's first year-round recreational resort was built. Although Swan Lake Hotel guests and local residents used the 94-hectare lake for swimming, fishing, boating, and ice-skating, it was never used for drinking water (humic and tannic acids leached from the soil gave the water a yellow-brown colour). After being destroyed by fire in 1894 and again in 1897, the hotel was not rebuilt.

In succeeding years, the water quality of Swan Lake deteriorated due to nutrient enrichment from the sulphides and yeast in effluent from two wineries; coliform bacteria contamination from sewage plant effluent discharged into waterways draining into the small lake; and biological oxygen demand problems resulting from past use of agricultural fertilizers, from cattle and waterfowl wastes, and from garden chemicals. Swan Lake became a smelly eutrophic lake that no one wanted to visit.

In the 1960s, the local municipality of Saanich began acquiring land around the lake, and, to protect the natural environment, the area was designated a nature sanctuary in 1975. Since then, the municipality has spent more than $2 million to develop facilities, and the nonprofit Swan Lake Christmas Hill Nature Sanctuary Society has raised and invested an equal amount. Provincial and federal agencies have ensured that projects meet public safety standards and habitat improvement criteria.

An interpretive centre has been built, about 4 kilometres of trails and boardwalks have been constructed, and a demonstration garden of native plants has been started with volunteer assistance from local contractors. In 1995, more than 15 000 school children, community group members, and casual visitors took part in the nature sanctuary's educational programs or enjoyed a quiet walk.

The society's mission is to foster understanding and appreciation of nature and to develop personal responsibility for the care of the natural environment. School programs are the main vehicle by which the society fulfills this mission, but volunteers also help maintain the sanctuary for other users. A growing appreciation of the value of this oasis in the midst of the city has contributed to growth in volunteer hours, as well as cooperation

Photo 7-13
Swan Lake is a nature sanctuary within a highly developed agricultural and urban region.

and partnerships among citizens, community businesses, and governments.

Though no longer ugly, Swan Lake remains threatened by use of fertilizers, pesticides, and herbicides in the watershed. Chemicals enter storm drains that run into the lake, leading to algae growth and associated problems. Education programs are needed to inform homeowners and residents about the consequences of excessive fertilizer use, to promote the benefits of gardening with native plants, and to conserve water. In the future, continued funding must be established for community-based environmental education and partnership activities, including the addition of some small parcels of private land around the lake to help meet the growing public demand for meaningful natural history and outdoor experiences.

As examples of effective stewards of land and water resources, the Swan Lake Christmas Hill Nature Sanctuary Society and its governmental, industry, and citizen partners deserve recognition. They are part of the movement toward ecological sustainability and public accountability that is changing our approach to managing our shared environment. Across Canada, small organizations such as Streamkeepers in British Columbia, Partners FOR the Saskatchewan River Basin, and the Sackville River Association are building a movement to maintain and enhance the quality of our watercourses.

SOURCES: "Back to Nature," M. Curtis, September 27, 1995, *Victoria Times Colonist,* p. B1; *Swan Lake Christmas Hill Nature Sanctuary: A Place to Explore; A World to Discover,* T. Roberts & T. Morrison, 1995, Victoria, BC: Swan Lake Christmas Hill Nature Sanctuary Society; "Gardening Chemicals Causing the Algae Growth in Swan Lake," July 5, 1995, *Saanich News,* p. 24; *Partners in Stream Restoration, Winter, 1995,* Swan Lake Christmas Hill Nature Sanctuary Newsletter, p. 2; *Information on Finances and Use, 1975–1995,* Swan Lake Christmas Hill Nature Sanctuary, 1995, Victoria, BC: Swan Lake Christmas Hill Nature Sanctuary Society; *1995 Annual Report,* Swan Lake Christmas Hill Nature Sanctuary, 1996, Victoria, BC: Swan Lake Christmas Hill Nature Sanctuary Society; *An Inventory of the Biota of Swan Lake with Some Basic Limnological Spects [sic] and Recommendations,* W. Zaccarelli, 1975, Victoria, BC: Swan Lake Christmas Hill Nature Centre Society.

Every 20 seconds, a child in the developing world dies from diarrheal diseases caused by polluted water. The BioSand Water Filter (BSF) may be the most positive single intervention affecting the health of people living in disadvantaged communities worldwide—and it was invented by Dr. David H. Manz from Calgary, Alberta. Formerly a professor in Civil Engineering (environmental and water resources engineering) at the University of Calgary, Dr. Manz developed the first BSF prototypes with his undergraduate and graduate students in 1990. The impetus for his invention came from his visit to South Africa to provide technical advice on environmental issues, where he learned of the difficulties people encountered in purifying their local water supplies.

Photo 7–14
David H. Manz

The idea behind the BSF is a "natural technology" called slow sand filtration, first used in England in 1832, in which water is poured continuously through a layer of fine sand and a naturally forming biological layer purifies the water. Known as the *schmutzdeke,* a German word meaning "dirty blanket," this biological layer (an accumulation of organic and inorganic debris) and the biofilm that forms on each of the particles near the surface of the filtering media enable sand filtration to remove particulate matter and virtually all of the parasites, bacteria, and viruses that cause diseases such as cholera, typhoid fever, and amoebic dysentery. Removal of water-borne pathogens such as helminths, encysted amoebas, *Giardia, Cryptosporidium,* and *E. coli* and fecal coliform bacteria has led to significant improvements in the health of the communities where the BSF is in use. Indeed, the water contamination problems in Walkerton and the Kashechewan reserve in Ontario and in North Battleford, Saskatchewan, would not have occurred if their water had been filtered using a BSF system.

Key to success of the BSF is the new filter that Dr. Manz designed, which does not require a continuous flow of water to keep the top layer of sand from drying out. His innovation was to retain some water in the filter

Photo 7–15
This is a cut-away side view of a standard concrete biosand filter (BSF) that produces about 60 litres of clean water per hour for household use. Such units are economical to construct and maintain. The lid is removed and contaminated water is poured into the unit. Gravity forces the water downward through the media (sand) to the underdrain, through the standpipe, and into the bucket below. Over time, the accumulation of organisms enables the biofilm to get better and better at capturing up to 99 percent of disease-causing bacteria and viruses.

to allow oxygen from the air above the water to diffuse into the retained water, keeping the schmutzdeke and biofilms alive and active even when water is not being filtered. While the prototype design was literally a garbage can with a faucet near the bottom, subsequent BSFs were made of concrete, a material readily available in most developing countries.

An estimated 300,000 BSFs are in use in more than 100 countries in Africa, Europe, Asia, and North, Central, and South America. Most of these filters are the smaller-scale, individual family size that produce between 20 and 60 litres of clean water per hour, but several commercial, community-sized systems are operating in North and Central America; using Manz's Low Operating Head Polishing Sand Filtration (LHPF) technology, these systems produce millions of litres per hour.

Dr. Manz retained the humanitarian rights to the BSF, and the first major NGO to embrace the technology was Samaritan's Purse Canada. Dr. Manz gives Samaritan's Purse the credit for global expansion of the water filter initiative and implementing BSF projects that have delivered safe water to more than 500 000 people around the world since 1997.

SOURCES: Campbell, C. (2002, February 22). *From South to North—the Sand Filter Takes Hold in Canada.* International Development Research Centre Archive. http://www.idrc.ca/en/ev-43234-201-1-DO-TOPIC.html; Manz, D. H. (2007). *BioSand Water Filter Technology: Household Concrete Design.* http://www.manzwaterinfo.ca/publications.html#academic_pubs; Manz, D. H. (2007). *Health Impact Study—BioSand Filter—Dominican Republic.* http://www.manzwaterinfo.ca/publications.html#academic_pubs; Samaritan's Purse Canada. (n.d.). *Our Work.* http://www.samaritanspurse.ca/ourwork/water/biosandfilter_general.aspx.

toxic metals, and persistent organic compounds) from distant sites, and acid drainage from abandoned mines, threaten water quality. In addition, the health of numerous citizens may be at particular risk from bacteria and pathogens in well water. This is particularly important for residents of rural areas. While progress has been made in slowing the degradation of freshwater resources in Canada, uncertainties such as future climate change and its potential impacts on water supply and distribution remain as challenges for water resource managers.

As changing economic conditions have resulted in declines in government-supported programs such as water monitoring, local stewardship will become an even more important element in reaching sustainability objectives. In order to protect and conserve water resources for future generations, communities and regions, public and private sectors will need to identify ways in which they can work together to monitor threats to freshwater supplies and ecosystems, and judge the effectiveness of prevention efforts, development practices, and remediation measures.

Chapter Questions

1. Given Canada's abundant water supply, should we be concerned about water availability in the future? Why or why not? What differences emerge from different parts of the country?

2. Discuss the range of pressures that humans place on water resources that lead to water quality concerns.

3. Compare the important environmental problems related to domestic and industrial uses of water. What are the differences and similarities between these sectors?

4. We often take our water supply for granted. The following questions may challenge us to think more carefully about water in our communities:

    a. What are the major sources of your community's water supply?

    b. How is water use divided among residential, commercial, industrial, and other uses? Which sector consumes the largest volume of water?

    c. How have water prices changed in the past 20 years? Do water prices encourage conservation? Where is water being wasted?

    d. What water supply and quality problems does your community experience?

    e. What plans does your community have in place to ensure an adequate supply of safe drinking water for the future?

5. How does knowledge of ecosystems contribute to your understanding of the challenges for water management in your community and your country?

6. If new energy developments are proposed in your province, what questions might you pose about their water requirements?

Agriculture and Agri-Food Canada. (2000). *The health of our water: Toward sustainable agriculture in Canada.* Ottawa: Minister of Public Works and Government Services.

Black, J. K. (2003). Three Gorges gates close on Chinese history: China builds the world's largest dam. *The Z Magazine, 16,* 7–8.

Boyd, D. (2003). *Unnatural law: Rethinking Canadian environmental law and policy.* Vancouver: UBC Press.

Brubaker, E. (2002, April 1). Lessons from Walkerton. *Fraser Forum.* www.environmentprobe.org

Bruce, J., & Mitchell, B. (1995). *Broadening perspectives on water issues.* Canadian Global Change Program Incidental Report Series No. IR95-1. Ottawa: The Royal Society of Canada.

Canadian Water Resources Association. (1994). *Sustainability principles for water management in Canada.* Cambridge, ON: Author.

Cayer, S. (1996). Lakes and ladders: Up and down the locks and channels of Ontario's Trent–Severn Waterway. *Canadian Geographic, 116*(4), 32–47.

Draper, D. (1997). Touristic development and water sustainability in Banff and Canmore, Alberta, Canada. *Journal of Sustainable Tourism, 5*(3), 183–212.

Environment Canada. (n.d.). *State of the environment in the Atlantic region.* http://www.ns.ec.gc.ca/soe/cha4.html

Environment Canada. (1990). *A primer on water: Questions and answers.* Ottawa: Supply and Services Canada.

Environment Canada. (1993). *Water works!* Freshwater Series A-4. Ottawa: Supply and Services Canada.

Environment Canada. (1995). *Water: No time to waste. A consumer's guide to water conservation.* Ottawa: Supply and Services Canada.

Environment Canada. (1996a). *DNAPLs.* http://www.cciw.ca/glimr/data/water-fact-sheets/facta5-e.html

Environment Canada. (1996b). *How we contaminate groundwater.* http://www.doe.water/water/en/nature/grdwtr/e_howweg.htm

Environment Canada. (1996c). *Leaking underground storage tanks and piping.* http://www.cciw.ca/glimr/data/water-fact-sheets/facta5-e.html

Environment Canada. (1999). *State of the Great Lakes report.* Ottawa: Environment Canada.

Environment Canada. (2002a). Science. *Environment bulletin: Tackling urban water pollution.* http://www.ec.gc.ca/science/sandenov02/article2_e.html

Environment Canada. (2002b). *Urban water indicators: Municipal water use and wastewater treatment.* http://www.ec.gc.ca/soer-ree/English/Indicators/Issues/Urb_H2O/

Environment Canada. (2004a). *Almost nine million Canadians depend on groundwater.* http://www.ec.gc.ca/water/en/nature/grdwtr/e_sixmil.htm

Environment Canada. (2004b). *2007 Municipal water use report: 2004 statistics.* http://www.ec.gc.ca/water/en/info/pubs/sss/e_mun2004.pdf

Environment Canada. (2005). *Canada's watery lifstyle.* http://www.ec.gc.ca/water/images/info/facts/e-Canada_domestic_water_use.htmz

Environment Canada. (2006). Canada-United States Air Quality Agreement-Program Report 2006. http:www.lc.gcca/clearair-airput/caol/canus/report/2006canus/c1_p1_e.cfm#s1_4

Environment Canada. (2007a). *How do we use it?* http://www.ec.gc.ca/water/en/info/facts/e_use.htm

Environment Canada. (2007b). *2007 municipal water use report.* http://www.ec.gc.ca/water/en/info/pubs/sss/e_mun2004.pdf

Federation of Canadian Municipalities. (1996). *Report on the state of municipal infrastructure.* Ottawa: Author.

Frederick, K. D. (1996, Spring). Water as a source of international conflict. *Resources, 123,* 9–12.

Gleick, P. H. (1996). Basic water requirements for human activities: Meeting basic needs. *Water International, 21,* 83–92.

Government of Canada. (1991). *The state of Canada's environment—1991.* Ottawa: Supply and Services Canada.

Government of Canada. (1996). *The state of Canada's environment—1996.* Ottawa: Supply and Services Canada.

Hunter, P., Colford, J., LeChevallier, M., Binder, S., & Berger, P. (2001). Waterborne diseases. Conference panel summary. *Emerging Infectious Diseases, 7*(3 Suppl.), 544–555.

Indian and Northern Affairs Canada. (2003). *National assessment of water and wastewater systems in First Nations communities: Summary report.* Ottawa: Author.

International Joint Commission. (1992). *Sixth biennial report under the Great Lakes Water Quality Agreement of 1978 to the governments of the United States and Canada and the state and provincial governments of the Great Lakes basin.* Ottawa: Author.

International Joint Commission. (2000, July 26). *Tenth biennial report on Great Lakes water quality.* http://www.ijc.org/ijcweb-e.html

Jones, J. A. (1997). *Global hydrology: Processes, resources and environmental management.* London: Longman.

Jones, M. L., Minns, C. K., Marmorek, D. R., & Elder. P. C. (1990). Assessing the potential extent of damage to inland lakes in eastern Canada due to acidic deposition: II. Application of the regional model. *Canadian Journal of Fisheries and Aquatic Sciences, 47,* 67–80.

Kreutzwiser, R. (1998). Water resources management: The changing landscape in Ontario. In R. D. Needham (Ed.), *Coping with the world around us: Changing approaches to land use, resources and the environment* (pp. 135–148). Department of Geography Publication Series No. 50. Waterloo, ON: University of Waterloo.

Laycock, A. (1987). The amount of Canadian water and its distribution. In M. C. Healey & R. R. Wallace (Eds.), *Canadian aquatic resources* (pp. 13–41). Canadian Bulletin of Fisheries and Aquatic Sciences, 215. Ottawa: Supply and Services Canada.

Li, H., Waley, P., & Rees, P. (2001). Reservoir resettlement in China: Past experience and the Three Gorges Dam. *The Geographical Journal, 167*(3), 195–212.

Manahan, S. E. (1994). *Environmental chemistry* (6th ed.). Boca Raton, FL: Lewis.

Mitchell, B., & Shrubsole, D. (1992). *Ontario conservation authorities: Myth and reality.* Department of Geography Publication Series No. 35. Waterloo, ON: University of Waterloo.

Nowlan, L. (2005). *Buried treaure: Groundwater permitting and pricing in Canada.* Report prepared for the Walter and Duncan Gordon Foundation. http://www.buriedtreasurecanada.ca/Buried_Treasure.pdf

Pearse, P. H., Bertrand, F., & MacLaren, J. W. (1985). *Currents of change: Final report, inquiry on federal water policy.* Ottawa: Environment Canada.

Pindera, G. (1997). Red River dance. *Canadian Geographic, 117*(4), 52–62.

Pope, H. (1996). Sharing the rivers. *People & the Planet, 5*(1), 5.

Royal Commission on the Future of the Toronto Waterfront. (1992). *Regeneration: Toronto's waterfront and the sustainable city, final report.* Toronto: Supply and Services Canada and Queen's Printer of Ontario.

Rutherford, S. (2004). *Groundwater use in Canada.* West Coast Environmental Law. http://www.buriedtreasurecanada.ca/Groundwater_Use.pdf

Sanderson, M. (1993). Climate change and the Great Lakes. In P. L. Lawrence & J. G. Nelson (Eds.), *Managing the Great Lakes shoreline: Experiences and opportunities* (pp. 181–193). Waterloo, ON: Heritage Resources Centre, University of Waterloo.

Schindler, D. W., & Bayley, S. E. (1991). Fresh waters in cycle. In C. Mungall & D. J. McLaren (Eds.), *Planet under stress: The challenge of global change* (pp. 149–167). Toronto: Oxford University Press.

Serrill, M. S. (1997, November). Wells running dry. *Time, 150*(17A), 16–21.

Sierra Legal Defence Fund. (2001). *Waterproof: Canada's drinking water report card.* www.sierralegal.org/reports/html

Sierra Legal Defence Fund. (2004). *The national sewage report card, number three, grading the sewage treatment of 22 Canadian cities.* http://www.sierralegal.org/reports/sewage_report_card_III.pdf

Sierra Legal Defence Fund. (2006). *Waterproof 2: Canada's drinking water report card.* http://www.sierralegal.org/reports/waterproof. II.report.pdf

Statistics Canada. (2000). *Human activity in the environment 2000.* Ottawa: Author.

Statistics Canada. (2003). *Population by sex and age group.* http://www.statcan.ca/english/Pgdb/demo31a.htm

Statistics Canada. (2007, March 13). Population and dwelling counts. *The Daily.* http://www.statcan.ca/Daily/English/070313/d070313a .htm

United Nations Educational, Scientific, and Cultural Organization (UNESCO). (2002). *Africa's hidden groundwater resources.* http://portal.unesco.org/en/ev.php-URL_ID=3026&URL_DO=DO_ TOPIC&URL_SECTION=201.html

Van Tighem, K. (1990). Heritage rivers: Preserving the spirit of Canada. *Canadian Geographic, 110,* 2.

Woo, D. M., & Vicente, K. J. (2003). Sociotechnical systems, risk management, and public health: Comparing the North Battleford and Walkerton outbreaks. *Reliability Engineering & System Safety, 80,* 253–269.

World Water Council. (2006). *Water crisis.* http://www.worldwatercouncil .org/index.php?id=25.

Wu, M. (1999). *Resettlement problems of the Three Gorges Dam.* International Rivers Network. http://www.irn.org/programs/threeg/ resettle.html#one

Photo 7–16

A UNICEF well in Vahun, Liberia, provides a welcome source of clean drinking water. Learn more about global access to drinking water in the Canada and the World section.

Photo 7–17

The Bronx Zoo's rainwater diversion spares treated water supplies and helps prevent oversubscription of water resources. Can Canadians say we do the same? Find out in Table C/W-11 in the Canada and the World section.

Chapter Contents

"We can no longer think of the sea as a bounteous provider whose mysterious depths contain an inexhaustible resource.... Overfishing and the fishing of ... distant stocks are unsustainable practices and are causing the depletion of important species. But it is not too late to implement policies to protect the world's fisheries for future generations."

Daniel Pauly and Reg Watson ("Counting the Last Fish," 2003)

Chapter Objectives

After studying this chapter you should be able to

- identify a range of human activities occurring in the marine environment

- discuss the effects of human activities on the marine environment

- describe the complexity and interrelatedness of marine environment issues

- specify Canadian and international responses to oceans and fisheries issues

- discuss challenges to a sustainable future for oceans and fisheries resources

INTRODUCTION

As a maritime nation, bordered by the Arctic, Atlantic, and Pacific oceans (see Figure 8–1a on the next page), Canada has the longest coastline (about 244 000 kilometres), the longest inland waterway, the largest archipelago, and the second-largest continental shelf (about 3.7 million square kilometres) of any country in the world. Canada also holds jurisdiction over an almost 5-million-square-kilometre **exclusive economic zone**, which we claimed in 1977 and was later enshrined in the United Nations Convention on the Law of the Sea (UNCLOS).

In spite of the geographical and historical importance of oceans, few Canadians realize how extensive and varied our ocean environments really are; few understand the wealth of natural resources that oceans contribute to the subsistence, social, economic, and cultural needs of the nation's people; and fewer still appreciate that Canada has international legal obligations and economic incentives to protect oceans from degradation.

In the sections that follow, a brief overview of selected biophysical characteristics and threats to ecosystem integrity in the Arctic, Atlantic, and Pacific oceans is provided. For each ocean and each coast, the discussion identifies important sociocultural, economic, ecological, and sustainability challenges facing oceans and fisheries in Canada and internationally. Discussion continues about human activities and their effects on marine environments. In addition to these issues, coastal development, overharvesting, climate change, and ozone depletion affect the living and nonliving resources of oceans and coasts in Canada and the world over. International, national, and local initiatives and strategies to regulate human behaviour toward coastlines and oceans are discussed later in the chapter.

CANADA'S MARINE ENVIRONMENTS

CANADA'S ARCTIC OCEAN ENVIRONMENT

Major Characteristics

Canada's coldest ocean area, the Arctic, contains about 173 000 kilometres of coastline (twice that of the east and west coasts combined) and over 1 million square kilometres of continental shelf waters that provide most of the country food for Canadian Inuit. The majority of this area is covered seasonally by ice 1 to 2 metres thick.

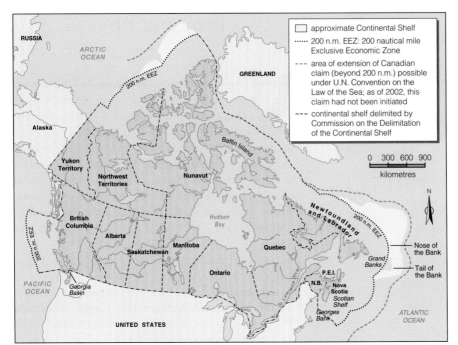

Figure 8–1a
Canada's marine environment

approximate Continental Shelf
200 n.m. EEZ: 200 nautical mile Exclusive Economic Zone
area of extension of Canadian claim (beyond 200 n.m.) possible under U.N. Convention on the Law of the Sea; as of 2002, this claim had not been initiated
continental shelf delimited by Commission on the Delimitation of the Continental Shelf

Figure 8–1b
Selected characteristics of Canada's Arctic Ocean environment

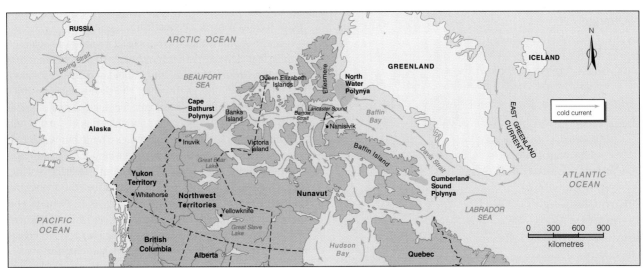

Figure 8–1c
Selected characteristics of Canada's Pacific Ocean environment

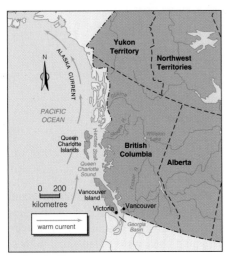

Figure 8–1d
Selected characteristics of Canada's Atlantic Ocean environment

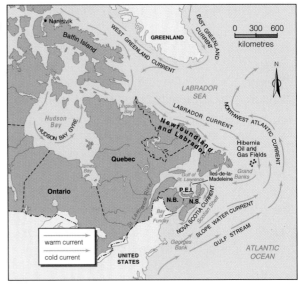

SOURCE: Adapted from *A Vision for Ocean Management,* B. Tobin, 1994, Ottawa: Fisheries and Oceans, p. 1.

Maximum sunlight enters the water column in July, after the ice breaks up, limiting phytoplankton production to the late summer. As a result, Arctic waters produce only about one-quarter of the organic biomass per unit area compared with that produced over the east and west coast continental shelves.

Major currents influencing Arctic waters include the flow of polar water southeast through the archipelago, the West Baffin Current, and the Hudson Bay gyre, a circular current that creates a small, nearly closed circulation system characterized by nutrient enrichment and high levels of biological productivity (see Figures 8–1b and d). Locally, currents help maintain open water areas called **polynyas** for much or all of the year. The largest of these polynyas, the North Water in north Baffin Bay (see Figure 8–1b), allows an early and persistent phytoplankton bloom. A biological hotspot, the North Water and other smaller polynyas serve as winter refuges for marine mammals such as polar bears, seals, whales, and sea birds that overwinter in the north. The ice edges that exist at polynyas and along floe edges (between landfast and drifting ice) are very important feeding and staging grounds for marine mammals and sea birds, particularly during spring and early summer migrations.

While subsistence hunting and fishing dominate the human use patterns in Arctic waters, some commercial fishing does take place. True polar Canadian waters have only limited commercial potential. The small Arctic char commercial fishery, for example, produced goods worth about $1.1 million in 1996, and Arctic char in northern Labrador are part of the commercial fishery that caught approximately 27 000 fish during the 2000 season (Fisheries and Oceans Canada, 2001b). There is concern, however, that most of the major Arctic char populations

have been harvested at or above maximum **sustainable yield** levels (Welch, 1995). The status of the species is unknown, as no subsistence or recreational catch data exist (Fisheries and Oceans Canada, 2001b). Other species such as redfish, round-nosed grenadier, Greenland sharks, clams, shrimp, and scallops may support small commercial operations. Although its commercial potential has not been assessed, there is a large biomass of kelp in nearshore shallow waters throughout the eastern Arctic.

Marine mammals and sea birds are the main biological components of the Canadian Arctic Ocean ecosystem. Generally, both sea bird and marine mammal populations have been stable through the last three decades. However, scientists from several countries have been monitoring the climate warming trend and its important implications for the size and location of the pack ice and for the many bird and mammal species dependent on the ice edge for their foraging and nesting areas. Increased scrutiny of sea ice conditions, water temperature, acidity levels, and other elements of the Canadian Arctic marine environment has raised considerable concern about the potential effects of climate change on marine ecosystems and their services (see Box 8–1).

Between 1990 and 2001, scattered, low-density Inuvialuit communities (in the Mackenzie delta of the western Arctic) such as Aklavik, Inuvik, and Tuktoyaktuk, whose residents depend on marine mammals for food and cultural continuity, landed an average of 111 beluga whales from the Eastern Beaufort Sea stock. During the 1992–2001 period, the community of Pangnirtung on Baffin Island hunted and landed an annual average of 36.5 belugas from the Cumberland Sound stock. Lumaaq, a beluga co-management committee established in 2003, co-manages the beluga hunt in eastern Hudson Bay,

BOX 8-1
INCREASING OCEANIC ACIDITY

Each year the world's oceans absorb approximately one-third of the carbon dioxide emitted by human activities (about 20 to 25 million tonnes of CO_2 are added to the oceans every day). Although this absorption has been considered a beneficial process because it reduces the concentration of CO_2 in the atmosphere and mitigates its impact on global temperatures, scientists now are concerned that the growing burden of CO_2 will lead to changes in the pH (acidity) of the ocean's upper layers, particularly in higher latitudes (e.g., the Arctic).

The direct chemical and biological impacts of CO_2 may seriously destabilize marine ecosystems. In addition to increasing acidity, scientists note that CO_2 absorption may cause lower nutrient concentrations in surface waters of high-latitude regions, less oxygenation of subsurface waters, and increased

exposure of phytoplankton to sunlight. Such changes would affect many species and change the composition of biological communities in ways that are not yet understood or predictable. At particular risk are many calcifying organisms such as corals, shellfish, and phytoplankton, which rely on calcium in seawater to build shells and which will be unable to grow and reproduce effectively at higher CO_2 and lower pH levels. The combination of rising temperatures, elevated CO_2, and decreasing pH poses a serious threat to coral reefs and may result in the destruction of some reefs by the end of this century.

Clearly, more research is needed to understand the consequences of the changes that are taking place, to appreciate the specific effects of more corrosive ocean waters on the variety of shelled creatures, and to better inform future policy decisions.

SOURCE: Adapted from "Research shows oceans becoming more acidic" 16-07-2004 UNESCO http://portal.unesco.org/en/ev.php-URL_ID=21758&URL_DO=DO_TOPIC&URL_SECTION=201.html

CHAPTER 8: OCEANS AND FISHERIES

Photo 8–1
Narwhals are an important source of country food for Inuit communities in the Canadian Arctic. Narwhals also are hunted for their ivory tusk.

Hudson Strait, and Ungava Bay areas with the Nunavut Wildlife Management Board and Fisheries and Oceans Canada (DFO). For the 2007 season, the quota increased from 170 to 204 belugas (George, 2007). However, hunters consistently have exceeded beluga quotas in the eastern Beaufort, Cumberland Sound, eastern Hudson, and Ungava Bay areas. Failure to comply with beluga management plans is a continuing concern for the Canadian Committee on the Status of Endangered Wildlife in Canada (COSEWIC), who designated the Cumberland Sound stock as endangered in 1990.

Since 1996 there has been a limited subsistence hunt for endangered bowhead whales in northwestern Hudson Bay. While the International Whaling Commission, ENGOs, and many scientists have criticized the Canadian bowhead hunt, Inuit people in Nunavut do not view this stock of bowheads as endangered, and they support a hunt because of its social and cultural significance. Balancing the needs of Arctic hunting cultures with the desire to maintain endangered species and biological diversity will require resource managers, scientists, and the Canadian public to become keenly attuned to the wildlife and people of the North.

Arctic ecosystems are particularly vulnerable to contamination by chemical compounds that have been transported over long distances (in gaseous or vapour form in the atmosphere, for instance). These compounds are persistent and lipophilic, which means they tend to concentrate in fatty or protein-rich tissues. Compounds such as PCBs and DDT **bioaccumulate** readily in fatty tissues of long-lived animals at the tops of food chains (such as marine mammals—polar bears, seals, whales), as well as terrestrial animals (caribou), sea birds (gulls), fish (Arctic char), and hunters and their families (see Figure 8–2).

The long and complex food web (with five trophic levels) in Arctic marine systems allows persistent contaminants to become highly concentrated in top predators. This concentration occurs because predators at each higher

level of the food chain accumulate the total chemical contaminant burden of all their prey. For instance, the bowhead whale sweeps up millions of copepods in a single day's foraging and, in doing so, accumulates the small amounts of chemical present in each individual prey item. The cumulative increase in the concentration of a chemical in successively higher levels of a food web is known as **biomagnification**. This explains why PCB levels in marine mammal blubber may be a million or more times higher than those in the Arctic ocean water. The issue of bioaccumulation is revisited briefly later in this chapter (see the pollution section of "Human Activities and Impacts on Marine Environments").

Threats to Ecosystem Integrity

Most of the major threats to Arctic ocean waters have impacts on the higher trophic levels, including marine mammals, sea birds, and polar bears. This is important not only because these species are of the most interest to local residents as well as tourists, but also because the roles of the top predators are important in the structure and function of the ecosystem. If top predators are affected by one or more of the threats described briefly below, feedback may alter the structure and function of the ecosystems.

Hydroelectric Development Hydroelectric dams and developments in Quebec, Ontario, and Manitoba will continue to affect rivers flowing to the Arctic primarily by increasing winter flows and decreasing summer flows. In turn, altered flows may cause changes in ocean currents, nearshore ice conditions, nutrient availability, the timing and magnitude of ice algal and phytoplankton production, the use of estuaries by marine mammals and **anadromous** fish that migrate into fresh water to spawn, and the ways in which coastal residents use the land and the sea. Although research programs are continuing, knowledge of many Arctic ecosystems is insufficient to predict long-term changes with certainty. Caution is necessary since, once put in place, hydroelectric developments are irreversible in the sense of meaningful human time horizons.

Long-Range Transport of Pollutants Ecosystem integrity is threatened by the long-range transport of pollutants (LRTAP) into the Canadian Arctic from agricultural and industrial activities elsewhere in the northern hemisphere. POPs, or persistent organic pollutants (halogenated compounds), and heavy metals are the most important groups of LRTAP contaminants. These substances are difficult to metabolize and excrete, so they bioaccumulate along the food chain, culminating in top Arctic predators.

PCBs evaporate from cropland, dumpsites, lands, and waters to the south. While they may enter the Arctic via ocean currents, their main pathway is atmospheric transport. Winter air flowing from Europe and Asia over the North Pole deposits thousands of tonnes of soil, fly ash particles, and

Figure 8–2

Biomagnification of PCBs in the Arctic

SOURCE: *The State of Canada's Environment—1991,* Environment Canada, Figure 15.6, page 15–18. © Her Majesty the Queen in Right of Canada, Environment Canada, 1991. Reproduced with permission of the Minister of Public Works and Government Services Canada, 2008.

associated pollutants on land and in the sea. When snowmelt occurs in June, these substances enter the oceans, are concentrated by algae and phytoplankton, and are passed on up the food chain. Biomagnification of contaminants reaches levels high enough to constitute potential health hazards for animals and humans higher up the chain.

Mercury occurs in natural ecosystems and is concentrated heavily in long-lived top predators such as seals, whales, and polar bears. Research has revealed that concentrations of mercury in the hair of humans and seals currently inhabiting Greenland are three to four times higher than they were in the hair of preindustrial humans and seals. While we do not know precisely what physiological and behavioural effects mercury concentration in top marine predators might be, we can surmise they are at risk, since they cannot switch to an alternative food source as humans might do. LRTAP contaminants pose one of the most important threats to the integrity of the Arctic marine ecosystem; the cultural and economic costs of the loss of polar bears, for example, are almost incalculable. Taking the required global actions to clean up these pollutants is difficult; Canadians can regulate directly only what happens within our own boundaries. However, we can help persuade political leaders to follow through with their commitments to ban POPs through such international agreements as the 2000 Stockholm Convention.

Climate Change   The 2007 report of the Intergovernmental Panel on Climate Change (IPCC) states, with high confidence (see Box 5–3, p. 147), that "continued changes in sea-ice extent, warming and acidification of the polar oceans are likely to further impact the biomass and community composition of marine biota as well as Arctic human activities" (p. 655). Scientific consensus is that, gradually, Arctic will be transformed into sub-Arctic; animals, ice edges, and other boundaries will shift, affecting species productivity. Analyses of changes in both body condition and cub production by polar bears in western Hudson Bay over the past two decades, in relation to the timing of sea ice breakup, suggest that climate change already is affecting this population (Lunn & Stirling, 2001).

Climate change also presents potentially serious security concerns. If ice in the Northwest Passage were to melt, as predicted, Canada's undefended Arctic coast would be open to sea-going vessels, water piracy, waste dumping, and oil spills. An open Passage also could threaten Canadian sovereignty (Canadian Arctic Resources Committee, 2002). However, dreams of an open waterway by 2030–50 may well be fantasy; research has shown that climate warming increases the likelihood of hull-penetrating, dense, multi-year sea ice occurring in high latitudes, which could cause major pitfalls for future navigation in some places in Arctic Canada (Stewart et al., 2007).

Research has identified ways in which a warming ocean climate, particularly the thinning and reduced coverage of Arctic sea ice, will drive changes in the biodiversity, distribution, and productivity of marine biota, negatively affecting the subsistence harvest and, thus, the health and well-being of Arctic residents. However, increased open water productivity will benefit the most important commercial fish stocks in the Arctic and sub-Arctic seas, including cod, herring, and pollock (Anisimov, Vaughan et al., 2007).

Nonrenewable Resource Extraction   Specific geographic sites, such as the Polaris and Nanisivik base metal mines (see Figure 8–1b) and the Bent Horn oil field in the High Arctic, appear to pose minor threats to local ecological integrity. Oil and gas exploration in the Beaufort Sea has been a source of hydrocarbon contamination (from drilling muds and fuel spills), but greater threats will occur during the production phase, perhaps during the next 20 years. Oil spills from wells, tankers, and pipelines around the world demonstrate that, in spite of stringent regulations, the Arctic will not be exempt from disasters. Depending on the time of year a massive oil spill might occur, Arctic marine ecosystem integrity would receive moderate to extremely severe damage.

Industrial growth in the Arctic has increased demands for more roads and port facilities. However, before such construction projects proceed in Nunavut, for example, they are expected to be reviewed by a co-management board set up through the Nunavut Land Claims Agreement. With equal representation of local people and government representatives, these boards promote a diversity of viewpoints in decision making necessary to consider effects on the environment. A road or port project may have severe effects on people and wildlife. For example, a proposed road might overlap with the calving grounds of an important caribou herd, and port development may result in heavy ship traffic through summer beluga whale concentrations. Infrastructure development in the Arctic already is challenging, and climate change is likely to exacerbate the difficulties.

CANADA'S PACIFIC OCEAN ENVIRONMENT

Major Characteristics

Of Canada's marine environments, the Pacific shoreline is the shortest (27 000 kilometres) and has the narrowest continental shelf (typically 16 to 32 kilometres wide), as well as the warmest waters (8 to 14°C at the surface) (see Figures 8–1a and c). The fusion of offshore currents (including the northward-flowing Alaska Coastal current; the southward-flowing California current; and weak coastal currents over the continental shelf, such as the Vancouver Island Coastal current, tidal streams, and upwellings) creates a complex oceanographic system that mixes the waters, giving the region a very high level of productivity.

Over 300 finfish species occur in this region, including anadromous species such as Pacific salmon (five species), steelhead, cutthroat, and Dolly Varden trout; **catadromous** eel family members; and other marine species such as Pacific cod, rockfish, flounder, lingcod, and herring. Numerous species of shellfish such as shrimps, scallops, crabs, and clams also proliferate in Pacific coastal waters. Millions of sea birds, both coastal and offshore species, and large numbers of marine mammals, such as whales, porpoises, dolphins, sea otters, seals, and sea lions, live and feed in or migrate through British Columbia waters.

The coastline is rocky, and only a few small estuaries exist. Mudflats are found at the head of fjords, especially in the southern part of the province, and deltaic deposits occur at the mouths of major rivers such as the Fraser, Skeena, and Stikine (see Figure 8–1c).

During the past decade, British Columbia's seafood harvest has remained relatively stable. In 2005, the commercial fishing sector employed about 54 000 people and generated an estimated $700 million in landed value (wholesale value was $1.2 billion). Commercial landed value of wild salmon declined 38 percent to $32.9 million, while during 2002 recreational fishing (which supported about 8900 jobs) generated revenues of $675 million. One of British Columbia's fastest-growing industries, the wholesale value of aquacultural production in 2005 reached $338.4 million, 40 percent above the 2004 value (British Columbia Ministry of Environment, Oceans and Marine Fisheries Division, 2006).

Threats to Ecosystem Integrity

Global Change   Not all is well in Canada's Pacific Ocean marine environment. Scientific evidence suggests that ocean surface temperatures are increasing on the Pacific coast, although clear answers as to why this is happening and what effects they will have on marine environments are not yet available. We do know that global environmental changes such as the El Niño–Southern Oscillation (see Chapter 5) not only reduce upwelling and lower productivity but also influence fish behaviour. In an El Niño year, salmon swim out away from the Alaska coast and closer to the British Columbia coast, resulting in record catches off British Columbia, and a scarcity for Alaska. These processes also have been implicated in very poor salmon returns in 1998, 1999, and 2000, possibly due partly to high ocean mortality from northerly movement of predatory mackerel.

Marine Pollution   There are growing threats to the sustainability of the natural resource base, particularly in areas such as the Georgia Basin, where growing human coastal populations generate increasing waste disposal, municipal wastewater, urban and agricultural runoff, and industrial, oil, and chemical discharges and spills. In part because of immigration, population numbers in Vancouver and Victoria have grown; in 2007, more than 50 percent of British Columbia's 4.4 million inhabitants lived in these two cities. As of 2006, Vancouver's Iona Island and Lions Gate sewage plants still provided only primary treatment of more than 6.75 million cubic metres per day of liquid waste. Both these sewage treatment plants failed bioassay toxicity tests, following which British Columbia's Minister of Water, Land and Air Protection required each plant to provide full secondary treatment by 2020 (Iona Island) and 2030 (Lions Gate).

Both Vancouver and Victoria discharge large amounts of effluent into fish habitats. Since 1962, Vancouver's effluent has contributed to the closure of shellfish harvesting in Boundary Bay, the Fraser River estuary, and Burrard Inlet. As of December 31, 2004, over 123 832 hectares of coastal marine habitat were closed to shellfish harvesting due primarily to sewage contamination, as well as contamination by toxic substances such as dioxins and furans (Environment Canada, 2005) (see Box 8–2).

CANADA'S ATLANTIC OCEAN ENVIRONMENT

Since John Cabot's small ship arrived off the coast of Newfoundland in 1497, the Grand Banks have been hailed as the world's richest hunting ground for Atlantic (northern) cod. The cod stocks, at one time so thick that ships were said to be slowed by them, seemed inexhaustible. But, in 1992, in light of unrestricted exploitation, stock declines, and fish plant closures, DFO placed a two-year moratorium on cod fishing in an attempt to avert ecological disaster. The moratorium remained in effect more than 16 years later.

Cod stocks off Newfoundland and Labrador have declined by 97 percent during the past 30 years, while stocks in the northern Gulf of St. Lawrence have declined by 81 percent. These statistics provide clear evidence of how a once bountiful resource can be decimated through ecosystem changes, human ignorance, and disregard of precautionary conservation principles. The declining biomass is the prime reason why, in May 2003, COSEWIC listed the Newfoundland and Labrador population of Atlantic cod as an endangered species and the northern Gulf of St. Lawrence cod stock as threatened (COSEWIC, 2003).

Major Characteristics

The eastern coastline of Canada is about 40 000 kilometres long, but the dominant physical feature of the east coast marine environment is the large, submerged continental shelf (see Figures 8–1a and d). Characterized by raised offshore areas of the seabed known as banks, with shallow water depths often of 50 metres or less, these areas of the continental shelf are associated with high levels of biological productivity and marine life. At 250 000 square kilometres, the Grand Banks is the largest bank in the northwest Atlantic.

Three interconnected ocean currents—the Labrador Current, Gulf Stream, and Nova Scotia Current—mix and exchange coastal and deeper ocean waters, causing

World Ocean Day was first proposed in 1992 by the Government of Canada at the Earth Summit in Rio de Janeiro. Although not yet officially designated by the United Nations, an increasing number of countries mark June 8th as an opportunity each year to celebrate our world ocean and our personal connection to the sea. (Note the use of the singular form-ocean, not oceans-to denote our global links to the ocean and the interconnectedness of our biosphere). Each year The Ocean Project and the World Ocean Network coordinate events and activities with aquariums, zoos, museums, conservation organizations, businesses, schools and universities to help people think about how the ocean affects them, how they affect the ocean, and to protect and conserve the world's ocean for present and future generations. These two organizations, working with their broad networks, are working to have the United Nations officially declare June 8 each year as World Ocean Day. Their homepage provides a link to the petition requesting official designation of World Ocean Day.

If you don't live near an ocean, why should you care about it? The Ocean Project (2008) suggests why:

The world's ocean:

- Generates most of the oxygen we breathe;
- Helps feed us;
- Regulates our climate;
- Cleans the water we drink;
- Offers us a pharmacopoeia of potential medicines; and
- Provides limitless inspiration!

Yet for too long, human society has:

- Treated the ocean as a garbage dump;
- Decimated fish populations;
- Destroyed critical habitat;
- Interrupted the fundamental reproductive capacity of life in the ocean; and
- Taken the world's ocean for granted.

SOURCE: "What Is World Ocean Day?" World Ocean Day homepage. 2007. http://www.theoceanproject.org.wod/wod_about.php © The Ocean Project

upwelling and bringing stored nutrients from the sea bottom up through the water column. This results in increased biological productivity, particularly along the edge of the Scotian Shelf and the southern Grand Banks. The Labrador Current brings cold Arctic waters down to the eastern margin of the Grand Banks, while the warm Gulf Stream flows up the east coast of the United States and over the southern Grand Banks. The Nova Scotia Current is a smaller coastal movement of cool water from the Gulf of St. Lawrence along the Scotian Shelf to the Gulf of Maine. The complex mixing of these major currents, local gyres, eddies, and tides, as well as spring discharge from northern rivers and melting ice from the Arctic, combine to increase biological productivity and marine life diversity.

Temperature and **salinity** have consequences for marine environments and climates. Atlantic Canada's offshore seawater is relatively cold, but a slight change in temperature can have great impacts on biological production. For instance, because each fish species has a range of tolerance to water depth and temperature, a change of 1°C can affect the distribution of a species, particularly if the species is living at the extreme limits of its distribution. A recent decline in water temperature may be a contributing factor in the collapse of the groundfish fishery. Similarly, declines in salinity resulting from increases in Arctic snowmelt may have contributed to the decline in cod and other groundfish (Meltzer, 1995). However, scientific knowledge of the effects of changes in temperature and salinity on cod stocks and other species is incomplete, and further research is needed.

For centuries, the spring phytoplankton bloom on the wide Atlantic continental shelf supported several major fisheries. In 1990, cod and other groundfish such as haddock, plaice, flounder, and halibut accounted for about 80 percent of total Canadian landings in weight and were valued at over $375 million. In 2004, groundfish accounted for less than 10 percent of Canada's total landed value ($2.26 billion). Catch values of pelagic species, such as herring, mackerel, tuna, salmon, and capelin, continued to decline, to $128 million in 2004. Invertebrate fisheries for crustaceans such as shrimp, lobster, and crab, and molluscs such as scallops and clams, have replaced groundfish as the major species and, in 2004, represented almost 70 percent of the total commercial marine fisheries landings in Canada. Their landed value in 2004 was $1.75 billion (Statistics Canada, 2007).

In 1995, then federal fisheries minister Brian Tobin announced that cod stocks may have declined to the point of commercial extinction. The dramatic drop in the 400-year abundance of northern cod and other groundfish species has continued. The Fisheries Resource Conservation Council (FRCC) report (2003) noted with alarm the sustained failure of most groundfish stocks in the Scotian Shelf and Bay of Fundy areas. (The FRCC was created in 1993 as a partnership between scientific and academic experts and representatives of the fishing industry. Twelve council members, appointed by the Minister of Fisheries and Oceans, make public recommendations to the minister on conservation measures for the Atlantic fishery. The four Atlantic provinces, Quebec, and Nunavut historically have held a seat on the council. A parallel partnership, the Pacific Fisheries Resource Conservation Council, was formed in 1998—see Box 8–9 on p. 331.) Fisheries scientists and inshore fishers cited predation by seals, reduced capelin populations, ongoing problems with by-catches, unaccounted mortality (such as dumping and discarding, and landing unreported catches), changes in ocean temperatures, seismic testing, food chain disruptions, and low biomass thresholds as causes for the continued decline in stocks.

The FRCC (2003, p. 5) recommended that every conservation recommendation should be explored—"we owe it to the fish to do so." COSEWIC's listing of Atlantic cod as an endangered species might be considered an appropriate conservation action because it forced the federal Cabinet to consider listing the cod as legally protected under the Species at Risk Act. On the other hand, once listed legally, it would be a crime to kill a cod fish. Such an action would preclude any possibility of reopening the fishery; Newfoundland fishers were angry and protested this designation (COSEWIC, 2003; Jaimet, 2003).

East coast waters support the feeding and breeding of many marine mammals and sea birds. While whales are not harvested commercially, they are vulnerable to fishing gear entanglement and ship collisions. As whale watching and other nature-based tourism activities have become more popular, the overall need to protect whales has been acknowledged, and DFO has established several whale conservation areas off New Brunswick and Nova Scotia. Seals, on the other hand, have been a controversial and politicized issue on the east coast for over 30 years. Landsmen in Newfoundland and residents of the Îles de la Madeleine currently undertake commercial fisheries for harp and hood seals. Public and scientific controversy still rages over the role played by rebounding seal populations in the biomass decline in groundfish.

Productivity of the Atlantic marine ecosystem is a function of diverse geographic and physiographic conditions such as shallow, rich estuaries and bays that provide ideal habitat for shellfish, and the oceanic currents, tidal flows, gyres, and upwellings on the continental shelf that influence the interactions of fish, mammalian, invertebrate, and plant communities. There are few comprehensive productivity studies, however, and limits to our knowledge have contributed to overfishing, marine degradation, and other problems.

In addition to its biological productivity, sedimentary formations underlying the continental shelf contain a variety of mineral resources, including petroleum, sand and gravel, silica sands, and precious metals. Commercial production of crude oil began in June 1992 in the Cohasset-Panuke oil field located 256 kilometres southeast of Halifax. The giant Hibernia project 312 kilometres east of St. John's on the northeast Grand Banks began pumping oil at a rate of 20 000 barrels per day in 1997. In 2003, Hibernia's average daily production was 220 000 barrels (about 80.4 million barrels per year) from an estimated recoverable reserve of 1.2 billion barrels. In 2006, Hibernia produced about 314 000 barrels per day of light crude in conjunction with the Terra Nova project. Total oil production from Hibernia and Terra Nova fields was 115 million barrels in 2004, and, as of May 2006, the White Rose project added 100 000 barrels per day of production. In 2005 Newfoundland accounted for 12 percent of Canada's crude oil production (British Columbia Ministry of Energy, Mines and Petroleum Resources, 2006; see Chapter 11).

Threats to Ecosystem Integrity

Lack of Knowledge   Much remains unknown about the highly variable yet interconnected Atlantic marine environment, and much research is required if scientists are going to be able to predict and prevent the negative consequences of human activities on marine ecosystems. The same is true if scientists are to understand the nature and implications of environmental changes. Fundamentally, this lack of knowledge underscores the importance of a precautionary approach toward use of ocean resources.

Anthropogenic Impacts and Marine Pollution
Although the coastal population of the Atlantic provinces is widely dispersed and there are few areas of industrial development, some hot spots of pervasive marine pollution exist, including the St. Lawrence River and estuary, Halifax Harbour, and St. John's Harbour. Hot spots are likely to grow in number and magnitude with increasing population, economic growth, and industrial development in coastal areas. Increasing competition for ocean space and limited resources also is anticipated, highlighting the need to have a coordinated approach to managing marine resources in the region.

Many productive shellfish areas have been contaminated by municipal or industrial effluents such as sewage, heavy metals, and polycyclic aromatic hydrocarbons. About 500 000 cubic metres of municipal sewage (50 percent untreated) are discharged daily into coastal waters. Since 1940, the number of shellfish area closures has increased steadily until, in 2004 for instance, over 33 percent (more than 2000 square kilometres) of the area classified as suitable for direct harvesting of shellfish in Atlantic Canada was closed (Environment Canada, 2004a; Menon, 1998). Similar conditions cause closures of recreational beaches, restrictions on siting of aquaculture operations, and limits on development options in general.

Other point sources of pollution occur adjacent to Canada's Atlantic Ocean environment, including effluents from pulp and paper mills, mines, and mineral processing plants; food processing plant discharges; and oil and hazardous chemical spills. Nonpoint sources of pollution include pesticides and other chemicals from agricultural and urban runoff, and atmospheric acid deposition.

Commercial Fishing   Experience has shown how difficult it is to set our fishing harvest levels in harmony with

Photo 8–2
Although a "nonconsumptive" use of marine life, whale watching may have negative effects on some species.

the ocean's level of productivity. Incomplete knowledge of the impacts of fishing and fishing practices on natural marine ecosystems and the role of other ocean changes means the effects of overfishing are not always clearly identifiable.

Other factors contributing to stock decline include discarded fishing nets and gear that continue to catch fish, marine mammals, and sea birds without human supervision (**ghostfishing**), and the dumping of plastics and other refuse. The use of mobile fishing gear, such as trawls, rakes, and dredges, has caused extensive structural destruction of ocean floor ecosystems. The trawl fishery drags nets and gear weighing more than 1 tonne along the ocean floor, removing important components of the marine habitat and affecting most fish and invertebrates that live and feed at the ocean bottom. Critical damage has been done to the continental shelf off Nova Scotia, at depths below about 200 metres, where 500-year-old seafan coral groves have been "clear-cut" by trawlers. Their recovery will take centuries. Such damage means the area's biodiversity is reduced and fish catches decline (McCallister, 2000; Willison, 2002).

Sea-Level Rise

Some scientists predict that global warming will have serious implications for Atlantic Canada, particularly with regard to sea-level rise. Under current climate change scenarios, much of the coasts of Prince Edward Island, New Brunswick, and Nova Scotia would face increased rates of bluff erosion, beach erosion, and destabilization of coastal dunes. While some parts of the coast would be submerged permanently,

in other places new beaches, spits, and barriers could form. With an increase in sea level, many communities could be damaged by storm surges. Environment Canada's (2006) report on the impacts of sea-level rise and climate change on the coastal zone of New Brunswick not only measured the impacts of climate change but also considered the kinds of adaptive strategies communities could develop.

SUMMARY OF CONCERNS FACING CANADA'S OCEAN REGIONS

Canada's coat of arms bears the motto *A Mari usque ad Mare*—from sea to sea—a clear designation of the significance of Canada's oceans to the life of the country. For centuries, different cultures in Canada have depended on the bounty of the oceans to support their traditional ways of life. From the Inuit groups in the Arctic and the First Nations peoples on the Pacific and Atlantic coasts, to the one thousand or so communities of fishers bordering the Atlantic, the ability to harvest various species of fish and shellfish, marine mammals, and sea birds to support both subsistence needs and commercial opportunities has been fundamental to continuation of their lifestyles.

Until relatively recently, these lifestyles were supported by generally stable, healthy ocean ecosystems that permitted growth in both fishing and processing industries based on what were thought to be renewable resources. Today, however, as humans have exploited fish stocks and other marine mammal and sea bird populations in order to earn a living, not only the renewability but also the sustainability of these resources has come into question.

In 2004, the global capture of fish reached 95.0 million tonnes, a 5 percent increase over 2003 (when total catch had declined to 90.5 million tonnes). The marine portion of the 2004 global catch was 85.8 million tonnes. Ten countries accounted for about 60 percent of the volume of the 2004 total world catch, comprising mostly Peruvian anchoveta, Alaskan pollock, blue whiting, and skipjack tuna. After increasing steadily for more than 30 years, the world catch of ocean fish had dropped sharply in 1990 and appeared to have peaked at between 85 and 90 million tonnes per year since then (Food and Agriculture Organization, 2007; see Box 8–3).

The United Nations Food and Agriculture Organization (FAO) estimated that catches of 75 percent of marine species have reached or exceeded sustainable levels, and concluded that "the maximum wild capture fishery potential from the world's oceans has probably been reached and reinforces the calls for more cautious and effective fisheries management to rebuild depleted stocks and prevent the decline of those being exploited at or close to their maximum potential" (2007, p. 7).

Given the need to conserve aquatic resources for the future, the FAO adopted a formal, global Code of Conduct for Responsible Fisheries in 1995. This nonmandatory code indicated that the right to fish carried with it the obligation to do so in a responsible manner in order to ensure effective conservation and management of living aquatic resources. Another important principle contained in this code was the admonition to all fisheries management organizations to apply a precautionary approach to conservation, management, and exploitation of aquatic resources and environments (Food and Agriculture Organization, 1997). In 1998, Canada became the first nation to apply the nine principles and 36 guidelines contained in the Code of Conduct (Department of Fisheries and Oceans, 2007).

In 2005, the FAO's Committee on Fisheries called for a "decade of implementation" for international fisheries management instruments, including the Code of Conduct, to ensure long-term sustainability of the world's fisheries. In trying to implement the code, various nations identified difficulties they had encountered, such as declining political support; lack of vision, leadership, and future planning to enable promotion of the code; and lack of accountability for implementation. These difficulties reflected mostly human resource and institutional capacity constraints. Since implementation of the code has contributed significantly to changes in attitude and behaviour in the fisheries sector, however, there is a need for continued participation of all stakeholders in fisheries decision making and management (Food and Agriculture Organization, 2005).

BOX 8-3
WORLD FISHERIES AND AQUACULTURE IN 2004

Together, capture fisheries and aquaculture provided the world with just under 106 million tonnes of fish for human consumption, supplying more than 2.6 billion people with 16.6 kilograms of fish per capita, the highest ever recorded (or, 13.5 kilograms per capita if data for China are excluded[1]). Aquaculture accounted for 43 percent of the total production. Fish provide about 20 percent of the world's intake of animal protein (and probably more, since subsistence fisheries are not included in official statistics).

BOX TABLE 8-1
WORLD FISHERIES AND AQUACULTURE PRODUCTION AND UTILIZATION

	2000	2001	2002	2003	2004	2005[a]
			(Million tonnes)			
Production Inland						
Capture	8.8	8.9	8.8	9.0	9.2	9.6
Aquaculture	21.2	22.5	23.9	25.4	27.2	28.9
Total inland	30.0	31.4	32.7	34.4	36.4	38.5
Marine						
Capture	86.8	84.2	84.5	81.5	85.8	84.2
Aquaculture	14.3	15.4	16.5	17.3	18.3	18.9
Total marine	101.1	99.6	101.0	98.8	104.1	103.1
Total Capture	95.6	93.1	93.3	90.5	95.0	93.8
Total Aquaculture	35.5	37.9	40.4	42.7	45.5	47.8
Total World Fisheries	131.1	131.9	133.7	133.2	140.5	141.6
Utilization						
Human consumption	96.9	99.7	100.2	102.7	105.6	107.2
Nonfood uses	34.2	31.3	33.5	30.5	34.8	34.4
Population (billions)	6.1	6.1	6.2	6.3	6.4	6.5
Per capita food fish supply (kg)	16.0	16.2	16.1	16.3	16.6	16.6

NOTE: Excluding aquatic plants.

[a] Preliminary estimate.

[1] The FAO indicates that statistics from China for capture fisheries and aquaculture are too high; this problem has existed since the early 1990s. Because of the uncertainty of its statistics, China's data generally are discussed separately from those of the rest of the world.

(continued)

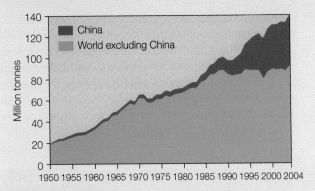

Box Figure 8–1a

World capture and aquaculture production

China reported fisheries production of 47.5 million tonnes in 2004 (16.9 megatonnes from capture fisheries, 30.6 megatonnes from aquaculture), including almost 70 percent of the quantity and over half the global value of the world's aquaculture production. Fish provide the Chinese domestic market with about 28.4 kilograms per capita, more than twice as much as consumed in low-income, food-deficit countries (14.1 kilograms per capita). Note the relatively steady capture and aquaculture production (minus China's portion) since about 1990.

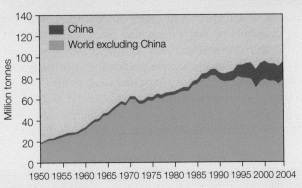

Box Figure 8–1b

World capture fisheries production

Capture fisheries (95 megatonnes in 2004) include inland fisheries (in lakes or rivers). A significant proportion of the inland fish catch is from the recreational fishery.

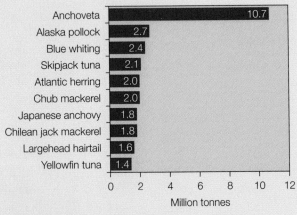

Box Figure 8–1c

Marine capture fisheries production: top ten species in 2004

The Peruvian anchoveta is by far the most-caught marine species, but catches of this species fluctuate widely. A result of the influence of El Niño effects on oceanographic conditions of the southeast Pacific, anchoveta catches ranged from a minimum of 1.7 megatonnes in 1998 to a maximum of 11.3 megatonnes in 2000.

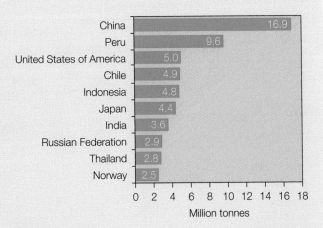

Box Figure 8–1d

Marine and inland capture fisheries: top ten producer countries in 2004

The recent top ten rankings of producer countries have not changed significantly, with the exception of Chile, whose rise to fourth place in 2004 was a function of fluctuations in anchoveta catches. In 2004, Canada ranked 18th with production of 1.19 megatonnes. Canada's commercial catch annually contributes about $2 billion in harvest value and $4.4 billion in export value.

SOURCE: *The State of World Fisheries and Aquaculture 2006*, Food and Agriculture Organization of the United Nations. Used with permission.

In addition to continuing ecological stresses such as growth in fishing pressure and stock or species collapses, a number of new human stresses as well as climatic and natural uncertainties have added to the difficulties in managing and protecting marine environmental resources for the future. For instance, the pace of coastal development, including tourism and recreational growth, has exacerbated problems relating to use of environmentally sensitive sites, water pollution, and waste disposal, while industrial growth has added new toxic chemicals such as dioxins and furans to effluent discharges. These stresses have ecological and economic implications, such as biomagnification of contaminants in fish, wildlife, and humans, reduced fish reproduction, fish die-offs, shellfishery closures, beach closures, and tourism losses.

Additional human stresses on the marine environment relate to energy supplies; as Canadian land-based supplies of petroleum resources decline, offshore oil and gas finds become more viable economically. Exploration and production activities may alter or contaminate habitats temporarily, whereas operational or accidental releases of toxic substances may degrade habitat for long periods. Marine transport safety and pollution issues continue to affect Canadian as well as international waters.

The volume of marine traffic carrying toxic or harmful substances is a major concern for ports and their approaches. The port of Vancouver, for example, annually ships millions of tonnes of chemicals and fuels to offshore markets. While marine accidents can cause spills of large volumes of oil and other hazardous substances, most spills from oil tankers result from routine operations such as loading and discharging. While on the high seas, some captains deliberately decide to pump out bilge water contaminated with leaked fuel oil or lubricating oil, or to discharge washings from fuel or cargo tanks over the ship's side. These negative actions, and the perception that oceans have an infinite capacity to absorb waste, need to be changed if long-term sustainability of ocean environments is to be assured. Canada's National Defence

aerial surveillance activity has resulted in the successful prosecution of offshore vessel captains who illegally discharge pollutants. Such enforcement activities help ensure environmentally responsible commercial marine operations in Canadian waters.

Global atmospheric, climatic, and sea-level changes are difficult to predict with certainty, but these changes will affect all three Canadian coasts, particularly the Arctic. Inundation of coastal communities and wetland habitats, for example, could displace coastal populations and affect marine species distribution patterns, potentially leading to major economic restructuring.

The effects of overharvesting both within and beyond Canada's 200-nautical-mile exclusive economic zone (EEZ) have been most evident on the Atlantic coast, where thousands of jobs were lost during the 1990s in Newfoundland and Labrador (see Coward, Ommer, & Pitcher, 2000). In both Atlantic Canada and British Columbia, the issues of excessive fishing capability and the power of fishing technologies have compounded the fundamental problem of too many fishers chasing too few fish. In the Arctic, there is concern about the potential consequences of opening a commercial char fishery when there is a lack of knowledge about the links between Arctic char and other species (Beckmann, 1995). This is a useful illustration of the importance of making decisions at an ecosystem, rather than species, level.

Seven major interconnected and strikingly similar threats to Canada's marine environmental sustainability exist (to varying degrees) on all three coasts: harvesting practices, industrialization, urban encroachment, pollution, habitat loss, atmospheric (climatic) change, and loss of biodiversity (see Figure 8–3). A selection of these threats is discussed in detail in the following section.

HUMAN ACTIVITIES AND IMPACTS ON MARINE ENVIRONMENTS

FISHERIES

The 1995 Canada–Spain Turbot Dispute

> The unthinkable has come to pass: The wealth of oceans, once deemed inexhaustible, has proven finite, and fish, once dubbed "the poor man's protein," have become a resource coveted—and fought over—by nations. (Parfit, 1995, p. 2)

The right of nations to exploit their coastal waters is well established in customary law and formal treaties, but it is only relatively recently that international oceanic law has come to grapple with the question of whether a coastal nation has a right to demand protection of migrating

Photo 8–3
The high volume of traffic carrying toxic cargo through the port of Vancouver is a continuing concern.

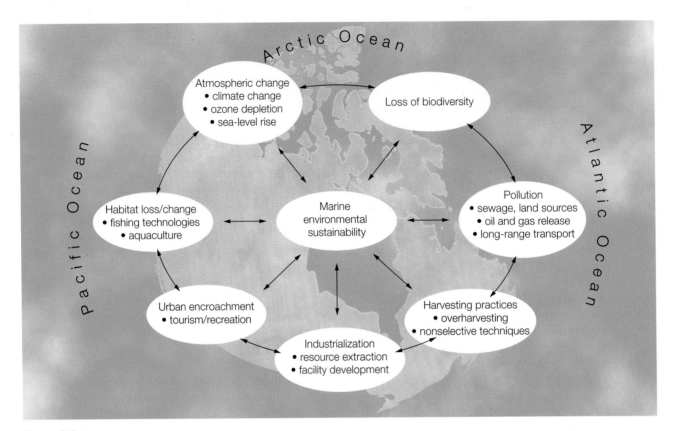

Figure 8–3

Common threats to Canada's marine environmental sustainability

species important to coastal economies even while these species are in international waters. Some nations that have large coastal fish stocks, such as Canada and the United States, argue for extending jurisdiction, while other nations that depend on fishing in distant waters argue for limitations to control overfishing beyond certain boundaries. The 1995 Canada–Spain conflict over turbot (or Greenland halibut—*Reinhardtius hippoglossoides*) is one incident that highlights the issue of transboundary stock protection.

As commercially valuable stocks of the bigger, slower-growing species have declined, commercial fishing fleets have turned to "fishing down the food chain," targeting increasingly large quantities of smaller species of fish with less commercial value (see Figure 8–4). In the case of the Spanish factory trawler fleet, their arrival on the Grand Banks in the mid-1980s was a result of their "fishing down African hake" and being "diverted to the Northwest Atlantic to find new fishing possibilities" (Department of Fisheries and Oceans, 1995c).

Canadian fishers have harvested turbot in our coastal waters for many years but, in 1986, European Union (EU) vessels, mostly from Spain and Portugal, began seriously to overfish groundfish stocks managed by the Northwest Atlantic Fisheries Organization (NAFO), an agency of the United Nations Food and Agricultural Organization. Some of these stocks were located on the "nose" and "tail" of

the Grand Banks just outside Canada's 200-mile limit. Turbot catches remained at about 20 000 tonnes from 1985 to 1988, then grew to 47 400 tonnes in 1989 and to 63 000 tonnes in 1992 (Department of Fisheries and Oceans, 1995a; Gomes, 1995; Nova Scotia Department of Environment, n.d.; Revel, n.d.).

In September 1994, NAFO adopted a 1995 total allowable catch (TAC) for turbot of 27 000 tonnes, less than half of what had been caught in 1993 and 1994. In January 1995, then Minister of Fisheries and Oceans Brian Tobin attended a special NAFO meeting in Brussels to determine how the turbot that migrated across the 200-mile limit should be shared. At the close of that meeting, Tobin claimed victory for Canada's conservation focus regarding turbot stocks, noting that most of NAFO's 15 major fishing nation members had voted for the allocation of 16 300 tonnes to Canada (a 60 percent share), and 3400 tonnes to the EU (a 12 percent share). The remainder of the TAC was allocated to Russia (3200 tonnes), Japan (2600 tonnes), and others (1500 tonnes) (Department of Fisheries and Oceans, 1995b, 1995c).

Under prevailing provisions of a NAFO objection procedure, however, the EU could reject the NAFO decision, set its own quotas, and allow EU vessels to fish virtually without restriction in the northwest Atlantic. Objection procedures seriously hamper the effectiveness of international ocean treaties, yet in some cases are the only way

Figure 8–4a

Fishing down the food chain

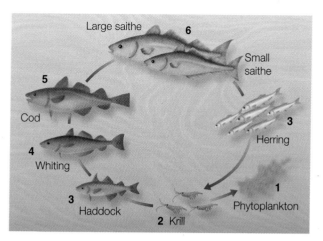

Figure 8–4b

Marine trophic levels

(a) The large arrow demonstrates that, over time, people have depleted stocks of the most prized food fish, the large fish that used to be located closer to shore, and are now targeting smaller fish and those located in deeper waters. That is, the average trophic level of the world catch has declined steadily since the start of industrial fisheries in the 1950s. When bottom fish are captured using trawls (heavy nets, some the size of football fields, that are dragged on the sea floor), habitat alterations are severe; from a sea bottom rich in organisms living on or near the bottom, the habitat becomes a near lifeless muddy substrate. Along with overfishing and the impacts of large-scale fisheries, habitat loss is a key reason for observed declines in numerous fish species. In the Black Sea, the overharvesting of predatory fish produced a boom in populations of competing predators—commercially worthless jellyfish. One solution is to set up protected, no-fishing zones so that nature may rebuild stocks of large fish.

(b) Two alternative food chains are illustrated here (who is eating whom). Within marine systems, large predators such as sharks and saithe are at a high trophic level (6), cod and sardines are in the middle, and shrimp are at a low trophic level (2); microscopic plants, mainly phytoplankton, are at the bottom of the trophic scale (1), but they sustain marine life. A single predator species may consume prey from several trophic levels, in which case its trophic level is calculated by the proportion of its diet that comes from each of the trophic levels it feeds on.

SOURCES: Artist: Cleo Vilett, © Pauly, D. and R. Watson. 2003. From "Counting the last fish." *Scientific American* July 2003: 42–47.

to activate treaties and bring all the resource users to the same table. As expected, the EU filed its objection to the turbot allocation in March 1995, and announced that its members would catch 18 000 tonnes of turbot, unilaterally setting the quota at 69 percent of the catch. Essentially, quota allocations sparked the confrontation that evolved into the Canada–Spain "turbot war."

In a move designed to permit Canada to conserve the turbot and other groundfish stocks that straddle the 200-mile limit, coastal fisheries protection regulations were amended in 1994 and in 1995. These regulations allowed Canada to seize Spanish and Portuguese vessels (and other ships flying flags of convenience) if they were caught fishing in defiance of NAFO quotas, outside the 200-mile limit. This step was necessary because many European Union vessels registered with non-NAFO countries such as Panama and then fished without quotas, thus exacerbating the effects of EU overfishing. Also, according to the Department of the Environment (n.d.), foreign fisheries on the nose and tail of the Grand Banks outside 200 miles harvested prespawning juveniles (immature fish), damaging future recruitment of the turbot stocks.

Diplomatic efforts to resolve these problems had continued, but it was under the coastal fisheries protection regulations that on March 9, 1995, Canadian authorities

boarded and seized the Spanish fishing trawler *Estai* after a chase at sea ended when warning shots were fired across its bow. The *Estai* captain was arrested and the ship was escorted into St. John's Harbour by Fisheries and Coast Guard vessels. Subsequently, Spain accused Canada of breaking international law when it seized the *Estai* in international waters. That case was put before the International Court of Justice; however, the case was dropped when Canada refused to let the court have jurisdiction (a requirement for this court to proceed). Some observers feel this was because, in strictly legal terms, Canada likely was in the wrong. However, in July 2005, a Canadian federal court ruled that Canada's actions were lawful when it seized the *Estai*.

Inspection of the *Estai* revealed that 79 percent of its catch was undersized turbot and that 25 tonnes of American plaice, an endangered species that NAFO had put under moratorium, were stored behind false bulkheads. The *Estai*'s net, which its crew had cut deliberately during the chase at sea, was recovered from the Grand Banks—its mesh measured 115 millimetres, although the smallest mesh size mandated for turbot by NAFO was 130 millimetres. Furthermore, the 115-millimetre net had an 80-millimetre mesh liner, to take even smaller fish (Bryden, 1995a). International regulations that have been

CHAPTER 8: OCEANS AND FISHERIES

BOX 8-4
FISHERIES AND THE "TRAGEDY OF OPEN ACCESS"

Renewable resources such the open ocean and its fish, as well as space, clean air, wildlife, and migratory birds, are classified as common property resources because no individual owns them and people have free access to them (i.e., at little or no cost).

In 1968, biologist Garrett Hardin described how we fail to manage these kinds of resources as the "tragedy of the commons." He suggested that resources that were held in common were subject to overuse because a rational user did not have to account for others. For example, overuse of the ocean's fish stocks occurs because each person or nation setting out to catch fish reasons that if they limit the amount of fish they catch (for conservation or other reasons), someone else will catch them anyway. Furthermore, they think the amount they catch is not enough to matter, since fish are a renewable resource. This "logic" works only when a small number of users make a few demands on the fish; when many people and nations try to exploit the free access to the ocean's fish, eventually the fish stocks are exhausted. Then, the tragedy is that no one benefits, and the resource is degraded or depleted.

Hardin's assessment captured the ways in which we have justified the extraction of many renewable resources. Yet, he confused open-access resources (those without owners) with true common-property resources, that is, those owned by collectives such as communities or nation-states. Resources owned by the state, such as Crown land or timber, also are a form of common property; these resources are subject to many regulations and also are susceptible to degradation. Research has illustrated that there are many other common-property systems where communities regulate the extraction of resources. Some of these have been operating sustainably for generations; others have been hampered because they are not recognized or enforced by higher levels of authority.

Actions that help prevent overuse of common property resources include setting catch limits at levels well below their estimated sustainable yields, establishing regulations that restrict access to the fish, and developing arrangements to share fish stocks among different users. Governments have enacted laws and regulations, and put international policies and treaties in place, to regulate who has access to which fish stocks, to set catch quotas, and to establish monitoring regimes. Community organizations (including Aboriginal forms of government) also may regulate access and use within a smaller geographic area. The original article and one follow-up are provided in the sources below so you can follow the debate yourself!

SOURCES: "The Tragedy of the Commons: Twenty-Two Years Later," D. Feeny, F. Berkes, B. J. McCay, & J. M. Acheson, 1990, *Human Ecology, 18,* 1–19; "The Tragedy of the Commons," G. Hardin, 1968, *Science, 162,* 1243–1248.

adopted into the United Nations Convention on the Law of the Sea decree that fish cannot be caught before reaching a certain spawning size, to ensure the survival of the species. Canada claimed that this illegal net would account for the undersized turbot catch aboard the *Estai*, and was proof of Spanish overfishing and violation of international rules intended to preserve endangered fish species.

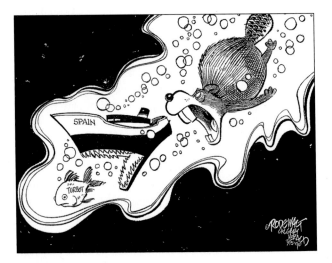

Photo 8–4
Calgary Herald, March 15, 1995, p. A4. Drawing by Vance Rodewalt.

The *Estai* was released on March 15, 1995, on payment of a $500 000 bond, and discussions with the EU to settle the dispute resumed. About two weeks later, then fisheries minister Tobin was in New York City on a public relations mission. As diplomats meeting at the United Nations Conference on Straddling Fish Stocks and Highly Migratory Fish Stocks were considering how to enforce fisheries rules on the high seas, Tobin displayed the 5.5 tonne net from the *Estai* on a barge on the East River across from the United Nations buildings. Holding up a tiny turbot in front of the illegal net, Tobin told "an army of international reporters and television crews" that "no baby fish can escape that monstrosity, that ecological madness. That's vacuuming the ocean floor and that's destroying and killing everything there" (Bryden, 1995b, 1995c). This was the day "a clever publicity stunt turned the tide in Canada's favor and the Spanish were … branded around the world as despoilers of the high seas unscrupulously vacuuming baby fish from the ocean floor" (Gessell, 1995).

On April 15, 1995, Canada and the EU reached an agreement on the conservation and management of transboundary stocks. The Canada–European Union Control and Enforcement agreement was a bilateral commitment to provide better rules, effective enforcement, and more severe penalties governing all Canadian and EU vessels fishing in specific areas regulated by NAFO. Among the major components of the new enforcement agreement were placement of independent, full-time observers on board vessels at all times; increased satellite surveillance and tracking; increased inspections and more rapid reporting of infractions; verification of gear and catch records; significant penalties to deter violations; and new minimum fish size limits. Also under the agreement, new catch quotas for both Canada and the EU were put in place for the remainder of 1995 (Canada and Spain would each receive 10 000 tonnes of the 27 000 tonne quota).

In conjunction with their bilateral negotiations with the European Union, Canadians had been working internationally toward a binding UN convention regarding conservation of migratory or straddling fish stocks on the high seas. This effort continued a major thrust Canada made in the original UNCLOS negotiations a decade earlier. An agreement relating to the conservation and management of straddling and highly migratory fish stocks was finalized and adopted without a vote by the United Nations General Assembly in August 1995. The agreement came into force in December 2001 (United Nations, 2003).

Turbot hostilities with Spain, from March 3 to April 15, 1995, were estimated to have cost the Canadian taxpayer over $3.24 million. This includes over $954 000 to operate ships that monitored the Spanish fishing boats, $231 000 for air surveillance, more than $752 000 in salaries for the RCMP and other law enforcement officers, and over $89 000 for fisheries and oceans minister Tobin's New York publicity campaign (Gessell, 1995).

Did Canada win the "turbot war"? A reduction in numbers of major violations of NAFO regulations (from 25 in 1994 to one in 1995) suggested that Spain and other members of the EU were cooperating with NAFO and Canada in regulation of the Grand Banks turbot fishery (Cox, 1996). The ability to cooperate in order to regulate catches and to conserve stocks is an important step toward sustainability of the resource. However, if sustainability is to be achieved, it is critical that all parties act responsibly and look to the best long-term interests not only of all participants but also of the fishery resources themselves. Responsible consumer choices regarding seafood play a role here (see Sustainable Seafood Canada's Seachoice Program: http://seachoice.org/Page/seachoicelaunch).

In 2002, however, given evidence of continuing irresponsible fishing practices, fisheries minister Robert Thibault announced that Canada would close its ports to fishing vessels that were believed to have committed serious violations of NAFO conservation and enforcement measures. In March and April, Canada closed its ports to vessels from the Faroe Islands and Estonia, respectively, for overfishing and misrepresentation of shrimp catches. Port closures had a negative economic impact on two Newfoundland communities that previously had supplied commercial cold storage and stevedoring operations. Minister Thibault indicated that residents in these communities understood that the long-term benefits of port closures would help to conserve fish stocks for future generations (Fisheries and Oceans Canada, 2002).

Following the "turbot war," the Canadian government continued to press for changes in NAFO operations to deal with illegal, unreported, and unregulated (IUU) fishing. On January 1, 2007, significant reforms to monitoring, control, and surveillance measures took effect. For instance, vessel owners caught misrepresenting their catch or fishing for moratoria species will be directed to port for immediate inspection. If vessel owners are caught breaking the rules, their countries must impose a fine, suspend or withdraw a licence or catch quota, or seize fishing gear or the illegal catch. In addition to these changes, improvements were made to NAFO's decision-making process, particularly relating to the objection procedure. Under the new procedures for dispute resolution, a country can no longer decide to fish a unilateral quota. Now, they must enter a dispute settlement process with an impartial panel. NAFO's fisheries management process is to base its decisions on science, and consider fish habitat and marine sensitive areas; the precautionary approach and the ecosystem approach must be taken into account.

The Northern Cod Moratorium

The unsustainable harvest of fish stocks is an increasingly important issue in Canada, perhaps nowhere felt more keenly than in outport Newfoundland. The northern cod (*Gadus morhua*) was the focal point of the distinctive culture of the small, once isolated communities scattered around the coast adjacent to fishing grounds. Peopled mostly by those of English and Irish descent,

Photo 8–5
Fisheries minister Brian Tobin displays an undersized turbot during his public relations mission in New York.

Newfoundland outports persisted for over 300 years based on small-scale, seasonal fisheries production. Although historical records indicate that northern cod have experienced general and localized cycles of abundance and severe decline, the fish always came back, and outport people adapted to these fish failures in a variety of ways (Coward, Ommer, & Pitcher, 2000; Ommer, 2002).

Change began in the 1930s with the decline of the saltfish trade, linked to the Great Depression among other things. When markets rebounded, the frozen-fish trade became the centre of development ideals, and traditional systems of merchant credit and old-fashioned processing methods began to disappear. A new scale of change began in the 1960s, led by the arrival on the Grand Banks of foreign trawlers built to withstand the icy winter storms of the North Atlantic. By 1968 their size and fishing power had boosted northern cod catches to over 800 000 tonnes, four times their historical average of 200 000 tonnes. This increase in catch clearly was the result of actions of the offshore foreign fleet, and this tragedy of open access came at the expense of the inshore Newfoundland fishers (see Figure 8–5 and Box 8–4). The 1968 catch, labelled "the killer spike," had two important impacts on the fishing industry in Newfoundland. Not only did the huge harvest in 1968 remove a large number of the northern cod population, it also appears to have reduced the resiliency of the stock to rebound from fishing mortality and changing environmental conditions, including ocean temperature changes (Department of Environment, n.d.). From a sustainability perspective, the 1980s expectation that northern cod stocks could sustain annual catches of at least 400 000 tonnes, double historical averages, was highly significant.

In 1977, in the context of negotiations at the United Nations Convention on the Law of the Sea, Canada declared a 200-nautical-mile exclusive economic zone (EEZ) (see Figure 8–1a). That zone excluded about 10 percent of the Grand Banks—the nose and tail—where important stocks of cod, flounder, and redfish moved between Canadian and international waters and were fished commercially, outside Canada's control. In 1979, NAFO assumed responsibility for conservation of 10 northwest Atlantic fish stocks (including cod) outside Canada's 200-nautical-mile limit. Within the EEZ, Canada imposed strict controls: foreign fishing was phased out, the offshore fishery became a Canadian fishery, and the federal government developed a science-based system of fisheries management (Department of Fisheries and Oceans, 1995d).

As a consequence of the extension of fisheries jurisdiction to 200 nautical miles, there was a perception of increased resource abundance and economic opportunity. Canadian fish-catching and fish-processing capacity expanded rapidly. After an initial period of increased catches in the late 1970s and early 1980s, however, groundfish stocks within and outside the EEZ declined drastically. By the mid-1980s, excess capacity and overcapitalization were evident in, for example, the

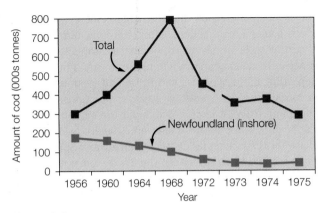

Figure 8–5

Newfoundland cod harvests showing the 1968 "killer spike" and impact on inshore fishers' catches

NOTE: These cod harvests took place in non-NAFO areas.

SOURCE: From McCay, Bonnie J. and A. Christopher Finlayson. 1996. "The Political Ecology of Crisis and Institutional Change: The Case of the Northern Cod." Published electronically, Arctic Circle (January 15, 1996) www.lib.uconn.edu/Arctic Circle; Data from Munro, G. 1980. Atlantic Report, A Promise of Abundance: Extended Fisheries Jurisdiction and the Newfoundland Economy. Ottawa: Minister of Supply and Services

development of jumbo draggers with larger hold capacities, bigger nets, more powerful engines, and higher price tags than conventional draggers.

About this time, DFO discovered serious inaccuracies in their stock assessments. In response, quotas were lowered, but it was not until 1992 that the magnitude of the problem was accepted—the fish had not come back, and maybe never would. By July 1992 it was estimated that the biomass of northern cod, Atlantic Canada's most important commercial fish stock, was about one-third its 30-year average and on the verge of commercial extinction. On this basis the Canadian government declared a two-year moratorium on the entire $700 million northern cod fishery: the intent of the moratorium was to allow the stock to rebuild.

Over 40 000 fishers and fish plant workers ultimately lost their jobs as a result of the moratorium; their families, businesses, and community organizations dependent on their work also were affected. Government assistance for the planned two-year closure was provided through programs such as the Northern Cod Adjustment and Recovery Program. In 1994 the northern cod stock was reassessed and results indicated a continued decline and concern for biological extinction of the stock. The moratorium continued, and with closure of the food fishery in the summer of 1994, it became illegal for Newfoundlanders to jig for cod to feed their families. The recreational (food) fishery reopened on a limited basis in 1996. Fishery-dependent workers and families in Atlantic Canada and Quebec were promised $1.9 million in income replacement and retraining assistance until the end of May 1999 (Department of Environment, n.d; Sinclair & Page, n.d.). However, the support program ended in August 1998 because it ran out of money. The moratorium remains in place, perhaps indefinitely, given the endangered status of certain key cod stocks.

The collapse of the groundfish fishery is a crisis of historic proportions for Newfoundland and the rest of Atlantic Canada as the displaced fishers and plant workers have lost their traditional livelihoods, independence, and way of life, and all levels of society and the economy have suffered (Blades, 1995; Coward, Ommer, & Pitcher, 2000; Davis, 2000). As understanding of the socioeconomic effects of the northern cod closure increased (Ommer, 2002), the difficulties associated with achieving intergenerational equity and finding a balance between protection of fish stocks and their habitat and provision of fish and fishing opportunities for Canadians now and in the future became clear. The causes of the crisis are many, complex, and interrelated, and include domestic and foreign overfishing, predation by seals, ghostfishing and **driftnetting**, seismic testing, government policies, corporate interests, the failures of international management, environmental and climatic factors, and the errors and uncertainties of science. Clearly, the knowledge base for fisheries decision making must be improved.

Critical gaps in knowledge and their role in the collapse of the northern cod stock were recognized by a broad spectrum of fishery stakeholders. For instance, some inshore fishers were among the first to identify the inaccuracy of DFO's science-based stock estimates, but the fishers' warnings went unheeded. Academics and other analysts were among those who called for an internal re-evaluation of scientific stock assessment and its methods. Scientists, too, who reassessed their estimates of stock sizes and showed that their earlier claims had overestimated the stock's abundance by as much as 100 percent and underestimated fishing mortality by about 50 percent, concurred that lack of knowledge had played a role in overfishing and, ultimately, the moratorium. In addition, it was recognized that the scientific side of fisheries decision making often was subject to

considerable political pressure and intervention. Thus, when changes in the process of assessing and allocating the resource were initiated, there was agreement that it was necessary to open up the decision-making process and promote greater transparency.

The value of a more participatory and inclusive decision-making process was reflected in the 1993 decision of the Minister of Fisheries and Oceans to create the Fisheries Resource Conservation Council (FRCC). The FRCC was given final authority for resource assessments and for recommendations to the minister regarding quotas and other conservation strategies. The spectrum of interests and expertise represented on the FRCC (scientists, academics, industry, and other representatives) adds important dimensions to decision making by providing more broadly based views and public input into the process. The FRCC's 2004–05 recommendations to the minister noted that the groundfish resource had not rebuilt to levels capable of supporting a significant commercial harvest, and that only limited fisheries should be permitted. However, the FRCC acknowledged the need for continued involvement of harvesters in rebuilding the resource.

As cod stocks collapsed, other groundfish, including hake, haddock, pollock, halibut, and redfish, became economically more important as substitutes for cod. However, despite increased measures to protect fish biomass, almost all stocks have continued to decline or have fluctuating biomass levels. Although no one seems able to explain fully why the decline continues, one possibility to consider is whether the threshold effect has occurred. Is the lack of recovery the result of gross ecosystem imbalance? Is it because of oceanic changes such as increasing warmth and acidity? At least part of the solution lies in good scientific research (conducted with sufficient funding) to increase understanding of the Atlantic Ocean ecosystem. Another part of the solution may lie in improving fisheries management processes. Modernizing the Fisheries Act is a case in point; see Box 8–5 on the next page.

Photo 8–6

Many of Atlantic Canada's fishing communities were affected economically and socially by the decline of fish stocks.

Pacific Herring and Salmon Stocks

The "turbot war" and the northern cod moratorium are just two examples of human effects on fisheries in the northwest Atlantic where harvesting practices have had critical impacts on fish stocks, their habitat, and biodiversity, as well as significant social and economic effects on fishing communities and regions. If we shift our attention to the west coast fisheries, we find similar long-standing issues. Pacific salmon and herring stocks have been overfished, and coastal development is having severe impacts on spawning habitats. Managers have responded with quota restrictions, gear restrictions, and area closures. More recently they have been able to reduce fleet capacity, an essential element of any program designed to ensure economic returns to Aboriginal, commercial, and recreational fishers. Here, too, scientists have been grappling with their

CHAPTER 8: OCEANS AND FISHERIES

ability to assess stocks accurately and set TACs, to model ecosystem interrelationships, and to deal with the uncertainty of the ocean environment.

Pacific Herring Pacific herring (*Clupea harengus pallasi*) are the most abundant fish species on Canada's west coast, providing employment for up to 6000 people. Herring harvests contribute millions of dollars to the provincial and national economies (wholesale value of herring products in 2005 was estimated at $85.8 million).

Just like capelin, herring are central to the marine food web: they are a key fish in the summer diets of Chinook salmon, Pacific cod, lingcod, and harbour seals, and herring eggs are important in the diet of migrating sea birds and grey whales (Environment Canada, 1994).

Pacific herring require abundant kelp beds and uncontaminated waters in which to spawn, but herring spawning habitat is threatened by coastal development. In addition, Pacific herring are sensitive to natural fluctuations in ocean climate and ecology, including ocean temperature changes and predators such as the Pacific hake. Waters off the west coast of Vancouver Island undergo alternating periods of cool and warm water that have been intensified by strong El Niño events (see Figure 8–6). Young herring survival is reduced during warm events because Pacific hake are abundant and also because large numbers of Pacific mackerel migrate north into British Columbia waters and feed on herring and other species during the summer. On average, the eight most abundant predatory fish off Vancouver Island's west coast consume

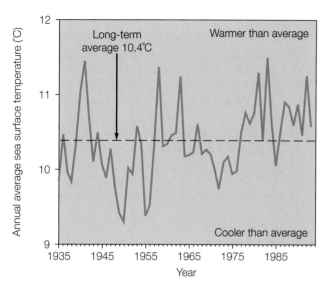

Figure 8–6

Variations in sea surface temperature off the west coast of Vancouver Island, 1935–1993

SOURCE: *Sustaining Marine Resources: Pacific Herring Fish Stocks,* © Her Majesty the Queen in Right of Canada, Environment Canada, 1994, SOE Bulletin, No. 94-5, Ottawa: Author, p. 6. Reprinted with permission of the Minister of Public Works and Government Services Canada, 2008.

an estimated 45 000 tonnes of herring annually (six times more than is harvested there each year). The spawning biomass declines because fewer young herring survive to join the spawning stock. Conversely, survival and growth are relatively strong when the summer biomass of hake is low and the annual water temperature is cool, about 10°C (Environment Canada, 1994).

Until the late 1960s, herring were harvested and reduced into low-value products such as fish meal and oil. Very large quantities of herring—up to 250 000 tonnes in 1962—were caught in this reduction fishery, exceeding the biomass that was left alive to spawn. By the mid-1960s, the commercial herring fishery could not be sustained as most of the older spawning fish had been removed from the populations. Coast-wide, only 15 000 tonnes of herring were left to spawn in 1965, and in 1967, the federal government closed all herring fishing, except traditional food and bait fisheries, for four years.

Fortunately, Pacific herring are among a group of fish species that can recover dramatically from a reduced population size; by 1993 the stocks had rebuilt to at least 100 000 tonnes and reached an estimated 165 000 tonnes in 2001. The fishery is managed by setting a fixed quota based on a 20 percent harvest rate of the forecast mature stock biomass. To meet conservation objectives, a minimum spawning stock biomass also is enforced. If the forecast biomass falls below the cutoff threshold (which varies by region), the commercial fishery is closed to allow stock recovery. One-year closures have occurred in 1985, 1986, and 2001 for west coast Vancouver Island stocks, and in 1988, 1994, and 2001 for the Queen Charlotte Islands roe

fishery, all because of low biomass. Fisheries and Oceans Canada admits that there is insufficient knowledge about the factors that affect recruitment in the different herring stocks, making it difficult to forecast future stock trends.

In 1972, a new fishery began to harvest British Columbia herring for its high-quality roe. Known as kazu-noko, herring roe is a traditional delicacy that has sold for $120 to $150 per kilogram in Japan. The highly controlled roe fishery removes about 31 000 tonnes per year (average for 1990–99). Even though only about one-tenth the amount of herring is taken compared with the 1960s reduction fishery, the landed value of the roe fishery averaged about $36.7 million annually between 2003 and 2005. The processed value of the catch is two to three times the landed value. First Nations people, for whom herring has been a traditional food, have been active participants in the food and commercial roe fishery. They have maintained their presence in the herring fishery for the past decade, owning about 25 percent of the herring roe fleet vessels and almost 75 percent of the licences to harvest roe spawned on kelp (Department of Fisheries and Oceans, 2001).

In 1991, 1200 boats participated in the lucrative roe fishery; herring contributed $214 500 to the gross income earned on each boat (in comparison, salmon accounted for $146 500 per boat) (Environment Canada, 1994). A combination of high financial stakes and stringent control efforts by DFO to ensure that quotas are not exceeded means the roe fishery is "an aggressive event where fishermen attempt to net as much herring as they can in the few minutes an opening is declared" (Meissner, 1995). In 1994, for example, the Strait of Georgia roe herring fishery for seine vessels was open for only 30 minutes. In 1995, herring roe openings on different parts of the coast ranged from 5 minutes to 24 hours, 50 minutes. In the latter case, in Barkley Sound (on the west coast of Vancouver Island), a pool system was set up to take the low quota of 1394 tonnes. Because of limited stocks, only 3 of the 23 seine boats were permitted

Photo 8–7

Herring spawning off the west coast of Vancouver Island.

to set their nets for the herring, but the value of the catch was to be split evenly among the 23 vessels. This decision to fish on a pool basis was made in an effort to come as close as possible to meeting DFO's quota. This style of management has been used with relatively high success for roe herring since that time.

Pacific herring play an important and complicated role in ocean food webs. The herring, their prey, and predators also interact with natural ocean change and human-induced changes. The corresponding high variability in spawning biomass between years makes this species a management priority for DFO. In addition, according to the Supreme Court of Canada, DFO must maintain conservation values, followed by the interests of First Nations in the fishery. In terms of maintaining conservation values, because the returns to the Queen Charlotte Islands and the west coast of Vancouver Island were forecast to be below the 20 percent cutoff in 2007 (linked to climatic conditions), no roe fisheries were planned for these areas. DFO also must consult with First Nations so that herring resources are managed to accommodate people's access for food, social, and ceremonial (FSC) purposes.

Coastal Salmon   Salmon stocks pose numerous challenges for managers, ranging from protection of biodiversity to improvement of habitat conditions and including political negotiations to apportion catch levels between Canadian and American fishers. Due to a combination of factors—*ocean regimes* (alternating periods of cool and warm water that are relatively stable for long periods of time, then shift abruptly, with dramatic effects on fish stocks), harvesting practices, and spawning habitat destruction resulting from forestry practices—wild Chinook and coho salmon stocks on the west coast of Vancouver Island and in the Gulf of Georgia have been severely depressed, some risking extinction. By 1990 in southwestern British Columbia (where urbanization and development pressures are greatest), one-third of

Photo 8–8

Herring punts used by First Nations fishers in the herring roe fishery.

the spawning locations known since the 1950s had been lost or so severely diminished that spawners were no longer monitored consistently (Fisheries and Oceans Canada, 2005a). Indeed, in 2002–03, COSEWIC designated three populations of salmon as endangered, namely the Interior Fraser River coho, the Cultus Lake sockeye in the lower Fraser, and the Sakinaw Lake sockeye in the Strait of Georgia (Fisheries and Oceans Canada, 2005a). COSEWIC's primary reasons for this designation were overfishing, changing marine conditions, and habitat perturbations (Canadian Legal Information Institute, 2006).

Endangered species are those facing imminent extirpation or extinction. If these salmon populations were to be identified officially as wildlife at risk, they would be added to Schedule 1 (the "List") and protected under the Species at Risk Act (SARA). The legislation would require development of a recovery strategy for these species. Having decided previously not to list the Cultus Lake or Sakinaw Lake populations, in 2006 the governor general (on the advice and recommendation of the ministers of environment and fisheries) decided that the Interior Fraser coho salmon population would not be added to the List of Endangered Species under SARA. The reasons were "based on uncertainties associated with changes in the marine environment and potential future socio-economic impacts on users associated with the uncertainty" (Canadian Legal Information Institute, 2006).

In 2006, an estimated 81 percent of the salmonid populations in British Columbia (excluding the Strait of Georgia) and the Yukon were thought to be at no risk or to have a low risk of extinction, and just over 13 percent of these stocks were either extinct (2 percent) or at high risk of extinction (Fisheries and Oceans Canada et al., 2006). Given these data, the governor general's decision may be interpreted as supporting the social and economic values that harvesting wild Pacific salmon provides to people, and the need for balance between protection and sustainable use of the stocks. Alternatively, this decision may be interpreted as a fisheries illustration of "the force of economics overpower[ing] conscience" (Parfit, 1995, p. 11). The rationale for not listing the Interior Fraser coho was that if marine survival rates were to improve, and if the required recovery strategy were not sufficiently flexible, there could be future loss of revenue from harvesting and processing in the 2009 to 2016 timeframe: "foregone gross combined revenue loss ... could range from $4.9 million to $52.9 million ... with direct total employment impacts ranging from 350 to 2160 person-years. In addition, losses in recreational sector revenue resulting from reduced angling opportunities could be between $41.9 million to $227 million" (Canadian Legal Information Institute, 2006).

The decision not to add the Interior Fraser coho to the list of endangered species was made despite clear scientific recognition that protecting diversity—"the irreplaceable lineages of salmon evolved through time"—is "the most prudent policy for future continuance of wild salmon as well as the ecological processes that depend on them and the cultural, social and economic benefits drawn from them" (Fisheries and Oceans Canada, 2005a, p. 2). While economics is an important decision-making factor, the decision not to protect the Interior Fraser coho salmon population appears not only to perpetuate the past failure to recognize the value of biodiversity in Pacific salmon, but also to denigrate the efforts of thousands of volunteer streamkeepers and many local watershed groups who have been working actively to protect and restore salmon species and habitats (Fisheries and Oceans Canada et al., 2006). This decision also does not exhibit a precautionary approach, even though uncertainty regarding the ability of the salmon stock to sustain human fishing and other pressures is evident.

Destruction of stream spawning beds has been cited as one of the primary causes of declining Pacific salmon stocks. In an effort to involve local communities in restoration and protection of this important salmon habitat, DFO, with funds from the Fraser River Action Plan, initiated the Streamkeepers Program. The objectives of the program are to provide training and support to volunteers interested in restoring and protecting local aquatic environments, to provide public education on the value of watershed resources, and to facilitate communication and cooperative efforts in watershed management. Since its inception in 1993, the Streamkeepers Program has supported local programs throughout British Columbia and the Yukon. Volunteers have removed dams, stabilized streambanks, improved salmon habitat, and created partnerships with local businesses with the goal of improving associated stream habitat.

The Pacific Streamkeepers Federation (PSkF) was initiated in May 1995, at a Community Involvement Workshop held in Williams Lake, British Columbia. More than 300 stream restoration volunteers from British Columbia and the Yukon attended. A nonprofit society committed to supporting community groups involved in Streamkeepers activities throughout British Columbia and the Yukon, the PSkF aims to provide an information exchange for streamkeeper and enhancement groups; lend a larger voice to streamkeeper and enhancement issues; facilitate training and provide support for streamkeeper and enhancement groups; foster cooperation among watershed stakeholders; and promote local management of aquatic resources.

A variety of influences has increased the challenges of managing Pacific salmon, including international agreements, Supreme Court decisions, Canadian legislation (i.e., SARA) governing species at risk (see Chapter 12), variations in ocean conditions and productivity, habitat loss and alteration of spawning and rearing habitat, shifts in global markets, conservation concerns, and altered public expectations. Public attitudes, science, and law have evolved to expect and promote more proactive, responsible stewardship and forward-looking approaches to conservation and protection of salmon biodiversity

than appeared in the decision to exclude Interior Fraser coho salmon from the endangered list. In this context, it is important to consider the adaptive approach to salmon conservation detailed in *Canada's Policy for Conservation of Wild Pacific Salmon.*

Conservation of wild salmon   Since 1995, the conservation of Pacific salmon has improved through such measures as reduction in the commercial fishing fleet, development and adoption of selective harvesting techniques, and renewal of the Pacific Salmon Treaty by Canada and the United States. Changes in the conservation ethic for Pacific salmon have come through greater understanding of the role of salmon as a keystone species (see Chapter 3) in Pacific regional ecosystems, and clear recognition that we need healthy, genetically distinct salmon runs to ensure the well-being and survival of small coastal fishing communities, whole forest systems, and British Columbia's economy.

Canada and the United States signed the Pacific Salmon Treaty in 1985. The treaty required both countries to conduct and manage their fisheries to provide for optimum production and equitable exploitation of salmon stocks. Treaty clauses indicate that each country is to receive benefits equivalent to the production of salmon originating in its waters, and each country is to avoid undue disruption to the other's fisheries. Periodically, bilateral agreements are negotiated to implement the treaty's principles for long-term conservation and harvest sharing. In addition, the Pacific Salmon Commission was established to advise both Canada and the United States on implementation of treaty provisions.

In practice, however, a variety of unilateral decisions and retaliatory actions—by both Canada and the United States—threatened the conservation objectives of the treaty. Canadian negotiators felt their concerns about American interceptions of salmon originating in Canada, and declines in key salmon stocks, were addressed inadequately. From 1992 through 1997, Canada and the United States were unable to reach a comprehensive, coast-wide agreement. However, in 1998, a new approach to treaty negotiations was advanced, enabling government-to-government negotiations to resume in 1999 and to culminate in the renewal of long-term fishing arrangements under the Pacific Salmon Treaty. Subsequently, both governments have agreed on smaller, annex agreements. These include two agreements signed in 2005 which focused on improving the management of transboundary river stocks and Fraser River sockeye and pink salmon.

Recognizing that the long-term well-being of wild salmon depends on protection of their genetic and geographic diversity, and recognizing that their habitat must be protected (or rehabilitated) effectively in order for salmon to flourish, DFO instituted its wild Pacific salmon policy in 2005. The policy is intended to protect the biological foundation of these salmon in order to provide the fullest

BOX 8-6

ABORIGINAL PEOPLE AND CANADA'S FISHERIES FRAMEWORK

Aboriginal people have fished Canada's coastal waters for thousands of years and have attached great cultural significance to the marine environment and its resources. In addition to their food and ceremonial fisheries, Aboriginal people are active participants in commercial fisheries.

The Government of Canada's legal and policy frameworks identify a special obligation to provide Aboriginal people the opportunity to harvest fish for food, social, and ceremonial purposes (FSC). This obligation derived from a 1990 landmark ruling of the Supreme Court of Canada in the *Sparrow* decision, wherein it was determined that the Musqueam First Nation had an Aboriginal right to fish for FSC purposes. The court found that where an Aboriginal group has a right to fish for such purposes, this right takes priority, after conservation, over other uses of the resource. In its 2004 decision (*Haida v. BC*), the Supreme Court also indicated the legal duty to consult with Aboriginal groups when their fishing rights might be affected.

In response to the *Sparrow* decision, and to provide stable fisheries management, DFO launched the Aboriginal Fisheries Strategy (AFS) in 1992. The AFS applies where DFO manages the fishery and where land claims settlements have not already put a fisheries management regime in place. The objectives of the AFS include

- providing a framework for management of fishing by Aboriginal groups for FSC purposes (consistent with the 1990 Supreme Court's *Sparrow* decision),

- providing an opportunity for Aboriginal groups to participate in fisheries management,

- contributing to the economic self-sufficiency of Aboriginal communities,

- providing a foundation for development of self-government agreements and treaties,

- improving fisheries management skills and capacity of Aboriginal groups.

With annual funding of about $35 million, the AFS is the principal mechanism that assists DFO personnel in managing the fishery appropriately (i.e., with respect to the *Sparrow* and subsequent Supreme Court decisions). DFO and Aboriginal groups negotiate about 125 mutually acceptable, time-limited fisheries agreements per year. If agreement cannot be reached, DFO reviews the consultations with the group, and the Minister of Fisheries and Oceans issues a communal fishing licence to the group for their FSC purposes. The fisheries agreements negotiated under the AFS could contain cooperative projects for improving the general management of fisheries, such as stock assessment, fish enhancement, and habitat management. The

agreements also could contain provisions related to communal licences under the Allocation Transfer Program (ATP).

An integral component of the AFS, the ATP facilitates voluntary retirement of commercial fishing licences. Providing the existing fishing effort is not increased, licences are issued to eligible Aboriginal groups. About 900 licences have been issued through the ATP (between 1994 and 2005). The ATP also helps Aboriginal people find other economic development opportunities.

The Aboriginal Aquatic Resources and Oceans Management (AAROM) program funds Aboriginal groups to build the capacity they require to coordinate fishery planning and program initiatives. AAROM focuses on developing affiliations between Aboriginal peoples to work together at a broad watershed or ecosystem level—where there are common interests and where decisions and solutions can be based on the integrated knowledge of several Aboriginal communities. AAROM bodies are striving for accountability to the communities they serve, while working to advance collaborative relationships between member communities, DFO, and other interests in aquatic resource and ocean management.

As part of the ongoing reforms in the Pacific fisheries, DFO is looking for opportunities to increase Aboriginal participation in new economic fisheries. Treaty stipulations are likely to provide for economic benefits, but new planning approaches and fishing techniques will be required to ensure an economically viable fishery. In recent years some "demonstration fisheries" have been initiated to explore facets of future fisheries. Similar projects were anticipated in 2007. In the lower Fraser River, DFO is working with First Nations and others with an interest in the salmon fishery to develop better collaboration for fishery planning.

The first "modern" treaty in British Columbia, the Nisga'a Final Agreement applies to the management of salmon originating in the Nass area. Taking effect on May 11, 2000, the agreement provides the Nisga'a Nation with the right to harvest Chinook, chum, coho, sockeye, and pink salmon originating in the Nass area. Under the terms of the agreement, representatives of the Nisga'a Lisims Government participate with representatives of the federal government on a Joint Fisheries Management Committee (JFMC). The purpose of the JFMC is to facilitate cooperative planning and conduct of Nisga'a fisheries and enhancement initiatives in the Nass area. The JFMC also provides advice about conservation requirements (such as escapement goals) and the management of fish and aquatic plants. The JFMC plays a key role in planning and implementing such initiatives as the wild Pacific salmon conservation policy in the local Nass area, and will be an important contributor in development of long-term strategic plans for wild salmon.

SOURCES: Aboriginal Fisheries Strategy, Fisheries and Oceans Canada, 2005, http://www.dfo-mpo.gc.ca/communic/fish_man/afs_e.htm; Pacific Region Integrated Fisheries Management Plan, Salmon, Southern B.C., June 1, 2007 to May 31, 2008, Fisheries and Oceans Canada, 2007, http://www-ops2. pac.dfo-mpo.gc.ca/xnet/content/MPLANS/plans07/salmon/southcoast/SCSalmon07IFMPcomplete.pdf; The Nisga'a Final Agreement, Indian and Northern Affairs Canada, 2004, http://www.ainc-inac.gc.ca/pr/agr/nsga/nisdex12_e.pdf

benefits for people today and for future generations. Both conservation (of genetic diversity, species, and ecosystems so that natural production processes are continued) and

sustainable use (where the resources are used in a way and at a rate that does not lead to their long-term decline) are part of this policy. DFO considers salmon to be "wild" if they have spent their entire life cycle in the wild and have originated from parents that also were produced by natural spawning and continuously lived in the wild. Salmon that originate directly from hatcheries and managed spawning channels are considered to be "enhanced," not wild, salmon. However, salmon that originate from habitat restoration or lake enrichment activities, because their reproduction has not been altered, are labelled "wild." The requirement that a wild salmon must complete more than one full generation in the wild safeguards against potential adverse effects resulting from artificial culture.

Figure 8–7 provides an overview of the wild Pacific salmon policy. The overall goal of the policy is to "restore and maintain healthy and diverse salmon populations and their habitats for the benefit and enjoyment of the people of Canada in perpetuity" (Fisheries and Oceans Canada, 2005a, p. 15). Of particular note are the four guiding principles that form the foundation of decisions and activities regarding conservation of wild Pacific salmon stocks:

- conservation of wild Pacific salmon and their habitats is the highest priority
- resource management processes and decisions will honour Canada's obligations to First Nations
- resource management decisions (about sustainable use) will consider biological, social, and economic consequences, reflect best science including Aboriginal Traditional Knowledge (ATK), and maintain the potential for future generations to meet their needs and aspirations
- resource management decisions will be based on meaningful public input and be made in an open, transparent, and inclusive manner (Fisheries and Oceans Canada, 2005a, pp. 8, 9).

In order to attain the policy goal for wild salmon stocks, DFO identified three objectives that must be accomplished, namely:

- safeguard the genetic diversity of wild Pacific salmon
- maintain habitat and ecosystem integrity
- manage fisheries for sustainable benefits.

Significant scientific and policy challenges arise in connection with these objectives. For instance, safeguarding genetic diversity means that geographic and genetic diversity, and habitats, must be protected, but how do managers know how much diversity is necessary to ensure the health of wild salmon? Salmon have a complex hierarchical

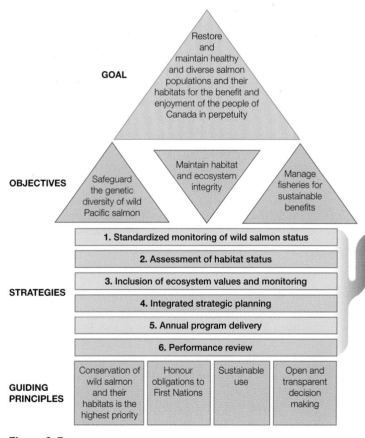

Figure 8–7a

Overview of the wild Pacific salmon policy

1. Standardized monitoring of wild salmon status
- Identify conservation units (CUs)
- Develop criteria to assess CUs and identify benchmarks to represent biological status
- Monitor and assess status of CUs

2. Assessment of habitat status
- Document habitat characteristics within CUs
- Select indicators and develop benchmarks for habitat assessment
- Monitor and assess habitat status
- Establish linkages to develop an integrated data system for watershed management

3. Inclusion of ecosystem values and monitoring
- Identify indicators to monitor status of freshwater ecosystems
- Integrate climate and ocean information into annual salmon management processes

4. Integrated strategic planning
- Implement an interim process for management of priority CUs
- Design and implement a fully integrated strategic planning process for salmon conservation

5. Annual program delivery
- Assess the status of CUs and populations
- Plan and conduct annual fisheries
- Plan and implement annual habitat management activities
- Plan and implement annual enhancement activities

6. Performance review
- Conduct post-season review of annual workplans
- Conduct regular reviews of the success of the WSP

Figure 8–7b

Strategies and action steps in the wild Pacific salmon conservation policy

SOURCE: *Canada's Policy for Conservation of Wild Pacific Salmon.* Fisheries and Oceans Canada. (2005). Vancouver: Fisheries and Oceans Canada, pp. 8 and 16. Reproduced with the permission of Her Majesty the Queen in Right of Canada, 2008.

structure that extends from groups of salmon at individual spawning sites right up to the taxonomic species. Because the genetic diversity of a species includes every individual fish, preserving maximum genetic diversity would mean that humans could not harvest salmon and any activities that might harm salmon habitat would be prohibited. Or, if managers tried to maintain a taxonomic species such as coho salmon, they would have to ignore the within-species structure of the population. Making that choice would reduce biodiversity and also would contravene the intent of the United Nations Convention on Biological Diversity and SARA.

With support from the provincial and territorial governments, Canada was the first industrialized nation to ratify the United Nations Convention on Biological Diversity (CBD), a document that had been signed by more than 150 countries at the 1992 Earth Summit in Rio de Janeiro. The convention's three main goals are conservation of biodiversity, sustainable use of the components of biodiversity, and fair and equitable sharing of the benefits that arise from commercial and other uses of genetic resources. The objective of the CBD is to achieve, by 2010, a significant reduction in the current rate of loss of biodiversity at the global, national, and regional levels. The convention advocates gene, species, and ecosystem conservation, but provides no guidance on which one should receive priority. Implementation of the CBD in Canada is guided by the 1996 Canadian Biodiversity Strategy.

To solve any contravention problem, DFO uses "conservation units" (CUs) that consist of a group of wild salmon that is sufficiently separated from other groups that, if it were extirpated, would be very unlikely to recolonize naturally within an acceptable timeframe (such as a human lifetime, or a specified number of salmon generations). Responsible management of CUs requires managers to ensure that the salmon remain and reproduce within the area, and that there is good connectivity for the fish among all their habitat (freshwater, coastal, and marine) areas. Ideally, since all local *demes* (spawning sites) and streams are valuable, protecting entire CUs with their networks of spawning groups would be the most effective way to protect individual salmon spawning groups and the interests of local communities. Given natural variations in salmon productivity, however, not all populations of salmon within a CU can be maintained at equal levels of productivity or have equal chance of loss. In practice, use of CUs to protect diversity requires protection of salmon populations and demes, but not necessarily all of them all of the time. DFO anticipates that there will be occasions when wild salmon populations will be lost, particularly when catastrophic events (including floods, droughts, disease, and climate change) cause habitat loss or destruction of spawning demes. DFO also recognized that we do not know enough about these fish, including how salmon are adapted to

their local streams, to take anything other than a precautionary and longer-term approach to conservation and management of wild salmon stocks (Fisheries and Oceans Canada, 2005a).

Efforts to maintain habitat and ecosystem integrity are challenged by human requirements and competition for accessible land, fresh water, and estuarine, coastal, and ocean spaces. Human activities affect water quality in freshwater and marine areas; human developments may affect wild salmon in estuaries during critical rearing and migration periods; and commercial fishing, shipping, and waste disposal may affect the marine habitat of salmon. To manage and protect aquatic systems, DFO must undertake integrated planning and work cooperatively and collaboratively with other federal and provincial agencies, Aboriginal governments, stewardship groups, industry, communities, and other stakeholders. Various strategies and action steps, identified in Figure 8–7 a and b, help facilitate implementation of the wild salmon policy: strategies 1 through 3 provide planning and decision-making information about wild salmon populations, their habitats, and ecosystems; strategy 4 integrates biological, social, and economic information to produce long-term strategic plans for salmon and habitat management; strategy 5 translates strategic plans into annual operational plans; and strategy 6 commits DFO to ongoing review of the success of the wild salmon policy.

Each of these strategies and action steps entails significant work to reduce the levels of uncertainty within which DFO operates. For instance, with regard to strategy 3 (including ecosystem values and monitoring), the lack of research that links salmon and their freshwater ecosystems with the effects of changes in climate and marine conditions on their survival and productivity means it is difficult to quantify ecosystem objectives. Similarly, while it is known that the ocean's capacity for salmon production can be limited, is highly variable over time, and greatly affects the abundance and condition of adult salmon, understanding the variability in salmon survival rates is challenging. From the time salmon enter the sea until they return as adults to coastal waters, their survival rates may vary by more than one hundredfold (and in some cases by a thousandfold). Add this sort of uncertainty to that associated with potential long-term climate change effects on marine and freshwater ecosystems, and it is clear that monitoring such variations and deriving appropriate management responses pose important challenges to current and future conservation efforts. DFO acknowledges that its ability to consider ecosystem values in salmon management currently is limited (Fisheries and Oceans Canada, 2005a). While the wild Pacific salmon conservation policy has limited ability to protect salmon from climate change, protection of genetic diversity and integrity of habitats is anticipated to allow the salmon time to adapt to future changes. If salmon productivity declines due to climate change, humans, too, might anticipate the need to adapt by reducing their allowable catches, or by taking other appropriate adaptive measures.

Attaining sustainable fisheries is a significant challenge, given the complexities of ocean ecosystems and human systems (governments and communities) that are involved. Nevertheless, it is possible to identify a number of principles that help guide our efforts to achieve sustainable fisheries:

1. Manage the entire marine ecosystem rather than individual stocks.
2. Adopt a precautionary approach to fisheries management.
3. Ensure that all relevant stakeholders have a meaningful say in fisheries management.
4. Decrease fishing fleet capacity and plan for stock fluctuations.
5. Protect ecological and species diversity.
6. Protect critical ocean habitat.
7. Create marine reserves to protect representative marine habitats.
8. Manage for and minimize by-catch and discards in commercial fisheries.
9. Ensure that aquaculture operates under sustainable standards.
10. Invest in monitoring, enforcement, and data acquisition (David Suzuki Foundation, 2004).

Photo 8–9
Fish hatcheries are one of several artificial means of increasing spawning production.

AQUACULTURE

Aquaculture is the farming of aquatic organisms, such as fish, shellfish, and plants, in controlled environments. Commercial aquaculture began in Canada in the 1950s, focused on trout in Ontario and British Columbia, and oysters in British Columbia, New Brunswick, and Prince Edward Island. It was not until the 1980s that the industry expanded to every province and the Yukon and the species base expanded to include Atlantic and Pacific salmon, rainbow and steelhead trout, mussels, clams, scallops, char, and marine plants. In 2005, 14 000 people were employed directly and indirectly in the aquaculture industry; over 90 percent of these jobs were in rural and coastal areas where the need for employment opportunities is great (Canadian Aquaculture Industry Alliance, 2005).

British Columbia and New Brunswick dominate the aquaculture industry; in both provinces, Atlantic salmon is the leading agri-export. In 2005, salmon (98 441 tonnes) and trout (4723 tonnes) were the major finfish species produced in Canada. Total value of finfish production was over $518 million, with salmon accounting for over $441 million. The value of shellfish production in 2005 was $64.8 million, and mussels (20 590 tonnes) accounted for $30.9 million of that total (Statistics Canada, 2005).

Aquaculture has grown significantly in Canada (and globally), partly in response to declines in wild fish stocks. With the collapse of local commercial fisheries, many people consider aquaculture to be a legitimate alternative that helps meet the demand for fish (for food) and reduces the economic hardship (including the need to relocate) on those who relied on wild stocks. Although socioeconomic benefits from expansion of the aquaculture industry have been important, particularly in coastal regions, concerns have been expressed about possible environmental effects of aquaculture operations on coastal ecosystems. The federal government's Standing Committee on Fisheries and Oceans (Wappel, 2003) heard evidence regarding major environmental effects of netcage salmon aquaculture, including

- risk of colonization of British Columbia rivers by escaped Atlantic salmon;
- genetic interaction of escaped domestic and wild salmon stocks (mainly an east coast concern);
- transmission of diseases from farmed salmon to wild stocks;
- effects of organic wastes from netcages;
- effects of the use of drugs, pesticides, and other chemicals by the aquaculture industry;
- question of the environmental sustainability of the aquaculture industry.

Although the aquaculture industry has addressed some of these issues, other concerns remain as challenges, in part because of the lack of information and research. For instance, in British Columbia, where the Atlantic salmon

Photo 8–10

British Columbia's salmon farms commonly use netpens to keep fish in captivity.

is a potentially invasive species, concerns were raised since the 1980s about escaped Atlantic salmon and their colonization of wild salmon streams. Environmentalists were concerned that Atlantic salmon might establish feral populations, which would then compete for food and habitat with native salmon species. Over the 12 years (1991–2002) that the Atlantic Salmon Watch Program (ASWP) kept statistics, 452 049 Atlantic salmon were reported as having escaped into British Columbia waters (Fisheries and Oceans Canada, Pacific Region, 2007b). This was likely a conservative estimate, as small escapes often were disregarded. DFO had maintained that Atlantic salmon could not survive in the wild and, even if they did, could not spawn successfully. However, Atlantic salmon are now found in fresh and salt waters in British Columbia and Alaska; in 1998, Atlantic salmon were found to be breeding in the wild in the Tsitika River (on northeastern Vancouver Island), and by 2002, they had spawned or were present in six additional rivers. In a similar fashion, rainbow trout, likely escapees from aquaculture operations in Cape Breton and New Brunswick, are breeding in streams in Newfoundland's Gros Morne National Park. DFO is concerned these non-native rainbows will out-compete wild Atlantic salmon for food resources (Canadian Broadcasting Corporation, 2003).

A cooperative research program operated by DFO and funded by the British Columbia Ministry of Agriculture and Lands, the ASWP studies the abundance, distribution, and biology of Atlantic salmon in British Columbia and adjacent waters in Alaska and Washington State. Commercial and sport catches (and other reported observations) are monitored by fishers, fish processors, government field staff, and hatchery workers in an effort to provide accurate and unbiased accounting of Atlantic salmon in British Columbia. Data from the ASWP have been published in the Manuscript Report Series of Fisheries and Oceans Canada.

A subprogram of the ASWP, the First Nations Atlantic Salmon Watch Program (FNASWP) commenced in 2001

and was funded by the British Columbia government's Interim Measures Fund (which specifically aids First Nations). Fifty members of First Nations were trained in fish identification, stream survey, and snorkelling techniques (snorkel surveys are the preferred survey technique for Atlantic salmon), as well as safety and first aid. From September to December 2001, 117 snorkel surveys were conducted on 55 different river systems; over 389 000 salmonids were counted (Fisheries and Oceans Canada, Pacific Region, 2007a, 2007c).

A major concern on the east coast of Canada is the potential for genetic interaction between wild and farmed salmon. For reasons that are not known fully, the 30-year decline in wild Atlantic salmon numbers coincided with the growth in salmon farming. Today, farmed Atlantic salmon vastly outnumber wild fish, and escapees dominate yearly spawning runs in salmon rivers in areas such as the Bay of Fundy, where 90 percent of the production facilities are located. Given that wild Atlantic salmon exhibit genetic distinctions based on the river systems from which they originate and to which they return to spawn, and given that farmed salmon have been selectively bred for genetic uniformity, scientists anticipate that interbreeding of the farmed and wild Atlantic stocks will reduce the fitness for survival of the wild stock. While more research about genetic interactions between farmed and wild fish is needed, so are improved efforts to reduce escapes and to recover escapees (Wappel, 2003).

Other criticisms of aquaculture relate to problems associated with fish health. Farmed salmon are stocked at high densities in netcages; stress associated with crowding may predispose farmed fish to disease, and the close physical proximity of fish facilitates transmission of pathogens. When farmed fish escape, or when wild fish swim close to the netpens, wild stocks may be at increased risk of disease and parasite transfers. The feces, vaccines, fungicides, and therapeutants that pollute the surrounding waters and sea floor underneath the netpens also may affect wild fish. In comparing fish farm wastes to municipal sewage, the Friends of Clayoquot Sound estimated that with production of 42 300 tonnes of salmon in 1998, British Columbia salmon farms generated raw sewage equivalent to a city of about one-half million inhabitants (Wappel, 2003). While municipal and salmon farm wastes are not the same, both may result in nutrient-loading issues; aquaculture critics note that the appearance of harmful algal blooms (see Box 8–7) in the Broughton Archipelago in British Columbia coincided with the arrival of the salmon farming industry. Improvements in feed formulations (see Box 8–8, p. 330) and feeding technology (such as use of computerized pneumatic feed machines, underwater video cameras, and feed detection instruments such as Doppler radar) have reduced environmental effects. For instance, despite a 300 percent increase in production, British Columbia salmon farmers release about one-third the amount of organic waste to the environment as 10 to 15 years ago (Wappel, 2003).

Parasites such as sea lice also pose threats to wild salmon (see Box 8–9, p. 331).

Among the solutions proposed to combat the serious environmental concerns raised by open netcage fish farming is the use of closed tank technologies. Floating closed tank systems eliminate escapes from the rearing facility; capture and treat the solid waste, eliminating its deposition to the marine environment; and eliminate marine mammal kills due to interactions with farmed fish and nets. Saltwater salmon have been grown successfully in closed tanks in trial projects in British Columbia and Norway and are produced commercially in Iceland.

As the lead federal agency for aquaculture, DFO has developed a variety of action plans to achieve both "well-informed and scientifically-based decisions" that will support sustainable development of the aquaculture sector (Fisheries and Oceans Canada, 2006b). Under the $75 million Program for Sustainable Aquaculture (PSA) initiated in 2000, DFO has established nine principles aimed at improving DFO's ability to support the industry's competitiveness in global markets and to increase public confidence in the sustainability of aquaculture development (Fisheries and Oceans Canada, 2006a). Among other things, the aquaculture policy framework of the PSA makes DFO both a regulator and an enabler of aquaculture development. In other words, DFO is charged with the simultaneous responsibilities of promoting the aquaculture industry and regulating it. How is the public interest in fisheries resources preserved if the government agency charged with their protection is also required to promote their development? DFO is aware that members of the public remain concerned about the effects of aquaculture

BOX 8–7
HARMFUL ALGAL BLOOMS AND SHELLFISH HARVESTING

Approximately 300 of the 4000 known species of microscopic phytoplankton (microalgae) undergo periodic explosions of growth in the ocean; dense growths of these microalgae are termed "blooms" and they can turn the water surface red, brown, yellow, green, or white (see Photo 8–11). About 40 species release powerful toxins that can move through the food web to affect sea birds, marine mammals, aquaculture operations, and humans—sometimes fatally. Human ailments— stomach cramps, nausea, memory loss, amnesia, paralysis, and even death—are contracted through breathing airborne toxins, making skin contact, or eating contaminated shellfish. Not all harmful algal blooms (HABs) are toxic; for example, some barbed species inflict physical damage by lodging in gill tissues and killing fish (including farmed fish, in which case the financial damage is considerable). Other species create unhealthy environmental conditions, such as decreased oxygen or reduced sunlight penetration.

In recent years, these HABs, often called "red tides," have been occurring more frequently over larger areas, are lasting longer, and are appearing in areas where they were unknown previously. Some scientists believe the increase in HABs reflects greater awareness and monitoring, but others have demonstrated the important contribution of human activities. Nutrient pollution from sewage outfalls, agriculture, mining, and direct discharges of raw sewage from moored or anchored boats create a nutrient-rich coastal environment in which certain phytoplankton may thrive. Chances of harvesting shellfish from polluted waters increase with proximity to highly urbanized or agricultural areas. Climate change also may be making some coastal environments more hospitable to harmful phytoplankton species. Many phytoplankton species are transported around the world in ships' ballast water and may be discharged in areas where they previously did not occur.

The shellfish-growing regions of Canada—British Columbia, Quebec, Nova Scotia, New Brunswick, Prince Edward Island, and Newfoundland—provide many seafood delicacies, including

Photo 8–11
British Columbia's coastal waters were in the world media spotlight after NASA posted an image collected by their MODIS satellite on June 25, 2006, showing an extensive, dramatically patterned, bright bloom off Vancouver Island. Samples collected from the Canadian Coast Guard ship *John P. Tully* confirm that this was due to a coccolithophore (nontoxic) species of phytoplankton. This was the largest such bloom ever observed in these waters.

(continued)

BOX 8-7
(CONTINUED)

oysters, clams, cockles, mussels, and quahogs. However, these shellfish (bivalve molluscs) are subject to the following natural biotoxins:

- Paralytic shellfish poison (PSP). PSP inhibits the passage of sodium ions, causing numbness, paralysis, respiratory failure, and death.

- Domoic acid, or amnesic shellfish poison (ASP). ASP attacks the human central nervous system, causing vomiting, abdominal cramps, diarrhea, and short-term memory loss.

Since bivalve mussels feed by filtering water above the shellfish bed, they bioaccumulate chemical or bacteriological pollutants from the surrounding water. For instance, a single mussel may filter up to 300 times its weight in one hour. Clearly, high water quality standards are demanded in areas where shellfish grow and harvesting takes place.

Environment Canada, DFO, and the Canadian Food Inspection Agency (CFIA) help protect consumer health through the Canadian Shellfish Sanitation Program (CSSP). Environment Canada undertakes sanitary and water quality surveys (based on fecal coliform measures) to help minimize potential health risks for people who harvest and eat molluscan shellfish. DFO is responsible for approving and opening or closing shellfish-growing areas, and for enforcing closure regulations. CFIA

manages the marine biotoxin monitoring program. Testing frequency is higher where PSP and ASP toxins are known to occur regularly.

Photo 8–12

This type of sign is found throughout Canada where DFO has determined that a closure is necessary due to natural toxins such as PSP.

SOURCES: *Toxic and Harmful Algal Blooms,* Bigelow Laboratory, n.d., http://www.bigelow.org/hab/impact.html; Shellfish and water quality. *Shellfish and Water Quality,* Environment Canada, Atlantic Region, 2005, http://atlenv.ns.ec.gc.ca/epb/factsheets/sfish_wq.html; *Harmful Algal Blooms and Toxins,* Seaweb, 2007, http://www.seaweb.org/resources/briefings/algae.php

BOX 8-8
FEEDING FARMED FISH

Globally, the majority of aquaculture is undertaken with noncarnivorous species such as shellfish, carp, tilapia, and milkfish. The long history of small scale, low intensity, and low technology employed in artisanal aquaculture suggests these operations are sustainable. In contrast, the sustainability of salmon farming has been questioned because salmon are carnivorous and consume more protein than they produce. High-quality fish meal is the major source of protein in marine fish feeds, and salmon require feed with a high percentage of fish meal (45 percent) and fish oil (25 percent) in order to replicate their diet in the wild. Approximately 3 kilograms of wild fish are required to produce 1 kilogram of farmed salmon. Fisheries and Oceans Canada notes that it takes 10 to 15 kilograms of wild fish to produce the same amount of wild salmon.

Where do the fish come from that make up the fish meal fed to salmon? The Canadian aquaculture industry depends heavily on South American imports of forage fish such as anchovies, sardines, herring, jack mackerel, capelin, and menhaden for

conversion to fish meal and fish oil. Some of these small pelagic species are suitable for human consumption; they also play an important role in the food chain, as they are the main food source for larger predators such as cod, tuna, whales, and sea birds. When these fish are harvested for fish meal, they are not available for consumption by these top-level predators (see Figure 8–4b on page 315). The FAO has estimated that currently one-third of the global catch of these species is turned into animal feed (31 percent is used by aquaculture), but within 10 years the global aquaculture could use two-thirds of the world's fish meal.

Aquaculture often claims that it has a small ecological footprint, largely limited to the farms themselves. But if the marine area required to sustain a fish farm is 40 000 to 50 000 times the area of the fish farm itself, then a 1-hectare fish farm is sustained by an ocean surface area of 50 000 hectares. In 2002, British Columbia's aquaculture industry consumed the biological productivity of approximately 7.8 million hectares of ocean—hardly a small footprint!

BOX 8-8
(CONTINUED)

Efforts are underway to investigate plant-based feeds as substitutes for fish meal, but there have been challenges with lower digestibility, slower fish growth, altered fish flavours, and increased levels of organic waste. Partial replacement of fish oils with canola and linseed oils seems to be successful in the culture of Atlantic salmon without affecting their growth.

Encouraging farming and consumption of noncarnivorous fish (i.e., eating lower on the food chain) would help reduce aquaculture's requirements for marine protein. Diversifying farmed species away from Atlantic salmon monoculture also would help reduce the industry's susceptibility to economic and biological risks.

SOURCES: *Aquaculture: Frequently Asked Questions, Fisheries and Oceans Canada, 2007,* http://www.dfo-mpo.gc.ca/aquaculture/faq_e.htm; *The Federal Role in Aquaculture in Canada: Report of the Standing Committee on Fisheries and Oceans,* T. Wappel, March 25, 2003, 37th Parliament, 2nd Session, No. 24, Ottawa: Queen's Printer, hhttp://cmte.parl.gc.ca/Content/HOC/committee/372/fopo/reports/rp1032312/foporp03/06-toc-e.htm;

BOX 8-9
WILD PINK SALMON, SEA LICE, AND AQUACULTURE IN BRITISH COLUMBIA

Photo 8–13
Sea lice find ideal breeding conditions on high-density fish farms.

In November 2002, the Pacific Fisheries Resource Conservation Council[1] (PFRCC) issued a warning to Canadian and British Columbia fisheries ministers that the number of spawning pink salmon in the Broughton Archipelago had decreased dramatically. Located near Campbell River, a well-known salmon sport fishing centre on Vancouver Island, the Broughton Archipelago is a group of islands that contains a high concentration of fish farms. The decline in numbers of spawning fish in 2002 (from over 3.6 million to 147 000) raised PFRCC's concerns about the potential impact of salmon aquaculture and sea lice on wild stocks. This concern led the PFRCC to recommend that

Canada and British Columbia act to maximize the passage of fish through the archipelago during April 2003.

The PFRCC indicated that while there was scientific uncertainty regarding the cause of the decline, European research had shown that sea lice infestations can be associated with salmon farming. Since the decline in spawning salmon was confined to the Broughton Archipelago, and since the pink juveniles in this area were infested with sea lice (a condition virtually unknown among juvenile pink salmon in the natural environment elsewhere), the conclusion was that the sea lice (and fish farming) were associated with the observed decline.

In advocating the precautionary approach in this situation, the chair of the PFRCC noted that in the absence of any evidence of some cause other than the sea lice, action was warranted. Among the options suggested were fallowing (closing) of all salmon farms in the Broughton Archipelago and implementation of rigorous sea lice control measures on the salmon farms to protect wild fish. The fallowing option would involve temporarily removing all salmon from the sea pens six weeks prior to when pink salmon entered the marine environment (as early as mid-April). Cooperative development of a Broughton Archipelago sea lice management plan could involve a variety of potential actions, including application of chemotherapeutants by all Broughton fish farms to kill (not just shed) the sea lice.

The PFRCC believed that fallowing was the lower-risk option and had the greatest likelihood of improving conditions for passage of juvenile pink salmon to the sea. In addition to noting that more research into the ecology and life history of sea lice was required, the PFRCC advised that monitoring of the environment, sea lice levels, and juvenile pink salmon was required immediately.

Strongly opposed to fish farming, the Union of British Columbia Indian Chiefs demanded (in a January 2003 letter

[1] Established in 1988, the role of the Pacific Fisheries Resource Conservation Council is to provide independent, strategic advice and relevant information to the fisheries ministers of both Canada and British Columbia, and to inform the Canadian public about the status and long-term sustainable use of wild salmon stocks and their freshwater and ocean habitats.

(continued)

BOX 8-9
(CONTINUED)

to the regional director general of DFO) that the federal government curb harmful activities of fish farms in the Broughton Archipelago. They asked DFO to fallow the fish farms from the end of February through mid-June to allow the wild juvenile fish to pass safely out to sea without the risk of infection from sea lice. DFO's response was to indicate that they were working on an action plan to address potential risks to wild pink salmon stocks. This action plan was to include freshwater and marine monitoring programs, an approach to salmon farm management, a long-term research plan, and a public consultation/dialogue process.

DFO is both enabler and regulator of the aquaculture industry; as such, DFO indicated it is "committed to the protection of wild salmon resources in British Columbia" (Fisheries and Oceans Canada, 2003). But, as the B.C. chiefs asked, did DFO fail to enforce the Fisheries Act and thus allow salmon farming to infect wild salmon stocks? Did DFO fail to take appropriate steps to minimize the possibility of a sea lice outbreak, given similar experiences in Norway, Ireland, and Scotland? Did DFO's approval of fish farm tenures on salmon migration routes reflect the lack of a scientific basis for siting criteria? Did DFO have a formal plan to manage the risks of salmon farming? These and other questions have been raised with respect to the sea lice outbreak in the Broughton Archipelago, and challenge the ability of a single agency (DFO) to promote both industry development and resource protection.

Since then, a number of sea lice research projects have been undertaken by the British Columbia Aquaculture Research and Development Committee, by DFO, and by university scientists. Results from some of this research have influenced management decisions in the Broughton Archipelago, including the use of fallowing along a prescribed "migration corridor" for juvenile salmon in 2003, and provincial sea lice management plans commencing in 2003. While DFO does not support the use of specific migration corridors to protect juvenile salmon, DFO notes that use of emamectin benzoate to control sea lice seems to be effective. However, the ecological toxicity of this product on the environment near a treated farm is not known. It is clear that additional, extensive research is required to provide the scientific basis for sustainable management of salmon aquaculture.

SOURCES: *Status Report on Sea Lice Monitoring in the Broughton Archipelago,* British Columbia Ministry of Agriculture, Food and Fisheries, 2003, http://www.agf.gov.bc.ca/fisheries/health/sealice_monitoring.htm; "Fish Farm Flap," *Disclosure,* Canadian Broadcasting Corporation, February 4, 2003, http://www.cbc.ca/disclosure/archives/030204_salmon/report.html; *News Release: A Collaborative Action Plan for Sea Lice to Be Implemented by Fisheries and Oceans in British Columbia,* Fisheries and Oceans Canada, 2003, http://www.dfo-mpo.gc.ca/media/newsrel/2003/hq-ac02_e.htm; *State-of-Knowledge Presentation for the Special Committee on Sustainable Aquaculture of the British Columbia Legislature,* Fisheries and Oceans Canada, 2006; *Summary of the Sea Lice Outbreak in the Broughton Archipelago,* Georgia Strait Alliance, 2001, http://www.georgiastrait.org/Articles2001/sealice2.php; *Communiqué: Pink Salmon in Broughton Archipelago in Crisis: Report,* Pacific Fisheries Resource Conservation Council, 2002, http://www.fish.bc.ca/html/fish3011.htm; *Impact of Fish Farms on the Salmon Runs of the Broughton Archipelago,* Union of British Columbia Indian Chiefs (letter), 2003.

on coastal environments and, in response, is developing a range of communications products to provide information intended to build "the public's confidence that aquaculture is developing in a sustainable manner" (Fisheries and Oceans Canada, 2006c).

DFO's State of Knowledge research review program is intended to improve knowledge of aquaculture's environmental effects in both marine and freshwater ecosystems. Three main areas of scientific knowledge are addressed in the 12 planned research reviews: the effects of wastes such as nutrient and organic matter on areas under netpens; the impacts of chemicals used by the aquaculture industry, including drugs, pesticides, and antifoulants; and the consequences of interactions between farmed fish and wild species, particularly regarding disease transfer and genetic and ecological interactions (Fisheries and Oceans Canada et al., 2006). In late 2006, after nine State of Knowledge reports had been published, DFO scientists presented some of their findings to the Special Committee on Sustainable Aquaculture of the British Columbia Legislature, which had been appointed earlier that year to examine and make recommendations regarding sustainable aquaculture in the province. It is clear that gaps remain in our knowledge of the ecological effects of salmon farms on wild salmon, and challenging research questions remain to be answered. More research and analysis are required to develop the sound science on which improved management actions may be taken.

POLLUTION

Coastlines are the primary habitat of the human species, probably because coastal ecosystems possess an extraordinary endowment of natural resources from which everyone can benefit (Olsen, 1996). Unfortunately, the litany of human effects on the marine environment is lengthy. Bacterial/viral contamination, oxygen depletion, toxicity, bioaccumulation, habitat loss or degradation, depletion of biota, and degradation of aesthetic values are among the notable effects of human-induced change in the coastal zone.

Contamination of Canada's oceans and coastlines is principally the result of human activities, including discharges of municipal sewage and wastewater; industrial effluents such as discharges from pulp and paper mills and other industrial sources; urban and agricultural runoff; solid waste and litter such as plastics, logs, and nets; ocean dumping; coastal developments such as housing, harbours, causeways, marinas, and aquaculture farms; and marine shipping. About 80 percent of the pollution load in the oceans originates from land-based activities; these contaminants affect the most productive areas of the marine environment, including estuaries and nearshore coastal waters (Environment Canada, 2004b). Because it is so difficult to clean up contaminants once they have been released to the environment, a precautionary approach with a focus on pollution prevention is appropriate and important to sustainability of the ocean environment.

In 1995, along with over 100 other nations, Canada adopted the Global Programme of Action for the Protection of the Marine Environment from Land-Based Activities, a program led by the United Nations Environment Programme (UNEP). As the first country to develop a national program in response to UNEP's initiative, Canada's National Programme of Action (NPA, published in 2000) is a partnership among federal, territorial, and provincial governments that focuses on coordinating actions to prevent marine pollution from land-based activities, and to protect habitat in coastal areas. The NPA also is responsive to Canadians' expectations of their governments to ensure clean oceans.

The NPA addresses two broad categories of marine pollution problems and protection issues at both national and regional levels:

1. *Contaminants*—Sewage, persistent organic pollutants (POPs), radionuclides, heavy metals, oils and hydrocarbons, nutrients, contaminated sediments, and litter.

2. *Physical alteration and destruction of habitat*—Shoreline construction/alteration, intertidal and subtidal alteration, mineral and sediment extraction/alteration, wetland and salt marsh alteration, and biological alteration (Government of Canada, 2006a). See Table 8–1 on the next page for examples of the regional areas, activities, and issues that the NPA identified as part of its assessment of the state of Canada's coastal and marine environment. Table 8–1 also identifies one example of NPA projects undertaken within each region between 2001 and 2006.

A committee composed of representatives from the federal government and the governments of British Columbia, Nunavut, Northwest Territories, Yukon, New Brunswick, Prince Edward Island, Nova Scotia, and Newfoundland and Labrador (Quebec is an observer) oversees the implementation of the program. Between 2000 and 2006, NPA activities focused on promoting collaboration, mobilizing communities, raising awareness, and coordinating government (Government of Canada, 2006a). In addition to the regional projects identified in Table 8–1, the NPA has undertaken several other projects toward those ends, including

- establishment of the NPA Information Clearing-House (www.npa-pan.ca) to provide access to information

to community groups, scientists, and governments, and to provide news and documents to the public;
- clarification of the definitions of "sewage" and "nutrients" to ensure that monitoring efforts link to federal legislation and science;
- publication of several reports, including the 2004 report, *Protecting Canada's Coastal and Marine Environment;*
- provision of funding and support for outreach and education efforts such as Oceans Day programming, community shoreline cleanups, biannual coastal zone conferences, and a nearshore marine monitoring workshop.

As the NPA committee tries to move forward from its past success in reaching the public, community groups, industry, NGOs, and ENGOs, as well as governments, with its messages and activities promoting marine environmental protection, it is difficult to know to what extent the federal government will support the NPA's regional and national activities in the future. The NPA committee is aware that governmental restructuring, changing priorities, and budgetary constraints are realities in the current political climate.

Environment Canada also was involved in coastal pollution prevention initiatives such as the Atlantic Coastal Action Program, St. Lawrence Action Plan Vision 2000, Great Lakes 2000, Northern River Basins Study/Northern Rivers Ecosystem Initiative, Fraser River Action Plan, Georgia Basin Ecosystem Initiative, and Northern Ecosystems Initiative. For the most part, these large,

Photo 8–14

The TD Great Canadian Shoreline Cleanup takes place annually in each province and territory, providing an opportunity for Canadians to develop and nurture a sense of stewardship toward our aquatic shorelines and habitats. Making these areas clean and healthy for people and wildlife to enjoy and raising awareness of the effects of litter and debris on these habitats are key goals. TD provides free supplies, instructions, and educational materials for groups that would like to clean up a local waterway during National Cleanup Week.

Region/Some Critical Areas	Activities, Issues	Examples of NPA's Regional Projects
Pacific		
• Georgia/ Puget Sound basin	• Rapid urban growth and associated development.	*Building First Nation Capacity to Undertake Marine Water Quality Monitoring*
	• Water quality and treatment in Vancouver.	• High fecal coliform bacterial counts have closed commercial and food/social/ceremonial shellfish harvests on Vancouver Island.
	• Nonpoint source pollution (onsite sewage systems and stormwater runoff).	• With the NPA team, the Kyuquot/Checleset and T'Sou-ke First Nations groups identified sources and patterns of fecal pollution, enhancing their capacity to identify problems in the shellfish industry.
	• Contaminated shellfish.	• Success of particular methods used in capacity building was documented.
Atlantic		
• Gulf of St. Lawrence	• Industrial drainage from Great Lakes area, the most urbanized and industrialized area of North America.	*Towards Best Management Practices for Land-Use Planning in Atlantic Canada*
• Bay of Fundy	• Contaminated dredged material.	• Because of limited capacity for watershed and coastal planning, the NPA Atlantic team developed fact sheets on saltwater marshes and coastal erosion.
	• Conservation and restoration of wetlands and associated uplands; waterfowl habitat.	• These information sheets describe issues and areas of concern and identify best management practices to help municipalities improve their decisions.
Arctic		
• Mackenzie River watershed	• Sparse population, fragile ecosystems.	*Technology Investigation for Enhancing Municipal Wastewater Treatment in Arctic Climates*
• Hudson Bay watershed	• Mining, hydroelectric, oil and gas exploration and development; ice platforms.	• Northern coastal communities rely on lagoon (primary treatment) systems that during thaw season may seep toward wetlands and other waterways.
	• Growing tourism industry.	• Two bio-remediation systems (aeration) were examined to determine if bio-remediation systems would work effectively.
	• Co-management approach and application of traditional ecological knowledge to resource regulation.	• If successful, this knowledge could be transferred to other communities; subsequent training in water sampling and operation and maintenance of such systems would enhance community members' capacity in coastal resources management.
	• Long-range transport of pollutants.	
Quebec		
• Saguenay Fjord	• Upper St. Lawrence basin has highly urbanized, industrialized, and agricultural regions.	*Inventory of Land-Based Sources of Pollution in Northern Quebec Watersheds*
• St. Lawrence River estuary	• Heavy industry (10 pulp and paper mills, three aluminum smelters, two ore pelletization facilities) on south shore of the estuary.	• Limited knowledge of the impacts of land-based activities on marine environments of Hudson and Ungava Bay areas existed, so to include the northern area, the NPA identified and evaluated land-based sources of pollution.
• North shore of the Gulf of St. Lawrence	• Long-range transport of pollutants.	• Subsequent monitoring of some specific sites was recommended.
	• Tracking of contaminants in marine environments.	• Priorities in this region need to be compared with those in the Arctic region of the NPA.
	• Limited data exist for northern Quebec's (Nunavik) coastal zone.	

SOURCES: "The Regions," Canada's National Programme of Action for the Protection of the Marine Environment from Land-Based Activities, n.d., http://www.npa-pan.ca/en/the_regions.cfm; *Implementing Canada's National Programme of Action for the Protection of the Marine Environment from Land-based Activities,* Government of Canada, 2006, Gatineau, QC: NPA Secretariat.

multiyear ecosystem initiatives were undertaken from the late 1980s through the late 1990s. These initiatives were successful; for instance, from 1988 to 1998, the St. Lawrence Action Plan reduced toxic effluent discharges from 50 industrial plants by 96 percent, protected 12 000 hectares of wildlife habitat, established the first federal–provincial marine park in the Saguenay, and saw beluga whale numbers in the St. Lawrence River increase from 500 to about 800. Similarly, results of the Fraser River Action Plan, completed in 1998, included a 90 percent reduction in toxic wood preservative releases and protection of almost 65 000 hectares of wild bird habitat (Environment Canada, 2007).

Some of Environment Canada's ecosystem initiatives have continued to benefit various communities and areas. Since 1991, individuals, communities, and governments associated with the Atlantic Coastal Action Program (ACAP) have undertaken over 400 collaborative projects ranging from restoring habitats, to upgrading sewage treatment facilities, to creating artificial wetlands (Environment Canada, 2007). For instance, during 2005–2006, the Northeast Avalon ACAP (Newfoundland and Labrador) undertook a monitoring project on a heavily polluted stream system in the outskirts of St. John's and generated public interest in future monitoring efforts to help prevent additional pollution events. Also in 2005–2006, ACAP staff and volunteers in St. Croix, New Brunswick, rejuvenated an important, 80-year-old community asset known as Camp Waweig so that stewardship learning opportunities about the natural environment could continue in the region. In both these cases, local NGOs were the most effective supporters of efforts to achieve sustainability in their communities (ACAP, 2007).

Environment Canada's efforts to empower individuals and communities, and to take a holistic approach toward protecting our coastal environments, were based on several key principles, including

- using an ecosystem approach (clearly recognizing the interrelationships between land, air, water, wildlife, and human activities),
- making decisions based on sound science (including both natural and social sciences in conjunction with local and traditional knowledge),
- working cooperatively with partners (federal, provincial, and territorial governments),
- building the capacity of citizens and communities to make better decisions and bring about change (individuals, communities, Aboriginal peoples, industry, and government working together to design and implement the initiatives),
- promoting a precautionary approach.

Other ENGO activities, such as Trout Unlimited Canada's Yellow Fish Road™ program, also were designed to educate the public about the hazards of using storm drains to indiscriminately dump unwanted chemicals directly into the nearest water course. In 1991, Trout Unlimited introduced the Yellow Fish Road Program in Calgary. Between 2005 and 2007, with the support of numerous municipal and other not-for-profit organizations in delivering the program, over 23,000 drains were marked and approximately 90,000 households were reached across Canada (see Photo 7–4, p. 271). Senior citizens, Girl Guides and Boy Scouts, school groups, and corporate green teams tried to remind people to dispose safely of toxic compounds such as used motor oil, antifreeze, paint, and solvents. Yellow fish-shaped door hangers (see Photo 8–15) were distributed to residences and businesses to explain the concept and to provide local contact information for disposal of unwanted chemicals.

Municipal Sewage

Municipal sewage, a point source of pollution, continues to be an issue in Canada. Although there has been progress in increasing the level of treatment and number of people serviced by wastewater treatment systems (see Chapter 7), concerns remain about environmental and human health effects of municipal sewage. Among the concerns are continuing eutrophication of lakes and rivers, contamination of domestic water supplies, shellfish harvesting closures due to fecal coliform contamination, heavy-metal contamination of sediments, risks associated with swimming in water contaminated with human fecal material, and aesthetic objections to the visible signs of sewage discharge.

In the Arctic, the extremely cold climate severely restricts the rate at which wastes break down in the environment. With local populations growing rapidly, it is not clear that traditional methods of sewage waste disposal will be sufficient to avoid contamination of coastal waters

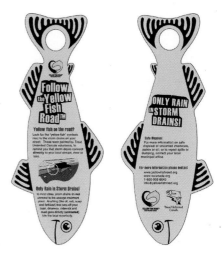

Photo 8–15

Fish-shaped door hangers remind residents not to pour household products down storm sewer drains because the chemicals in the products will flow through underground pipes into creeks and streams and potentially harm fish and other aquatic life.

in the long term. Research is required into alternative treatment methods that will be effective in cold climates. In Atlantic Canada, where many communities are located on or near marine waters, the proportion of the population served by waste treatment facilities is lower than in the rest of Canada. Prince Edward Island is the exception: almost all of its municipal waste undergoes treatment in order to protect the important coastal-oriented tourism industry and shellfish resources and to avoid groundwater contamination. In Nova Scotia, 250 years of dumping industrial effluents and sewage into Halifax Harbour has resulted in complaints about odours and floating debris as well as bacterial contamination of beaches and (former) shellfishing areas. Cleaning up the harbour is expected to cost over $300 million.

In the lower Fraser River basin, municipalities release about half of the wastewater (much of it untreated or primary-treated sewage) entering the river system. Anticipating that the population of Vancouver and its suburbs may reach 3 million during the next two decades, it should be possible to plan—in advance—to implement any necessary sewage treatment improvements and to protect the sustainability of ocean waters that receive municipal discharges. For over 30 years, the city of Victoria, British Columbia, has used a "natural treatment system" (deep ocean outfalls) to dispose of its municipal sewage. Conflicting viewpoints about the appropriateness of this disposal system versus a land-based system highlight the challenges of balancing science and politics in wastewater management (see Enviro-Focus 8).

ENVIRO-FOCUS 8

Science, Politics, and Public Health: Treating Victoria's Sewage

Victoria's attractive marine environment draws many residents and tourists to water activities: sailing, scuba diving, wind and kite surfing, and whale watching. For more than 30 years, British Columbia's capital city has discharged its sewage wastes into the Strait of Juan de Fuca via two deep ocean outfalls extending more than 1 kilometre from shore. The sewage (about 130 million litres per day in 2005–2006) passes through 6-millimetre screens before it enters the outfalls. At the end of the outfalls, the effluent moves through 200-metre-long diffusers located 60 metres below the ocean surface.

During most of the year, ocean currents (driven by large volumes of fresh water from rivers such as the Fraser that flow into the Georgia/Puget Sound basin) rapidly dilute and disperse the effluent plume below sea level. During slack tides in the winter months, the diluted (about 1000:1) effluent plume reaches the surface between 10 and 20 percent of the time; models suggest the plumes last, on average, for 92 and 69 minutes at the Macaulay and Clover Point outfalls, respectively. This situation provides the potential to transfer a variety of pathogens (viruses, bacteria, and parasites) from the sewage to humans who come into contact with marine water in the vicinity of the outfalls. Bacterial tests have

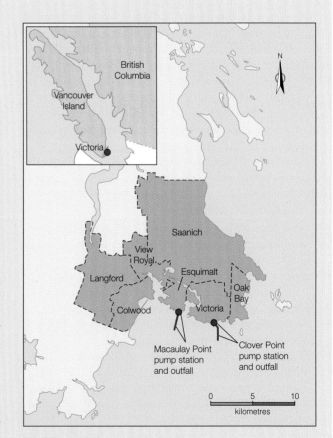

Box Figure 8–2
Location of Clover Point and Macaulay Point outfalls, Victoria, British Columbia

Photo 8–16
Activities such as kite surfing near the Macaulay Point outfall may expose recreationalists to increased risk of contact with pathogens in marine water.

detected the diluted plume, but there is a great deal of uncertainty about precise human health risks that occur from exposure to this water. Previously, the regional medical health officer had advised the Capital Regional District (CRD) that beach contamination was a public health risk because of the potential exposure to sewage-contaminated water coming from stormwater drain discharges, but the deep ocean discharges were not a risk to public health.

The CRD's monitoring program focuses on sea floor organisms and communities around the outfalls. Adjacent to the Macaulay Point outfall, pollution-tolerant invertebrates such as sea worms dominate the sediment-dwelling organisms. At Clover Point, mussel tissues show elevated levels of copper and lead, PCBs, and PBDEs, but the observed tissue concentrations are well below the levels known to cause adverse effects. The Scientific and Technical Review Panel members who were appointed in 2005 to evaluate aspects of the CRD's Liquid Waste Management Plan (LWMP) cautioned that there were gaps in the CRD's knowledge about the marine ecological community. For instance, the direct toxicity of the effluent and its effects on water column–dwelling organisms were unknown. While the CRD's environmental monitoring program to evaluate the effects of sewage in marine environments is among the most comprehensive programs in the world, the panel suggested that a higher frequency of monitoring and the addition of specific bacterial indicators would

help assess human health and environmental risks more precisely. Given the lack of sewage treatment, the panel recommended that several "traditional" (e.g., chlorinated pesticides) and new "compounds of concern" (e.g., pharmaceuticals, endocrine-disrupting compounds) should be added to the CRD's monitoring program.

Given Victoria's desirability as a city and its projected population growth, as well as the reputation of its marine recreational opportunities and its significant tourism industry, wastewater systems undoubtedly will face an increased sewage load, and the footprint of the wastewater discharges will increase proportionally with the increased volume of discharges. While Victoria uses source control efforts to reduce inputs of certain contaminants to the wastewater, the panel felt this approach would not be fully effective in the future. For instance, endocrine-disrupting compounds are difficult or impossible to control in the CRD's current collection system; if the effluent remains untreated, there likely would be estrogenic responses in exposed organisms (e.g., male fish would develop female characteristics such as egg development in the male sex organs). The panel recommended a combination of sewage treatment processes and oxidation techniques to reduce the risk of environmental impacts; they noted that sewage treatment produces sludges that also must be treated and managed.

The issue of whether to treat or not to treat Victoria's wastewater has been a longstanding one, and was the subject of a public referendum in 1992 (voters opted for continuation of the existing method of sewage treatment). The Scientific and Technical Review Panel developed an eight-week public submissions process to enable interested groups and individuals to make technical submissions for the panel to consider. While the panel was not designed or directed to account for social, political, regulatory, or policy considerations, its members recognized that some questions (about the "to treat or not to treat" issue) could not be answered through technical and scientific input alone. Nine different groups and 43 individuals submitted 82 written documents to the panel. Submissions dealing with public and social values included statements in favour of sewage treatment because of impacts in the immediate area of the outfalls (e.g., sewage smells), the future inadequacy of dilution as a sewage treatment approach, and cumulative effects on the ocean as a whole, including high toxicity levels in whales. Other submissions suggested the lack of sewage

(continued)

treatment tarnishes Victoria's tourism reputation, while still others noted that treatment is the "morally right thing to do," regardless of what scientists say.

Some submitters cautioned against investing in sewage treatment when other discharges could be the source of contamination. The metals and other chemicals found in ocean sediments near the outfalls may have come from Victoria's historical practice of dumping solid waste from barges into the ocean, or from stormwater outfalls that continue to discharge runoff from roads, as well as fecal coliforms from cross-connections of sewer and stormwater collection systems.

Responsible Sewage Treatment Victoria (RSTV), an association of environmentalists, scientists, engineers,

Photo 8–17
This stormwater drain empties onto the beach between the Clover Point and Macaulay Point outfalls in Victoria and is a known source of sewage contamination.

health care professionals, and concerned citizens, was formed to promote the existing "natural treatment system" (with additional improved source controls and infrastructure upgrading). RSTV developed a website (www.rstv.ca) to publicize their concerns and to raise public awareness about the advantages of the natural treatment system. RSTV members objected to the change in government policy that required the CRD to develop a $1.2 billion land-based sewage treatment system because they felt the natural treatment system was already the best ecological practice. RSTV pointed out that conditions off the present outfalls are similar to those off the outfalls from secondary treatment plants in other municipalities. The group's arguments extended to the significant environmental impacts a land-based treatment plant would have, including consumption of large amounts of energy (enough to power between 1000 and 1500 average British Columbia homes), production of large amounts of greenhouse gases, habitat loss, and generation of a minimum of 1000 tonnes per year of biosolids (sludge) that must be kept isolated from land-based aquifers. In addition, RSTV was concerned about the long-term economic cost of construction and operation of the plant to taxpayers, and about the CRD's decision not to undertake the repair, which would cost about $100 million, of the cross-connected stormwater drains (sewer lines improperly connected to stormwater systems) before embarking on plant construction.

In essence, RSTV and other groups challenged the scientific necessity to construct land-based sewage treatment systems in order to protect human health and the marine environment before conducting the research necessary to determine whether or not, and to what degree, serious harm might be being done by the existing discharges. In this case, accurate comparison of social, economic, and environmental benefits and costs of land-based treatment versus marine effluent discharges requires more knowledge regarding how contaminants enter the marine environment and whether the sewer system is a significant pathway. Similarly, RSTV noted that more research was needed to determine whether land-based sewage treatment would deal effectively with the substances of concern or whether they would remain in the treated effluent and be discharged into the ocean or in contaminated sludge (which would present human health and environmental issues on land).

The priorities in protecting the marine environment also needed to be made explicit; habitat protection in the Georgia/Puget Sound basin previously had been identified as a critical issue, and Victoria's sewage disposal practices were viewed as a minor issue relative to habitat concerns. RSTV and other groups recognized the continuing scientific uncertainties and suggested that greater value for money could be attained through a variety of other actions to control input of deleterious or toxic substances that cause degradation of the marine environment.

The political debate continues; up to mid-2007, RSTV members (in particular, a previous regional medical health officer) continued to provide comments to such agencies as the CRD's Liquid Waste Management Committee and the CRD Board about how 20 years of monitoring have shown the lack of public health risks associated with human exposure to marine water from the two deep-sea outfalls and current level of preliminary treatment. Spending public funds on increasing treatment levels without clear scientific justification of those expenditures is an issue that continues to challenge decision makers in Victoria and elsewhere in coastal communities. The RSTV and other groups have helped to point out that the weight of evidence needs to be clearly established in order for appropriate sewage treatment decisions to be made.

SOURCES: *Storm Water Quality Annual Report,* Capital Regional District, 2005, http://www.crd.bc.ca/es/environmental_programs/stormwater/monitoring.htm; *Is Victoria Dumping Raw Sewage?* Responsible Sewage Treatment Victoria, 2006, http:/www.rstv.c a/is-victoria-dumping-raw-sewage/; *Scientific Review of Environmental Issues,* Responsible Sewage Treatment Victoria, 2006, http:/www.rstv.c a/scientific-review/; *What Is RSTV?* Responsible Sewage Treatment Victoria, 2006, http://www.rstv.ca/what-is-rstv/; "Fireproof Killer Whales (*Ornicus orca*): Flame-Retardant Chemicals and the Conservation Imperative in the Charismatic Icon of British Columbia, Canada," P. H. S. Ross, 2006, *Canadian Journal of Fisheries and Aquatic Sciences, 63*(1), 224–234; *Scientific and Technical Review: Capital Regional District Core Area Liquid Waste Management Plan,* W. A. Stubblefield et al., 2006, http://www.crd.bc.ca/es/review_panel.htm

Photo 8–18
Hypodermic needles and other medical waste are among the debris found on beaches around the world.

MARINE SHIPPING, OCEAN DUMPING, AND PLASTICS

Marine Shipping

As noted previously, shipping activity contributes to degradation of marine environments. From contaminated bilge water to major oil spills, most impacts and problems are caused by human error; many can be avoided. As low temperatures and limited species diversity make Canada's North exceptionally sensitive to pollution, northern Canadians are concerned about accidental pollution of Arctic waters, which could occur through shipping incidents or during hydrocarbon exploration. Furthermore, effective spill cleanup in ice-covered areas may be impossible, particularly since the effects of oil on the Arctic system are incompletely understood. As early as 1972 the government recognized the need for special consideration of the region with the passage of the Arctic Waters Pollution Prevention Act, and again pushed for special consideration in the Convention on the Law of the Sea for ice-covered areas.

Aquaculture operations also may be particularly vulnerable to marine shipping, as the 1993 stranding of the oil tanker *Braer* on the Shetland Islands, Scotland, demonstrated. Heading to Canada when it grounded on Sumburgh Head, the *Braer* spilled 96 million gallons of light crude oil, threatening salmon farms 80 kilometres away from the accident site. The Shetland Salmon Farmers Association determined that approximately 2.5 million fish at 16 aquaculture sites were tainted by the oil spill, resulting in a loss of $67.5 million (Golden, 1993).

Oil spills may kill farmed fish and shellfish by direct toxicity or by smothering them, and can damage them by tainting their flesh. Even the hint of oil contamination may cause consumer uncertainty and affect world fish

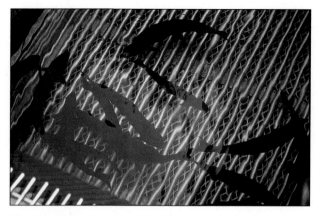

Photo 8–19
Aquaculture operations may be highly sensitive to any degradation in the marine environment.

markets. Given that the salmon (aquaculture) industry in the Bay of Fundy is similar in scope to that of the Shetland Islands, fish farmers in both areas were concerned that the environmental quality around their operations could be destroyed by a tanker accident. With hundreds of tankers passing through the Bay of Fundy annually, a serious oil spill might be difficult to contain, particularly if the very high tides in the area were combined with high seas. Such a potential threat emphasizes the need for protection of unpolluted environments in which to raise salmon and other marine species.

Ocean Dumping

Ocean dumping is defined under the Canadian Environmental Protection Act as deliberate disposal at sea from ships, aircraft, platforms, and other human-made structures. Dredged material, fish waste, scrap metal, decommissioned vessels, and uncontaminated organic material of natural origin are among those inert, nonhazardous substances permitted to be dumped. Permits for ocean dumping are granted after an evaluation has been conducted regarding the type of material to be dumped, the intended locations for the loading and disposal, potential environmental impacts, and alternatives to ocean disposal. A permit is not issued if practical opportunities are available for recycling, reuse, or treatment of the waste. Furthermore, Canada banned the disposal of industrial and radioactive wastes at sea in September 1994.

From 1987 to 1997, Environment Canada issued 1781 permits for disposal at sea of excavated earth and material from dredging of waterways, fish processing waste, retired vessels, and "other" wastes including scrap metal. More than 98 percent of wastes disposed at sea were from dredging of harbours and land excavation activities, while in Atlantic Canada, most permits were issued for disposal of fish waste (Statistics Canada, 2000). Permits to dispose of vessels also have been issued, one of which was an artificial reef-building project (see Box 8–10).

A permit is issued only if there are no practical alternatives to disposal at sea. In 1997, a new fee of $470 per thousand cubic metres of material to be disposed, in addition to the $2500 nonrefundable application fee, came into effect as an incentive to companies to reduce the amount of waste disposed of at sea. Still, 2 to 3 million tonnes of material are disposed of in 130 disposal sites each year on Canada's east and west coasts. While the number of permits has declined since the early 1990s, the World Wildlife Fund of Canada (WWF) has charged that fines levied against ships that discharge bilge water at sea are less than the cost of legally disposing of bilge water in port. This suggests that it "pays to pollute"—and foreign ships have taken advantage of that situation, dumping oil in Canadian waters before returning to their home ports. Instead of tolerating illegal oil discharges that kill 300 000 birds a year, the WWF noted that stricter laws and better air, ship, and satellite surveillance, ship traffic monitoring, and in-port inspections would help reduce the amount of oil dumped into the oceans. "These are … major crimes against nature, and there should be major fines to stop them" (Chandarana, 2002).

As part of Transport Canada's National Aerial Surveillance Program (NASP), high-technology aircraft and satellite systems help detect and document ship pollution in Canadian waters. To ensure compliance with environmental regulations, Canada's pollution surveillance aircraft can detect illicit discharges at sea during nighttime and in poor weather. NASP aircraft carry equipment such as side-looking airborne radar (SLAR) to detect anomalies that may be oil slicks on the ocean surface, ultraviolet infrared line scanners to analyze oil slicks, and electro-optical infrared cameras to identify vessels at long distances. In 2005, NASP flew 1548 hours over 9724 vessels and discovered 78 pollution incidents (Government of Canada, 2006b; Sorum, 2007).

In waters off Newfoundland and Labrador, and in the Arctic, the I-STOP program (Integrated Satellite Tracking of Polluters) uses RADARSAT imaging to identify possible oil slicks on the ocean surface. In no more than 90 minutes from the time the satellite image is taken, authorities responsible for responding to oil spills receive the data and subsequently may direct surveillance aircraft to areas where suspected pollution incidents have occurred. Up to 2005, however, because of prohibitions on the use of digital imagery as evidence in court cases, not a single pollution case had been prosecuted successfully in Canada. Instead, Environment Canada attempted to use the DNA of oil from a spill and match it with oil in the tanks of the suspect ship, using the satellite data simply to inform the authorities of the incident (de Selding, 2005).

Plastics

Plastics in the marine environment are an increasing problem. In high demand because of their durability, light

BOX 8-10
DECOMMISSIONED NAVAL SHIP BECOMES ARTIFICIAL REEF

With a loud bang and clouds of brown and white smoke, the decommissioned Canadian destroyer escort *Mackenzie* sank 18 metres below the waters off Sidney, British Columbia, on September 17, 1995, ending a 34-year naval career in just over four minutes. A popular new tradition for old ships, the *Mackenzie* was the third ship sunk in British Columbia waters by the Artificial Reef Society of British Columbia. Within two years of settling on the bottom, the new artificial reef and diving attraction was expected to be home to over 120 species of marine life.

The sinking of the *Mackenzie* had been preceded by the scuttling of HMCS *Chaudière* off Sechelt, British Columbia, in 1992 and the HMCS *Saguenay* in Nova Scotia in 1994. The *Matthew Atlantic* followed, sunk near Port Mouton, Nova Scotia, in 1998 to enhance an underwater diving park.

A special ocean disposal activity permitted by Environment Canada under the Canadian Environmental Protection Act, preparing the *Mackenzie* or any other ship to become an artificial reef requires removal of potentially polluting materials such as PCBs, oil, and gauges containing radioactive materials. In addition, holes are cut between compartments and decks to allow safe access for divers. Before the ship is sent to the bottom, Environment Canada officials inspect the ship for environmental readiness.

Turning the 2370-tonne destroyer HMCS *Chaudière* into an artificial diving reef north of Vancouver was a proving ground for this activity. Environmentalists and First Nations people objected to its sinking because of potential pollution fears. However,

Photo 8–20
The sinking of the *Mackenzie* off Sidney, British Columbia.

Environment Canada instituted a program to observe any effects at the disposal site, and in 1993 data showed the old destroyer was home to a wide variety of marine life. In 1994, further videos showed a rich abundance of marine life completely covering the vessel, and no evidence of chemical contamination in the water and nearby sediments has been found.

SOURCES: "Former Destroyer to Be Sunk off Sidney Today," J. Bell, September 16, 1995, *Victoria Times Colonist*, p. B3; "That Sinking Feeling," M. Eggen, 1997, *Alternatives, 23*(1), 7; "Ocean Disposal: Waste Management and Remediation, the Atlantic Region," Environment Canada, 2002, http://www.pyr .ec.gc.ca/EN/ocean-disposal/English/fact2_e.htm; "Mackenzie Goes Below as Artificial Reef," N. Gidney, September 17, 1995, *Victoria Times Colonist*, p. A7; *Canadian Environmental Protection Act: Report for the Period April 1994 to March 1995,* Minister of Supply and Services, 1996, Ottawa: Author.

weight, and relatively low cost, plastics do not break down readily and tend to remain in the marine environment for three to five years or longer. In 1990, volunteers with the British Columbia Coastal Cleanup Campaign found more than 1000 pieces of debris per kilometre on some beaches; most of the debris they catalogued was plastic and foam. As the amount of plastic released into the environment grows each year, plastic in the marine environment is accumulating faster than it can break down; tides, winds, and storms deposit plastic all over the world's coastlines and seabeds. One study on Sable Island, 160 kilometres east of Nova Scotia, estimated 8 tonnes of debris washed up on the island each year, 94 percent of which was plastic. About 6.4 million tonnes of garbage reach the oceans each year (Allsop et al., n.d.)

Marine sensitivity to plastic is high: marine birds and other creatures are hurt or killed when they mistakenly eat or become entangled in it. Plastic can kill by blocking a digestive tract, by releasing toxins as a byproduct during digestion, or through starvation by giving a false sense of being full. Entanglements in plastic often lead to starva-

tion, exhaustion, infection from wounds, and drowning. People, too, are affected by plastic debris when it gets caught in boat propellers, clogs water intakes, or blocks pumping systems. Repairs, lost fishing opportunities, and rising insurance claims cost individuals and the fishing industry both time and money. Communities also may face increasing costs for litter collection (Environment Canada, n.d.)

Marine plastic debris comes from many sources, including careless boaters, beach users, and tourists; cargo vessels, passenger ships, and commercial fishing vessels discharging garbage or accidentally losing cargo; workers at construction sites or other industrial sites who thoughtlessly dispose of waste into marine waters; and poor management practices at landfills (if uncovered, materials may blow into the ocean) and municipal sewage outlets (people dispose of plastic wastes in sewer systems). Rope, containers, grocery and garbage bags, cups and cup lids, and foam pieces are some of the most prevalent forms of plastic debris encountered in the marine environment.

A National Marine Plastic Debris research, information, and education program was established by Environment Canada when the Green Plan was operative, in order to improve efforts to deal with the problem. Debris pollution is one of those problems that requires international cooperation because the oceans carry lightweight plastics over long distances. While Canada harmonizes its own legislation with international standards, nations that do not regulate effectively and ships that fly flags of convenience and exist outside of most national and international regulation can dump plastic debris that lands on Canada's coasts.

COASTAL DEVELOPMENT

Growing human populations in coastal areas are posing increasing problems to marine ecosystems as a result of sewage, municipal and industrial wastes, litter, and urban runoff. As well, habitat loss through construction activities and physical alteration of coastal environments is an issue of concern in several parts of the country. One of the main attractions of living on the coasts is their aesthetic appeal, which can be lost through poorly planned development.

Urban Runoff

Urban runoff is one of the most significant examples of nonpoint-source (NPS) pollution. Not only is NPS pollution hard to track, it is also hard to control using conventional regulations. Nothing short of a change in our overall behaviour as "urban humans" will combat this problem. The lower Fraser Valley, with its urban, industrial, and agricultural growth, is one of Canada's best examples of this problem's complexity.

When rainwater runs off farmland in the lower Fraser River valley into ditches or washes city streets and industrial sites before draining away, it picks up all kinds of contaminants that eventually end up in the river. Manure is one major potential pollutant in agricultural runoff, especially in the Fraser Valley, which supports high livestock densities. If improperly applied on fields, pesticides can be problematic if they enter the drainage systems and reach the river untreated or reach groundwater aquifers. Wastewater from poorly maintained septic systems can have the same potential effects. All of these nonpoint sources of polluted runoff are diffuse and hard to quantify, but can have serious effects (as in Walkerton, Ontario; see Chapter 7).

It is known, however, that runoff from urban areas collects sediments and chemical pollutants such as trace metals, PCBs, and hydrocarbons (from cars and trucks). The volume of urban runoff for the Fraser River basin as a whole amounts to 500 million cubic metres per year— enough to fill B.C. Place Stadium 250 times (Fraser River Action Plan, n.d.). That volume is more than the annual discharge from municipal and pulp and paper sources combined (see Figure 8–8). Because of its large population and extensive urban areas, the lower Fraser River basin contributes the largest amounts of urban runoff in British Columbia, including almost 55 000 tonnes of suspended solids that enter the Fraser basin each year.

The changes that growing urban pressures in the Fraser Valley bring to Fraser delta shorebirds are worrisome to researchers. Who believe that environmental changes in the Fraser delta could affect migrating shorebirds profoundly. If an oil spill or any other mishap reduced the birds' feeding, many would arrive too late at their Arctic breeding grounds to nest and produce a brood. In other words, habitat degradation on the Fraser River and delta could hinder the shorebirds' success on a breeding ground 3000 kilometres away (Obee, 1996). Such interconnections between human activities and environmental impacts on migrating birds give important meaning to the adage "think globally, act locally."

Physical Alterations

Physical restructuring of coastal environments often affects the biotic as well as the abiotic components of an area. The current expansion of Deltaport, the fifth-largest container port on the west coast of North America, illustrates a range of anticipated biotic effects from construction activity in the Fraser River estuary. Vancouver's Port Authority (VPA) proposed to add a third berth to the existing container terminal at Roberts Bank in Delta, British Columbia, thereby increasing the port's capacity by 44 percent. This expansion project was intended to enable the Port of Vancouver to capture an increasing share of west coast container traffic. The $272 million expansion is to be achieved through various construction activities, including building

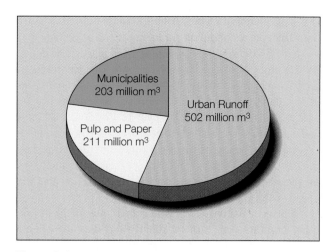

Figure 8–8

Urban runoff in the Fraser River basin

SOURCE: *Fact Sheet 2: Pollution in the Fraser,* Fraser River Action Plan, n.d.

a new 427-metre-long concrete wharf, dredging the Fraser estuary and using the dredge spoil to fill in a 22-hectare area to expand the container storage yard, and dredging to deepen the existing ship channel to accommodate ships as long as three football fields and 14.5 metres deep (Fisheries and Oceans Canada & Environment Canada, 2006).

The Deltaport project triggered a federal Environmental Assessment (EA) under the Canadian Environmental Protection Act (CEAA) because DFO and Environment Canada were required to issue statutory or regulatory approvals for various aspects of the project. For instance, expansion of Deltaport required DFO to authorize destruction of fish habitat and, under the CEAA, a permit was required for disposal of the dredged material at sea. A provincial EA also was required, but the federal and provincial EA processes were harmonized (undertaken together).

The EA or Comprehensive Study Report released by DFO and Environment Canada in 2006 indicated that, except for two written submissions from members of the public that supported the project, all other submissions expressed concerns about or objected to the project. A fundamental challenge was whether there was a need for the project. With regard to biotic elements of the project, these concerns included negative impacts on and loss of wildlife habitat in the Fraser River estuary, and the project's adverse impacts on COSEWIC-listed species. Dredging and the accompanying increased turbidity, for instance, could disturb killer whales and their food sources such as Chinook salmon. Dredging and the placement of fill potentially could affect fish, invertebrates, and marine

mammals as well as the eelgrass and other biotic elements of the ecosystem that support these species. Underwater noise associated with dredging could affect marine mammals and their behaviour (e.g., leading to avoidance of an area, tissue rupture, hearing loss, disruption of echolocation, pup/calf abandonment), and the potential exists for collisions between marine vessels and marine mammals such as whales and seals. Increased lighting planned for the expanded site also raised concerns about the potential for increased glare and sky brightness, as well as effects on marine life (migrating salmon), migratory birds, and wildlife. DFO raised specific concerns about night lighting facilitating nocturnal predation on juvenile salmon by piscivorous birds.

Marbled murrelets, great blue herons, and long-billed curlews are among the 34 bird species listed as at risk (either federally or provincially) that potentially occur within the project area. Not yet endangered, but declining, the entire world population (3.6 million) of western sandpipers migrates along this portion of the British Columbia coast. The habitat and wildlife values of the Roberts Bank ecosystem have been recognized globally, and the Fraser River estuary has been declared a Globally Significant Important Bird Area and a Hemispheric Site in the Western Hemisphere Shorebird Reserve Network. The Fraser River is a vitally important salmon-producing river, and Environment Canada has recognized in the past the need for improved salmon fishery management in the Fraser estuary. The Boundary Bay Conservation Committee's comments on the EA/Comprehensive Study Report indicated that Environment Canada did not assess the Deltaport project with the same level of concern it had expressed in the past about the ecology of the Fraser River estuary (Boundary Bay Conservation Committee, 2006).

On September 29, 2006, the VPA received a provincial environmental assessment certificate (i.e., approval) for its proposed Deltaport expansion project. The British Columbia Ministry of the Environment (2006, p. 1) indicated that "all potential significant adverse environmental, economic, social, heritage and health effects identified are manageable to an acceptable level" provided that project design components are followed along with the 152 commitments that the VPA must implement. While the federal Minister of the Environment must approve the project before it can proceed, among the key commitments to protect the environment required by the British Columbia Ministry of Environment is that the VPA must implement a habitat compensation plan to establish new fish and bird habitat or to enhance existing habitat. Key aspects of that plan are identified in Photo 8–22 (next page) and the following paragraphs. The VPA also must establish an adaptive management strategy to monitor conditions in the marine environment between the existing Deltaport and Tsawwassen ferry causeways. VPA is required to prepare an environmental plan for the 32-month construction period that addresses

Photo 8–21
Shown at high tide, the 50-hectare bulk-handling coal facility (on the left) and the 65-hectare Deltaport container terminal (on the right) at Roberts Bank were constructed in a naturally shallow area of the globally significant Fraser River delta. These terminals are connected to the mainland by a 4.1-kilometre causeway that carries rail and road traffic. Deltaport expansion will add three new gantry cranes like the ones shown on the right, each of which has its own lighting system. If you look closely, you might also see the 35-metre-tall poles that hold high-pressure sodium floodlamps.

dredging, surface water quality and sediment control, hazardous waste management, noise, wildlife and vegetation impacts, marine environment, marine water quality, air quality impacts, and lighting configurations.

The east causeway enhancements involve converting the eastern shoreline of the port causeway to high-quality marsh habitat for fish and water birds. Removal of excessive log debris accumulation and restoration of the regionally rare salt marsh area will enhance its biological productivity and habitat function. Creation of new reef segments (in addition to the four subtidal reefs constructed previously) is intended to increase the productive capacity and habitat diversity of the Deltaport area by providing new habitat for fish such as lingcod, invertebrates, and algae. Unstable sand bars (in the dendritic channel area) that can no longer support eelgrass are to be stabilized and eelgrass re-established over time.

Container terminal docks usually are constructed of reinforced concrete caisson structures; marine refugia are created when openings (1 metre diameter) are created in the caisson face and various intertidal and subtidal species and communities can move into the inside of the dock. Typically, shrimp, sea stars, barnacles, and anemones take advantage of the feeding opportunities along the wharf face and entrances to the refugia. However, the area of new habitat represented by the caisson refugia is small—0.3 to 0.5 hectares on the Deltaport site. VPA also is working with Ducks Unlimited Canada, DFO, and the Canadian Wildlife Service to provide off-site habitat compensation for fish and migratory birds (Williams & Millar, 2006). The question that usually is asked about such mitigative measures is whether they effectively can replace the original environmental conditions and qualities that are affected by physical alteration of the area through development.

OFFSHORE HYDROCARBON DEVELOPMENT

Marine ecosystems may be affected directly or indirectly and for the short or long term by hydrocarbon exploration and production activities. Our still-limited abilities to deal with iceberg collisions with production rigs or with spills, well blowouts, and containment in the Atlantic and Arctic ocean environments are key issues related to offshore development. In 1972, the British Columbia government imposed a moratorium on offshore exploration, and on the east coast, in response to fishing industry lobbying, exploration activity was banned by the federal and Nova Scotia governments in the Georges Bank area until the year 2000. As of mid-2007, British Columbia's moratoria had not been lifted.

Oil drilling off the British Columbia coast has been prevented by three moratoria, those of the federal and provincial governments and a First Nations suspension

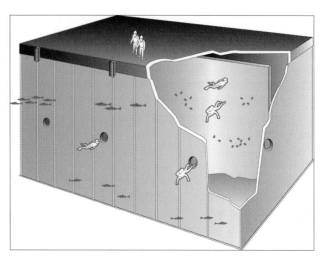

Photo 8–22

This schematic diagram of a caisson refugia shows how marine species may gain access to increased habitat area. Most organisms that use these components of the wharf system are lower-order species such as the calcareous tube worm; habitat complexity is low, and efforts need to be made to improve the habitat functionality for fish migration and feeding behaviour.

on oil and gas development. The provincial government now strongly supports offshore oil and gas drilling, and can lift their moratorium unilaterally. If the federal moratorium were not in place, oil and gas companies could conduct exploration and drilling activities along most of the coast. The provincial government has requested that the federal government examine its moratorium on offshore oil and gas drilling, particularly in the Queen Charlotte basin.

Keeping the moratoria in place is important, as potential drilling and extraction sites in British Columbia often are located near shore. For instance, some leases have been granted near the mouth of the Fraser River, the largest salmon-producing river in North America. Wind and current patterns would bring oil spills onto the coast and could devastate areas of high economic and ecological importance. The Queen Charlotte Islands are known internationally for their rich marine flora and fauna, including more than 400 species of fish, 121 species of birds, and 29 species of marine mammals. The world's only known living glass-sponge reefs, proposed as a UNESCO World Heritage Site (see Chapter 12), could be exposed to toxic, daily pollution from oil rig drilling cuttings (see Box 8–11) that would affect their filtering actions and their survival. The Scott Islands, proposed as a wildlife conservation area, is home to more than 2 million sea birds, including globally significant populations of Cassin's auklet, rhinocerous auklet, and tufted puffin, The island's birds could be devastated by an oil spill.

These and other concerns challenge the idea that developing offshore oil and gas would be in the best economic interest of coastal communities. When development of offshore oil and gas threatens existing coastal

An issue of concern in the drilling of an oil well is that drilling muds and drill cuttings (typically in the order of 200 to 500 cubic metres) are discharged directly into the ocean. Mud additives used in this process are of particular concern to marine life because they may contain a variety of contaminants, including heavy metals, hydrocarbons, and biocides.

Exploration for petroleum hydrocarbons began in the Arctic in 1973 and, by 2000, 134 wells had been drilled off the Arctic coast; as well, 346 wells were drilled off the Atlantic coast. The Hibernia project off Newfoundland, smaller projects on the Scotian Shelf, and the gas field near Sable Island are in production. These projects provide economic development and expansion opportunities for the region, but also pose potentially significant threats to local marine life on the Grand Banks and to grey and harbour seals on Sable Island breeding grounds. In 2002, COSEWIC uplisted (to endangered) the status of the Scotian Shelf population of bottlenose whales, in part because this species is threatened by the loud noises associated with oil and gas exploration. Living in small, deep (greater than 800 metres) water areas at the entrances to major underwater canyons such as the Gully off the southeast coast of Nova Scotia, the 130 bottlenose whales benefited from the Minister of Fisheries and Oceans' designation of the Gully Marine Protected Area (MPA). Regulations prohibit disturbance or damage to any living organism or habitat within the Gully. DFO also requested that vessels avoid the Gully MPA in an effort to reduce the chance of collisions. In April 2006 the Minister of Fisheries and Oceans announced that the bottlenose whale would be added to the list of species protected under SARA. Such a decision may be perceived as an effort to balance industrial development impacts and marine protection policies.

Legislation establishing the drilling moratorium on Georges Bank expired on January 1, 2000; subsequently, a panel conducted a public review of the environmental and socioeconomic impacts of hydrocarbon drilling. An important source of new environmental information for the panel was a multidisciplinary research program on the effects of drilling wastes conducted by researchers at the Bedford Institute of Oceanography in Nova Scotia. Scientists studied the physical oceanography and sedimentology of Georges Bank, the flocculation behaviour of drilling wastes, drilling waste dispersion around an active rig on Sable Island Bank, and the sublethal effects of drilling wastes on sea scallops, the most important commercial species on Georges Bank. Particular attention was paid to water circulation so that the horizontal dispersion and transport of particulate drilling wastes could be understood, particularly in the benthic boundary layer. That layer of water, just above the sea floor, is where scallops filter their food particles. Scientists used the models they developed to explore the potential impacts of specific hypothetical drilling scenarios on Georges Bank and conveyed that information to the review panel for their consideration (*Drilling on Georges Bank*, n.d.). This and other socioeconomic consultations by the panel allowed them to submit a recommendation to extend the moratorium until the end of 2012, which was accepted jointly by the governments of Canada and Nova Scotia.

SOURCE: *Fate and effects of offshore hydrocarbon drilling waste,* T. G. Milligan et al., 1996, http://www.mar.dfo-mpo.gc.ca/science/review/1996/Milligan/Milligan_e.html; *Georges Bank moratorium extended,* Nova Scotia Petroleum Directorate, 1999, http://www.gov.ns.ca/news/details.asp?id=1999 12 2004

industries such as fishing and tourism (would even the sight of oil rigs be a disincentive to cruise ship tourism?), and when sustainability of the marine environment may be compromised, the precautionary principle should be applied. Alternatives to oil and gas, such as improvements in fuel efficiency, wind power, and other renewable energy sources, also require investigation. Additionally, Aboriginal land claims and jurisdictional issues would need to be considered prior to any decision to lift the ban. These issues illustrate some of the challenges that managers face in making appropriate decisions for resource sustainability.

RESPONSES TO ENVIRONMENTAL IMPACTS AND CHANGE

Are Canada's commercial fisheries sustainable? How can the health of major aquatic ecosystems be maintained? How do we balance social, environmental, and economic interests in areas that are important for fisheries, shipping, and urban and industrial development? These questions and many others like them reveal the worries that people have regarding the present effects of human activities and the need to plan and manage resources for a sustainable future. While we know that we need improved ecological knowledge to answer such questions and to move toward sustainable ocean resource use, there have been efforts at all levels, from international to individual, to try to make a difference. This section outlines some of these efforts.

INTERNATIONAL INITIATIVES

A variety of international agreements and programs are in place to safeguard the oceans and their resources for present and future generations. The Organization for Economic Cooperation and Development (OECD) and UNEP run oceans and coastal area programs. UNEP's Regional Seas Programme, for example, emphasizes integrated coastal zone management, pollution control measures, and climate change issues. Earlier in the chapter we noted NAFO's difficulties with enforcing international law to preserve high-seas turbot (and other species) for future generations (Schram & Polunin, 1995). The United Nations Convention on the Law of the Sea and Agenda 21, described briefly below, are important international initiatives.

United Nations Convention on the Law of the Sea

On November 16, 1994, the United Nations Convention on the Law of the Sea (UNCLOS) came into force, concluding a process that had begun in the mid-1930s. Prior to the First World War, it had been recognized that the world needed to develop a legal order for the oceans that would "promote the peaceful uses of the seas and oceans, the equitable and efficient utilization of their resources, the conservation of their living resources, and the study, protection and preservation of the marine environment" (UNCLOS, 1982, cited in Alexandrowicz, 1995).

While the history of UNCLOS is both lengthy and complex, the legal regime was developed through international political negotiations during three Law of the Sea (LOS) conferences. The Third LOS Conference took 10 years (until 1982) to negotiate a final agreement, which, in turn, took 12 years to come into force (in 1994). The resulting United Nations Convention on the Law of the Sea is the centrepiece of the international regime for managing the world's oceans. UNCLOS reconciled the widely divergent interests of 150 independent states, and also established the ideal for a new equity in use of oceans and their resources. The Food and Agriculture Organization of the United Nations also has established fishing areas for management purposes.

Among other items in UNCLOS agreements, exclusive economic zones (EEZs) were established that gave coastal states legal power and international obligation to apply sound principles of resource management to oceans. In addition, UNCLOS declared that more than 45 percent of the seabed area and its resources were "the 'common heritage of mankind,' a concept that represents a milestone in the realm of international cooperation" (World Commission on Environment and Development, 1987, p. 273). This concept means that the world's oceans are inextricably linked and that Canada, as every other maritime nation, has an international responsibility to manage the ocean as a shared global resource. Having ratified the convention in 2003, Canada is a strong supporter of the UNCLOS process and is a major beneficiary of its provisions (United Nations Convention on the Law of the Sea, 2004).

Agenda 21

Chapter 17 of Agenda 21 of the United Nations Conference on Environment and Development (UNCED) deals with the marine environment. Linked directly with UNCLOS, Agenda 21 sets out the international basis on which

Photo 8–23
Marinas expand as recreational demand grows. Marinas may cause wetland destruction through dredging for access to sheltered water.

protection and sustainable development of marine and coastal environments and their resources are pursued. Agenda 21 calls for new approaches to marine and coastal area management and development that integrate knowledge from all sources and that are both precautionary and anticipatory (Gerges, 1994).

Agenda 21 focuses on a number of areas such as integrated management and sustainable development of coastal areas, including EEZs, marine environmental protection, climate change, and strengthening regional and international cooperation and coordination in dealing with ocean issues. Given the continued growth of human settlement along the world's coasts, increased coastal recreation, the concentration of industrial development in coastal areas, and the wealth of exploitable, living marine resources, emphasis is placed on protecting the health of coastal waters. Particular attention is paid to the land-based sources of marine degradation that contribute 70 percent of ocean pollution (International Development Research Centre, n.d.). The real challenge, of course, is to implement these approaches effectively in order to achieve the desired goals.

CANADIAN LAW, POLICY, AND PRACTICE

Oceans and Fisheries Legislation

Canada's history of governance of marine environments has reflected both federal and provincial responsibilities and jurisdictions. The federal government has responsibility for all matters in waters below the mean high-water mark (except in aquaculture, where certain responsibilities have been delegated to provinces through specific memoranda of understanding). Provincial jurisdiction covers provincial lands, shorelines, and freshwater resources (except navigable waters, inland fisheries, and federal lands), and certain areas of the seabed. Federal and provincial jurisdictions overlap in matters of species and habitat conservation, and provincial and municipal jurisdictions include many of the land-based activities that affect the marine environment. With establishment of some major land claims agreements in the Arctic, Aboriginal governments also are involved in the management of human activities in marine environments.

The main federal responsibility for the marine environment and economy lies with DFO. Primarily, DFO has managed commercially harvestable marine species, but it also is responsible for all marine species (except sea birds) and marine mammals. Other key departments and their major responsibilities are identified in Table 8–2.

The multiple and overlapping jurisdictions that characterize Canadian government in general give rise to fragmentation, duplication, and lack of coordination in marine environmental management and decision making (Beckmann, 1996). Aware that fragmentation tends to cause environmental considerations to be lost among the competing, more powerful economic interests, the federal (Liberal) government had generated policies and guidelines to deal with that problem. Among the legislation and policies developed were the National Marine Conservation Areas Act (2002) and the Canadian Arctic Marine Conservation Strategy.

Despite some excellent plans for marine conservation, pollution control, and species and habitat protection, collapse of numerous fish stocks indicates that Canada has had difficulty managing the commercial fishery in its own waters (Beckmann, 1995). Despite the government's commitment to environmentally sustainable development, reasons for Canada's failure to prevent degradation of marine waters and species include political inertia and fragmentation of responsibility.

In the early 1990s, four key events looked very promising for the advancement of marine conservation. The first event was the 1994 release by the National Advisory Board on Science and Technology (which reports directly to the prime minister) of its report on oceans and coasts (National Advisory Board on Science and Technology, 1994). Recommendations made by the advisory board included a comprehensive marine environment protection system that would safeguard Canada's oceans for the health, enjoyment, and economic welfare of future generations. The second event was Parks Canada's release of its revised "Guiding Principles and Operational Policies," which included a section on establishing marine conservation areas and which recognized the need to design these areas to accommodate varying levels of human activity within them.

TABLE 8–2
FEDERAL DEPARTMENTS WITH SIGNIFICANT MARINE RESPONSIBILITIES

Department and Selected Legislation	Selected Major Responsibilities
Fisheries and Oceans Canada (DFO) • Oceans Act • Fisheries Act • Species at Risk Act	• Management of commercially harvestable marine species, and all marine species (except sea birds) and marine mammals; safeguarding of Canada's oceans; Coast Guard functions
National Defence	• Border patrol
Natural Resources Canada	• Extraction of marine resources such as oil, gas, minerals, and aggregates south of 60°N latitude
Environment Canada • Canada Wildlife Act • Migratory Birds Convention Act • Species at Risk Act	• Protection of marine environmental quality; pollution prevention; sea bird and sea bird habitat protection
Parks Canada • Canada National Marine Conservation Areas Act • Canada National Parks Act • Species at Risk Act	• Establishment of national marine conservation areas and national parks through Parks Canada
Indian and Northern Affairs Canada	• Environmental issues and offshore oil, gas, and mineral development north of 60°N latitude
Foreign Affairs Canada	• Marine-related negotiations with other countries (as in the case of turbot negotiations with Spain, and the Pacific Salmon Treaty)
Emergency Preparedness Canada	• Response to natural and human-made disasters such as oil spills (on land and at sea)

SOURCES: *Seas the Day: Towards a National Marine Conservation Strategy for Canada,* L. Beckmann, 1996, Ottawa: Canadian Arctic Resources Committee/ Canadian Nature Federation; *Canada's Federal Marine Protected Areas Strategy,* Communications Branch, Fisheries and Oceans Canada, 2005, Ottawa: Author; *Overview of the East Coast Marine Environment,* E. Meltzer, 1995, Ottawa: Canadian Arctic Resources Committee/Canadian Nature Federation.

The conservation area program that originated from the Guiding Principles document resulted in the planning of three national marine conservation areas. These are Gwaii Haanas, a potential national marine conservation area (NMCA) off the Queen Charlotte Islands, British Columbia; Fathom Five National Marine Park, established adjacent to Bruce Peninsula National Park in Georgian Bay, Ontario; and Saguenay–St. Lawrence Marine Park, established near Tadoussac, Quebec. The need for additional marine protected areas is great as highlighted by COSEWIC's identification of more than 100 marine ecosystem species in British Columbia that require protection. In January 2008, a new Marine Advisory Committee met for the first time to provide general comments about, and specific recommendations for, the development of an interim management plan for the proposed Gwaii Haanas NMCA. When the NMCA is established, it will be one of the only places in the world to protect an area stretching from the mountain tops to ocean depths.

Amendments to the Canada Wildlife Act, which enabled the establishment of wildlife areas out to 200 nautical miles, was the third event. This is an important means of extending environmental regulation to protect marine mammals and their habitat. The fourth event was DFO's release of *A Vision for Ocean Management,* a document that not only outlined the essentials of a new oceans management strategy for Canada but also recommitted DFO to the creation of a Canada Oceans Act.

Another significant action occurred in December 1995 when the Minister of Fisheries and Oceans, Brian Tobin, tabled the first major rewrite of the Fisheries Act since 1868, updating the legal basis for conservation and fisheries management. In particular, these changes provided greater opportunity for shared management of the resource through partnerships, more effective enforcement, and more flexible regulations—the kinds of changes that had been advocated for a long time by various analysts. Tobin indicated that changes to the Fisheries Act were designed to allow government and industry to move forward into the "fishery of the future." This future fishery was to be guided by such principles as "conservation comes first," basing the fishery on resource capacity, government and industry operating in partnership, and respecting the rights of Aboriginal people (Department of Fisheries and Oceans, 1995e).

The Canada Oceans Act was passed by the House of Commons and given royal assent in 1996. The Canada Oceans Act recognized Canada's jurisdiction over its ocean areas by declaring a contiguous zone and an EEZ, and provided the legislative basis for an oceans management strategy based on the principles of shared stewardship, sustainable development, and the precautionary approach. There were high hopes for the Canada Oceans Act because it was the basis on which cooperative work with the provinces could begin, and through which all Canadians interested in the marine environment and economy could help build an oceans management strategy. However, since the Oceans Act was "enabling legislation" only and required designation of either management plans or marine protected areas to be effective, DFO was criticized for its failure to follow through on its implementation.

Prior to the passing of the Canada Oceans Act, the provinces had been active in coastal issues. For example, Nova Scotia and New Brunswick had formulated coastal zone management policies and plans. Other cooperative initiatives were undertaken as well, such as the Burrard Inlet Environmental Action Plan (involving Environment Canada, DFO, Transport Canada, the British Columbia Ministry of Environment, Metro Vancouver, and the Vancouver Fraser Port Authority) to reduce toxic loadings in the inlet. The Inuvialuit Final Agreement (for the western Arctic) and the Nunavut Final Agreement (for the eastern Arctic) provided for a joint federal–territorial–Aboriginal management system that fosters integrated decision making. (These co-management initiatives are noted briefly in the section "Canadian Partnerships and Local Actions" later in this chapter.) Municipalities, with their solid waste and sewage management responsibilities, also played, and continue to play, important roles in improving the health of Canada's marine systems through careful urban planning and appropriate waste management practices.

In 2002, when Canada's Oceans Strategy was released, the creation of marine protected areas (MPAs) became possible. MPAs are areas of the ocean designated for special management measures under the Oceans Act. This means that enforceable regulations can help protect the area and its marine organisms. In March 2003, Canada's first MPA was designated: the Endeavour Hydrothermal Vents Area, southwest of Vancouver Island, British Columbia, contains 12 species of marine life that exist nowhere else in the world. Other locations considered for designation as MPAs include an area in the southern Beaufort Sea to protect critical beluga whale habitat, and an ancient subsea volcano (Bowie Seamount) located 189 kilometres offshore to the west of the Queen Charlotte Islands that provides an uncommon shallow-water habitat.

Following passage of the Oceans Act in 1996 and the Ocean Strategy in 2002, the federal government announced its intention to develop an Oceans Action Plan, Phase I of which began in 2005. The Oceans Action Plan (OAP) established the framework on which an integrated federal oceans agenda was to be promoted; Phase I focused on improving oceans management and preserving the health of marine ecosystems. For two years, Phase I actions were targeted to four "pillars":

- *International leadership, sovereignty, and security:* As part of this line of action, $800 000 was allocated to advance the Arctic Marine Strategic Plan and to improve oceans management in the Gulf of Maine.

- *Integrated oceans management for sustainable development:* Actions within this $15 million pillar included setting up planning forums with industry, Aboriginal groups, communities, and other governments to identify common objectives that would help protect fragile ecosystems.
- *Health of the oceans:* DFO, Environment Canada, and Parks Canada were invested with almost $10 million for work on the federal Marine Protected Areas Strategy, including establishment of a network of marine protected areas on all three coasts (to protect important species, habitats, and critical ecosystems), protection of Sable Island's unique scientific and ecological value, and increased air surveillance on the east coast (to better protect our waters from ship-source pollution).
- *Science and technology:* $2 million was invested in an Oceans Technology Network (Internet based) for sharing coastal and ocean data and information, demonstrating leading oceans technology, and linking NGOs, community groups, First Nations, industry, academia, and governments toward sustainable use and well-being of marine resources and coastal communities (Fisheries and Oceans Canada, 2005b).

Unfortunately, despite the importance of marine protected areas as a key tool to help protect ecosystems from the effects of industrial activity, less than one-ten-thousandth of the world's oceans are fully protected and Canada has protected less than 0.1 percent of its oceans. In contrast, New Zealand has indicated that before 2010 it will protect 10 percent of its coastline in MPAs, and Australia has plans to create the world's largest marine reserve (David Suzuki Foundation, 2007). While Canada's Oceans Act and Oceans Strategy are based on appropriate principles such as the ecosystem approach, integrated and adaptive management, and the precautionary principle, the federal government has not established any new MPAs or provided sufficient funding to achieve appropriate protection of our common heritage. To proceed with effective implementation (i.e., comprehensive planning, scientific research, management reforms) of Phase II of the Oceans Action Plan would require several hundred million dollars. The 2007 federal budget provided less than $19 million toward ocean conservation under the Oceans Action Plan. Clearly, the federal government's failure to provide adequate funding to accomplish its Ocean Act mandate means that important marine resources and areas will remain unprotected and improperly managed.

Coastal Zone Management Efforts

As the preceding discussion illustrates, Canada has made progress in revising existing legislation and in creating new legislation pertaining to the marine environment. Efforts to implement coastal zone management in Canada, however, continue to lag.

To mitigate the negative aspects of increasing stress on coastal environments, a number of countries have adopted national coastal zone management (CZM) programs. Coastal zone management may be defined as "the process of implementing a plan designed to resolve conflicts among a variety of coastal users, to determine the most appropriate use of coastal resources, and to allocate uses and resources among legitimate stakeholders" (Hildebrand, 1989, p. 9). Canada does not have a national coastal zone management program; however, regional efforts exist in parts of the country where resource allocation conflicts and problems of environmental degradation are, or have been, severe.

In 1978, in an effort to establish a national CZM program, the Canadian Council of Resource and Environment Ministers (CCREM) sponsored a national seminar on coastal zone issues. Although a national strategy did not emerge from this symposium, 10 principles were developed to guide local and regional coastal management efforts. The principles, along with the early initiative for CZM, disappeared before the end of the decade, leaving coastal management to be implemented through a variety of regional initiatives such as the Fraser River Estuary Management Program, the Fraser River Action Plan (FRAP), and the Atlantic Coastal Action Program.

Canada's oceans legislation provides the potential to achieve the objectives of coastal zone management, but as noted previously, with insufficient funding allocated by the federal government to implement the programs, the lack of progress is not unexpected. Canada must commit to funding an effective oceans management program if it is to move ahead with meaningful planning, protection, and management of marine resources within our coastal and economic zones.

CANADIAN PARTNERSHIPS AND LOCAL ACTIONS

Many Canadians care deeply about what happens to their environment, oceans included, and take a variety of individual or group actions, to help ensure the environment in their location is protected. A national awards program—Canadian Environment Awards—was established in 2002 to recognize Canadians dedicated to helping protect, preserve, and restore Canada's environment through the work that they do in their communities. The awards program is a partnership between the Government of Canada and Canadian Geographic Enterprises with financial support from the private sector.

Table 8–3 highlights some past award winners whose actions have contributed broadly or specifically toward oceans protection. You can read more about these awards, and the people who try to make a difference, either individually or in partnership with others, at www.canadiangeographic.ca/cea2006/home.asp.

TABLE 8-3

SELECTED CANADIAN ENVIRONMENT AWARDS RELATED TO OCEANS AND FISHERIES

Awardee	Year	Project	Location	Description
Alain Branchaud and Andrée Gendron	2002	Aquatic biologists	Quebec	Branchaud and Gendron were rehabilitating spawning sites of a fish that they had renamed *chevalier cuivré*. The pair worked with a brewing company to feature the fish on a beer label. Proceeds from sales of Rescousse are directed to Fondation de la Faune du Québec, which manages funds for restoration of the fish's critical habitat.
David Loewen	2002	Wild salmon advocate	Inuvik to Los Angeles	In 2001 David Loewen began the Wild Salmon Cycle, a 10 000-kilometre bicycle expedition from Inuvik to Los Angeles. He wanted to raise awareness and educate people about threats to the Pacific salmon and inspire people to make positive changes in their lives. Money raised on the trip was to help establish Salmon Watch, a program to facilitate observing salmon in their natural habitat.
Clive Callaway and Sarah Kipp	2002	The Living by Water Project	British Columbia	Callaway and Kipp have developed printed material that informs rural waterfront residents about health-related, financial, and recreational benefits of protecting shore-line ecosystems.
North Vancouver Outdoor School (NVOS)	2005	Environmental education program and facility	Brackendale, British Columbia	NVOS hosts wild-salmon spawning channels, ancient red cedars, and bald eagle winter habitat. The school is a hands-on environmental learning centre.
Humber Arm Environmental Association (HAEA)	2007	Trading Books for Boats	Cornerbrook, Newfoundland	HAEA developed the Trading Books for Boats program to educate students on oceanography. Using their marina classroom, students discuss marine debris, water quality, oil-spill prevention, and municipal waste-water treatment, followed by a hands-on at-sea experience where students learn about the Bay of Islands marine ecosystem and conduct research.

These projects and many others undertaken individually or cooperatively by a variety of ENGOs, private sector businesses and agencies, and governments have been vital not only in protecting locally valued resources, but also in pointing the way toward attaining and maintaining future sustainability of fisheries and oceans. While these award winners may be leading the way, there is a great need for each of us to follow these examples and work in whatever ways we can to promote environmental sustainability.

FUTURE CHALLENGES

What would characterize a sustainable future for Canadian oceans and fisheries? A number of points may be identified, including deliberate application of a sound ecological approach to management; ethical principles, including interpersonal and intergenerational equity; appropriate technology; and improved science with clear and objective data. Other features would include achievement of a tolerable level of human pressure on natural resources and ecosystems, an acceptable quality of life (which recognizes the interdependence of humans and their environment), respect for and maintenance of diversity (both cultural and ecological), and people striving cooperatively together toward agreed-on goals that meet environmental, social, and economic objectives.

As the examples in this chapter have illustrated, human development activities in and relating to marine environments have resulted in a wide variety of impacts on coastal waters and species. International, national, regional, and local agreements and actions are helping to resolve some of these problems. In general, however, challenges for the future regarding sustainability of Canada's oceans, fisheries, and environments lie in ongoing efforts

Photo 8–24

With the *Sedna IV* in the background, Jean Lemire meets an Antarctic penguin "up close" during his 15-month-long Antarctic Mission (2005–6).

Jean Lemire is a marine biologist, adventurer, and documentary filmmaker who received a Lifetime Achievement Citation from the Canadian Environment Awards program in 2007 for his visionary efforts to popularize environmental stories, particularly the effects of climate change on the endangered ecosystems of the Arctic and Antarctic. He has reached hundreds of millions of people around the world with his award-winning productions, and is helping to unite scientists and the public in environmental action.

Lemire completed his bachelor's degree at the University of Sherbrooke in 1985, and got his first job with the Canadian Wildlife Service. But what really focused his future career were his summers spent working on photo-identification of whales for the non-profit Mingan Island Cetacean Study. By the time he began his PhD at Laval University, he had gained considerable field experience and developed the sophisticated piloting skills required to approach whales in a Zodiac. These skills and his knowledge of whales enabled him to participate in many international whale research projects. In addition to conducting his own academic research, he was asked frequently to take film crews with him—eventually he bought a camera himself.

In 1987 Lemire established Les Productions Ciné-Bio, a firm that specialized in scientific consulting and script development for documentary productions. There he produced such acclaimed films as *Marine Mammals Mission* (1994), *Encounters with Whales of the St. Lawrence* (1996), and *The Last Frontier* (1998). He left academia in 1998 to join Montreal's Max Films, where he produced award-winning TV programming. Despite his success, Lemire felt that environmental themes were a "tough sell," so in 2001 he formed Glacialis Productions Inc., specifically to enable him to lead a five-month Arctic expedition through the Northwest Passage with a crew of scientists and filmmakers. In taking this step, Lemire believed that his films connected with people in ways that made them care about climate change issues; he used money from the movie business to advance research and to link science and the public to help engage the world in the fight against climate change.

The three-masted 51-metre steel sailboat that Lemire acquired and christened with the Inuit name for sea goddess, the *Sedna IV*, was outfitted with high-precision navigational equipment for polar travel and a cutting room for high-definition film production, making her the best floating studio in the world. Lemire's Arctic trip was the basis for his five-part *Arctic Mission* production (2003–4), which aired on *The Nature of Things* with David Suzuki and on Radio-Canada and Télé-Québec. *Arctic Mission* received great popular acclaim and won the prestigious Earth Watch Award presented by the National Geographic Society. In 2006, Lemire helped produce and direct *The White Planet*, a powerful, feature-length environmental film that gives visual testament to the impacts of climate change on the Arctic.

During 403 days of sailing on his Antarctic trip, Lemire maintained 10 direct satellite links for schools, while another 820 schools logged on through the Internet, and up to 830 000 people visited the Antarctic Mission site daily. This level of interest was proof to Lemire that the environment does matter to Canadians and that "if we learn to be close to nature again and think of ourselves as part of it, the problems we face might be solved." Watch for the feature-length film, documentary series, and adventure series to come.

SOURCES: Radio-Canada. (n.d.). *The Mission: Sedna's Course*. http://www.radio-canada.ca/sedna/index.html?p=/eng/crew/lemire.php; Radio-Canada. (n.d.). *The Mission: Objectives*. http://www.radio-canada.ca/sedna/index.html?p=/eng/crew/lemire; Canadian Geographic. (2007). *Citation of Lifetime Achievement*. http://www.canadiangeographic.ca/cea/archives/archives_lifetime.asp?id=199

to improve our stewardship, protection and monitoring, and knowledge-building activities.

Stewardship, the management of oceans and fisheries resources so that they are conserved for future generations, requires an active, shared awareness of both ethical and ecological principles on which safeguarding the future of marine environments depends. Equity and respect for all other users of oceans and fisheries resources, and a holistic understanding of ecosystems and their interdependencies at all levels, are among the characteristics required to develop attitudes and practices that will help achieve a sustainable future. This is as true for professional fishers as it is for recreational users. One related challenge arising here is to educate everyone who uses or impacts marine environments to include care and respect not only for themselves, but also for other people, and to be aware of the interactions that may occur from their decisions.

New agreements, such as Canada's Oceans Act, that are intended to work toward and achieve sustainability, and new fishing management agreements that are intended to protect particular fish species and stocks, may assist improved stewardship practices. Follow-through is required, however, to ensure the agreements are put in place, implemented effectively, supported financially, and enforced. Increasingly—and this applies to all environments, not just ocean and fisheries resources—stewardship implies that the necessary attitudinal characteristics on the part of individuals, agencies, corporations, and governments should include awareness of human effects, receptivity to change, accountability for decisions taken, and acceptance of responsibility to rectify any negative impacts.

Sustainability depends on many related factors, some of which are little understood or poorly defined, and most of which are very difficult to predict. If Canada's oceans and fisheries resources and environments are going to be protected for the future, monitoring efforts need to be incorporated for measuring the environmental, social, and economic parameters of our development activities. In addition, monitoring effects of variables ranging from effluent discharges to climate change may, over time, help us overcome the problem of inadequate data on which to base management decisions (although there is no guarantee that the acquired knowledge will satisfy the questions that need to be answered). In the meantime, as Canada and other countries present at the 1992 Earth Summit recognized, when the "weight of evidence" suggests that action to protect the environment should be taken to prevent serious or irreversible damage, then the lack of full scientific "proof" is not a reason to postpone measures to prevent that degradation. In light of this precautionary principle, perhaps fisheries minister Tobin's actions regarding protection of turbot stocks were both effective and appropriate.

Observer programs for fisheries (as in the case of European Union vessels and others who fish stocks that cross the Canadian 200-nautical-mile limit), and the establishment and application of standards for various types of coastal development activity, including housing construction, port expansion, and other infrastructure facilities, are means by which marine protection can be promoted. A shared sense of the responsibility for establishing and effectively implementing programs and regulatory mechanisms to ensure continued ecological functioning of marine environments should enable all parties to cooperate and achieve desired common goals, including sustainability. An important part of any cooperative effort is the ability to anticipate what our future needs might be—for instance, what impacts climate change might have on marine environments—and the ability to develop appropriately sensitive environmental protection and monitoring approaches and devices. Protection measures also can be applied to those marine environments that have been restored or rehabilitated.

Given the lack of knowledge of fundamental as well as more sophisticated elements of marine environments and species functions, a key current and future challenge is to enhance research programs and data collection opportunities to build the necessary knowledge. Partnerships at all levels are appropriate here, and are particularly valuable when they involve First Nations' traditional ecological knowledge (TEK), and the knowledge of fishers and others with long-term experience in marine environments. Opening up the research process to include TEK and the environmental understanding and contributions of people with extensive fishing and other ocean experience should enable a fuller appreciation of stock status and regeneration methods, for example, as well as an earlier identification of critical gaps in knowledge. Additionally, support for and participation of those affected by decisions may encourage meaningful domestic (and perhaps international) partnerships in identifying alternative economic and employment opportunities.

Rachel Carson, Jacques Cousteau, and many other observers since the 1970s have pointed out that the oceans do not hold the key to humanity's burgeoning needs and wants. The collapse of the northern cod fishery and the more recent downward trends in Pacific salmon stocks should be very clear and ominous calls for the attention of all Canadians. During the heyday of those fisheries, few believed they would collapse with such harsh echoes resounding over the now-quieted fishing harbours of maritime Canada. As discussed above, governments are moving in new directions, but they require the support and critique of an informed public to create a better future for Canada's oceans.

Chapter Questions

1. Most biological productivity in the oceans occurs near continents, in areas of upwelling currents, on continental shelves, or near river estuaries. For each of the Arctic, Atlantic, and Pacific oceans, identify the kinds of threats that Canadians and their activities (on land and sea) pose to these areas of biological richness.

2. Fish do not respect political or administrative boundaries such as the 200-nautical-mile limit to Canada's exclusive economic zone. What difficulties does this characteristic of fish bring to efforts to protect transboundary fish stocks from overharvesting? What are the implications for sustainability of fish stocks?

3. Discuss the effects that climate change may have on Canada's coastal and offshore fisheries and ocean environment.

4. In what ways can traditional environmental knowledge and scientific research help us make decisions that will enhance the sustainability of oceans and their resources?

5. In what ways might protecting our marine environment help to safeguard human health?

6. Debate the value of the precautionary principle or approach in dealing with international and national oceans and fisheries issues.

7. What kinds of activities within Canada's urban areas are affecting the quality of our marine environments and the sustainability of oceans or fishery resources? What kinds of action were taken (or could be taken) to address the issue(s)? What could you do to make a difference in a current issue?

references

Alexandrowicz, G. (1995). *Law of the sea: A Canadian practitioner's handbook.* Kingston, ON: Faculty of Law, Queen's University.

Allsopp, M., Walters, A., Santillo, D., & Johnston, P. (n.d.). *Plastic debris in the world's oceans.* http://oceans.greenpeace.org/raw/content/en/documents-reports/plastic_ocean_report.pdf

Anisimov, O. A., Vaughan, D. G., et al. (2007). Polar regions (Arctic and Antarctic). In M. L. Parry et al. (Eds.), *Climate change 2007: Impacts, adaptation and vulnerability. Contribution of Working Group II to the Fourth Assessment Report of the Intergovernmental Panel on Climate Change* (pp. 653–685). Cambridge, UK: Cambridge University Press.

Anonymous. (June 22, 1995). Fish fight will cost taxpayers $3 million. Calgary Herald, p. A18.

Atlantic Coastal Action Program (ACAP). (2007, Winter). *Ebb & Flow.* Newsletter of the Atlantic Coastal Action Program.

Beckmann, L. (1995). Marine conservation—keeping the Arctic Ocean on the agenda. *Northern Perspectives, 23*(1), 1–2.

Beckmann, L. (1996). *Seas the day: Towards a national marine conservation strategy for Canada.* Ottawa: Canadian Arctic Resources Committee/Canadian Nature Federation.

Blades, K. (1995). *Net destruction: The death of Atlantic Canada's fishery.* Halifax: Nimbus.

Boundary Bay Conservation Committee. (2006). *Deltaport Third Berth Expansion Project: Response to Comprehensive Study Report.* http://www.wildernesscommittee.org/campaigns/communities/gateway/reports/Final_BBCC_Submission.pdf

British Columbia Ministry of Energy, Mines and Petroleum Resources. (2006). Offshore oil and gas around the world. http://www.offshoreoilandgas.gov.bc.ca/world-offshore-oil-and-gas/

British Columbia Ministry of Environment. (2006). *Information bulletin: Deltaport expansion receives approval from province.* http://www2.news.gov.bc.ca/news_releases_2005-2009/2006ENV0088-001171.htm

British Columbia Ministry of Environment, Oceans and Marine Fisheries Division. (2006). *2005 British Columbia seafood industry year in review.* Victoria: Ministry of Environment.

Bryden, J. (1995a, March 14). Ship loaded with tiny turbot. *Calgary Herald,* p. A2.

Bryden, J. (1995b, March 29). Canada delivers proof of "ecological madness." *Calgary Herald,* p. A3.

Bryden, J. (1995c, March 29). Lonely, unloved turbot clinging by its fingernails, Tobin says. http://www.southam.com/nmc/waves/depth/fishery/turbot032295.html

Canadian Aquaculture Industry Alliance. (2005). *Canadian aquaculture industry profile.* http://www.aquaculture.ca/index.htm

Canadian Arctic Resources Committee. (2002). Action on climate change. *Compass,* p. 7.

Canadian Broadcasting Corporation. (2003, January 30). Rainbow trout may push out Atlantic salmon. *CBC Radio News.* http://cbc.ca/cgi-bin/templates/print.cgi/2003.01.30/salmon trout

Canadian Legal Information Institute. (2006). *Order giving notice of decisions not to add certain species to the list of endangered species, annex 1.* http://www.canlii.org/ca/regu/si2006-61/part244288.html

Chandarana, R. (2002, September 25). Ships dumping bilge are slaughtering birds off Canada. *Reuters.* http://www.enn.com/news/wire-stories/2002/09/09252002/reu_48512.asp

Committee on the Status of Endangered Wildlife in Canada. (2003). *Two Atlantic cod populations designated at risk.* http://www.cosewic.gc.ca/eng/sct7/sct7_3_1_e.cfm

Coward, H., Ommer, K., & Pitcher, T. (Eds.). (2000). *Just fish: Ethics and Canadian marine fisheries.* St. John's, NF: Institute of Social and Economic Research.

Cox, K. (1996, March 16). Who won the great turbot war? *The Globe and Mail.* http://www.docuweb.ca/~pardos/globe.html

David Suzuki Foundation. (2004). *Seas of change: Ten recommendations for sustainable fisheries on the B.C. coast.* Vancouver: Author.

David Suzuki Foundation. (2007). *Marine protected areas.* http://www.davidsuzuki.org/Oceans/Healthy_Oceans/Marine_Conservation/

Davis, D. (2000). Gendered cultures and conflict and discontent: Living "the crisis" in a Newfoundland community. *Women's Studies International Forum, 23*(3), 343–352.

Department of Environment. (n.d.). *Sustainability for commercial fisheries.* http://www.ns.doe.ca/soe/ch6-43.html

Department of Fisheries and Oceans. (1995a, January 27). *Tobin says NAFO must decide equitable sharing arrangement for Greenland halibut.* News release. http://www.ncr.dfo.ca/communic/newsrel/1995/HQ08E.htm

Department of Fisheries and Oceans. (1995b, February 2). *Canada wins critical vote on turbot at NAFO.* News release. http://www.ncr.dfo.ca/communic/newsrel/1995/HQ10E.htm

Department of Fisheries and Oceans. (1995c, February 15). *Tobin says Canada will not let the EU devastate turbot.* News release. http://www.ncr.dfo.ca/communic/newsrel/1995/HQ08E.htm

Department of Fisheries and Oceans. (1995d, July). *The fisheries crisis in the northwest Atlantic.* Backgrounder. http://www.dfo-mpo.gc.ca/media/backgrou/1995/hq-ac16_e.htm

Department of Fisheries and Oceans. (1995e, December 11). *Tobin tables Fisheries Act amendments.* News release. http://www.ncr.dfo.ca/communic/newsrel/1995/HQ140E.htm

Department of Fisheries and Oceans. (2001a). *Herring and minor finfish. Pacific region roe herring fishery: Overview of the fishery.* http://www.pac.dfo-mpo.gc.ca/ops/fm/Herring/ROE/roe.htm

Department of Fisheries and Oceans. (2001b). *North Labrador Arctic char.* DFO Science Stock Status D2-07 (2001). http://www.dfo-mpo.gc.ca/csas/Csas/status/2001/SSR2001_02-07e.pdf

Department of Fisheries and Oceans. (2007). *History: Overfishing and international fisheries and oceans governance.* http://www.dfo-mpo.gc.ca/overfishing-surpeche/history_e.htm

de Selding, P. B. (2005, March 2). Courts limit use of satellite imagery for prosecuting suspected polluters. *Space News.* http://www.space.com/spacenews/oillegal_022805.html

***Drilling on Georges Bank.* (n.d.).** http://biome.bio.dfo.ca/science/drilling.html

Environment Canada. (n.d.). *Marine plastics debris.* http://www.ns.ec.gc.ca/udo/cry.html

Environment Canada. (1994). Sustaining marine resources: Pacific herring fish stocks. *SOE Bulletin,* No. 94-5. Ottawa: Author.

Environment Canada. (2004a). *Canadian Shellfish Sanitation Program (CSSP).* http://www.atl.ec.gc.ca/epb/sfish/cssp.html

Environment Canada. (2004b). *Protecting Canada's coastal and marine environment.* http://www.npa-pan.ca/en/publications/oceas/oceas_e.pdf

Environment Canada. (2005). *What is happening?* http://www.ecoinfo.org/env_ind/region/shellfish/shellfish_e.cfm

Environment Canada. (2006). *Impacts of sea-level rise and climate change on the coastal zone of southeastern New Brunswick.* http://atlantic-web1.ns.ec.gc.ca/slr/default.asp?lang=En

Environment Canada. (2007). *Ecosystem initiatives.* Backgrounder. http://www.ec.gc.ca/ecosyst/backgrounder.html

Fisheries and Oceans Canada. (2003). *Sustainable aquaculture: DFO's Aquaculture Action Plan.* http://dfo-mpo.gc.ca/aquaculture/response_details_program.htm

Fisheries and Oceans Canada. (2005a). *Canada's policy for conservation of wild Pacific salmon.* Vancouver: Author.

Fisheries and Oceans Canada. (2005b). *Oceans Action Plan—Phase I.* http://www.dfo-mpo.gc.ca/media/backgrou/2005/hq-ac47a_e.htm

Fisheries and Oceans Canada. (2006a). *DFO's aquaculture action plan.* http://www.dfo-mpo.gc.ca/Aquaculture/ref/AAP_e.htm

Fisheries and Oceans Canada. (2006b). *Pacific Region, Integrated Fisheries Management Plan, Salmon, Southern B.C.* Ottawa: Minister of Fisheries and Oceans.

Fisheries and Oceans Canada. (2006c). *A scientific review of the potential environmental effects of aquaculture in aquatic ecosystems. Vol. IV.* http://www.dfo-mpo.gc.ca/science/environmental-environnement/sok_enviroeffects_aquaculture/volume_4/VolIV_English.pdf

Fisheries and Oceans Canada, British Columbia Ministry of Environment, University of British Columbia Fisheries Centre, University of Victoria Geography Department, & Environment Canada. (2006). *Alive and inseparable: British Columbia's coastal environment: 2006.* Victoria: Government of British Columbia.

Fisheries and Oceans Canada & Environment Canada. (2006). *Deltaport Third Berth Expansion Project: Comprehensive study report.* Vancouver: Government of Canada. http://www.ceaa-acee.gc.ca/050/documents/16090/16090e.pdf

Fisheries and Oceans Canada, Pacific Region. (2007a). *Atlantic salmon watch program.* http://www-sci.pac.dfo-mpo.gc.ca/aquaculture/aswp/default_e.htm

Fisheries and Oceans Canada, Pacific Region. (2007b). *BC reported escapes from aquaculture facilities.* http://www-sci.pac.dfo-mpo.gc.ca/aquaculture/aswp/Atl_escapes.pdf

Fisheries and Oceans Canada, Pacific Region. (2007c). *First Nations Atlantic salmon watch.* http://www.pac.dfo-mpo.gc.ca/sci/aqua/pages/firstnat_e.htm.

Fisheries Resource Conservation Council. (2003). *2003/2004 conservation requirements for groundfish stocks on the Scotian Shelf and in the Bay of Fundy (4VWX5Z), in Subareas 0, 2 + 3 and redfish stocks.* http://www.frcc.ca/2003/sf2003.pdf

Food and Agriculture Organization. United Nations. (1997). *Code of conduct for responsible fisheries.* http://www.fao.org/DOCREP/005/v9878e/v9878e00.htm

Food and Agriculture Organization. United Nations. (2005). *The code of conduct for responsible fisheries: Moving into the second decade of implementation.* http://www.fao.org/docrep/009/a0699e/A0699E06.htm#6.1

Food and Agriculture Organization. United Nations. (2007). *The state of world fisheries and aquaculture 2006.* Rome: Communication Division, FAO.

Fraser River Action Plan. (n.d.). *Fact sheet 2: Pollution in the Fraser.* http://yvrwww1.pwc.bc.doe.ca/ec/frap/fr-fs2.html

George, J. (2007, June 15). Beluga hunters laud quota increase. *Nunatsiaq News.* http://www.nunatsiaq.com/test/archives/2007/706/70615/news/nunavik/70615_209.html

Gerges, M. A. (1994). Marine pollution monitoring, assessment and control: UNEPs approach and strategy. *Marine Pollution Bulletin, 28*(4), 199–210.

Golden, S. (1993). Shetland tanker spill worries Canadian fish farmers. *Alternatives, 19*(4), 13.

Gomes, M. C. (1995, March 20). Turbot affair: The EC vs Canada. Message posted on fish-ecology mailing list of the Bedford Institute of Oceanography. http://hed.bio.ns.ca/lists/war/msg00050.html

Government of Canada. (2006a). *Implementing Canada's National Programme of Action for the Protection of the Marine Environment from Land-based Activities.* Gatineau, QC: NPA Secretariat.

Government of Canada. (2006b). *Marine pollution prevention: Aerial surveillance program.* Backgrounder. http://www.marinepollution.gc.ca/en/surveillance/backgrounder/menu.htm

Hildebrand, L. P. (1989). *Canada's experience with coastal zone management.* Halifax: Oceans Institute of Canada.

Intergovernmental Panel on Climate Change. (2007). *Climate change 2007: The physical science basis. Contribution of Working Group I to the Fourth Assessment Report of the Intergovernmental Panel on Climate Change.* New York: Cambridge University Press.

International Development Research Centre. (n.d.). *Ocean facts: Land-based sources of ocean pollution.* Ottawa: Author.

Jaimet, K. (2003, May 3). Scientists add Atlantic cod to endangered list. *Calgary Herald,* p. A15.

Lunn, N., & Stirling, I. (2001). Climate change and polar bears: Long-term ecological trends observed at Wapusk National Park. *Research Links, 9*(1), 1, 6–7.

Meissner, D. (1995, March 1). Boat owners set to throw book at roe protesters. *Victoria Times Colonist,* p. B2.

Meltzer, E. (1995). *Overview of the east coast marine environment.* Ottawa: Canadian Arctic Resources Committee/Canadian Nature Federation.

Menon, A. (1998). Shellfish water quality protection program. *Fisheries and Oceans Canada.* http://www.mar.dfo-mpo.gc.ca/science/review/1996/AmarMenon/ Menon_e.html

National Advisory Board on Science and Technology. (1994). *Opportunities from our oceans: Report of the Committee on Oceans and Coasts.* Ottawa: Author.

National Programme of Action. (n.d.). *About the NPA.* http://www.npa-pan.ca/en/about.cfm

Nova Scotia Department of Environment. (n.d.). *Sustainability for commercial fisheries.* http://www.ns.doe.ca/soe/ch6-43.html

Obee, B. (1996). Fragile havens for millions of shorebirds. *Beautiful British Columbia, 38*(2), 24–29.

Olsen, S. (1996, February 29). The primary habitat of our species. *Providence Journal-Bulletin.* http://brooktrout.gso.uri.edu/ProJoEd.html

Ommer, R. (Ed.). (2002). *The resilient outport: Ecology, economy, and society in rural Newfoundland.* St. John's, NF: Institute of Social and Economic Research.

Parfit, M. (1995). Diminishing returns: Exploiting the ocean's bounty. *National Geographic, 188*(5), 2–37.

Pauly, D., & Watson, R. (2003, July). Counting the last fish. *Scientific American, 289*(1), 42–47.

Revel, B. (n.d.). *The fish: The Greenland halibut, or turbot.* http://www.sfu.ca/~revela/thefish.htm

Schram, G. G., & Polunin, N. (1995). The high seas "commons": Imperative regulation of half our planet's surface. *Environment Conservation, 22*(1), 3.

Sinclair, M., & Page, F. (n.d.). *Cod fishery collapses and North Atlantic GLOBEC.* http://www.usglobec.berkeley.edu/usglobec/news/news8/news8sinclair.html

Sorum, A. (2007). *National aerial surveillance plan: Transport Canada program to detect ship source pollution.* http://boatingsailing.suite101.com/article.cfm/national_aerial_surveillance_plan

Statistics Canada. (2000). *Human activity and the environment 2000.* Ottawa: Minister of Industry.

Statistics Canada. (2005). *Aquaculture statistics 2005.* Ottawa: Author.

Statistics Canada. (2007). *Canadian fisheries statistics 2004.* http://www.dfo-mpo.gc.ca/communic/statistics/publications/commercial/cfs/toc_e.htm

Stewart, E. J., Howell, S. E. J., Draper, D., Yackel, D. J., & Tivy, A. (2007, December). Sea ice in Canada's Arctic: Implications for cruise tourism. *Arctic, 80*(4), 370–380.

United Nations. (2003). *The United Nations agreement for the implementation of the provisions of the United Nations Convention on the Law of the Sea of 10 December 1982 relating to the conservation and management of straddling fish stocks and highly migratory fish stocks (in force as from 11 December 2001): Overview.* http://www.un.org/Depts/los/convention_overview_fish_stocks.htm

United Nations Convention on the Law of the Sea. (2004). *Chronological list of ratifications of, accessions and successions to the Convention and the related Agreements as at 16 July 2004.* http://www.un.org/Depts/los/reference_files/chronological_lists_of_ratifications.htm

Wappel, T. (Chair). (2003). *The federal role in aquaculture in Canada: Report of the Standing Committee on Fisheries and Oceans,* 37th Parliament, 2nd Session, No. 24. Ottawa: Queen's Printer. http://cmte.parl.gc.ca/Content/HOC/committee/372/fopo/reports/rp1032312/foporp03/03-cov2-e.htm

Welch, H. E. (1995). Marine conservation in the Canadian Arctic: A regional overview. *Northern Perspectives, 25*(1), 5–17.

Willison, M. (2002). Science and policy for marine sanctuaries. *Biodiversity, 3*(2), 15–20.

Willson, M. F., Gende, S. M., & Marston, B. H. (1998). Fishes and the forest. *Bioscience, 48*(6), 455–462.

World Commission on Environment and Development. (1987). *Our common future.* Oxford: Oxford University Press.

Photo 8–25

Respect for quotas helps prevent overfishing by fishers such as these in Grand Manan, New Brunswick. To learn how well or how poorly Canada performs when it comes to world overfishing, turn to Table C/W-15 in the Canada and the World section.

Forests
and Forestry

Chapter Contents

Chapter Objectives

After studying this chapter you should be able to

- explain the nature and distribution of global forests and Canada's forest resources

- identify a range of human uses of and values associated with forest resources

- describe the impacts of human activities on forests and forest environments

- discuss how historical forest practices have affected the abundance and diversity of present forests

- appreciate the range of ecological, social, and economic issues associated with forestry and how they are interrelated

- consider opportunities for and challenges of achieving sustainable forests and forestry in Canada

INTRODUCTION

As biologically diverse as the people who live here, Canada's forests are a symbol of our national heritage. From the lofty Douglas fir and Sitka spruce in the old-growth temperate rain forests of British Columbia, to the rare sassafras and endangered cucumber trees in the Carolinian forests of southern Ontario, to the ground-hugging black spruce, jack pine, and tamarack of the boreal forest that drapes "like a great green scarf across the shoulders of North America," forests continue to enrich the lives of all Canadians (Natural Resources Canada, 1996a). Indeed, the goal set out by the Canadian Council of Forest Ministers in 1992 (see epitaph) is as relevant today as it was when it was written.

More than 330 communities and 864 000 people are directly and indirectly supported economically by Canada's forests (Natural Resources Canada, 2006). Moreover, forest products are the biggest net contributor to Canada's visible trade balance, to a considerable degree defining Canada's global economic role. Capital investment in the forest industries is massive (Natural Resources Canada, 2000a, b). Yet, employment, trade, and investment figures are only part of the story of the values, products, and services associated with forests. As suggested by the report of the Clayoquot Sound Scientific Panel (1995), Canadian values are shifting from solely supporting timber, to a broader range of nonconsumptive and even spiritual, values. Canadians realize that forests are more than a source of timber and fibre for newsprint and other industrial commodities. Left standing, forests are complex systems that provide many important ecological services such as moderating climate (carbon storage), improving air quality, stabilizing soil, regulating water flow, protecting aquatic ecosystems (in rivers and streams), and providing habitats for plants, fish, and wildlife, including nesting and breeding grounds for many migratory bird species (Environment Canada, 1995; McKibben, 1996; Sierra Club of Canada, 1996).

Recreation and tourism are increasingly important activities in forested environments. The spiritual and cultural values associated with forests, long important to First Nations peoples, are also of great interest to many Canadians and visitors seeking solitude and sanctuary from urban lifestyles (Davidson, 1996). Conversely, many First Nations are exploring how they may use the forests for commercial purposes while retaining species and stands that will serve their spiritual and cultural needs. Specific life forms such as spotted owls and marbled murrelets also rely on large trees within forested ecosystems. Thus, forests are valued for a range of commercial, spiritual, and intrinsic reasons (see Table 9–1).

If Canadian forests are to continue to provide opportunities for jobs, recreation, spiritual expression, and

TABLE 9–1
FOREST ECOSYSTEM–BASED VALUES

Forest Value	Comment
Air quality	Most life on earth depends on a unique chemical reaction—photosynthesis—that happens inside the cells of green plants. The green pigment chlorophyll combines carbon dioxide gas from the air with water from the soil to produce carbohydrates and oxygen. Since plants began to photosynthesize, almost all life has relied on this reaction to produce food, generate oxygen, and remove carbon dioxide. The oxygen people breathe comes from green plants; large forests are major producers of oxygen and also filter pollutants from the air.
Water and soil	Forests act like massive pumps, helping to recycle water, making it repeatedly available for plant growth. Through this action and their extensive rooting systems, forests also help to maintain a regular pattern of water flow in streams and reduce erosion, thus helping to maintain soils and their nutrients. In doing so they help maintain stream conditions favourable for fish and other species.
Climate	Forests capture carbon dioxide and store vast amounts of carbon that might otherwise accumulate in the atmosphere and contribute to global warming. By producing oxygen and absorbing carbon dioxide, forests provide a vital air-conditioning service to the planet.
Biodiversity	Natural (unmanaged) forests are remarkably rich in species. Survival of many species depends on the structural complexity and variety of habitats found in old, natural forests. Managed forests are deliberately simplified to make management easier. This simplification alters resident biodiversity, sometimes dramatically.
Scenic values	People experience scenery over a large area. Thus, to understand scenic resources, it is necessary to look at broad patterns in the landscape. For residents, scenery provides a backdrop to their lives and reflects on their lifestyles. For tourists, scenic resources often provide the context for a trip or recreational activity. Forests are part of many of the world's most highly valued landscapes. To many people, removal of the forest reduces scenic resource values.
Cultural and spiritual values	Forests have values that go beyond specific resource attributes, such as the presence of large trees or deer. They provide traditional foods, materials, and medicinal plants important to Indigenous cultures. As systems, they provide a context in which physical and spiritual events take place. Because of their longevity and many values, forests often form part of the cultural identity of the people who inhabit or live near them.
Economic values	Forests provide many goods, such as wood and its diverse products, fish, wildlife, and water—all of which support human society. The sale of forest products and forest-based experiences generates funds that support health, education, and other social services.
Intergenerational values	Many forest trees, especially those in the Pacific Northwest, are potentially long-lived, some reaching ages greater than 1000 years. Thus, the values associated with any individual forest can benefit many human generations. Values attributed to forests have changed over human history, and it is reasonable to expect that they will continue to change. The obligation of current generations is to sustain forest systems without damaging their potential value for future generations.
Intrinsic Values	Forested ecosystems also have values associated with their existence. Many Canadians believe that forests are part of the country's landscape and simply allowing them to continue to persist for their own sake is an important value to protect.

SOURCE: Adapted from *A Vision and Its Context: Global Context for Forest Practices in Clayoquot Sound,* Clayoquot Sound Scientific Panel, 1995, Report 4 of the Scientific Panel for Sustainable Forest Practices in Clayoquot Sound, Victoria: B.C. Ministry of Forests, p. 4. Copyright © 2000 Province of British Columbia. All rights reserved. Reprinted with permission of the Province of British Columbia.

wildlife habitat, then a central concern is how to maintain the biological diversity on which the multiple benefits and roles of forests depend. In turn, biodiversity conservation requires forest management practices that sustain the health and productivity of forest ecosystems. Within the past two to three decades, a major challenge—internationally as well as in Canada—has been to develop an understanding of the complex environmental, economic, social, and political dimensions of forests (see the section "Canada and the World" at the end of Part III). Both national and provincial governments in Canada

have responded to the growing public concern regarding forests and the environment. They have begun to take actions intended to shift forest management from its historical focus on maintaining timber harvests toward sustainability of forest ecosystems that protect both timber and nontimber values through ecosystem-based land use planning initiatives.

In this chapter, we describe the Earth's forested ecosystems and the ways in which forest practices in Canada have been conducted. We explain the ecological importance of forests, with an emphasis on old-growth forest systems. Along with the impacts of human activities on forests, we discuss Canadian efforts to achieve environmental and social sustainability of forests and forestry.

THE EARTH'S FORESTS

GLOBAL DISTRIBUTION

About 40 percent of the Earth's land surface supports trees or shrub cover. Although estimates vary considerably, one conservative suggestion indicates that forests occupy about 4.0 billion hectares (30.3 percent) of the world's land area, and open woodland and mixed vegetation occupy almost 1.47 billion hectares. The Russian Federation contains the largest concentration of forests and wooded areas (809 million hectares), followed by North America (677 million hectares), Europe (193 million hectares), and the Pacific nations of Australia, Japan, and New Zealand (197 million hectares). Combined, the forests of Brazil, Russia, the United States, Canada, and

China contain more than 50 percent of the Earth's forests (Food and Agriculture Organization, 2007).

Globally, forests may be classified as temperate, boreal, or tropical (see Figure 9–1). Tropical forests, found between the tropics of Cancer and Capricorn, form the most species-diverse ecosystem in the world, containing more than 50 percent of all living species on this planet (Natural Resources Canada, 1996b). In 1990, tropical forests occupied about 1.79 billion hectares, while boreal and temperate forests occupied about 1.67 billion hectares. The predominantly coniferous boreal forests cover 920 million hectares and are located between the Arctic tundra and the temperate zone.

TROPICAL FORESTS: DEGRADATION AND DEFORESTATION

Although tropical rain forests occupy only about 6 percent of the world's land area near, the equator in Latin America, Africa, and Asia, they provide habitat for over one-half of the Earth's plant and animal species, and homes and livelihoods for about 100 million people. The

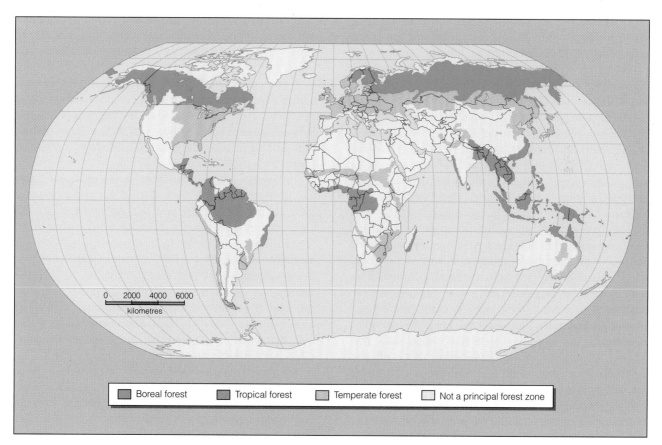

Figure 9–1

Principal forest zones of the world

SOURCE: *The State of Canada's Forests: Sustaining Forests at Home and Abroad, 1996,* Natural Resources Canada, Ottawa: Author, p. 25. Reprinted with permission of the Minister of Public Works and Government Services Canada, 2008.

global importance of tropical forests relates to their ecological functions as well as to the products produced from their plants—nuts, fruits, chocolate, gums, coffee, wood, rubber, pesticides, fibres, and dyes. In particular, people with high blood pressure, Parkinson's or Hodgkin's disease, multiple sclerosis, and leukemia have been treated with drugs made from tropical plants. Scientists believe many more plants with medicinal values remain to be discovered. Despite the range of values, tropical rain forests have been depleted at alarming rates over the past century.

It is difficult to make global assessments of **deforestation**. Internationally, the United Nations Food and Agricultural Organization (FAO) compiles statistics provided by countries themselves. Because the ability of countries to assess their forest resources varies, the accuracy of these data also may vary. Nevertheless, the picture is stark. During the 1980s the area of tropical forests declined dramatically—by an average of 15.4 million hectares annually. An additional 56.3 million hectares were deforested between 1990 and 1995 (Food and Agriculture Organization, 1999). Between 1990 and 2005, Brazil had the dubious distinction of being the leader in forest loss, having cleared 42.3 million hectares. This area is about the size of California. Another way of thinking about deforestation is to calculate the proportion of the forest land base that has been harvested in each country. Comoros (an island nation north of Madagascar) cleared nearly 60 percent of its forests between 1990 and 2005, followed by Burundi (47 percent), Togo (44 percent), Honduras (37 percent), and Mauritania (36 percent) (Lindsey, 2007).

Many interrelated factors, which vary by region and by country, combine to cause deforestation. These include clearing land for crops or livestock (a practice that has been conducted for over 2000 years), providing wood for fuel or building materials, and building infrastructure such as roads or cities. In Latin America, rain forests often are converted to pasture land; in sub-Saharan Africa, they are cleared to meet increasing demands for farmland and firewood; and in Southeast Asia, rain forests provide hardwood products for export to industrialized countries. In some cases, such as in the Amazon, forests have been cleared for large-scale cattle ranching and soybean production to serve a global market. State policies may encourage expansion into forested areas by providing subsidies or tax incentives to increase agricultural production. A country's financial health also may be a factor, especially if a country seeks to use revenues from timber harvests or alternative land uses to pay its foreign debt.

The burden of debt carried by many tropical and developing countries has placed pressures on them to overexploit their resources. Many of the countries with the highest rates of deforestation in the 1980s were also the largest debtors at that time. Furthermore, structural adjustment programs, designed by the World Bank and the International Monetary Fund to address the indebtedness of many developing countries, encouraged countries to engage in export-led economic growth. The result was a massive liquidation of natural resources. For example, Ghana lost 75 percent of its forest area during its economic adjustment in the 1980s (Elliott, 1999). To provide funds for debt servicing, austerity measures by governments often required reductions in programs and agencies that addressed environmental management, health provision, and poverty alleviation. If these countries were able to reduce their payments toward debt relief, they may be able to reduce pressures on environmental resources and improve the infrastructure to protect both their natural resources and social systems. However, decisions about how debts may be reduced frequently are made by the World Bank, the International Monetary Fund, and individual lending countries that historically have not considered environmental protection, poverty alleviation, or improved social welfare in these countries as primary criteria when deciding how best to restructure a country's economy.

The need for foreign exchange also may lead to accelerated timber harvesting. Since 1950, the consumption of tropical hardwoods has increased by a factor of 15, satisfying markets in Japan (which consumes about 60 percent of annual tropical timber production), the United States, and Great Britain. Developing countries often sell off their forests to pay their debts and to create jobs. Surinam, a country on the northeast coast of South America which is 90 percent covered by virgin rain forest, granted large timber concessions to an Indonesian logging company in 1994. This decision was based on the fact that children in Surinam were dying of hunger and cutting forests would provide people with the jobs they needed to purchase food (Bequette, 1994).

Firewood consumption adds to the problem of tree loss in developing countries. Half of the world's wood is used as fuel for cooking and heating, and yet in 1985, about one in three people on Earth were unable to get enough fuelwood to meet basic needs or were forced to meet those needs by consuming wood faster than it was being replenished. Wood scarcity creates considerable hardship for poor families, as buying fuelwood or charcoal can take 40 percent of a family's small income. Women, especially, often have to walk long distances to gather fuel. If they cannot get enough fuelwood, poor families often burn dried animal dung and crop residues. This means that these natural fertilizers are not returned to the soil, and, as cropland productivity declines, hunger and malnutrition increase. In addition, cutting trees for fuelwood often results in increased erosion and may even lead to permanent lowering of water tables.

The effects of these multiple factors can be extreme: countries that once exported timber—Nigeria and the Philippines, for example—now import it. Other Southeast

Photo 9–1

People in developing nations rely heavily on fuelwood cutting, which threatens renewability of forests and associated resources.

Asian and Central American nations have almost totally deforested their lands: Haiti has lost 98 percent of its original forest cover, the Philippines 97 percent, and Madagascar 84 percent (International Tropical Timber Organization, 1999). Most cleared tropical forests are not replanted, in part because timber companies are held responsible for few of the costs of environmental degradation, and in part because of corrupt, deeply entangled local practices (Dauvergne, 1997). And yet, people in developing countries also have demonstrated a deep commitment to forest protection. The Chipko movement of India where men and women hugged trees to protect them from being harvested and the intensive planting of trees in Guinea as human populations increased illustrate this commitment. We cannot assume that poor people living in developing countries are more likely to degrade their forest environments because of their economic circumstances. Examples of forest degradation and renewal alike illustrate how environmental sustainability cannot be achieved without an understanding of and action on economic and social fronts.

FORESTS AND FORESTRY IN CANADA

Among the 12 regions classified in Figure 9–2 (p. 362), eight are considered to be major forest regions in Canada, covering approximately 46 percent of our land base. The three types of boreal forests occupy more than one-third of Canada, constituting the country's largest biome and providing direct employment for an estimated 339 900 people. British Columbia's high-volume coastal (temperate) forests, however, produce a relatively large share of Canada's forest products and, because of the large size of the trees, account for about 46 percent of the annual volume cut in Canada. The other major forest regions shown in Figure 9–2 are the Columbian, Deciduous, Great Lakes–St. Lawrence, and Acadian. With about 402.1 million hectares of forested land, Canada is caretaker of about 10 percent of the world's forests, including about 19 percent of the world's softwood supply (see Table 9–2, p. 363, for additional Canadian forest facts).

Worldwide, the amount of forest is decreasing. Most of the loss of forests is recent, 60 percent having occurred since the Industrial Revolution. In North America, 64 million hectares were cleared for settlement and agriculture between 1860 and 1978 (Clayoquot Sound Scientific Panel, 1995). In Canada, between 1979 and 1997, the average area harvested (logged) was almost 1 million hectares (or 0.4 percent of Canada's productive forest) per year, and the average annual volume of wood harvested was 163 million cubic metres.

Unlike most nations, the vast majority (94 percent) of Canada's forests are publicly owned. Provincial governments manage 71 percent of forest lands, federal and territorial governments manage 23 percent, while the remaining 6 percent of Canada's forest lands are owned privately (see Figure 9–3, p. 364). Forest management in Canada is a matter of provincial jurisdiction; each province, as well as the Northwest Territories and Nunavut, has its own legislation, policies, and regulations to govern forest activities within its boundaries.

While most forest land is considered provincial Crown land, in Prince Edward Island (92 percent), Nova Scotia (69 percent), and New Brunswick (51 percent), most land is privately held, often in private woodlots. Woodlot owners are not subject to provincial regulations, so the challenges of sustainable management are different than in the rest of Canada, where Crown land dominates. Forest management practices on woodlots in the Maritimes are highly variable, and, in New Brunswick, logging continues at a faster rate than replanting on most woodlots (see Box 9–1, p. 365). Bearing in mind the deep criticisms of corporate forestry in the rest of Canada, experiences in the Maritimes suggest that neither private nor public ownership of land will necessarily ensure that forestry practices are sustainable or achieve a balanced set of objectives.

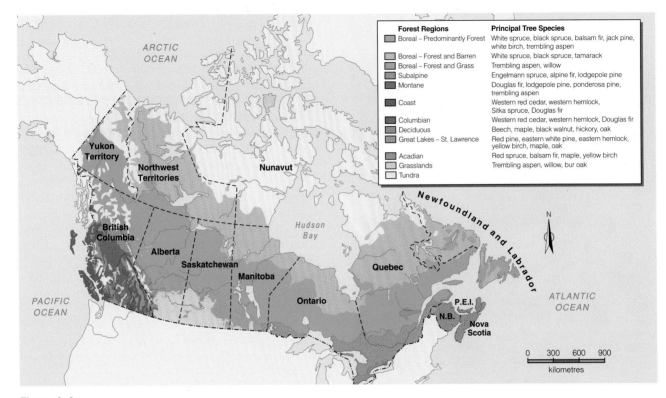

Figure 9–2

Forest regions of Canada

SOURCE: *The State of Canada's Forests: A Balancing Act,* 1995, Natural Resources, Ottawa. Reprinted with permission of the Minister of Public Works and Government Services Canada, 2008.

Forest products continue to be one of the largest contributors to Canada's balance of trade (Natural Resources Canada, 2000a). In 2006, for instance, Canada's forest products exports were valued at approximately $38.2 billion; softwood lumber, newsprint, and wood pulp account for most of these exports (Natural Resources Canada, 2007). In 2006, the forest sector contributed $36.3 billion to Canada's gross domestic product and $28.1 billion to Canada's balance of trade (Natural Resources Canada, 2007).

Until recently, deforestation was a term applied mostly to tropical rain forests, but deforestation also occurs in Canada. In regard to our timber-cutting practices, during the 1990s, environmental activists referred to Canada—particularly British Columbia—as the "Brazil of the North" (Hammond, 1991; Friends of the earth, n.d.). The timber industry and the provincial government denied the comparison, pointing out that Amazon rain forests are being cleared for agricultural uses, whereas Canada's forests are being regenerated for timber. However, some critics estimate that until the 1990s, about 50 percent of the logged area in Canada did not regenerate to productive species within five years of cutting (Diem, 1992). In addition, during the period 1979 to 1993, only 36 percent of the area harvested was replanted or seeded; the remainder was left to "regenerate naturally," in an effort

to "help maintain the natural diversity of the forest *and reduce costs*" (Natural Resources Canada, 1996b, p. 88; emphasis added). Nevertheless, basic silviculture has been significantly extended, especially in British Columbia and Quebec (Hayter, 1996, p. 105). In British Columbia, for many years now, the number of trees planted has exceeded the number of trees harvested, planting frequently has involved a variety of species to suit site-specific conditions, and slash burning has been reduced greatly. In 2005, 569.2 million seedlings were planted on provincial Crown lands in Canada, accounting for 446 000 hectares (Natural Resources Canada, 2007). Of these seedlings, it is estimated that almost 183 million were planted in British Columbia and 126 million were planted in Ontario (Canadian Council of Forest Ministers, 2005). In 2004, 362 036 hectares of trees were planted throughout Canada. The majority of trees planted are spruce, followed by pine and other softwoods. In total, 43 percent of trees are replanted and 4 percent are direct-seeded.

The federal department Natural Resources Canada is examining the feasibility of increasing forest cover on agricultural lands to help Canada meet its commitments to reducing carbon emissions (see Chapter 5). It is not clear, however, whether the amount of land that could be returned to forest cover would be sufficient to make a significant contribution to these commitments.

TABLE 9–2
SELECTED FACTS ABOUT FORESTS IN CANADA

Forested Lands

- Forests cover 402.1 million hectares (almost 46 percent) of Canada's land base (882.1 million hectares).
- 56 percent, or 234.5 million hectares, are considered commercial forests.
- 38 percent, or 156.2 million hectares, are open forests consisting of muskeg, marshes, and sparse tree cover.
- Most (94 percent) are publicly owned: provincial governments manage 71 percent, federal and territorial governments manage 23 percent, and the remaining 6 percent is private property of 425 000 landowners.

Commercial Forests

- 143.7 million hectares are managed for timber production.
- Over 12 percent, or 50 million hectares, are protected from harvesting by legislation (heritage forests) or policy (protection forests).
- Annually, in recent years, about 0.3 percent of the accessible commercial forest is harvested, removing an average of 30.9 million hectares of timber and contributing about $37.6 billion to Canada's gross domestic product.

Forest Regions (see Figure 9–2)

- Boreal
- Subalpine
- Montane
- Coast
- Columbian
- Deciduous
- Great Lakes–St. Lawrence
- Acadian

Forest Type (2000)

- Softwood (e.g., pine, spruce)   62 percent
- Hardwood (e.g., poplar, maple)   16 percent
- Mixed wood   22 percent

Tree Species

- Approximately 180

Total Annual Allowable Cut Estimates (millions of cubic metres)

Year	Total	Softwoods	Hardwoods
1994	239	179	60
1995	236	176	60
1996	236	176	60
1997	239	177	62
1998	238	176	62
1999	239	177	62
2000	235	174	60
2001	237	177	60
2002	238	178	60
2003	239	179	60
2004	246	186	60

SOURCES: *Compendium of Canadian Forestry Statistics 1996,* Canadian Council of Forest Ministers, 1997, Ottawa; "Sustaining Canada's Forests: Timber Harvesting," Environment Canada, 1995, *Overview SOE Bulletin,* no. 95-4 (Summer); *Wood Supply Introduction,* National Forestry Database Program, 2006, Ottawa: Author; *The State of Canada's Forests 1995–1996: Sustaining Forests at Home and Abroad,* Natural Resources Canada, Canadian Forest Service, 1996, Ottawa: Author; *The State of Canada's Forests 1996–1997: Learning from History,* Natural Resources Canada, Canadian Forest Service, 1997, Ottawa: Author; *The State of Canada's Forests 1997–1998: The People's Forests,* Natural Resources Canada, Canadian Forest Service, 1998, Ottawa: Author; *The State of Canada's Forests 1998–1999: Globally Competitive through Innovation,* Natural Resources Canada, Canadian Forest Service, 1999, Ottawa: Author; *The State of Canada's Forests 1999–2000: Advancing into the New Millennium,* Natural Resources Canada, Canadian Forest Service, 2000, Ottawa: Author; *Natural Resources Fact Sheet,* Natural Resources Canada, 2000, http://www.nrcan.gc.ca/statistics/factsheet.htm; *The State of Canada's Forests 2000–2001: Sustainable Forestry: A Reality in Canada,* Natural Resources Canada, Canadian Forest Service, 2001a, Ottawa: Author; *The State of Canada's Forests 2002–2003: Looking Ahead,* Natural Resources Canada, Canadian Forest Service, 2004, Ottawa: Author; *The State of Canada's Forests 2005–2006: Forest Industry Competitiveness,* Natural Resources Canada, Canadian Forest Service, 2006, Ottawa: Author.

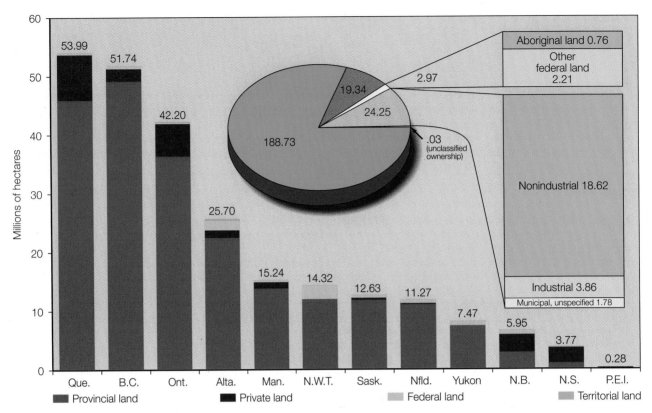

Figure 9–3

Ownership of timber productive forest lands

SOURCES: Data from *Compendium of Canadian Forestry Statistics, 1996,* Canadian Council of Forest Ministers, 1997, Ottawa: Author, Figure 1, p. 1; *The State of Canada's Forests 2001–2002,* Natural Resources Canada, Canadian Forest Service, 2002, Ottawa: Author; *Canada's National Forest Inventory* (CanFI 92, V. 94), Natural Resources Canada, Canadian Forest Service, 2002, http://cfs.nrcan.gc.ca/subsite/canfi/data-summaries-2/1

Questions have been raised about whether current rates of production are too high to permit forests to replenish themselves and to promote forest sustainability (Hammond, 1991; M'Gonigle & Parfitt, 1994; Sierra Club of Canada, 1996). Related to questions about the rate of wood cutting in Canada are concerns about the impacts of different harvesting systems, the feasibility of establishing tree plantations, the "timber bias," and the implications of the inevitable shift from harvesting old-growth to newer-growth forests (called the fall-down effect). A brief discussion of these concerns follows.

Harvesting Systems

Clear-cutting remains the dominant method of harvesting in Canada. In 2005, 87.8 percent of Canada's timber harvest was clear-cut, while 5.2 percent was cut by selection methods (Canadian Council of Forest Ministers, 2005). These data probably include other forms of logging referred to in Table 9–3 and Figure 9–4, such as patch cutting, as well as other variations such as partial retention. Interestingly, the highest level of clear-cutting occurred on provincially owned land, while the lowest

level of clear-cutting took place on federally owned land (see Table 9–4). Timber companies prefer clear-cutting because it is normally the most cost-effective way to harvest trees. It is also the safest system for loggers, and foresters have argued that on many sites it is ecologically the most appropriate form of logging (Kimmins, 1992).

Clear-cutting is sometimes defended as a method of logging that mimics natural disturbances. To some degree this may be true in boreal forests, where fire means renewal (for example, seeds in cones of black spruce and lodgepole pine are released by fire). Clear-cutting, like fire, may establish site conditions conducive to regeneration (Hebert et al., 1995). In ancient temperate rain forests, however, there is no forest-fire dependent cycle and clear-cutting may have numerous negative effects, including landslides, water pollution, loss of plants and animals, and soil degradation. Replanting after clear-cutting can be extremely difficult.

In practice, clear-cutting throughout Canada (and elsewhere) typically focused first on the most accessible, high-quality forests, leaving less-accessible, often lower-quality forest areas for later harvest. This is a practice known as **highgrading**. While highgrading typically

BOX 9-1
PRIVATE WOODLOTS IN THE ATLANTIC PROVINCES

The fact that more than half of Atlantic forests are in the hands of private owners has different implications for sustainable forest management than in the rest of Canada, where the vast majority of forests are on Crown land. In the Atlantic provinces, private woodlots are not subject to provincial forestry regulations but are considered freehold property where owners may use the resource as they choose.

There are more than 425 000 private forest owners in Canada who own more than 18 million hectares or 12 percent of Canada's commercially productive forest land. While some of this land is owned and operated by large forestry corporations, most is classified as private woodlots, private property used for, or capable of, growing trees, and with an average size of 40 hectares (National Round Table on Environment and Economy [NRTEE], 1997). Because they represent such a large percentage of forested lands in the Atlantic provinces, private woodlots are critically important for all the economic, social, cultural, and ecological reasons discussed in this chapter. However, there has been serious concern about the sustainability of woodlot forestry in this region in the last two decades. For example, the NRTEE (1997) found that a combination of overharvesting, lack of forest stewardship practices, and a perception that there are no apparent economic incentives to manage woodlot forests sustainably could create a forest industry collapse in the Maritimes similar to the collapse of the ground fishery in Atlantic Canada (see Chapter 8).

Unlike Crown lands used for forestry, private forest lands do not have an assigned annual allowable cut. Consequently, it is difficult to determine how much will be cut in any given year. Silvicultural investment is critical for sustaining current harvest levels yet public funding for silviculture in the 1990s and 2000s has been highly variable. Private woodlot owners are also interested in becoming certified, however, undertaking certification is difficult because private landowners typically do not draw up management plans. Additionally, the spruce budworm, a major pest that affected forest yields in the 1970s, is only temporarily halted and landowners are bracing for another infestation.

Nevertheless, there is movement on these challenges. In 1997, the NRTEE made several recommendations to promote sustainable forest practices through voluntary measures, tax incentives, and industry-supported trust funds (NRTEE, 1997). In Nova Scotia, a regulation was introduced that placed the onus on buyers of large quantities of primary forest products to undertake some of the responsibility toward sustainable forestry. On the industry side, one Maritime pulp and paper company pays a bonus for fibre from private woodlots and is providing private owners with nominally priced seedlings to encourage replanting (Natural Resources Canada, 2000). Additionally, the Fundy Model Forest worked with private landowners in the early 2000s to demonstrate good silvicultural practices and to promote the cultivation of non-timber forest products. Additionally, in 2003, they established an informal network with organizations and government agencies in Canada and Maine to provide educational materials and promote family forest owner education and communication. Together, these initiatives help encourage environmental, economic, and social sustainability of Atlantic forests.

SOURCES: *State of the Debate on the Environment and the Economy: Private Woodlot Management in the Maritimes,* National Round Table on the Environment and Economy (NRTEE), 1997, Ottawa: Author; *The State of Canada's Forests, 1992–2000. Forests in the New Millennium. Species at Risk,* Natural Resources Canada, 2000, Ottawa: Author, http://www.nrcan.gc.ca/cfs/proj/ppiab/sof/sof00/spart3.html; *Innovations: The Canadian Model Forest Association Newsletter,* Canadian Model Forest Association, 2005, http://www.modelforest.net/CMFN/uploadedDocuments/Innovations_5-2_en.pdf *The Canadian Forest Resource in Atlantic Canada: an overview of issues that impact wood production,* Canadian Forest Service, n.d. Ottawa: Author.

TABLE 9-3
FOREST HARVESTING METHODS

Method	Characteristics
Selective (or selection) cutting	• The original forest is of varied species and ages. • Only the most valuable species of trees or only trees of prescribed size or quality are cut. • The forest is left to regenerate naturally. • Trees are cut individually or in small clusters. • About 7 percent of Canada's timber has been cut using selective techniques.
Shelterwood cutting	• The original forest may be evenly or unevenly aged. • All mature trees are removed in a series of cuttings, stretched out over about 10 years. • First cut removes most canopy trees, unwanted tree species, and diseased, defective, and dying trees.

(continued)

TABLE 9–3
(CONTINUED)

Method	Characteristics
	• After a decade or so, when enough seedlings have taken hold, a second cut removes more canopy trees but leaves some of the best mature trees to shelter the young trees.
	• After perhaps another decade, a third cut removes the remaining mature trees and the remaining uniformly aged stand of young trees grows to maturity.
Seed tree cutting	• The original forest is harvested in one cutting, but a few uniformly distributed trees are left to provide seeds for regeneration.
	• After the new trees have become established, the seed trees may be cut.
	• About 4 percent of Canada's timber is cut using the shelterwood cutting and seed tree methods.
Clear-cutting	• Clear-cutting removes all the trees from an original forest at the same time.
	• Trees may be cut as whole stands, as strips, or as patches.
	• After the trees are cut, the forest may be left to regenerate naturally or may be replanted.
	• Clear-cut areas have varied in size (from small patches to thousands of hectares).
	• Almost 90 percent of Canada's timber is cut using clear-cutting.
Patch (clear) cutting	• Patch clear-cutting leaves small-scale clear-cut areas, perhaps 100 to 200 hectares in size.
	• Several clear-cut patches adjacent to one another can result in a continuous clear-cut.
Strip cutting	• Strip cutting involves clear-cutting narrow rows of forest, perhaps 80 metres wide, leaving wooded corridors that may serve as seed sources.
	• After regeneration, another strip is cut above the first, and so on, allowing the forest area to be clear-cut in narrow strips over several decades.
Whole tree harvesting	• Machines harvest entire trees (including roots, leaves, bark, small branches) and cut them into small chips to be used as pulpwood or fuelwood products.
	• Another variation of clear-cutting, this method deprives soil of plant nutrients and can support replanted trees only if they are fertilized.

(a) Selection cutting

(b) Shelterwood cutting

(c) Clear-cutting

(d) Patch cutting

Figure 9–4
Major systems of tree harvesting

SOURCE: *The State of Canada's Forests: A Balancing Act,* Natural Resources Canada, 1995. Reprinted with permission of the Minister of Public Works and Government Services Canada, 2008.

TABLE 9-4

PERCENTAGE OF LAND HARVESTED IN 2005 BY CLEAR-CUTTING AND SELECTION CUTTING BY OWNERSHIP TYPE

	Provincial Crown Land	Private Land	Federal Crown Land*	Total
Clear-cutting (includes shelterwood cutting)	88.7	81.6	69.7	87.8
Selection cutting	4.2	11.7	14.4	5.2
Commercial thinning	6.9	6.7	15.1	6.9

* Harvest type on a small amount of federal land is not specified. The numbers are too low, however, to change the overall proportions

SOURCE: "Silviculture Quick Facts," *National Forestry Database Program,* © Canadian Council of Forest Ministers, 2005, http://nfdp.ccfm.org/compendium/silviculture/summary_e.php

Photo 9–2
This clear-cut area shows signs of initial regrowth.

yields high short-term economic returns, it may have long-term ecological consequences. Since accessibility and timber quality often overlap (if by no means perfectly), many of the highest-quality forests across Canada have long since been logged. Consequently, some nonindustrial values, such as high-quality seed sources (with genetic codes adapted precisely to sites), have been lost forever.

In Canada, highgrading rarely means "cherry picking" the very best individual trees from a forest. Rather, highgrading typically occurs within the system of clear-cutting, where all trees are removed from large continuous tracts and from entire watersheds. The removal rate may occur in a short time (five years) or over a longer period of 20 or 30 years, but the impacts that occur are similar.

Until recently, clear-cuts across Canada were extremely large (hundreds of hectares), and the practice of **continuous clear-cutting**—in which cut blocks are located adjacent to each other in successive years—rapidly laid bare much larger areas. Since 1995 in British Columbia, continuous clear-cutting has been banned and the size of permissible clear-cuts greatly reduced as part of efforts to create a more environmentally sensitive forest sector (Hayter, 2000).

Clear-cutting results in—and is defined by—altered microclimates (Kimmins, 1992). Clear-cutting removes cover needed by wildlife and new plant growth, degrades the soil, damages fish habitat and water quality, and destroys the forest diversity needed to sustain all forest uses, including future timber supplies (Hammond, 1991). With very large clear-cuts, especially in association with continuous clear-cutting, these problems become more serious. The tendency to cut the most accessible and the best first also means that every year both the quality and the value of the remaining forest declines (Clapp, 1998). The timber now standing in many provinces is less valuable per tree and costs more to log than the average-quality timber of a few decades ago.

As clear-cutting–highgrading depletes high-volume, high-value old-growth forests, it also results in a decline in the average volume of timber per hectare in remaining old-growth forests. This means that for the same land area, the volume and the quality of the timber removed are less. If timber managers seek to "sustain" the volume or the value of their cut, they must log a larger forest area each year. As British Columbia's coastal old-growth forests were clear-cut, for instance, timber companies moved into the interior of the province, to higher elevations, and to more remote parts of the coast where the trees are smaller, requiring more land area to be cleared to supply the volume of wood needed to feed local mills. Elsewhere

CHAPTER 9: FORESTS AND FORESTRY

in Canada, after a century or more of clear-cutting, the loss of the Atlantic hardwood forests and almost 90 percent of the Carolinian forests has forced companies in the eastern and central provinces to reach into more remote regions of their provinces to supply societal demands. In New Brunswick, for instance, clear-cutting of the remote Christmas Mountains region, the only old-growth forest left in the province, began in 1992.

After clear-cutting, forest firms engage in some form of **silviculture** or managed forestry, defined as the "theory and practice of controlling the establishment, composition, growth and quality of forest stands. Basic silviculture means planting and seeding; intensive silviculture includes site rehabilitation, spacing and fertilization" (Natural Resources Canada, 2000b, p. 110). Traditionally, the most common approach to re-creating a forest, albeit in much simplified form, first emphasized slash burning, where debris (natural supplies of woody material on the ground and in the soil) was removed by fire. The conventional wisdom was that slash burning facilitated regeneration, including natural regeneration. Moreover, as commitment to planting trees in slash-burned areas increased after the 1960s, there was a strong tendency to plant one or two species only (known as monoculture), to be grown and cut again in short cycles of 60 to 120 years. In a third silvicultural step, brush may be removed, often with chemical pesticides, as forest managers attempt to maximize timber growth by controlling or eliminating competing forms of life from the forest.

This kind of three-step basic silviculture—slash burning, monoculture, and brush removal—poses problems, however. Slash burning increases greenhouse gases, increases the likelihood of soil erosion, decreases the availability of soil nutrients, and creates human health problems. Respiratory ailments are of particular concern as slash-burning smoke contains two carcinogens, namely formaldehyde and polynuclear aromatic hydrocarbons.

While it is easy to criticize clear-cutting and its associated practices, alternatives to clear-cut logging also pose challenges for sustainability. At least four issues arise, if we criticize clear-cut logging. First, under contemporary arrangements, clear-cutting is undoubtedly the least expensive means of logging. Other strategies such as patch-cutting or selective logging may require specialized equipment that is very expensive to operate (e.g., helicopters), or the construction of more access roads.

Second, where selective forms of harvesting require more patches to be protected from harvest, both economic and ecological concerns arise due to the cost of building access roads. Road building is the most ecologically damaging activity related to timber harvesting, often resulting in undesirable environmental effects such as soil compaction and erosion, disturbance of natural water courses, and loss of soil cover and nutrients. With the exception of helicopter logging (which is the most expensive option), the smaller the cut area, the larger the number of access roads required, and the greater the ecological impact.

Third, safety of forest workers is also a key issue. Logging is a dangerous occupation and clear-cutting remains the safest method of felling trees. In other methods of selective logging where trees are left standing within an active logging area, loggers themselves are at high risk for fallen trees and other "debris" in the area. In some cases, worker compensation boards require that clear-cutting be undertaken in order to protect the safety of forest workers.

Fourth, where logging historically has been undertaken using a particular regime (e.g., clear-cut logging), a change to new harvesting methods may result in job lay-offs, increased training requirements, and the shedding of a long-standing workforce. In many cases, loggers have built their livelihood and identity on skills they have learned over many years of work in the woods. They believe that they make a key contribution to society by providing a product that is in heavy demand by urbanites and others who build homes, city infrastructure, and paper products from timber. Changes in logging practices may threaten both the incomes and long-held beliefs of woods workers related to their value in contemporary society. Politicians who are sensitive to their constituents may be reluctant to make policy decisions about harvesting if they believe such decisions would be vehemently opposed by their electorate. This is part of the issue of being "trapped by staples," described in Box 10–2 (p. 412). These issues illustrate the complexity of sustainability. As we consider changes that we believe are ecologically responsible, we face challenges related to social and economic elements of sustainability. The choices are not always clear (see also Box 4–5, p. 129).

Tree Plantations

One type of forestry practice is the tree plantation, where trees of uniform size grow in straight rows and are logged by machines. This practice works best in warmer climates where some species, such as eucalyptus, can be grown in 20 years. In Canada, however, such practices are controversial. Tree plantations tend not to be labour intensive. Plantations that produce products (such as disposable chopsticks) made from single-species trees of a uniform size require much less labour because production systems are highly mechanized and the range of products is very limited. The wood that comes from monoculture forests can be made into pulp and composite products such as fibre board. Consequently, over time, as natural forests are reduced to fibre farms, both tree sizes and employment will decline (Hammond, 1991; M'Gonigle & Parfitt, 1994). In addition, tourism and recreational values and opportunities that depend on more diverse forest values may be reduced or even destroyed. Biological diversity is lost, as is the ability of the forest to buffer climate change, because large carbon sinks are gone (see Chapter 5), water quality is frequently reduced (due to possible contamination from pesticides used in the clearing of brush), and species are eliminated.

Research is being conducted in many countries to determine what benefits genetically modified (GM) trees may offer. Most of the research is being conducted in laboratories in Europe, North America, and Asia, but some countries have introduced GM trees, including China. In 2002, China planted 1.4 million poplars in an effort to produce more fibre quickly and introduced nine other trial plantings across the country. GM trees grow more quickly than their native counterparts and they contain less lignin. This makes the trees cheaper to make into pulp, but it also may reduce their fitness in the environment and lead to decreases in biomass and biodiversity. Because forestry is not as large an industry globally as agriculture, it is not clear that the benefits of using GM trees outweigh the economic, environmental, and social costs of their development and introduction.

Replacement of diverse old-growth forests with monoculture stands brings potential problems, including rapid spread of wildfires in evenly aged stands, blowdown

Photo 9–3

Most tree plantations are characterized by stark rows of one or two species of similar age. Underbrush is absent.

due to poor root formation in planted trees, and loss in the number and variety of mycorrhizal fungi needed for seedling growth (Hammond, 1991). Additionally, monoculture may increase the risk of massive losses through pest infestations. Some studies are seeking to determine whether GM trees can be created that can withstand pest infestations without the use of pesticides; however, other ecological risks of such introductions have not yet been considered carefully. Finally, brush provides shade for young trees and cover for animals, enriches the soil, and repels unwanted insects. In natural forests, brush plays an important role in sustaining the whole forest (as does every other organism). While economically viable from a forest industry perspective, development of plantation forests potentially reduces both economic and biological diversity (M'Gonigle & Parfitt, 1994; Taylor, 1994). In short, tree plantations are not the same as old-growth forests.

Yet, even though single-species plantations are not forests, there may be a place for some plantations under particular circumstances. There is the possibility that plantations of hybrid cottonwoods or genetically uniform Douglas fir—if not grown on good forest land and not displacing natural forests or their regeneration—could become sources of employment and regional income. Some new towns could be based on scientific research related to plantation forestry as well as exploitation of these unnatural forests (Schoonmaker, von Hagen, & Wolf, 1997).

The Timber Bias and the Consequences of a Volume-Based Economy

For many decades, a great number of Canadians and their governments have viewed trees as timber and forests as log supply centres; Canada's institutional approach to forest management has evolved out of that perspective. Typically, politicians legislated for timber cutting and production, and not for forest protection and the stewardship of diverse ecosystems. The "timber bias" prevalent in our use of forests has resulted in a number of ecological, economic, and sociocultural impacts visible on the landscape and in communities.

Early timber industry barons viewed forests as a limitless timber supply. As evidence accumulated that this was not the case, government and industry embraced the idea of **sustained-yield** forest management. The commonly held interpretation of sustained yield is that timber should be cut no faster than new trees can grow so that an even flow of timber in perpetuity may be obtained. In effect, this concept means that, if yield is to be maintained, all the trees cut down should be replaced each year with new trees that are allowed to mature to a size comparable to the original trees on the site before they are logged. This simple concept becomes obscured in practice, however.

Tree growth data show that the average annual accumulation of wood *volume* (not wood *quality*) peaks

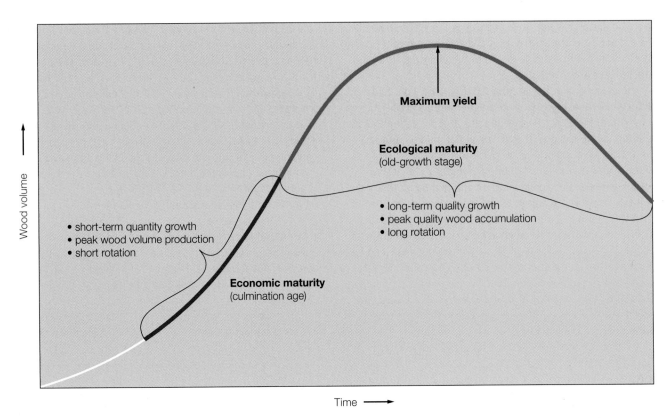

Figure 9–5

Timber volume production

before the old-growth stage (see Figure 9–5). Timber managers want to grow trees to the point where average timber volume production is greatest (this is called the *culmination age*), and then clear-cut the trees to produce the greatest timber volume over time. Timber managers consider trees at culmination age—60 to 120 years old—to be "mature"; they rationalize that old-growth or "decadent" timber should be cut down because it grows timber volume too slowly.

The word "mature" is used differently by foresters and by scientists. Foresters use the term to mean the *economic maturity* of a tree or forest stand—the youngest age at which the trees can be cut and sold for a profit. On the other hand, scientists call wood mature when it has developed its maximum fibre length—that is, the *natural* or *ecological maturity* at which trees develop their strongest and highest-value wood. A tree is not ecologically mature until it has passed through all forest stages from shrub to old growth. For short-lived tree species, this may be 200 to 300 years, but in long-lived species, trees may take up to 1500 years to reach ecological maturity. Trees and forests may live for centuries after reaching maturity, during which time they perform vital ecological functions and accumulate the highest-quality wood of their lifetimes (Franklin, 1984). Clearly, economic maturity is reached far sooner than ecological maturity.

Cutting trees at economic maturity versus ecological maturity, however, is a little like picking green tomatoes instead of waiting for ripe tomatoes. When green, tomatoes have nearly the same volume as red, ripe tomatoes, but the ripe fruit of the tomato is far more desirable and far more valuable. Just as ripe tomatoes sell for a lot more money than green tomatoes, high-quality, old-growth wood can be sold for a lot more than economically mature wood (Hammond, 1991).

In order to calculate how much timber should be cut in any one year (called the annual allowable cut, or AAC), current Canadian forestry practice relies on a measure called the *rotation period*. For any given species, its rotation period is the length of time required to grow a tree to economic maturity. Actual calculations of the annual allowable cut are complicated, however; the rotation period, the total available natural old-growth timber volume, and the annual growth of the forest are the most important factors affecting calculation of the AAC.

A serious issue with respect to forestry is the declining number of people who are required to undertake it. In British Columbia, for example, total forest sector employees (in logging and processing) declined from 1.32 per 1000 cubic metres harvested in 1963 to 0.85 in 1995 (Marchak, Aycock, & Herbert, 1999). This decline suggests that to maintain the workforce in forestry, either more wood must be cut or better use must be made of it. It is often argued that secondary wood processing—such as making cabinets, mouldings, panelling, furniture, and guitar tops from lumber—adds value and results in higher levels of employment generated from each tree cut. In fact, value can be added by capital and technology, as well as labour, and greater efficiency requires less labour. Nevertheless, in British Columbia, which has the highest quality and highest volume of timber per hectare of any province in Canada, the value added to wood products in 1984 was only about half that added in the rest of Canada. In spite of its large timber production, for every one job per 1000 cubic metres of timber (about 33 truckloads of logs) produced in British Columbia in 1984, 2.2 jobs were produced from the same amount of timber in the rest of Canada (Hammond, 1991; Hayter, 2000; Travers, 1993). This discrepancy suggests that there are unrealized value-added potentials in British Columbia.

In 2005, of the 79 700 forest sector workers in British Columbia, about 45 800 were employed in wood manufacturing (including sawmills), 21 600 in logging and reforestation, and 12 300 in the paper industry (British Columbia Ministry of Advanced Education, 2006a, 2006b). Overall, employment in the wood industry (sawmills and wood manufacturing) has been stable the past 15 years despite the softwood lumber dispute with the United States. However, 36 percent fewer people work in paper industries and 18 percent fewer people work in logging than 15 years ago. As access to timber declines (see the next section), the employment in all sectors of the industry is also expected to drop. To maintain employment, some researchers and organizations have advocated a shift toward increasing the value of wood products through additional manufacturing.

The Falldown Effect

Diversity is the cornerstone of a stable, healthy forest and of a stable, healthy economy. Given that forest diversity is achieved through forest protection, and that we do not understand fully how forests work, it would seem reasonable that forest management activities should give priority to, and be consistent with, protection and ecological sustainability. However, timber managers are aware that their monoculture tree plantations and managed natural stands will never produce the amount or quality of timber provided by the old natural forests they are replacing.

Foresters call the reduction in the volume of production caused by the shift from exploiting old-growth forests to producing managed (monoculture or more diverse) forests *falldown*. Government projections of falldown estimate that future harvests will be 20 to 30 percent below allowable annual cuts; other forecasts are highly variable. Falldown occurs because old-growth forests have typically had a long time to produce the fibre for which they are renowned. Although definitions vary (see Kimmins, 1992), old-growth forests often are thought of as forests that contain trees 200 to 1000 or more years old and that have not been seriously changed by human action. Yet, when these forests are harvested, they are typically placed on a rotation schedule of approximately 60 to 120 years. That

means that an old-growth tree that may be cut after 200 years would be replaced by a tree that is "ready to harvest" in 60 to 120 years. The shorter period between harvests means there is less time to build the biomass, hence the resulting reduction in harvest volume. If falldown is to be avoided—both biologically and economically—new-growth forests would have be cut on 200- to 400-year cycles or rotation periods (Hammond, 1991). (See also the section "The Need for Protection" later in this chapter.)

Falldown and loss of biological diversity have clear economic impacts. Once the historical diversity of tree species and sizes is gone, employment levels in traditional timber cutting and wood manufacturing will decline, and the wood products industry may be unable to adjust rapidly to local, national, and international demands. In addition to reduced quantities of timber, reductions in quality of timber produced in the second-growth forests are of concern. Old-growth wood from slow-growing trees is clear, soft, fine-grained, strong, and easy to work with. In contrast, second-growth wood is frequently knotty, hard, coarse-grained, weak, and more difficult to work with. Old-growth trees contain about 80 percent mature wood, while 60-year-old second-growth trees contain about 50 percent juvenile wood. Long-fibre, mature wood is not formed on the stem of the tree until branches die (natural pruning), while juvenile, short-fibre wood is produced on the stem as long as wood is growing around green or living branches.

Forintek, a Canadian industry–government research cooperative, analyzed the wood fibre of second-growth Douglas fir and determined that it had low structural strength and problems with warping and workability. Almost no high-quality lumber could be milled from the short rotation second-growth trees (Kellogg, 1989). This decline in quality (strength and workability) is due largely to the shorter length of fibres that make up the new-growth wood. Even pulp products such as paper also are stronger when produced from old-growth timber. Forintek's research revealed that second-growth Douglas fir trees grown on average or better sites needed to reach the age of 90 years and be pruned to increase wood quality in order to have positive dollar value. This finding suggests that annual cutting rates need to be reduced by at least one-third to accommodate a lengthening of rotation periods from 60 to more than 90 years, so that wood will have sufficient value to realize a profit in the long term.

Moving from a Volume-based to a Value-based Economy

Some industry analysts suggest that future timber management in Canada can be based on a "fibre" or "volume" economy. This means that technology can be used to provide us with the ability to fabricate construction materials from bonded composites of chips or from pulp obtained from plantation-grown trees or natural regeneration trees grown on short rotations. The flaws in this plan include

CHAPTER 9: FORESTS AND FORESTRY

the fact that improvements in technology have typically been used to shed labour rather than to increase labour and the fact that high-quality wood equates to high-value wood, both today and in the future.

Critics of high extraction volumes of timber suggest that "as if in a process of reverse alchemy, we still convert our old-growth gold into the dull lead of … two-by-fours" (M'Gonigle & Parfitt, 1994, p. 44). They argue that sustainable cutting of old growth and manufacturing of high-quality wood products can provide more jobs in both the short and long term than can plantation forestry and pulp or wood fibre or volume economies (e.g., Travers, 1993). Selective cutting systems in natural forests require the highest labour per volume logged of all conventional logging systems. Timber products from old-growth forests can feed a diverse sustainable industry, including large log sawmills, small log sawmills, pulp mills, paper mills, cabinet shops, millwork plants, furniture factories, beam and truss lamination plants, and so on. Similarly, labour-intensive operations such as commercial thinning in older diverse forests provide growing space for old trees and furnish intermediate timber products for wood manufacturing. In addition, if planned sensitively, selective harvesting can protect forest-based recreation, although the latter itself can cause environmental damage.

Instead, the pursuit of economic productivity through high-volume, low-labour logging has resulted in declining forests, closure of community mills, and loss of jobs throughout the country (Hammond, 1991; Marchak, 1995; M'Gonigle & Parfitt, 1994; Taylor, 1994). As the most accessible and highest-quality (usually old-growth) forests have been clear-cut (often with considerable wood waste) to achieve short-term maximum profit, younger and smaller trees have been logged, shortening the rotational period. These practices have contributed to the "falldown effect" and to the potential loss of future economic and ecological diversity.

Furthermore, the qualities of longer-growing timber continue to command higher prices. A study in Washington State, for example, revealed that Douglas fir aged 160 or more years was 56 percent more valuable than wood of the same species aged less than 100 years (Wigg & Boulton, 1989). In a separate example, in 2001, the value of an old-growth fir saw log was $444 per cubic metre, while a second-growth saw log was valued at only $110 per cubic metre. A second-growth log of spruce could claim $68 per cubic metre compared to an old-growth spruce at $430 per cubic metre (David Suzuki Foundation, 2006). It seems reasonable to assume that high-quality wood produced by older trees will always be in demand for manufacture of fine wood products, quality pulp and paper, and other specialty products, particularly as its availability diminishes.

Much of the high-quality, long-fibre, old-growth timber left in the world is located in western Canada. This supply can be liquidated and sold cheaply, or it can be cut more slowly to make high-quality wood products and command premium prices. From an economic standpoint, scarcity favours the latter strategy. World demand for high-quality old-growth wood suggests that the costs of careful stewardship and labour-intensive practices could be recovered. However, such a strategy would reverse historical practices and require a fundamental rethinking of land tenure arrangements, fees and royalties paid by private operators to provincial governments, and management practices required of forest companies. To date, no government has demonstrated the political will to dismantle and replace the current system of land allocation and forest management.

The shift away from the old-forest economy, based on volume cutting and unsustainable economics of corporate and bureaucratic growth, toward a value-based forest economy brings many opportunities. One caveat to this perspective is that the costs such a strategy entails will have to be paid for by revenues generated from anticipated value-added activity. This is an assumption and should not be taken for granted (Hayter, 2000), and the performance of woodlots in New Brunswick should be kept in mind in this regard. But old-growth forests offer nonindustrial values as well. Part of the challenge in learning to value forests differently and in considering strategies for conservation-based development is to understand why old-growth forests are so important ecologically. Another part of the challenge will be to figure out how forest workers can be retained and retrained for new kinds of jobs in a value-based forest economy.

Nevertheless, many groups in Canadian society are now challenging governments at all levels to manage public forests for a wider range of interests and over longer time periods. These groups include Aboriginal people, nature-based tourism operators, rural water users, ranchers, trappers, small-business owners in forest-based communities, wilderness users, scientists, artists, educators, and future generations of Canadians. As these groups continue to express their interests in forests and forestry management, governments are finding ways to work directly with stakeholder groups and may be required to move away from the old volume economy, and to develop a new forest economy, one based on value-added industries that can be locally generated.

THE ECOLOGICAL IMPORTANCE OF OLD-GROWTH FORESTS

Old-growth or ancient forests share characteristics (in terms of life cycle, carbon storage, and biological diversity) that make them important legacies for the future of Canadian forests. These characteristics, and the need for their protection, are considered briefly below.

THE LIFE CYCLE IN THE OLD-GROWTH FOREST

Large, old living trees are virtual forest communities in themselves and provide an excellent example of the connectivity of species within ecosystems described in Chapter 3. For example, the foliage of a single old-growth Douglas fir may have a surface area of over 2800 square metres that, because of the microclimatic differences created by the lean of the tree, may attract epiphytic (aerial) plants such as mosses and lichens to the moist cool portions of the crown and lichens to the drier portions of the canopy. Up to 1500 species of insects have been found in the irregularly shaped branches of a single stand of old-growth forest (Hammond, 1991). Small mammals such as squirrels and tree voles depend on the large accumulations of organic matter in the crowns of individual old-growth trees for their food and shelter. Certain birds such as the northern spotted owl and the marbled murrelet need old-growth canopies for nesting areas and as habitat to rear their young.

No tree lives forever. Within a dying tree, the processes of matter recycling and energy flows, along with the roles of producers, consumers, and decomposers, become apparent (see also Chapter 3). However, when large, old trees die, their extensive root systems enable them to remain upright for 50 to 75 years in the case of Douglas fir, and up to 125 years in the case of western red cedar. Large snags are a distinct feature of old-growth and unmanaged forests. They provide habitat for many nesting birds and mammals such as woodpeckers, flickers, and marten. Many birds prefer the large, old-tree snags that require centuries of tree growth, growth that is not part of the life cycle in the managed forest (see Figure 3–11, p. 82). Managed forests and young forests simply do not provide the diversity of habitat options available in old-growth forests over 200 years of age (because snag density increases as forests age). A reduction in the number of snags means a reduction in the numbers of hole-nesting birds that assist in balancing insect populations.

A fallen tree is literally the soil for future generations of forests. Carpenter ants (which eat insect eggs and larvae, and help keep the defoliating spruce budworm in check), bark beetles, wood borers, and mites invade the wood of the fallen tree, using it as a home and contributing to its decay. As the decaying wood gets wet, it acts like a giant sponge, holding water and slowly releasing water and plant nutrients to the forest. The mycorrhizal fungi that assist forest plants in obtaining the elements needed for growth thrive in this medium (see Box 9–5, p. 386; Ricklefs, 1993).

A healthy, living, large tree in an old-growth forest may have 30 to 40 species of mycorrhizal fungi attached to its roots as opposed to three to five in managed forests. These fungi provide a rich source of nitrogen to the host tree and enable a fallen tree to become a nurse tree, an ideal place for the germination and growth of the next generation of trees and many other plants. If a nurse tree is broken or spread apart, its moisture-holding and nutrient-cycling functions are greatly reduced or destroyed.

Over the 250 years it would take a 400-year-old Douglas fir to decompose (or 400 years if the fir were 800 years old), the fallen tree performs other functions, including maintaining the stability of forest slopes. When large living trees or snags fall across the slope, a natural retaining wall is created, holding organic material and soil behind the terrace or barrier, and preventing slumps and erosion. Also, the water and nutrients collected here provide rich conditions for plant growth. Animal habitat is created along the sides of (and often underneath) large fallen trees, providing travel routes for squirrels, mice, and rabbits, and their predators.

Trees that fall into or across streams act as dams or breakwaters to slow the erosive forces of the stream and add diversity to the stream channel. They provide a variety of spawning and rearing habitats for fish, including sites for aquatic plants and insects needed for fish food. Fallen trees that land in streams help stabilize sediment transport by acting as barriers for movement of debris. Over time, as the tree decomposes, parts of it may move down the stream and become embedded in a bank, contributing to the formation of a new forest community.

CARBON STORAGE

As we saw in Chapter 3, maintaining the 0.03 percent carbon dioxide in the Earth's atmosphere is crucial to maintaining life as we know it. Old-growth forests are the planet's most important land-based storage systems for carbon. Huge amounts of carbon are stored in branches, trunks, roots, fallen trees, and soil organic matter, and the older the tree, the more it can store. For instance, a 450-year-old Douglas fir forest stores more than double the total amount of carbon stored in a 60-year-old Douglas fir forest. There is evidence that the northern hemisphere's land-based carbon sinks are

Photo 9–4

Various stages of growth are evident in this part of a British Columbia rain forest.

more important for carbon storage than the oceans. This means that Canada's old-growth forests—particularly the vast northern boreal forests—are immensely important in regulating Earth's carbon dioxide levels (Jardine, 1994). With this realization, the Canadian government initiated two programs, the Shelterbelt Enhancement Program and a Feasibility Assessment of Afforestation for Carbon Sequestration, to determine the potential for the large-scale creation of new forests on lands currently used for agriculture. The first program, ending in 2007, helped land-owners improve shelterbelt planting success and provided landowners with mulching equipment. The second program produced a series of provincial reports in 2005 related to best practices for afforestation on agricultural lands.

KEYS TO DIVERSITY

The keys to diversity in an old-growth forest are its multiple canopy layers, canopy gaps, and understory patchiness. Just as the diverse canopy provides varied microhabitats for plants and animals, so too do the canopy gaps and understory patches. The Pacific yew, for example, needs the shade, cool temperatures, and high humidity provided by old-growth canopies (see Enviro-Focus 3). Specialized mammals such as the northern flying squirrel and fisher require the massive spreading branches, deformed tops, hollow trees, and open spaces of the old-growth canopy for their homes. Ungulates such as mule deer, moose, and Roosevelt elk use the dense forest patches for winter shelter and browse the vegetation within the canopy gaps. In fact, of the native mammals on Vancouver Island, 85 percent reproduce in ancient forests (Hammond, 1991).

In contrast, the closed canopies of young forests result in forest simplicity. When a forest is growing, most of the forest's energy is diverted to growing trees, resulting in a uniform, closed canopy that blocks almost all usable light from reaching the ground. Understory trees, shrubs, and herbs are very limited or absent, and populations and species diversity of many life forms decrease during this period of forest development. Natural diversity rebounds when the forest canopy begins to open due to individual tree mortality in the early old-growth phase.

Biological Diversity

Humans have identified only a small number of the organisms in an old-growth forest, and we know even less about plant, animal, fungi, and bacteria functions than we do about the number of species. We do know, however, that the biomass (total amount of living matter) in a Canadian northwest old-growth rain forest is three to eight times as great as the biomass of a tropical rain forest. And if plants, animals, and microorganisms above, at, and below soil level are included, a northwest old-growth temperate rain forest may be more biologically diverse than a tropical rain forest (Kelly & Braasch, 1988).

Our ignorance of the functioning of Canadian forests is immense, in part because of this diversity. In contrast to tropical rain forests, where the diversity and functioning depend on about 500 different tree species and less than 10 mycorrhizal fungi, the boreal forest contains about a dozen tree species and may depend on as many as 5000 species of mycorrhizal fungi to sustain their integrity. We know that each of these mycorrhizal fungi has a specific role in growth and development of boreal forests, but for the most part we do not know the nature of these functions (Hammond, 1991).

The ongoing existence of forests depends on the biological diversity or richness of old-growth forests. If measured by numbers of species only, recently disturbed forests have the greatest variety of species. The species that colonize openings created by fire, wind, or the falling of a single tree are called *aggressive generalists*, as these species grow in harsh environments. Since disturbances are created constantly by nature and by humans, neither these species nor their habitats are at risk of loss.

In contrast, old-growth species are specialist species that require the ancient forests to survive. Humans cannot create old growth: "lichens which fix nitrogen, small mammals which move mycorrhizal fungi around, and predator insects which eat foliage-consuming insects are some of the gifts of old growth forests which benefit all phases of a forest" (Hammond, 1991, p. 32). While some species require old growth, others may need it only for certain periods in their lives. Grizzly bears need the hiding cover provided by the large crowns of old-growth trees, and they utilize the berry supplies of old-growth canopy gaps. Salmon, required by grizzlies, thrive on the quality of water and habitat supplied only by old-growth forests. In turn, the old trees benefit mutualistically from nutrients provided by salmon carcasses, left partially eaten at their bases, by grizzly and other bears. Scientists are beginning to understand the extensive land–sea food web and its importance in forest and fisheries management.

In unmanaged forests, every organism is different genetically, allowing each organism to adapt to its particular environment today and to meet the uncertainties in tomorrow's environments. Maintaining genetic diversity is a natural process in a healthy forest. Just as the complexity and diversity of each individual's contribution within human societies enables societies to continue and thrive, so genetic diversity enables forests to survive. This is why managed forests, such as the genetically identical clones of Douglas fir or white spruce planted to replace logged, old-growth forests, are not adequate substitutes for the complexity and diversity found in old-growth, natural (unmanaged) forests. Because of their variety of species and long lives, old-growth forests are a vital storehouse of genetic material, from soil microorganisms to giant trees.

Old-growth forests exhibit extremely large ecosystem diversity in their multilayered canopies and patchy under-growth. Yet the old-growth soil with its thousands of organisms is the most biologically rich part of the old-growth forest. If this biological legacy of old-growth forests were to be lost, it could lead eventually to critical losses in all forests. Without old-growth forests, essential parts required to maintain forests through time are lost. This is perhaps most evident in water and forest relationships. The canopies of standing giant trees catch snow while their root systems and the organic, rich soil filter, purify, and slowly release the water. Fallen trees serve as reservoirs for water and as buffers for stream flows so that most parts of the forest get the water they need, seldom too much or too little. Old growth is a necessary part of any forest ecosystem, a necessary phase in the life of any forest.

SPECIAL FORESTS IN CANADA

THE TEMPERATE RAIN FOREST

In British Columbia, and internationally, the Clayoquot (pronounced *klak-wot*) Sound area became an important focal point in the conflict over forest values and issues

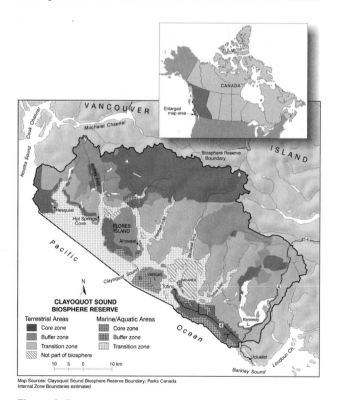

Figure 9–6a

Clayoquot Sound area

SOURCE: *A Vision and Its Context: Global Context for Forest Practices in Clay-oquot Sound,* Clayoquot Sound Scientific Panel, 1995, Report 4 of the Scientific Panel for Sustainable Forest Practices in Clayoquot Sound, Victoria: B.C. Ministry of Forests, pp. i. Copyright © Province of British Columbia. All rights reserved. Reprinted with permission of the Province of British Columbia. www.ipp.gov.bc.ca

of environmental and economic sustainability. Located on the west coast of Vancouver Island, British Columbia (see Figure 9–6a), the Clayoquot Sound area is rich in forest values, including spectacular natural, unmanaged forests; a long history of First Nations' settlement; world-class scenic and tourism resources; and major commercial fishery and timber industries.

Local and international concern about Clayoquot Sound arose because of its significance within the coastal temperate rain forest biome. Although they are found around the world in places such as Chile, Norway, and Tasmania, coastal temperate rain forests are a rare forest type, originally covering less than 0.2 percent of the Earth's land surface. British Columbia forests contain an estimated 18 to 25 percent of the world's coastal temperate rain forests (Kellogg, 1992). About 60 percent of the world's unlogged coastal temperate rain forests and over 95 percent of the unlogged coastal temperate rain forests Pacific Northwest occur in British Columbia and Alaska (see Figure 9–6b, p. 376) (Clayoquot Sound Scientific Panel, 1995). (The Pacific Northwest geographical region includes southeast Alaska, British Columbia, Washington, Oregon, Idaho, western Montana, and northern California.)

In North America, the distribution of these globally important, vigorously growing forests is centred on Vancouver Island and "attains its most dramatic expression around Clayoquot Sound" (Clayoquot Sound Scientific Panel, 1995, p. 8). Tall trees are evidence of this "dramatic expression"—for example, the two tallest western red cedars in British Columbia (59.2 and 56.4 metres), the tallest Sitka spruce (95.7 metres), the tallest Douglas fir (82.9 metres), the tallest western hemlock (75.6 metres), and the two tallest yellow cedars (45.4 and 44 metres) are located near Clayoquot Sound (Clayoquot Sound Scientific Panel, 1995). In addition, as scientists have begun to study the complexity of forest ecology, including the canopies of coastal rain forests, they have discovered hundreds of new species that previously were unknown to science (Moffett, 1997).

About 62 percent of the Clayoquot Sound area has been assessed as commercially productive forest land, with 74 percent of this land being old-growth forest of which about 22 percent has already been clear-cut logged. In 1995, about 70 percent (or 90 400 hectares) of the remaining unlogged, merchantable forest was primary or old-growth forest (Clayoquot Sound Scientific Panel, 1995).

This region has been subject to longstanding public debate, the most publicized being the summer of 1993 when thousands of concerned citizens and environmentalists from British Columbia and around the world congregated at Clayoquot Sound to protest the British Columbia government's decision to allow major timber companies to clear-cut log more than two-thirds of the Sound's rain forests.

To address the controversy, in 1993 the provincial government created a Clayoquot Sound Scientific Panel whose mandate was to help "make forest practices in

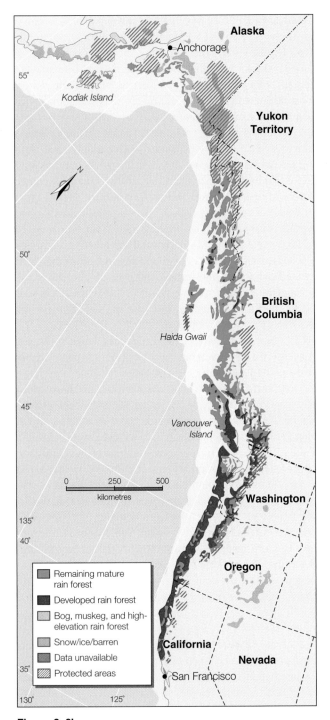

Figure 9–6b

Western North America's coastal temperate rain forest

SOURCE: Reprinted with permission of Ecotrust from *The Rain Forests of Home: An Atlas of People and Place,* 1995, page 4.

Photo 9–5

A researcher examines a 320-year-old Douglas fir in Canada's temperate rain forest.

the Clayoquot not only the best in the province, but the best in the world" (Clayoquot Sound Scientific Panel, 1995, p. 1). Upon seeing the recommendations of the committee, in 1996, the major corporation active in the area negotiated a joint venture, controlled by local First Nations, known as Iisaak Forest Resources. This company is now undertaking logging operations in the region, using criteria associated with sustainable forestry (Hayter, 2000).

In 2000, Clayoquot Sound was designated a United Nations Biosphere Reserve (see Chapter 12). The biosphere reserve is 349947 hectares including terrestrial and marine components. Additionally, a memorandum of understanding was signed by environmental organizations and Iisaak to preserve the remaining forested areas in Clayoquot Sound for cultural, ecological, nontimber, and ecotourism values. The significance of old-growth forests as a bank for genetic variability, as a wildlife sanctuary, and as a place of cultural and spiritual importance, among other values, were rationales for the designation. Clayoquot Sound made national headlines again in 2006 when a joint government–First Nations panel, the Central Region Board, agreed to eight new watershed management plans that would allow road building and logging in the region. Environmental organizations immediately denounced the plans (CBC News, 2006). This region is undeniably "special" for its ecological, social, and political significance. Because of these special characteristics, the status of the region will continue to be debated for years to come.

THE BOREAL FOREST

By contrast, Canadian and international citizens have heard relatively little about the status of Canada's boreal forest—a forest region that covers about 50 percent of the country and about 70 percent of Canada's forested and wooded areas (see Figure 9–7). In 1999, the Senate Subcommittee on the Boreal Forest (n.p.) declared "the world's boreal forest, a resource of which Canada is the major trustee, is under siege." What are the characteristics of this forest ecosystem, and why is it so important to Canadians?

The boreal ecoregion is the largest forest ecosystem in the world, a circumpolar area extending across Canada, the United States, and Eurasia. In North America, it is a region that runs from Alaska in the west to Newfoundland in the east, bordering the tundra at the north and the Great Lakes at the south. There is also a small portion in northwestern New Brunswick. The boreal forest is one of the largest biomes in the world, covering some 12 million square kilometres. Approximately one-half of this area is contained in Canada. The biome has a harsh climate—long, extremely cold, dry winters and short, cool, moist summers—that favours evergreen species such as spruces and firs. Species growing here take longer to regenerate than those logged in temperate and tropical regions.

Fire is a crucial disturbance for the maintenance of the boreal forest. It destroys old, diseased trees and their pests, stimulates the reproductive cycles for some trees such as aspen and jack pine, and once spent, leaves nutrient-rich ash to stimulate new growth. Different tree populations burn naturally at different intervals. Jack pine forests burn every 15 to 35 years, certain spruce forests every 50 to 100 years, some pine stands perhaps only once every 200 years. Aspen burns every three to five years. In Canada, an average of 2.1 million hectares is burned every year, virtually all in the boreal forest. In comparison, about 800 000 hectares of Canadian forest are cut down each year.

In Canada, about 20 percent of the boreal ecosystem is covered by wetlands, consisting of bogs, fens, marshes, an estimated 1.5 million lakes, and some of the country's largest river systems. The North American boreal forest provides breeding grounds to over 200 bird species. More than 75 percent of North America's waterfowl rely on Canada's boreal wetlands and forests at some point in their lives to breed, stage, and molt. This biome is also home to mammals such

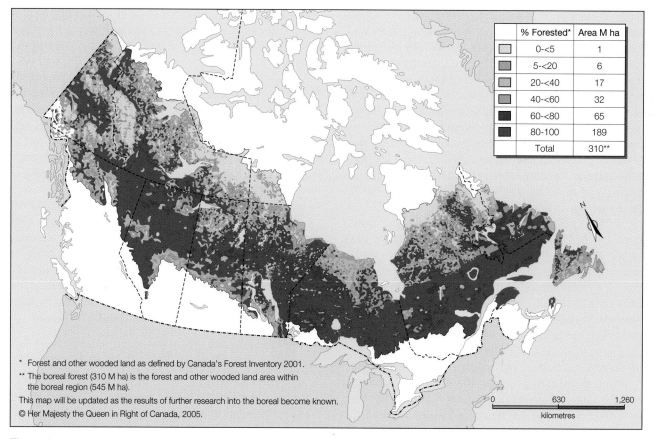

% Forested*	Area M ha
0–<5	1
5–<20	6
20–<40	17
40–<60	32
60–<80	65
80–100	189
Total	310**

* Forest and other wooded land as defined by Canada's Forest Inventory 2001.

** The boreal forest (310 M ha) is the forest and other wooded land area within the boreal region (545 M ha).

This map will be updated as the results of further research into the boreal become known.

© Her Majesty the Queen in Right of Canada, 2005.

0   630   1,260
kilometres

Figure 9–7
Canada's boreal forest

SOURCE: *The State of Canada's Forests,* Natural Resources Canada, 2005. Reproduced with the permission of the Minister of Public Works and Government Services, 2008, and the courtesy of the Canadian Forest Service. http://canadaforests.nrcan.gc.ca/maps

as caribou, lynx, black bears, moose, coyotes, timber wolves, beaver, and wood bison. Because of wide-ranging activities in this region, some mammals are already threatened.

The boreal forest is home to an estimated 2.5 million Aboriginal and non-Aboriginal people. More than 600 First Nations communities, including the Cree, Innu, Dene, Swich'in, and Athabascan peoples, have long resided in the boreal forest, yet only an estimated 15 000 work for the forestry industry (Canadian Boreal Initiative, 2003). In many parts of the country, increased exploitation of the boreal forest has conflicted with Aboriginal people's traditional use and occupancy of those lands. Increasingly, Aboriginal people are becoming involved in forestry by asserting their rights of occupancy and use, by participating in planning processes that assess access and exploitation for commercial purposes, and by becoming participants in the waged forest economy.

Boreal forests contain vast amounts of carbon and therefore play an important role in understanding and addressing climate change. Canada's role as a signatory to the Biodiversity Convention of 1992 and its commitment at Kyoto to reduce greenhouse gas emissions such as carbon dioxide are closely related to how we manage the boreal forest.

The Senate subcommittee (1999, n.p.) recognized that the boreal forest provides multiple values, including "a home and a way of life for Aboriginal communities, habitat for wildlife, an attraction for tourism and a place where biodiversity and watersheds are protected." Indeed, this forest is home to a rich array of birds and wildlife and is one of the world's largest sources of fresh water. The forest is a significant air purifier and helps regulate climate through its vast amounts of vegetation and soils. After consultations across the country, the Senate subcommittee and the Council of Forest Ministers stated that there is "no doubt that this wide range of functions is not only not being met, but is vitally important to the people of Canada to whom this forest belongs" (Senate Subcommittee on Boreal Forest, 1999, n.p.).

About one-half of Canada's wood harvest comes from the boreal forest region. About 200 000 hectares of boreal forests have been opened up for exploitation since the 1980s, doubling the amount of boreal forest harvested in Canada since the 1920s. Provincial governments have opened public lands to multinationals from North America, Europe, and Asia (especially Japan), supporting their plans for pulp, paper, and saw mills, simulated plywood plants, and chopstick factories, often with subsidies on the order of millions of Canadian taxpayer dollars.

Timber extraction is not the only resource-based activity—about 50 percent of the boreal land area has been given over to forestry and mining industries. According to the Senate subcommittee, the forest faces many threats, including climate change, ozone depletion, acid deposition, overcutting and exploitation arising from mineral and petroleum exploration and extraction, and hydroelectric development. There are also concerns about the effects of air pollution from smelters and power plants, radioactivity from atomic power and weapons testing, water pollution and disruption of habitats along transportation corridors, and threats to endangered species. For example, the woodland caribou have been extirpated from more than half of the range they occupied before European settlement in Canada (Sierra Club of Canada & Canadian Parks and Wilderness Society, 2006).

Insect infestation also has been a significant concern in the boreal forest. Between 1980 and 1993, over 6.6 million hectares of land in the eastern boreal forest was affected by spruce budworm. This insect has created management challenges in the Prairie region, as well. In British Columbia, vast tracts of the boreal forest are now threatened by the epidemic of mountain pine beetle (see Box 9–2).

Given the range of activities that threaten the boreal forest, what can be done? Scientific understanding of the boreal forest's significance in the carbon cycle and its role in controlling greenhouse gases is incomplete. The Canadian-based Boreal Ecosystem-Atmosphere Study (BOREAS) project is an international experiment aimed at determining how boreal forests interact with the atmosphere, how much carbon they can store, and how climate change will affect them. Scientists also study particular species to identify their habitat requirements. Aboriginal people have made modest inroads in the management of these places. For example, in Saskatchewan, new forest licences must be accompanied by co-management agreements with Aboriginal people who reside in the regions.

The Senate subcommittee made 35 recommendations to improve forest management and protect the range of values it identified with the boreal ecosystem. As most of Canada's forests are managed directly by provincial and territorial governments, the federal government's role is limited to data gathering, research, or protection through specific environmental legislation (e.g., the Migratory Birds Convention Act, the Fisheries Act). Nevertheless, the federal government can work with provincial and territorial agencies to improve large-scale land use planning, ensuring a national network of protected areas and national parks, strengthening the involvement of Aboriginal people in land use planning and forest management, and improving data collection and monitoring of natural attributes of the boreal region to help inform efforts to achieve sustainability (Canadian Boreal Initiative, 2003).

THE CAROLINIAN FOREST

Clearing of forest lands for agriculture and grazing, and to accommodate community and urban development, has been ongoing in Canada since settlement began. Perhaps nowhere are the effects of these human activities seen more clearly than in the Carolinian forest in Ontario. Located on the fertile plain north of Lake Erie, less than 10 percent of the area remains in forest cover, the remainder having

BOX 9–2

SMALLER THAN A GRAIN OF RICE, FASTER THAN A FOREST COMPANY: IT'S THE MOUNTAIN PINE BEETLE!

The mountain pine beetle, or *Dendroctonus ponderosae,* is smaller than a grain of rice. Yet, when it teams up with other forest pests in periodic outbreaks, it can cause devastation to Canadian forests. Since the late 1990s, mountain pine beetles have consumed 12 to 13 million hectares of lodgepole pine forest in central and northern British Columbia. This is an area nearly twice the size of New Brunswick that includes about $50 billion of the province's most commercially valuable timber (Nikiforuk & Narayana, 2007).

Photo 9–6

The mountain pine beetle.

In September 2006, the Province of British Columbia stated that "the epidemic [of mountain pine beetle] has now affected over 400 million cubic metres of timber. About 8.7 million hectares were affected in 2005 alone" (British Columbia, 2006, n.p.). This amount is about five times the annual allowable cut in the entire province. It is estimated that by 2013, about 80 percent of the province's mature pine will be affected (Natural Resources Canada, 2006). While British Columbia has been the hardest hit, the beetle also has affected the foothills of the Canadian Rockies, moved into Alberta, and has been observed at Cypress Hills in southwestern Saskatchewan.

The mountain pine beetle is a longstanding member of boreal ecosystems. It plays a role in lodgepole forests by thinning aging forests that then become susceptible to wildfires. Wildfires force lodgepole cones to open and release their seeds. Fires also have held the beetle in check. However, the creation of larger stands of lodgepole pines and effective fire-fighting techniques during the 20th century increased the area of mature pine threefold throughout British Columbia. Consequently, extensive areas of mature pine provided the perfect conditions for the pine beetle. Additionally, climate change has reduced the incidence of very cold winters (–40°C) in British Columbia's interior, so the beetles do not die off during winter. In fact, they have a built-in form of antifreeze that allows them to survive milder temperatures.

Beetles attack pine trees by laying eggs under the bark. When the eggs hatch, the larvae mine the phloem area beneath the bark and eventually cut off the tree's supply of nutrients. The beetles also carry a fungus that causes dehydration, inhibits a tree's natural defences against beetle attacks, and causes decolouration. Yet, the wood remains structurally sound and infested timber can retain at least some of its commercial value for up to 18 years after attack. Nevertheless, the infestation affects a forest-based economy in several ways. The beetle tends to attack the largest and most valuable trees first; it reduces the aesthetic value of forests in recreational areas; and it increases fire hazard. The blue stain caused by the beetle may result in reduced commercial values of the trees used for lumber and pulp, although there is a small market for the blue-stained wood for use as panelling (Langor, 2003).

Ironically, in the short term, some timber-dependent communities are thriving. Increases have been awarded in the annual allowable cuts for salvaging or recovering greatest value possible from affected timber. For example, because of the beetles, the annual allowable cut near Quesnel, British Columbia, increased from about 2 million cubic metres in 2001 to about 5 million cubic metres in 2004. This is a very short-term gain that inevitably will be followed by long-term reductions in timber harvests. Both the province and the federal government have established plans for mitigating the adverse effects of the infestation and creating economic diversification strategies to address future losses.

Photo 9–7

Landscape affected by a mountain pine beetle infestation.

SOURCES: "Summary," *Mountain Pine Beetle Action Plan 2006–2011,* British Columbia, 2006, www.for.gov.bc.ca/hfp/mountain_pine_beetle/actionplan/2006/SUM_Action_Plan.pdf; *Mountain Pine Beetle,* Forestry Leaflet 36, D. W. Langor, 2003, Edmonton: Natural Resources Canada, Canadian Forest Service, Northern Forestry Centre, www.cfs.nrcan.gc.ca/factsheets/pine-beetle-nofc/cat.entomology; *Mountain Pine Beetle: The Economics of Infestation,* Natural Resources Canada, 2006, Ottawa: Author, http://canadaforests.nrcan.gc.ca/articletopic/8; "Pine Plague," A. Nikiforuk & A. Nrayanan, 2007, *Canadian Geographic, 127,* 68–76.

been cleared since the time of the European settlers. More than 95 percent of the Carolinian forest is privately owned, and less than 1 percent is contained in national and provincial parks. The nature of this forest, its importance, and an indication of efforts being undertaken to conserve what remains of it are discussed in Box 9–3 on page 380.

THE NEED FOR PROTECTION

Sustainable human communities require healthy forests. One way to maintain healthy forests and healthy communities is to apply the principles of ecological responsibility and balanced use (Kimmins, 1992). *Ecological responsibility*

Photo 9–8

This BOREAS site is in Prince Albert National Park.

means that all human activities within forest landscapes must be carried out in a way that protects and maintains necessary forest structures and functions. *Balanced use* means that all forest users, both human and nonhuman, are entitled to a fair and protected land base on which to carry out their various activities. In turn, this means that sufficient natural forest reserves must be protected from all but the gentlest of human uses. Protection of natural areas is required to maintain landscape connections, to maintain a reservoir of species and genetic components, and to provide natural benchmarks so that we can evaluate impacts of forest activities and restore degraded forests.

In effect, acknowledging the importance of all life forms provides the impetus to fully protect biological diversity in order to maintain healthy forests and healthy communities. Sustaining biological diversity means protecting the integrity of the forest—the biological diversity

BOX 9-3
CANADA'S CAROLINIAN LIFE ZONE

Canada's Carolinian forest covers the southernmost part of Ontario, stretching from the Rouge River Valley in Toronto to the shore of Lake Erie. The forest represents the northern extreme of the eastern deciduous forest region that covers a vast area south of the Great Lakes. The Carolinian forest supports natural habitats and species found nowhere else in Canada. Sixteen endangered plants and animals are native to the Carolinian region, and at least one-third of our country's rare, threatened, or endangered species depend on its natural habitats. More than half of Canada's bird species are found in the Carolinian forest; so is the highest representation of reptiles in Canada. The Carolinian forest is home to the opossum, North America's only marsupial. The forest area is one of the few places in North America where the American chestnut has not been eradicated by chestnut blight. Other Carolinian tree species include the tulip, Kentucky coffee, black gum, cucumber, sycamore, and sassafras.

Early settlers were attracted to the region's relatively warm climate and highly productive agricultural lands. Today more than 20 percent of Canada's population lives in the Carolinian zone. As a result of extensive urbanization in the Toronto to Windsor corridor, less than 10 percent of the land has any forest cover. In fact, all of the counties within the Carolinian zone have less than 20 percent natural forest cover remaining, while some townships are approaching zero cover. Clearly, southern Ontario's Carolinian forests have been and are influenced greatly by human activities.

Although large tracts of Carolinian forests containing similar habitats and range of species remain in the United States, Canada's Carolinian zone is particularly worthy of conservation. Ontario's small patch is considered crucial because species living near the limit of their range have unique characteristics—such as exceptional hardiness—that can be passed on to and strengthen those species over their entire range (see the section in Chapter 3 entitled "Tolerance Ranges of Species").

Protecting Carolinian habitat is especially challenging because most forest remaining in Ontario is fragmented. A variety of complex issues, such as understanding the problem of natural succession, must be considered when managing fragmented natural areas. As a forest matures, new species take over from older ones in a cycle of replacement. In large wilderness areas, most plant species normally survive because occasional natural disturbances, such as fires, storms, and insect infestations, merely slow or reduce the natural succession of the area. While an isolated forest fire may be healthy to a large forest, the same size fire could be devastating to a forest remnant. Conversely, if the remnant is left alone, succession by new species may replace existing ones. The possibility of Carolinian species being replaced by more northerly species is a significant threat in Ontario's Carolinian forests.

One of the best remaining examples of mature Carolinian forest in Canada is the 265-hectare Backus Woods, located a few kilometres from Lake Erie. The site was owned by the Backus family, operators of a flour mill and sawmill beginning in 1798. Backus Woods remained largely intact because the family recognized the value of preserving their forest to protect the watershed for the creek that powered their mills. Backus Woods presently is owned by the Long Point Region Conservation Authority and managed by an advisory committee. In the Backus Woods management plan, half the forest is designated as a natural zone, where no human interference is allowed. The remaining half is a conservation zone where action may be taken to stop natural succession if Carolinian species are threatened.

Both conservationists and forest managers agree that Carolinian forests must be further protected and expanded in Ontario. By expanding Carolinian forests, genetic exchange between adjacent forest remnants can be encouraged. Genetic exchange is important to ensure that plants can build up the tolerance needed to respond to environmental changes such as global warming. Organizations such as the World Wildlife Fund and Long Point Region Conservation Authority are working toward enlarging the woods by buying adjacent properties and encouraging voluntary stewardship initiatives.

BOX 9–3
(CONTINUED)

Photo 9–9
Cucumber tree.

Photo 9–10
Tulip tree.

Stewardship initiatives in Canada's Carolinian zone began in 1983 with the Carolinian Canada project. The initiative was conceived by the Natural Heritage League (a network of 38 private organizations and public agencies linked by mutual interest and involvement in the identification, protection, and management of Ontario's natural heritage), the Nature Conservancy of Canada, and the World Wildlife Fund.

Between 1984 and 1994, 38 priority unprotected Carolinian forest sites were identified, two-thirds (9800 hectares) of which were privately owned. A landowner contact program was established to target these landowners and encourage their willingness to enter into stewardship agreements. Voluntary agreements were then negotiated by the league's Natural Heritage Stewardship Program, based at the University of Guelph. By 2002, over 950 landowners had been awarded Ontario's Natural Heritage Stewardship Award to recognized their stewardship commitment. Voluntary agreements applied to 14,000 hectares of natural areas.

In 1996, Carolinian Canada developed a conservation strategy for a regional approach to environmental education and conservation. It relies on its member organizations to undertake initiatives to protect specific areas and species.

SOURCES: *What Is the Big Picture?* Carolinian Canada, n.d., www.carolinian.org/ConservationPrograms.htm; *What Is Carolinian Canada?* Federation of Ontario Naturalists, n.d., brochure; "The Enchanted Woodland," P. Gorrie, 1994, *Canadian Geographic, 114*(2), 32–42; *The State of Canada's Forests 1993: Forests, a Global Resource,* Natural Resources Canada, Canadian Forest Service, 1994; "Natural Heritage Protection: Voluntary Stewardship or Planning Control?" M. Van Patter & S. Hilts, 1990, *Plan Canada, 30*(5), 20–28; Hilts, S. 2002. Ontario's natural heritage stewardship project. http://www.slv2000.qc.ca/st_laurent_facettes/bulletins_habitats/vol_3_no_1/patrimoine_a.htm

of forests—at the species, genetic, and ecosystem levels. Because diversity works in interconnected and interdependent ways, biological diversity must be protected in at least two ways. One way is by limiting the fragmentation of the forest so that the patterns of, and connections between, the various clusters or stands that compose a forest landscape are maintained. Another way requires the protection of the structure and composition of the individual parts that constitute the forest landscape, including the fallen trees, the soil, the old growth, the riparian and upland corridors, and the natural flows of water, nutrients, and other forms of energy throughout the forest (Hammond, 1991; Ness & Cooperrider, 1994; Quinby, 1996). Ultimately, protection requires managers to act on the understanding that each forest stand requires old trees, snags, and fallen trees, that brush or competing vegetation is biologically necessary for forest integrity, and that insects and disease are essential parts of a fully functioning forest. Sustainable forestry relies on incorporating alternative models of forestry into landscape-scale and ecosystem-based land use planning approaches, as opposed to volume-based management planning.

Photo 9–11a   **Photo 9–11b**   **Photo 9–11c**   **Photo 9–11d**   **Photo 9–11e**

Among the tallest trees in Canada's west coast forests are (from left) the western red cedar, Sitka spruce, Douglas fir, western hemlock, and yellow cedar.

HUMAN ACTIVITIES AND IMPACTS ON FOREST ENVIRONMENTS

Canadians depend on their forests for a wide range of services, products, and values. The key to sustaining all of these uses and values—in order that the forest needs of both present and future generations of Canadians may be met—lies in maintaining the health, diversity, and productive capacity of forest ecosystems. This means that forests in Canada and everywhere must be managed so that their sustainability is assured. However, recognition of this challenge is relatively recent, and we continue to see a wide range of problems resulting from practices that did not, or do not, promote sustainability. This section provides a brief context of human activities in Canadian forests and illustrates the ecological, social, and economic effects of these activities.

TIMBER PRODUCTION ACTIVITIES AND THEIR EFFECTS

Historical timber production activities in Canada have shifted from small-scale, low-impact use of forests by small numbers of Aboriginal people to increasingly large-scale, high-impact forest cutting by settlers, speculators, entrepreneurs, and, ultimately, large corporations on Crown land. Basically, in Canada, forest policy has been equated with industrial policy, and clear-cutting has become the dominant form of harvesting (Figure 9–8). Although the fundamental problem of failure to protect forests for the future was recognized more than a century ago, it is only recently that actions toward sustainability have begun to be developed. Before examining these actions and efforts in more detail, a number of examples of the impacts of timber production on

selected forest elements, as well as other effects of human activities on forest ecosystems, are identified.

Habitat, Wildlife, and Life-Support Effects

Timber cutting, especially clear-cutting, can have significant negative effects on habitats for all species, on wildlife, on humans, as well as on ecological life-support systems. From their place in the world's carbon storage system to their reservoir of genetic diversity, old-growth forests across Canada provide a range of immensely important global functions. After so much of the country's old-growth timber has been clear-cut, or committed to being logged, it is only recently that the search for appropriate levels of forest use has begun. Only in recent years, as well, have increased levels of knowledge provided some basic premises on which to make more informed choices about management efforts.

Canada's forest regions are home to more than two-thirds of all species found in Canada, including about 76 percent of our land-dwelling mammals and 60 percent of breeding bird species (Natural Resources Canada, 1996b). Of the roughly 200 000 species that depend on forest habitats, 85 have been identified as species at risk (see Table 9–5 on page 384). The decline in numbers of many of these forest-dwelling species may be attributed partly to habitat loss due to timber harvesting.

The very rare Queen Charlotte goshawk, for example, was assigned "vulnerable" status in 1995 by COSEWIC—the Committee on the Status of Endangered Wildlife in Canada (see Tables 12–3, p. 497, and 12–4, p. 498). Only three nests have been reported on the Queen Charlotte Islands and six have been reported on Vancouver Island. The goshawk prefers to nest in large, contiguous stands of mature forests with closed canopy cover. The dense vegetation provides ideal breeding habitat, with cover and protection from predators. In addition to threats from poaching and pesticides, the Queen Charlotte goshawk

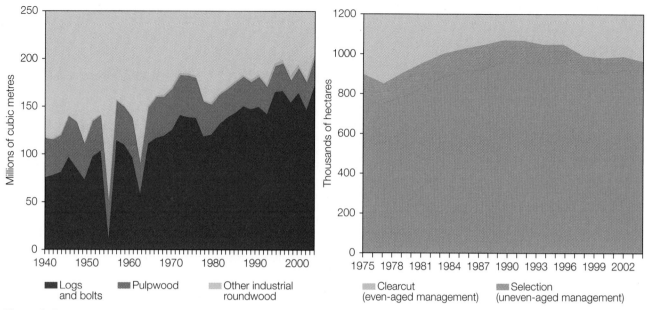

Figure 9–8

Annual volume and area of timber harvest in Canada

NOTES:

- *Roundwood* is the term applied to the major types of products harvested from Canadian forests. Roundwood includes sections of tree stems (with or without bark), logs, bolts (short logs to be sawn for lumber or peeled for veneer), pulpwood, posts, pilings, and other products "still in the round." Industrial roundwood also includes fuelwood for industrial or institutional needs, and firewood for household or recreational needs.
- Regional harvest trends vary substantially from this national picture.

SOURCE: *Compendium of Canadian Forestry Statistics 2004,* © Canadian Council of Forest Ministers, 2004, Ottawa. Reprinted with permission of the Canadian Council of Forest Ministers, http://www.ccfm.org

has lost suitable nesting trees and foraging habitat due to timber harvesting (Natural Resources Canada, 1996b). In recent years, the situation has not improved; the goshawk is now declared to be "threatened," that is, "a species likely to become endangered if limiting factors are not reversed" (COSEWIC, 2003).

As trees disappear through logging, so do other living things. The woodland caribou, for instance, lives in mature forests, where it feeds on lichen. While some populations are not at risk, others—for example, in the boreal habitat in northwestern Ontario and parts of British Columbia—are declining because of logging, road and pipeline construction, and hunting (Natural Resources Canada, 1995). The Queen Charlotte woodland caribou population is extinct and the Atlantic-Gaspésie population in Quebec is in the endangered category (COSEWIC, 2003). Migratory birds such as the Cape May warbler, whose summer range includes Ontario's boreal forests, are affected by the loss of habitat caused by logging. As recent research findings have shown, loss of neotropical migratory birds from forests has important implications for control of insect outbreaks (see Box 9–4 on page 385). In other parts of the world, similar wild species losses occur. Australia has lost 18 of its native mammals in the recent past, many from Western Australia, where 95 percent of the natural woodland has been cleared (Pimm, 1996).

Other habitat losses occur as soil and debris from clear-cut slopes erode into rivers and streams, suffocating aquatic species. Rainfall can exacerbate erosion problems: in the Clayoquot Sound area in January 1996, for instance, heavy rain generated over 250 landslides, mostly in clear-cut logged areas (Rainforest Action Network, 1996). Companies responsible for other damage to British Columbia streams and fish habitat allegedly caused by logging roads and operations have been difficult to prosecute (Friends of Clayoquot Sound, 1996).

Such effects are found worldwide; for instance, in the northern Philippines, logging roads were found to have caused erosion more than 200 times greater than on undisturbed sites (Ryan, 1990). Millions of dollars of damage to fisheries and coral reefs caused by logging-induced sedimentation has been documented. Near Palawan in the Philippines, fisheries in Bacuit Bay were depleted after logging began on surrounding hillsides. Sediment entering the bay smothered up to half of the living coral that supported the fishery, depriving local people of their source of protein (Ryan, 1990). In the mid-1960s, harvesting $14 million worth of timber from the watershed of the South Fork of the Salmon River in central Idaho caused an estimated $100 million damage to the river's Chinook salmon fishery. That industry still has not recovered.

A SAMPLE OF FOREST-DWELLING SPECIES AT RISK IN CANADA, 2006

	Mammals	Birds	Plants	Reptiles & Amphibians
Endangered	Vancouver Island marmot (BC) Wolverine (QC, NFL) Woodland caribou (QC)	Acadian flycatcher (ON) Kirtland's warbler (ON) Northern spotted owl (BC) Western screech owl sub. macfarlanei (BC) Prothonotary warbler (ON) White-headed woodpecker (BC) Williamson's sap-sucker (BC) Yellow-breasted chat sub. auricollis (BC)	American chestnut (ON) American ginseng (ON, QC) Bashful bulrush (ON) Bird's-foot violet (ON) Boreal felt lichen (NB, NS) Cucumber tree (ON) Deltoid balsamroot (BC) Drooping trillium (ON) Heart-leaved plantain (ON) Hoary mountain-mint (ON) Howell's triteleia (BC) Large whorled pogonia (ON) Nodding pogonia (ON) Prairie lupine (BC) Purple twayblade (ON) Red mulberry (ON) Seaside centipede lichen (BC) Small whorled pogonia (ON) Spotted Wintergreen (ON) Tall bugbane (BC) Wood Poppy (ON)	Blanding's turtle (NS) Blue racer (snake) (ON) Northern leopard frog (BC) Rocky mountain tailed frog (BC) Sharp-tailed snake (BC) Tiger salamander (BC)
Threatened	American, marten (NFL) Ermine sub. haidarum (BC) Grey fox (MB, ON) Pacific water shrew (BC) Pallid bat (BC) Wood bison (AB, BC, NT, YT) Woodland caribou (NT, BC, AB, SK, MB, ON, QC, NL) Boreal pop. Woodland caribou (BC, AB) Southern Mountain pop.	Hooded warbler (ON) Marbled murrelet (BC) Northern goshawk sub. laingi (BC) Red-headed woodpecker (SK, MB, ON, QC)	Goldenseal (ON) Blunt-lobed woodsia (ON, QC) Common hoptree (ON) Crooked-stemmed aster (ON) Deerberry (ON) Dwarf hackberry (ON) False rue-anemone (ON) Goldenseal (ON) Kentucky coffee tree (ON) Lyall's mariposa lily (BC) Phantom orchid (BC) Pocket moss (BC) Purple sanicle (BC) Round-leaved greenbrier (ON) Van brunt's jacob's ladder (QC) Wild hyacinth (ON) White wood aster (ON, QC) White-top aster (BC) Wild hyacinth (ON) Yellow montane violet (BC)	Allegheny mountain dusky salamander (QC) Coastal giant salamander (BC) Eastern Massasauga rattlesnake (ON) Jefferson salamander (ON) Eastern ribbon snake (NS) Atlantic pop. Coastal giant salamander (BC)
Special concern	Eastern mole (ON) Eastern wolf (ON, QC) Grizzly bear (AB, BC, NT, YT, NU) Mountain beaver (BC) Nuttall's cottontail sub. nuttallii (BC) Spotted bat (BC) Wolverine (AB, BC, MB, NT, ON, SK, YT, NU) Woodland caribou (AB, BC, MB, NT, ON, SK) Woodland vole (ON, QC)	Bicknell's thrush (NB, NS, QC) Cerulean warbler (ON, QC) Flammulated owl (BC) Lewis's woodpecker (BC) Louisiana waterthrush (ON, QC) Western screech-owl sub. kennicottii (BC) Yellow-breasted chat sub. virens (ON)	American columbo (ON) Blue ash (ON) Boreal felt lichen (NL) Broad beech fern (ON, QC) Coastal wood fern (BC) Cryptic paw lichen (BC) Green dragon (ON, QC) New jersey rush (NS) Oldgrowth specklebelly lichen (BC) Seaside bone lichen (BC) Shumard oak (ON)	Coast tailed frog (BC) Coeur d'Alène salamander (BC) Eastern ribbon snake (ON) Great Lakes pop. Five-lined skink (ON) Milk snake (ON, QC) Red-legged frog (BC) Rubber boa (BC) Pacific giant salamander (BC) Spring salamander (ON, QC) Western skink (BC) Western toad (AB, BC, NT, YT) Wood turtle (NB, NS, ON, QC)

SOURCE: "Search by Species," *Species at Risk,* Environment Canada, 2004, http://www.sararegistry.gc.ca/sar/index/default_e.cfm. *The State of Canada's Forests 2002–2003: Looking Ahead,* Natural Resources Canada, Canadian Forest Service, 2004, Ottawa: Author. http://bookstore_cfs.nrcan.gc.ca

BOX 9-4

SAVING OUR BIRDS TO SAVE OUR FORESTS

Neotropical migratory birds such as the rufous hummingbird, the western tanager, or the several warbler species that inhabit the Pacific Northwest and boreal forests spend only one-third of their lives in Canada or the United States. The remainder of their time is spent in tropical regions such as Mexico, the Caribbean, and Central and South America (or areas in between their summer and winter homes). Of the nearly 200 species of neotropical birds, some travel thousands of kilometres twice a year.

These neotropical birds, as well as resident birds, such as juncos, thrushes, pine siskins, chickadees, nuthatches, and some woodpeckers, play an important role in helping to keep forest trees healthy. While not all birds eat insects, the majority do: as many as 300 insects per day during the summer months. A pair of breeding evening grosbeaks, for example, can devour 25 000 to 50 000 caterpillars just in the period it takes them to raise their brood.

United States Forest Service biologists in the Pacific Northwest learned that 35 species of birds, including 24 neotropical migrants, feed on the western spruce budworm and the Douglas fir tussock moth, which are the two most destructive defoliating insects there. When the caterpillars (or larvae) of the western spruce budworm and Douglas fir tussock moth eat the needles of these trees, they weaken them, making them vulnerable to attack by other insects or to diseases that ultimately kill the trees. Severe outbreaks of these insects can result in the loss of millions of trees over thousands of hectares of forested land.

One of the responses to these insect outbreaks has been to spray insecticides to kill the budworm and tussock moth. However, this partially effective action kills beneficial insects and spiders along with the pests. Killing the beneficial insects affects forest birds and animals that depend on all types of invertebrates for food.

Knowing that both neotropical and resident birds feed on budworm and tussock moth larvae, the Forest Service scientists planned an experiment to see just how effective the birds were in eating budworms off fir trees. The scientists enclosed entire,

30-foot-tall fir trees in cages of PVC pipe and plastic netting to prevent birds from feeding on the caterpillars on those trees. The results showed that six times more budworms survived on the caged trees than on uncaged trees. This means that the birds were eating five of every six caterpillars, and were making a tremendous difference to the health of the forests.

Unfortunately, the populations of dozens of species of neotropical migratory birds that spend their summers in the forests of the Pacific Northwest and the boreal forests of northern Canada have declined during the past two to three decades. Biologists believe these declines are the result of changes in nesting or wintering habitat (or both). Activities such as logging and land clearing result in less available food, fewer nesting sites, and less protection from natural enemies for these birds. Logging and land clearing also affect streamside (or riparian) habitats, which are favourite nesting or foraging sites for many bird species. Building roads and allowing grazing near streams also have caused problems for birds.

If healthy forests are to be maintained, responsible managers need to realize that essential forest-dwelling birds need suitable nesting and foraging areas. This implies that managers need to plan for forest diversity with a variety of tree species of different ages, including standing snags and fallen logs. One international effort to help stem the decline in populations of neotropical birds is the Partners in Flight–Aves de las Americas Neotropical Migratory Bird Conservation Program.

Initiated in 1990, the Partners in Flight program brings public and private partners, including Canadian, American, Mexican, Caribbean, and Latin American conservation organizations, together in efforts to conserve migratory songbirds. The basic principles of their strategy, known as the Flight Plan, include promotion of conservation of habitats in breeding, migration, and wintering areas when it should be done—before species and ecosystems become endangered. Conservation based on sound science, such as that described here, is also an important principle of the Flight Plan. Saving our birds is indeed a way to save our forests.

SOURCES: *Partners in Flight—Canada,* Canadian Wildlife Service, 2006, http://www.cws-scf.ec.gc.ca/mbc-com/default.asp?lang=en&n=7AEDFD2C; *Neotropical Migratory Bird Conservation,* National Fish and Wildlife Foundation, 2008, http://www.nfwf.org/nfwfne.htm; Ruth, J. M. 2006. Partners in Flight—U.S. Website. Served by the USGS Patuxent Wildlife Research Center, Laurel, Maryland, USA. http://www.partnersinflight.org

Many types of plants are threatened by timber operations, too. The white wood aster, a perennial herb that is known to grow in only ten sites in Quebec and fifteen in the Carolinian forests of Ontario, was designated by COSEWIC as a threatened species in 1995. It was re-examined and confirmed in 2002 to be threatened (see Table 9–5). This aster is threatened largely because of habitat loss resulting from human and natural changes in the forest ecosystem (Natural Resources Canada, 1996a). In Alberta, about 100 plant species are known to grow only in the boreal forest, and about half of these are rare already (Acharya, 1995).

In the Pacific Northwest, existing wild mushroom harvests likely would be destroyed should logging occur in the old-growth forests where the fungi grow (see Box 9–5, p. 386). The case of the "worthless" Pacific yew tree (see Enviro-Focus 3, p. 81) also highlights the need for enhanced awareness of the importance and protection of what may appear to be insignificant species in our forests. If people are to gain a full range of benefits from forest products and avoid the irrecoverable losses of biodiversity and ecological function that can occur under certain harvesting regimes, the precautionary principle (see Chapter 1) is applicable.

BOX 9-5
FORESTS AND WILD MUSHROOMS

The Pacific Northwest has been recognized for a long time for its rich mycota—such as mushrooms, truffles, conks, puffballs, and cup fungi—that are found in conjunction with old-growth forests. The richness of the mycota is related directly to the region's expansive forest communities, diversity of tree species, and weather patterns. Under these conditions, forest tree species form beneficial root symbioses (mycorrhizae) with specialized fungi that obtain their carbohydrate nutrition via the roots of the host trees and, in return, provide access to nutrients to much larger tree roots (Brady & Weil, 1999). The wood of both live and dead trees and the abundance of other organic debris on the forest floor provide rich resources for numerous fungi. In turn, these fungi are important contributors to the dynamic functioning of forest ecosystems, providing food for organisms from microbes to mammals and contributing to the overall resiliency and diversity of forest ecosystems. "If we are to succeed at managing forest ecosystems in their entirety, we must integrate the biological and functional diversity of forest fungi into future management plans" (Pilz & Molina, 1996, p. 1).

Pushing through the mossy floor surrounding 100- to 200-year-old lodgepole pine, Douglas fir, and western hemlock, the firm, white to pale brown pine mushrooms (*Tricholoma magnivelare*) are found along the coast and interior mountain ranges of western North America. In Canada, pine mushrooms also are found in the eastern Maritimes and throughout the boreal forests of Manitoba and Saskatchewan. Under ideal conditions, pine mushrooms can grow to more than 2 kilograms each!

Of the more than 30 species of wild edible mushrooms that are harvested in British Columbia, the pine mushroom is one of the few that is picked commercially on a large scale. Pickers who harvest top-grade pine mushrooms can command anywhere from $8 to $300 per pound for these fungi.

The pine fungi are closely related to the very popular Japanese *Tricholoma matsutake* mushroom, which, because of the medicinal qualities it is believed to contain, has been an integral part of the Japanese diet for centuries. In the 1980s, however, Japanese matsutake crops declined as a result of "the ailing health of its red pine forests, the symbiotic partner of the matsutake" (Welland, 1997, p. 66). (Of note are similar declines in European fungi that have been linked to pollution such as acid precipitation and sulphur dioxide [Amaranthus & Pilz, 1996].) At the same time as supplies of the pine mushroom declined, the demand for it grew; by the early 1990s, Canada was the world's fourth leading exporter of pine mushrooms to Japan.

The pine mushrooms are "fussy fungi, needing an undisturbed forest floor to propagate; any pawing or raking of the moss covering can set future growth back for years" (Welland, 1997, p. 64). Extensive harvesting of several species of edible

Photo 9–12
Pine mushroom of the Pacific Northwest.

forest mushrooms during the past decade has heightened awareness and concern for forest fungi on the part of the public and resource managers. While economic benefits are sizable—such as the $40 million that wild mushroom picking contributed to the economies of Oregon, Washington, and Idaho in 1992, or the almost $4 million earned by harvesters in 1994 in the Nass Valley in northern British Columbia—so are the concerns about the potential overharvesting of wild mushrooms and the impact of mushroom harvesting on forest ecosystems. Clear-cut logging, scheduled to occur in the Nass Valley also is a concern.

In the United States, legislation and permit systems to regulate the commercial harvest of wild mushrooms on public lands have been instituted. As well, then-president Clinton's 1993 Forest Ecosystem Management Assessment Team report identified the need to study and protect fungi throughout Pacific Northwest forests and to integrate these forest fungi into ecosystem management plans.

In British Columbia, regulation of the mushroom harvesting industry has been resisted. The Nisga'a First Nation's land claims settlement may signal a change, however. As they now own all forest resources within some 2000 square kilometres of the Nass Valley, the Nisga'a have patrolled the valley to contain the harvesters within main camping centres. As well, through their company, Nass Valley Resources, Inc., they hope to develop a food processing facility in the area for mushrooms, fish, and other local foods. Obviously, none of these actions will result in the opportunity to study or protect the pine mushroom should logging occur. Thus, an adaptive management process is recommended in which, as new information is acquired, it may be incorporated continuously into revised management plans.

SOURCES: "Productivity and Sustainable Harvest of Wild Mushrooms," M. Amaranthus & D. Pilz, 1996, in D. Pilz & R. Molina (Eds.), *Managing Forest Ecosystems to Conserve Fungus Diversity and Sustain Wild Mushroom Harvests* (pp. 42–61), Portland, OR: United States Department of Agriculture, Forest Service, Pacific Northwest Research Station: General Technical Report PNW-GTR-371; *The Nature and Property of Soils*, N. C. Brady & R. R. Weil, 1999, Englewood Cliffs, NJ: Prentice-Hall; "Introduction," D. Pilz & R. Molina (Eds.), 1996, *Managing Forest Ecosystems to Conserve Fungus Diversity and Sustain Wild Mushroom Harvests* (pp. 1–4), Portland, OR: United States Department of Agriculture, Forest Service, Pacific Northwest Research Station: General Technical Report PNW-GTR-371; "Mushroom Madness," F. Welland, 1997, *Canadian Geographic, 117*(1), 62–68.

Photo 9–13

The central Swan Hills area, 35 kilometres north of Whitecourt, Alberta, September 27, 1949 (9.1 × 9.1 km). North is to the top of the image, as it is in the two accompanying photos.

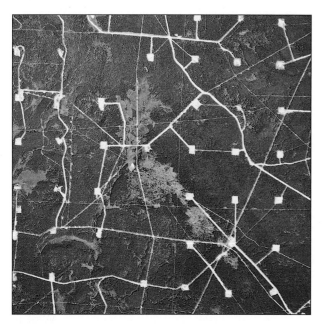

Photo 9–14

The central Swan Hills area, July 2, 1964 (7.2 × 7.2 km). The grey lines are roads, pipelines, and transmission lines; small squares are well sites; large patches are clear-cuts.

POLLUTION

Pollution is a widespread problem for Canada's forests. Pulping operations release toxic organochlorines, such as dioxins, and other substances into water bodies. Sometimes disastrous effects on aquatic life occur, and often damaging effects on the health of First Nations

Photo 9–15

The central Swan Hills area, October 7, 1991 (13.6 × 13.6 km). In just 42 years a wilderness area is transformed into an intensely fragmented, ecologically dysfunctional landscape.

people are observed. Examples abound: in Ontario, long-term discharge of mill effluent threatened local people with Minamata disease (mercury poisoning) from eating contaminated fish from the Wabigoon River system. In the case of the largest bleached kraft mill in the world, Mitsubishi's Alberta-Pacific mill located on the Athabasca River, chlorine is used to bleach 1500 metric tonnes of pulp per day (Acharya, 1995). Completed in 1993, this mill releases dioxins and other toxins that require long-term monitoring to prevent cumulative toxic damage. Throughout British Columbia, the health of Aboriginal people and others who rely on marine species has been threatened for many years by the eating of fish and shellfish contaminated by pulp mill effluents; however, increasing understanding of the causes of these health problems and improvements in technology have reduced contemporary releases of such substances.

Some of the world's most serious cases of air pollution causing damage to forests are found in Russia. Russian mining and smelting operations produce among the world's highest sulphur emissions, which, in turn, have killed off entire Russian forests and damaged forests outside of Russia. During the 1950s and 1960s, huge smelters were built on the mineral-rich Kola Peninsula bordering Norway and Finland. These plants use obsolete technology, and produce nearly as many tonnes of sulphur emissions as they do metals and minerals. In 1988, for instance, the Severo-Nickel smelter on the Kola Peninsula produced 243 000 tonnes of nickel, copper, and cobalt, and 212 000 tonnes of sulphur dioxide (Acharya, 1995).

These sulphur emissions have killed forests outright on 40 000 to 100 000 hectares and damaged 3 million hectares of forest in Russia alone. The damage extends into Norway and Finland; both countries regarded the pollution as a major foreign policy problem and offered to help upgrade the Russian plants. The offer was declined, and the plants continued to operate using imported ores that contained even higher sulphur content than the exhausted local ores.

Elsewhere in Russia, such as at Krasnoyarsk in the south-central part of the country, fluorine emissions from aluminum smelters are identified as the prime cause of 3.2 million hectares of dead and dying forests. Southern Sweden and Norway are affected by the long-range transport of acid precipitation and other forms of air pollution from this area. Deposition of sulphur dioxide and nitrous oxides has affected soils so radically that some of them may not be able to support another generation of trees. Radioactive pollution is another problem affecting forests in parts of the former Soviet Union, including about 1 million hectares around Chernobyl. As fires in contaminated forests release dust and smoke, radioactive pollution drifts on air currents for hundreds of kilometres (Acharya, 1995).

In Germany, the word *Waldsterben* (meaning "forest death") describes the forest decline that has affected more than one-third of the country's forests, as well as up to 25 percent of the fir and spruce trees in Switzerland and more than 1.2 million acres of forest in Poland and the Czech Republic (Hammond, 1991). The primary cause of this forest decline is the long-range transport of airborne pollutants (LRTAP) from combustion of fossil fuels in vehicles and from many industrial processes, including thermal power generation and smelting.

The acid deposition that results from this LRTAP causes direct damage and loss of foliage and needles to trees by leaching out nutrients, causing thinning and perhaps fatal damage to the tree's crown. As well, indirect damage through soil acidification (in which heavy metals

are released in forms taken up by tree roots) occurs. In Canada, acid precipitation contributes to, and may well be the major cause of, forest decline in southwestern British Columbia, as well as the loss of sugar maple trees in Quebec. Slash burning and the pulp manufacturing process also contribute to the problem of forest decline in Canada.

TOURISM AND RECREATION

Natural forest landscapes are an important factor in the health of the tourism industry across Canada. Valued at billions of dollars per year, forest-related tourism occurs in national and provincial parks and in provincial forests through activities such as hunting and fishing, wilderness hiking, river rafting and canoe tripping, skiing, and camping and picnicking. While these activities disperse revenues in the communities where the tourism occurs to some degree, many goods and services used by tourists are supplied by major urban centres. This is a concern, as is the seasonal nature of tourism and the often low wages paid to tourism workers. Nevertheless, the overall scale of tourist activities occurring in, or related to, forest areas is substantial.

Wildlife viewing—from waterways, forest trails, and viewing stations—is a multimillion-dollar, "nonconsumptive" forest use and activity in Canada. Provided that forest-based tourism occurs in forest areas that are protected and used wisely, long-term annual benefits can accrue to communities. Old-growth forests are prime wildlife habitat and provide superb scenic backdrops for visitors who have come to the forest for their interest in birds, mammals, fish, and plants. Even the trees themselves are visitor attractions. Cutting old-growth forests for their timber values potentially precludes the economic benefits that come from sustainable, nontimber values such as wildlife viewing, even though logging has been important for facilitating access for recreationists. Although it is difficult to calculate a precise dollar value, trees are worth highly valuable to the tourism industry.

As a growth industry in Canada, tourism and recreational services will continue to depend on healthy, natural amenities, including unlogged forests. In 1995, foresters and environmentalists clashed over plans to clear-cut much of the 700 square kilometres of the Algoma Highlands, 150 kilometres northeast of Sault Ste. Marie, Ontario. A 60-square-kilometre conservation reserve was excluded from harvesting, as was a large (temporary) area around Megasin Lake in the centre of the highlands. Wilderness outfitters in that area argued that logging was incompatible with their successful remote tourism operations, and forced the provincial government to undertake its first ever environmental assessment of a forest management plan. The environmental assessment, however, focused only on the impacts of logging on tourism, and did not consider other environmental impacts (Leahy, 1995).

Photo 9–16
Acid rain has had a detrimental effect on the world's forests.

Photo 9–17
Canada's forests provide economic returns through recreation and tourism as well as commercial forestry.

For instance, human-started fires occur, and demands for improved infrastructure (such as toilets, roads, and parking lots) may arise, especially as numbers escalate. Forest values can be destroyed by recreational activities, most obviously in the case of skiing, snowmobiling, and golfing but also from hiking, cycling, and visiting. Backcountry hiking may introduce exotic species into previously inaccessible regions. Indeed, where tourism becomes a successful industry, the large-scale presence of visitors may reduce the values they came to appreciate. In Squamish, British Columbia, the popularity of the winter bird count for Bald Eagles coincided with temporary declines in returning birds. Local and provincial officials took strong measures (including designation of a protected area and provision of public information at the site) to ensure the safety of bald eagles that congregate there by the hundreds in the winter. Caution must be exercised in interpreting such activities as "nonconsumptive." In addition, governments and private landowners may face increased liability if natural forest events such as wildfires or falling trees damage equipment or injure or kill visitors. These realities, however, do not diminish the "multiple values" of natural forests.

A proposed "view-scape cut," where narrow bands of trees would be left to ring the major lakes and streams used by tourists, may hide clear-cut slopes beyond the tree ring, but does not provide the healthy, natural forest amenities that are part of the expected quality experience for wilderness visitors. Outfitters worry that this lack of a quality experience could lead to a decrease in repeat customers that, in the longer term, could cause a reversal in the economic viability of their operations.

Yet, possibilities for complementary relationships between the forest industry and ecotourism exist, as the experience of Fiddlehead Farm near Powell River, British Columbia, reveals. Fiddlehead Farm is surrounded by extensive tree farm licences and could have been threatened by logging slated for the adjacent Giovanno Valley. Visitors to the 32-hectare wilderness hostel arrive by boat and then walk in through 2 kilometres of second-growth, mixed-conifer forest, including Douglas fir, hemlock, and cedar. The forest company's logging plan anticipated clear-cuts in the valley adjacent to the farm and a mainline logging road across the walk-in access route (McPhedran, 1997). Indeed, since 1997 more roads have been built and more cut blocks have been created, including a logged site that extends to the shore of Giovanno Lake. Nevertheless, despite the farm owner's initial fears regarding noise and visual impact of summer logging, both the farm and logging co-exist.

Admittedly, recreational activities that access public or private forests themselves impose risks and problems.

ECONOMIC AND SOCIAL CIRCUMSTANCES FACING CANADA'S FOREST INDUSTRY: PAST AND PRESENT

Before this country became a nation, many Aboriginal peoples derived their basic means of survival—food, clothing, shelter, and tools—from the forests. Forests also were a fundamental dimension in their cultural and spiritual lives. Among the wealthiest nonagricultural (traditional) societies ever known, the First Nations people on the west coast based their lives on the use of the abundant cedar trees and the salmon that spawned in the coastal rain forest streams. These people carved wooden totem poles and masks, highly notable elements of their culture, that represented the integration of the forces of natural and spiritual realms that surrounded them (Knudtson & Suzuki, 1992). The wealth of the coastal forests enabled these First Nations to develop the potlatch economy, where masks and other goods were redistributed according to social status.

The European settlers, who challenged the original forest inhabitants for possession of lands, had a different conception of, and relationship with, nature and the forest. From the 17th to the 19th centuries, the vast majority of European immigrants wanted to establish farms. The forests of butternut, oak, white pine, walnut,

Photo 9–18
First Nations people from Canada's west coast used wood to carve artworks in addition to a great number of more utilitarian items.

industry grew rapidly after 1920, as did the chemical pulp industry after 1945. In contrast to sawmilling operations, where small entrepreneurs were still numerous, pulp and paper mills were invariably large and capital intensive, and thus more often under the control of large companies. Moreover, these companies, with the help of favourable government policies, were able to gain large timber concessions that assured access to adequate supplies of pulpwood and the necessary loans.

Most of the 20th century was marked by increasing concentration of control over timber harvesting by a small number of large companies. In British Columbia, by the 1940s, 58 firms held about 52 percent of the 1.6 million hectares under timber licence. By 1973, 54 percent of the harvesting rights were held by 10 large companies that were multinational in scope with integrated forest management operations around the world. "In 1975, the four largest firms accounted for 22 percent of timber production, but 75 percent of plywood, 52 percent of market pulp, and 94 percent of newsprint production" (Hayter, 2000, p. 55). This level of concentration remains.

The turn by government to large-scale companies was a deliberate policy of the 1950s and 1960s. Governments of the day believed that a sustained or steady harvest of timber would achieve to socially desirable objectives such as community stability (Byron, 1978), and that large-scale companies were in the most favourable position to meet them (Marchak, 1983). Yet, a steady supply of timber did not account for changing market demand and fluctuating prices, while large companies did not provide more stable employment for workers than smaller companies. Instead, larger companies had significant political influence in setting policy priorities related to payments made to governments, allocation of harvesting rights, and management practices (Williston & Keller, 1997). As the history of labour strikes and continuous shedding of employees indicates, larger companies did not provide a high level of stability for forestry workers, and ultimately their actions increased dependency and vulnerability of workers and forestry communities to globalizing forces (Burda & M'Gonigle, 1998; Marchak et al., 1999; M'Gonigle, 1997). This concentration of ownership and the pattern of instability forms part of the social and political characteristics of the resource cycle described in Chapter 4.

Like other resource-based industries, forestry has tended to be male-dominated. In 2007, across Canada, only 14 percent of forestry workers were women. While some have argued that this imbalance is due to the physical nature of forestry work, women are also underrepresented in jobs that are not physically challenging such as forest assessment (using computer-based technologies such as GIS and remote sensing), planning, regulation, and decision making. For example, a recent survey of the Canadian Forest Service revealed that in

maple, and black cherry trees, as well as the Aboriginal people's, were seen as obstacles, something to be conquered and to be driven back to permit homesteading to proceed. With more powerful technology, Europeans used force, treaties, or both to remove Aboriginal peoples from lands the newcomers wanted to settle. With axes and oxen, European settlers slowly but surely began removing the forest cover.

At the beginning of the 19th century, Britain and the United States began to be interested in extracting Canadian forest products for large-scale export to support shipbuilding in those places (Lower, 1973). Following Confederation, from 1867 to 1906, the governments of Quebec and Ontario received millions of dollars through the liquidation of their forests, collecting various rents and fees from the timber industry. For instance, between 1867 and 1899, forest-generated income contributed 28 cents out of every dollar collected by the Ontario treasury (Swift, 1983).

At the beginning of the 20th century, the growth of literacy, the increased importance of newspapers, and the growth in consumer spending in Canada became the impetus for a new pulp and paper industry. The newsprint

this government agency, women composed 34 percent of the workforce overall. Women were overrepresented in administrative/support positions (where 94 percent of workers were female) but underrepresented at the executive level (where 16 percent of the workers were female) and in operations (where only 6 percent of the workers were female) (Fullerton, 2006). Although in other sectors of the economy women are typically overrepresented in support positions and underrepresented in executive decisions, the skewed division of labour is particularly acute in forestry and other resource extraction industries dominated by large-scale employers.

Aboriginal peoples lived as part of the North American forests for centuries before Europeans arrived in this land. Hammond (1993, p. 134) claims that their sovereignty "has never been diminished through conquest, prior discovery, purchase, or fair treaties by the various governments of European descendants which have controlled Canada for the last two centuries." Displacement of Aboriginal peoples from their traditional homelands by European settlers and the subsequent suppression and sometimes abuse of Aboriginal cultures have diminished the opportunity to learn about sustaining the forests from those people who once were part of them. Throughout Canada, land questions remain largely unresolved. From Alberta to the east coast, treaties were signed; however, disputes still arise over their interpretation. Most Aboriginal peoples in British Columbia have never signed treaties. Nevertheless, governments have sometimes already given away rights to access resources to third parties such as timber or mining companies. These "third-party" interests also must be considered as governments and Aboriginal peoples come to the negotiating table about Aboriginal rights.

For Aboriginal peoples, pursuing the land claims process embodies an enigma: Why must something be claimed that was never given up? Even though the land claims process is far from complete, Aboriginal influence over British Columbia's and Canada's forests is growing. A concern is that logging means not only that these people will be denied timber sale royalties, but also that they will lose traditional hunting and gathering territories. While struggles are ongoing to address Aboriginal title adequately and to settle land questions justly, the timber industry is said to be "swiftly foreclosing on the options that indigenous people will have following any agreement" (Hammond, 1991, p. 135). Consequently, First Nations people have sought injunctions to stop logging on these lands so that their rights are acknowledged, and so that First Nations people themselves will have the right to decide how the lands will be used.

In recent years, timber companies in British Columbia have been extremely active in negotiating joint ventures with Aboriginal peoples (Hayter, 2000). For example, Iisaak Forest Products is a company formed as a joint venture between Weyerhaeuser and the Ma-Mook (Aboriginal) Development Corporation, with the Central Region Nuu-chah-nulth First Nations holding controlling interest. Iisaak has primary rights of access to Tree Farm License (TFL) 57 in Clayoquot Sound. In 2001, the World Wildlife Fund recognized Iisaak for its outstanding environmental and social commitment to the forests. In 2006, Ecotrust Canada entered into a two-year partnership to manage Iisaak along with Triumph Timber, a forest management company. Additionally, the Central Region Chiefs, through Ma-Mook, formed a partnership with Coulson Forest Products to manage the former Interfor TFL 54. This partnership means that Central Region First Nations on Vancouver Island have a controlling interest in all forestry activities in Clayoquot Sound.

In other parts of Canada as well, Aboriginal peoples are active in forestry. In Saskatchewan, Mistik Management is a joint venture between the Meadow Lake Tribal Council, Norsask Forest Products (Meadow Lake Tribal Council became owner in 1998), and Millar Western Pulp. Mistik has been in operation for over 30 years, gradually increasing the numbers of First Nations peoples it employs and developing practices that are consistent with ecological aspects of sustainability. In December 2006, the Meadow Lake pulp mill was purchased by the Sinar Mas Group, an Indonesia-based paper company that owns Asia Pulp and Paper. The new owners have stated that they will run the mill for at least five years with about 150 people working there (CBC News, 2006). Given the large proportion of Aboriginal peoples living in northern Saskatchewan (where most of the timber is harvested), in the late 1990s the Saskatchewan government declared that any new forest management arrangements must be co-managed by Aboriginal and industry partners. In Labrador and Quebec, in the summer of 1994, the Innu living in Nitassinan were involved in land rights negotiations with Canada and Newfoundland when the Newfoundland Forest Service constructed new access roads in Forestry Management District 20, despite legislation requiring an approved forestry management plan before any new activity took place (Innu Nation, 1995). While the forests were not exploited actively by large-scale industrial forest operations at that time, the wood deficit forecast for the island of Newfoundland meant that large pulp interests were looking to Nitassinan to fill the gap. Subsequently, a land claims agreement has been reached in principle (Department of Indian Affairs and Northern Development, 1999).

Aboriginal organizations are not the only ones attempting to gain more control over timber operations. In many communities, Aboriginal and non-Aboriginal people are working toward environmentally sustainable, socially acceptable, economically feasible, and community-based forestry practices. A sample of these efforts is described in the next section.

Canada's Role in Addressing Environmental and Social Sustainability of Forests

INTERNATIONAL AND FEDERAL INITIATIVES

Many countries that produce and consume forest products are trying to come to grips with the need to balance economic and environmental requirements in order to ensure healthy, vigorous forests that can meet the needs of today as well as tomorrow. Over time there has been a continued focus on balancing economic development and conservation, although the relative emphasis placed on development and conservation has varied. In Canada, at least, a small but growing emphasis has been placed on seeking a balance between conservation and development that considers social objectives such as ensuring adequate employment and including Aboriginal peoples in forestry. Table 9–6 reveals this growing emphasis as it describes international and national initiatives in which Canada has participated.

SETTING STANDARDS AND CODES OF PRACTICE

Consumer pressure, especially in Europe, has been driving efforts to establish certification standards or methods to identify forest products that have been produced in ways that do not degrade the environment. Slow to react at first, over the past decade or so, the forest industry has become increasingly conscious of the need to respond to environmental and social imperatives. A growing number of forest firms are seeking **ISO 14000** registration and various forms of **eco-certification** (see Box 9–6, p. 394). For instance, the Canadian Sustainable Forestry Coalition is promoting the development by the Canadian Standards Association (CSA) of an international system of forestry certification using the ISO 14000 series of Environmental Management Systems standards. The International Organization for Standardization (ISO) focuses on developing systems standards so that quality products of a particular type (such as pharmaceuticals or chemicals) are known to have similar or identical manufacturing histories. With regard to forestry, the ISO emphasizes whether a logging company, for instance, has an adequate forest management planning process in place; the ISO does not focus on their actual on-the-ground performance (note, however, that the Sustainable Forest Management System is based on the six Canadian criteria for sustainable forest management outlined in Table 9–6).

The ISO 14000 system has been criticized for failing to require a clearly documented and verifiable "chain of custody" (see Box 9–6) back to the forest from which the wood originated. Although participants in this system must define a "designated forest area" where their management system will apply, there is no requirement that the entire output of a specific mill, for instance, originate from that area. That is, there is no clear link between the products sold by a company and its forest management system (von Mirbach, 1997).

Nevertheless, some companies have worked with environmental organizations to become registered and thereby gain a competitive advantage. A noteworthy example is the accord between the World Wildlife Fund and Tembec Inc., an innovative Quebec-based corporation that also has extensive interests in southeast British Columbia, to promote sustainable forestry practices (World Wildlife Fund, 2001). In its British Columbia operations, Tembec received ISO 14001 certification for its mills. It also developed ecosystem land use plans; shifted away from sole reliance on clear-cutting while reducing the size of remaining clear-cuts; practised more intensive silviculture; and participated in various cooperative efforts with local institutions. These practices are now part of its overall operations.

Other agencies also have undertaken certification (Box 9–6). For example, in November 2002, the Ontario Ministry of Natural Resources signed a memorandum of understanding with the Standards Council of Canada (SCC) to recognize each other's requirements for forest certification. Federal model forests of eastern Ontario and Bas-Saint-Laurent have gained resource manager forest certification in accordance with the principles and criteria of the Forest Stewardship Council. The first boreal certification in Canada was granted to Gordon Cosens Forest, an area of 2 million hectares located in northern Ontario managed by Tembec.

British Columbia's Forest Practices Code

The Forest Practices Code of British Columbia Act (1995) was a major attempt to balance the full range of industrial and nonindustrial values within a framework of sustainable forest management. Achieving such a balance has been difficult, however (Cashore et al., 2001). The government acknowledged public concern for the protection of landscape values and wildlife habitat, and the Forest Practices Code was an attempt to regulate industrial forestry in a way that would satisfy these desires while preserving jobs (British Columbia Ministry of Forests, 1997). During the late 1990s, the code regulated all aspects of forestry and rangeland management on Crown lands and some private lands in British Columbia, including all aspects of logging and road construction, silviculture policies, fire protection, and the safeguarding of environmental and recreational values. Unlike most previous forestry-related

International Initiative	Description
UNCED (Earth Summit) Forest Principles (1992)	A nonbinding statement of principles for a global consensus on the management, conservation, and sustainable development of all types of forests. This statement included understanding forests as integrated ecosystems with diverse values; promoting public participation in decision making, particularly women and Aboriginal peoples; developing the skills, education, and knowledge needed to support forest conservation and sustainable development; strengthening international cooperation and assistance for forests in developing countries; developing policies to ensure the conservation and sustainable development of forests; identifying and dealing with outside pressures; and encouraging fair international trade in forest products.
Agenda 21 (1992)	An international agenda for development and the environment in the 21st century. Agenda 21 recognized humans are responsible for widespread and often uncontrolled degradation and depletion of forests and called for national action and international cooperation to achieve sustainable development. The chapter on forestry contained no recommended policy for sustainable forest management.
The Convention on Biological Diversity (1992)	A legally binding agreement, signed by Canada, committing the country to preparing and adhering to a national biodiversity strategy, including ensuring that a representative sample of Canada's forests is protected. Canada established a biodiversity strategy in 1996.
United Nations Forum on Forests (UNFF) (2000)	Established in October 2000 with the main objective of facilitating and promoting implementation of the proposals for action of the Intergovernmental Panel and Forum on Forests.
Montreal Process on Criteria and Indicators (2003)	A group of 12 countries, representing 90 percent of all temperate and boreal forests (and 45 percent of all trade in forest products), working together to develop and implement criteria and indicators for the conservation and sustainable management of temperate and boreal forests. Its first report was released at the 12th World Forestry Congress in Quebec City in 2003.
Federal Initiative	**Description**
National Forest Strategy (1992)	First released by the federal government in 1992. New strategies have been released approximately every five years, the most recent being developed for 2003–8. This strategy identified nine goals intended to: (1) conserve the natural diversity of our forests, maintain and enhance their productive capacity, and provide for their continued renewal; (2) improve our ability to plan and practise sustainable forest management; (3) increase public participation in the allocation and management of forest lands and provide an increased level of public information and awareness; (4) diversify and encourage economic opportunities for the forest sector in domestic and international markets; (5) increase and focus research and technology efforts to benefit our environment and economy; (6) ensure that we have a highly skilled and adaptable workforce; (7) increase participation by and benefits for Aboriginal peoples in the management and use of forests; (8) assist private forest owners in continuing to improve their individual and collective abilities to manage and exercise stewardship of their land; and (9) reinforce Canada's responsibilities as trustee of 10 percent of the world's forests.
Model Forests and Forest Communities (1992 and 2007)	Implemented in 1992. Canada now has 11 model forests developed to determine how to establish and nurture sustainable forestry. Model forests range in size from 100000 to 2500000 hectares and are created on a mix of public and private lands to represent a range of forest ecosystems across the country. Model forests have many partners, including provincial governments, forest industries, First Nations, recreational users, community organizations, private landowners, environmental organizations, and researchers. Each model forest undertakes sustainability initiatives that reflect the issues relevant to the region. As of 2006, model forests began to place a greater emphasis on community sustainability and how forests can contribute. To this end, in April 2007, the Canadian Forest Service launched the Forest Communities Program to help forest-based communities develop environmentally sustainable, diverse, and robust rural economies.
Criteria and Indicators of Sustainable Forest Management (1993)	Begun in 1993 by the Canadian Council of Forest Ministers to report on six criteria and indicators for sustainable forest management in Canada. The four ecological criteria are conservation of biological diversity; maintenance and enrichment of forest ecosystem condition and productivity; conservation of soil and water resources; and forest ecosystem contributions to global ecological cycles. The two socioeconomic criteria include multiple benefits to society and accepting society's responsibility for sustainable development. Each year, the State of Canada's Forests report documents practices and challenges associated with attempts to meet these criteria.

BOX 9-6

SETTING STANDARDS FOR SUSTAINABLE FOREST MANAGEMENT

As public concerns about forests and forest practices have grown, and environmental groups have gained increasing public recognition, there has been a corresponding growth in industry support for independent assessments of forest operations to ensure continued or enhanced market access. The objective is to provide purchasers with a form of guarantee that the forest products they buy were managed according to sustainable forest management principles.

The Forest Stewardship Council (FSC), an international nongovernmental organization, was established in 1993 with the support of the World Wildlife Fund. Members of the council include representatives of environmental groups, Indigenous peoples, certification organizations, and other nongovernmental groups from 25 countries. The council's goal is to provide consumers with information about forest products and their sources through certification.

There are important similarities between the objectives and approaches of the Canadian Standards Association (CSA) and the FSC. For instance, both organizations promote better forest management and require third-party audits. However, there are also important differences in their processes. The FSC focuses on product labelling and tracking of forest products to their origin (the "chain of custody"). Wood that is guaranteed to have come from environmentally well-managed forests is sometimes called "certified wood" (Polson, 1996). The CSA's registration program does not involve tracing products but assesses a company's ability to manage in an environmentally sound manner and includes performance indicators tailored to specific sites. The CSA process is not an eco-labelling program because the standards do not apply to consumer products at the retail level.

Another difference is that the FSC's certification is based on a series of principles developed independently to apply to all forest types. Specific requirements of the FSC are outlined in 10 principles that cover topics such as management planning, assessment of environmental impacts, and maintaining community relations. Forest operators must satisfy the requirements of all 10 principles to be certified by the FSC. The CSA's Sustainable Forest Management system is based on both the Canadian criteria and the ISO 14000 system, which deal with the quality of the management systems, not the quality of the products themselves. CSA's Technical Committee on Sustainable Forest Management has met with FSC representatives to discuss the potential for aligning the two processes.

In March 2000, two small woodlot operators became the first two forests in western Canada to be certified under the FSC certification system. In 2001, Mistik Management, a joint venture in Saskatchewan, was granted certification. In 2001, Tembec Inc. made a commitment to certify all of its operations to the standards of the FSC. In total, by 2001, 17 million hectares were certified. In January 2002, the Forest Products Association of Canada committed its membership to achieving Sustainable Forest Management (SFM) certification based on one of three systems on all lands under their management by the end of 2006. These three systems are the Canadian Standards Association (CSA), the Forest Stewardship Council (FSC), and the Sustainable Forestry Initiative (SFI). By June 2006, 119 million hectares were certified to one of the three SFM certification programs in Canada; 78 percent of the certified forests (by area) were members of the Forest Products

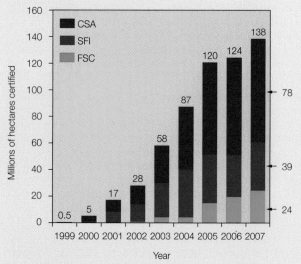

Box Figure 9–1

Sustainable Forest Management certification in Canada, 1999–2007

SOURCE: © Canadian Sustainable Forestry Certification Coalition, December 2006.

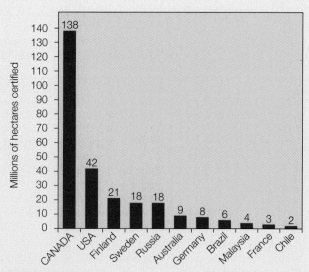

Box Figure 9–2

Canadian certification status compared to other countries in 2006

SOURCE: © Canadian Sustainable Forestry Certification Coalition, December 2006.

Association of Canada. By 2007, 159 companies operating across 128 million hectares had become certified. Current levels of certification by companies can be reviewed at http://www.certifiedwoodsearch.org/certificationcanada/. As Box Figures 9–1 and 9–2 illustrate, certification has been rapid and extensive. Canada now has the largest area of third-party certified forests in the world.

Products acquired from certified forest operations are in high demand, fuelled by the purchasing policies of large retailers such as Home Depot and IKEA that give preference to certified wood (Vasbinder & Brewer, 2001). It is anticipated that the demand for certified products will continue to grow, increasing pressure on producers to identify and implement approaches to certification that are consistent and clear for consumers.

SOURCES: *Branching Out: Case Studies in Canadian Forest Management,* A. Berry, 2006, Bozeman, MT: Property and Environment Research Centre, www.iisd.org/greenstand/default.htm; *The State of Canada's Forests 1995–1996: Sustaining Forests at Home and Abroad,* Natural Resources Canada, Canadian Forest Service, 1996; "Cutting with Conscience," S. Polson, 1996, *E Magazine, 7*(3), 42–43; "The Promise of Forest Certification," W. Vasbinder & C. Brewer, 2001, *Encompass, 5*(3), 8–9, 28; "Demanding Good Wood," M. von Mirbach, 1997, *Alternatives, 23*(3), 10–17. Canada-wide status, Certification Canada, 2006. http://www.certificationcanada.org/english/status-intentions/canada.php

regulations, which were contractual, the code was statutory, enforceable by law.

Nevertheless, environmental groups and the industry continued to criticize the code based on whether it worked to improve management practices or whether it simply added costs to industry (Hayter, 2000). In 2001, government revised the code, in part to reduce what was considered a bureaucratic burden on industry. Environmental groups were alarmed at what they saw as a weakening of an already too weak and inadequately enforced code. In 2002, the provincial government introduced a new Forest and Range Practices Act. The Act came into effect in January 2004 and became fully operational by 2006, replacing the Forest Practices Code. Government policymakers suggested that the code was highly prescriptive, rigid, and expensive to enforce. In its place, government introduced a results-oriented system in which government sets objectives to enforce forest values, and forest companies are granted greater flexibility to determine how best to meet those objectives. Monitoring and enforcement remain part of the new Act (see British Columbia Ministry of Forests, 2003). Environmental groups have argued that the new legislation further weakens government commitment to protection of forest values, while forest industry advocates disagree. Thus, while the Forest Practices Code was considered a radical policy innovation, it was short-lived and ultimately failed to reconcile competing values in British Columbia's forests.

ESTABLISHING PARTNERSHIPS FOR WILDLIFE PROTECTION

Grizzly bear populations in Alberta have declined from an estimated historic population of 6000 to about 800 today, and are at risk of extinction if their needs are not integrated into land use planning and hunting quotas. The Eastern Slopes Grizzly Bear Research Project began in 1993 as a partnership between researchers at the University of Calgary and about 30 other conservation groups, resource users, developers such as the cattle and the oil and gas industries, and government agencies. Researchers are attempting to understand grizzly bear habitat as it relates to all human activities. If this understanding can be developed, then it may be possible to design an enduring land use system that would include movement corridors for the endangered bears and enable them to repopulate their former home ranges in Banff National Park and the Kananaskis Country areas.

There are no regulations requiring the Alberta forest industry to demonstrate concern for grizzly bear habitat. However, an Alberta forest products company, Spray Lakes Sawmills Ltd., became a partner in the Eastern Slopes Grizzly Bear Research Project in 1996, donating $10 000 to support the conservation project ("Grizzly Study Finds Forestry Friend," 1996). The woodlands manager, aware that logging can be made compatible with other forest values, entered the project with the willingness to develop creative ways to change the company's forest management practices. Committed to learn from researchers about habitat and movement corridors that are important for grizzlies in areas they proposed to log, the company gained crucial information for making environmentally responsible decisions.

Clearly, being a partner in this research project helped the company identify how to manage the impact of its forestry operations on sensitive wildlife species such as the grizzly bear. In addition, researchers gained an important opportunity to learn how to integrate grizzly bears' needs into the design of future forest harvesting plans for the eastern slopes of the Rocky Mountains. By protecting grizzly bears and their habitat, this partnership also helped maintain habitat for many other species in healthy ecosystems. The Eastern Slopes Grizzly Bear Research Project is an important demonstration of the win-win situation that can evolve through sharing information about cumulative impacts and being willing to change management practices.

Whitetail deer reach the northern limits of their natural habitat in Quebec. Their survival is influenced strongly by availability of winter habitat that provides shelter and food. When establishing their winter habitat, deer seek out mature coniferous stands that provide shelter from the cold and wind. Coniferous stands also facilitate the animals' movements, because the trees permit only minor accumulations of snow on the ground. Since twigs constitute the deer's basic winter diet, an abundance of young broad-leaved trees also is necessary. The greater the diversity of food and shelter opportunities within an area, and the shorter the distance deer have to travel during harsh winters, the lower will be their vulnerability to winter weather and predators (Fondation de la faune du Québec, n.d.; Natural Resources Canada, 1995).

To secure this important winter habitat, the forest industry, Quebec government departments, Natural Resources Canada, Wildlife Habitat Canada, and the Fondation de la faune du Québec developed and funded the Deer Yard Program. The program works in cooperation with the forest industry by increasing woodlot owners' awareness of their land's wildlife potential and by providing landowners with technical and financial assistance to plan timber harvesting and tree-planting regimes that are suitable to the habitat needs of whitetail deer. The more severe the winter, the more local landowner yards become essential to the survival of the species. The Deer Yard Program initiative is helping to ensure the continued sustainability of Quebec's deer population.

WORKING DIRECTLY WITH ABORIGINAL PEOPLE

First Nations have become important participants in forestry across the nation. In British Columbia, efforts have been made to increase First Nations' participation in the forest sector through "interim measures agreements" that have been signed prior to resolution of the land question through treaties. In Alberta, the Aboriginal Apprenticeship Project, announced in September 2002, encourages Aboriginal people to take up careers in many trades, including forestry jobs. In October 2002, the Government of Newfoundland and Labrador and the Labrador Métis First Nation signed a memorandum of understanding to facilitate Métis participation in forest management. The Government of Canada renewed the First Nations Forestry Program from 2003 to 2008 to provide financial assistance to activities that encourage opportunities for First Nations people to participate in Canada's forest sector.

Additionally, First Nations and private forest companies have formed joint business ventures to undertake sustainable forestry that employs Aboriginal people. In Saskatchewan, for example, forest companies can no longer have access to a forest management agreement unless they are partnered with a First Nation. Mistik Management is a company jointly owned by Millar Western and NorSask Forest Products, the latter of which is owned by the Meadow Lake Tribal Council. Since the late 1980s, Mistik has attempted to conduct sustainable forestry, working with nine community-based advisory boards to guide its operations, ensuring that most of its contractors are owned by First Nations or Métis community members, and engaging in practices and research to assure the long-term sustainability of the resource base.

INVOLVING COMMUNITIES

Beyond these initiatives, there is a growing interest in providing conditions for communities to be more directly involved in undertaking and regulating forestry. There are many ways in which local communities might be directly involved in forestry. For example, Saskatchewan developed a new policy framework for managing wildland fire and forest insects and diseases following extensive public consultation. In Quebec, the government has been testing an approach known as the *Forêt Habitée* ("inhabited forest"). This is a concept of joint forest management that allows diverse users to make management decisions. In Manitoba, a government report released in 2002 outlined ways for government, industry, and First Nations to work together to enhance forest stewardship and to ensure that both scientific and traditional knowledge are considered to help promote a sustainable forest economy. In Toronto, the Urban Forestry and Natural Environment and Horticulture Section of Toronto's Parks and Recreation Division has undertaken several projects related to urban forestry and biodiversity protection that demonstrate the benefits of community stewardship in ecosystem protection. On northern Vancouver Island, the North Island Woodlot Association has promoted a type of grassroots, small-scale forestry that involves local people in forest management.

In every province except Prince Edward Island, Canadian forest managers have introduced new processes and sometimes even legal requirements to incorporate public interest and values in the management of Crown lands. The advisory or citizen committee has become a key tool among these processes; these committees are an entry point for local residents, communities, and stakeholder groups to express their interests in forest management.

Women make up only 17 percent of participants in these committees across Canada, although there is some variation. Women are represented in higher proportions in British Columbia (32 percent) and in lower proportions in Saskatchewan (8.1 percent) (Reed & Varghese, 2007). As several studies have revealed that women are more likely to support environmental conservation generally and forest protection specifically exclusion of women likely has reinforced a timber extraction bias and has restricted women's contributions to advancing the aims of sustainable forestry (Arora-Jonsson, 2004; Davidson & Freudenburg, 1996; Mohai, 1992; Tindall et al., 2003; Uliczka et al., 2004).

Community forests, in all their diversity, are small but important examples of people working toward the social, economic, and environmental objectives of sustainability (Box 9–7). More common in developing countries than in Canada, community forests offer locally tailored models for consideration when pursuing sustainability.

BOX 9-7
COMMUNITY FORESTS

About 94 percent of Canada's forest land is publicly owned and managed by governments, primarily provincial governments. Large-scale, integrated, and globally connected forest product companies typically have access to the largest tracts of forest land. Since at least the 1970s, these companies as well as governments have been subject to criticism because they have put profitability over ecosystem protection and community well-being.

What if communities rather than governments owned, managed, and harvested products from their own forests? Would community forests be more successful in meeting environmental, economic, social, and political goals than government-owned forests? Research has suggested that meeting this range of goals simultaneously is a significant challenge.

Around the world, communities can and do hold title to forest lands and manage the use of the forests collectively. Pagdee et al. (2006, 34) suggest that "community forestry focuses on improving the livelihood and welfare of rural people and conserving natural forest systems through participation and cooperation. Local community groups negotiate, define, and guarantee among themselves equitable sharing of the management functions, entitlements, and responsibilities for a given set of natural resources." In theory, then, owners of community forests can manage the forest resources to meet a wide range of community needs.

In Canada, experience with community forests is limited. Only a few small areas have been dedicated to community tenures. This does not necessarily mean that a community owns the land, but rather that a community holds a limited-time licence for which it is required to meet certain conditions. In Ontario, the Westwind Forest Stewardship Inc. is a nonprofit organization that manages the publicly owned French/Severn Forest. Westwind is directed by a local board that includes community and forest industry representation. As a nonprofit organization, Westwind has been successful in reducing the overall harvest of timber to accommodate nontimber values. Additionally, the forest products derived from the forest have been certified by the FSC.

What happens when local communities that are timber-dependent gain a community forest licence? In 1998, the British Columbia government initiated 11 pilot projects for

community forest agreements. Two of these community forests, at Revelstoke and at Burns Lake, were established where commercial forestry had long been important to the local economy. Employment and revenue generation were at the top of the list of priorities for these forests. These community forests have focused on creating jobs, supplying logs for local processing, and boosting the local economy while maintaining environmental standards. On the positive front, community forests typically meet and often exceed environmental standards set by provincial governments. Additionally, supporters believe that they can respond quickly to economic and environmental issues as they arise (Berry, 2006). But critics argue that community tenures do not provide enough incentives for ecosystem-based forestry and that annual cutting rates may still be set too high to be sustainable over the long term (Berry, 2006).

Other concerns have been raised about whether all members of local communities have equal opportunities to be represented. For example, a study of the Burns Lake Community Forest noted that greater participation by Aboriginal people was imperative, although in practice, this involvement was restricted to Aboriginal leaders rather than general community members. Additionally, the Burns Lake Community Forest did not have a better record of involving women or migrant forest workers in forestry activities or decision making than conventional forestry conducted by larger companies. The dominant focus has remained on providing timber rather than improving access to and development of nontimber forest products (Reed & McIlveen, 2006).

It is difficult to objectively assess the success of community forest management. A study of community forests around the world concluded that specific attributes of property rights regimes, institutional arrangements, incentives and interests of the community, and decentralization are directly associated with the success of community forest management (Pagdee et al., 2006). While strong leaders with effective organizational skills and experience also are important, these factors (expertise, experience, leadership) are commonly associated with exclusive forms of management (Bradshaw, 2007). What do you think? What attributes of community forests are important? How can we achieve multiple objectives simultaneously?

SOURCES: *Branching Out: Case Studies in Canadian Forest Management*, A. Berry, 2006, Bozeman, MT: Property and Environment Research Center; "On Definitions of 'Success' and Contingencies Affecting Success in Community Forestry: A Response to Reed and McIlveen (2006) and Pagdee et al. (2006)," B. Bradshaw, 2007, *Society and Natural Resources, 20*(8), 751–758; "What Makes Community Forest Management Successful: A Meta-Study from Community Forest Throughout the World," A. Pagdee, K. Yeon-Su, & P. Daugherty, 2006, *Society and Natural Resources, 19*, 33–52; "Toward a Pluralistic Civic Science? Assessing Community Forestry," M. Reed & K. McIlveen, 2006, *Society and Natural Resources, 19*, 591–607.

FUTURE CHALLENGES

Forests require careful stewardship, both internationally and within Canada. Balancing the demands on forest ecosystems to attain sustainability requires that the full range of forest values—ecological, economic, and social—be integrated into decision making. And, in a time when scarcity of forests is an issue, protecting forest ecosystems is paramount.

One way to protect forests and forest ecosystems is to identify an alternative source of fibre, such as hemp (see Enviro-Focus 9). New drug-free strains of hemp are revitalizing what was once a major source of fibre for paper, textiles, and other composite materials such as fibreboard. Since hemp is an agricultural crop grown on farms, it has significant implications for providing high-quality fibre with lower costs and fewer environmental impacts, potentially reducing the pressure on Canada's remaining old-growth forests. Other nonwood fibres may be poised for a comeback also (Rosmarin, 1997).

ENVIRO-FOCUS 9

Hemp: Fibre of the Future?

Humans have used hemp for fibre for thousands of years; in fact, in about 150 B.C., the Chinese made the world's first paper out of hemp. Until about 1850, hemp was used for making textiles, fishing nets, sails, rope, and the caulking between ship planks. The grain of the hemp plant was stewed, roasted, and milled for food. Hemp seed is second only to soybeans in complete protein. Its oil has been used for cosmetics, lighting, paints, varnishes, and medicinal preparations. More recently, hemp has been identified as an excellent source of biomass for alternative fuels, as a substitute for petrochemicals in the manufacture of some plastics, and in the manufacture of particle board, fibreboard, and other composites used in the construction industry.

Perhaps better known as the marijuana plant, hemp used to be grown throughout the western and central provinces of Canada as a textile crop. By 1937, hemp was extremely profitable, as the hemp combine and other new machinery had simplified harvesting and made production more cost-effective. Manufacturers became interested in the byproducts of hemp, including seed oil for paint and lacquer, and "hurds" (the woody inner portion of the stalk) for paper. However, in September 1937, the U.S. government banned hemp production. In spite of the benefits of the plant for industrial uses, and established markets for paper, textiles, and medicine derived from hemp, Canada followed suit, banning production under the Opium and Narcotics Act in 1938. The plant "disappeared" from cultivation for over 55 years.

Photo 9–19
Textiles made from hemp have multiple uses.

The U.S. government's reasons for banning such a beneficial plant were purely economic. Timber baron William Randolph Hearst (who controlled large tracts of forested land for pulp and paper), and the multinational DuPont (which owned the patents on new sulphate/sulphite processes for making paper out of wood), stood to lose billions of dollars if low-cost hemp became widely used. Across the United States, Hearst used the newspapers he owned to create a new perception of hemp as "the assassin of youth." Hearst's tactics resulted in the criminalization of hemp.

Although it made a brief comeback during the Second World War, hemp might never have been heard of again, except that a new strain of the plant was engineered in France. This plant contains very low levels of THC (the active ingredient responsible for the marijuana "high"). The new "drug-free" hemp was legalized in many parts of Europe and crops were growing again by 1993. In June 1996, the Canadian government amended the Narcotic Control Act to make it legal to cultivate industrial grades of hemp. Health Canada approved 27 varieties of industrial hemp for the 2006 growing season. The total number of hectares licensed for hemp cultivation across Canada grew from 2400 in 1998 to 9725 in 2005. Of the 2005 total, 52 percent was grown in Manitoba and 35 percent was grown in Saskatchewan. Hemp has generated much interest in Prairie rural communities as farmers seek alternatives to traditional commodities.

Switching from wood to hemp fibre has enormous implications. Fibreboard industry representatives claim that anything that can be made out of a tree can be made out of hemp, more cost-effectively and with less negative impact on the environment. Since hemp is an annual crop that can be grown on existing farmland, there is no need to build and reclaim expensive logging roads, and no need to clear-cut vast areas of forest using heavy equipment that damages the interconnected elements of the ecosystem and reduces its biodiversity. Hemp thrives without herbicides, it reinvigorates the soil, it is not a big consumer of water, it matures in three to four months, and it can yield four times as much paper per hectare as trees. Hemp fibres are ideal for producing superior-quality paper; long and light-coloured, hemp fibres require less bleaching than wood pulp, resulting in the production of lower levels of organochlorines.

Today, the export of hemp fibres has been highly variable, between zero and 389 tonnes. Only in 2004 were hemp food products legally allowed in the U.S. food market. Hemp oil and hemp seed are just beginning to gain an export market. It appears that the industry may develop if growers can produce hemp as a dual purpose crop, using both the grain and the fibre of the same plant. If hemp becomes an internationally significant alternative fibre source, it could reduce harvesting pressure on remaining old-growth forests in Canada and elsewhere. The forest industry could then focus on sustainable forest management, value-added production, and community health and sustainability. The viability of the concept of sustainability could become crystal clear to consumers; it makes much more sense to use plant material that grows in 100 days to build a house that lasts 50 years than it does to use plant material that takes between 200 and 500 years to grow. Hemp may be one of the fibres that helps achieve stewardship (conservation) of Canada's forests for the future.

SOURCES: "Back to the Future: Hemp Returns," S. Black & A. Guthrie, 1994, *Earthkeeper, 4*(3), 18–25; *Hemp and the Marijuana Conspiracy: The Emperor Wears No Clothes,* J. Herer, 1991, Van Nuys, CA: Hemp Publishing; "Harvesting Opportunity," P. Marck, June 23, 1997, *Calgary Herald,* p. C4. Agriculture and Agri-Food Canada, 2007. Canada's Industrial Hemp Industry. http://www4.agr.gc.ca/AAFC-AAC/display-afficher.do?id=1174595656066&lang=e

If Canadians wish to have sustainable forests, sustainable forest industries, and sustainable environments, there is a great deal that we yet need to know and predict about forests and forest ecosystems. We also must gain an understanding of the social effects that may result from changes in land allocation and management strategies. Knowledge building remains a critical part of developing sustainable forests, sustainable forest communities, and sustainable forest management. This is one reason why Canada's old-growth forests, boreal and temperate, must be considered as living laboratories. By considering the forests as laboratories, we can test new systems of harvest, new silvicultural methods, and new ways to gain additional value from timber. We also can try new methods and participatory processes to learn how to respect other cultural and nontimber values of the forests, and how to address concerns over displacement of forest workers as we move toward a value-based forest economy.

Knowledge-building technology, such as satellite imagery and GIS, can be used effectively to augment our understanding of the impacts of human activities on forest systems. For instance, satellite imagery of the world's forests, evaluated by experts around the world, enabled the World Resources Institute to specify what percentage of natural forests remained on the planet. There is a need, as well, to provide and expand these technical forms of assistance to developing nations to enable them to determine what constitutes sustainable forest management.

On a different level, knowledge-building processes help facilitate community understanding of forest uses and values that, ultimately, find expression in community-based and landscape-level land-use-planning decisions. Knowledge of ways to create sustainable forests and forest-based communities is improved, too, when partnership experiences and successes are shared with others. Overall, there is a critical need to combine natural sciences, social sciences, and even intuition and spirituality in our quest for a more sensitive and sustainable relationship between people and forests. Finally, we should recognize that across Canada, there has been a "re-regulation" of

"There are two ways of going at a forest," says Merv Wilkinson. "You can destroy it, or you can harvest it sustainably." Merv Wilkinson chose the latter route, offering us a model to consider. A sustainability pioneer born in September 1913, Merv Wilkinson spent most of his life learning how to manage a forest ecosystem.

Wildwood Forest, located on southern Vancouver Island, has been widely recognized as a model for ecoforestry. Although Wilkinson began stewarding Wildwood in 1938, he took time to learn about managing forests, rather than individual trees, and did not begin logging his property until 1945. He pioneered sustainable forest practices in western Canada, which he learned from a Scandinavian teacher. He began by applying sustained yield theory, a practice new to the West but well known in Scandinavia.

Wilkinson logged his property 11 times. He harvested trees selectively, never taking more than 10 percent of the standing timber in a given year. By 1999, he had logged approximately 2.1 million board feet (5000 cubic metres) from his 137-acre (55-hectare) property and neighbouring properties. In 1996, the standing volume at Wildwood was estimated at 1.65 million board feet (2500 cubic metres), 10 percent more than in 1938.

Wilkinson managed Wildwood by attempting to maintain a multiage, multispecies forest, including Douglas fir, western red cedar, grand fir, arbutus, bigleaf maple, red alder, western hemlock, bitter cherry, cascara, and Pacific dogwood. Wilkinson's management model stands in stark contrast to attempts in other parts of British Columbia to achieve a "normal forest" or a rotation based on even-age classes. His strong opposition to clear-cutting got him arrested in 1993 when he took part in the blockade in Clayoquot Sound.

"Mr. Wildwood" has supported public use of and public education about his forest. Since the 1980s, Merv Wilkinson has taught his methods to school children, college and university classes, environmentalists, journalists, film crews, and foresters from around the world.

In early 1999, the Land Conservancy of British Columbia and the Ecoforestry Institute entered into negotiations to purchase Wildwood, to maintain its capability as an ecoforestry demonstration site and

Photo 9–20
Merv Wilkinson.

learning facility. They finalized their purchase in December 2000.

Wilkinson, now a member of the Order of British Columbia (2001) and the Order of Canada (2002), continues to have life tenancy at Wildwood. His efforts illustrate how, through commitment and perseverance, one person can become a model for others.

Through his small parcel of land, Merv Wilkinson has demonstrated how we can make our forest resources both renewable and sustainable. His exemplary ecoforestry illustrates that this is not simply a philosophy but also a practice and a way of life. We must consider how to apply these lessons broadly if we are to encourage sustainable forest management.

SOURCES: "A Matter of Method: Merv Wilkinson's Wildwood Tree Farm," P. Donovan, 1999, *Managing Wholes,* http://managingwholes.com/merve.htm; "Merv Wilkinson's Wildwood," *The Land Conservancy,* 2005, http://www.conservancy.bc.ca/content.asp?sectionack=wildwood; "Community Hero: Merv Wilkinson," H. Rock, 2006, *Dogwood Initiative,* http://www.dogwoodinitiative.org/bulletins/CoomHeroMervewilkinson/; *Wildwood: Creating a Legacy for the Future,* Ecoforestry Institute, 2002, http://ecoforestry.ca/Wildwood/default.htm

forest policy (Hayter, 2000). The last decade or two has witnessed a remarkable level of experimentation in forest legislation that is seeking a more balanced use of the forest. As Canadian and international public interests in forests are likely to continue, the need to experiment with new harvest practices and management strategies, driven by a heightened commitment to protecting ecological, social, and cultural integrity, is likely to continue.

Chapter Questions

1. What is falldown? In what ways are the falldown effect and the life cycle in old-growth forests interrelated?

2. Outline the range of impacts that human activities have on forests and associated resources. If you live in a community or an area in which forestry activities are important, which types of impacts are most visible? Can you classify impacts as economic, environmental, social, or cultural? Which kinds of impacts are most important? Why?

3. Comment on the following statement: "clear-cutting is appropriate and necessary for forest management." In what ways would your comments be different for the statement, "clear-cutting is appropriate and necessary for forest sustainability"?

4. If clear-cutting were banned today, what would be the implications for people who work in the forests and live in forestry communities? What would be the impacts on government revenues on the forest itself? What recommendations might you make to address these impacts?

5. What cultural and social values do you hold in relation to forests? Of these, what values do you think are consistent with the aims of environmental, social, cultural, or economic sustainability?

6. If all the world's remaining tropical forests were to be destroyed, in what ways might your life change? What difference could the loss of all old-growth forests in Canada have on your life and on the lives of your descendants?

7. Discuss the value of the Canadian Council of Forest Ministers' criteria and critical elements (outlined in Table 9–6 on page 393) to achieve sustainability of Canada's forests. Are there additional elements that you would add to the list?

references

Acharya, A. (1995, May–June). Plundering the boreal forests. *World Watch*, 21–29.

Arora-Jonsson, S. (2004). Relational dynamics and strategies: Men and women in a forest community in Sweden. *Agriculture and Human Values, 21*, 355–365.

Bequette, F. (1994, November). Greenwatch: Red alert for the Earth's green belt. *The Unesco Courier*, 41–43.

British Columbia Ministry of Advanced Education. (2006a). Forestry and logging. *A guide to the BC economy and labour market.* http://www.guidetobceconomy.org/major_industries/foresty.htm

British Columbia Ministry of Advanced Education. (2006b). Manufacturing. *A guide to the BC economy and labour market.* http://www.guidetobceconomy.org/major_industries/manufacturing.htm

British Columbia Ministry of Forests. (1997). *BC's new Forest Practices Code: A living process.* FPC 1. www.for.gov.bc.ca/pab,publctns/fpcliv/process.htm#begin

British Columbia Ministry of Forests. (2003). *British Columbia's forests and their management.* Victoria: Author.

Burda, C., Gale, F., & M'Gonigle, M. (1998). Eco-forestry versus the state(us) quo. *BC Studies, 199*, 45–72.

Byron, R. N. (1978). Community stability and forest policy in British Columbia. *Canadian Journal of Forestry Resarch, 8*, 61–66.

Canadian Council of Forest Ministers. (1992). *Sustainable forests: A Canadian commitment.* Ottawa: Author.

Canadian Council of Forest Ministers. (2005). *Compendium of Canadian forestry statistics.* http://nfdp.ccfm.org

Cashore, B., Howlett, M., Wilson, J., Hoberg, G., & Rayer, J. (2001). *In search of sustainability: British Columbia forest policy in the 1990s.* Vancouver: UBC Press.

CBC News. (2006, December 15). *Meadow Lake mill sold to Indonesian company.* http://www.cbc.ca/canada/saskatchewan/story/2006/12/15/mill.html

Clapp, R. A. (1998). The resource cycle in forestry and fishing. *The Canadian Geographer, 42*, 129–144.

Clayoquot Sound Scientific Panel. (1995). *A vision and its context: Global context for forest practices in Clayoquot Sound.* Report 4 of the Scientific Panel for Sustainable Forest Practices in Clayoquot Sound. Victoria: British Columbia Ministry of Forests.

Committee on the Status of Endangered Wildlife in Canada (COSEWIC). (2003). *Canadian Species at Risk.* Ottawa: Author.

Dauvergne, P. (1997). *Shadows in the forest: Japan and the politics of timber in Southeast Asia.* Cambridge, MA: MIT Press.

Davidson, B. (1996). Forests: A symbol of national heritage. *World Conservation, 3*(October), 16.

Davidson, D., & Freudenburg, W. (1996). Gender and environmental concerns: A review and analysis of available research. *Environmental Behavior, 28,* 302–339.

David Suzuki Foundation. (2006). *The falldown effect.* http://www. davidsuzuki.org/forests/canada/bc/overcut/falldown.asp

Department of Indian Affairs and Northern Development (DIAND). (1999). *Agreement in principle reached between the Innu nation, Canada and Newfoundland.* http://www.inac.gc.ca./nr/prs/ s-d1999.1~99167.html

Diem, A. (1992). Clearcutting British Columbia. *The Ecologist, 22*(6), 261–266.

Elliott, J. (1999). *An introduction to sustainable development.* London and New York: Routledge.

Environment Canada. (1995). Sustaining Canada's forests: Overview. *Overview SOE Bulletin,* no. 95-4 (Summer).

Fondation de la faune du Québec. (n.d.). *Deer yard program.* Brochure. Sainte-Foy, PQ: Author.

Food and Agriculture Organization. (1999). *State of the world's forests, 1999.* http://www.fao.org/forestry/FO/SOFO/sofo-e.htm

Food and Agriculture Organization. (2005). *Global forest resources assessment 2005: Progress towards sustainable forest management.* http://www.fao.org/DOCREP/008/a0400e/a0400e00.htm.

Food and Agriculture Organization. (2007). *State of the world's forests, 2007.* http://www.fao.org/docrep/009/a0773e/a0773e00.htm

Franklin, J. F. (1984). Characteristics of old-growth Douglas-fir forests. In *New forests—forests for a changing world.* Proceedings of the 1983 Society of American Foresters Conventions, Bethesda, MD.

Friends of Clayoquot Sound. (1996, October 2). *Province drops prosecution of MacMillan Bloedel in Clayoquot Sound.* News release. http://www.island.net/~focs/nr100296.htm

Friends of the Earth. (n.d.). Sustainability and logging in Canada's forests. http://www.foc.co.uk/Pubsinfo/briefings/html/1997 1215 15 00 12.html # Fpptnote 3

Fullerton, M. (2006). Gender structures in forestry organizations: Canada. In UNECE/FAO Team of Specialists on Gender and Forestry (Eds.), *Time for action: Changing the gender situation in forestry* (pp. 20–26). Rome: Food and Agriculture Organization of the United Nations.

Grizzly study finds forestry friend. (1996). *University of Calgary Gazette, 26*(10), 6.

Hammond, H. (1991). *Seeing the forest among the trees: The case for wholistic forest use.* Vancouver: Polestar Press.

Hammond, H. (1993). Forest practices: Putting wholistic forest use into practice. In K. Drushka, B. Nixon, & R. Travers (Eds.), *Touch wood: B.C. forests at the crossroads* (pp. 96–136). Madeira Park, BC: Harbour Publishing.

Hayter, R. (1996). Technological imperatives in resource sectors: Forest products. In J. N. H. Britton (Ed.), *Canada and the global economy* (pp. 101–122). Montreal: McGill–Queen's University Press.

Hayter, R. (2000). *Flexible crossroads: The restructuring of British Columbia's forest economy.* Vancouver: UBC Press.

Hebert, D. M., Sklar, D., Wasel, S., Ghostkeeper, E., & Daniels, T. (1995). Accomplishing partnerships in the boreal mixed wood forests of northeastern Alberta. Transactions of the 60th North American Wildlife and Natural Resources Conference, pp. 433–438.

Innu Nation. (1995). *Adaptive mismanagement proposed for Nitassinan forests.* http://www.web.net/~innu/adaptivemm.html

International Tropical Timber Organization (ITTO). (1999). *Annual review and assessment of world timber situation.* Prepared by the Division of Economic Information and Market Intelligence, International Tropical Timber Organization. Yokohama, Japan. http://www .itto.or.jp/inside/review1999/index.html

Jardine, K. (1994). Finger on the carbon pulse: Climate change and the boreal forests. *The Ecologist, 24*(6), 220–223.

Kellogg, E. (Ed.). (1992). *Coastal temperate rain forests: Ecological characteristics, status and distribution worldwide.* Occasional Paper No. 1. Portland, OR: Ecotrust/Conservation International.

Kellogg, R. M. (Ed.). (1989). *Second growth Douglas fir: Its management and conversion for value.* A report of the Douglas-fir Task Force. Special Publication No. SP-32. Vancouver: Forintek Canada Corporation.

Kelly, D., & Braasch, G. (1988). *Secrets of the old growth forest.* Layton, UT: Gibbs Smith.

Kimmins, H. (1992). *Balancing act: Environmental issues in forestry.* Vancouver: UBC Press.

Knudtson, P., & Suzuki, D. (1992). *Wisdom of the elders.* Toronto: Stoddart.

Leahy, S. (1995, September/October). Clayoquot Sound East. *Equinox, 83,* 14.

Lindsey, R. (2007, March 30). Tropical deforestation. *Earth Observatory.* http://earthobservatory.nsas.gov/Library/Deforestation/ deforestation_update3.html.

Lower, A. R. M. (1973). *Great Britain's woodyard: Britain, America and the timber trade, 1763–1867.* Montreal: McGill-Queen's UP.

Marchak, M. P. (1983). *Green gold: The forest industry in British Columbia.* Vancouver: UBC Press.

Marchak, M. P. (1995). *Logging the globe.* Montreal: McGill-Queen's University Press.

Marchak, M. P., Aycock, S. L., & Herbert, D. M. (1999). *Falldown: Forest policy in British Columbia.* Vancouver: David Suzuki Foundation and Ecotrust Canada.

McKibben, B. (1996). What good is a forest? *Audubon, 98*(3), 54–63.

McPhedran, K. (1997, Spring). Fiddlehead Farm—out of tune? *Beautiful British Columbia Traveller, 7.*

M'Gonigle, M. (1997). Reinventing British Columbia: Towards a new political economy in the forest. In T. Barnes & R. Haytor (Eds.), *Troubles in the rainforest: British Columbia's forest economy in transition* (pp. 15–35). Canadian Western Geographical Series no. 33. Victoria: Western Geographical Press.

M'Gonigle, M., & Parfitt, B. (1994). *Forestopia: A practical guide to the new forest economy.* Madeira Park, BC: Harbour Publishing.

Moffett, M. W. (1997). Climbing an ecological frontier: Tree giants of North America. *National Geographic, 191*(1), 44–61.

Mohai, P. (1992). Men, women, and the environment: An examination of the gender gap in environmental concern and activism. *Society and Natural Resources, 5,* 1–19.

National Round Table on the Environment and the Economy (NRTEE). (1997). *State of the debate on the environment and the economy: Private woodlot management in the Maritimes.* Ottawa: Author.

Natural Resources Canada. (2007). *Canada's forests: Annual report 2007.* http://canadaforests.nrcan.gc.ca/rpt#tables

Natural Resources Canada, Canadian Forest Service. (1995). *The state of Canada's forests 1994: A balancing act.* Ottawa: Author.

Natural Resources Canada, Canadian Forest Service. (1996a). *The boreal forest.* Poster-map. Ottawa: Author.

Natural Resources Canada, Canadian Forest Service. (1996b). *The state of Canada's forests 1995–1996: Sustaining forests at home and abroad.* Ottawa: Author.

Natural Resources Canada, Canadian Forest Service. (2000a). *Natural resources fact sheet.* Ottawa: Author. http://www.nrcan. gc.ca/statistics/factsheet.htm

Natural Resources Canada, Canadian Forest Service. (2000b). *The state of Canada's forests, 1999–2000: Forests in the new millennium.* Ottawa: Author.

Natural Resources Canada, Canadian Forest Service. (2006). *The state of Canada's forests 2005–2006: Forest industry competitiveness.* Ottawa: Author.

Ness, R., & Cooperrider, A. Y. (1994). *Saving nature's legacy: Protecting and restoring biodiversity.* Covelo, CA: Island Press.

Pimm, S. (1996). The lonely earth. *World Conservation, 27*(1), 8–9.

Quinby, P. A. (1996). *A critique of the proposed management of old-growth white and red pine forest in Temagami, Ontario resulting from the comprehensive planning process of 1996 with a case study analysis of the Owain Lake old-growth pine stand as a representative ecosystem.* http://www.sll.fi/TRN/index2.html

Rainforest Action Network. (1996, February). Clayoquot Sound landslides add to mountain of evidence against rainforest clearcut. *Rainforest Action News.* http://www.ran.org/ran/info_center/press_release/landslide.html

Reed, M. G., & Varghese, J. (2007). Gender representation on Canadian forest sector advisory committees. *Forestry Chronicle, 83,* 515–525.

Ricklefs, R. E. (1993). *The economy of nature.* New York: W. H. Freeman.

Rosmarin, H. (1997). Rethinking paper: Non-wood fibres poised for comeback. *Global Biodiversity, 7*(2), 33–36.

Ryan, J. S. (1990, July/August). Timber's last stand. *World Watch,* 27–34.

Schoonmaker, P. K., von Hagen, B., & Wolf, E. C. (Eds.). (1997). *The rain forests of home: Profile of a North American bioregion.* Washington, DC: Island Press.

Senate Sub-Committee on the Boreal Forest. (1999). *Competing realities: The boreal forest at risk.* Ottawa: Government of Canada.

Sierra Club of Canada. (1996). *Canadian forests fact sheet.* http://www.sierraclub.ca/national/forests/forests-fact-sheet-1996.html

Sierra Club of Canada & Canadian Parks and Wilderness Society. (2006). *Uncertain future: Woodland caribou and Canada's boreal forest. A report on government action.* http://www.cpaws.org/files/report-caribou-2006.pdf

Swift, J. (1983). *Cut and run: The assault on Canada's forests.* Toronto: Between the Lines.

Taylor, D. M. (1994). *Off course: Restoring balance between Canadian society and the environment.* Ottawa: International Development Research Centre.

Tindall, D. B., Davies, S., & Mauboules, C. (2003). Activism and conservation behavior in an environmental movement: The contradictory effects of gender. *Society and Natural Resources, 16*(10), 909–932.

Travers, O. R. (1993). Forest policy: Rhetoric and reality. In K. Drushka, B. Nixon, & R. Travers (Eds.), *Touch wood: B.C. forests at the crossroads* (pp. 171–224). Madeira Park, BC: Harbour Publishing.

Uliczka, H., Angelstam, P., Jansson, G., & Bro, A. (2004). Non-industrial private forest owners' knowledge of and attitudes towards nature conservation. *Scandinavian Journal of Forest Research, 19,* 274–288.

von Mirbach, M. (1997). Demanding good wood. *Alternatives, 23*(3), 10–17.

Wigg, M., & Boulton, A. (1989). Quality wood, sustainable forests. *Forest Watch, 9*(7), 7–12.

Williston, E., & Keller, B. (1997). *Forests, power and policy: The legacy of Ray Williston.* Prince George, BC: Caitlin Press.

World Wildlife Fund. (2001). *World Wildlife Fund and Temebc Inc. reach historic accord to promote long-term sustainability of Canadian forestry.* http://www.wwf.ca/NewsAndFacts/NewsRoom/default.asp?section=archive&page=display&ID=1293&lang=EN

Photo 9–22

Forests soak up atmospheric CO_2 and also provide good resting sites for fauna such as these Monarch butterflies. High levels of CO_2 may reduce the abundance of milkweed plants, the sole food source for Monarch larvae, so forests benefit these butterflies in two ways. At the global level, CO_2 is often tied to economic indicators, which do not have such visual cues. For more information about CO_2 per GDP, see the Canada and the World section.

Photo 9–21

Using sustainable timber harvesting practices, such as this combination of old and new technologies with a horse-drawn wagon and mechanized lifting, reduces the effects of tree removal at this Nova Scotia woodlot and helps Canada conserve its forest resources. The Canada and the World section shows how our practices rank internationally.

CHAPTER 10

Minerals and Mining

Chapter Contents

"Environmentally responsible mining exploration, development, operations and public policies are predicated on maintaining a healthy environment and, on closure, returning mine sites and affected areas to viable and, wherever practicable, self-sustaining ecosystems that are compatible with a healthy environment and with human activities."

Principles and Goals of the Whitehorse Mining
Initiative (1995–96, pp. 3–4)

Chapter Objectives

After studying this chapter you should be able to

- understand the nature and distribution of Canada's mineral resources
- describe the impacts of mining on Canada's natural environments
- outline Canadian and international responses to mining issues
- discuss definitions of and challenges to sustainable mining in Canada

INTRODUCTION

Earth's mineral resources, including sand, gravel, clay, rock, minerals, and fossil fuels, touch almost every aspect of our lives. Mineral products are essential in the construction of our homes and workplaces (concrete, bricks, tiles, and structural steel; saw, hammer, and nails); in the provision and distribution of energy and water (coal and uranium, electrical wires and copper pipes); in our transportation (roads, gasoline, trains, and bicycles); in many luxury goods (televisions, stereos, telephones, and computers; gold and diamond jewellery; CDs; aluminum baseball bats); and in medicines, vitamins, and other products to keep us healthy (including zinc, an essential ingredient in sunscreen). Consider your place setting at dinner tonight: your drinking glass, your plate, and your cutlery all may be composed of minerals. Clearly, minerals are necessary to sustain us!

The mining industry is a vital contributor to the Canadian economy—every province and territory in Canada supports mining and oil drilling activities. In 2005, the mining and mineral processing industries directly employed more than 388 000 Canadians; 45 000 were employed in mining, 84 000 in smelting and refining, and 259 000 in the manufacture of mineral and metal products (Natural Resources Canada, 2007b). In 2006, the value of minerals produced in Canada reached $75 billion, and the mining and mineral processing industries contributed $40 billion to the Canadian economy, or 3.7 percent of the national gross domestic product. About 80 percent of our mineral and metal production is exported.

Although Canada does not have accurate data on the nature and extent of land used by the mining industry, in 1982 it was estimated that less than 0.03 percent (279 477 hectares) of Canada's land area was disturbed, used, or alienated by mining activities since metal mining began more than 150 years ago (Government of Canada, 1996b). This intensive use of a relatively small area (less than half the size of Prince Edward Island) produces all the minerals we use every day. However, there is concern that habitat destruction, increased access to natural areas resulting from construction of infrastructure (including mine access roads), and effects of acidifying mine waste runoff on fish, wildlife, and water quality are among the most important and extensive effects of mining. Mineral staking rushes, such as in the cases of the Northwest Territories diamond fields and Voisey's Bay nickel deposit, can also affect or block land uses.

The discovery, extraction, transportation, processing, and consumption of minerals often result in significant environmental, economic, and social alterations. Despite the intensive land use at the point of extraction, mining increasingly has come into conflict with other environmental resources and user groups, including forestry, wildlife habitat, water quality, harvesting and other Aboriginal peoples' land uses, recreation, and tourism. Where mining involves extraction and transportation, these activities may conflict with agriculture, recreation, and even urban development. Since many of these environmental resources and resource uses do not have established "economic prices" in a marketplace, they cannot compete against a market valuation of minerals. However, the environmental and social impacts of mining are real to people living in areas adjacent to mine sites. Because impacts often extend beyond the site of extraction, responsibility for environmental protection may extend well beyond the working operations of a mine to include neighbouring lands and the watershed(s) within which the mine is located.

Because of how atmospheric, lithospheric, and hydrologic cycles combine with human processes of disposal, trade, and transportation, harm and disruption can take place in areas that are quite a bit larger than or distant from the actual sites of mineral extraction. In Western economies, heightened environmental policies and regulations have prompted the mining industry to improve its practices, to invest in research and development, and to develop new environmental technology. Additionally, there are regulations and unions in place that serve to safeguard the health and safety of mine workers and neighbouring communities. However, as Box 10–1 reveals, in its activities in developing nations, the mining industry does not always display the same level of active support for environmental sustainability or for the health of workers and neighbouring communities as it does at home (Holden, 2003; Johnson, 1999).

With growing worldwide demand for minerals and mineral products, Canada is faced with the challenge of developing our mineral resources in a way that fosters our economy without compromising the sustainability of our environment. This chapter begins by describing the rock cycle and the classification of minerals into resources and reserves. We then describe mineral development in Canada and provide an overview of the environmental disturbances that result from mining activity. Finally,

BOX 10–1
CANADA AND THE WORLD: MINING RESPONSIBILITIES IN A GLOBAL ECONOMY

Canadian mining companies are major players in the global exploration for minerals. In fact, there are more mineral exploration companies based in Canada than in any other country in the world (Natural Resources Canada, 2003). About 48 percent of total mining properties held by companies listed on the Canadian stock exchanges are foreign properties (Natural Resources Canada, 2006). At least 2200 firms in Canada advertise that they offer specialized mining goods and services (Natural Resources Canada, 2003b). Box Figure 10–1 illustrates that Canada's larger mining companies (those that spend at least $3.7 million annually on mineral exploration) undertake exploration work all over the world.

Given their reach around the globe, to what extent should Canadian companies comply with Canadian-type standards for environmental and social protection? Not surprisingly, companies and watchdog organizations have different opinions. Companies involved in exploration and exploitation overseas typically are not subject to the same level of scrutiny as they might be at home. In some places, environmental impact assessments are voluntary. As a consequence, their level of detail and the subsequent commitment to protection are uneven. In Chile, for example, monitoring and enforcement of environmental laws are rare, obtaining access to information on environment and development impacts is difficult or impossible, and health and safety standards are inadequate (Environmental Mining Council of British Columbia, 1996; Padilla, 2005). Industry leaders, such as Canada's Barrick Gold, have praised the attitude of Chile toward mining companies, while others, including the World Bank, have been critical of the absence of regulations and the administrative obstacles in Chile that make it difficult to assess or enforce environmental standards. The environmental and worker safety conditions within many South American mines would not be tolerated in Canada.

Mining operators in Chile and Ghana have been criticized for compromising local water and air quality, providing inadequate compensation for workers, and securing lands for mining that previously provided housing or food for local people. In some cases, rights of Indigenous people have not been recognized. Mining companies have responded by stating that they voluntarily act responsibly. Yet, often they are not required to disclose the full nature of these voluntary activities to their shareholders. Impact-benefit agreements that are negotiated with local communities in Canada are not pursued vigorously elsewhere. In Canada, **impact-benefit agreements** are negotiated among private companies, government agencies, and local communities to provide benefits to local residents (such as employment) from resource production. Civic watchdogs such as Mining Watch Canada have countered that voluntary codes typically fail to ensure the necessary protection of environmental or social conditions. Indeed, environmental assessment procedures in Canada are not always automatically applied. Furthermore, critics point out that while local laws may be strong, local enforcement regimes are often weak or subject to corruption. Canadian governments have not regulated companies' overseas operations through securities legislation or other mechanisms.

BOX 10-1
(CONTINUED)

As discussed in the case of the EKATI mine later in the chapter, a company's reputation overseas may affect its welcome in Canadian communities. Given the impetus to promote sustainable mining at home, what more do you think should be done to improve the environmental and social record of Canadian companies operating overseas? The websites of two organizations and one government agency are listed below. They offer different perspectives that may help you formulate your opinion.

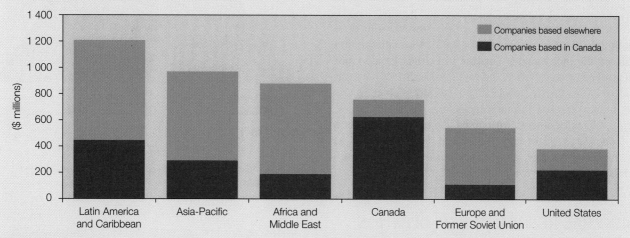

Box Figure 10–1

Exploration budgets of the world's larger companies for selected regions of the world, 2005

Companies with worldwide budgets of at least $3.7 million for precious-metal, base-metal, or diamond exploration

NOTES: The worldwide exploration budgets of companies that intended to spend less than $3.7 million (US$3 million) in 2005 are excluded. The worldwide exploration budgets for other commodities such as uranium or industrial minerals are also excluded.

SOURCE: Canadian Minerals Yearbook, 2005, Natural Resources Canada ©, Her Majesty the Queen in Right of Canada, 2008.

SOURCES: Taylor, M.E. 1998. Economic Development and the Environment in Chile. *Journal of Environment and Development,* 7:(4); 422–436; Mining in Canada, Natural Resources Canada, 2007, http://www.nrcan.gc.ca/mms/top-suje/min_e.htm; Community Rights and the Environment: Recommendations for Canadian Legislation, C. Padilla, April 2005, prepared for Mining Watch Canada, http://www.miningwatch.ca/updir/Chile_case_study.pdf

strategies that governments, industries, and nongovernmental organizations use to reduce the environmental and social impacts of mining are discussed.

THE ROCK CYCLE

Mining relies on natural cycles of the Earth, just like any other process of natural resource extraction. The rock cycle is the slowest of Earth's cyclic processes and consists of several processes that produce rocks and soil and redistribute chemical elements within and at the surface of the Earth. Based on the way they form, rocks are classified as igneous, sedimentary, or metamorphic. **Igneous rock** is produced from molten materials crystal-

lizing at the Earth's surface (such as lava from volcanoes) or beneath the surface (such as granite). **Sedimentary rock** forms when small bits and pieces of matter and sediments are carried by wind or rain and then deposited, compacted, and cemented to form rock. As the deposited layers grow larger, increasing pressure causes their particles to bond together to form sedimentary rocks such as shale, limestone, and bituminous coal. **Metamorphic rock** is formed when pre-existing rocks lying deep below the Earth's surface are subjected to high temperatures, high pressures, chemically active fluids, or a combination of these agents, causing the rocks' crystal structure to change. For example, marble is formed from limestone that has been heated and recrystallized.

Rocks located at or near the surface are subject to physical and chemical processes of weathering that, over time, can change them. For instance, freeze–thaw actions can break rock apart by repeated expansion and contraction, and rocks may be dissolved by weak acids that form in the presence of carbon dioxide, organic material, and water; such actions produce sediments that may be transported by wind, water, or ice. The interaction of all processes that change rocks from one type to another is the rock cycle; it is responsible for concentrating the mineral resources on which humans depend.

Given the very long time periods over which different types of rocks are created, it is not really possible to classify minerals as renewable resources. However, this does not mean that their availability is static. Although the first law of thermodynamics (matter is neither created nor destroyed) suggests that the total availability of minerals is fixed, the effective availability of resources changes due to human-created circumstances. As discussed below, the availability of static resources like minerals increases or decreases according to societal interests such as demand, technology, and price. Those who exploit minerals describe their availability in different ways.

MINERAL RESOURCE EXPLOITATION

Mineral resources are broadly defined as elements, chemical compounds, minerals, or rocks concentrated in a form that can be extracted to obtain a usable commodity. The mass of mineral resources available for extraction depends on physical characteristics of the site as well as social characteristics, such as technology, market demand, costs of production and processing, prices that can be obtained for the resource, availability of substitutes, and societal rules relating to exploitation, development, and use. When calculating how much of a resource is available, one can consider the resource base as the total quantity available in an ecosystem (see Figure 10–1). However, the actual amount used is usually considerably smaller than the total quantity. The resource base is often classified into smaller subdivisions of *reserves* and *resources* to reflect the different potentials for use.

The difference between reserves and resources is like comparing a person's current bank accounts to his or her potential lifetime earnings. For miners, reserves can be likened to a current account, while resources describe potential earnings. This classification can be further divided. *Proven reserves* are deposits that already have been discovered and can be extracted economically under current circumstances of demand, price, technology, and societal rules. *Conditional reserves* have been discovered as well, but they are not economically feasible to work at present-day price levels with current technology and extraction methods. Most of the oil sands in Alberta were conditional reserves in the 1960s and 1970s (the first mine began operation in 1967) until the price of oil rose sufficiently in the 1990s to provide conditions for their broad-scale exploitation in the 2000s. *Hypothetical*

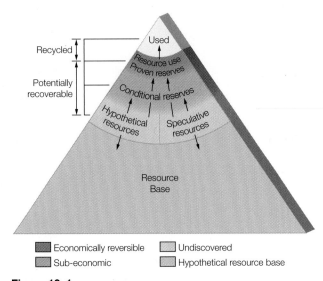

Figure 10–1

Resource base classification into smaller subdivisions

SOURCE: Adapted from *Natural Resources: Allocation, Economics and Policy,* 2nd Edition, Judith Rees, 1995, Routledge. Figure 2.2, page 20. Used with permission of the publisher.

resources are not currently known for certain, but they are likely to be found in the future in areas that have been partially surveyed or developed. These are often difficult to estimate accurately without undertaking the exploration work. *Speculative resources* are even more uncertain. These are resources that are considered likely because of favourable geological conditions, but there has been no exploration to confirm their extent or quality. Exploration may raise or lower the status of these resources. The main distinction between a reserve and a resource is the degree of certainty of their existence and the likelihood that they will be exploited. Note that the distinction between the two is based on economic and physical criteria.

HUMAN ACTIVITIES AND IMPACTS ON NATURAL ENVIRONMENTS

PRODUCTION, VALUE, AND DISTRIBUTION OF MINERAL RESOURCES IN CANADA

Canada's mineral resources comprise both mineral fuels and nonfuel minerals. **Mineral fuels**—crude oil and equivalents, natural gas, coal, and natural gas byproducts—accounted for about 77 percent of the total value of Canada's mineral production in 2002. **Nonfuel minerals** are categorized as metallic (e.g., iron ore, gold), nonmetallic (potash, asbestos), and structural (lime, sand, and gravel). In 2002, nonfuel minerals accounted for the remaining 23 percent of the total value of Canada's mineral production. Between 2002 and 2007, Natural Resources Canada did not continue reporting oil and natural gas with other nonmetal minerals. Consequently, it is difficult to compare the production levels and value of these resources with other minerals (Table 10–1). According to preliminary data for 2007, metals, including nickel, copper, and iron ore, accounted for 62.1 percent of the value of Canada's mineral production (which no longer includes oil or natural gas). Nonmetals (for example, potash, cement, and sand and gravel, not including oil or natural gas) accounted for 29.4 percent of the total value, and coal accounted for 8.5 percent. The total value of Canada's mineral production in 2007 (without accounting for oil and natural gas) was almost $34 billion (Natural Resources Canada, 2008). But these data may not strictly be comparable to earlier years

(e.g., 2002) in which oil and natural gas were classified as nonmetallic minerals by Natural Resources Canada. In 2005, Statistics Canada reported that of mining establishments in operation, 19 were coal mining establishments, 55 metal ore mining, 739 nonmetallic mining and quarrying, 34 smelting and refining of nonferrous metals, 19 primary production of alumina and aluminum, 42 clay products, 25 cement, and 12 lime (Statistics Canada, 2005). Canada's principal metal and mineral mining regions are identified in Figure 10–2 on the next page.

Canada produces more than 30 metallic minerals; six of these—copper, gold, iron ore, nickel, uranium, and zinc —accounted for almost 91 percent of the total value of metal mining production in 2007. Canada produced just over 34 574 500 tonnes of copper, nickel, uranium, iron ore, and zinc in 2007. In terms of 2007 production value,

TABLE 10–1
PRODUCTION VOLUME AND VALUE OF CANADA'S LEADING MINERALS (2007*)

Category/Commodity	Production (000 tonnes unless noted otherwise)	Value (CDN$ millions)
METALS		
Nickel	245.1	9 902.2
Copper	577.3	4 533.2
Uranium	9.1	2 522.7
Iron ore	33 158.3	2 512.1
Gold (kg)	100 156.8	2 376.9
Zinc	584.7	2 087.9
Other metals	n/a	2 410.0
Total metals	n/a	26 344.9
NONMETALS		
Potash (K$_2$0)	11 426.2	3 142.3
Cement	14 737.5	1 802.4
Diamonds (000 ct)	17 007.9	1 444.7
Stone	145 824.5	1 333.1
Sand and gravel	234 658.4	1 316.5
Other nonmetals	n/a	2 230.6
Total nonmetals	n/a	11 269.5
FUELS		
Crude oil and equivalent (000 m³)	160 584	n/a
Natural gas (million m³)	167 104	n/a
Natural gas byproducts (000 m³)	n/a	n/a
Coal	69 360.0	2 761.0
Total fuels	n/a	58 974.3

* Numbers for production and value are preliminary.

SOURCES: *Information Bulletin: Mineral Production,* March, 2008, http://www.nrcan-rncan.gc.ca/mms/pdf/minprod-08_e.pdf; *Production of Canada's Leading Minerals,* January, 2008, http://mmsd1.mms.nrcan.gc.ca/mmsd/data/2008/08MTLY03.pdf. Used with permission of the Ministry of Public Works and Government Services, Canada, 2008.

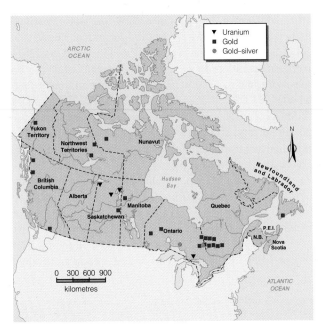

Figure 10–2a

Principal mining regions of Canada: uranium and precious metals mines

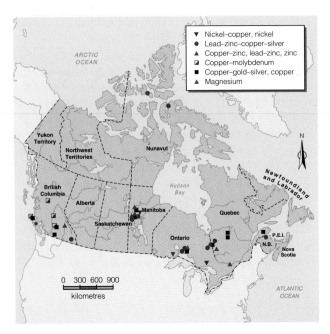

Figure 10–2b

Principal mining regions of Canada: base metal mines

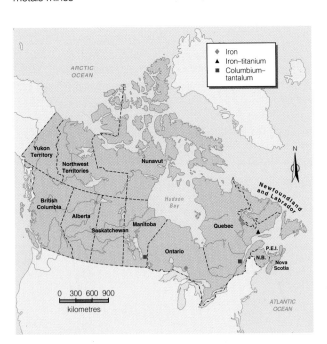

Figure 10–2c

Principal mining regions of Canada: ferrous metal mines

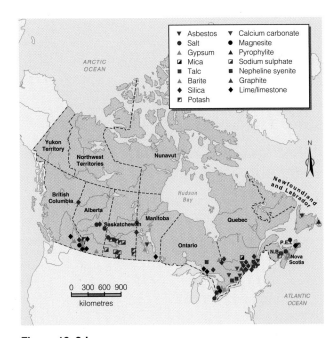

Figure 10–2d

Principal mining regions of Canada: industrial mineral mines

SOURCE: *The State of Canada's Environment—1996,* © Her Majesty the Queen in Right of Canada, Environment Canada, 1996, Figure 11.27. Reprinted with permission of the Minister of Public Works and Government Services Canada, 2008.

the four most important metals were nickel ($9.90 billion), copper ($4.53 billion), uranium ($2.52 billion), and iron ore ($2.51 billion). Potash, the most important commodity in the nonmetals category, was valued at $3.14 billion in 2007 (Natural Resources Canada, 2008b).

About 65 percent of expenditures on mineral exploration in 2007 were focused in Ontario, Quebec, British Columbia, and Nunavut. Typically, **precious metals**, particularly gold, account for the largest share of total Canadian exploration expenditures. However, one of the largest staking rushes in recent Canadian history was prompted by the 1991 discovery of diamonds in the Northwest Territories. By 2007, the value of diamond production was $1.44 billion, making diamonds Canada's third-largest nonfuel mineral commodity in terms of value of production (Natural Resources Canada, 2008a). Canada now ranks third in terms of the value of diamond production worldwide, behind Botswana and Russia.

HISTORICAL OVERVIEW OF MINING IN CANADA

Many communities have strong ties to mineral extraction; in fact, much of Canada's regional and infrastructural development has proceeded in parallel with the development of natural resources. We all have heard tales of the Klondike gold rush where thousands of people from around the world flocked to the Yukon in the hopes of striking it rich. Despite treacherous conditions, prospectors made their way over icy mountain passes and down the Yukon River to Dawson City. By 1898, three years after the first discovery of gold by George Carmack, more than 40 000 people had set up camp in Dawson.

Then referred to as the Paris of the North, Dawson became a thriving community, creating wealth for both prospectors and the Canadian government. Although few of the men made their fortunes (because the rich gold claims had been staked before most prospectors arrived), the tax earnings from gold and alcohol sales prompted the federal government to make the Yukon a separate territory in 1898. Major infrastructure projects, such as the White Pass and Yukon Route Railway (opened in 1900 between Skagway, Alaska, and Whitehorse, Yukon), were constructed to accommodate the growing population.

Not everyone appreciated the economic boom generated by the gold rush. Encroaching populations disrupted traditional ways of life of Aboriginal people. Miners and other new residents joined in the hunt for game, leaving Aboriginal hunters to travel farther for food. While some Aboriginal people elected to earn wages packing supplies for miners or cutting fuelwood for steamships, others were forced to leave their lands to escape the growing mining towns.

By 1928, about $200 million worth of gold had been produced in the region, mostly by individual placer mines—that is, the mining of sand and gravel beds in ancient or existing streambeds. For years, gold dredges had operated in the creeks near Dawson City, removing gold until the level of recovery declined sufficiently that it was no longer profitable to run the dredges. Despite the end of the gold rush in the early 1900s, and the depopulation of Dawson City, mining activity remains a valuable component of the Yukon economy.

The Yukon gold rush illustrates the boom and bust cycle associated with the mining industry and the history of mining in Canada. Like all sectors of the economy, the mining industry is affected by recession and growth periods within the business cycle. However, mining is especially vulnerable to short-term changes in the supply, demand, and price of an individual commodity. These

Photo 10–1
In the rush to extract gold, 19th-century mining communities often were erected hastily. This photo of Barkerville, British Columbia, was taken the day before it was razed by fire in September 1868.

market conditions have a great deal of influence over the regions and communities where mining takes place.

We know that there is a significant imbalance between the distribution of people (south) and the distribution of mineral resources (north) in Canada. This distribution gave rise to a large number of single-resource, **one-industry towns** or **company towns**, established to provide a pool of labour to operate and service a mine effectively. When a town's mine is booming, additional workers and support services are required, drawing people into the community. During these good times, one-industry towns are very successful economically, with low unemployment and relatively high personal income levels. In 2006, for example, a worker in the metal, nonmetal, or coal mining industries earned an average of $1109 per

Photo 10–2
Many of Canada's communities, such as Sudbury, Ontario, built their wealth on the extraction of mineral resources.

week; the national average weekly earnings were $762 (Natural Resources Canada, 2007b). However, once there is a downturn in the commodity price, or reserves are exhausted, mines close, workers leave, and the community is left with little or no economic base. Quite often, entire communities are abandoned, leaving usable facilities and infrastructure behind. The costs to establish and abandon towns can be very high. Some researchers have described the link between the resource cycle and the ups and downs of resource-dependent communities and regions as "the staples trap" (see Box 10–2).

The problems associated with one-industry towns are not as prevalent today as they were in the past. Improvements in air transportation and communication have fostered a regime of **long-distance commuting**, in which miners fly in to a mine to work for a designated period and then are flown back to their homes in larger communities for another period. Workers are provided with food and temporary lodging, but no expensive infrastructure or support services are constructed at the mine site. Changes in the regulatory environment have also led to fewer one-industry towns being established.

BOX 10–2
TRAPPED BY STAPLES? RESOURCE COMMUNITIES AND THE RESOURCE CYCLE

The resource cycle described in Box 4–5 has important implications for the development of resource communities, regions, and countries. Once a community has been established around primary resource extraction, there are few incentives to diversify and create sustainable economies. Harold Innis, one of Canada's most important economic historians, referred to this pattern as "the staples trap". According to Innis, specializing in staples production—commodities that dominate an export economy—based on natural resources gives rise to unstable and incomplete economic development for a region or country. Staples-producing regions and nations typically export these products with limited or no processing and become dependent on more powerful core areas to accept their exports. This pattern narrows the range of development opportunities and locks communities, regions, and nations in a staples trap.

At the local level, communities are subject to boom and bust cycles. According to William Freudenberg (1992), communities may even become addicted to the primary commodity as periodic increases in resource prices and the resulting (short-term) increases in employment opportunities provide intermittent positive reinforcement of the status quo. During the boom stage, the revenues generated by extraction and sale of the associated commodities allow communities to postpone making hard economic choices to diversify their economic base. As exploitation begins to peak, extensive restructuring may result as industries begin to reduce the number of jobs within specific operations or shut down particular operations altogether. Once resources are abandoned, communities begin to decline as people leave to look for new jobs, the tax base is reduced, and the costs to maintain the infrastructure are spread across a smaller number of people. Consequently, communities have insufficient funds, people, or social or economic capital to support regional diversification, just when diversification becomes vital to their survival. So while single-industry resource communities may be encouraged to diversify their economies, they have very little capacity to act on such advice.

Government policies frequently have reinforced this pattern. Politicians want to support local industries for the jobs and

revenues they will provide. Civil servants that regulate resource use often share the same values about resource use and revenues with the companies they regulate. Simultaneously, legislation and incentives are created to encourage industries to expand, while very few, if any, efforts are made in the early stages of development to consider alternative strategies to complement the primary industry. When the first signals of decline emerge, there is often a strong political disincentive to act immediately to address diversification. Nevertheless, the social costs of failing to diversify the local economy mean that governments (local, provincial, and federal) will be obliged to spend more money on social programs such as employment insurance, retraining expenses, and subsidies to promote alternative economic activities. Thus, when times are good, they are "very very good," but when times are bad, "they are horrid."

Photo 10–3
Situated in the Shunda Valley, the abandoned coal mining town of Nordegg, Alberta, was designated a National Historic Site of Canada in February 2002. Nordegg's Brazeau Collieries were once the largest supplier of coal briquettes in Canada. Operations ceased due to the upsurge of oil usage in June 1955.

SOURCES: "Addictive Economies: Extractive Industries and Vulnerable Localities in a Changing World Economy" W. R. Freudenburg, 1992, *Rural Sociology, 57,* 305–332. Innis, H. 1995. The importance of staple products in Canadian development. pp. 3–23 in Drache, D. (ed). *Staples, Markets, and Cultural Change, Selected Essays of Harold Innis,* Montreal, McGill-Queen's University Press. First appeared in Innis, H. 1956. *The Fur Trade in Canada. Rev. ed. (Toronto, 1956)* 383–402.

In the past, little attention was paid to community planning; often, the urban environment in single-resource towns was of poor quality. Today, in response to concerns of governments and miners' families, new towns are subject to impact assessment processes, structured planning efforts, and substantial infrastructure investments (Shrimpton & Storey, 1988). Tumbler Ridge, British Columbia, for example, was created in the early 1980s within a strong planning and governance framework. Nevertheless, the town was still subject to cycles in mineral production and the population has declined since the 1990s (see Box 10–3). Planning and infrastructure requirements for new towns, combined with companies' striving to increase productivity, reduce costs, and rationalize

BOX 10-3
CAN COMMUNITIES OVERCOME THE STAPLES TRAP?

The role of communities in mining activities has changed over time. At the beginning of the 20th century, mining companies provided bunkhouses for their male workers, a company store, and little else. Companies were accused of controlling all aspects of community life because, having paid their workers, companies controlled the types of goods and services provided within the communities and how they would be offered to residents. In fact, many resource towns were effectively "company towns." After the Second World War, companies recognized that miners were not solely single men—many of them were married with families. Resource communities were still characterized by their isolation from larger centres; their limited infrastructure, services, and amenities (education, recreational, health, and commercial services); the majority of young, single men and a relatively small number of retirees and families; high labour turnover; and large fluctuations in the availability and affordability of housing. To attract a stable workforce, governments began to work with mining companies to provide better access to affordable housing and services, and to plan for winding down communities, should that be required.

Box 10–2 describes the staples trap in resource economies. The boom and bust pattern that characterizes resource regions affects the stability of communities that rely on resources as well. In 1971, Rex Lucas suggested that single-industry communities undergo four stages: construction, recruitment of citizens, transition, and maturity. In the first two stages, the population is characterized by a high rate of turnover, a predominance of young people and young families, a mixture of ethnic groups, an unbalanced sex ratio, and a high birth rate. As communities move into the third stage, the involvement and commitment of residents grow as responsibility for amenities and services shifts from the company to the community. The last phase, maturity, is characterized by a less mobile adult workforce and an increasing number of retirees in the town. This characterization of single-industry communities implies that they will remain sustainable: for a time it was thought that if communities remained in place for at least two generations, they would become stable. However, this outcome has been achieved only rarely. After reviewing experience in the iron ore town of Schefferville, Quebec, John Bradbury and Isabelle St-Martin (1983) added two more stages: winding down and abandonment. These six stages roughly parallel the three stages described in the resource cycle (see Box 4–5 on page 129).

Although the authors point out that these six stages do not always occur in sequence, they paint a rather gloomy picture for the prospects of single-industry towns. Communities may take a more active role in determining their fates by establishing impact-benefit agreements with private companies that describe employment and training opportunities, and monitoring of health, safety, and environmental effects of planned activities. These agreements keep a mine open longer than might otherwise be the case. Governments and industry no longer promote the establishment of new towns. Many forestry and mining resource operations now rely on flying workers to the site for periods of time. This strategy allows workers to raise families in larger, regional centres where infrastructure and services are easier to provide economically.

Can the single-industry communities that continue to exist move beyond these predicted outcomes and overcome the staples trap? Several have tried to do so. For example, Sudbury, located in northern Ontario, was first established for the production of nickel. In 1970, Inco and Falconbridge employed almost 30 000 people; by 1986, the number had dropped to 7700. In 1983, unemployment was 17 percent. Sudbury reconfigured itself, becoming a regional centre for services and a major government tax centre for Canada. Efforts to reclaim the surrounding landscape and build new attractions such as an important regional science centre and mining museum began to bring tourists to the city. The population of Regional Municipality of Sudbury in 1970 was about 170 000. By 1986, this number had dropped to about 152 000. In 2006, the population of the Greater City of Sudbury had rebounded somewhat to 158 000 (amalgamations and name changes occurred during this time). So, although the city has not achieved its earlier population level and its rank size has dropped relative to other Canadian cities, Sudbury's economy is now more diversified and more robust.

The northeastern British Columbia coal mining community of Tumbler Ridge was planned jointly by government and industry. When it opened in 1984, its population was close to 5000. Efforts were made to create a vibrant town centre and to ensure that housing would be subsidized by the industry benefiting from the mining development. Coal markets declined in the late 1990s, and by 2003, the two main mines were closed. Today, only about 3775 people live in Tumbler Ridge. Slowly, efforts to diversify the economy by developing tourism and other sectors have helped to stabilize the population, albeit at a lower level.

Some communities have managed to retain a healthy economic base after the closure of a mine. In 1996, Island Copper Mine on northern Vancouver Island was closed after 24 years in operation. Most employees lived in Port Hardy. Despite the fact that hundreds of employees lost jobs at the site, its economic impact was considered small because of the long lead

(continued)

CHAPTER 10: MINERALS AND MINING

BOX 10-3
(CONTINUED)

time to closure, the ability of the company to find alternative employment for most of the workers, the transitional provision of services negotiated between the company and the local governments, and the ability of Port Hardy to draw on its local advantages to diversify its economic base.

When the coal mines and timber mills restructured or closed near Chemainus, British Columbia, tourists came to view the large heritage murals painted on community buildings and to enjoy shopping and socializing over tea or coffee in the many small businesses that were established following the success of the murals.

But these options are never painless. People involved in the tourist trade typically are not the same as those who previously were employed in the primary resource industry. The process of transition is often wrenching for resource workers, leaving distinct "winners" and "losers" during the process. And some communities may never be able to move from activities like mining to tourism. Sydney, Nova Scotia, has the dubious distinction of being Canada's most toxic site due to the longstanding smelting operations (see Chapter 11). One can now take "toxic tours" to learn this history, but its potential for expanding as a tourism or amenity destination is limited.

Photo 10-4

Tourism allows communities affected by mine closures to maintain their viability. Here at Elliot Lake, Ontario, the community focused on providing services to seniors and becoming a desirable retirement location.

SOURCES: "Winding Down in a Quebec Mining Town," J. Bradbury & I. St-Martin, 1983, *The Canadian Geographer, 27*, 128–144; *Minetown, Milltown, Railtown: Life in Canadian Communities of Single Industry*, R. A. Lucas, 1971, Toronto: University of Toronto Press.

unproductive operations, have led to a movement away from one-industry towns. Even so, mining is the mainstay of employment in over 100 Canadian communities, mostly in rural and remote areas, and especially in the North (Natural Resources Canada, 2007a).

From the coal mines of Nova Scotia to the asbestos mines of Quebec and the uranium mines in Saskatchewan, over the years mineral exploration, development, and processing have taken many lives and affected the health of countless mine workers. In the early days of mining, health and safety concerns were of minimal importance to mine operators. For example, beyond the obvious threats from collapsed mineshafts, equipment failures, and site explosions, little thought was given to the long-term effects of exposure to hazardous substances, mine dust, and other emissions. Black lung disease, silicosis, asbestosis, and cancer are among the common diseases that miners and other workers have contracted.

Today we recognize these threats; however, workers continue to be employed in conditions that place their health at risk. The mining industry is concerned about worker health and safety, and most mine sites now have programs to monitor exposure to hazardous substances, assess noise impacts, and protect respiratory health. Even so, a key problem confronting the industry is the uncertainty surrounding the long-term, cumulative effects of exposure to mining operations. Governments and industry must continue to strive for continual enhancement of workplace safety through reliable monitoring programs, technical innovation, and enforceable regulatory measures.

CANADA'S FIRST DIAMOND MINE

Since the discovery of diamonds, the central region of the Northwest Territories (known as the Slave Geological Province) has attracted intense mineral exploration and development. Encompassing an area approximately one-third the size of Alberta, the Slave Geological Province extends north from Great Slave Lake to Coronation Gulf on the Arctic coast. Between 1993 and 1996, the diamond boom accounted for 20 percent of Canada's total exploration expenditures, or $560 million (Natural Resources Canada, 1996a). By 1996, close to 60 companies were active in diamond exploration, attempting to find reserves as lucrative as the EKATI mine located northeast of Yellowknife.

The Broken Hill Proprietary Billiton (BHP Billiton) diamonds project (referred to as the EKATI mine), located in the Lac de Gras region 300 kilometres north of Yellowknife, is the largest mineral project in the

Northwest Territories and the first diamond mine in North America (see Figure 10–3). Its creation was followed by the opening of the Diavik diamond project in 2003, and the Jericho mine (owned by Tahera Diamond Corporation) in Nunavut in 2006. Efforts to determine the environmental and social effects of the EKATI mine set important precedents for other developments in the North.

On June 21, 1996, a Canadian Environmental Assessment Review Panel (EARP) approved the EKATI diamonds project. Twenty-nine recommendations were made in the EARP report regarding the ecological and social impacts of the mine. Most of these concerns were expected to be satisfied through the terms and conditions of the project's water licence, land lease, and land use permits. However, a number of EARP recommendations fell outside the scope of these regulatory instruments. To satisfy these concerns, the federal government required BHP Billiton to enter into an environmental agreement and to negotiate impact-benefit agreements with the Treaty 11 Dogrib, the Yellowknives Dene, the Inuit of Coppermine, and the Métis Nation who live in various parts of the remote region. Recall that impact-benefit agreements are negotiated between a private company, various levels

of government, and local communities to enhance local benefits from resource production. Normally, these agreements are limited to Aboriginal communities where issues such as employment and training; economic development and business opportunities; social, cultural, and community support; implementation and coordination; and funding of various initiatives may be addressed (Kennett, 1999). The federal government has used similar agreements in the North for several mines in the Yukon, as well as for the Norman Wells Pipeline.

In consultation with the government of the Northwest Territories and Aboriginal groups, the federal government negotiated the required environmental agreement with BHP Billiton. The agreement obliged BHP Billiton to establish an environmental advisory group in addition to developing monitoring and management plans for birds and caribou. Annually, BHP Billiton was to submit public monitoring reports on social and environmental effects that, in turn, would be used in the preparation of longer-term monitoring reports every three to five years. Water quality issues that were not included in the water licence also were to be addressed (Department of Indian and Northern Affairs, 1996b). However, even though there was a commitment to monitor social effects as well environmental ones, only the environmental effects have actually been monitored under the independent environmental monitoring agency. Social effects of the mine operation have received very little formal attention. Yet, as mining proceeds, it is clear that numerous social and environmental issues remain.

At the time of the environmental assessment, numerous criticisms were raised about the way in which the environmental assessment of the diamond project was conducted. Intervenor groups, for instance, noted that BHP Billiton's environmental impact statement was deficient in traditional knowledge, monitoring, mitigation, community impacts, and handling of issues related to land claims. Given this and other northern EARP experiences, questions were raised about the ability of Canada's environmental assessment process to ensure fair, effective, and efficient decision making (Wismer, 1996).

In 2006, about 685 people were employed directly at the EKATI mine site; 69 percent were northern residents. At Diavik, the number of people employed was estimated at 760 in 2006, of which 77 percent were northern residents. About half of these northern resident employees were Aboriginal. A third project at Snap Lake is anticipated to begin full production in 2008, and will employ approximately 500 people (Northwest Territories Industry, Tourism, and Investment, 2006).

BHP Billiton and the Government of the Northwest Territories signed a Socio-Economic Agreement in 1996, which set employment targets for the EKATI diamond mine. This agreement set the target for hiring northern residents at 62 percent and the target for hiring Aboriginal

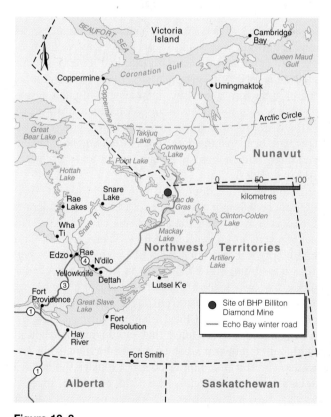

Figure 10–3

Great Slave Lake area and location of BHP Billiton (EKATI) diamond mine

SOURCE: Adapted from "The Nasty Game," S. Wismer, 1996, *Alternatives, 22*(4), 12. Reprinted courtesy of Alternatives Journal: Environmental Thought, Policy and Action.

Photo 10–5
A diamond mine northeast of Yellowknife, Northwest Territories.

workers at 31 percent. According to BHP Billiton's 2006 annual report on northern employment and spending, 60 percent of employees were northern residents, and 33 percent were Aboriginal.

In the construction phase, the mine operated on a shift of two weeks fly-in/two weeks fly-out. Although BHP Billiton indicated this schedule suited employee needs, there were no provisions for workers to take time off on a seasonal basis. The costs of social and family disruption and loss of opportunity to participate adequately in community life arising from such a schedule were not addressed (Wismer, 1996). The Canadian Arctic Resources Committee (CARC), a nongovernmental organization, continues to advocate for mining practices that will allow Aboriginal peoples to maintain their cultural and social values while participating in the economic activities of the North (see Box 10–4).

Beyond the social effects described above, the World Wildlife Fund (Canada) expressed public concerns over the rapid pace of the approvals process. The organization filed for a judicial review of the EARP's procedures in an effort to obtain commitments for action on protected areas in the region. The international conservation organization was concerned that the diamond mining area is located at the centre of the migration route of the Bathurst caribou herd. After the governments of Canada and the Northwest Territories committed to produce a Protected Areas Strategy (PAS) for the entire Northwest Territories by 1998, the World Wildlife Fund withdrew the court action (World Wildlife Fund, 1997). On September 30, 1999, the Northwest Territories Protected Areas Strategy was signed by the federal Minister of Indian Affairs and Northern Development and the territorial Minister of Resources, Wildlife and Economic Development. Although the PAS is a consensus-built strategy and is intended

to provide greater certainty to industry interested in northern investment, concerns about the effectiveness of such protected areas strategies remain. One indication that such strategies might work occurred in the case of Tuktut Nogait National Park, established in 1996 to protect the tundra hills natural region and the calving grounds of the Bluenose caribou herd. The mining industry wanted park boundaries amended to permit mining on 415 square kilometres of land. In 1998, Parliament refused, perhaps an indication that approaches such as the PAS will achieve their objectives (McNamee, 1999).

Aboriginal groups also expressed concern over the EKATI mine project. The site falls within the traditional hunting and trapping grounds asserted by the Yellowknives Dene and Dogrib Nation. As the mine project was undergoing the approval process, both the Yellowknives Dene and the Dogrib were in the process of negotiating land claims agreements with the federal government. The Yellowknives Dene entered into treaty land entitlement negotiations, while the Dogrib were negotiating a comprehensive land claim and self-government agreement. Both groups were concerned that mining development would compromise the government's ability to conduct negotiations (Department of Indian and Northern Affairs, 1996c).

The Dene were concerned that without a land agreement they risked becoming an "embittered minority," as mining development would attract many new residents to the area (Freeman, 1996). Although BHP Billiton negotiated impact-benefit agreements with Aboriginal groups, there is concern about the enforcement of such agreements because no provision for enforcement was set out in the EARP recommendations. Attention to equity issues may have been insufficient to ensure that northern people and their communities can remain healthy and sustainable (Wismer, 1996).

Aboriginal leaders also were skeptical of BHP Billiton because of the company's environmental performance record, including problems with the Ok Tedi copper mine in Papua New Guinea. There, BHP Billiton operated without a mine tailings system for more than 10 years, dumping 80 000 tonnes of waste rock per day into the Ok Tedi and Fly rivers, and rendering 70 kilometres of the Ok Tedi River almost biologically dead (Institute for Global Communications," 1996). Aboriginal leaders claimed that although BHP Billiton might offer monetary compensation for damaging the waters and the land, money does not replace the natural values and opportunities the land provides. In particular, the Yellowknives Dene were concerned about the fuel oil, arsenic, and cyanide that would be hauled on winter roads across their hunting grounds (Wismer, 1996). What troubles many Aboriginal groups and environmentalists is the increased potential for accidents and spills as additional mining companies show interest in developing the area.

The environmental impact statement prepared by the project's proponents outlined the methods and techniques that were to be used to mitigate environmental damage. Although diamond production avoids the use of toxic chemicals, land and water resources are severely altered by diamond mining. For instance, the mine will have to dig through 6 tonnes of granite for every 1 tonne of kimberlite diamond ore that will be processed. The mine is expected to process about 9000 tonnes of ore per day; that will yield about 2 kilograms of diamonds per day, enough to fill a coffee can (BHP Billiton, 2003; Weber, 1997). In addition, the EKATI project will drain six lakes and use another for tailings storage. Over the planned 25-year operation of the diamond processing plant, 133 million tonnes of tailings will be impounded at the storage lake (BHP Billiton Minerals Canada Ltd. & DIA Met Minerals, 1995). At full capacity, the mine is expected to supply 3 million carats annually, or about 5 percent of the world's diamonds (Natural Resources Canada, 2000). In 2007, the mine accounted for 6 percent of the value of the world's supply of rough diamonds (BHP Billiton, 2007).

As noted above, new mines may open in the region where BHP Billiton is developing its Panda mine. In early March 2000, the Government of the Northwest Territories signed off on the environmental agreement with the second diamond mine, that of Diavik Diamond Mines Inc.

This agreement, too, addressed environmental provisions identified in the Diavik Comprehensive Study Report that would not be covered by existing regulatory instruments, such as a water licence or land permit (Government of the Northwest Territories, 2000). The mine opened in 2003.

Beyond the mines in Nunavut and the Northwest Territories, diamond mines are being developed in the northern portions of the provinces as well. Construction of the Victor Project mine in northern Ontario began in February 2006. It is estimated that it will employ about 600 people during construction and create 375 permanent positions. The project was approved under the Federal Environmental Assessment Act, and an impact-benefit agreement was established with the Attawapiskat First Nation, 85.5 percent of whose members voted in favour of the agreement. Private companies in Saskatchewan also are beginning exploration in that province.

Diamond mining poses important environmental and social challenges. Notwithstanding the industrial uses of some diamonds, most are produced for the luxury market. One might question the effects of diamond mining to satisfy nonessential needs, yet diamond mining provides employment in a region where steady jobs are hard to come by. Canadians might ask: can diamond and other types of mining contribute to the longer-term health and the sustainability of northern communities? This question is considered in Box 10–4.

BOX 10–4
SUSTAINABLE MINING: FUEL FOR THOUGHT?

The Brundtland Commission described sustainable development as "development that meets the needs of the present without compromising the ability of future generations to meet their own needs." Is sustainability possible in light of human extraction of nonrenewable resources? Recently, industry, government agencies, nongovernmental organizations, and Aboriginal peoples in Canada have been thinking about how sustainability might apply to the mining industry. While these groups' concerns deal only with the production of minerals and fossil fuels rather than their consumption, these concerns provide an opportunity to consider whether sustainability and mining are compatible.

In 1994, the Whitehorse Mining Initiative Leadership Council Accord was signed by members of the industry, senior governments, labour unions, Aboriginal peoples, and the environmental communities. This accord was aimed at maintaining healthy and diverse ecosystems in Canada, and sharing opportunities with Aboriginal peoples. In 1995–96, the northern watchdog organization Canadian Arctic Resources Committee (CARC) stated that the accord was not fully effective and suggested that several issues still needed to be addressed in relation to northern mineral exploration and development. Although neither the accord nor CARC explicitly used the language of

"sustainable mining," the issues raised are consistent with later efforts to consider sustainability and mining. The outstanding issues included

- ensuring notification of, consultation with, and consent for exploration and development by affected Aboriginal organizations and communities;

- ensuring regulation of the impacts of exploration to protect environmental as well as social and cultural effects;

- using traditional knowledge to create regulatory requirements for resource development;

- negotiating fair impact-benefit agreements;

- developing regional baseline studies using traditional knowledge and appropriately directed science;

- providing Aboriginal people with opportunities to become familiar with mining practices so that they can become involved in identifying and assessing potential impacts;

- providing opportunities for cross-cultural awareness programs for members of the mining industry (including some in government), possibly modelled on programs developed for the petroleum industry in the western Arctic;

(continued)

BOX 10-4
(CONTINUED)

- ensuring that all stages of mineral development focus on protecting cultural, economic, and environmental concerns—that is, infusing resource development decisions with the customs, traditions, and values of Aboriginal peoples; because women, in particular, give testimony to these cultural issues, some believe that women can and should play more central roles in development decision making.

In the 1990s, the environmental impact assessment panel investigating the impacts of the Voisey's Bay nickel project in Newfoundland required the proponent to include sustainability objectives in its application; this was the first mine operation with an explicit "sustainability mandate" in its review and approvals process. The Environmental Impact Assessment panel noted that to contribute to sustainability, the mine must

- not impair ecosystem integrity or biodiversity,

- not significantly damage local and regional ecosystem functions,

- not reduce the capacity of renewable resources to support present and future generations,

- deliver durable and equitable social and economic benefits (even after mine closure), with special attention to the needs of Aboriginal peoples,

- proceed in a manner compatible with stewardship of nonrenewable resources,

- respect Aboriginal rights and land claims agreements.

Based on the panel's review and recommendations, the rate of extraction was slowed to extend the life of the mine operation and to promote longer social and economic benefits for the local community. Would these recommendations "fit" your definition of sustainability?

In 2001, the Mining Association of Canada (2004) developed a set of guiding principles to demonstrate the commitment of its members to sustainable development. Part of these guiding principles state,

In all aspects of our business and operations, we will:

- respect human rights and treat those with whom we deal fairly and with dignity;

- respect the cultures, customs and values of people with whom our operations interact;

- obtain and maintain business through ethical conduct;

- comply with all laws and regulations in each country where we operate and apply the standards reflecting our adherence to these Guiding Principles and our adherence to best international practices;

- support the capability of communities to participate in opportunities provided by new mining projects and existing operations;

- be responsive to community priorities, needs, and interests through all stages of mining exploration, development, operations, and closure;

- provide lasting benefits to local communities through self-sustaining programs to enhance the economic, social, educational, and healthcare standards they enjoy.

In May 2002, a workshop was held involving geological scientists from across Canada. Participants recognized that resource development may be a key contributor to future economic independence and stability (for Canada's northern regions), but preservation of the social and environmental values also must be paramount to any development decision. Workshop participants defined sustainable mining as ensuring that its economic benefits are shared fairly with affected, communities and are not offset by long-term negative impacts to the environment.

In 1999, nine of the world's largest mining companies launched the Global Mining Initiative aimed at defining, promoting, and implementing sustainable development in the mining, metals, and minerals industry. This initiative led to a written report and a global conference in Toronto in 2002. Following the work of the Global Mining Initiative, the International Council on Mining and Metals was established. The role of the council is to promote sustainable business practices in order to enhance economic performance and to recruit and retain talented employees. The council has declared that demonstration of environmental, economic, and social responsibility in the mining sector is necessary in order to maintain access to land, capital, and markets. While these initiatives are voluntary, they do illustrate that the mining industry is sensitive to increased public vigilance of its operations and to increasing demands that their operations are conducted responsibly.

What considerations do you think are important if mining is to be considered under the heading of sustainable development?

SOURCES: "Aboriginal Communities and Mining in Northern Canada," R. F. Keith, 1995/96, *Northern Perspectives, 23,* 3–4, http://www.carc.org/pubs/v2n3-4/mining2.htm; *Towards Sustainable Mining: Guiding Principles,* Mining Association of Canada, April 2004, http://www.mining.ca/english/tsm/principles~eng.pdf; Personal communication, B. Noble, 2003; *Whitehorse Mining Initiative,* Natural Resources Canada, 2003, http://www.nrcan.gc.ca/mms/poli/wmi_e.htm; *Sustainable Mining in the 21st Century (SUM 21)—A Workshop for Geoscientists Conference Report,* Geological Association of Canada, n.d., http://www.cim.org/geosoc/sum21_report.cfm; *Global Mining Initiative,* International Council on Mining and Minerals, 2006, www.icmm.com/gmi.php.

ENVIRONMENTAL IMPACTS OF MINING

Since mineral deposits often are located in areas desirable for other land uses, such as forestry, agriculture, and recreation, mining is not always an activity located in remote regions. In the case of sand and gravel mining, these deposits frequently are located near or within urban areas. Using ecosystem-based approaches to make environmental decisions helps us realize that the environmental effects of a mine operation extend far

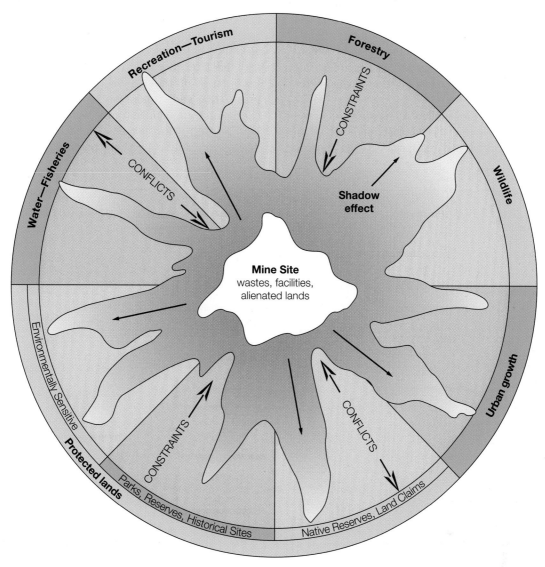

Figure 10–4

Conceptual land use conflicts and constraints for mining

SOURCE: Adapted from *Mining, Land Use and the Environment: A Canadian Overview*, I. B. Marshall, Land Use in Canada series. No. 22–23, p. 194. © Her Majesty the Queen in Right of Canada, Environment Canada, 1982. Reprinted with permission of the Minister of Public Works and Government Services Canada, 2008.

beyond the mine site. Mining has a considerable influence on land surrounding the mine, and the range of interaction between mining and other land uses has become increasingly complex. Both the direct uses at the mine site and the accompanying indirect uses beyond the immediate site have the potential to conflict with other land use activities (see Figure 10–4). As a result, a mining company's responsibility for environmental protection extends beyond its working operations to include neighbouring lands, watersheds, and transportation corridors.

Increasingly, mineral claims have been staked in areas designated for environmental protection; this action has sparked some intense land use conflicts. For example, a mining development proposed by a subsidiary of the Canadian multinational Noranda Inc., adjacent to Yellowstone National Park, was halted in 1996 by U.S.

president Bill Clinton following a lengthy period of public opposition. Similarly, a proposal to develop a copper mine on British Columbia's Windy Craggy Mountain, in the Tatshenshini watershed, was denied and a land swap compensation package was negotiated in 1993. The region around the Tatshenshini River now is preserved as the Tatshenshini-Alsek Wilderness Park and is permanently closed to mining (Newcott, 1994). In 1994, the area was designated as a World Heritage Site. Yet these decisions never seem to be final. The Canadian Zinc Corporation has established a mine site about 15 kilometres from the boundary of the Nahanni National Park Reserve and 43 kilometres upstream of the South Nahanni River. This area is also a UNESCO World Heritage Site and is characterized by limestone caves and karst formations. Although the company has not obtained the necessary permits to

CHAPTER 10: MINERALS AND MINING

operate the mine, it has expressed interest in establishing a winter road in the same area as a proposed park expansion. Any proposal to develop the mine will have to consider the unique and easily disturbed landscape features and will have to address outstanding land claims issues with local Aboriginal people.

Most mining operations follow a four-stage sequence of development: exploration, development and extraction, processing, and closure and reclamation (each stage is described briefly in the following sections). The environmental impact at each stage of development varies according to the mineral type, consistency, and location, and the form in which the final product is delivered. Each stage of the mineral production process—from prospecting and exploration to mine development and extraction to refining and processing—introduces potentially disruptive environmental impacts. Figure 10–5 summarizes the waste impacts and potential hazards of mining

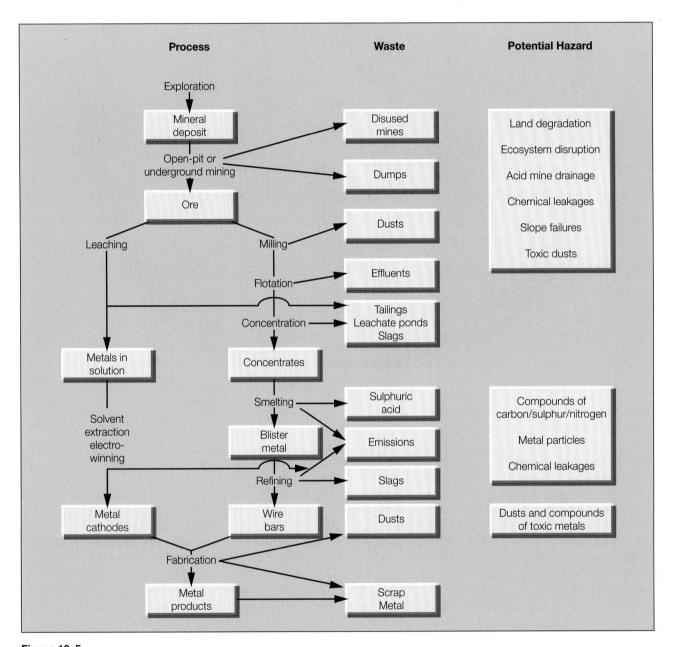

Figure 10–5

The mining process and the environment

NOTE: Please refer to Table 10–2 for information on potential environmental impacts of mining phases illustrated in this figure.

SOURCE: Adapted from *Environmental Degradation from Mining and Mineral Processing in Developing Countries: Corporate Responses and National Policies*, A. Warhurst, 1994, Paris: Organization for Economic Cooperation and Development, p. 14.

at each stage of the production process, while Table 10–2 highlights a broad range of impact issues associated with the mining activities illustrated in Figure 10–5.

The extent of environmental impact from a mine depends on a range of factors, from the type of mineral and its chemical properties to the local ecology, geology, and climate characteristics at the mine site. For example, most metal (gold, copper, zinc, and nickel) mines in Canada contain sulphide materials. When exposed to air and water, the sulphide materials oxidize and generate sulphuric acid, resulting in **acid mine** (or acid rock) **drainage**. Acid mine drainage is the most serious environmental problem facing the mining industry (see the discussion under "Mine Closure and Reclamation"). Climatic variables, such as strong winds and precipitation, may further compound problems of acidic drainage and increase the risk of freshwater contamination.

Smelting, refining, and fabrication processes use chemicals that may leak or be discharged into the environment. These processing activities also require a large amount of energy—the mining industry accounts for about 20 percent of Canadian industrial energy demand. Generally, energy is provided by burning fossil fuels, which releases carbon dioxide and other gases into the atmosphere.

Mineral Exploration

Mineral exploration involves finding geological, geophysical, or geochemical conditions that differ from those of their surroundings (Marshall, 1982). Discovering such anomalies in the landscape may signal the presence of significant mineral deposits. Even though there are extensive geological mineral records compiled over the

TABLE 10–2
POTENTIAL ENVIRONMENTAL IMPACTS OF MINING PHASES

Mining Phase	Potential Impacts
Exploration	• Generally low or no impact
	• When exploration stage requires trenching, drilling, or road access, there is increased habitat disturbance and the potential for discharge of contaminants
Extraction and processing	• Acid mine drainage containing contaminants is released to surface water and groundwater; there are particular concerns relating to
• Mining and milling	– heavy metals that originate in the ore and tailings (their release may be accelerated by naturally occurring acid generation);
	– organic compounds that originate in the chemical reagents used in the milling process;
	– cyanide, particularly from gold milling processes;
	– ammonia.
	• Alienation of land as a result of waste rock piles and tailings disposal areas
	• Increased erosion; silting of lakes and streams
	• Dust and noise
• Smelting and refining	• Discharge to air of contaminants, including heavy metals, organics, and SO_2
	• Alienation of land as a result of slag disposal
	• Indirect impacts as a result of energy production (most of the energy used in mining processes is used for smelting and refining)
Closure and reclamation*	• Continuing discharge of contaminants to groundwater and surface water (particularly heavy metals when naturally occurring acid generation exists)
	• Alienation of land and one-time pulse discharge of contaminants and sediment to water as a result of dam failure

NOTE: A particular concern centres on the responsibility for orphaned mine sites; liability falls to society through the government.

* Does not apply everywhere.

SOURCE: Adapted from *The State of Canada's Environment—1996,* Environment Canada, 1996, Table 11.15. © Her Majesty the Queen in Right of Canada, Environment Canada, 1996. Reprinted with permission of the Minister of Public Works and Government Services Canada, 2008.

past century in Canada, actually detecting an anomaly can be like finding a needle in a haystack. A company's expenditures are high during the exploration stage, and there is no guarantee of turning a discovery into an economically feasible mine.

During exploration, construction of access roads, trenches, pits, and drill pads disturbs the land surface, and may interfere with wildlife and local drainage. In some instances, where vegetation is stripped to accommodate testing activities, soil erosion and sedimentation (and possible disruption of fish habitat) follow. The more extensive effects of constructing roads in areas previously devoid of them include opening up access to potentially sensitive areas and permitting hunters, wilderness tourists, guides, outfitters, and others to cause potentially significant impacts, ranging from noise to harassment of wildlife. Companies involved in exploration are required to follow guidelines aimed at reducing the disruptive environmental effects of their activities. In addition, most provinces require companies to have reclamation plans and adequate financing to rehabilitate exploration sites.

Having discovered a mineral deposit, a company must first assess the technical and economic requirements of bringing a mine into operation. Costs of extraction, transportation, and processing are considered, as well as costs of environmental controls and reclamation procedures. A company's commitment to operate within an acceptable environmental standard must be demonstrated before a project is approved. As with proposals for many large-scale developments, mining proposals are subject to environmental review. Decisions to proceed with, modify, or restrict development normally are reached through the **environmental impact assessment** (EIA) process.

An EIA aims to provide decision makers with scientifically researched and documented evidence to identify the likely consequences of undertaking new developments and changing natural systems (Wiesner, 1995). The magnitude of a review and the requirements to be satisfied vary from project to project and from province to province. A key component of the overall EIA process is the preparation of an **environmental impact statement** (EIS). In Canada, it is the responsibility of the project proponent (individual or company proposing the project) to prepare the EIS and ensure that all provincial and federal policy requirements are satisfied. A balanced EIA should consider the scope of a project from a systems perspective. Figure 10–6 outlines the procedural elements involved in the EIA process.

While project proponents are required to publish terms of reference for their EISs, and opponents are entitled to respond to these terms, the nature and complexity of the EIA process often leads to frustration for all interested stakeholders. In spite of the possibility of review under the federal Environmental Assessment Act, many people are

Project description	• description of the proposed action, including its alternatives, and details sufficient for an assessment
Screening	• determination of whether the action is subject to an EIA under the regulations or guidelines present, and if so what type or level of assessment is required
Scoping	• delineation of the key issues and the boundaries to be considered in the assessment, including the baseline conditions and scoping of alternatives
Impact prediction and evaluation	• prediction of environmental impacts and determination of impact significance
Impact management	• identification of impact management and mitigation strategies, and development of environmental management or protection plans
Review and decision	• technical and public review of EIS and related documents, and subsequent recommendation as to whether the proposed action should proceed and under what conditions
Implementation and follow-up	• implementation of project and associated management measures; continuous data collection to monitor compliance with conditions and regulations; monitoring the effectiveness of impact management measures and the accuracy of impact predictions

Public consultation

Figure 10–6

Elements of a generic EIA process

SOURCE: *Introduction to Environmental Impact Assessment: A Guide to Principles and Practice* by Bram F. Noble, p. 13. © Copyright Oxford University Press Canada 2006. Reprinted by permission of the publisher.

critical of impact statements because they are commissioned by the developer and prepared by consultants and researchers hired by the developer. The EIS for the EKATI diamond mine in the Northwest Territories, for example, was described as superficial and totally inadequate in assessing the effects of the mine on the environment (Freeman, 1996).

Opponents of development projects are not the only ones critical of environmental assessment procedures. In 1996, the Cheslatta Carrier Nation of northern British Columbia obtained documents that revealed "extraordinary corporate pressure to obtain federal approval for the proposed Huckleberry mine near Houston, BC" (Nelson, 1996, p. A5). Japanese investors in the mine opposed "unreasonable delays" in the environmental assessment process and threatened to withdraw from the project and reduce mining investment in Canada. Such corporate pressure undermines the federal environmental assessment process and may have led to the report entitled "Streamlining Environmental Regulation for Mining" tabled in the House of Commons in November 1996. In the report, the Standing Committee on Natural Resources made 11 recommendations for reforming the federal environmental regulatory regime for mining.

Mine Development and Mineral Extraction

Mining development may have a double impact on the environment, not only as a result of the mine site development but also because of the infrastructure put in place to service the mine. As noted above, roads increase access to remote areas and result in additional environmental pressure from nonmining activities such as hunting, fishing, and recreation. In the case of sand and gravel pits, increased traffic on existing roads brings increased levels of dust, noise, and maintenance costs that must be borne by local residents and municipalities.

Effective transportation links are essential for servicing mining operations. Although a large degree of processing occurs at the mine site, large shipments of minerals are transported to smelters, refineries, and other processing locations. In 2001, for instance, Canadian railways earned 59 percent of their total freight revenue from transporting mineral products, and between 60 and 70 percent of the volume of all products loaded at Canadian ports in international trade was from mineral-related products (Natural Resources Canada, n.d.). Environmentalists, and others, are concerned about spills of minerals, mine wastes, and processing chemicals en route to or from mine sites. Roads constructed beside rivers are of special concern, as an accident could release toxic substances into the watercourse and threaten aquatic habitat. Mine sites located in areas of seismic activity also are of concern due to the threat of an earthquake rupturing tailings ponds and subsequently washing out roads and bridges.

Until the early 1900s, mining activity was concentrated underground. To extract the desired materials, shafts were sunk or tunnels were driven on a slope or horizontally into the ore zone (Figure 10–7). Then the ore was drilled, blasted, and collected for transport to the surface by ore hoists or wheeled haulage vehicles.

Development of surface mining allowed lower-grade ore bodies to be mined over a wider, more dispersed land area. Surface mining involves two basic techniques. In **open-pit mining**, ore is extracted from deposits by making a progressively larger and deeper pit from which **overburden** and waste rock are removed. In **strip mining**, material that lies relatively flat and is not buried too deeply is exposed by shovels or draglines, and the waste materials are thrown back into the previous cut

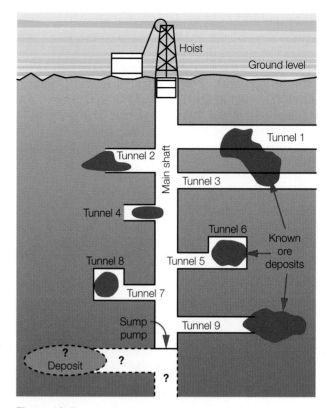

Figure 10–7
Cross-section of a mineshaft

NOTE: Sump pumps keep the mine dry, and sophisticated ventilation systems, usually requiring a second shaft, must be installed in most underground mines to remove explosive and radioactive gases and provide fresh air.

SOURCE: Adapted from *Conservation of Natural Resources: A Resource Management Approach*, D. C. Castillon, 1992, Dubuque, IA: Brown, p. 325.

made where the ore or coal was extracted. Placer mining is a form of surface mining, such as panning for gold, that occurs mainly in the Yukon and involves mining river- and streambeds for eroded particles of minerals. In 1992, over 70 percent of mineral production in Canada was from surface mining operations.

Another form of mining has recently drawn attention in Canada—the mining of coalbed methane (see Box 11–4, p. 457). Methane is the primary source of natural gas, and coalbed methane is found in coal seams. Gas is released from the coal by removing water from the coalbed. Sometimes large amounts of water must be removed; the deeper the coalbed, the less water that is present, but the more saline the water becomes. While mining for coalbed methane is not as intrusive as strip mining, critics point to the extensive effects of mining, including road building, drilling pads, compression stations, pipelines, and the disposal of wastewater (National Parks Conservation Association, 2004; U.S. Geological Survey, 1997). Disposing of water may introduce additional sediments, heavy metals, salts, and changes in acidity and temperature; finding methods to dispose of water that are environmentally and economically sound remains a significant challenge. Water may be discharged on the surface if it is considered fresh, although the preferred option is to inject the water back into the host rock. This is required by regulations in Alberta, but not in British Columbia.

Open-pit mining has allowed mineral companies to exploit economies of scale by using larger mining equipment and large-scale extraction techniques (Warhurst, 1994). However, extensive surface excavations of overburden material may clog streams, create excessive dust, and disturb habitat. In 1989, surface mines produced eight times as much waste per tonne of ore as underground mines (Warhurst, 1994). Land disruption from surface mining also reduces land available for alternative uses, such as forestry, agriculture, recreation, and wildlife habitat.

Photo 10–6
Gold, coal, potash, and salt are among the minerals extracted in underground mining.

Photo 10–7
Open-pit mines may have environmental impacts beyond land disturbance and aesthetic degradation, including altered surface drainage patterns and the release of harmful trace elements.

Processing of Minerals

The processing of minerals through milling, smelting, and refining is less land intensive than exploration and extraction; however, the environmental impacts are more significant and long term. The **milling** process involves the crushing and grinding of ores to separate the useful materials from the nonuseful ones. **Tailings**, the nonuseful materials, are removed from the mill after the recoverable minerals have been extracted. Generally, the amount of concentrate produced per tonne of ore is small in comparison with the amount of rock waste.

Photo 10–8
Usually, pure minerals constitute a tiny fraction of the material extracted to obtain them.

Photo 10–9
A potash slag heap at Vanscoy, Saskatchewan.

Most metal ores require crushing and grinding, plus additional treatment with chemical or biological reagents to extract the desired minerals. Base-metal milling commonly uses a flotation process that mixes the ore with chemicals (such as kerosene, organic agents, and sulphuric acid) and water to produce a fine mineral concentrate (subsequently shipped to a smelter for the next stage of recovery). Following the flotation process, tailings are normally filtered and washed to remove most of the reagents. Once tailing solids have settled, the effluent is discharged to natural water bodies, providing it meets regulatory standards.

The milling of gold uses cyanide, which is lethal to fish at concentrations as low as 0.04 milligrams per litre (Government of Canada, 1996a). Once the milling of gold is complete, cyanide must be treated because the retention time in tailing ponds normally is not long enough for cyanide to break down naturally. Various processes are used to treat cyanide in gold mill effluents and tailings pond waters, where cyanide concentrations are high. Most of the cyanide and metallocyanide complexes can be destroyed or recovered. However, some metallocyanides are more stable and difficult to treat; they may end up in the aquatic environment and harm fish. Provincial regulations specify limits on the amount of cyanide that may be released through effluent discharges.

Usually, mine wastes are treated and stored on site in tailings retention facilities, such as dams and ponds. Effluents containing metals are treated with lime during retention to precipitate the dissolved metals as hydroxides. Such treatment generally removes up to 99 percent of metals and suspended sediments from mine and mill effluent (Government of Canada, 1996b). Serious aquatic damage may result if tailings retention facilities leak or rupture, as was the case with tailings dike failures at Canadian-owned or operated mines in Spain (Los Frailes) and Kyrgyzstan during 1998. These failures were preceded by the failure of a drainage tunnel at the Marcopper mine in the Philippines in 1996, and by the crash of a truck carrying sodium cyanide into a local river near the Kumtor mine in Guyana during 1995 (Johnson, 1999). Each of these accidents caused severe contamination of surrounding lands and rivers. There have been past instances in Canada, too, where leaking or ruptured tailings ponds have affected local water bodies and contaminated community water supplies, such as when the tailings pond at Western Mines discharged into Buttle Lake on Vancouver Island, British Columbia, over 30 years ago. Mines that have long been abandoned pose enormous environmental costs today. Toxic substances deposited into Howe Sound, British Columbia, from the Britannia mines continue to destroy fish habitat, while no government or private company is prepared to take responsibility for its cleanup. Even today, many sites are highly toxic.

Production of most base metals (copper, lead, zinc, and nickel), all ferrous metals (iron and steel), and aluminum, occurs in smelters and blast furnaces that operate at high temperatures (pyrometallurgy) and emit various pollutants into the atmosphere. Particulate matter, nitrogen oxides, sulphur dioxide, metals, and organic compounds may be deposited locally or transported over long distances. Since the 1970s, stricter emission control standards, new, smelting technologies and processes, and voluntary pollution prevention efforts by the mining industry have helped to reduce sulphur dioxide and other emissions. Figure 10–8 (next page), which illustrates total emissions in Canada as well as those from Eastern Canada, demonstrates the high proportion of emissions coming from this part of the country due to the larger, industrial and manufacturing base, relative to other parts of the country. However, a substantial portion of the Boreal Shield ecozone continues to receive elevated levels of acidic deposition (Government of Canada, 1996a).

Tailings and waste rock that are naturally high in sulphide materials and are stored at working and abandoned mines can result in acid mine drainage. Acid mine drainage, the most serious control problem facing the Canadian and global mining industry, is discussed in the following section.

Mine Closure and Reclamation

In common with other nonrenewable resources, mineral reserves are finite. Once deposits become depleted or extraction becomes uneconomical, a mine site will close. Efforts to extend the life of a mine include introducing exploration programs to find nearby ore deposits, increasing recovery efficiencies, and providing financial incentives. Regardless of the efforts employed, the eventual closure of a mine is inevitable. As described in Box 10–2, mine closures may have devastating impacts on communities whose economies have been built on mineral exploitation.

Mine closure not only affects the social fabric of a community but can have far-reaching negative effects on the environment. In the past, in keeping with environmental and mining practices of the day, mine sites were abandoned with minimal or no rehabilitation work. Little, if any, concern was shown for land restoration, environmental stability, or even public safety. Today, most mining projects will be denied approval if the proponents fail to provide a detailed closure plan or do not have the financial security to ensure site rehabilitation. To be effective, these plans must include a long-term monitoring program to safeguard against future environmental damage.

In Canada, jurisdiction over mineral resources is assigned to the provinces. As a result, **reclamation** standards are determined by each province. The federal government has direct responsibility for reclamation in the Yukon and the Northwest Territories and in relation to uranium. As well, the federal government influences mine reclamation issues at the national level through the Fisheries Act and the Canadian Environmental Assessment Act, and through tax policies and science and technology activities.

CHAPTER 10: MINERALS AND MINING

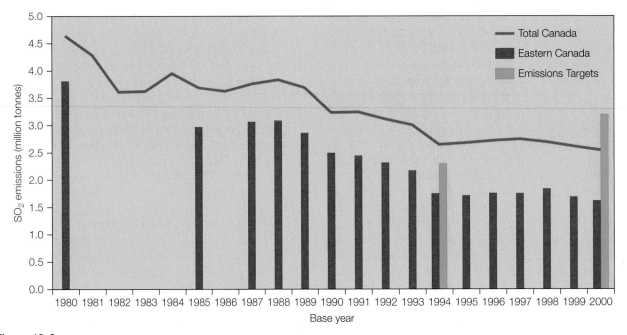

Figure 10–8

Sulphur dioxide emissions for all of Canada and eastern Canada (million tonnes), 1980–2000

SOURCE: *Environmental Signals, Canada's National Environmental Indicator Series 2003,* © Her Majesty the Queen in Right of Canada, 2005. Reproduced with the permission of the Minister of Public Works and Government Services Canada, 2008. http://www.environment-canada.ca/soer-ree/English/Indicators/Issues/ acidrain/Bulletin/arind1_e.cfm

Photo 10–10

Recent reclamation efforts have reintroduced vegetation and improved air and water quality in the area of Sudbury, Ontario, where mining slag heaps had historically been left unattended.

Mine reclamation seeks to rehabilitate a mine site to a viable and, wherever practicable, self-sustaining ecosystem that is compatible with a healthy environment and other human activities (Government of Canada, 1996a). Returning land disturbed by mining activity to a condition that is safe, stable, and compatible with adjoining lands requires a well-planned series of activities that incorporate sustainability objectives at all stages of mineral production. Ideally, rehabilitation should be a continual activity that occurs over the life of the mine. In addition to initial studies, such as an EIA and closure plan, rehabilitation reports should be prepared annually and the site should be continuously monitored to identify ecological and land use changes.

Mines are no longer abandoned; they are closed following legislated federal or provincial procedures and, when maintained according to these procedures, have fewer downstream impacts. Mines were abandoned in the past, however, and Canada still has many abandoned mining sites scattered across the landscape that have never been reclaimed. Abandoned metal mines potentially introduce the most serious mining-related environmental problems. The tendency of sulphide-bearing rocks to oxidize and generate acidic effluents was noted earlier in the chapter. Every year, the Canadian mining industry generates approximately 650 million tonnes of tailings and waste rock, about half of which are from sulphide ore operations. In the absence of naturally occurring (or applications of) acid-neutralizing materials such as calcite or limestone, toxic metals from surface tailings and mine wastes may leach into nearby watercourses in the form of acid mine drainage. When tailings contain high levels of sulphide material, the potential for acid generation is severe. Untreated acidic wastes also carry toxic concentrations of metals and high levels of dissolved salts. Rainfall and melting snow flush the toxic solutions from waste sites to the surrounding watershed, contaminating watercourses and groundwater.

Although the process of acid mine drainage can be slowed, and the acidic effluent can be treated, it is difficult to prevent completely. Current treatment facilities at mine sites are effective in preventing environmental contamination downstream provided they are well maintained and operated. Unfortunately, acid generation may continue for hundreds of years following mine closure, making treatment plants neither financially nor operationally viable. Furthermore, conventional treatment using lime offers limited long-term benefit as the volume of sludge produced in the treatment process would exceed the volume of tailings in only a few decades.

In 1994, over 12 500 hectares of tailings and 740 million tonnes of waste mine rock were generating acid drainage in Canada. According to these figures, acidic drainage liability in Canada was estimated at between $2 billion and $5 billion. New data are not readily available; however, the liability remains. Promoting the growth of vegetation on tailings and waste rock was expected to alleviate acid drainage so that mining companies could close sites without future liability. However, it was discovered that the presence of vegetation did little to improve the quality of water drainage. The Canadian mining industry and governments realized that new reclamation technology needed to be developed, and in 1986 established a task force to conduct research on acidic drainage.

Recommendations from the task force led to the creation of the Mine Environmental Neutral Drainage (MEND) program in 1989 (see Box 10–5). The MEND program has advanced research and led to improved technology for reducing problems associated with acid mine drainage. Many mine operators favour underwater disposal of mine tailings as part of a decommissioning program. An anaerobic (without oxygen) environment prohibits the production of sulphuric acid in tailings kept underwater. In the long term, natural sedimentation will cover the tailings, preventing their contact with oxygen.

In 2000, Mackasey undertook a study of abandoned mines across Canada, estimating that there were at least 10 100 abandoned mines (see Table 10–3, next page), including eight Atomic Energy Control Board uranium mines. The cost to clean up abandoned mine sites across Canada was estimated in 1996 to be $6 billion (Young, 1996). A large portion of this total can be attributed to degradation resulting from past practices that are no longer permitted. Abandoned mine sites that represent an unacceptable risk to the environment or human health and safety need to be rehabilitated. Most provincial and territorial governments have surveyed abandoned (no longer operating, but owners known) or orphaned (no

BOX 10–5
CANADA'S MEND PROGRAM

Canada's initial Mine Environmental Neutral Drainage (MEND) program was a cooperative program financed and administered by the Canadian mining industry, several federal government agencies (including Natural Resources Canada, Environment Canada, and Indian and Northern Affairs), and provincial governments.

The program was a collaborative effort to research and develop technologies that would prevent or substantially reduce environmental problems caused by acid mine drainage and the financial liabilities that accrued to public agencies at abandoned mine sites. For tailings and waste rock piles of many existing and orphaned mines, however, the best that can be expected is long-term containment and treatment to neutralize acid drainage and remove dissolved metal contaminants. The MEND program confirmed that prevention is the best solution for acidic drainage.

More than $18 million has been spent on the MEND program, resulting in such research advances as

- development of precise methods to predict and measure the extent of acidic drainage before it occurs,
- subaqueous tailings disposal (such as at the Polaris mine),
- layered earth covers,
- engineered wetlands (such as in Elliot Lake),
- use of solid covers and wet barriers to prevent and control acid runoff,
- use of biotechnology to treat small acidic seeps.

Through this investment, Canadian mining companies and government departments suggest that they have reduced the liability due to acidic drainage by at least $400 million.

MEND is funded equally by the Mining Association of Canada and Natural Resources Canada, and supports research, monitoring and information to further reduce the environmental liability associated with acidic drainage.

SOURCES: *The State of Canada's Environment—1996*, Government of Canada, 1996, Ottawa: Supply and Services Canada; *Mine Environmental Neutral Drainage Program*, Natural Resources Canada, 1996, http://www.emr.ca/mets/mend/; *Mine Environment Neutral Drainage*, Natural Resources Canada, 2008, www.nrcan.gc.ca/mms/canmet-mtb/mmsl-lmsm/mend/default_e.htm

TABLE 10-3

ABANDONED MINES IDENTIFIED AND ON FILE IN CANADA (2000)

Jurisdiction	Number of Abandoned Mines
Alberta	2100
British Columbia	20 (estimated)
Manitoba	n/a
New Brunswick	60
Newfoundland and Labrador	39
Nova Scotia	300
Ontario	6015
Prince Edward Island	No mining in province
Quebec	1000
Saskatchewan	505+
Yukon	120
Nunavut	3
Northwest Territories	37
Atomic Energy Control Board	8

SOURCE: *Abandoned Mines in Canada,* W. O. Mackasey, 2000, http://www.miningwatch.ca/publications/Mackasey_abandoned_mines.html. Reprinted by permission of WOM Geological Associates Inc.

longer operating, owners unknown) mine sites to identify the number involved and to assess the level of degradation and cleanup efforts required. Responsibility for cleaning up many of these abandoned sites is often left with provincial governments, as the previous owner or operator of the property can no longer be identified, is insolvent, or is otherwise unable to pay. However, governments are reluctant to take responsibility and frequently have more immediate demands on public funds.

It is important to note that governments and nongovernmental organizations believe that the list in Table 10–3 is in complete (Mackasey, 2000); indeed, one source from Natural Resources Canada estimates there are at least 27 000 abandoned mines (Natural Resources Canada, 2007c). Unfortunately, there has been no systematic study to monitor sites and update these data. The numbers likely grossly underestimate the number of abandoned mines found in Canada today.

Each of the provinces and territories has legislation in place to administer abandoned mines and mine reclamation (Mackasey, 2000). Mining-related Acts are employed in British Columbia, Newfoundland and Labrador, Nova Scotia, New Brunswick, Quebec, Ontario, and the Yukon. Environment-related Acts are used in Saskatchewan, Northwest Territories, Nunavut, and the

Yukon, while Alberta uses the Coal Conservation Act. Manitoba has a policy document in place. Environment-related Acts also apply in Alberta, British Columbia, and Newfoundland and Labrador. Federally, Acts that apply to abandoned mines and reclamation include Environmental Assessment, Environmental Protection, Fisheries, and the Atomic Energy Control Act. In May 2000, the Atomic Energy Control Board became the Canadian Nuclear Safety Commission, with a mandate to be more active in regulating and licensing sites with significant radioactive substances resulting from nuclear operations (see also Chapter 11).

Mined-out shafts do not necessarily have to be closed and capped, as is commonly assumed. For example, a mined-out chamber of a zinc–copper mine in Manitoba has been converted into a garden supporting a wide variety of plant species. Long-term results of this experiment, however, have received mixed reports (see Enviro-Focus 10 on page 430). Reclamation of gravel mine sites is now quite common as, in order to obtain permits to extract gravel, mining companies are required to establish remediation strategies that may include planting new vegetation and providing recreational facilities (e.g., small lakes, picnic areas) on site after the gravel has been removed. Across the country, abandoned underground mines have been considered possible locations for mine tailings and for disposal of solid and nuclear wastes generated elsewhere. Proposals for such uses are often controversial, as they require safe transportation, disposal, and maintenance of wastes over considerable periods of time. No one knows, for example, if we can guarantee the safety of nuclear wastes for thousands of years. The use of mine sites for these purposes, however, draws attention to the fact that sustainable mining must consider the entire life cycle of the materials that are extracted and of the sites where extraction takes place.

In a very curious example of remediation of toxic sites, one location in the United States has been called the "World's Most Ironic Nature Park." The Rocky Mountain Arsenal, located just outside Denver, Colorado, was the location of a major chemical weapons manufacturing facility of the U.S. Department of Defense during the Second World War. After the war, the land was leased to companies that made commercial pesticides. For nearly 40 years, millions of gallons of highly poisonous chemicals were deposited in landfills and waste basins on the site. The chemicals also contaminated soils and groundwater. Yet, there was no urban sprawl from Denver in this direction, and in 1986, scientists discovered that the Arsenal was home to a large population of wintering eagles. Since then, other wild flora and fauna have been observed, and the site now boasts wildlife populations that are more diverse and abundant than anywhere else in the central Rockies. In 1992, Congress passed an Act to designate the site a future wildlife refuge. The Rocky Mountain Arsenal National Wildlife Refuge is now managed by the U.S. Fish and Wildlife Service in association with the army, Shell Oil Company, and regulatory agencies. Staff members at the refuge now work with biologists and other scientists to make it one of the largest urban national wildlife refuges in the United States. Efforts are being focused on restoring the landscape to the prairie ecosystems that characterized the region prior to the Second World War. The refuge also has a large public education campaign to provide environmental education for visitors who come to enjoy its "natural" beauty. From efforts at this site, we might learn a great deal about how best to remediate abandoned mine sites that have also experienced severe biophysical and chemical degradation.

Beyond mining activities directly, the recycling of minerals and metals has become an important economic venture. Reuse and recycling practices, combined with the long life span of minerals and metals, can help maintain the stock of extracted minerals and metals and reduce the need for primary extraction. Because Canada has developed a large metal smelting and refining capacity, and because scrap and recycled metals follow the same metallurgical pathway through smelters and refineries as do primary metals, Canada has an excellent base for metal recycling.

Most metal products produced in Canada are made from a mixture of primary and recycled metals. For instance, about 50 percent of the 15 million tonnes of iron and steel produced annually in Canada comes from recycled iron and steel scrap. More than 90 percent of the lead consumed in Canada can be recycled economically; today, almost 50 percent of Canada's total refined lead production comes from secondary lead sources. Currently, over 1000 scrap metal recycling companies operate in Canada, providing direct employment to about 20 000 people (Natural Resources Canada, 2003b). They handle over 11 million tonnes and $3 billion worth of metals annually.

Metal recycling has significant environmental benefits when compared with primary production of metals. The reduced demand for raw material means more efficient use of minerals and increased energy conservation. Energy savings are gained through the reduced quantity of fossil fuels used to generate electricity or operate smelters. Reduced use of fossil fuels means reduced levels of air emissions such as carbon dioxide, sulphur dioxide, and nitrogen oxides, as well as reductions in effluent discharges. Typical energy savings realized by recycling are 95 percent for aluminum, 85 percent for copper, 65 percent for lead, and 60 percent for zinc. Producing steel from recycled materials results in energy savings of 74 percent when compared with the energy used in primary production.

RESPONSES TO ENVIRONMENTAL IMPACTS AND CHANGE

PARTNERSHIPS FOR ENVIRONMENTAL SUSTAINABILITY

Major players in Canada's mining industry realize that they have to work hard to overcome a long history of environmental neglect. Abandoned operations, high emissions, and dangerous human health conditions have given the mining industry a reputation that is less socially desirable than that of other forms of economic and land use activities. Government regulations, at both the federal and provincial levels, have prompted mining companies to invest in research and environmental technologies to improve their operations. Environmental nongovernmental organizations (ENGOs) and networks, such as the Environmental Mining Council of British Columbia (EMCBC) and Mining Watch Canada, act as environmental watchdogs over industrial practices at home and abroad. In the past decade or so, a variety of cooperative programs and initiatives have been working toward fostering sustainable development of mining and mineral processing activities.

In response to growing public concern about provincial mining regulations and assessment processes, the EMCBC initiated an education and advocacy program

Photo 10–11

As the demand for mineral resources continues to increase, the recycling of metals remains an important means to reduce waste. Aluminum products such as these beverage cans are among the most commonly recycled metals. However, recycling often requires large quantities of fossil fuel energy, which does not resolve the issue of how much we consume in the first place.

Precious Metals, or Petals?

Exhausted mineshafts and tunnels do not necessarily have to end up abandoned. In a fully operational copper mine in Flin Flon, Manitoba, a rich diversity of plant species flourishes 365 metres below the surface.

Canada's adventure in underground gardening began in the late 1970s when Inco began growing market vegetables at one of the company's mines in Creighton, Ontario. In 1984, the company switched to growing pine seedlings, replacement trees for those damaged by mine activity. Looking to make use of its kilometres of exhausted mine tunnels, the Hudson Bay Mining and Smelting Co. Ltd. approached Saskatchewan-based Prairie Plant Systems to evaluate the potential of using the spent tunnels for biotechnology research. The mining company also was interested in the possibility of growing plant material for use in mine site reclamation.

The spectacular level of growth may be attributed to the reduced amount of stress plants endure in mine tunnels. Conditions underground—everything from lighting and temperature to moisture and fertilizer—are close to ideal. In the mine, aboveground stresses such as drought, wind, excess sun and water, insects, and disease are avoided. The president of Prairie Plant Systems believes that with conditions such as these, a plant's genetic system is able to direct all its energy toward growth.

Drug companies also are intrigued by the potential of mines to provide high-quality, rapidly growing plants for medicinal purposes. The Pacific yew, for

Photo 10–12
Underground gardening in Flin Flon.

instance, is in high demand because its bark contains taxol, used in the treatment of ovarian cancer (see Enviro-Focus 3, pp. 81–82). As a result, the Flin Flon mine is cultivating yew trees with the intention of easing pressure on the wild Pacific yew. The federal government also has been using the mine site in Flin Flon to grow marijuana for medicinal purposes. Nevertheless, this experiment has been controversial for social and environmental reasons. There are recent concerns that contaminated soils, water, and air in Flin Flon may affect the quality of the products grown in the abandoned mine shafts. The nongovernmental organization Canadians for Safe Access advises Health Canada to stop distributing cannabis from this source to legal users and researchers until independent analysis of the product is conducted and the extent and results of the safety testing are revealed. These concerns highlight the challenges of remediation of former mines and impress on us the need to be cautious about both the immediate and long-term ecological effects of mining activities.

SOURCE: "Health Canada's Dirty Little Secret—Flin Flon Area Contamination," Canadians for Safe Access press release, October 1, 2003, http://www.medicalmarihuana.ca/toxic.html; "Roses from Rock," B. Ryan, January–February 1995, *Equinox, 79*, 50–55. Reprinted by permission of the author.

called BC Mining Watch. The program aimed to build the capacity of activists to respond to environmental threats posed by mineral development, from exploration to mine abandonment. The BC Mining Watch project carried out its central objective in three main ways: (1) by supporting effective documentation of environmental mining conflicts; (2) by supporting communication and alliances among ENGOs, First Nations, and labour groups

on environmental mining issues; and (3) by coordinating and communicating a clear agenda for environmentally appropriate mining regulations and practices (British Columbia Spaces for Nature, n.d.).

One of most successful advances in reducing environmental impacts of mineral processing involves the initiatives taken to lower sulphur dioxide emissions (see Figure 10–8). Ontario's Countdown Acid Rain program, initiated in 1985, was a key motivator in prompting companies to attain the required reductions in sulphur dioxide emissions. At Inco's nickel smelter in Sudbury, Ontario, the program prompted a 90 percent reduction in emissions. This positive event was tempered by intensification of continued emissions, however.

Efforts to reduce emissions in other parts of Canada also have generated positive results. For instance, at Flin Flon, Manitoba, the Hudson Bay Mining and Smelting zinc smelter implemented a new hydrometallurgical pressure process rather than conventional ore roasting. This process leached toxic metals and sulphur ore out of wastes in solution. Installation of a new zinc plant resulted in significant emission reductions—up to 98 percent of the sulphur contained in the ore was captured. In addition, use of Gore-Tex fabric for filtering purposes greatly reduced particulate emissions and allowed mine operators to aim for particulate emissions as low as 16 percent of the allowable limit (Government of Canada, 1996a).

The Accelerated Reduction/Elimination of Toxics (ARET) program is another initiative that helps companies reduce emissions of particulate matter and sulphur dioxide from industrial smelters. As part of the ARET program, 17 base-metal production companies committed to reduce emissions of arsenic, cadmium, lead, mercury, and nickel by 80 percent by 2008, from 1988 levels (see Tables 10–4 and 10–5). Between 1988 and 1993, the companies reduced releases by 43 percent, and by 1998 had achieved a reduction of 73 percent (5824 tonnes) from 1988 levels. Among the companies contributing to major reductions in zinc, lead, arsenic, and cadmium emissions were Hudson Bay Mining and Smelting and Noranda's Horne smelter. Increases in lead and copper emissions were reported at Inco. (Other air quality initiatives are discussed in Chapter 5.) Sources of data, and the specific foci of data collection efforts, change over time, however, making it difficult to determine clearly whether we are reducing or accelerating our effects on the environment (with respect to smelting emissions).

Nevertheless, cooperative efforts in the minerals sector extend beyond atmospheric antipollution programs. In 1993, the Aquamin program was initiated to assess the impacts of mining on aquatic environments. Aquamin's multistakeholder group included representatives from various federal government departments, eight provincial governments, the Mining Association of Canada, Aboriginal groups, and ENGOs. The final report of Aquamin made a

TABLE 10–4
MINING AND SMELTING EMISSIONS, 2000

Substance	Percentage of Emissions (total: 2226 tonnes)
Lead	22
Zinc	24
Copper	27
Nickel	17
Arsenic	7
Cadmium	3
Other	0

SOURCE: *Environmental Leaders 4: ARET, Voluntary Action on Toxic Substances, 2003.* http://dsp-psd.pwgsc.gc.ca/Collection/En40-492-2000E.pdf

TABLE 10–5
PERCENTAGE OF CANADIAN EMISSIONS RELEASED FROM THE BASE METALS SMELTING SECTOR IN 2005, EXCLUDING ARSENIC AND NICKEL

Substance	Base Metals Smelting (tonnes)	Canadian Total (tonnes)	Percentage of Emissions Attributed to Base Metals Smelting
Arsenic	153	201	76
Cadmium	31	33	94
Lead	196	223	88
Mercury	1.7	3	58
Nickel	258	475	54
Total particulate matter	10757	523319	2
Sulphur dioxide	669967	1419520	47

SOURCE: "Base Metals Smelters," *Clean Air Online,* © Her Majesty the Queen in Right of Canada, Environment Canada, 2007. Reproduced with permission of the Ministry of Public Works and Government Services Canada, 2008. http://www.ec.gc.ca/cleanair-airpur/Base_Metals_Smelting-WSB06262AE-1_En.htm

number of key recommendations, including improving federal effluent regulations and updating the Environmental Code of Practice for Mines.

Canada's role in fostering technological development in the mining and metals industry is an important one. Research activities of federal agencies such as the Canada Centre for Mineral and Energy Technology (CANMET) include the pursuit of sustainable development objectives in advancing mineral science. The federal government also supports stronger links between the scientific community and policy organizations to advance sustainability objectives (Government of Canada, 1996a).

The Ottawa-based International Council on Metals and the Environment (ICME) represents major nonferrous and precious-metal producers from five continents. Canadian companies help ICME foster environmentally sustainable economic development by defining environmental management systems for the mining industry, including the ISO 14000 series of international standards.

The Whitehorse Mining Initiative (WMI) was established in 1992 in order to find solutions to economic and environmental realities in the Canadian and global mining industry. Initiated by the Mining Association of Canada, the WMI accord is perceived as an important key to the future of the Canadian mining industry. The accord advocates change toward a sustainable mining industry within the context of a commitment to social and environmental goals and within the framework of an evolving and sustainable Canadian society (Natural Resources Canada, 1996b; see also Box 10–4, pp. 417–418).

FUTURE CHALLENGES

STEWARDSHIP AND REDUCING WASTE

The cooperation demonstrated by the various parties in preparing the Whitehorse Mining Initiative is an important step toward the stewardship of Canadian mineral resources. Successful implementation of the WMI accord would demonstrate to the world Canada's commitment to environmental sustainability through sound economic, social, and ecological frameworks and policies. Efforts made toward improving the stewardship of minerals in Canada, and other parts of the developed world, should be transferable to the developing world.

The stewardship of mineral resources, particularly metals, is demonstrated by efforts to reduce, reuse, and recycle. Recycling extends the efficient use of metals, reduces pressure on landfills and incinerators, and results in energy savings relative to the level of energy inputs required to produce metals from primary sources. In fact, many minerals and metals can be reused indefinitely because of their value, chemical properties, and durability.

With these kinds of characteristics in mind, Germany instituted an extended producer responsibility (EPR) policy through its Packaging Ordinance of 1991. Subsequently debated (and frequently copied) throughout the world, this approach extends "the responsibility of producers for the environmental impacts of their products to the entire product life cycle, and especially for their take-back, recycling, and disposal" (Fishbein, 1998). That is, environmental costs are incorporated into product costs, and the costs of collecting, sorting, and recycling used car parts, computers, televisions, or refrigerators, following their use by consumers, are shifted from municipal governments to private industry. The idea is that making producers (not the public) pay for waste management would give them an incentive to make less wasteful and more economically recyclable products. In addition, EPR was expected to stimulate new recycling technologies and enhance Germany's competitive position as a major exporter of environmental technologies.

Industry responded to the challenge of designing and implementing its own system to take back and recycle packaging waste (the first sector targeted for EPR) by initiating the Dual, or Green Dot, System. In this system, households have two bins, one for regular garbage that they pay their municipality to collect, and one for packaging that the Duales System Deutschland (DSD) collects for free (DSD is the nonprofit company established to operate the recycling system). Between 1991 and 1999, packaging consumption per person decreased from 95.6 kilograms to 82.5 kilograms almost 14 percent. Between 1993 and 1996, packaging recycling increased from 52 to 84 percent. By 1999, 52 million tonnes of packaging had been forwarded for recycling. In 2002, approximately 6.3 million tonnes of garbage were collected from households and containers. Of this total, 5.3 million tonnes of sales packaging were forwarded for recycling. It was estimated that used sales packaging saved 67.5 billion megajoules of primary energy in 2002 while it prevented the emission of 1.5 million tonnes of greenhouse gases. This is the equivalent to the exhaust emissions that

Photo 10–13
Recycling plant in Burlington, Ontario.

Photo 10–14

Plastic containers are recycled into durable picnic tables and benches.

would be caused by city buses driving 1.2 billion kilometres (Der Grüne Punkt, 2003). At least 28 countries now have packaging take-back laws. The Packaging Ordinance also stimulated development of high-tech sorting and recycling technologies using infrared and laser beams. Germany already is licensing some of its new technologies in Japan and expects to expand its exports of environmental technology within Europe and Asia (Fishbein, 1998).

Vehicles are an excellent example of how extended producer responsibility can have an impact on product design. European vehicle producers have been redesigning their cars for disassembly and recycling since the early 1990s. They have increased the recycled content, reduced the number of plastic resins, labelled plastics, marked parts to permit draining of fluids (to avoid contamination of recycling feedstock), and used fasteners that facilitate disassembly. In the United States, where no EPR policies are in place for end-of-life vehicles (ELVs), members of the voluntary Vehicle Recycling Partnership, including Chrysler, Ford, and General Motors, are working on design changes to make it easier to recycle discarded vehicles.

As experience has shown, EPR policies can result in reduced consumption of energy and materials, lower toxicity of products, fewer negative environmental effects of manufacturing, and improved efficiency in resource use. Canada likely has something to gain by considering the contributions EPR policies can make to stewardship as well as to sustainability.

PROTECTION AND MONITORING

With increased global competition in the minerals and metals sector, Canada is striving to maintain its role as a leading mineral producer. To attract foreign investment and retain a competitive edge, domestic policy- and decision-making processes must be responsive to international factors.

Federal initiatives, such as the streamlining of environmental regulations for mining, are intended to promote a positive investment climate. For the mining industry to remain an important component of the Canadian economy, new mineral deposits must be discovered. Because mineral reserves are finite, exploration will advance into more remote regions of the country and conflicts will arise over key wilderness areas. For example, the initial phases of a coal mining operation have been established only 2 kilometres from Jasper National Park, a UNESCO World Heritage Site. The initial operation that has been approved includes the development of a haul road and the first five of 40 proposed open pits. Environmental organizations have taken the federal government to court for failing to obtain approval under the Canadian Environmental Assessment Act and failing to fulfill its requirements under the Migratory Birds Convention Act. Similarly, the Canadian Zinc Corporation is proposing to develop a large high-grade deposit of zinc, lead, and silver at Prairie Creek mine. The mine, built in 1982 but not yet operated, is located in an environmentally sensitive area within the watershed of the South Nahanni River and close to the Nahanni National Park Reserve. This region also is claimed by the Dehcho First Nations as their traditional territory, and no land claim settlement agreement has been reached between Canada and the Dehcho. These examples illustrate the need for constant vigilance in order to maintain the ecological integrity of protected areas and the cultural integrity of Aboriginal peoples.

Aboriginal communities have started to participate actively in providing due diligence. In 2000, a joint community–industry committee in northern Saskatchewan called the Athabasca Working Group (AWG) began to conduct environmental monitoring of uranium developments (Cameco, 2007). Three uranium companies and seven Athabascan communities jointly designed and implemented a community-based environmental monitoring program. Water, sediments, vegetation, air, and fish and animal tissues such as caribou and moose are sampled in and around the communities with the help of local hunters and other residents. Samples are sent to independent laboratories, where samples from "reference" stations outside the region are compared to "effects" stations located within the affected region. To date, the testing has shown no environmental effects from the present uranium mining operations. AWG members also visit uranium mine sites, discuss mine plans and projects, and ensure that mining companies are aware of community issues.

It is important that the exploration and development of new mineral deposits be conducted with ecosystem sustainability in mind. Canada must identify and protect areas of significant terrestrial and marine habitat from mineral and other forms of development. Protected areas strategies should be coordinated with the provinces to ensure critical regions are safeguarded. Where mining is permitted, monitoring strategies should be implemented to assess the effect of development on ecosystem health and community well-being.

Not long after he was called to the Bar, Thomas Berger began working with a small group of lawyers who decided to devote their professional skills to establishing fundamental Aboriginal and treaty rights. Berger's work led to several landmark legal decisions that advanced Aboriginal rights in land and resource management.

In 1971, when he was 38 years old, Berger was appointed to the Supreme Court of British Columbia. In 1974, the Government of Canada appointed him commissioner of the Mackenzie Valley Pipeline Inquiry, whose mandate was to determine the social, economic, and environmental consequences of building a natural gas pipeline from the Arctic to mid-continent. Berger released the inquiry's findings on May 9, 1977, under the title *Northern Frontier, Northern Homeland*. This is the first and perhaps the only royal commission report to make the Canadian bestseller list. It had to be reprinted, it was so popular. The Canadian Broadcasting Corporation described the report as a "deathblow" to the pipeline, since it recommended "a 10-year moratorium on pipeline construction while native land claims are settled, and a permanent ban on any pipeline from Alaska across the northern Yukon" (Canadian Broadcasting Corporation, 2006).

Berger's inquiry did not kill our thirst for oil. Rather, the inquiry became a model for listening to and learning from Aboriginal peoples in managing and developing environmental resources. Following this inquiry, the federal government began to negotiate seriously with the First Nations and Inuit people of the Mackenzie Valley to establish agreements of use and occupancy of the region. These agreements were signed during the 1990s. In these agreements, Aboriginal people have specific entitlements as well as co-management rights and responsibilities related to resource use. As we continue to look north for our energy requirements, Aboriginal people will be important contributors to decisions about resource extraction, transportation, and development and the implications of these activities for Aboriginal people and the environment in which they live.

Thomas Berger resigned from the Supreme Court of British Columbia in 1983 but continued to be involved in work defending Aboriginal rights. He led

Photo 10–15

Thomas Berger listening to testimony in 1975, when he was commissioner of the Mackenzie Valley Pipeline Inquiry.

the Alaska Native Review Commission and was also instrumental in including Aboriginal rights in the Canadian Constitution. For his landmark work, he has received honorary degrees from 13 universities. Justice Berger also received the Order of Canada (1990) and the Order of British Columbia (2004), and was made a Freeman of the City of Vancouver (1992).

The concerns raised by the Berger Inquiry more than 30 years ago continue to be important today as both Aboriginal and non-Aboriginal communities consider the environmental, economic, and social effects of large-scale and rapid energy resource development. Berger's work set the example against which contemporary efforts will be assessed.

SOURCES: *The Berger Report Is Released,* Canadian Broadcasting Corporation, 2006, http://archives.cbc.ca/400i.asp?IDCat=73&IDDos=295&IDCli= 1552&IDLan=1&NoCli=8&type=clip 9; *Northern Frontier —Northern Homeland,* The Empire Club Foundation, n.d., http://www.empireclubfoundation.com/ details.asp?FT=yes&SpeechID=1680; *Thomas R. Berger—Vancouver,* Order of British Columbia, 2007, http://www.protocol.gov.bc.ca/protocol/prgs/obc/ 2004/2004_TBerger.htm; *University History: Honorary Degree Recipients. Honourable Thomas R. Berger,* University of Saskatchewan Archives, 2007, http://www.usask.ca/archives/history/hondegrees.php?id=383&view=detail&keyword=&campuses=

KNOWLEDGE BUILDING

As land-based mines become exhausted and extraction becomes less cost effective, we may turn to the oceans for many of our mineral requirements. The extraction of mineral fuels from the ocean floor has become a major economic activity; however, deep-sea mining of nonfuels remains in its infancy.

However, the industry is growing quickly. The first company to explore the commercial production of gold, copper, zinc and other base minerals on the ocean floor is Nautilus Minerals Inc., a Canadian company, that hopes to produce minerals from its Solwara projects in the territorial waters of Papua New Guinea beginning in 2010. "Nautilus" has a number of ongoing environmental studies intended to support its commitment to undersea mining that will be "conducted in an environmentally responsible manner" and where "all the modern knowledge of the environment can be brought to bear" on their projects (Nautilus Minerals Inc., 2008). As mineral exploration of the seabed increases, we must consider the diverse physical and ecological processes that occur in our oceans and proceed with development on a sustainable basis. Development decisions, both on land and in the ocean, should be based on the precautionary principle.

Research efforts in the mining field focus on all aspects of mineral production, from exploration to processing and site decommissioning. Recently, we have seen important scientific advances in controlling toxic emissions and acid mine drainage. However, much more work needs to be done in the areas of waste management, aquatic effects monitoring, and reduced energy consumption. For instance, there are over 10 000 active, abandoned, and orphaned tailings sites in Canada (see Table 10–3 on page 428). There is no comprehensive inventory of the risks these sites pose. This is one of the significant gaps in knowledge about the environmental effects of mining that needs to be filled.

Coordination of research efforts through national partnerships may increase technical innovation and allow programs to be delivered with maximum efficiency. International collaboration and the sharing of expertise are essential for meeting the challenge of sustainable development, particularly in the developing world. As a leader in mining, Canada has an important role to play in fostering the global sustainability of mining operations by establishing sound industrial practices, and continual improvements through vigorous application of research, technology, regulation, planning, and corporate and public policy.

Chapter Questions

1. If mining operations occur on only 0.03 percent of Canada's land surface, why is there so much environmental concern about them?

2. Imagine your friend saying, "I am more concerned about running out of clean water for drinking than running out of coal for energy." Why might that be the case?

3. Which of the four phases of mineral development do you think has the greatest environmental impact? Why?

4. What mineral resources are extracted in your local area and in your region? What mining methods are used? What laws and regulations require restoration of the landscape after mining is completed? How stringently are these laws and regulations enforced? What parallels are there between the impacts and regulation of urban development and those of mining?

5. Discuss several harmful environmental effects that mining and processing minerals have on atmospheric, aquatic, and land environments.

6. A mining company is coming to town offering new job opportunities for residents in your community. As the local mayor or band leader, what kinds of issues would you like to negotiate?

7. Reusing and recycling mineral and metal resources is one way to extend the availability of these nonrenewable resources. What kinds of mineral and metal recycling occur in your educational institution? In your community? What more could be done in your community or region to encourage reuse and recycling of mineral resources?

8. What are the similarities and differences between the mines developed by Canadian companies in northern Canada and mines developed by Canadian companies in South America? How does public opinion in each country affect the outcome of mining activities?

9. Mining contributes to economic well-being, while mining activities, both directly and indirectly, affect economies, society, and environments. How do you balance these three elements in your definition of sustainable mining?

BHP Billiton. (2003). *Processing diamonds.* http://ekati.bhpbilliton. com/common/downloads/ProcessingDiamonds.pdf

BHP Billiton. (2006). *Annual report on northern employment and spending, 2006 Operations Phase—Ekati diamond mine.* http://ekati. bhpbilliton.com/common/downloads/2006_SEA_AR.pdf

BHP Billiton. (2007). *BHP Billiton sustainability report: Full report 2007.* http://www.bhpbilliton.com/bbContentRepository/200710338624/ sustainabilityreport.pdf

BHP Billiton Minerals Canada Ltd. & DIA Met Minerals. (1995). *NWT diamonds project: Environmental impact statement/BHP; DIA MET.* Vancouver: BHP Diamonds.

British Columbia Spaces for Nature. (n.d.). http://www.sunshine.net/ www/0/sn0004/bc-miningwatch/

Cameco. (2007). *Athabasca environmental monitoring.* http://www. cameco.com/sustainable_development/clean_environment/ awg.php

Department of Indian and Northern Affairs. (1996a). *Canada's diamond mine project: Canada's gross domestic product to grow by $6.2 billion.* Backgrounder #3. http://www.INAC.ca

Department of Indian and Northern Affairs. (1996b). *Canada's diamond mine project: Environmental agreement.* Backgrounder #7. http://www.INAC.ca

Department of Indian and Northern Affairs. (1996c). *Canada's diamond mine project: Land claims near the BHP site.* Backgrounder #2. http://www.INAC.ca

Der Grüne Punkt. (2003). *Duales System Deutschland AG.* http:// www.gruener-punkt.de

Fishbein, B. K. (1998). *EPR: What does it mean? Where is it headed?* http://www.informinc.org/eprarticle.htm

Freeman, A. (1996). Government approves largest diamond mine in North America. http://www.igc.apc.org

Government of Canada. (1996a). *The minerals and metals policy of the Government of Canada.* Ottawa: Minister of Public Works and Government Services.

Government of Canada. (1996b). *The state of Canada's environment— 1996.* Ottawa: Supply and Services Canada.

Government of the Northwest Territories. (2000). *GNWT signs off on Diavik Environmental Agreement.* http://www.gov.nt.ca/ RWED/99news.htm#diaviksignsoff

Government of the Northwest Territories, Investment and Economic Analysis. (2004). *NWT economic trends,* Issue 2, 2nd quarter. http://www.gov.nt.ca/RWED/iea/index.htm

Holden, W. N. (2003). *The role of environmental protection as a loca-tional determinant of the nonferrous metals mining industry: A synec-dochic investigation of a stylized fact.* Unpublished PhD dissertation, University of Calgary.

Institute for Global Communications. (1996). *Papua New Guinea: BHP agrees to settlement for Ok Tedi spill.* http://www.igc.apc.org

Johnson, E. (1999). Canadian mining companies build a shaky reputa-tion abroad. *Alternatives Journal, 25*(4), 29.

Kennett, S. A. (1999). *A guide to impact benefits agreements.* Calgary: Canadian Institute of Resources Law.

Mackasey, W.O. (2000). *Abandoned mines in Canada.* http://www. miningwatch.ca/publications/Mackasey_abandoned_mines.html

Marshall, I. B. (1982). *Mining, land use and the environment: A Canadian overview.* Ottawa: Environment Canada. Land use in Canada series, p. 22.

McNamee, K. (1999). Undermining wilderness: The Canadian mining industry is abandoning its support for a national network of protected areas. *Alternatives Journal, 25*(4), 24–31.

National Parks Conservation Association. (2004, Summer). Coal developers eyeing Glacier's Flathead Valley. *National Parks Magazine.* http://www.npca.org/magazine/2004/summer/ news3.html

Natural Resources Canada. (n.d.). *Canada's minerals and metals.* Video production. http:www.nrcan.gc.ca/mms/video/ vhp_e.htm

Natural Resources Canada. (1996a). *Canadian mining facts.* http://www.nrcan.gc.ca

Natural Resources Canada. (1996b). *Whitehorse mining initiative.* http://www.emr.ca/ms/sdev/wmi_e.htm

Natural Resources Canada. (2000). *Canadian mining facts.* http://www.nrcan.gc.ca/mms/efab/mmsd/facts/canada.htm

Natural Resources Canada. (2002). *Minerals and metals sector, year in review.* http://www.nrcan.gc.ca/mms/cmy/2002revu/ con_e.htm

Natural Resources Canada. (2003a). *Canadian mineral production demonstrates continued strength in 2002.* Information Bulletin, Mineral Production. http://mmsd1.mms.nrcan.gc.ca/mmsd/ production/default_e.asp

Natural Resources Canada. (2003b). *Canadian mining facts.* http://mmsdl.mms.nrcan.gc.ca/mmsd/facts/canFact

Natural Resources Canada. (2007a). *Canadian minerals yearbook— 2005.* General review. http://www.nrcan.gc.ca/mms/cmy/ content/2005/01e.pdf

National Resources Canada. (2007b). *Information bulletin 2007: Employment.* http://www.nrcan.gc.ca/mms/pdf/employment- 2007_e.pdf

Natural Resources Canada. (2007c). *Sustainable management and rehabilitation of mine sites for decision support.* http://sst.nrcan. gc.ca/2002_2006/sdki/mine/site_rehab_e.php

Natural Resources Canada. (2008a). *Canadian diamonds: Mining our way toward a responsible future.* http://www.nrcan-rncan.gc.ca/ com/elements/issues/06/diam-eng.php

Natural Resources Canada. (2008b). *Information bulletin: Mineral pro-duction.* http://www.nrcan-rncan/gc/ca/mms/pdf/minprod-08_e.pdf

Natural Resources Canada. (2008c). *Production of Canada's leading minerals.* http://mmsd1mms.nrcan.gc.ca/mmsd/ data/2008/08MTLY01.pdf

Nautilus **Minerals Inc. (2008).** Environmental. http://www. nautilusminerals.com/s/Projects-Environment.asp

Nelson, J. (1996, March 14). Environmental review process put under pressure. *Victoria Times Colonist,* p. A5.

Newcott, W. R. (1994). Tatshenshini-Alsek Wilderness Park: Rivers of conflict. *National Geographic, 185*(2), 122–134.

Northwest Territories Industry, Tourism, and Investment. (2006). *Diamond facts: 2006 diamond industry report, Northwest Territories Canada.* http://www.iti.gov.nt.ca/diamond/pdf/diamondfacts_ 2006.pdf

Padilla, C. (2005, April). Canadian mining exploitation in Chile, com-munity rights and the environment: Recommendations for Canadian legislation. Prepared for Mining Watch Canada. http://www. miningwatch.ca/updir/Chile_case_study.pdf

Principles and goals of the Whitehorse Mining Initiative. (1995–96, Fall/Winter). *Northern Perspectives, 23*(3–4), 9–11.

Shrimpton, S., & Storey, K. (1988). *The urban miner: Long distance commuting to work in the mining sector and its implications for the Canadian north.* Paper presented to the Canadian Urban and Housing Studies Conference. Institute of Urban Studies, University of Winnipeg.

U.S. Geological Survey, Energy Resource Surveys Program. (1997). *Coalbed methane—an untapped energy resource and an environmental concern.* USGS Fact Sheet FS-019-97. http://energy .usgs.gov/factsheets/Coalbed/coalmeth.html

Warhurst, A. (1994). *Environmental degradation from mining and mineral processing in developing countries: Corporate responsibilities and national policies.* Paris: Organisation for Economic Cooperation and Development.

Weber, R. (1997, July 18). Diamond mine rises from tundra. *Calgary Herald*, p. A8.

Wiesner, D. (1995). *The environmental impact assessment process.* Dorset: Prism Press.

Wismer, S. (1996). The nasty game. *Alternatives, 22*(4), 10–17.

World Wildlife Fund. (1997, January 13). *WWF Canada withdraws court action on BHP diamond mine.* News release.

Young, A. (1996, October 22). *Achieving investor security through environmentally sustainable mining.* Speech presented to the Fraser Institute.

Photo 10–16

Tapping the power available in underground hot water sources has been described as akin to mining energy, the subject explored next in Chapter 11. New Zealanders have been "mining energy" at the Wairakei geothermal power station since 1958. The greater the amount of energy a country uses from renewable sources, the better its global renewable energy ranking. See Canada's results in the Canada and the World section.

Chapter Contents

*"The continuing prosperity and high
quality of life of Canadians depend on
a secure supply of affordable energy,
produced with minimal impact on the
natural environment. Our ability to
sustain this supply will depend on two
factors. First, there must be a critical
mass of people with the right knowledge and a passion for achieving this
goal. Second, these people must be able
to become experts at collaboration,
applying their diverse skills, perspectives, and interests to the creation of
technological breakthroughs.... When
it comes to production of this energy,
'business as usual' is not an option.'*

Len Bolger & Eddy Isaacs (2003, pp. 58, 61)

Chapter Objectives

After studying this chapter you should be able to

- understand the characteristics of energy resources in Canada

- identify a range of human uses of energy resources

- describe the effects of human activities related to the production and use of Canada's energy resources

- appreciate the complexity and interrelatedness of energy issues

- outline Canadian and international responses to energy issues

- discuss challenges to sustainable energy production and use in Canada

INTRODUCTION

CANADIANS AND ENERGY

Canadians use energy every day to heat our homes, travel to work, and cook our meals. Business and industry depend on abundant, reliable sources of energy to produce goods and deliver services. While we may change our preferences for the products we consume, we cannot choose to abandon the use of energy. In fact, many of us take our use of energy for granted. For example, when we flip on a light switch, we tend not to think about the coal or hydropower that may have been used to produce electricity. However, this is not the case in many parts of the world, where electricity is considered a luxury and much thought is given to how to obtain light (see Box 11–1 on the next page).

While our need for energy may be constant, our sources of energy are variable. Canada is fortunate to have an abundant supply of fossil fuels, and these have provided us with most of our energy requirements over the last century. Although a driving force behind our economy, the production and consumption of fossil fuels affects our environment. Concern over climate change and air pollution (see Chapter 5) provides an impetus for rethinking how energy is produced and delivered. Consumer demand for "green" energy, such as wind power, is leading governments and businesses to invest in renewable energy resources and solutions.

Photo 11–1

If electricity for electric vehicles (EVs) is produced by wind and solar technologies, these vehicles are pollution-free. Solar-powered cars, such as this one shown crossing the finish line, competed in the 2005 North America Solar Challenge race from Austin, Texas, to Calgary, Alberta. Five Canadian teams participated in this race, the longest solar car race in the world (4015 kilometres), demonstrating the potential of solar technology in transportation. Several hybrid gasoline/electric vehicles are available from major automobile manufacturers, and new zero-emission options such as compressed air vehicles are close to commercial production.

BOX 11–1
LIGHT UP THE WORLD GLOBAL INITIATIVE

The Light Up the World (LUTW) Foundation was founded by Dr. Dave Irvine-Halliday, a professor of electrical and computer engineering at the University of Calgary, following a 1997 visit to rural Nepal. Alerted to the fact that schools and homes lacked adequate lighting, Dr. Irvine-Halliday set out to find a simple, safe, healthy, reliable, and economic source of light for the villagers.

In many parts of the world, rural homes are lit by kerosene wick lamps and, to a lesser extent, by candles or resin-soaked twigs—if they are lit at all. Each of these forms of lighting constitutes a fire hazard and leads to serious and well-documented health problems in poorly ventilated homes. Dr. Irvine-Halliday recognized the potential, afforded through the development of white light–emitting diodes (WLEDs), to bring a bright and affordable source of light to homes that otherwise would be unable to acquire traditional electrical grid–based lighting. Batteries that supply power to the WLED lamps may be recharged using forms of renewable energy, such as human-powered pedal generators, solar **photovoltaic** panels, pico hydro and wind generators, and biomass, biodiesel, and biofuel cells. A child is able to read a book with the light emitted by a single 0.1-watt WLED lamp, and a room can be lit to an acceptable level using a 1-watt WLED lamp (life expectancy of 40 years).

Since electrical energy is very costly in the developing world, LUTW's initial objective is not to light up entire rooms or homes to North American standards of illumination but to provide adequate light to those areas where it is most useful—essentially, task lighting. As a community development tool, Solid State Lighting (SSL; the WLED lamp) has had an enormous impact on the social, economic, and physical well-being of many people who live in poverty-stricken parts of the world. In many areas, the one-time cost of the LUTW's SSL system is approximately equal to what people are spending on fuel-based lighting in a single year! The ability to read and study after dark, and to operate cottage industries at night, using either fixed or mobile task lighting helps people improve their education and augment their income.

From the initial and subsequent projects in Nepal, LUTW's activities have grown to include lighting initiatives in Africa (Ghana, South Africa, Virunga/Bwindi Gorilla), Asia (Papua New Guinea, Tibet, India, Pakistan, Sri Lanka, Philippines), the Middle East (Afghanistan), and Latin America (Costa Rica, Dominican Republic, Ecuador, Mexico, Peru). As part of the legacy for Captain Nichola Goddard (a captain in the 1st Regiment of the Royal Canadian Horse Artillery when she was killed while serving in Afghanistan), LUTW is working with her family, school children, and people across Canada to raise funds to light up 1820 first aid posts in Papua New Guinea (where Nichola was born).

Photo 11–2
Children reading by the light of a 6-diode WLED lamp at Child Haven Orphanage, Bhaktapur, Nepal.

In 2004, LUTW implemented its first pilot project in Canada to install and evaluate the potential of the foundation's WLED lamps in the off-grid First Nation community of Xeni Gwet'in (located in the Chilcotin region of British Columbia). Participants in this project replaced their flashlights and propane lamps with WLED lamps, saving an estimated $220 per household annually in disposable battery costs alone. LUTW is in the early planning stage of a comprehensive University of Calgary fourth-year engineering student SSL project for multiple First Nation communities.

Partnering with international NGOs and solar and LED companies around the world, and through the support of interested individuals, host country organizations, and international foundations and grants, the foundation has lit approximately 20 000 homes, schools, clinics, hospitals, temples, churches, and mosques in 42 countries. The LUTW Foundation believes that with a virtual *one-time* cost of US$150 for the WLED lighting system, compared to the US$40 to $200 *annual* cost of kerosene, the prospect of providing almost permanent lighting systems for the world's 2 billion people who do not have electricity is a challenging, yet reachable, goal. Since the LUTW continues to work to provide the capacity for host communities to continue, independently, after initial projects are completed, the foundation is helping to ensure that lighting, literacy, equality, and economic and social progress are inseparable allies.

SOURCES: Adapted from text provided by Dr. Dave Irvine-Halliday, the Light Up the World Foundation website (www.lutw.org), and LUTW's newsletter, *Enlightenment*. Courtesy of Dave Irvine-Halliday.

This chapter examines some of the obstacles in adopting new energy sources into our energy use mix. Our reliance on nonrenewable fossil fuels is discussed, as are other energy supplies such as nuclear and hydroelectric power. The environmental effects of energy production and use are investigated, along with steps taken to improve energy efficiency. We begin by considering Canada as a producer and consumer of energy.

HUMAN ACTIVITIES AND IMPACTS ON NATURAL ENVIRONMENTS

ENERGY SUPPLY AND DEMAND IN CANADA

Canada's high standard of living is attributed partly to a reliable and relatively low-cost supply of energy. Because of such factors as our cold climate, vast distances (which encourage car use), and an energy-intensive industrial base, Canadians are the second-largest per capita consumers of energy in the world (Statistics Canada, 2006). In 2004, Canada's energy consumption was 363 gigajoules per person; our energy consumption has been growing an average of 1 percent per year since the mid-1970s (Statistics Canada, 2006). Canadians spent almost $135 billion in 2004 to heat and cool their homes and offices and to operate their appliances, cars, and industrial processes (Natural Resources Canada, 2006b). Directly employing 290 400 people in 2005, the energy sector plays a major role in the Canadian economy. Consistently during the past four decades, the energy sector constituted 6 to 10 percent of Canada's gross domestic product (GDP); in 2005, the energy industry directly accounted for 9.9 percent of Canada's GDP (National Energy Board, 2007a). Figure 11–1 illustrates Canada's primary energy consumption from 1958 to 2004 as well as growth in Canada's GDP during those years. Our energy consumption per dollar of GDP has been declining since the 1974 oil crisis, largely as a result of two factors: (1) energy conservation practices and improved energy-efficient technologies have reduced the energy intensity of the economy, and (2) energy consumption has increased at a slower rate than the GDP, causing a decline in the energy consumption per dollar ratio (Statistics Canada, 2002).

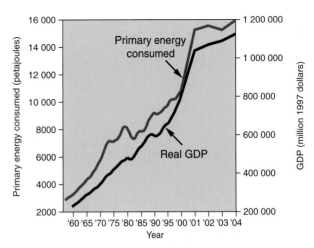

Figure 11–1

Primary energy consumption in Canada and GDP, 1958 to 2004

[1] Energy units: A joule is the international unit of measure for energy. The energy content of a 40-litre tank of gasoline is about 1.36 billion joules. One gigajoule (GJ) is 10^9 (1 000 000 000) times larger than one joule, one petajoule (PJ) is 10^{15} (1 000 000 000 000 000) times larger than one joule, and one exajoule (EJ) is 10^{18} (1 000 000 000 000 000 000) times larger than one joule. One petajoule represents the amount of energy consumed by a town of 3700 people in one year for all uses, including transportation, housing, local services, and industry, while one exajoule is roughly equivalent to 28 billion litres of motor gasoline.

[2] These data exclude the use of wood and wastes as energy sources.

SOURCES: *Human Activity and the Environment: Annual Statistics 2006,* Cat. no. 16-201-XPE, Statistics Canada, 2006, Ottawa: Minister of Industry; *Energy Efficiency Trends in Canada 1990 to 2004,* Natural Resources Canada, 2006. Reprinted by permission of Statistics Canada.

Throughout Canada's history, different types of energy have dominated. About the time of Confederation, wood accounted for almost 90 percent of Canada's energy market, while today wood accounts for less than 5 percent. The use of coal for energy peaked about 1920, when it commanded 75 percent of the market. By 1996, the market share for coal had declined to roughly 12 percent. With industrialization and the widespread adoption of the combustion engine, oil (with a market share of 60 percent) became the dominant energy source during the 1960s. In 2004, the surge in natural gas production caused the market share of oil to drop to about 35 percent, while natural gas accounted for 43 percent of the energy market. Figures 11–2 and 11–3 (next page) illustrate changes over time in production and consumption of primary energy in Canada. **Alternative energy** sources, such as solar and wind power, are increasing their market share as the technologies become more viable. (See Box 11–2, p. 443, for a snapshot of energy in Canada and the world.)

HOW DO WE USE ENERGY?

Energy use can be described as primary or secondary. **Primary energy** (energy as it is first produced)

Photo 11–3

In Canada, long corridors of transmission lines carry power from generating facilities to consumer markets.

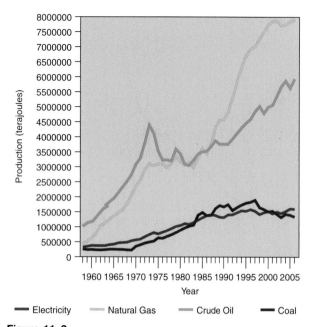

Figure 11–2

Canadian primary energy production by source, 1958–2006

SOURCE: *Human Activity and the Environment: Annual Statistics 2005,*
Cat. no. 16-201-XIE, Statistics Canada, 2005, Ottawa: Minister of Industry;
Tables 125-0002 and 128-0009, Statistics Canada CANSIM database,
http://cansim2.statcan.ca.

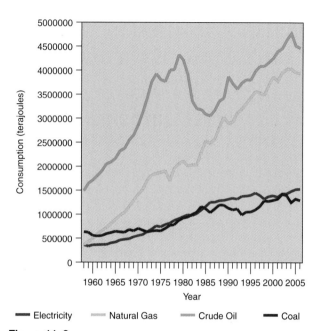

Figure 11–3

Changes in primary types of energy consumed in Canada,
1958–2006

NOTE: One terajoule is 10^{12} (1 000 000 000 000) times larger than one joule.

SOURCES: *Human Activity and the Environment: Annual Statistics 2005,*
Cat. no. 16-201-XIE, Statistics Canada, 2005, Ottawa: Minister of
Industry; *Human Activity and the Environment: Annual Statistics 2006,*
Cat. no. 16-201-XPE, Statistics Canada, 2006, Ottawa: Minister of Industry;
Tables 125-0002 and 128-0009, Statistics Canada CANSIM database,
http://cansim2.statcan.ca.

represents the total requirement for all users of energy, including energy used by final consumers, energy used in transforming one energy form to another (e.g., coal to electricity), energy used by suppliers in providing energy to the market (e.g., fuel to run pipeline compressors), as well as imported energy minus exported energy. The major forms of primary energy in Canada are fossil fuel hydrocarbons (coal, crude oil, natural gas, natural gas liquids) and electricity from nuclear and hydroelectric power plants. From 1990 to 2004, total primary energy use in Canada increased 27.9 percent from 9743 to 12 463 **petajoules**. Of the energy available in Canada in 2004, the industrial sector (including pulp and paper, metal smelting, steel making, mining, cement manufacturing, and petrochemical industries) consumed the most (38.4 percent), transportation used 28.9 percent, residential consumers used 16.6 percent, commercial and institutional users consumed 13.7 percent, and agriculture used 2.4 percent (Natural Resources Canada, 2006b).

Secondary energy (produced by processing primary energy, such as electricity produced from coal, and gasoline from crude oil) is energy used by Canadians (final consumers) to heat and cool their homes and workplaces and to operate their appliances, vehicles, and factories. The secondary, or end-use, sector comprises the residential, agricultural, commercial/institutional, industrial, and transportation sectors. Between

1990 and 2004, secondary energy use increased by 23 percent (from 6951 to 8543 petajoules). As a result, greenhouse gas emissions related to secondary energy (including GHGs related to electricity generation), increased 24 percent, from 408 to 505 megatonnes (see Figure 11–4 on page 445) (Natural Resources Canada, 2006b, 2006d).

Net Useful Energy

It takes energy to produce energy and, as described in Chapter 3, converting energy sources into useful energy products leads to waste. One example is the one-third efficiency of converting coal into electricity, and the subsequent losses in transmission of electricity to consumers. In addition to the waste that comes from the degradation of energy to low-quality energy (the second law of energy), some waste is brought about by avoidable human practices.

Changing the way we use energy to meet our needs (energy conservation) and using the most efficient equipment we can (energy efficiency) are essential actions if we are to meet future energy needs and help transform energy markets toward more energy-efficient products and practices. Taking the bus, walking to the corner store, and joining a car-sharing service help to reduce our energy consumption and energy waste, and also help to address climate change effects of GHGs. Upgrading appliances to more energy-efficient models

and ensuring our homes are properly insulated are two actions we can take to improve energy efficiency.

The Energy Star program is one approach to improving energy efficiency in Canada. Energy Star is

---

BOX 11-2
A SNAPSHOT OF ENERGY IN CANADA AND THE WORLD

A. The Global Context

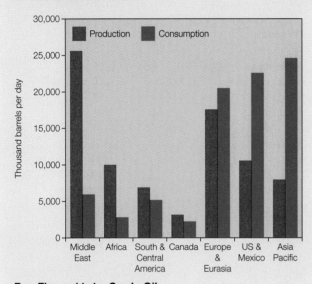

Box Figure 11–1a Crude Oil

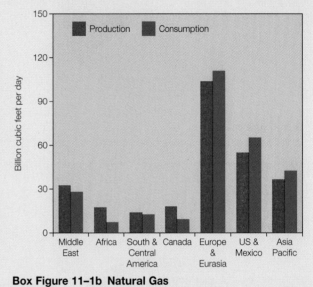

Box Figure 11–1b Natural Gas

Global production and consumption of oil and natural gas, by area, 2006

SOURCE: Data from *BP Statistical Review of World Energy, June 2007,* pages 8 and 11. HYPERLINK "http://www.bp.com/statisticalreview" www.bp.com/statisticalreview

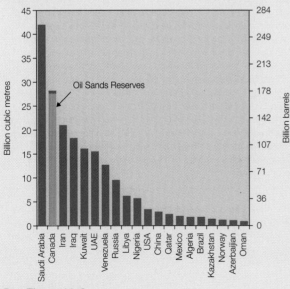

Box Figure 11–2
Estimated proved oil reserves, 2005

SOURCE: Data from *BP Statistical Review of World Energy, June 2007,* pages 8 and 11. www.bp.com/statisticalreview

- Saudi Arabia is the world's top crude oil producer at 1.7 million cubic metres per day (10.8 million barrels per day); Canada ranks seventh (16 refineries produce about 1 343 595 barrels of conventional crude oil per day and 1.2 million barrels of oil from oil sands per day)

- The United States is the world's largest market for oil, constituting almost 25 percent of total oil demand (3.27 million cubic metres per day, or 20.6 million barrels per day). Canada accounts for 2.5 percent of total world oil demand (353 000 cubic metres per day, or 2.2 million barrels per day)

- 60 percent of the world's natural gas reserves are located in Russia, Iran, and Qatar. In 2006, Russia remained the world's largest producer of natural gas, producing 21 percent (1.67 mil-lion cubic metres per day); the United States was second, while Canada ranked as the world's third-largest producer (over 6 percent; 20 billion cubic feet of natural gas daily)

(continued)

BOX 11-2
(CONTINUED)

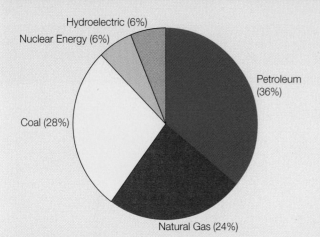

Box Figure 11–3

World primary energy consumption by fuel type, 2006

SOURCE: Data from *BP Statistical Review of World Energy, June 2007,* pages 8 and 11. HYPERLINK "http://www.bp.com/statisticalreview" www.bp.com/statisticalreview

B. The Canadian Context

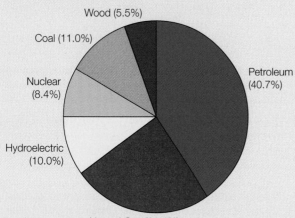

Box Figure 11–4

Canadian primary energy consumption by fuel type, 2004

SOURCE: Data from *Energy Use Data Handbook 1990 and 1998 to 2004.* Natural Resources Canada, August 2006. http://www.nrcan.gc.ca/statistics/energy/default.html

BOX TABLE 11–1
CANADIAN ENERGY RESOURCES

Energy Resource	Year	Reserves or Potential	Production or Capacity
Oil	2005	4.2 billion barrels	134 billion barrels/day
Oil sands	2006	173 billion barrels	1.26 million barrels/day
Natural gas	2005	57.9 trillion cubic feet (2005)	20 billion cubic feet/day (2006)
Coal	2005	10 billion tonnes (2005)	62 928 kilo-tonnes (2006)
Nuclear	2006	92.4 billion kilowatt-hours	92 000 000 gigawatt-hours (electrical) net
Hydroelectric	2006	163 173 megawatts	143 227 173 megawatt-hours
Wind	2007	>40 gigawatts	1 587 megawatts
Solar	2006	70 gigawatts	22 836 kilowatts
Tidal	2006	3 gigawatts	20 megawatts/day
Wave	2006	10–16 gigawatts	0

SOURCES: *Alberta's Oil Sands 2006,* Alberta Department of Energy, 2007, http://www.energy.gov.ab.ca/News/1032.asp; *Canada Statistics,* Canadian Centre for Energy Information, 2007, http://www.centreforenergy.com/FactsStats/statistics.asp?template=5,0; Canadian Industrial and End-Use Data and Analysis Centre, 2004, http://www.cieedac.sfu.ca/CIEEDACweb/; *Environmental Solutions through Technology Innovation and Partnerships,* Environment Canada, 2003, Gatineau, QC: Author; *Canada's Energy Future: Reference Case and Scenarios to 2030,* National Energy Board, 2007, Calgary: Author; *Statistics on Natural Resources—Statistics and Facts on Energy,* Natural Resources Canada, 2007, http://www.nrcan.gc.ca/statistics/energy/default.html; *Energy Statistics Handbook, January to March 2007,* Statistics Canada, 2007, Ottawa: Author; *Coal,* K. Stone, 2006, *Canadian Minerals Yearbook,* 2006, http://www.nrcan.gc.ca/ms/cmy/2006CMY_e.htm; *Electrical Production by Canadian Nuclear Reactors in 2006,* J. Whitlock, 2008, *Canadian Nuclear FAQ,* http://www.nuclearfaq.ca/nuke-gen-monthly-2006.htm; *World Nuclear Power Reactors 2006–08 and Uranium Requirements,* World Nuclear Association, 2008, http://www.world-nuclear.org/

NOTE: Although Canada adopted the metric system in the 1970s, American measurements—barrel for crude oil, thousand cubic feet for natural gas—are used frequently by the industry and the media. There are 159 litres (42 US gallons) in one barrel of oil. One cubic metre of natural gas is 1 000 litres, roughly the same volume of a large office desk, or about 6.3 US barrels.

the easily recognized, international symbol of energy efficiency for producers and consumers of homes, appliances, and energy-using equipment. The Energy Star symbol identifies products that are high-efficiency performers in their category, including appliances; residential heating and cooling equipment; office equipment such as computers; consumer electronics such as TVs, VCRs, audio equipment, and DVD products; and lighting equipment

Figure 11–4

Greenhouse gas volumes

One tonne of carbon dioxide (CO_2) emissions would fill the volume of approximately two average-sized houses in Canada—and one megatonne would fill about 2 million average-sized houses.

SOURCE: *Energy Efficiency Trends in Canada 1990 to 2004,* Natural Resources Canada, 2006, Ottawa: Author.

such as compact fluorescent light bulbs. In Ontario and Saskatchewan, new homes may be built to Energy Star technical specifications.

Energy Star–labelled products must meet and exceed minimum Canadian federal energy efficiency standards (e.g., to qualify for the Energy Star mark, standard-sized clothes washers in 2007 were to be at least 36 percent more efficient than the minimum federal energy performance standard specified in Canada's Energy Efficiency Regulations). As a consumer, if you were to choose an Energy Star product, not only would you save money on energy costs, you also would help the environment—needing less energy to operate Energy Star equipment helps reduce air pollution and GHGs (by requiring less energy to be produced). In Canada, the Energy Star program is promoted by the Office of Energy Efficiency, a division of Natural Resources Canada.

Another important action we can take to improve overall energy efficiency is to implement full-cost accounting to ensure that environmental, economic, and social costs are accounted for in decisions relating to land, resource use, species depletion, and economics of energy (Taylor, 1994). Full-cost accounting principles suggest that market prices of oil should reflect accurately the actual costs of production, distribution, consumption, and environmental impacts. In 2002, for instance, 20 percent of Canada's GHGs came from the oil and gas industry, but this impact was not included in the accounting. If market prices were to reflect true costs, perhaps alternative energy sources such as wind power

Photo 11–4

Only manufacturers and retailers whose products meet the Energy Star criteria are permitted to use the Energy Star symbol on their labels.

would become more viable. Currently such renewable sources of energy have limited markets, while nonrenewable sources such as oil and gas receive significant government subsidies and incentives. Investments in oil sands, for instance, received significant tax concessions: companies could write off all capital costs for a project before they paid any federal income taxes on the profits earned from the project, thus making such investments more attractive than they would be otherwise (see Box 11–3, p. 451). If these financial advantages were removed, would petroleum resources continue to dominate our energy industry?

Net useful energy is the usable amount of energy available from an energy source over its lifetime. To determine the net useful energy of an energy resource, all losses are subtracted, including those automatically wasted (second energy law) and those wasted in the discovery, processing, and transportation phases. For example, if 10 units of coal energy are required to supply 15 units of electricity, the net useful energy gain is 5 units of energy. If it takes 15 units of coal energy to produce 10 units of electricity, there is a net energy loss of 5 units over the lifetime of the system. Presently, oil has a relatively high net useful energy, as it is readily accessible and easily transported; however, as deposits decline and their locations become more remote, net useful energy of oil will decrease. The concept of net useful energy is important in understanding why governments, utilities, and private-sector suppliers (and even individual consumers) are exploring the efficiency of alternative technologies and considering new incentive and regulatory regimes.

Environmental concern over energy use is reflected throughout the life cycle of the energy source. During exploration and production, there is often disturbance to the land where facilities are located, conflict with other land uses, and the risk of spills or accidents. For example, large-scale wind farms place a large footprint on land, and little is known about the biophysical impacts of wind farms on microclimatology and hydrology as wind patterns change. Delivering energy to users requires some form of transport (such as oil through pipelines or electricity through power lines) that may be intrusive to natural ecosystems. In addition, the risk of accidents or spills increases as the distance or number of transfers increases. At the point of consumption, burning fossil fuels or wood releases emissions that affect air quality, contribute to acid precipitation, and influence global climate. At the end of the life cycle, finding a safe long-term disposal solution for radioactive waste is one of the most controversial issues in energy decision making today (see Box 11–6, p. 463).

ENERGY RESOURCES

Canada's economic well-being is tied to the energy sector, and relatively inexpensive and abundant energy has been

CHAPTER 11: ENERGY

Photo 11–5a
Thirty cars carry 40 people …

Photo 11–5b

paramount to the Canadian way of life. As Canada begins to emerge as an energy superpower, however, Canadians realize that our well-being is achieved with certain social, environmental, and economic effects. Construction of large energy developments, or megaprojects, has been heralded by government and industry as critical in helping to secure Canada's national and international economic success. Government-supported ventures, such as offshore oil and gas projects, oil sands development in Alberta, and the James Bay hydroelectric project in Quebec, have offered the promise of jobs and economic security for residents of the respective regions. But at what cost have, and will, these energy developments occur? Are communities associated with energy developments, and Canadians in general, realizing the full benefits and understanding the full costs of developing our energy resources?

The following sections review some of the societal and economic benefits and environmental challenges of Canada's primary energy resources: fossil fuels (oil, heavy oil, coal, and natural gas), hydroelectricity, and nuclear power. Selected alternative energy sources also

are considered. Offshore oil and gas operations and development of the Alberta oil sands are considered, as exploitation of these resources is changing the face of Canada as well as Canada's global energy position.

Fossil Fuels: Oil

Oil is a mixture of hydrocarbon compounds, those containing hydrogen, carbon, and other elements. Most oil is found in sedimentary rock located deep below the surface of the land and sea floor; Canada's most important sedimentary basins are illustrated in Figure 11–5 on the next page. Most **hydrocarbons** are the remains of prehistoric animals, forests, and sea-floor life, hence the name **fossil fuels**. Buried in layers of sediment, these plants and animals decomposed very slowly and eventually were converted into crude oil.

The world's most important traded commodity, oil has a high energy value per unit of volume. However, fossil fuel combustion releases gases that contribute to climate change, acid precipitation, and photochemical smog. If

Photo 11–5c
… but one bus carries 40 passengers and takes up a lot less space.

Photo 11–5d

spilled, crude oil and other petroleum products often are toxic to wildlife and in some cases can result in drastic changes to wildlife ecosystems. Although we tend to hear only about the largest oil spills, every day in Canada there are about 12 reported spills of 4000 litres or more that flow into the oceans on our three coasts, and one of those spills occurs in navigable waters (Anonymous, 2005). An oil spill can occur at any point from production to consumption; accidental spills and deliberate discharges (illegally dumped bilge wastes from ships) are most likely to occur during transportation.

Offshore Oil and Gas Development   The offshore oil and gas industry has spent billions of dollars to conduct seismic surveys and drill test wells in exploring the petroleum potential of sedimentary basins beneath the ocean floors off Canada's Arctic, Atlantic, and Pacific coasts (see Figure 11–5). Exploration from the 1960s to the 1980s in

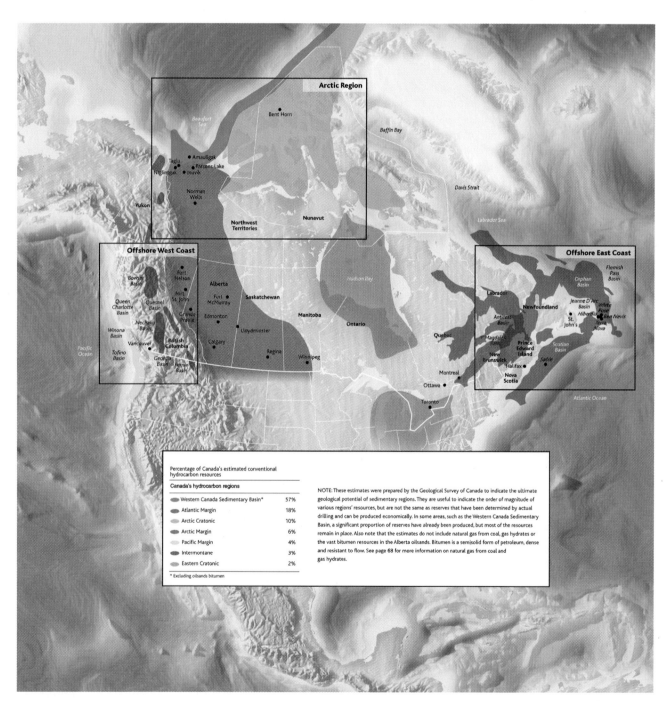

Figure 11–5

Canada's seven hydrocarbon regions and areas of offshore drilling

SOURCE: *Canada's Evolving Offshore Oil and Gas Industry,* R. Bott, 2004, Calgary: © Canadian Centre for Energy Information, p. 3.

the Northwest Territories and Nunavut revealed substantial crude oil and natural gas reserves, including discovery of the Amauligak oilfield under the Beaufort Sea, one of the largest crude oil discoveries in North America during the past three decades.

Future development of Arctic offshore oil and gas reserves depends partly on the construction of safe and economical transportation systems, potentially including pipelines, to ship these resources to markets in southern Canada, in the United States, and throughout the world. However, the World-Wide Fund for Nature (also known as the World Wildlife Fund [WWF]) is concerned about exposing the highly ecologically sensitive Arctic marine environment to the risk of a catastrophic oil spill given the lack of adequate emergency response capacity. The WWF (2008) has called for a moratorium on additional oil exploration in the Arctic until the spill response technologies are field proven and market ready. Pending such spill response technologies, the WWF has called for an international, mandatory instrument to regulate shipping in the Arctic, including such measures as routes and areas to avoid, and zero-discharge zones.

On the Atlantic coast, Canada's first offshore development (Cohasset-Panuke off Nova Scotia) produced crude oil from 1992 to 1999. Three major crude oil production projects off Newfoundland and Labrador (Hibernia, White Rose, and Terra Nova) and the Sable Offshore Energy Project, which produces natural gas off Nova Scotia, have come onstream since the 1980s. Local communities and regional economies may benefit directly and indirectly from the economic stimulus of offshore oil and gas developments. For instance, residents of Newfoundland and Labrador provided 66 percent of the 63 million person-hours of labour required to construct the production

system, and, in operation (in 2004), Hibernia directly employed about 875 people, about 89 percent of whom were from Newfoundland and Labrador. Similarly, Nova Scotians provided 54 percent of the labour and materials expenditure for the Sable Offshore Energy Project (Bott, 2004).

However, while Hibernia had generated $1.2 billion for Newfoundland's coffers by the end of 2006, the project returned $8.8 billion to the consortium of oil companies that ran it and another $4.8 billion to the federal treasury. Yet, outside of the capital, St. John's, the province's outport (fishing) communities continued to show signs of a depressed economy; clearly the benefits of oil production have not been distributed equally. These disparities helped fuel Premier Danny Williams's aggressive pursuit of equity (ownership) stakes in the offshore sector, particularly the 8.5 percent stake that Ottawa holds in Hibernia (Canadian Press, 2007).

The offshore industry's primary focus on development of east coast petroleum resources reflects their proximity to energy-hungry markets in the northeastern United States. Atlantic Canada's offshore wells also have higher productivity compared to onshore wells: an average onshore well in western Canada produces less than 8 cubic metres of crude oil per day, whereas the first Hibernia well flowed initially at a rate of more than 9000 cubic metres of crude oil per day. In 2004, the 24th well drilled from the Hibernia platform reached 6000 cubic metres per day. While the output of these wells will decline over time, their high output is advantageous in offsetting Canada's use of imported oil (Bott, 2004).

On the Pacific coast, exploration began in 1958 in geologically promising areas (particularly the Queen Charlotte Basin), but in 1972 the British Columbia and

Photo 11–6
The floating drill rig Kulluk (left) and supply vessel *Fennica* in the Beaufort Sea near Herschel Island in summer 2007. The Kulluk was being refitted prior to the 2008 drilling season.

Photo 11–7

These oil drilling ships with towers are frozen in pack ice on the Beaufort Sea, Northwest Territories. Arctic winter conditions, including a lack of natural light, extreme cold, moving ice floes, high wind, and low visibility, pose challenges to oil and gas operations and contribute to oil spill risks.

federal governments called a moratorium on offshore petroleum development (in part because of concerns about a proposed route for Alaskan crude oil tankers through Canadian waters). The British Columbia government reaffirmed its moratorium following the 1989 oil spills from the tanker *Exxon Valdez* and the barge *Nestucca*, and the federal government indicated (also in 1989) that no offshore exploration or development activities would be considered until the British Columbia government asked Ottawa to do so.

Between 2001 and 2004, at least six major reports were written concerning scientific, technical, and economic issues associated with "responsible development" of British Columbia's offshore oil and gas resources. According to the director of British Columbia's Offshore Oil and Gas Branch of the Ministry of Mines and Petroleum Resources, these reports revealed science gaps that must be addressed before offshore activity takes place, but no scientific or technical barriers were identified that warranted continuation of the blanket moratorium over west coast offshore oil and gas development. However, environmental concerns, (lack of) First Nations support, and uncertainties of jurisdiction and ownership, including Aboriginal title and rights, have not yet been resolved fully. Coastal communities are concerned not only about ensuring safeguards are put in place to prevent damage to existing tourism, sport fishing, and commercial fishing industries, but also about seeking royalties from the government and compensation for oil and gas development activities or environmental accidents.

Several ENGOs have opposed opening the British Columbia coast to offshore oil and gas development. For instance, the Sierra Club of Canada (British Columbia chapter), the David Suzuki Foundation, the Living Oceans Society, Greenpeace, and the Georgia Strait Alliance

identified key reasons to leave the moratorium in place, including ecological risks from seismic testing and the risk of oil spills, concern about the inadequacy of environmental regulations to protect the natural environment, and the need to look beyond fossil fuel energy sources to develop alternative energy sources that will reduce GHG emissions. Since an average-sized crude oil tanker takes about 2 kilometres to come to a stop or to make a significant change in its course, and given that the waters surrounding the Queen Charlotte Islands often are treacherous, with many rocky outcroppings less than 350 metres from shore, one can understand the concerns that communities along the shipping routes might have about lifting the moratorium. Among other activities, these ENGOs are working toward implementation of legislation that will permanently protect the British Columbia coast, and are promoting the need for First Nations and other coastal communities to have meaningful roles in the environmental reviews and other regulatory processes necessary to assess the benefits and risks of lifting the moratorium.

Currently, the province is undertaking initiatives that will enable offshore development to occur, including identifying potential benefits and risks of such development, developing comprehensive fiscal and regulatory regimes, and advancing scientific knowledge. The provincial government has established research partnerships with universities, signed a 2005 protocol agreement with the Nisga'a First Nation, and launched a new marine-planning process called the Pacific North Coast Integrated Management Area to ensure the inclusion of offshore oil and gas development opportunities in decision making. British Columbia's 2007 Energy Plan confirms the province's commitment to offshore development, and notes that a request has been made to Canada to lift the federal moratorium (the provincial moratorium would be lifted simultaneously).

As dependent as Canada is on oil and gas for much of its energy requirements, scientific information and multidisciplinary research studies are required to address such concerns as detrimental ecosystem effects from exploratory seismic operations and the ocean discharge of "production water." Extracted along with oil and gas in the drilling process, produced water contains a wide variety of contaminants, including heavy metals, radionuclides, petroleum hydrocarbons, and alkylphenols, all of which are known to be harmful to fish in their sensitive early-life stages (Lee, 2006). If the offshore oil and gas industry expands as expected, the potential for acute and chronic toxicity responses of fish (including commercially valuable species) to increases in production water discharges also will rise. Appropriate regulatory and habitat management actions will depend on research that predicts and monitors the environmental risks associated with produced water discharges and identifies acceptable disposal limits of these waste products into our oceans.

In 2002, Fisheries and Oceans Canada (DFO) set up the Centre for Offshore Oil and Gas Environmental Research (COOGER) to provide scientific data intended to support environmentally focused decision making associated with oil and gas development in Canadian waters. The overall goal of COOGER's activities is to protect the health of Canada's three oceans and inland waters and the sustainability of their renewable resources. For example, it may be possible to identify and map sensitive habitats (fish nurseries or migration routes) that need protection (through exclusion zones or seasonal limitations on activities) from oil and gas exploration and development. Similarly, as interest in Arctic oil and gas has increased, and as climate change effects may open the Northwest Passage to shipping and simultaneously put the area at increased risk of oil spills, research into cleaning up spills that occur in ice is ongoing. Off the west coast, COOGER is working to establish a baseline for naturally occurring hydrocarbons in the environment, information that will be valuable if the oil and gas development moratorium is lifted. And, with the push toward alternative energy resources, COOGER is expected to help answer the questions that inevitably will arise about the impact of wind and tidal power developments on the marine environment.

Photo 11–8

Oil spills from ocean-going tankers are serious because of the large volume of oil that may be spilled and the uncertainty about the nature and extent of environmental damage that may result from the spill itself and from cleanup efforts.

Fossil Fuels: Heavy Oil

Oil deposits, in the form of shale and oil sand, are found close to the Earth's surface. **Oil shale** is rock that contains a solid mixture of hydrocarbon compounds called kerogen. Once crushed and heated, kerogen vapour is condensed to form heavy, slow-flowing shale oil. Oil shale is more expensive and difficult to extract and process than conventional oil, and its net useful energy yield is lower. Because oil shale is extracted on land, many of the same problems associated with above-ground mining, including altering the landscape and interfering with wildlife, are evident with shale processing. In addition, salts and toxic compounds from processed shale can leach into watercourses and contaminate groundwater.

Substantially heavier (more viscous) than other crude oils, **oil sands** (also known as tar sands) are crude oil deposits that consist of sand, bitumen, mineral-rich clays, and water. **Bitumen**, a black oil rich in sulphur, requires upgrading to synthetic crude oil, or dilution with lighter hydrocarbons, to enable transportation by pipelines and to be usable by refineries. Canada is home to the largest known oil sands deposits in the world: located principally in the boreal forest zone of northern Alberta, the oil sands cover an area (140 200 square kilometres) about twice the size of New Brunswick (Alberta Energy, 2006). The major oil sands deposits are found in the Peace River, Athabasca (Fort McMurray area), and Cold Lake (north of Lloydminster) regions, and are estimated to contain approximately 1.7 trillion barrels of bitumen initially in-place, of which 173 billion barrels are proven reserves that can be recovered using current technology (see Box 11–3).

The net useful energy yield from oil sands is lower than for conventional oil because more energy is required to extract and process bitumen than conventional crude oil resources. Specifically, it takes about 34 cubic metres of natural gas to produce one barrel of bitumen from in situ projects and about 20 cubic metres for integrated mining projects. The oil sands industry uses about 21 million cubic metres per day of natural gas, an amount equal to about 5 percent of the Western Canada Sedimentary Basin production. By 2015, natural gas consumption is expected to increase to about 60 million cubic metres per day (National Energy Board, 2007b). The energy intensity of bitumen extraction means that oil sands mining operations are major emitters of GHGs; for example, in 2005, Syncrude emitted 10.3 million tonnes of GHGs (equivalent to emissions from 2.7 million private vehicles) (Dyer et al., 2008).

Deriving oil from oil sands introduces significant landscape changes, notably open pit mines and large waste disposal ponds. Mining the bitumen within the boreal forest means that rivers must be diverted, wetlands drained, and all vegetation and non–oil-bearing overburden removed. The process also releases large quantities of nitrogen oxides (NO_x), sulphur dioxide (SO_2), and volatile organic compounds (VOCs); in 2005, oil sands operations emitted

Bitumenous sands found in Alberta consist of 10 to 12 percent bitumen, 80 to 85 percent mineral matter (sand and clays), and 4 to 6 percent water. Each grain of oil sand is composed of three layers: the grain of sand at the core is surrounded by a layer of water that, in turn, is surrounded by the bitumen to form the outer layer. Of the total 177.9 billion barrels of proven oil reserves found in Canada, Alberta's oil sands and oil fields account for 175.3 billion barrels, over 98.5 percent of the total. Note the expanse of the (heavy) oil sands areas compared to conventional oil fields; the potential scale of energy development will bring major environmental changes to Alberta.

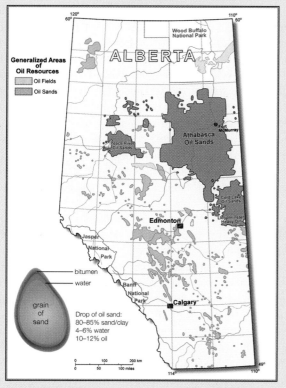

Box Figure 11–5

Oil sands and oil fields in Alberta

SOURCE: Oil Reserves and Production, Alberta Department of Energy. 2006. page 4. http://www.energy.gov.ab.ca/Oil/pdfs/AB_OilReserves.pdf Used with permission.

Oil sands mining also requires large volumes of water in processing operations. Both water quantity and quality issues are of concern. In November 2007, residents of Fort Chipewyan (located about 260 kilometres north of Fort McMurray and downstream of major oil sands plants) called for a moratorium on new oil sands mining projects in the region. A study released by the town's health authority found unsafe levels of arsenic, mercury, and polycyclic aromatic hydrocarbons (PAHs) in the fish of Lake Athabasca as well as in sediments, water, and wildlife. Villagers feared that oil sands developments may be responsible for poor water quality, rare types of cancer, and other health issues in the Aboriginal community (de Souza, 2007; Haggett, 2007).

Development of the oil sands is changing the face of Canadian energy production and, with more than 3000 square kilometres projected to be mined to extract bitumen, dramatically altering the boreal forest environment in northern Alberta. Canadians are beginning to realize the importance of this energy resource and are becoming aware of the environmental impacts of oil sands mining on Alberta's (and Canada's) natural capital and GHG emissions.

Producing Oil from Alberta's Oil Sands Oil sands development incorporates either mining (conventional) or in situ (nonconventional) production methods. Minable bitumen deposits are located near the surface and, following removal of the overburden (trees, soil), are excavated using open pit mining methods. Near Fort McMurray, Alberta, the Syncrude and Suncor oil sands mining operations use the world's largest trucks and shovels to remove oil sands formations. About 2 tonnes of oil sands must be dug up, moved, and processed to produce one barrel of oil. Approximately 75 percent of the bitumen can be recovered from the sand; after being processed, the sand is returned to the pit and the site is reclaimed. Oil sand

Photo 11–9

Companies extracting bitumen from Alberta's oil sands rely heavily on technology, including massive equipment such as the 80-tonne shovel, shown here loading a 240-tonne truck.

70 000 tonnes of NO_x, 147 000 tonnes of SO_2, and 59 000 tonnes of VOCs. By 2015, these figures are expected to rise to 196 000 tonnes of NO_x, 166 000 tonnes of SO_2, and 300 000 tonnes of VOCs—and to exceed a variety of Alberta and international air quality measures. Over 40 percent of the increase in GHG emissions in Canada between 2003 and 2010 will be the direct result of new oil sands development (Dyer et al., 2008).

tailings (waste) management is a major consideration in oil sands production activity.

In situ ("in place") methods are used to recover oil from bitumen deposits that are more than 75 metres underground. Today, about two-thirds of bitumen production derives from conventional mining methods and one-third through use of in situ methods. Since about 80 percent of Alberta's oil sands are located at depths of more than 400 metres, too deep to be open pit mined, the ratio will reverse over time. Currently, five in situ methods of bitumen extraction are in use: steam-assisted gravity drainage (SAGD), cyclic steam stimulation (CSS), vapour recovery extraction (VAPEX), toe to heel air injection (THAI), and cold flow/cold heavy oil production with sand (cold flow/CHOPS). Each of these methods is explained briefly below. Four of the five methods remove the bitumen by injecting wells with steam, air, or hydrocarbon solvents; the cold flow/CHOPS method involves pumping the bitumen. Oil recovery rates vary, with SAGD recovering about 60 percent of the oil, while CSS recovers 20 to 25 percent, and cold flow/CHOPS about 5 to 6 percent (Budgell, 2006; National Energy Board, 2007b).

Once separated from the sand, the bitumen is upgraded into synthetic crude oil. Some of the oil sands companies carry out the upgrading on site, others pipe the bitumen to off-site upgraders for processing, while still others do not upgrade but sell different types of oil products according to market demands.

The industry invests billions of dollars annually in the development and expansion of the oil sands resource. Technological innovations that have enabled oil to be recovered from sand reflect the importance of continuing to conduct energy research through such agencies as the Alberta Energy Research Institute. Now, new research and innovations are required to reduce the impacts of GHGs and other emissions, to reduce the consumption of oil and gas, and to manage the environmental and social impacts of oil sands development.

Environmental Effects of Oil Sands Mining Burgeoning interest in secure oil supplies, particularly by the United States, and growing interest from China, has markedly increased the demand for oil from the oil sands. As demand grows, environmentalists and many citizens increasingly are concerned that weak environmental review processes will fail to safeguard Alberta's boreal forest ecosystem from the cumulative effects of oil sands projects. Although the federal government has exclusive authority over fish and migratory bird habitats, key components of forest ecosystems, the federal government's role in assessing the environmental impacts of oil sands development has been limited. Under the Canadian Environmental Assessment Act, federal environmental assessments are required when the federal government exercises authority over a project. Federal authority is triggered when a federal department or agency proposes a project, or provides

land or money to facilitate a project. To varying degrees, provinces also require environmental reviews. Under "harmonization" agreements, where two or more governments are required by law to assess the same project, a single assessment and review process takes place.

In the absence of federal reviews, companies prepare environmental impact assessments (EIAs; refer to Figure 10–6 on page 422) and submit them to the province for review before a project licence is issued. Ideally, an EIA should consider all potential environmental impacts from a project, including the cumulative effects of other developments, and outline measures to minimize negative effects. Many company environmental reviews have been criticized for being narrow and lacking depth, and have been challenged by ENGOs.

The Pembina Institute has worked for more than a decade to address environmental issues emanating from oil sands development. A member of the Oil Sands Environmental Coalition, the Pembina Institute has led the review of environmental assessments for proposed oil sands developments and intervened in both provincial and federal regulatory hearings. The institute also has been engaged in multistakeholder initiatives focused on regional environmental management and monitoring in the oil sands. The institute's research is communicated via outreach efforts to the public, media, and policymakers. In 2008, the Pembina Institute released its first oil sands "report card," in which it was noted that the technologies companies use to mine, extract, and upgrade the bitumen to synthetic crude "make the product among the most environmentally costly sources of transport fuel in the world" (Dyer et al., 2008, p. vii).

Pembina's oil sands report card notes that a typical oil sands mine in Alberta represents billions of dollars in capital investment, employs over 1000 people, and has a lifespan of over 50 years (Dyer et al., 2008). However, the mining and extraction of bitumen produces a number of environmental problems that contribute to cumulative environmental degradation in the oil sands region. Part of the challenge of managing environmental impacts of the industry derives from Alberta's emphasis on voluntary efforts by industry rather than regulatory requirements. Alberta has no mechanisms for third-party scrutiny and validation of environmental performance, with the result that companies may approach environmental matters in a variety of ways and with a range of consequences. This approach helps explain the following environmental effects described in the oil sands report card (Dyer et al., 2008).

Freshwater and Groundwater Consumption Freshwater and groundwater consumption during oil sands production significantly affects the environment (see also Box 7–4 on page 283). Oil sands mining operations are licensed to divert 349 million cubic metres of water per year from the Athabasca River (twice the amount of water used by the more than 1 million inhabitants of

Calgary) and to withdraw water even during winter low flow conditions, when fish and fish habitat may be damaged. If proposed projects are approved, more than 500 million cubic metres of fresh water may be withdrawn, raising concern about the sustainability of water use from the Athabasca River. Not one oil sands company voluntarily committed to halt water withdrawals during low flow periods on the Athabasca River, even if fish and habitat damage were occurring. In February 2007, in an unprecedented action, the Alberta government, with Fisheries and Oceans Canada, developed the Athabasca River Water Management Framework, which introduces a world standard policy for protecting in-stream flow needs to apply to year-round water withdrawals in a northern climate.

The production of 1 cubic metre of synthetic crude oil from the oil sands requires 2 to 4.5 cubic metres of water (some surface water is used, but most operations use fresh and saline groundwater). In SAGD operations, even though 90 to 95 percent of water is reused, every cubic metre of bitumen produced requires about another 0.2 cubic metres of groundwater. At current rates of withdrawal, water volume is insufficient to support all announced projects. Water use by oil sands companies is one of the most urgent environmental challenges in the region, yet not one of the projects or companies has reported water intensity reduction targets (formal targets to reduce water use and to reduce impacts on aquatic systems).

Mature Fine Tailings   Mature fine tailings (MFT) are the fine particles of sediment, suspended in water, created by most oil sands extraction processes; the MFT end up in the massive waste lagoons located north of Fort McMurray. Management of liquid mine wastes is a daunting challenge; the long-term plan for disposal of MFT is to place them in end pit lakes, but there is debate on whether the tailings ponds can be reclaimed to become biologically productive ecosystems. Although not yet proven commercially, a filtered tailings technology that produces a dry tailings and thickened tailings stream enables the dry waste material to be trucked offsite or to be used for reclamation or backfill and the thickened tailings to be placed in tailings ponds without the creation of MFT. Several companies have proposed to use the new technology in the future.

Air Emissions and Climate Change   Air emissions and climate change are also concerns associated with oil sands mining. Oil sands projects emit many chemical pollutants; of particular importance are NO_x, SO_2, and VOCs. NO_x and SO_2 contribute to acid precipitation, and all three types of emissions contribute to smog and have potential human health effects. NO_x can cause respiratory problems and, in combination with VOCs and sunlight, form ground-level ozone. Oil sands SO_2 emissions are expected to increase to 166 000 tonnes per year by 2015; at this level, SO_2 pollution will exceed 24-hour Alberta and World Health Organization air quality objec-

Photo 11–10
Oil sands mining has a substantial impact on the environment; here, both air emissions and landscape alteration from open pit mining activity are evident.

tives. About 500 square kilometres of land surrounding the current operations are at risk from acidic emissions; if all planned projects proceed, the at-risk area will increase to 1000 square kilometres.

Oil sands mining operations are major emitters of GHGs; respectively, Syncrude and Suncor are Canada's third- and sixth-largest emitters. The oil sands are projected to contribute close to half of the growth in national emissions between 2003 and 2010. In direct contrast to the need for significant reductions in global GHG emissions, the intensity targets identified by the Canadian government will not provide those reductions and may lead to companies receiving up to $700 million in credits through expected efficiency gains but with a doubling or tripling in absolute carbon emissions. No oil sands projects have publicly stated any voluntary emission reduction targets for NO_x, SO_2, or VOCs.

Land Reclamation   The Alberta government requires mining operations to reclaim disturbed land to an "equivalent land capability," and the government will certify reclaimed land that meets that standard. Suncor has the longest legacy in the oil sands region and in 40 years of operation has disturbed 13 093 hectares of land and reclaimed only 949 hectares. It was not until March 19, 2008, that the first provincial reclamation certificate was issued to Syncrude (with 19 973 hectares disturbed in 29 years of operation) for a 104-hectare parcel that had been undergoing reclamation since the early 1980s (O'Meara, 2008). Prior to this date, not a single hectare of land had been certified as reclaimed by the provincial government, despite more than 40 years of oil sands mining—concern exists for the 3000 square kilometres of boreal forest that already have been leased for future oil sands mining activity (Dyer et al., 2008).

In 2007, the Pembina Institute and WWF-Canada examined activities undertaken by oil sands companies to minimize their cumulative environmental effects. Ten oil sands mining companies were asked to complete a survey about their environmental performance and management, including air emissions, land and water management, and climate change. In the report card that the institute prepared based on the results of the survey, as well as consultation with the companies and other research, nine of the 10 operating oil sands mines received a failing environmental grade. Only one mining operation came close to a passing grade, and the average score was only 33 percent. Clearly, substantial improvement is required in the environmental performance of oil sands mining operations.

The research conducted by the Pembina Institute and WWF-Canada highlighted where the oil sands mining companies were falling behind in their environmental performance. For example, while most of the companies had comprehensive environmental policies in place, only Albian Sands and Imperial Oil had an independently accredited environmental management system (such as ISO 14001) in place. No company had established voluntary targets to limit absolute greenhouse gas emissions, and no company had reported publicly any water intensity reduction targets. This weak environmental performance reflects poorly on the oil sands mining companies, particularly since they include the largest and most profitable major oil companies in the world. The reputations of oil sands companies and their social licence to operate may be at risk if they fail to implement best practices to protect the environment and to minimize their environmental footprint in the oil sands region.

The recommendations of the Pembina Institute and WWF-Canada (Dyer et al., 2008) to improve environmental management of oil sands mining operations in Alberta involved both government and industry actions (see Table 11–1).

Fossil Fuels: Coal

Coal is the most abundant fossil fuel in the world, with proven reserves exceeding 900 billion tonnes, enough coal to last for about 150 years at current rates of consumption. Canada holds 6.6 billion tonnes of proven recoverable coal reserves. Coal is burned to generate about 16 percent of Canada's electricity, and roughly 40 percent of the world's electricity. Coal has a relatively high net useful energy yield and is highly effective for providing industrial heat. As a result, 70 percent of the world's steel is produced from coal energy. Globally, over 3 billion tonnes of coal are consumed per year, 66 million tonnes of which were produced in Canada's 25 operating mines in 2006 (Stone, 2006). The combined impact of coal mining, coal transportation, and coal-fired electricity on the Canadian economy is 73 000 jobs and over $5 billion in GDP.

Of all the fossil fuels, coal burning produces the most CO_2 and air pollution per unit of energy. Concern over climate change and acid precipitation has led the coal industry to develop advanced pollution control technologies, and others to investigate clean coal technologies and zero emissions coal technology. In January 2007, the federal government announced a $230 million ecoENERGY Technology Initiative to research and develop clean energy technologies. Until emissions-free energy production and use occur, air pollutants from coal burning will continue to kill thousands of people, cause thousands of cases of respiratory disease, and account for several billion dollars in property damage every year. Extracting coal from underground mines endangers human lives directly through accidents (explosions, shaft collapses) and prolonged exposure to coal dust (black lung disease). Surface coal mining severely alters the landscape, causes soil erosion, and can pollute nearby water supplies. Despite coal's drawbacks, energy analysts forecast that the world demand for coal will increase significantly over the next two to five decades, driven by what appears to be a continuously increasing demand for energy. To improve the environmental acceptability of coal, technologies to

TABLE 11–1
RECOMMENDATIONS FOR ENVIRONMENTAL MANAGEMENT IN ALBERTA'S OIL SANDS REGION

Provincial Government	Oil Sands Mining Industry
• needs to protect the public interest and enforce acceptable standards of environmental performance, and continuously to improve regulations and incentives to ensure environmental impacts are minimized • needs to report on environmental impacts to public lands and to ensure that annual data regarding companies' environmental performance are accessible easily to the public • federal and provincial data collection must be based on consistent industry-wide standards, and must allow for meaningful comparisons among mining operations	• needs to implement best available practices, including adopting and focusing on development and implementation of new technologies and processes that lead to reductions in environmental impacts • should make project-specific oil sands environmental performance information more widely available to the public and in a consistent format

SOURCE: *Under-Mining the Environment: The Oil Sands Report Card*, S. Dyer, J. Moorhouse, K. Laufenberg, & R. Powell, 2008, Drayton Valley, AB: The Pembina Institute, http://www.pembina.org/pub/1571/

Figure 11-6

Sydney, Nova Scotia, and the Sydney tar ponds

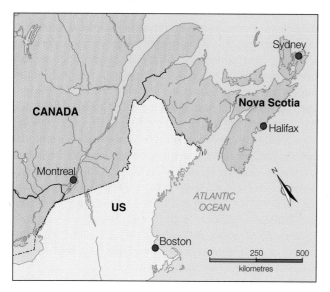

a) Location of Sydney, Nova Scotia

b) Aerial view of the Sydney tar ponds. The north pond, open to the harbour, contains an estimated 360 000 tonnes of contaminated sediments in an area of 19 hectares. Separated from the north pond by a dam, the 13-hectare south pond contains an estimated 350 000 tonnes of contaminated sediments.

c) Aerial view of the cooling pond lagoon (round water body); the south end of the south tar pond is in the middle of the photo. The dam separating the north and south tar ponds is on the right side of the photo; this dam limits the tidal influences of the harbour on the south pond but, prior to remedial works, the north pond was open to the harbour and estuarine area.

d) In addition to the tar ponds, the 68-hectare coke oven site (foreground) required demolition of the derelict building and smokestacks and cleanup of an in-ground tar cell containing 25 000 tonnes of tars and contaminated soil. This site was used for almost 100 years to produce coke (a clean, hard, lightweight fuel; byproducts of its manufacture include heavy metals and PAHs), a key ingredient in steel production. Remediation of this site is expected to be completed by 2011.

reduce emissions and improve combustion efficiency are being developed. The challenge is to commercialize clean coal technologies while keeping a competitive price.

For nearly a century, the Sydney steel plant (Cape Breton Island, Nova Scotia; see Figure 11-6) was the lifeblood of the community, providing employment for 1500 workers in its prime. But virtually every day from 1905 to 1988, pollution from the plant's coke (coal) ovens poured into the air and untreated effluent from the coking operations was dumped into Muggah Creek. The steel mill closed in 2000, and today, the 31 hectares of the Sydney

tar ponds, which once were the tidal flats of the Muggah Creek watershed, contain an estimated 700 000 tonnes of toxic coal-tar deposits. Among the contaminants are PAHs, PCBs, and heavy metals (Gjertson, 1997; Hamilton, 1997). With each tide, contaminants were flushed into Sydney Harbour from the north pond; scientists estimated that about 800 kilograms of PAHs were released annually. In 1980, Environment Canada closed the fishery in the harbour's south arm due to contamination—PAH levels in lobsters were 26 times the norm.

Early cleanup efforts began in 1986 when the federal and provincial governments signed a five-year, $34.2 million agreement to clean up the tar ponds and to establish a date for closing the coke ovens, a significant employer as well as a major polluter. The tar ponds were to be dredged, and the dredged sediment pumped through a mile-long pipeline to an incinerator, but the thick, lumpy sludge repeatedly clogged the pipeline. By 1994, rising costs triggered a premature end to the project. In 1996, the province's proposal to cover the tar ponds with slag from the steel plant was loudly condemned by some residents. Later that year, federal and provincial ministers called for a public consultation process to search for a solution, and the Joint Action Group (JAG) was formed. A highly empowered community group, with a mandate to seek consensus around cleanup options, JAG and three levels of government signed a $62 million cost-sharing agreement in 1999 to fund scientific studies, surface cleanup, and JAG activities.

In 2000, the Acting Minister of Nova Scotia's Department of Environment stated that managing contaminated sites and prioritizing them for remediation was a first priority for his ministry. He cited the Sydney tar ponds as an example of this problem and called it Canada's worst contaminated site (Baker, personal communication, 2000). In 2001, the province closed the steel plant and created the Sydney Tar Ponds Agency (TPA) to manage the cleanup of the tar ponds and coke ovens. Following JAG's cleanup recommendations to government in 2003, Canada and Nova Scotia committed $400 million to a 10-year cleanup. In May 2005, then Environment Minister Stéphane Dion ordered a full panel review of the cleanup plan, the most rigorous form of environmental assessment. By December 2005, the province (the Tar Ponds Agency) had submitted its seven-volume, 3000-page EIS and requested public comment until February 2006. Three weeks of public hearings were held in April and May 2006, and by July the EIS Review Panel delivered its report and 55 recommendations for the cleanup plan. Remediation work has been initiated, and the Cape Breton Regional Municipality, responsible for land use planning, has been leading the effort to design and redevelop the former industrial sites (Sydney Tar Ponds Agency, 2006). Finding effective solutions to energy-related contamination issues continues to challenge us. Often our solutions are less than optimal, reminding us of the importance of developing sustainable strategies for meeting our energy demands (see Enviro-Focus 14 on page 562).

Fossil Fuels: Natural Gas

Conventional, or associated, **natural gas** is located underground above most reserves of crude oil and is a gaseous hydrocarbon mixture of methane combined with smaller amounts of propane and butane. When found on its own in dry wells, natural gas is called nonassociated or unconventional natural gas. Approximately 72 percent of world reserves of natural gas are of the nonassociated type, and the remaining 28 percent are the associated type. Typically, it has been more economical to extract associated reserves; however, advances in extraction technology have improved the cost effectiveness of nonassociated production. Natural gas production had been rising faster than oil, making it increasingly more important to the Canadian economy. By 2000, natural gas represented almost 30 percent of Canada's total primary energy production (International Energy Agency, 2003). However, some experts estimate that conventional natural gas production has peaked and by 2006 will start to decline (Bolger & Isaacs, 2003). As older natural gas fields in western Canada have become less productive, the National Energy Board (2007a) anticipates that new gas supplies (to meet a projected 45 percent increase in demand between 2005 and 2030) will come from the North, offshore, and unconventional gas resources such as coalbed methane (see Box 11–4).

Many analysts view natural gas as the bridge from "dirty" hydrocarbon-based energy to cleaner renewable energy. Natural gas burns more efficiently than oil, and produces one-third less carbon dioxide per unit of heat energy and fewer pollutants overall. Simply substituting natural gas for coal in electrical generation facilities could reduce carbon emissions by 50 to 70 percent, depending on efficiency of individual facilities. However, because methane is 30 times more powerful than carbon dioxide as a greenhouse gas, it is critical that turbines and associated machinery in natural gas–burning facilities be sealed against leaks. If only 3 to 4 percent of the methane finds its way to the atmosphere, the lower emission benefit of burning natural gas is nullified (Hill, O'Keefe, & Snape, 1995). Natural gas generally is less expensive than oil and transports easily over land through pipelines (see Figure 11–7 on page 458). Pipeline construction, however, can have impacts on sensitive aquatic, grassland, and other environments.

The process of **flaring** also is a source of concern. Flaring is a way of disposing of unwanted, unprocessed natural gas; the industry burns this gas to release hydrogen sulphide (sour gas) and to avoid the buildup of potentially explosive levels of gas at work sites. In Alberta, for instance, only about 1.4 percent of the natural gas processed in the province is flared, but that amount translates into more than 2 billion cubic metres of gas burned off each year (Francis, 1997). For decades, people living near flares have expressed their concern about the impacts of flaring emissions.

Research has revealed that emissions from many flares are greater than was assumed previously; that even though flaring destroys many sulphur compounds, others are created; and that the risks to cattle and humans from exposure to many of the emissions from flaring are not well understood. Following a five-year study, the Alberta Research Council identified more than 200 chemical compounds produced by flaring, including more than 30 varieties of cancer-causing benzene (Francis, 1997). Public frustration over flaring escalated in the late 1990s when two residents of Alberta were convicted following acts of "eco-terrorism" against an oil company. The two citizens, concerned about the health of their families and livestock, bombed an oil well shed in northern Alberta. Evidence of the health risks of flaring mounted, and in July 2000, claiming that his herd of cattle had experienced reproductive failure, a central Alberta rancher accepted a settlement from a major oil company after an eight-year legal battle (Lau, 2000).

An advisory committee appointed by the Alberta Energy and Utilities Board recommended a series of measures to develop a better understanding of the effects of sour gas on human health and improve the public consultation process (Public Safety and Sour Gas, 2000). Alberta also introduced regulations requiring petroleum companies to reduce flaring by 25 percent from 1996 levels, by the end of 2001 (Alberta Energy and Utilities Board, 2000). By 2001, the industry had reduced flaring in Alberta by 53 percent (Canadian Association of Petroleum Producers, 2001). However, residents continue to express their concerns about sour gas releases (Kom, 2007), and, given the potential seriousness of chronic exposure to risks from flaring, including increased costs of medical care, precautionary approaches continue to be warranted.

Photo 11–11
Installation of the Trans-Canada pipeline near North Bay, Ontario.

Photo 11–12
In Los Angeles in 1979, gasoline rationing resulted in long lineups at local gas stations.

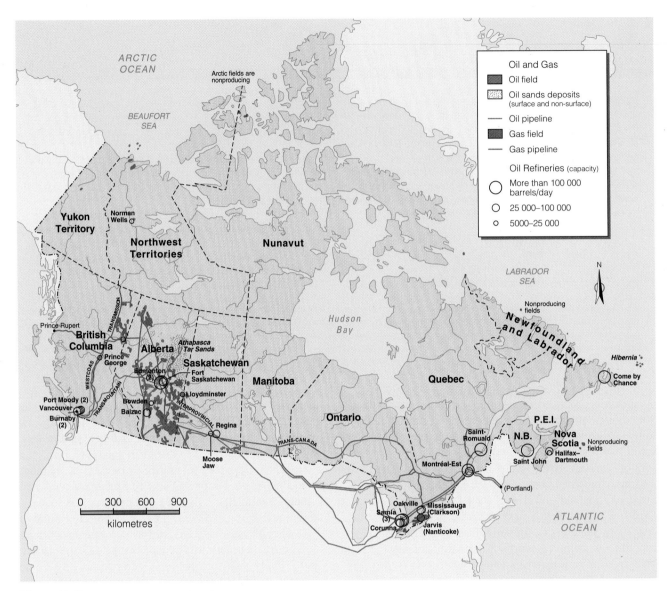

Figure 11–7

Oil and natural gas fields and pipelines in Canada

SOURCE: Adapted from *Canadian Oxford World Atlas: New Edition,* Q. H. Stanford (Ed.), 1992, Toronto: Oxford University Press, p. 250. Used by permission of Oxford University Press, Inc.

Fossil Fuels: The 1970s Energy Crisis

In 1973, a then little-known cartel, the Organization of Petroleum Exporting Countries (OPEC), disrupted global supplies of imported oil. The OPEC embargo, combined with the U.S. energy policy, resulted in an energy crisis in the United States that had far-reaching economic, social, and political effects. In addition to high prices and long lines at gas stations, the "oil shock" raised concerns over energy policy, particularly U.S. dependence on imported petroleum.

The energy crisis prompted critical thinking on energy futures in areas such as estimates of global fossil fuel supplies, ways to improve energy efficiency, and use of alternative energy sources. In hindsight, the oil shock helped

the North American economy to realize the volatility of energy markets. The energy crisis has been credited with improving our understanding of environmental and societal consequences of energy use (Feldman, 1995).

Bioenergy and Biomass

Bioenergy is energy that is made available by the conversion of materials derived from sources of living organisms or their metabolic byproducts. **Biomass** is organic matter, including wood, agricultural wastes and manure, and some types of garbage, that can be converted into solid, liquid, or gaseous sources and used in a number of different ways; it supplies 15 percent of the world's energy. Biomass can be burned directly to produce heat and/or electricity, converted biochemically to produce liquid fuel (biodiesel, ethanol—see Chapter 6), or digested or gasified to produce gaseous fuel. Canada relies on biomass—principally waste wood chips from pulp mills—to supply about 6 percent of our energy requirements, and this amount of renewable bioenergy ranks second to hydropower (Natural Resources Canada, 2006a). Less-developed countries are much more dependent on biomass, relying on it for up to 50 percent of their energy requirements.

When trees and plants are replaced at a level equal to or greater than the rate at which they are harvested, biomass is considered a renewable energy resource. In addition, no net increase in atmospheric carbon dioxide occurs if replacement equals harvest. Sound land use management practices must be in place to avoid problems associated with land clearing, such as soil erosion, water pollution, flooding, and habitat loss. Unfortunately, in many parts of the world, harvesting practices are not sustainable and fuelwood shortages occur. Many forested lands in developing countries are disappearing to accommodate agriculture and urbanization, not to provide fuelwood to meet energy needs and demands.

Increasingly, developing countries are turning to agroforestry to meet their energy needs. Agroforestry is a multipurpose land use system that combines indigenous trees (to provide erosion protection and fuelwood) in areas used to plant crops and graze animals. Land use activities reflect local sociocultural values. Agroforestry initiatives, such as the Kenyan Woodfuel Development Program, have been successful in encouraging farmers to increase the amount of woody biomass on their farms (Hill et al., 1995). The introduction of similar initiatives in other developing countries may improve the sustainability of biomass fuels, enabling people to use wood for fuel while meeting the increasing energy demands of local populations.

For 20 years, Natural Resources Canada (through CETC-Ottawa, that is, the CANMET Energy Technology Centre) has operated a Bioenergy Development Program in association with the Canadian Biomass Innovation Network. Since the two largest sources of biomass supply in Canada come from forestry and agriculture, CETC has assisted Canadian firms in making ethanol from biomass a commercial reality. Major breakthroughs are being made to convert lignocellulosic biomass products (wood chips, sawdust, straw, perennial grasses) into ethanol. Canada also is taking an active role in managing the residuals from its municipal and industrial sectors and developing technology to convert biomass and/or landfill or anaerobic digester gas into ethanol (Natural Resources Canada, 2006c).

Hydroelectricity

Hydroelectric power supplies almost 17 percent of the world's electricity, while in Canada 60 percent of our electricity is produced via hydropower (see Figure 11–8 on the next page). Canada is the world's largest producer of hydroelectricity, generating 353 terawatt-hours per year (nearly 13 percent of the global output of hydropower). Notably, in the developed world, about 70 percent of hydroelectric power generation potential has been developed already, whereas in the developing world, only about 10 percent of the potential has been exploited.

In Canada in 2003 there were 933 large dams (defined as those with a height of 15 metres or more from the foundation), many thousands of smaller dams, and over 450 hydropower facilities. In 2006, the installed production capacity of all hydro plants in Canada was 70 858 megawatts; technically, another 163 173 megawatts could be developed, mostly in Quebec, British Columbia, and the Yukon (Canadian Hydropower Association, 2007). Canada's largest hydroelectric power development, the James Bay project in Quebec, began generating electricity in 1982. The project's eight dams and 198 dikes contain five reservoirs covering 11 900 square kilometres (half the size of Lake Ontario), and have a combined output of 15 237 megawatts.

Hydroelectric projects are expensive to build but have low operating and maintenance costs. In addition, their life spans are two to ten times greater than those of coal or nuclear plants. Hydroelectric stations emit no air pollutants or GHGs and help regulate downstream irrigation. Unfortunately, construction of large dams (such as in the James Bay project) to provide hydroelectric power introduces far-reaching landscape changes that displace people and wildlife, destroy cropland and forests, and interfere with aquatic ecosystems. Because of the negative environmental and social effects of large-scale dams, some critics consider them not to be renewable energy, even though the "fuel source" (the water) is renewable. Small, run-of-river hydropower systems generally have fewer environmental and social impacts, but sustainable hydropower may be attainable, regardless of size, provided sustainability guidelines are followed (see Box 11–5, p. 461).

The International Hydropower Association (IHA, 2004) adopted a set of Sustainability Guidelines that promote "sustainable development" as a fundamental component of social responsibility, sound business practice, and natural resource management in hydroelectric development. During the past decade there have been major improvements in our understanding of the impacts of (hydroelectric) dams on riverine environments. Growth in knowledge has helped to improve the management of environmental issues arising from hydropower developments and enabled decision makers to optimize the positive outcomes for hydropower schemes. Selected examples of the issues for management consideration to achieve sustainable hydropower schemes are identified in Table 11–2 (p. 462).

On November 9, 1997, engineers finished dumping 60 000 cubic metres of rockfill and cement to dam the Yangtze River, irrevocably changing the landscape of this part of China. In building the world's largest dam across the world's third-largest river, China displaced 1.4 million people from fertile farmlands along the river to less

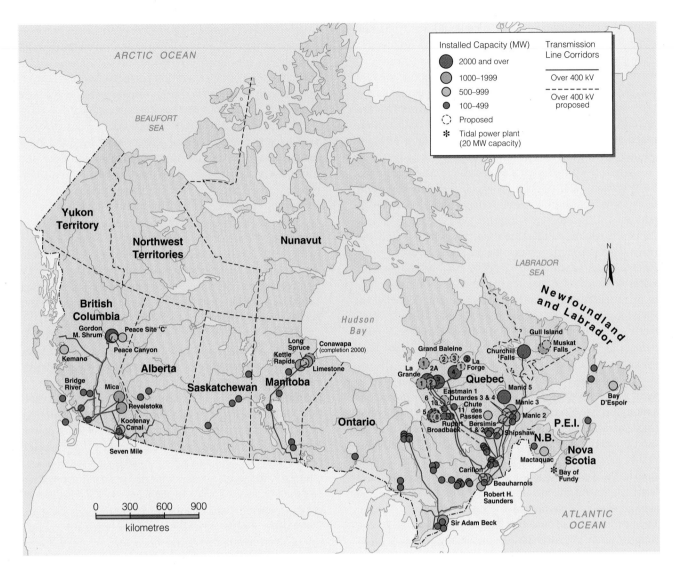

Figure 11–8

Major hydroelectric dams and transmission line corridors in Canada

SOURCE: Adapted from *Canadian Oxford World Atlas: New Edition,* Q. H. Stanford (Ed.), 1992, Toronto: Oxford University Press, p. 23. Used by permission of Oxford University Press, Inc.

productive, steeper hillsides. The dam flooded farmland that had produced 40 percent of China's grain crops and 70 percent of its rice crops. The lives of about one-quarter of the Chinese population (400 million people) who lived along its banks were affected. By the time the US$180 billion Three Gorges project is completed in 2009, 140 towns and 326 villages will be submerged under 670 square kilometres of water, along with 657 factories, 953 kilometres of highway, and 139 power stations (Sly, 1997; Yang, 2007).

The primary purpose of the dam is to provide energy for China's increasingly industrial economy. Proponents of the dam note that it will produce 18.2 million kilowatts of clean electricity (the equivalent of 18 nuclear power stations) needed for China's economic growth and modernization and reduce China's reliance on coal-fired electric power, thus reducing GHG emissions from China. In addition, the dam will control flooding in the lower reaches of the river (International River Network, 1998; Zich, 1997). Critics charge that the dam's ability to control floods may be limited because the river's lower reaches are fed by three other tributaries that also contribute to flooding. A string of smaller dams would have had the same effect on floods and produced as much electricity without as many environmental side effects.

Other effects of the dam and reservoir include the loss of the famous Three Gorges as a landmark; they will be flooded and the ancient (Stone and Bronze Age) archaeological sites they contain will be submerged. Also, the river supports numerous endangered species, including the Yangtze dolphin, Chinese sturgeon, finless porpoise, giant panda, and Siberian white crane. How many of these species will survive in the dramatically changed environment is uncertain. Some hydrologists warn that trapping the silt behind the dam could make downstream riverbanks more vulnerable to flooding—already there have been numerous landslides and riverbank collapses along the steep shores of the reservoir and the Yangtze. Water quality in the river tributaries is deteriorating rapidly, as the lower flows of the dammed river are unable to disperse pollutants effectively. Algae blooms have increased since the reservoir was completed in 2006 (Yang, 2007). Reports that Chinese officials are discussing the environmental and sociopolitical issues related to the Three Gorges dam project may be an indication that greater attention will be paid to environmental issues in the future.

Nuclear Energy

Nuclear energy generates approximately 75 million megawatt-hours of electricity in Canada each year, equivalent to about 15.5 percent of the total electricity consumed in Canada in 2006. Fifty-four percent of Ontario's electricity was supplied by nuclear energy in 2006. The nuclear industry is an important aspect of Canada's economy, contributing $2 billion to Canada's GDP annually in uranium production, nuclear energy generation, reactor sales and service, fuel and isotope production, research and development, and in providing direct employment for over 21 000 people. Of the 22 nuclear reactors in Canada in 2006, 18 were operating: 16 in Ontario, one in Quebec,

and one in New Brunswick. The other reactors were either laid up for refurbishment or have been decommissioned. Canada has developed a strong competitive advantage in the nuclear technology sector, primarily through development and export of the Canada Deuterium Uranium (CANDU) reactor. There are CANDU reactors operating in Argentina, China, Pakistan, India, Romania, and Republic of Korea. Atomic Energy of Canada Limited (AECL), a Crown corporation, generates about 60 percent of its revenue through export of nuclear expertise, technology, and services to foreign governments and utilities, and currently is developing an Advanced CANDU Reactor (Canadian Nuclear Association, 2007).

Nuclear energy emits one-sixth the amount of CO_2 per unit of electricity than coal. Excluding subsidies, generation of nuclear energy is less expensive than energy produced from fossil fuels and creates minimal land disturbance. Once regarded as the energy of the future, the capacity of nuclear fission to provide the world with energy has not lived up to expectations. In the 1950s, researchers predicted that 1800 nuclear power plants would supply 21 percent of the world's commercial energy by the end of the century. At the outset of 2007, 435 commercial reactors in 30 countries supplied 16.2 percent of the world's electricity generation (Canadian Nuclear Association, 2007). Government subsidies, cost overruns,

TABLE 11–2

OPTIMIZING ENVIRONMENTAL OUTCOMES FOR HYDROELECTRIC POWER SCHEMES: SELECTED ISSUES AND ILLUSTRATIVE MITIGATION OPTIONS AND STRATEGIES

Issue for Management Consideration	Illustrative Mitigation Options/Strategies
1. Water quality • Longer residence times of reservoir-impounded water influence reduced oxygenation, temperature, pollutant inflow, propensity for disease proliferation, and algae bloom potential.	• Adequate data collection and an EIA process that identifies potential problems prior to dam design are required. • Working with local communities and regulatory authorities to improve catchment management practices can have significant water quality benefits for hydro reservoirs.
2. Rare and endangered species • Loss of rare or threatened species may be a significant issue arising from dam construction (because of loss of or changes to habitat during construction, or from reservoir creation, or altered downstream flow patterns). • When significant changes cannot be avoided, mechanisms to protect remaining habitats at the local and regional scale should be considered as compensation.	• Need plans to manage this issue before construction begins. • Habitats of critical importance should be identified (in a regional context) and impacts avoided or minimized as much as possible during the design phase. • Specific management plans (e.g., for translocation or habitat rehabilitation) need to be developed for species of conservation significance, along with a backup habitat management location and plan.
3. Passage of fish species • Many fish species require travel along lengths of rivers during their life cycles. Annual migrations may be halted or disrupted by dams and other instream structures and barriers. In some cases, the long-term sustainability of fish populations depends on this migration; in developing countries local economies may rely heavily on fish for income.	• Fish passage is an issue that must be considered during the design and planning stages (e.g., dam site selection), and consideration must be given to appropriate mechanisms for fish transfer (fish ladders, mechanical elevators, guiding devices, translocation programs). • Large downstream migrations of some species may require mitigation measures to reduce mortality by passage through turbines. • Options for facilitating fish passage within existing developments need to be considered also.
4. Health issues • Hydropower developments may affect human health: transmission of disease, human health risks associated with flow regulation downstream, and the consumption of contaminated food sources (e.g., raised mercury levels in fish) must be considered. Potential health benefits also should be identified.	• Public health and emergency response plans should be developed in conjunction with local authorities and based on monitoring levels of risk and uncertainty. • Health benefits due to improved water supply, economic improvements, and flood control should be recognized and valued.

SOURCE: *Sustainability Guidelines,* International Hydropower Association, 2004, pp. 14–16. http://www.un.org/eas/sustdev/sdissues/energy/op/hydro_scanlon.pdf

accidents, and public concerns about safety have affected growth of the nuclear industry.

Despite Canada's investment in nuclear energy, its future is unclear. Two catastrophic accidents raised serious concerns about the safety of nuclear energy. In the United States in 1979, a series of human errors and mechanical failures allowed unknown quantities of radioactive material to move through an open valve to the containment building inside the Three Mile Island reactor. Subsequently, radioactive material escaped to the atmosphere through leaky pipes in the building's exhaust system. Two days after the accident, 200 000 people within a 40-kilometre radius were evacuated from the area. Officially, no deaths were linked to the Three Mile Island accident (although some contradictory claims exist). This incident sparked the anti-nuclear movement and severely reduced public trust in nuclear power.

Then, in 1986, the world's worst commercial nuclear accident occurred at the Chernobyl plant in the former Soviet Union (now Ukraine). Two explosions occurred at the nuclear power plant as a result of human error. The first explosion released fission products to the atmosphere. A second explosion ejected fragments of burning fuel and graphite from the core and allowed air to rush in, causing a graphite fire that burned for nine days. Forty-two exposed workers died immediately, childhood thyroid cancers increased 25 times in nearby Belarus, and experts estimated that 6500 more cancer deaths were likely to occur in nearby populations (Macfarlane, 2003). Winds carried radiation particles thousands of kilometres from the site. The accident went unreported in Russia for three days, and another two days elapsed before the rest of the world was alerted. Local residents were unaware that they had been exposed to an estimated 30 to 40 times the radioactivity of the bombs dropped on Hiroshima and Nagasaki during the Second World War.

Although Canada's nuclear industry has been operating for over 45 years without a serious accident, issues associated with the "power of the Promethean fire" must be recognized (see Box 11–6). Ultimately, Canadians must examine nuclear power in terms of its risks, impacts, and sustainability—this is true of all other energy sources as well. Recently, Innovative Research Group, a national public opinion research and strategy firm, presented the results of its October 2007 online survey (of almost 1100 "representative" Canadians) on selected energy issues. Regarding nuclear power, this poll revealed that 48 percent of Canadians agreed with the statement "while we may not like nuclear power, if we want to get serious about climate change we have to use it as a way to reduce greenhouse gas emissions," while 39 percent agreed that "we should never rely on nuclear power as a way of reducing greenhouse gas emissions, and that we should

Photo 11–13
A concrete sarcophagus encloses the damaged reactor at Chernobyl.

BOX 11-6
NUCLEAR ENERGY: THE POWER OF THE PROMETHEAN FIRE

By Dr. William N. Holden (BA, LLB, ME, PhD), nonpractising member of the Law Society of Alberta, and cross-appointed assistant professor in the Department of Geography and the BSc Program in Environmental Science at the University of Calgary. Used with permission.

In recent years, the generation of electricity by means of nuclear fission (the splitting of uranium atoms) has generated substantial attention from prominent environmentalists concerned about climate change brought on by the combustion of fossil fuels and the resultant emission of CO_2 into the Earth's atmosphere. In May 2004, Sir James Lovelock, inventor of the Gaia hypothesis (which postulates that the Earth is one superorganism), stated that nuclear energy is the only green solution to climate change. In October 2004, Hugh Montefiore, a long-time trustee of Friends of the Earth, said that the solution to the problem of climate change is to make more use of nuclear energy. Patrick Moore, one of the founders of Greenpeace, testified before the United States Congress in defence of nuclear power. Paul Allen and Peter Harper, directors of the Center for Alternative Technology, stated that "the worst possible nuclear disasters are not as bad as the worst possible climate change disasters."

Nuclear energy contains a tremendous scope to generate massive amounts of electricity with minimal emissions of CO_2. In Canada, in 2006, the use of nuclear energy prevented almost 78 million tonnes of CO_2 from being released; what facilitates such a scope for CO_2-free electricity is uranium's high energy density. One tonne of natural uranium produces the electricity equivalent of 15 000 tonnes of coal. Over the course of a year, a 1000-megawatt power plant will require 2000 train cars of coal, or only 12 cubic metres of natural uranium.

Uranium's high energy density also trumps hydroelectricity, biomass, wind power, and solar power. If half of Ontario were to be flooded to a depth of 60 metres and placed behind a hydroelectric dam, the resulting 11 000 megawatts of electricity would equate to only 80 percent of that produced by Canada's existing fleet of nuclear reactors. Replacing the electricity produced by a 1000-megawatt nuclear reactor would require 2500 square kilometres of biomass, a 770-square-kilometre wind farm, or 150 square kilometres of solar panels. Nuclear power plants are expensive to build, costing between $1 billion and $3 billion, but they operate with minimal variable costs and, given the small amounts of uranium required to operate them, are relatively immune to price fluctuations. The spectacular 1986 accident at the Chernobyl nuclear power station in Ukraine notwithstanding, nuclear power has demonstrated itself to be safe and reliable, with no serious injuries or deaths being attributed to the operation of a CANDU nuclear power plant.

Nuclear power also can act as an excellent energy source for extracting hydrogen from water; hydrogen, in turn, becomes a CO_2-free fuel source for automobiles. When hydrogen is extracted from water, deuterium (or "heavy water") is produced as a byproduct. Deuterium is used as the moderating substance that slows the free neutrons emitted from uranium atoms in

(continued)

BOX 11-6
(CONTINUED)

CANDU reactors, thus allowing them to split, or "fission," other uranium atoms, and generating the heat that is used to turn water into steam and spin an electricity-generating turbine. This process presents the opportunity of a synergy between nuclear power, for electricity generation, and hydrogen, as a fuel source for automobiles: hydrogen is extracted from water, deuterium is created as a byproduct, deuterium is used to moderate nuclear power plants, nuclear power plants generate electricity, and electricity is used to extract hydrogen from water.

However, nuclear power is not without its problems. Uranium may have a high energy density, but uranium mining is an activity with substantial potential for environmental harm. Proponents of nuclear energy stress the substantial adverse environmental effects of the entire fuel cycle when they discuss fossil fuels (the environmental degradation inherent in coal mining, the news reports that surround the frequent Chinese mine accidents, and the environmental effects of burning coal to generate electricity) and then declare the environmental superiority of nuclear power. This narrow focus on the power generation aspects of nuclear energy is somewhat disingenuous.

Nuclear energy can have some of its most serious environmental effects early in the fuel cycle, that is, during the mining of uranium. Uranium mining can release radionuclides into the atmosphere through the crushing and grinding of ore, from fugitive dust emissions, and from the release of radon gases. Uranium has the geological attributes of metals and, like most nonferrous metals (such as copper, gold, lead, nickel, silver, and zinc), often is found in what are called "sulphide ore deposits." When oxygen and water come in contact with the sulphur in the ore deposits, acid is generated. The problems of uranium's radioactivity and acid mine drainage have a perverse synergy in that the acidity created by acid mine drainage leads to the further dissolution of radionuclides, thus enhancing the radioactivity given off by the uranium. Consequently, the fine-grained tailings left behind by uranium mining operations will pose a potential environmental risk for centuries and will require perpetual monitoring.

Often the people and places that have to deal with the hazards of uranium mining are forgotten in discussions of the environmental costs of nuclear fuel. Frequently, these *people* are Indigenous peoples and these *places* are their ancestral lands. Indeed, uranium mining has occurred with such frequency on lands inhabited by Indigenous people that it has become known as "radioactive colonialism." On the Navajo reserve on the Colorado plateau of the southwestern United States, for example, concerns surrounding the environmental effects of uranium mining have led to the Dine Natural Resources Protection Act of 2005, which bans all uranium mining and processing anywhere on the reserve. These are important questions as Canada remains the world's largest exporter of uranium, and the Saskatchewan government, elected in November 2007, is considering accelerating the development of nuclear energy within the province.

Reprocessing spent fuel, and separating out reusable uranium, plutonium, and nonrecoverable waste products, can avoid the mining of fresh uranium for use as fuel, but this practice is dangerous as plutonium is the ideal material for nuclear weapons, which can be developed with as little as 8 kilograms of diverted plutonium.

If spent fuel is not reprocessed it must be disposed of, generating another controversial issue. In their 1972 book, *Only One Earth: The Care and Maintenance of a Small Planet,* Barbara Ward and Rene Dubos described the generation of power by means of nuclear energy as the Promethean act of stealing fire from the gods. In ancient Greek mythology, Prometheus stole fire from the gods and, as a result, gave humankind a limitless source of energy. However, as punishment for his hubris, Prometheus was chained to a rock for all eternity where an eagle would perpetually feed upon his flesh. Nuclear energy may provide us with virtually limitless energy, but it also will produce wastes that will remain radioactive for thousands of years. Humans, like Prometheus chained to his rock, will be left with the consequences of this waste for eternity. Should we choose to acquire the limitless energy of the Promethean fire, we automatically choose to deal with the perpetual consequences of this act. It is not enough to assert that "perpetuity is a long time away," as Lorne Scott, Saskatchewan's former Minister of Environment and Resources Management, did during the 1997 environmental impact assessment of the Saskatchewan uranium mines.

Lastly, there are the issues of *risk* and *trust.* If wide-scale adoption of nuclear power is implemented as a way of forestalling climate change (brought on by the use of CO_2-emitting fossil fuels), the public (knowledgeable about the Chernobyl disaster) will be consoled by experts, such as engineers and nuclear physicists, who will assure them that nuclear energy is safe and that they, being the experts, can be trusted. This is an excellent example of what Anthony Giddens would call "the juggernaut of modernity." In premodern times, humans faced risks (such as crop failures, droughts, earthquakes, epidemics, famines, and storms) that were *naturally* occurring events. Today, we still face these risks, but we also face risks, such as accidents at nuclear power plants or terrorists acquiring weapons-grade plutonium, that are created by our *own technology.* For the public to accept these risks, the experts who assure them that the risks are acceptable must be trusted, and this may be the biggest challenge of all to nuclear energy.

SOURCES: *Yellowcake Towns: Uranium Mining Communities in the American West,* M. A. Amundson, 2004, Boulder: University of Colorado Press; "Renewable and Nuclear Heresies," J. H. Ausubel, 2007, *International Journal of Nuclear Governance, Economy, and Ecology, 1*(3), 229–243; "Implementing Kyoto in Canada: The Role of Nuclear Power," D. Bratt, 2005, *The Energy Journal, 22*(1), 107–121; "Nuclear Power's New Dawn," D. Butler, 2004, *Nature, 429,* 238–240; *Canadian Nuclear FAQ,* 2007, http://www.nuclearfaq.ca/nuke-gen-monthly-2006.htm; "McArthur River Uranium Mine Environmental Assessment Process," H. Cotton, 1999, *Journal of Environmental Law and Practice, 9,* 71–91; *The Consequences of Modernity,* A. Giddens, 1990, Stanford, CA: Stanford University Press; "When the Price Is Right," J. Giles, 2006, *Nature, 440,* 984–986; "Nuclear Is the New Black," A. Ma'anit, September 2005, *New Internationalist, 382,* 2–6; "Uranium-Sustainable Resource or Limit to Growth?" C. MacDonald, 2004, *Nuclear Energy, 43*(2), 99–105; "Is the Friendly Atom Poised for a Comeback?" E. Marshall, 2005, *Science, 309,* 1168–1169; "The Need for Nuclear Power," R. Rhodes & D. Beller, 2000, *Foreign Affairs, 79*(1), 30–44; *Environmental Effects of Mining,* E. A. Ripley, R. E. Redmann, & A. A. Crowder, 1996, Delray Beach, FL: St. Lucie Press; *Only One Earth: The Care and Maintenance of a Small Planet,* B. Ward & R. Dubos, 1972, New York: Norton.

just focus on changing the way we are living by reducing personal consumption of energy." The remaining 13 percent "did not know" (Innovative Research Group, 2007). Interestingly, however, when asked whether they would support or oppose the idea of Canada as a world leader in developing nuclear energy or in energy conservation and technology, 62 percent strongly supported Canada as a world leader in conservation, and only 20 percent strongly supported Canada as a world leader in nuclear energy (Innovative Research Group, 2007). The variability in Canadians' opinions is just one of the challenges in making sustainable energy policy decisions.

RESPONSES TO ENVIRONMENTAL IMPACTS AND CHANGE

EMERGING ENERGY RESOURCES AND TECHNOLOGIES

While energy is essential to Canada and Canadians, we face key challenges in producing and using energy in ways that minimize environmental impacts and provide the kind of balanced and desirable future we imagine. The availability of energy resources in the future is not anticipated to be a concern for Canadians (but prices might be), and fossil fuel energy is expected to continue to dominate our supply for the next few decades. However, growing interest in emerging energy resources and new technologies reflects concerns in several parts of the country about the adequacy of our electrical supply, the interest in diversifying energy sources including "renewables," regional concerns about air quality, and overall concerns about climate change.

Emerging energy resources and technologies include wind power, biomass, small hydro, geothermal energy, fuel cells, solar cells, ocean energy, and clean coal, among others. Breakthrough technologies related to gas hydrate resources, nuclear fusion, or a hydrogen economy also could change the ways Canadians produce and use energy. This section provides a brief overview of the advantages and disadvantages of some of these emerging technologies (see Table 11–3) as well as examples of mechanisms that promote and constraints that hinder the development of emerging energy resources and technologies.

Currently, emerging power generation technologies constitute about 3 percent of the installed generating

TABLE 11–3
EMERGING ENERGY RESOURCES AND TECHNOLOGIES

Emerging Energy Resource and/or Technology (cost = $/MWh)	Advantages/Benefits/Potential	Disadvantages/Costs/Barriers
Wind power • cost: 50–100 • size: 1–2 MW (wind farms 50–150 MW)	• three provinces have established renewable portfolio standards and requested proposals for wind power developments • strong wind resources in many regions • short construction and installation lead times	• intermittency of wind resources requires backup power or energy storage to ensure reliability • gaining economical access to existing transmission facilities affects decisions about project siting and feasibility
Small hydro • cost: 40–150 • size: <25 MW	• largest contributor to Canada's green power sector • conceptually simple, mature technology • low capital and low operating costs • large number of potential sites in Canada means good near- and long-term prospects	• output is subject to seasonal variations • developers may face difficulties with site approval and environmental assessments (disproportionate to project size) that impose costs and time delays • projects may be constrained by local opposition (usually environmental basis, NIMBY)
Biomass • cost: 40–150 • size: 10–50 MW	• second-largest renewable energy source after small hydro • produced through industrial **co-generation**, mostly in pulp and paper industries • improved prospects in Canada (higher natural gas prices, shift away from coal-fired generation, limitations on new hydro development, intermittency issues associated with other renewable technologies)	• wide regional variability in potential for biomass generation from landfill gas, municipal waste, and agricultural operations • development may be constrained by relatively high start-up and operating costs *(continued)*

TABLE 11-3

(CONTINUED)

Emerging Energy Resource and/or Technology (cost = $/MWh)	Advantages/Benefits/Potential	Disadvantages/Costs/Barriers
Geothermal • cost: 40–100 • size: 100–200 MW	• extracts naturally occurring underground steam to power conventional steam turbine and generating unit • fuel costs are low; operating and maintenance costs are competitive with other technologies • extremely reliable, once operational, and suitable for base-load power	• upfront investments are high • long-term prospects are limited because there are few high-quality sites in Canada • potential for high grid connection costs depending on location
Solar photovoltaic (PV) cells • cost: 200–500 • size: varies at consumer level	• solar cells made of semiconductor materials (silicon) produce energy directly from sunlight • well suited to distributed energy applications (energy generation at the point of consumption in residences, commercial buildings, or industrial applications)	• although technology is well proven, advancements need to be made to be cost competitive in the Canadian market • barriers to distributed generation (such as restrictive or unclear grid connection standards) make installing modules difficult
Fuel cells (hydrogen) • cost: 100–150 • size: 1–100 MW	• electrochemical devices produce electricity (and water and heat) by combining hydrogen and oxygen • operate at high efficiencies (40–50 percent; up to 80 percent if waste heat is used) • can be manufactured in a wide range of sizes (fully scalable) • well suited to distributed generation applications	• technological breakthroughs required before fuel cells can be competitive with other generation sources (about five years to commercial stage) • still expensive • niche applications
Ocean energy • cost: 80–190 • size: <1 MW	• one tidal power plant exists in Nova Scotia • best prospects are west and east coasts due to tidal current and wave power	• in early stages of development; costs are uncertain • tidal currents are intermittent but predictable
Clean coal • cost: 50–60 • size: 250–500	• involves methods to reduce emissions resulting from coal-fired generation • global warming concerns have focused technology on reducing CO_2 emissions • integrated coal gasification combined cycle (IGCC) has lower capital costs and is more reliable to date	• Alberta is most likely to build coal-fired generation facilities because of abundant coal, but favours a less efficient but more reliable coal-fired technology (supercritical coal-fired technology) • development of CO_2 sequestration techniques needed to improve prospects for IGCC power generation • expensive compared with conventional coal • few commercial projects currently
Demand management • cost: 0–50 • size: varies at customer level	• includes demand side management (DSM), specifically energy conservation and energy efficiency, and demand response (DR), actions by consumers to reduce demand on short notice in response to a pricing initiative • helps stabilize prices • improves reliability of electricity supply • provides environmental gains	• to what extent DSM or DR programs can be deployed is uncertain • some measures require significant investment • potential benefits are not always perceived to be achievable, thus limiting uptake

SOURCE: *Emerging Technologies in Electricity Generation,* National Energy Board, 2006, Calgary: Author.

capacity in Canada. In terms of electricity, this low penetration is partly a result of the low costs of electricity generated from conventional sources (large-scale hydro, coal, nuclear power, and natural gas), and partly a result of the large publicly owned utilities using large central generating stations. Technology, an important part of the solution for energy supply and for environmental challenges, has made rapid advances over the last few decades. On the supply side, for instance, technological advances have permitted continuation of current levels of conventional production, enabled people to gain access to unconventional resources, and facilitated development of alternative sources of energy. More energy-efficient technologies are being developed on the demand side also. Key challenges remain: to consider which technologies should be supported, to what extent, and to what end (National Energy Board, 2007a, 2007b). Other interesting policy questions are likely to be debated by Canadians, such as whether renewable resources should become a required part of energy generation and acquisition by public utilities, and whether consumers should pay an emissions (carbon) tax.

Incentives for Emerging Energy Resources

Mechanisms to promote the development of emerging energy resources and technologies include both provincial and federal incentives. At the provincial level, requests for proposals, establishing renewable portfolio standards, and *net metering* (allowing utility customers with generation capacity to sell power to the grid) are offered. Net metering is an important mechanism, because the rules that have permitted access to the transmission grid for small-scale or remote producers often have been unclear and restrictive (because the rules were established to connect large-scale generating stations to load centres using the extensive transmission network set up by centralized power systems). These issues are being addressed particularly in jurisdictions where electricity markets have been opened to competition.

Renewable Portfolio Standards   Several U.S. states, including California, have enacted statutes that require public utilities to obtain a portion of their energy load from renewable resources. Known as renewable portfolio standards (RPS), this tool is often used in the United States as a climate change "fix," but RPS also can be used to increase energy self-sufficiency and national security. Typically, RPS use results in increased research and development of alternative energy sources such as wind, biomass, geothermal, tidal, small hydro, and solar.

Canadian provinces have been slow to adopt formal RPS requirements. Public utilities in Quebec are required to obtain certain amounts of energy from certain types of renewable resources, Ontario has set a renewables target,

and British Columbia has indicated that a portion of new load must come from renewables. Part of the reason there has not been a rush to enact RPS legislation in Canada may be that many of the provinces, including Quebec, British Columbia, and Manitoba, obtain most of their power from large-scale hydro operations. While it may be reasonable to identify both large- and small-scale hydro as renewable energy resources, policy decisions have specified that large hydro cannot be used to meet RPS requirements. Designing a workable RPS without including large hydro sources seems unlikely; effective use of RPS in Canada may require government cooperation to alter of policy requirements (Cassidy, 2008).

Emissions (Carbon) Tax   The National Round Table on the Environment and the Economy defines an emissions (carbon) tax as "a fee imposed by a government on each unit of CO_2-equivalent emissions by a source subject to the tax. Since virtually all of the carbon in fossil fuels is ultimately emitted as carbon dioxide, a levy on the carbon content of fossil fuels—a carbon tax—is equivalent to an emissions tax for emissions caused by fossil fuel combustion" (NRTEE, 2007, p. 60).

The Green Party of Canada put it a little more simply when it noted that almost all goods and services in Canada involve some emission of GHGs—such as the fossil fuel used to heat factories, the electricity used to make goods, and the fuels used to transport items. Fossil fuels themselves involve the most emissions, as well as electricity produced by burning fossil fuels. The effect of a carbon tax is to incorporate a price for those emissions in every good and service in Canada; those goods and services that cause high emissions would incur higher fees and become relatively more expensive. Increasing the cost is intended to create an incentive for everyone to make economic choices that contribute less to global warming. Effectively, a carbon tax reflects the true social, political, and environmental costs of fossil fuels.

In its advisory report to the Harper government, the NRTEE echoed prominent economists in recommending that an economy-wide price on carbon be established as soon as possible to achieve the deep cuts required in GHG emissions (Pole, 2008). However, a carbon tax stands in contrast to the federal government's current approach, which involves a blend of regulations, consumer incentives, and fiscal transfers to the provinces and territories. Federal Environment Minister John Baird's response to the NRTEE's report was to ignore the main recommendation and to focus on the need for long-term policy certainty, improved technologies, and a global approach.

Government Incentive Programs   Federally, a variety of incentive programs such as the Wind Power Production Incentive (WPPI) and the Renewable Power Production

Incentive (RPPI) have been directed toward renewables. After industry participants called for a comprehensive renewable strategy, Natural Resources Canada agreed to work toward this goal. Canada's Office of Energy Efficiency (OEE) was established in 1998 to manage energy efficiency and alternative fuels programs aimed at the residential, commercial, industrial, and transportation sectors. One of the OEE programs, EnerGuide for Houses, aims to improve energy performance in the residential sector by helping homeowners obtain individualized professional advice on how to improve the energy efficiency of their homes. The R-2000 home program provides some

standards for homeowners to follow to improve energy efficiency (see Box 11–7).

In its May 2006 budget, the Harper government cut most of Canada's climate change programs, including the successful WPPI and the EnerGuide program for houses. Internationally, the Canadian government withdrew support for the United Nations Climate Change Secretariat, which implemented the Clean Development Mechanism (CDM). Established under the Kyoto Protocol, the dual goals of the CDM are to promote sustainable development in developing countries and to allow industrialized countries to earn emissions credits from their investments

---

BOX 11–7
FEATURES AND BENEFITS OF AN R-2000 HOME

In 1982, the Department of Energy, Mines and Resources (now Natural Resources Canada) introduced the R-2000 program in partnership with the Canadian Home Builders Association. The R-2000 "environmentally friendly" home can generate up to 40 percent savings in energy consumption over a traditional house of the same size.

The central feature of an R-2000 home is the strict requirement for air sealing and the use of the heat recovery ventilator (HRV) or the air-to-air heat exchanger. Located near the furnace, an HRV unit draws fresh air into the house while expelling existing air. As the air streams pass each other, incoming air is either heated or cooled by outflowing air, resulting in improved heating and cooling efficiency. R-2000 standards require an HRV unit to exchange all the air in a house at least once every three hours. Although the placement of windows, doors, and roof overhangs is taken into consideration in energy-efficient homes, virtually any house design can accommodate the R-2000 approach. However, only houses built by R-2000–certified builders may be certified as R-2000 homes.

The Built Green Society of Canada owns and manages the voluntary Built Green program, which encourages builders to build homes that have better energy efficiency, indoor air quality, resource use (including waste management), and overall environmental impact. Natural Resources Canada's EnerGuide for New Houses provides the mandatory energy efficiency component of the Built Green Checklist. The checklist identifies the "green" criteria such as energy efficiency, and the "green" items from which builders can select to meet the platinum, gold, silver, and bronze achievement levels in the program. The Built Green program currently is available only in British Columbia and Alberta; Built Green municipal incentives offer a building permit rebate fee for homebuilders who achieve R-2000 or Built Green certification. Over 7600 new single-family homes and row homes were enrolled in the program by early 2008.

Features and benefits of R-2000 homes include

- a whole-house, continuous ventilation system, resulting in better air quality and health advantages;

Photo 11–14
The R-2000 symbol.

- more environmentally friendly (low-emissions) building materials and equipment;
- advanced heating and cooling systems;
- energy-efficient appliances and lighting;
- energy-efficient windows and doors, resulting in fewer drafts and cold spots;
- a "tight" building envelope to reduce drafts and heat loss;
- less noise and dust;
- high levels of insulation;
- greater comfort, with lower energy bills.

So why the name R-2000? The "R" is a value normally assigned to the insulation capacity of a building surface, such as R-35 walls, and the "2000" represents the futuristic building standard the federal government wanted to see in place by the year 2000.

SOURCES: *About Built Green,* Built Green Society of Canada, 2008, http://www.builtgreencanada.ca/content.php?id=260; About R-2000, Natural Resources Canada, Office of Energy Efficiency, http://www.oee.nrcan.gc.ca/residential/personal/new-homes/r-2000/About_r-2000.cfm?attr=4. Reprinted with permission. R-2000™ is an official trademark of National Resources Canada.

---

in emission-reducing projects. The 2006 federal budget did not provide a strong commitment to real solutions to climate change—such as renewable energy, energy efficiency, and conservation—but made nonspecific promises to cut GHG emissions and issued an expensive tax credit for transit passes.

In January 2007, the federal government announced the ecoEnergy Renewable Power program to support the addition of 4000 megawatts of renewable energy between 2007 and 2011. The Canadian Wind Association anticipates that, because of high demand, the funding available through the program will be allocated fully by the end of 2009. Compared to other parts of the world, Canada has lagged behind in wind power, but with both provincial and federal support, wind energy installed capacity is predicted to grow to 12 000 megawatts and meet 5 percent of Canada's total electricity demand by 2016 (Canadian Wind Energy Association, 2008). If Canada intends to become a global clean energy leader, governments must ensure that wind energy is one of the key elements in future energy development strategies.

BARRIERS TO EMERGING ENERGY RESOURCES AND TECHNOLOGIES

A major constraint to the development of emerging energy technologies is that the external costs (negative externalities) associated with air pollution and other environmental costs are not included in the price of energy products. If market prices were to include these factors (that is, if external costs were "internalized"), many people feel that emerging technologies would be more competitive and possibly even lower cost than conventional generation. In some cases, such as electricity, prices do not always reflect actual costs because the prices may be based on historical rates that are below the cost of developing new generation capacity. "Heritage resources" (such as low-cost, large-scale hydro projects) often are used as policy instruments to mitigate costs of more expensive new generation, but such an approach results in higher consumption and reduces the motivations to conserve and to invest in emerging technologies. Levelling the playing field (evening out the differentials in price treatments) would help enhance the competitiveness of emerging technologies (National Energy Board, 2007a).

Another barrier to emerging technologies is dealing with regulatory requirements to gain project approvals. Emerging technology projects often are smaller than their conventional generator counterparts, yet both types of projects face the same regulatory processes. Not only may the requirements seem relatively more burdensome to the emerging technology proponent, but the new entrants may not have the expertise required to deal with the regulatory process. Both established and emerging technology proponents may have to face the NIMBY ("not in my backyard") effect.

Canadians have expressed their concerns about climate change, greenhouse gases, and other environmental effects of energy production and use, and many individuals have responded favourably to federal and provincial programs to reduce overall and peak demands for energy. Individual consumers also appear to be responding to increased energy costs by adjusting their lifestyles and spending habits, including purchasing "green power" certificates (see the following section). However, lack of awareness of and access to funding are two barriers to demand-side management efforts that have reduced the effectiveness of energy conservation and energy efficiency programs (National Energy Board, 2007a). To the degree that governments have tended to support traditional sources of generation, and have developed standards, infrastructure, and other systems to support conventional energy sources, it is time to establish similar support systems for emerging energy resources and technology, as well as for improvements in energy efficiency.

Buying Green Power in Canada

Green power (green energy) is electrical power derived from a range of clean, renewable energy sources. There are two key criteria for green power: it must be generated from renewable resources, and it must have minimal impact on the environment. While there is no consensus about what constitutes green power, most people think of wind turbines, solar cells, and hydroelectricity as green energy sources. Nuclear power is not a green power source because it uses uranium, a nonrenewable resource.

Currently, electricity generated from green power sources costs more than electricity from conventional sources, although costs of green power are declining as the technologies become more established. Because our electricity pricing systems do not take into account the savings to society when green power is used (cleaner environment, reduced climate change impacts), consumers who buy green power are paying a premium. Essentially, they pay the difference between the standard price the developer is paid for the sale of electricity and the cost to generate it through green power—often the amount paid by utilities for green power does not cover all the costs of generating that power. Consumers who pay the premium are helping to build a market for green power, but not all consumers are able or willing to pay this premium.

Buying green power is becoming easier for Canadians in certain parts of the country; where bundled green power is available, customers can pay the premium as part of their regular electricity bill, or they can pay it separately by buying federal or provincial Green Power certificates (known also as Green Tags) that add a specified amount

TABLE 11–4

GREEN POWER AVAILABILITY IN CANADA

Province	Utility	Program	Power source(s)	Availability[1]	Comments
British Columbia	BC Hydro	Green power certificates	Small hydro, biomass	I, C	$15 per certificate, representing 1 MWh of green power
Alberta	Bullfrog Power	Bullfrog Power	Wind	R, C	EcoLogo certified; 2¢ per kWh
	Canadian Hydro Developers	Green certificates	Wind, small hydro	R, C	EcoLogo certified; $20 per MWh
	EPCOR	Envest	Wind, solar, biomass, run-of-river hydro	C (large), I	Green Tags are EcoLogo certified; customized pricing per MWh
	ENMAX	Greenmax	Wind	R, C	EcoLogo certified; residential: $6.50 for 50% or $12.00 for 100% green power per month (about $1.25 per kWh); small and medium business: $15 for 50% or $30 for 100% green power; powers Calgary's light rail transit system
	Vision Quest	Green Tags, Green Energy to bundled power customers	Wind	C	Green Leaf– and Green E–certified Green Tags offered to retail customers through the Pembina Institute; commercial customers: customized pricing
Saskatchewan	Sask Power	Green Power (bundled power)	Wind	R, I, C	EcoLogo certified; $2.50 per 100 kWh
Ontario	Ontario Power Corporation	Evergreen	Small hydro, wind, biogas, solar PV	Large C, I	EcoLogo certified; power generated from pre-1990 facilities is not certified but is blended with power from newer facilities; three rates depending on blended power structure. Average price $35 per MWh
	Energy Ottawa	Green Power	Small hydro	R, C	EcoLogo certified; customized pricing
	Oakville Hydro	Green Light Pact	Small hydro, wind, biogas, solar PV	R, C	EcoLogo certified; Green Light Pact program is a certificate marketing program; $30 per 500 kWh, $60 per 1000 kWh
	Bullfrog Power	Bullfrog Power, Green Power certificates to bundled power customers	Wind, low-impact hydro	R, C	EcoLogo certified; direct sales to residential customers at 8.9¢ per kWh
New Brunswick	JD Irving	Green Power	Small hydro	Direct marketing to large customers only	GreenLeaf certified; 3¢ per/kWh
Nova Scotia	Nova Scotia Power	Green Power	Wind, hydro, tidal	R, G	EcoLogo certified; 125 kWh at $5 above standard electricity price

[1] Customers are categorized as R = residential; I = industrial; C = commercial/corporate.

[2] Currently there are no bundled power offers and no Green Power certificates in Manitoba or Quebec; no bundled power offers in British Columbia or New Brunswick; and no Green Power certificate programs in Saskatchewan or Nova Scotia.

SOURCE: *A consumer guide to green power in Canada,* Pollution Probe. (July 2007) http://www.pollutionprobe.org/whatwedo/greenpower/consumerguide/index.htm

of green electricity to the grid on behalf of the customer. (Even though a utility might be generating green power and putting it into the grid, it is physically impossible to ensure that "green electrons" from a green power facility are being delivered to a certain location. However, the utility can guarantee that green power is part of the overall power mix in the quantities it retails to its customers.) Revenue from the "tags" or certificates helps green power developers to compete in the wholesale electricity market by covering the extra cost of producing this power. Table 11–4 identifies selected details of these options for Canadian consumers.

When customers purchase green power, they pay for clean, renewable energy to be supplied to the power pool for a certain number of kilowatt-hours. Their purchase displaces emissions from coal- and gas-fired generation facilities, reducing air contaminants including SO_2, NO_x, and GHGs. Green power is certified (see Photo 11–15) and tracked by independent third parties that verify the source, quality, and amount of clean energy supplied. If a customer were to purchase 1000 kilowatt-hours of electricity from wind power instead of the same amount of electricity generated from a coal-fired plant, the positive benefits would be the same as

- leaving 3454 kilograms of coal in the ground,
- avoiding 1000 kilograms of GHGs,
- not driving your car 4350 kilometres,
- planting five trees.

Whether the issue is wind farms or CBM gas wells, green power certificates or R-2000 homes, public awareness and engagement is vital to achieving energy and environmental sustainability objectives. As the footprint of energy extraction, production, and distribution grows, an increasingly informed and committed Canadian public is asking for access to information and knowledge, for interaction with the energy industry, and for evidence of the societal benefits and costs of energy technology and developments.

Photo 11–15

The EcoLogo program, launched by the Canadian government in 1988, is North America's oldest and most widely recognized and respected environmental standard and certification organization. The program sets standards and certifies environmentally preferable (green) goods and services. The EcoLogo program is the only North American standard accredited by the Global Ecolabeling Network as meeting the international ISO 14024 standard for environmental labels.

With its enormous reserves of oil sands, Canada is being touted as an energy superpower, but for many Canadians, sustained development of the energy sector potentially conflicts with other objectives such as environmental sustainability. A "smart" and flexible energy policy is required to ensure the role of emerging energy resources and technologies within a changing global environment and within a framework that takes into account the regional differences in energy supply systems and energy-related emissions. This is a highly challenging route to take into the future because of the difficulties in integrating the entire energy chain, all the jurisdictions, and multiple layers of government into developing policies and programs that will establish and guide Canada's future energy paths.

Ground-source heating and an aquifer thermal energy storage project in Canada are considered briefly in Enviro-Focus 11 on the next page.

ORGANIZED INITIATIVES

Canadians expect that heat and light for our homes, fuel for our vehicles, and power to operate our businesses and factories will be available on demand. In Western society, much of this energy comes from nonrenewable fossil fuels. Use of oil, coal, and natural gas is a major cause of air and water pollution, land disruption, and long-term changes in global climate. Similarly, use of other common energy sources, such as hydroelectricity, nuclear power, and biomass energy, also affect the natural environment and can have devastating effects on ecosystem sustainability. In response to the detrimental environmental effects of energy use, Canada has developed a number of initiatives and has become a partner in international agreements aimed at conserving energy, reducing the output of GHGs (discussed in Chapter 5), and developing renewable energy sources.

The United Nations Framework Convention on Climate Change, opened in 1992 at the Earth Summit in Rio de Janeiro, Brazil, acknowledged for the first time that human activities have an influence on global climate. The parties agreed to work toward preventing the predicted effects of climate change, such as sea-level rise and changes to agricultural production zones. In 1997, international commitments were strengthened when the Kyoto Protocol established targets for reducing GHG emissions. The Kyoto Protocol, to which Canada was a signatory, committed nations to reduce GHG emissions to 6 percent below 1990 levels by 2008–12. Many nations who signed the Kyoto Protocol were not on track to meet the reduction target. In 1999, Canada realized that a reduction of 26 percent in our GHG emissions from business-as-usual forecasts would be necessary if we were to reach the international objective.

The Conference of the Parties (CoP) is the primary decision-making body of the United Nations Framework

Ground-Source Heating and Cooling

Both earth and water maintain a relatively constant temperature below the surface, making them an ideal heating source in the winter months or cooling source in the summer months. Tapping backyards, ponds, or lakes for geothermal energy is an environmentally friendly and efficient way to heat and cool many types of buildings.

Tapping geothermal energy is basically a way of moving (rather than generating) heat. A sealed or closed-loop system, in which a water-based solution is pumped through a polyethylene pipe extending vertically or horizontally below the Earth's surface, can operate effectively with ground temperatures ranging from –5°C to 38°C.

In the winter, for example, the solution absorbs heat and carries it to a geothermal unit, which compresses the heat to a high temperature (similar to the process used in conventional refrigerators) and delivers it to the home or building. A small electric pump operates the system, but the energy generated is often four or five times greater than the energy used. In comparison, if a conventional natural gas furnace achieves a one-to-one ratio, it is considered to be highly efficient.

The idea of geothermal energy use in Canada is not a new one. Open-loop heat pumps, which use the water and discard it, have been used in Canada since 1912, and closed-loop technology has been available since the 1940s. A 300-room hotel in Winnipeg has used geothermal power since the 1930s, and it is used extensively in British Columbia.

Although start-up costs of geothermal systems are about 40 percent higher than for conventional systems, savings in operating costs usually make up for the difference in three to five years. Because there is no combustion of fossil fuel, and no greenhouse gases are produced, geothermal systems are safe. They produce less dust and provide better indoor air quality. Ground-source heating maintains a relatively constant heating in winter, provides greater control over humidity in summer, and is suitable for use in private residences and commercial and public buildings such as schools.

In Sussex, New Brunswick, an aquifer thermal energy storage (ATES) system at the Sussex Hospital complex has been fully operational since January 1995. The hospital uses the ATES system to reduce the cost of preheating air and saves approximately $86 000 in energy consumption annually. The system works by using two well fields, one cool (7.5°C) and the other warm (10°C), located on either side of the hospital complex. During the cooling season, the groundwater is transferred from the cool well field through the exchange systems within the buildings to the warm well field; the process is reversed during the heating season. In the cooling season, heat is transferred from the air through, for example, a water-to-air coil to the groundwater, thus reducing the temperature of the air in the supply system. The system was expanded in 1999 to increase its thermal efficiency.

Using a hospital to demonstrate the ATES concept is significant because hospitals depend on secure energy supplies for heating and cooling. While large-scale ATES systems are not used widely in Canada, the Pacific Agricultural Research Park in Agassiz, British Columbia, Carleton University in Ottawa (since 1990), and the Scarborough Centre in Ontario operate ATES systems.

SOURCES: "Ground-Source Heating: The Wave of the Future?" D. Burke, March 18, 1997, *Canmore Leader,* p. A14; "Underground Thermal Energy in Sussex, New Brunswick," F. Cruickshanks, 1997, *Water News, 16*(2), 3–6; "Underground Thermal Energy Rises to Future Challenges," F. Cruickshanks & J. L. Sponagle, June 1997, *Technical Bureau Supplement, Water News,* i–viii.

Convention on Climate Change. Representatives from all signatories to the Kyoto Protocol have met annually to negotiate implementation measures, chart progress, review new technologies, and provide support in reaching Kyoto commitments. Recognizing that developed countries have contributed the most to the GHG problem, CoP requires industrialized countries to provide leadership through emission reduction as well as technological and financial support to developing countries. On February 16, 2005, the Kyoto Protocol officially entered into force, and because Kyoto is the only binding, international agreement that sets targets to reduce GHGs, it was an important step forward in the global fight against climate change.

Canada had ratified the Kyoto Protocol in December 2002. Between 1998 and 2003, even without a formal plan, the federal government invested $3.7 billion to support the reduction of GHGs by individual Canadians, industry and business, and governments and communities (Government of Canada, 2003). Some of the activities eligible for funding included new technology and alternative fuel development measures, energy efficiency incentives, research, and public education programs (Government of Canada, 2003). The government invested in real solutions to climate change, including a variety of programs associated with renewable energy, energy efficiency, and conservation. Efforts to meet the Kyoto target (6 percent below the 1990 level by 2008–12) included mandatory emissions cuts for large factories and power plants and a voluntary agreement with automakers to improve the fuel efficiency of Canadian vehicles. Provinces and territories developed action plans, as did all sectors of the economy. Studies showed that implementing the Kyoto Protocol would stimulate the hi-tech and construction industries, create jobs, reduce health care costs from air pollution, and help protect our ecosystems (David Suzuki Foundation, 2002). Even if the plan relied too heavily on incentives and voluntary initiatives, the Chrétien government was working toward meeting Canada's Kyoto target.

Following its election in January 2006, the Harper government backed away from the preceding government's commitments to fight climate change, announcing that the new government would not even try to meet the Kyoto target. Instead, funding for Canada's climate change plan was cut, as were most of the climate change policies and programs implemented previously. In October 2006, the Harper government indicated that it planned to address smog and climate change by consulting for another three years with industry and by using an intensity-based approach to setting targets. Initially, the specified target on tackling climate change was set for 2050 and was less than half the reduction that scientists indicate is necessary to avoid the most dangerous effects of climate change. Strong criticism of this vague position (expressed in the Clean Air Act, Bill C-30, in October 2006) challenged the government to revise its GHG targets to 20 percent below 2006 levels by 2020, and 60 to 70 percent below 2006 levels by 2050. And, since opinion polls in Canada consistently reveal the public's increasing awareness of the need to address climate change, the federal government responded with its ecoACTION plan to address atmospheric emissions and climate change. This plan marked a significant policy shift, but did not satisfy fully the criticism that the government had failed to make a genuine effort to meet international commitments specified in the Kyoto Protocol.

OUR ENERGY FUTURE

In January 1999, crude oil prices averaged about US$12 per barrel; less than a decade later, in mid-2008, crude oil traded at over US$130 per barrel. Energy price is one of several factors influencing Canada's energy systems and futures. Other factors include global growth in energy demand (led by developing countries, particularly China and India) and associated concerns about security of supply for the large-consuming countries; changing energy and environmental policies; consumers' responses to increased energy costs; development of new and innovative technologies; new infrastructure requirements and additions to existing infrastructure such as pipelines; the vital economic role that industry plays in the Canadian economy; energy exports, particularly the issue of processing lower-value raw resources within Canada to obtain higher value products for export; and reserves of conventional resources.

While not all of the preceding factors have been discussed in this chapter, it is clear that the growing importance of energy issues has stimulated provincial governments to develop energy strategies and policy directives, as well as climate change action programs. For instance, British Columbia, Alberta, Manitoba, Nova Scotia, Newfoundland and Labrador, and the Northwest Territories have released climate action plans. Nova Scotia has released policy directives focusing on alternative energy sources such as tidal power and hybrid transit systems, energy efficiency measures, and GHG emission reductions. Released in 2006, Quebec's energy strategy emphasizes accelerated development of hydroelectric resources and wind power, energy efficiency across all forms and uses, and innovation. Ontario has released several policy directives pertaining to conservation, small-scale alternative energy projects, and net metering, all promoting improved efficiency in use of energy while reducing emissions. Another Ontario policy directive in April 2007 focuses on energy efficiency and changes in the electric sector.

In the same vein, Alberta's focus on emission intensity reductions from final large emitters is specified in its Climate Change and Emissions Management Amendment Act, while intent to expand the bioenergy industry is contained within the Nine Point Bio-Energy Strategy document. Early in 2007, British Columbia released its Vision for Clean Energy Leadership, focusing on energy efficiency, electricity self-sufficiency, net zero emissions from thermal generation, renewable portfolio standards, and alternative fuels. The Northwest Territories has produced a Greenhouse Gas Strategy as well as an Energy Plan, recognizing the need for increased conservation and efficiency while maintaining the integrity of the northern environment. Manitoba is working on developing wind power, and

New Brunswick has promised a Climate Change Action Plan. Saskatchewan is exploring net metering and in 2007 introduced a Green Strategy that includes initiatives dealing with climate change.

Cities, too, are examining ways to reduce their greenhouse gas emissions. Despite the fact that the United States did not sign the Kyoto Protocol, in November 2007, more than 100 mayors from across the country held a summit to discuss the effects of climate change on their cities and to identify steps they are taking to reduce greenhouse gas emissions. The U.S. Mayors Climate Protection Agreement has been signed by more than 720 mayors from 50 states (Seattle Government, Office of the Mayor, 2008). Canadian cities also are taking action. Saskatoon formally has adopted a greenhouse gas emission strategy to reduce emissions. Universities across Canada are challenging one another to do the same. Large-scale events, such as the Olympics, also provide opportunities to demonstrate our commitment to using energy in ways that support sustainability (Box 11–8).

Increasing numbers of Canadians are realizing that they have a personal responsibility for environmental action, and their efforts to seek action and accountability from politicians and industry representatives have helped drive more robust policies and programs. The federal government's 2007 plan, *Turning the Corner: An Action Plan to Reduce Greenhouse Gases and Air Pollution*, which targets absolute reductions in GHGs and calls for reduction of industrial air pollution by half by 2015, may be seen as a response to political opposition and to growing public pressure for action on energy issues. Although not all provincial and territorial governments have reached the same level of policy development, and not all sectors of the industry are targeted equally for improvements in energy consumption and GHG emission reductions, some progress has been made in seeking balance between economic, energy, and environmental objectives (National Energy Board, 2007a).

While Canadian energy policy is continuing to evolve, an apparent global shift also is occurring in the way we produce and use energy—from wasteful and environmentally destructive consumption toward cleaner and more efficient forms of power. Wind power, for example, is growing by 40 percent annually in Europe, and the U.S. government actively promotes wind energy. The fastest-growing energy source in the world, wind power (in some areas) is economically competitive with electricity generated by burning fossil fuels. Canadians, who pride themselves on being innovators in the energy field, could learn from other nations such as Denmark: growing faster than the cellular phone industry, Danish manufacturers have quadrupled their production of wind turbines since about 2003. If this growth rate were to be sustained, within the next 15 years the entire Danish population could be employed in the wind industry. Canadians appreciate that there is great economic growth potential in improving energy efficiency and in producing clean, sustainable energy that reduces the risk of climate change, yet brings jobs, investment income, improved health, and quality of life.

A long-term energy vision and strategy for Canada is necessary to ensure that social, economic, and environmental sustainability goals are achieved and that policies and regulations effectively integrate conventional, new, and emerging energy resources and technologies into our

BOX 11–8
CARBON NEUTRAL AT THE VANCOUVER 2010 OLYMPIC AND PARALYMPIC WINTER GAMES?

The Vancouver 2010 Olympic and Paralympic Winter Games have the opportunity to be one of the most climate-friendly Games ever. This will require delivery of a comprehensive climate change strategy that effectively manages the GHGs associated with the 2010 Winter Games. The Vancouver Organizing Committee (VANOC) can move toward a zero net emissions Games by adopting a carbon neutral strategy. This strategy involves calculating GHG emissions associated with the organization's activities, reducing those emissions wherever possible, and purchasing high-quality carbon offsets to mitigate remaining emissions. There are major, unavoidable emissions sources associated with the 2010 Winter Games, including ground transportation of people and goods, energy consumption at events (electricity, heating, snow making, freezing ice rinks, and sliding tracks), and air travel for participants and spectators.

A credible carbon neutral strategy for VANOC would use best practices to reduce GHG emissions from all aspects of its activities, followed by the purchase of carbon offsets, thus resulting in zero net emissions for the Games. As one of the highest-profile international events in the world, the 2010 Winter Games has an opportunity to establish legacies of improved public transportation, energy efficiency, and renewable energy capacity, and to significantly advance public understanding and action regarding global warming and its solutions. While it will not get the same visibility as the athletic performances the world comes to see, perhaps VANOC will earn a gold medal for its carbon neutral performance.

For more information on the carbon neutral proposal for the 2010 Winter Games, see D. Carlson and C. Lingl, 2007, *Meeting the Challenge: A Carbon Neutral 2010 Winter Games Discussion Paper*. Vancouver: David Suzuki Foundation. http://www.davidsuzuki.org/files/reportsMeeting-the-Challenge.pdf.

evolving energy system. Canadians are likely to adjust their energy consumption behaviour as electricity and other energy prices rise, and as the policies and programs designed to reduce GHG emissions change the way we live and produce our goods and services. Canadians will need to understand the implications of such changes, and it is their participation in discussions of Canada's energy future that will help foster good decision making and ensure balanced outcomes. Canadians, along with many others in the world, are on the verge of a profound shift in thinking about energy; will this generation be the one to make the transition to renewables and sustainability?

MAKING A DIFFERENCE 11
STEVE NASH

Steve Nash is best known for his skills on the basketball court, having twice been named Most Valuable Player in the National Basketball Association (NBA). What may be less well known is that this Canadian sports star, raised in Victoria, British Columbia, uses his celebrity status to make a difference in the environment and in society.

The Steve Nash Foundation works to ensure that children have the rights outlined in the United Nations Convention on the Rights of the Child—the right to health, the right to play, the right to live without abuse, and the right to learn. His website states,

> I started this Foundation because I really felt the need to try to help people. As a professional athlete, you are in a position and given the opportunity to really have an impact on more than just your immediate surroundings.... Every day, all of us—together and as individuals—have an opportunity as citizens to contribute to the vision of what we want to see in the world.... At the Steve Nash Foundation, we believe strongly that every child has the right to be healthy, to have a good education, to live in an environment that contributes to her well-being, to his personal development.

These are strong words that Steve Nash puts into action through his foundation; he has supported dozens of organizations, events, and charities that work toward healthy lifestyles for children, particularly children who are disadvantaged economically, physically, or socially. His website also makes several suggestions for ways individuals may contribute to positive environmental change.

Steve Nash is committed personally to protecting the environment for future generations. An example of his commitment to reducing energy consumption is his endorsement of an athletic shoe made of recycled material (from worn-out shoes) and reused materials (leather). Steve wore this "Nike Trash Talk" shoe at the 2008 All-Star NBA game. Subsequently, Nike committed to design all its footwear to a higher environmental standard. In 2006, to promote his many social and environmental causes, Steve Nash initiated an annual, carbon neutral charity basketball game to be played in Vancouver.

In 2007, the Steve Nash Sports Club opened in Vancouver, reflecting sustainability principles. The club was built according to "Silver" Leadership in Energy and Environmental Design (LEED) standards for commercial interiors—the first fitness facility in Canada to do so. The club's wood floors are made of renewable, quick-growing bamboo and the rubber flooring is made of recycled car tires. Area rugs composed of recycled athletic shoelaces were chosen for their recycled content and contribution to air quality. Add in energy-efficient lighting and the Steve Nash Sports Club isn't just a place to work out—it is a sports club where people who spend energy also save it.

Steve Nash's actions can help spur a new generation to take actions within their own lives to reduce their energy consumption and to protect the environment.

Photo 11–16
Steve Nash at the opening of the ecofriendly Steve Nash Sports Club in Vancouver, 2007.

SOURCES: "Steve Nash and Nike Turn Garbage into "Trash Talk," *Nikebiz,* February 13, 2008, http://www.nikebiz.com/media/pr/2008/02/13_Nash.html; "The Steve Nash Foundation: About," *The Steve Nash Foundation,* n.d., http://stevenash.org/html/about.html; "The Steve Nash Foundation: Growing Health in Kids," *The Steve Nash Foundation,* n.d., https://stevenash.org; "Fitness and Health in a Green Designed Building," Steve Nash Sports Club, 2007, http://www.stevenashsportsclub.com/a_healthy_environment.html.

Chapter Questions

1. The world consumes about 84 million barrels of oil a day; currently, people consume two barrels of oil for every barrel discovered. And, according to some, world demand for oil will continue to grow by over 40 percent by 2025. Should you be worried about this issue? What are some of the steps that need to be taken by the oil industry, governments, automakers, energy technology companies, and consumers to deal with this challenge?

2. An advantage of various forms of renewable energy (wind and solar energy, for instance) is that they cause no net increase in carbon dioxide. Is this true for biomass? Why or why not?

3. Excluding fossil fuels, what other forms of energy have the greatest potential where you live? What would be some of the advantages to your community of developing these energy sources? What might be some of the barriers to developing these energy sources? Are there any federal or provincial incentive programs available to assist in the development of these energy resources?

4. Discuss why or how energy conservation and improved energy efficiency might be considered major "sources" of energy.

5. Why is the permanent storage of high-level radioactive wastes such a problem in Canada and elsewhere?

6. What kinds of energy conservation measures could you adopt for each of the following aspects of your life: washing dishes, doing laundry, lighting, bathing, cooking, buying a car, driving a car?

7. How can governments and the private sector support the efforts of citizens to reduce overall energy consumption and move toward more sustainable sources of energy?

references

Alberta Energy. (2006). *What is oil sands.* http://www.energy.gov. ab.ca/OilSands/793.asp

Alberta Energy and Utilities Board. (2000). Guide 60: Upstream petroleum industry flaring guide. http://www.eub.gov.ab.ca/bbs/products/newsletter/2000–01/atb_jan2000_fea02.htm

Anonymous. (2005, January 13). Oil spills: Cleaning up the mess. *EnviroZine, 50,* Feature 2. http://www.ec.gc.ca/EnviroZine/english/issues/50/home_e.cfm

Bolger, L., & Isaacs, E. (2003). Shaping an integrated energy future. In A. Heintzman & E. Solomon (Eds.), *Fueling the future: How the battle over energy is changing everything* (pp. 55–81). Toronto: House of Anansi Press.

Bott, R. (2004). *Canada's evolving offshore oil and gas industry.* Calgary: Canadian Centre for Energy Information.

Budgell, P. (2006). *State of the industry review.* http://oilsands. infomine.com/commodities/soir/oilsands/

Canadian Association of Petroleum Producers. (2001). *Action on energy—Industry continues to surpass gas flaring targets.* http://www.capp.ca/default.asp?V_DOC_ID+816_

Canadian Hydropower Association. (2007). *Hydropower: Clean and renewable energy to power our development. Submission to the Council of Energy Ministers.* http://www.canhydropower.org/hydro_e/pdf/CEM_2007.pdf

Canadian Nuclear Association. (2007). *Canada's nuclear energy: Reliable, affordable and clean electricity.* http://can.ca/english/Nuclear_Facts/Nuclear_Energy_Booklet-EN/2007/CAN-07NucFactsBklt_EN.pdf

Canadian Press. (2007, November 15). 10 years after: Hibernia oilfield has surpassed expectations. http://www.cbc.ca/canada/newfoundland-labrador/story/2007/11/15/hibernia-decade.html

Canadian Wind Energy Association. (2008, January 30). *Wind energy sets global growth record in 2007.* News release. http://www.canwea.ca/news_releases.cfm

Cassidy, P. (2008). Carbon tax and spread of RPSs likely key themes during 2008. *Environment Policy and Law, 18*(.8), 1031.

David Suzuki Foundation. (2002). *The bottom line on Kyoto: Economic benefits of Canadian action.* http://www.davidsuzuki.org/Climate_Change/Kyoto/

De Souza, M. (2007, November 12). Doctor alleges oilsands coverup. *Calgary Herald,* p. A3.

Dyer, S., Moorhouse, J., Laufenberg, K., & Powell, R. (2008). *Under-Mining the environment: The oil sands report card.* Drayton Valley, AB: The Pembina Institute. http://www.pembina.org/pub/1571/

Feldman, D. L. (1995). Revisiting the energy crisis: How far have we come? *Environment, 37*(4), 16–20, 42–44.

Francis, W. (1997). Burning questions about gas flares. *Environment Views and Network News, 1*(1), 18–19.

Gjertson, H. (1997). Still the worst. *Alternatives, 23*(3), 5.

Government of Canada. (2003). *Taking action on climate change: Government of Canada announced $1 billion toward implementation of the climate change plan for Canada.* http://www.climatechange.gc.ca/english/publications/announcements/news_release.html

Haggett, S. (2007, November 9). Natives fear oilsands pollution causing cancer. *Calgary Herald,* p. A13.

Hamilton, G. (1997, February 16). Emblem of death. *Calgary Herald*, p. A13.

Hill, R., O'Keefe, P., & Snape, C. (1995). *The future of energy use.* London: Earthscan.

Innovative Research Group. (2007). *Canadian Defence and Foreign Affairs Institute, fall conference study 2007 poll.* http://www.cdfai.org/PDF/CDFAI2007Poll.pdf

International Energy Agency. (2003). *Key energy indicators in 2000: Canada.* http://www.iea.org/stats/files/selstats/ketindic/country/canada.htm

International Hydropower Association. (2004). *Sustainability guidelines.* http://www.hydropower.org/sustainable_hydropower/sustainability_guidelines

International River Network. (1998). *The river dragon has come.* www.irn.org/programs/threeg/dragon.html

Kom, J. (2007, November 10). Family says sour gas leaks are making it sick. *Calgary Herald*, p. B2.

Lau, M. (2000, July 24). Rancher's gas battle still flares. *Calgary Herald*, p. B1.

Lee, K, (2006, November). Hibernia project: Monitoring environmental effects associated with produced water discharges. *The COOGER Update, 3*(1), 1–2.

Macfarlane, A. (2003). Is nuclear energy the answer? In A. Heintzman & E. Solomon (Eds.), *Fueling the future: How the battle over energy is changing everything* (pp. 127–151). Toronto: House of Anansi Press.

National Energy Board. (2007a). *Canada's energy future: Reference case and scenarios to 2030.* Calgary: National Energy Board. http://www.neb.gc.ca/clf-nsi/rnrgynfmtn/nrgyrprt/2007/nrgyftr2007-eng.pdf

National Energy Board. (2007b). *Canada's oil sands—Opportunities and challenges to 2015: An update questions and answers.* http://www.neb-one.gc.ca/clf-nsi/rnrgynfmtn/nrgyrprt/lsnd/pprtntsndchllngs20152006/pprtntsndchllngs20152006-eng.html

National Round Table on the Environment and the Economy. (2007). *Getting to 2050: Canada's transition to a low-emission future.* Ottawa: Author.

Natural Resources Canada. (2000). *Energy in Canada 2000.* Ottawa: Author.

Natural Resources Canada. (2006a). Bioenergy and biomass. http://www.nrcan.gc.ca/es/etb/ctec/cetc01/htmldocs/Publications/factsheet_bioenergy_e.htm

Natural Resources Canada. (2006b). *Energy efficiency trends in Canada 1990 to 2004.* Ottawa: Author.

Natural Resources Canada. (2006c). *Ethanol the "green gasoline."* http://www.nrcan.gc.ca/es/etb/ctec/cetc01/htmldocs/Publications/factsheet_ethanol_the_green_gasoline_e.htm

Natural Resources Canada. (2006d). *Improving energy performance in Canada—Report to Parliament under the Energy Efficiency Act for the fiscal year 2005–2006.* Ottawa: Author.

O'Meara, D. (2008, March 20). Syncrude scores reclamation win. *Calgary Herald*, p. E5.

Pole, K. (2008). NRTEE report supports carbon tax, cap-and-trade. *Environment Policy and Law, 18*(8), 1025–1026.

Public Safety and Sour Gas. (2000, December 18). *Provincial Advisory Committee on Public Safety and Sour Gas releases final report: Findings and recommendations.* http://www.publicsafetyandsourgas.org/FinalRec.htm. Accessed January 2001.

Seattle Government, Office of the Mayor. (2008). *U.S. Mayors Climate Protection Agreement.* http://www.seattle.gov/mayor/climate/

Sly, L. (1997, January 18). Upheaval on the Yangtze. *Calgary Herald*, p. C3.

Statistics Canada. (2002). *Human activity and the environment: Annual Statistics 2002.* Ottawa: Minister of Industry.

Statistics Canada. (2006). *Human activity and the environment: Annual Statistics 2006.* Ottawa: Minister of Industry.

Stone, K. (2006). *Coal.* Canadian Minerals Yearbook, 2005. http://www.nrcan.gc.ca/ms/cmy/2005CMY_e.htm

Sydney Tar Ponds Agency. (2006). *What a long, strange trip it's been.* http://142.177.37.250/_clients/stpa/wwwRoot/default.asp?T=2&M=14

Taylor, D. M. (1994). *Off course: Restoring balance between Canadian society and the environment.* Ottawa: International Development Research Centre.

Yang, L. (2007, Oct. 12). China's Three Gorges dam under fire. *Time.* http://www.time.com/time/world/article/0,8599,1671000,00.html

Zich, A. (1997). China's Three Gorges: Before the flood. *National Geographic, 192*(3), 2–33.

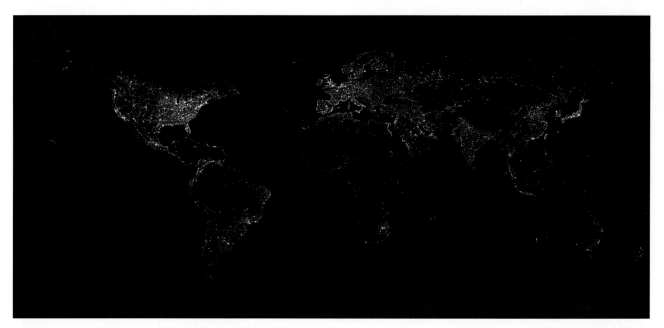

Photo 11-17

Waste energy creates the light pollution that enables NASA's composite view of the world at night from space. After you consider which countries are brightest and darkest, you may not be surprised to learn that no industrialized nation ranks near the top of the energy efficiency scores in the Canada and the World section.

Chapter Contents

"The endangered spaces that must be loved and protected are the irreplaceable landscapes and waterscapes whose mosaics contribute to the health, beauty, permanency, and productivity of the globe. To perceive native landscapes and waterscapes, parks and wildernesses, as beyond price, as sacrosanct, is the saving goal that humanity must pursue."

J. Stan Rowe, in Hummel (1989)

Chapter Objectives

After studying this chapter you should be
able to

- understand the importance of biodiversity
  for economic, ecological, and social
  well-being

- describe the impacts of human activities on
  wild species and their habitats

- appreciate the complexity of trying to
  measure biodiversity and to determine
  how best to protect it

- discuss Canadian and international strategies to protect biodiversity

- consider the implications of climate change
  for the protection of biodiversity

- debate challenges and opportunities for
  biodiversity protection for sustainability

INTRODUCTION

Biodiversity is a nonrenewable resource. Despite the fact that many of its components, such as flora and fauna, are renewable, the structure, networks, and cycles that make up the whole cannot be reproduced in a timeframe that is meaningful to humans. For example, one may replant trees, but, as pointed out in Chapter 9, trees are not the sole component of an old-growth forest. The rich and biodiverse ecosystem of an old-growth forest is lost once a key component is extracted.

Additionally, biodiversity is not replaceable. Unlike other nonrenewable resources such as coal or copper, we have been unable to find or create adequate substitutes for key components such as water or for interactions such as a food web. Once a region's biodiversity is degraded, it is very difficult to reproduce the complex interactions and hence to regain its ecological health and integrity. Consequently, if we consider biodiversity as a resource—something that is used for human benefit—then biodiversity is one of the most precious. Given that many of the values we attri-bute to biodiversity, such as spiritual and intrinsic values, are not exchanged in the marketplace, biodiversity is extremely susceptible to degradation and loss.

There are currently between 1.5 and 1.8 million named species in the world. About one-half of these are insects; only 4500 species of these are mammals (McGill University, 2007). An estimated 5 to 20 million species exist: in total the range is large because so little is known about the diversity of life on this planet. Despite their rel-atively small numbers, mammals tend to be better known than insects, fungi, and other less popular species. While it is estimated that at least 7 million species of insects remain unknown (Environment Canada, 1996), there are still occasional discoveries of mammals. Just as important as the threatened wild species themselves are the land-scapes or ecosystems they inhabit. From the coasts of Newfoundland to the rain forests of British Columbia, and from the prairie grasslands to the Arctic tundra, Canada is losing wilderness at the rate of more than 0.4 hectares (1 acre) every 15 seconds (World Wildlife Fund Canada, 2000b). Figure 12–1 (on the next page) illustrates areas of risk to biodiversity in Canada.

The purpose of this chapter is to describe and illus-trate the importance of biodiversity and the challenges associated with its protection for the sustainability of the planet. The chapter begins by describing changes in amphibian populations around the world to illustrate vul-nerability of ecosystems to degradation and uncertainties surrounding our scientific understanding of associated changes. Next, we draw attention to the ways in which scientists understand and measure biodiversity as well as the multiple ways in which we value it. We then turn to

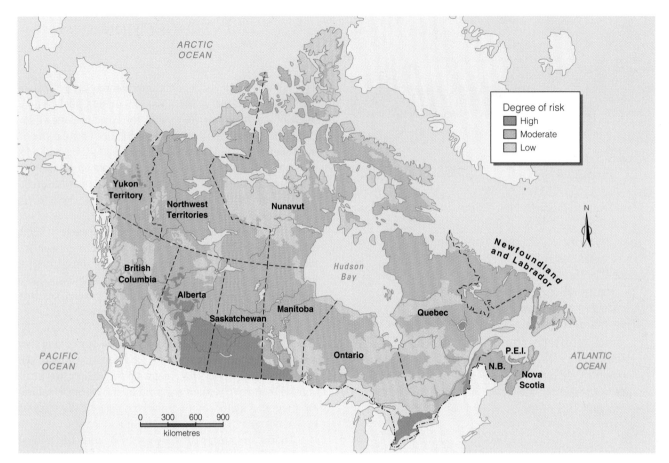

Figure 12–1

Risk to biodiversity in Canada

SOURCE: Adapted from *Protect Canada's Biodiversity,* Western Canada Wilderness Committee, Spring 1995, *14*(4), 4–5. Based on *Biodiversity in Canada: A Science Assessment for Environment Canada,* Minister of Supply and Services, 1995, p. 2.

the effects of human activities on biodiversity and identify strategies for protection. The chapter ends by discussing future challenges and opportunities.

AN ILLUSTRATION OF LOSS: GLOBAL CHANGE IN AMPHIBIAN POPULATIONS

The vulnerability of and uncertainties associated with habitat and species loss are illustrated by the rapid decline of frog species throughout the world. Once the most widespread frog species in North America, the northern leopard frog experienced a population crash in the mid-1970s all across the continent. "Piles of dead and dying frogs were reported from many Lake Manitoba shorelines, [and] heaps nearly a metre high were recorded from the major frog holes" (Zolkewich, 1995, p. 3). By 1989, the realization that a variety of frog species had disappeared almost simultaneously from large, well-protected national parks and nature reserves around the world raised particular concern. Golden toads, for instance, disappeared from the Monteverde Cloud Forest Reserve in Costa Rica, and gastric breeding frogs vanished from

a remote national park in Australia. The golden toad has not been seen since 1989, and the gastric frog since 1981 (Campbell, 1999; Pounds et al., 1999). Research has shown that red-legged frogs have disappeared from pristine habitat near Yosemite National Park, California (Drost & Fellers, 1996), and apparently are extirpated (National Parks Service, 2000).

Most previously observed amphibian (frog, toad, salamander, and newt) population declines and extirpations were attributed directly to habitat destruction by logging, urbanization, and drainage of wetlands, and indirectly to pollutants. Local amphibian populations also could have been affected greatly by factors such as weather (particularly drought), predation, and extensive commercial harvest such as occurred with bullfrogs in Algonquin Provincial Park, Ontario (Brooks & MacDonald, 1996; Amphibiaweb, 2008).

The loss of frogs from geographically dispersed and apparently pristine protected areas suggested one or more global agents might be adversely affecting amphibians. Possible candidates for the causes of these global declines include an increase in UV-B radiation resulting from ozone layer depletion; chemical contamination including the effects of acid precipitation, pesticides, herbicides, and

Photo 12–1a

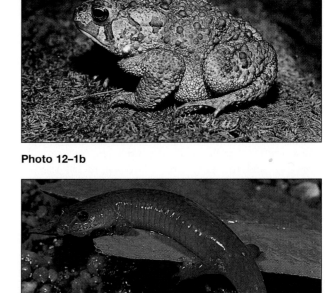

Photo 12–1b

Photo 12–1c

Photo 12–1d

Amphibians, such as frogs (12–1a), toads (12–1b), newts (12–1c), and salamanders (12–1d), are highly sensitive to a variety of environmental stressors. Because they do not migrate, because they reside in aquatic and terrestrial environments, and because their skins are permeable, they are excellent indicators of chemical changes in the environment.

fertilizers; introduction of exotic competitors and predators; and disease (Declining Amphibian Populations Task Force, n.d.; Dunn, 1996).

Frogs and other amphibians are highly sensitive to a variety of environmental stressors and are good indicators of ecological problems (see Chapter 3). Their permeable skins, through which they breathe, make them extremely vulnerable to both airborne and waterborne pollutants. In addition, their low mobility and complex life cycles (involving both aquatic and terrestrial habitats) make them vulnerable to subtle habitat changes. Of all the vertebrate classes, they may be the best indicators of ecological health, able to pinpoint degradation of terrestrial and aquatic habitats better than even the more commonly monitored bird populations (Bishop et al., 1994).

Why does the loss of amphibians matter? Vanishing amphibians not only signal a loss of biodiversity, a cause of concern in itself, but also may indicate "profound environmental change affecting all life on earth" (Dunn, 1996, p. 4). There is a sense that if frogs are in trouble, humans are not far behind (Zolkewich, 1995). In addition to their significance as a measure of the health of the environment, amphibians are an important part of the ecological balance

of many habitats. As predators, frogs and salamanders consume many times their weight in invertebrates, including many pest species, and, as prey, they control the abundance, distribution, and health of numerous aquatic and terrestrial predators (Bishop et al., 1994). Amphibians also have biomedicinal value: for example, we are just beginning to appreciate the potential and value that the skins of amphibians have in yielding drugs useful to medicine.

In spite of amphibians' ecological significance, scientists have only a rudimentary understanding of amphibian population dynamics, and baseline data on the populations of the 140 types of salamanders and 90 frogs and toads occurring in Canada and the United States are almost nonexistent (Bishop et al., 1994). Since the populations of most amphibian species exhibit large natural fluctuations, extensive research and long-term monitoring are necessary to determine whether the extirpations and large population declines are following natural patterns or are accelerating.

In response to international declines in frog populations, the IUCN (the World Conservation Union, formerly known as the International Union for the Conservation of Nature and Natural Resources) Species Survival Commission struck the Declining Amphibian Populations

Task Force (DAPTF) in 1991. Over 3000 scientists and conservationists now belong to the network of 90 working groups around the world (including one in Canada) attempting to determine the nature, extent, and causes of global declines of amphibians and to promote means by which the declines can be halted or reversed and species diversity maintained (Declining Amphibian Populations Task Force, 2000).

The documented disappearance of amphibian species emphasizes the urgency of establishing reliable inventories and long-term monitoring programs in general, and of establishing them in national parks and other protected areas in particular. Inventories in Mount Revelstoke and Glacier national parks in British Columbia, for example, have revealed the presence of two amphibian species (western toads and spotted frogs) that have undergone severe population declines elsewhere. Monitoring these

species within the parks should contribute data to a national database and help analysts identify and understand both the internal and external threats to biodiversity and ecological integrity (Dunn, 1996). (For further information about amphibian monitoring programs in Canada, see Box 12–1.)

Saving remaining populations and their habitat also is critical to the survival of some amphibian species, and Ducks Unlimited is one organization that has been active in this area. Their Prince's Spring project, a northern leopard frog breeding colony located about 190 kilometres southeast of Hanna, Alberta, is a protected site where this species has a good chance for survival. The frog population has remained stable since the early 1980s, when Ducks Unlimited constructed two dykes to create a spring-fed freshwater marsh, and built five nesting islands within the marsh (Zolkewich, 1995).

BOX 12-1
AMPHIBIAN MONITORING IN CANADA

In 1992, volunteer observers began monitoring the mating calls of male amphibians in Canada. By 1995, over 400 observers were involved in large-scale monitoring programs in Nova Scotia, Quebec, Ontario, Manitoba, and Saskatchewan. Each night for three minutes during the April to July mating season, observers report on the species calling and the intensity of the calling. Observers choose their own monitoring sites, which can be a favourite pond or marsh, a rural road, or even their own backyard. This program has become very popular with the general public, partly because volunteers are sent tapes of the frog calls, and people enjoy the opportunity to learn the calls of animals other than birds.

In Ontario, the Long Point Bird Observatory and Environment Canada's Marsh Monitoring Program combine sight and sound surveys of marsh birds and amphibians in Great Lakes wetlands to assess the need for rehabilitation of a marsh or to determine whether a rehabilitation project has been successful. In 1995 and 1996, 5502 amphibian choruses were recorded on 256 routes.

In Nova Scotia, the monitoring program focuses on the spring peeper; volunteers call the provincial museum on the first date in spring when they hear the spring peepers. These data collected by volunteers not only provide information on the presence or absence of the spring peeper, but also promote awareness, because the locations of the first dates of calling are reported on television weather maps.

There is also an extensive cooperative amphibian monitoring program between Canada and the United States. The North American Amphibian Monitoring Program (NAAMP), established in 1994, is a collaborative effort of the amphibian research and conservation community in North America.

The broad goal of NAAMP is to develop a statistically defensible program to monitor the distribution and abundance of amphibians. So far, provinces and states have focused on

implementing calling surveys and establishing herpetological (reptile and amphibian) atlases. Collaboration among researchers and volunteers is important to the success of projects such as Saskatchewan's Amphibian Monitoring Program and Ontario's Herpetofaunal Atlas. The NAAMP provides data reports to such atlas projects, and the atlas projects assist monitoring programs through analysis of data, development of additional survey routes, and "frog watch" programs.

Participants in NAAMP's monitoring programs come from federal governments, provincial and state natural resource groups, national parks, wildlife refuges, academia, ENGOs, and the public. Both the Canadian and North American amphibian monitoring programs rely to a considerable extent on partnerships between professional biologists and volunteer observers. These partnerships also serve as educational and training opportunities, as volunteers learn how to identify the calls of adult amphibians and develop other skills in order to help collect high-quality data (Orchard, personal communication, 1997).

The Canadian Amphibian and Reptile Conservation Network (CARCNET) is a proactive group, principally of biologists, working to reverse the trends in habitat loss and to better understand frogs, toads, salamanders, turtles, snakes, and lizards. This organization helps coordinate public involvement in frog and toad monitoring programs across Canada and has developed a system to identify Canada's most critical and valuable amphibian and reptile habitats. This system is used to forewarn Canadians of places that have special significance for the conservation of amphibians and reptiles so that these places can be protected. By December 2000, two sites had been identified: Pelee Island in Ontario and the south Okanagan Valley in British Columbia. For additional information about CARCNET's Important Amphibian and Reptile Areas (IMPARA) project, see their website: http://www.carcnet.ca

SOURCE: *Important Amphibian and Reptile Areas,* Canadian Amphibian and Reptile Conservation Network, 2003. Reprinted by permission of CARCNET, http://www.carcnet.ca

In addition to amphibians, there are many other wild animal and plant species in Canada whose continued healthy existence is threatened by loss and degradation of habitat through human economic development activities. The following discussion about the definition of biodiversity, its measurement and patterns, reveals the connections between individuals and the landscapes they inhabit. It also reveals a high level of scientific uncertainty in our understanding of these relationships.

SCIENTIFIC APPROACHES TO UNDERSTANDING BIODIVERSITY

DEFINING BIODIVERSITY

The Canadian Biodiversity Strategy (n.d., n.p.) defines biodiversity as "the variety of species and ecosystems on Earth and the ecological processes of which they are a part." As described in Chapter 3, biological diversity, or biodiversity, involves three different concepts: genetic diversity, species diversity, and ecological diversity. **Genetic diversity**, as noted previously, is the variation in genetic makeup among individuals within a single species. Genetic diversity can be measured at different scales, including population, species, community, and biome. Genetic diversity is important because it represents the raw materials needed for evolution and adaptation. **Species diversity** refers to the number of different species (that is, species richness) and their relative abundance in different habitats on Earth. This is the easiest type of biodiversity to understand because species frequently can be identified in the field without laboratory equipment. **Ecological diversity**, sometimes called habitat diversity, is the variety of biological communities—oceans, lakes, streams, wetlands, forests, grasslands, deserts—that interact with one another and with their physical and chemical (nonliving) environments. Ecological diversity includes associations, networks, and communities. It is challenging to understand the complex interactions among these elements. Indeed, simply determining the boundaries of a community is a major challenge, let alone determining the interactions among communities. Because of conceptual and practical difficulties, ecological diversity is the least-understood level of biodiversity.

MEASURING BIODIVERSITY

There are three common ways to measure biodiversity: by counting numbers, by assessing evenness, and by determining difference. Biodiversity can be measured by counting the number of species in an area or how many taxonomic groups higher than species are present in an ecosystem. These numbers can be expressed as the number of species found per unit area, per unit mass, or per number of individuals identified. The measurements used depend on the purpose of the study. There is no clear way to standardize measures that are taken at different scales so, different measures are not always comparable. Evenness refers to the extent to which individuals are evenly distributed among species. Several different abundance indices exist, although some are more commonly used than others. Difference relates to comparing diversity across two different units. For example, a site with many species that are all very closely related exhibits a smaller difference than a site with fewer species that are more distantly related. Measurements of difference typically provide some indication of disparity or diversity in character. These three types of measurement do not always provide the same results. For example, Figure 12–2 (on the next page) illustrates that different measures of biodiversity can give us a different indication of the level of biodiversity in a given area.

Just as for humans, biodiversity can be measured by taking sample surveys or by monitoring. Different types of surveys may be established, depending on the purpose. For example, a study designed to determine the number of species in an area may examine every species within a particular grid, while one that seeks to determine changes in populations of specific species may seek to monitor only specific species. While species diversity is most commonly measured, genetic diversity can be measured by taking samples from the field and analyzing them in the laboratory. In some cases, only estimates of the number of species most likely to be found in an area are determined by undertaking a proxy measure, such as the amount of energy available in a system.

PATTERNS OF BIODIVERSITY ACROSS SPACE AND TIME

Biodiversity is dynamic. By this, we mean that the level of biodiversity changes over space and time. For virtually all species, biodiversity increases closer to the equator and decreases toward the poles. Diversity also increases as elevation declines. This is also true, to a point, in oceans. There is more marine diversity on the ocean floor than in the water column. Typically, there are more species contained in larger areas than smaller ones, although this is not a straight-line relation.

The number of species present across the seasons is about the same, although the number of individuals and the total weight of biological material (due to shedding) may be reduced. There have been numerous times when biodiversity has been reduced through natural causes. Glaciations are large-scale disturbances that can affect a region for a long time. For example, amphibians in Canada have not moved back into regions in which they

Figure 12–2

Measuring biodiversity

a) This picture illustrates the greatest number of species, but half of the individuals are from the same species.

b) This picture illustrates a smaller number of species but the numbers of individuals are more evenly distributed.

c) This picture illustrates the smallest number of species but there is the greatest difference between the size of each population.

SOURCE: "Biodiversity Theory: Gaining and Losing Biodiversity," *The Canadian Biodiversity Web Site,* n.d., Torsten Bernhardt, Redpath Museum, McGill University. Used with permission. http://canadianbiodiversity.mcgill.ca/english/theory/gainingandlosing.htm

lived before the last glaciation, even though the last one reached its peak about 20 000 years ago. Mass extinctions also are well known, such as the one that wiped out the dinosaurs 65 million years ago. Nevertheless, in no period except the present have humans had such a rapid and dramatic effect on all levels of biodiversity.

The Importance of Biodiversity

The diversity of life in Canada and on this planet sustains us. Biological diversity supports vital ecological processes, including oxygen production, water purification, conversion of solar energy into carbohydrates and protein, and climate moderation. Indeed, human health and ultimately our survival depend on these ecological processes. Beyond its life-supporting contributions, biodiversity also has tremendous economic value. In a landmark study, Costanza et al. (1997) estimated that the value of the world's ecosystems services and natural capital was $33 trillion. Although this study was undertaken more than a decade ago and has not been replicated, the basic point is that the number calculated is larger than the global gross domestic product. This means that the economic value of the world's biodiversity is greater than the economic value of all the goods and services that we create. But the argument for protecting biodiversity is important for at least four additional reasons: maintaining livelihoods through employment and subsistence, spiritual inspiration and cultural identity, intrinsic value, and maintaining future options.

The diversity of Earth's life forms enables people to satisfy many of their needs, including that of gainful employment. Millions of people who work in the fishing, forestry, agriculture, tourism and outdoor recreation, pharmaceutical, and biotechnological industries depend directly on high-quality biological resources to earn their living. As a resource-based economy, Canada relies on its abundance of biodiversity to support many of its rural communities and its balance of payments.

Particularly in the north of Canada, many Aboriginal communities derive a large portion of their food and income from harvesting of biological resources. As we have seen in the cases of east coast fishers and Aboriginal peoples, loss of wildlife species or their habitats affects traditional lifestyles and reduces the quality or availability of country foods, as well as opportunities to undertake other hunting, gathering, and guiding activities (see Chapter 8). The attendant economic repercussions are important also.

In part, Canada's cultural identity has been shaped by the wild, elemental beauty of our natural landscapes. Aboriginal cultures developed intimate relationships with nature, and many non-Aboriginal Canadians also have found that the country's diversity of species and spaces provides spiritual, emotional, and artistic inspiration. Painters, writers, and musicians have captured landscape and wildlife elements in their work and have helped define Canada domestically as well as internationally (see Making a Difference 1 on page 31).

Many Canadians also believe that each of the wild species that inhabits our landscape has **intrinsic value**—a value based on the inherent qualities of that species, independent of its value to humans. As recognized by the Convention on Biological Diversity, the concept of intrinsic value suggests that human society should be built on respect for the life that surrounds us, and that biodiversity should be conserved for its own sake, regardless of its economic or other values. Loss of biodiversity in wild species and spaces means that certain intangible values also are lost, ranging from relationships with the natural world to aesthetics. Conversely, maintaining biodiversity increases the genetic variation among individuals within populations and provides an insurance policy for species survival when environmental conditions extend to threshold limits (see Chapter 3).

As insurance, biodiversity helps us to maintain the flexibility to maximize our options and respond to unforeseen environmental changes and circumstances. These options include using our biodiversity to develop new foods, medicines, and industrial products in the future—for example, the genetic material contained in many of our native plants that enables them to endure both cold winters and hot summers may be used to develop agricultural crops that can withstand even greater temperature ranges. Canada's 138 tree species have at least 40 recorded pharmaceutical or medical uses in addition to industrial products such as cellophane, glue, and turpentine.

If Canadians fail to conserve biodiversity, we foreclose future options, flexibility, and economic opportunities, and pass on the enormous costs of this failure to future generations. Given the current rate of environmental change, and the likelihood that species of unknown (but valuable) ecological, medical, and economic potential are vanishing before their existence has even been confirmed, striving to conserve biodiversity is an investment in the future and makes good business sense. Conserving biodiversity also is one way to help provide for intergenerational equity.

A major global threat to species diversity is that many of the areas richest in endemic species—such as Vancouver Island and the Queen Charlotte Islands in British Columbia—also are prime targets for intensive economic development, including urbanization and forestry.

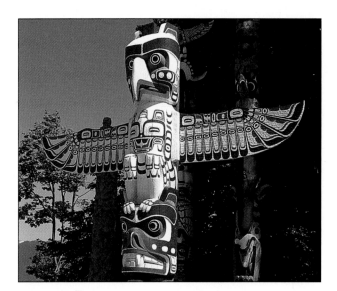

Photo 12–2
First Nations people on Canada's west coast derived distinctive art forms from their close relationship with wildlife species.

In other areas, such as the large sand dunes on the south shore of Lake Athabasca, Saskatchewan, the 10 endemic plant species that occur there could be put at risk by large-scale removal of sand, or unrestricted use of all-terrain vehicles. Recall from Chapter 3, protecting biodiversity involves protecting function, structure, and processes that support the life of plants and animals. Thus, it is necessary to support the protection of habitats in order for flora and fauna to co-exist with humans.

Having briefly reviewed some reasons to protect the biodiversity and sustainability of Canada's species and spaces, the following sections note the nature of Canada's wildlife species and protected areas, and highlight relevant concerns regarding biodiversity and sustainability. As we shall see later in the chapter, national and international efforts are being made to address the loss of species diversity and wild spaces.

HUMAN ACTIVITIES AND IMPACTS ON CANADA'S BIODIVERSITY

CANADA'S BIODIVERSITY

Many of the natural processes that affect biodiversity (such as speciation, succession, extinction) are described in Chapter 3. Because the numbers of species in most **taxonomic** groups tend to decrease from equatorial to polar latitudes, Canada, in spite of its large size, has less species richness than many other nations. Brazil, for instance, has close to 55 000 known species of flowering plants, while Canada has less than one-tenth that amount, including about 2980 species of native flowering plants.

With regard to the total species in Canada (that is, the total of all plants, animals, and microorganisms, of both terrestrial and aquatic ecosystems), estimates are that there are more than 138 000 species in Canada (Government of Canada, 1996). This total includes more than 4000 known plants, as noted above, plus nearly 1800 known vertebrate animals, more than 44 000 known invertebrates, and about 30 000 known species of insects (see Table 12–1 on the next page). These are conservative estimates, as only about one-half of all species and one-third of Canada's insects have been identified. One-half of these species are terrestrial, one-quarter freshwater, and one-quarter live in marine ecosystems. The proportion of species varies within each of these habitats. For example, although 25 percent of species are found in freshwater ecosystems, 80 to 98 percent of algae, 32 percent of bacteria, 15 percent of native flowering plants, and 7 percent of fungi species live in Canada's fresh waters (McGill University, 2007).

TABLE 12-1
THE DIVERSITY OF WILD SPECIES IN CANADA

Kingdom	Major Subdivisions and Common Names	Estimated Number of Species: Reported to Date	Suspected but Not Reported
Procaryotae	bacteria, cyanobacteria (blue-green algae), chloroxybacteria	2400	20800
Protista	algae, diatoms, protozoa	6303	2980
Fungi (Eumycota)	zoosporic fungi, mushrooms, rusts, smuts, lichen, etc.	11800	3831
Plantae	mosses and liverworts	965	50
	conifers and kin	34	0
	dicots and monocots*	3864	75
	club mosses, horsetails, and ferns	141	11
Animalia	molluscs (snails, bivalves, octopus, squid, etc.)	1500	135
	crustaceans (crabs, lobsters, shrimp, etc.)	3139	1411
	arachnids (spiders, mites, ticks, and kin)	3275	7731
	insects	29913	24653
	other invertebrates	6444	4417
	sharks, bony fishes, and lampreys	1091	513
	amphibians and reptiles	84	2
	birds	426	0
	mammals	194	0
Total		71573	66609

* Of the dicots and monocots, about 77 percent (2980) are native and the rest are exotic. Dicots are a group of flowering plants that have two seed leaves. They include many herbaceous plants and most families of trees and shrubs. Monocots are flowering plants with a single seed leaf, including grasses and lilies.

NOTE: Viruses also contribute to Canada's biological diversity. Almost 150 000 species are suspected to exist in the country, but only 200 species had been reported up to 2006.

SOURCE: *The State of Canada's Environment—1996*, © Her Majesty the Queen in Right of Canada, Environment Canada, 1996, Table 10.17. Reprinted with permission of the Minister of Public Works and Government Services Canada, 2008.

Only 1 to 5 percent of Canadian species are endemic—found only in Canada. It is possible that about 800 plant species in Canada are exotic. Most of Canada's biodiversity is found in the southern parts of the country and declines as one travels north. Areas in the south are also home to the largest proportions of endangered species, primarily because of the conversion of land to agriculture and land use and pollution arising from urbanization and the consequent losses in habitat. Resource extraction such as forestry, mining, and fishing also threatens biodiversity. The establishment of roads throughout the country has had a cumulative negative effect on biodiversity by fragmenting habitats. Located in southern Canada as well are the largest number of invasive species that have been introduced deliberately (game fish, starlings) or unintentionally (sea lamprey, zebra mussels).

Beginning with European settlement, Canada's ecosystems have been altered significantly through settlement, cultivation, industrial and domestic pollution, and harvesting of commercially valuable life forms such as fish and trees. Some of the greatest losses to biodiversity have occurred historically as new land uses such as agriculture and urbanization competed with natural ecosystems. The drainage of wetlands (among the habitats richest in species), much of it undertaken in the early and mid-20th century to facilitate agriculture and city formation, reduced these habitats by as much as 90 percent. Habitats have been altered through physical changes, competition from non-native biota, and other cumulative agents of change. Figure 12–3 provides an overview of the level of human activity occurring on Canada's ecosystems; note the overlap with areas of risk to biodiversity shown in Figure 12–1 (refer also to Figure 3–6 on page 73). Table 12–2 indicates in summary form some of the key areas, characteristics, and environmental stresses relating to biodiversity within Canada.

The state of biodiversity in Canada reflects natural changes, such as periodic fluctuations in populations due

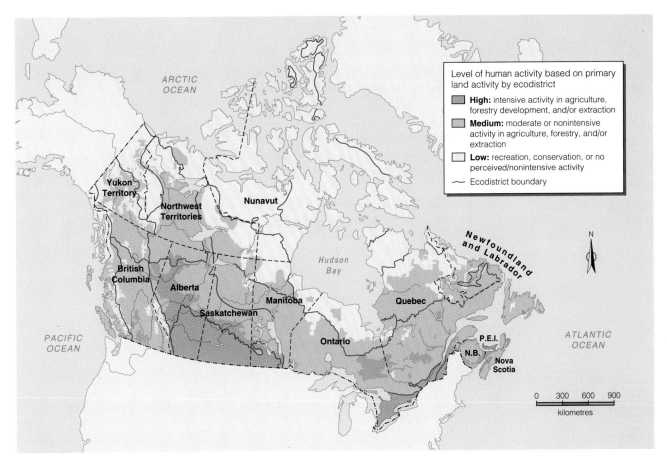

Figure 12–3

Degree to which human activity has changed Canada's ecosystems

SOURCE: *The State of Canada's Environment—1996,* © Her Majesty the Queen in Right of Canada, Environment Canada, 1996, Figure 14.5. Reprinted with permission of the Minister of Public Works and Government Services of Canada, 2008.

to disease, weather events, naturally occurring fires, competition among species, and predation, as well as human activities that alter habitats or introduce non-native species. Major types of habitat alteration, as well as their causes and effects, are outlined briefly in the following sections.

THE EFFECTS OF HABITAT ALTERATION

Humans have been enormously "successful" at exploiting their surroundings for resources that they need or desire. Indeed, key factors in human development described in Chapter 4—more effective technologies, including the technologies of war; increases in human population; and rising levels of consumption and associated waste—have contributed to biodiversity losses. These activities have fundamentally altered the habitat conditions of species. In the following sections, we explore more specifically some of the ways in which human activities have altered habitat and reduced (or exterminated) the populations of non-human species on the planet.

Habitat Alteration Due to Human Activities

Physical changes to habitats have resulted from activities in forestry, agriculture, urban development, and other human pursuits. In forestry, logging and clear-cutting result in loss or fragmentation of habitat for certain species but may enhance habitat for other species. In addition, replanting and reseeding are based on commercial preferences of the forest industry and are not likely to reproduce the original species mix and balance. This results in simplified, evenly aged forests of the tree-farm variety. Fire suppression activities deter the return to early or pioneer stages of natural succession, with implications for species reliant on young-growth forest. Fire suppression also may change the species composition of the climax forest in the area affected.

Agriculture has distorted the original habitat balance of forests, grasslands, and wetlands as they were converted to agricultural lands. Over time, however, previously farmed lands that proved to be marginal for agriculture have been allowed to return to their wild state, while other marginal agricultural lands have been

TABLE 12-2

KEY AREAS, CHARACTERISTICS, AND ENVIRONMENTAL STRESSES RELATING TO CANADA'S BIODIVERSITY

Area	Key Characteristics and Environmental Stresses
Arctic diversity	• Arctic ecosystems occupy about 10 percent of the world's land area; Canada has jurisdiction over about 20 percent of these lands • Arctic regions sustain a wealth of lichens and plant species • Seasonally high productivity of the marine ecosystem attracts sea birds and marine animals to Arctic waters • Atmospheric and oceanic currents carry pollutants to polar regions, causing toxic contamination of the food chain up to marine mammals, birds, and people; over time this places species at risk of decline and possible extinction
Forest diversity	• Close to 10 percent of the world's forests, and a much greater percentage of all boreal forests, grow in Canada • Forests provide a valuable economic resource and a vital habitat for temperate organisms • On the global level, forest biodiversity is being compromised seriously by continuing loss of tropical rain forests • Forest ecosystems filter and purify the atmosphere; provide a living substrate for complex communities of organisms (such as insects, birds); protect watersheds against soil erosion; and moderate impacts of extremes of temperature, wind, and precipitation. Living trees contribute oxygen to the atmosphere, and breakdown of their leaves and other organic debris sustains microorganisms and invertebrates that contribute to soil formation • In Canada, forest biodiversity is threatened by reductions in the extent of forest types (such as southern Ontario's Carolinian species, northern boreal forests, and British Columbia's old-growth forests that provide habitat for specialized species such as the spotted owl) • Logging and clear-cutting result in fragmentation of forested habitat areas so that forests can no longer support species that rely on large, contiguous forest habitat
Grassland diversity	• Grassland biomes represent about 20 percent of Earth's land area; most have been altered dramatically by human activities • At the time of European settlement, prairie grassland ecosystems covered about one-half million square kilometres of western Canada, sustaining a rich, highly specialized floral and faunal community • Since then, more than 80 percent of Canada's grasslands have been converted to agricultural use; their original diversity has been altered profoundly—only about 1 percent of Canada today remains in grassland ecosystems • An important part of the conservation challenge is to protect and enhance native prairie biodiversity within modern agricultural landscapes
Wetland diversity	• Canada has about 24 percent of the world's wetlands as well as a much greater proportion of its boreal fens and bogs • Wetlands are among the world's most varied and biologically productive ecosystems, supporting a great diversity of plants and providing ideal breeding and feeding sites for many kinds of invertebrates, fish, amphibians, and waterfowl • Wetlands also perform important ecological functions, including water retention and purification, and flood and erosion control • Removal of wetlands for agricultural or urban development eliminates habitat for wetland-dependent wildlife species and can seriously disrupt the seasonal supply of fresh water over large areas
Freshwater diversity	• Canadian runoff to the sea is about 9 percent of the world's freshwater runoff; freshwater ecosystems cover more than 7 percent of Canada's surface area, having significant climatic effects (cooling the summer heat, moderating the winter cold) • Canada's freshwater ecosystems sustain about 180 fish species, a rich variety of aquatic plants, and many invertebrates, including some groups of arthropods that appear to achieve greatest diversity in temperate latitudes • Pollution by industrial activities and urban wastes is a significant threat to the quality of freshwater habitats; point-source release of industrial effluents, discharges from urban settlements, and airborne pollutants that fall as wet (acid rain) or dry deposition are of concern

TABLE 12-2

(CONTINUED)

Area	Key Characteristics and Environmental Stresses
Marine diversity	• Globally, the range and diversity of marine ecosystems is only beginning to be understood and measured • Canada has five major marine ecozones spread over 5 million square kilometres of ocean; these ecozones contain some of the most productive marine ecosystems in the northern hemisphere; the total marine food web contains thousands of different kinds of organisms • Threats to Canada's marine ecosystems include overfishing, by-catch (nontargeted species in the catch), destruction of habitat, pollution, and global environmental changes such as climate, temperature, and ocean current changes. Thinning of the ozone layer globally places phytoplankton (the biological foundation of the marine ecosystem) at risk

SOURCE: *The State of Canada's Environment—1996,* © Her Majesty the Queen in Right of Canada, Environment Canada, 1996, Chapters 10, 14. Reprinted with permission of the Minister of Public Works and Government Services Canada, 2008.

restored through conservation programs such as the North American Waterfowl Management Plan.

Other human activities, including urbanization, large- and small-scale hydroelectric facilities, multi-lane highways, railways and transportation infrastructure, and various industrial activities, have impacts on wildlife habitat through physical removal of land. Hiking, use of off-road vehicles, and other recreational pursuits may seem environmentally benign as their effects may not be visible, but even they may result in widespread damage, especially if wildlife populations are stressed already.

Fragmentation Human activities (such as those described above, and others) result in varying degrees of habitat fragmentation. Divided highways and logging and recreational access roads cut off usable portions of some animals' home ranges and create barriers to movement; other animals are reluctant to cross extensive open areas. In both cases, individual animals that attempt to

Photo 12–3
Wildlife viewing and nature photography may cause local environmental stress.

cross highways or large open areas are exposed to greater threats of predation and mortality. Box 12–2 describes some of the effects of transportation corridors on wildlife.

Chemical Changes Terrestrial and aquatic habitats can be degraded by hydrocarbon spills, industrial and municipal effluents, and application of pesticides, herbicides, and other chemical compounds. Acidic deposition, such as from long-range transport of atmospheric pollutants, can degrade life-support systems and reduce overall productive capacity of ecosystems. Some chemical alterations, including increases in nitrogen and phosphorus, can enhance life-support systems for certain species and result in an increase in overall productive capacity of ecosystems. In the case of eutrophication, however, oversupply of nutrients results in detrimental effects on ecosystem functioning.

Climate Change Climate change has the potential to lead to dramatic alterations in ecosystem structure over the long term. Recall from Chapter 5 that climate change includes temperature change, changing rainfall patterns, declining water balances, increased extreme climate events, and changes in oscillations such as El Niño. Some species could find evolving climatic conditions favourable, while others—especially those at the limits of their ranges—could disappear.

It is estimated that in Canada 75 to 80 percent of national parks will experience shifts in dominant vegetation if carbon dioxide levels double (Hannah et al., 2002). In the Great Basin region of the United States, a warming of 3°C would result in a loss of between 9 and 62 percent of mammal species located in the mountain ranges in this region. Small-scale producers of tropical foodstuffs also may experience large economic losses, while globally traded commodities such as coffee, cocoa, and soy may be widely affected (Hannah et al., 2002).

BOX 12-2

WILDLIFE, THE TRANS-CANADA HIGHWAY, AND THE CANADIAN PACIFIC RAILWAY: COLLISION COURSE?

As a place where one can view wild animals close up, Banff National Park has become a favourite vacation destination for Canadian and international visitors alike. However, the pressure on the transportation network that brings about 5 million visitors to Banff annually is increasing, as are collisions and congestion on the highway. To cope with the expected increase in visitors and the anticipated 3 to 4 percent annual increase in traffic on the Trans-Canada Highway through 2015, a decision was made to extend the twinned (expanded from two to four lanes) portion of the highway.

The Trans-Canada Highway has serious effects on wildlife populations in the park: not only does the highway fragment habitat and act as a barrier to natural movements in the Bow Valley, it also is a significant factor in wildlife mortality. About half of the reported wildlife deaths in the park can be attributed to highways—statistical records confirm that known wildlife losses are in the thousands for several species. This is ironic, and unacceptable, given the park's role as a core refuge for wildlife protection.

Upgrading and twinning of the Trans-Canada Highway in Banff National Park began in 1980 and continued in phases throughout the 1990s. Wildlife exclusion fencing was erected to keep animals off the highway right of way, as records showed that fencing the Trans-Canada Highway reduced ungulate (principally elk and deer) collisions by 96 percent. In addition to the fencing, there are 22 wildlife underpasses along the 45-kilometre section of fenced and twinned highway. The section of the highway that was twinned in 1997 incorporated two experimental overpasses to enable wildlife to cross the highway. Costing over $2 million each, these 50-metre-wide overpasses were based on successful European overpasses. Within terrain limitations, they were constructed along known wildlife corridors and were planted with ground cover, shrubs, and other vegetation selected for wildlife security. There was a learning curve for animals to feel sufficiently secure to use the overpasses (in the case of wary species such as grizzlies and wolves, up to five years), but as of November 2007, 11 species of large mammals

Photo 12–5

An example of a wildlife underpass.

have used the wildlife crossings in the park, including the overpasses, more than 94 000 times.

Construction currently is under way to twin a 10-kilometre stretch of the Trans-Canada Highway near Lake Louise; this $87 million project will be completed in late 2008. The federal government is considering the expenditure of between $200 and $250 million to widen the remaining 32 kilometres of the highway to the British Columbia border. Eighteen more wildlife crossings will be built as the twinning of the highway continues.

Another transportation corridor passing through Banff National Park is the Canadian Pacific Railway line and right of way. The railway, too, is a source of considerable wildlife mortality, although little research has been done on railway impacts on wildlife populations. At a 1997 "Roads, Rails and Environment" workshop in Revelstoke, a locomotive engineer presented some observations about train-killed wildlife on the main line between Field and Revelstoke, British Columbia. The collected statistics indicated that trains killed two species of birds (bald eagle and great horned owl) and 12 species of mammals, including black bear, cougar, beaver, bighorn sheep, elk, wolf, and wolverine. Numerous other small mammals and birds were killed also.

It appears that birds are attracted to the railway track to feed on the mice that eat the various grains that spill from passing grain trains. Other wildlife come to the tracks to feed on the carcasses of large animals killed by trains (carcasses are not removed as they are along the Trans-Canada Highway and in national parks). For example, the engineer observed that all bald eagles and almost all coyotes and wolves were killed near carcasses. Other factors such as snow depth, wildlife using the railway right of way as a travel corridor because it is plowed in winter, and the type of seed with which cleared slopes and right of ways are planted (such as clover and other grasses—nutrient-rich food sources that attract bears) contribute to wildlife kills by trains. Changing some of the current management strategies, such as removing train-killed animals from the railway right of way, would help reduce the number of wildlife killed.

Photo 12–4

A wildlife overpass under construction (before landscaping).

SOURCES: "Highway Effects on Wildlife in Banff National Park," A. Clevenger, 1997, *Research Links, 5*(1), 1, 6; "10 Quick Facts about Highway and Wildlife Crossings in the Park," Parks Canada, 2008, http://www.pc.gc.ca/pn-np/ab/banff/docs/routes/routes2_E.asp; *Wildlife Mortality on the Canadian Pacific Railway between Field and Revelstoke, British Columbia,* P. Wells, 1997, paper presented at the Roads, Rails and Environment Workshop, April 9–10, Revelstoke, B.C.

Climate change likely will result also in a shift in location of many wildlife habitats. For instance, coastal wetlands could be displaced or created as sea levels rise, aquatic and semiaquatic habitats could recede as wetlands dry up, and boreal forest plants and animals could shift northward. The implications of such a shift for the establishment of protected areas is explored later in the chapter.

Habitat Alteration Due to Competition from Non-native Biota

Non-native (alien, exotic, nonindigenous, or introduced) species have become established in Canada intentionally and accidentally. In either case, native species must compete with non-native species for space, water, food, and other essentials of life. Virtually every region of the country has an introduced species that is actively displacing a native, rare, or endangered species. Released in Central Park, New York, the European starling has spread throughout North America, displacing native species that require tree holes or other cavities for nests.

Similarly, raccoons released on the Queen Charlotte Islands (to provide local trappers with a new species to harvest) have put sea bird colonies at risk, killing about 10 percent of the breeding colonies of burrow-nesting alcids (auklets, guillemots, and ancient murrelets—the murrelet is listed as a vulnerable species) in only five years. Plants such as Scotch broom, purple loosestrife, and crested wheatgrass also have competed aggressively with and replaced native species. Currently, about 23 percent of wild flora (mostly weeds) and about 1 percent of fish in Canada are exotic species.

Habitat Alteration Due to Harvesting

Harvesting has the potential to cause short- and long-term changes in populations and species composition, regardless of the type of wildlife harvested or the methods employed. Logging, for example, causes temporary (sometimes permanent) reduction in tree populations, which affects trees' delivery of ecological functions such as habitat provision, carbon fixation, and oxygen production. Logging also affects the structure of the forest community as older-growth stands are replaced with younger trees. Harvesting of fish not only targets large, older specimens, but also extracts enormous numbers from the population pools of aquatic species. In 2005, for example, commercial landings of fish were more than 1 million tonnes with a commercial value of over $2 billion (Fisheries and Oceans Canada, 2007). Harvesting of species for collection purposes cannot be overlooked; some butterfly species and at least nine nationally endangered plants already at risk face some threat from collectors.

Habitat Alteration Due to Toxic Contaminants

Toxic substances may occur naturally (mercury, lead) or be generated **anthropogenically** by human activities such as industrial discharges, municipal waste disposal, agriculture, and forestry. These contaminants may spread over great distances through air and water currents. Mercury and lead do not appear to have any nutritional or biochemical function; at higher concentrations, however, they can adversely affect plant and animal growth and health.

Lead poisoning of waterfowl and other birds occurs when ducks and other bottom-feeding species ingest the lead pellets from lead shot used in hunting ammunition. Lead enters the gizzard and becomes available for absorption into the body. Ten to 15 percent of the mortality of golden and bald eagles has been attributed to secondary lead poisoning (from feeding on waterfowl carrying lead pellets embedded in their bodies). A national ban on the use of lead shot for all migratory game bird hunting has been in place since 1997.

Use of lead sinkers in recreational fishing also causes secondary lead poisoning; when fish escape from anglers with the "hook, line, and sinker" attached, loons or other fish-eating birds can swallow the fish whole, including the lead sinkers, and subsequently die of lead toxicosis. In the fall of 1996, it became illegal to use lead fishing sinkers or jigs (weighted lead hooks) in Canada's national parks and national wildlife areas.

Persistent organochlorines and metals are two notable groups of toxic substances. Organochlorines, including pesticides, industrial chemicals, and byproducts of certain industrial processes, take decades or centuries to break down naturally (thus their persistence). This persistence and their high solubility in fat leads to bioaccumulation in animal tissues, which are then passed on through food webs, reaching very high concentrations in the tissues of predators at the top of the food web, a process known as biomagnification (see Chapter 7). Interestingly, certain wildlife species are used as environmental indicators to monitor levels of organochlorines and toxic contaminants in ecosystems (see Box 12–3 on the next page).

Flooding for hydroelectric developments frequently results in mercury contamination; this is because naturally occurring inorganic mercury in submerged organic material is converted into methylmercury by anaerobic bacteria. Methylmercury easily bioaccumulates in many organisms and also biomagnifies through food webs. Advisories have been issued regarding human consumption of fish above certain sizes from both reservoirs and natural lakes in Canada.

Habitat Alteration Due to Urbanization

While we do not frequently identify wildlife with urban areas, in fact, many wild animals do live in or near cities. Certainly, they live in and about small towns that are located in natural settings such as national parks (e.g., Banff, Alberta; Waskesiu, Saskatchewan; Clear Lake, Manitoba). Urban settlements and small "resort" municipalities are under great pressure to expand their

Indicators are selected key statistics that represent or summarize some aspect of the state of ecosystems. By focusing on trends in environmental change, they convey how ecosystems are responding to both stresses and management responses.

The insecticide DDT was widely used in Canada between 1947 and 1969 to control agricultural and forest insects. The main breakdown product of DDT is dichlorodiphenyldichloroethylene (DDE), a compound that interferes with enzymes necessary for the production of calcium carbonate in female double-crested cormorants, bald eagles, peregrine falcons, and other birds. Eggshells with less calcium carbonate are thinner and more likely to crack or break during incubation. Because of these and other toxic properties, most uses of DDT were banned in Canada by the mid-1970s. Concentrations of DDE have declined substantially since the 1970s. In recent years, declines have levelled off, possibly as a result of the slow release of contaminant residues from bottom sediments or long-range atmospheric transport from countries still using DDT.

Certain toxic organochlorines, including DDE, PCBs, and some dioxins and furans, have been monitored in species of wildlife since the early 1970s. Tracking concentrations in wildlife simplifies the detection of some chemicals that are present in extremely low concentrations in air and water and are therefore difficult to measure directly. Levels of some organochlorine contaminants in the eggs of fish-eating birds, for example, may be as much as 25 million times the concentrations in the waters in which the fish live, because of the processes of bioaccumulation and biomagnification.

The double-crested cormorant has been selected as a national indicator species for organochlorine levels in wildlife because of its broad distribution across southern Canada, especially in areas of concentrated human activity, and because it is a top predator that eats live fish. A disadvantage of using the double-crested cormorant as an indicator, however, is that, like many Canadian birds, it migrates south in the winter. It is therefore not known what proportion of the contaminants measured in its eggs comes from non-Canadian sources.

Photo 12-6

The double-crested cormorant (*Phalacrocorax auritus*) is an excellent swimmer and diver. In pursuit of its fish prey it may remain underwater for 30 seconds or longer, sometimes using its wings for propulsion in addition to its webbed feet. It nests in colonies and builds its nest on the ground or in a tree.

SOURCE: *The State of Canada's Environment—1996*, © Her Majesty the Queen in Right of Canada, Environment Canada, 1996, Box 10.5. Reprinted with permission of the Minister of Public Works and Government Services Canada, 2008.

populations and services. Processes of urbanization place enormous pressures on wildlife and habitat. Clearing of land to build more principal residences or second homes may reduce habitat for indigenous flora and fauna, alter natural waterways, and destroy trails and migration routes used by animals. Pollution of the air, water, and land may negatively affect the ability of species to thrive.

When urban growth alters local habitats, some species actually thrive. In these cases, however, the population of wild animals can become out of synch with the availability of food and other resources they need to survive. For example, in the townsite of Banff, conditions have become favourable for large ungulates like elk. A visitor to the townsite might be delighted that the elk are so numerous. However, in their search for food, elk destroy much vegetation and ultimately become "problem animals," dealt with by calling or removing them from areas of human population. In a related situation, in January 2002, the Ontario Ministry of Natural Resources introduced a 30-month moratorium on wolf killing in townships surrounding Algonquin Park. Environmental organizations suggested that two-thirds of wolf deaths were human-caused, as wolves were shot, snared, trapped, hit by vehicles, and sometimes even poisoned. The development of new subdivisions for primary housing or cottages also can have devastating effects as habitats are destroyed and domesticated pets and exotic plants are introduced and compete with and even disrupt conditions necessary for the maintenance of indigenous species.

Habitat Alteration Due to Cumulative Agents of Change

Wildlife and habitat changes frequently are the result of a combination of factors that act directly or indirectly to cause change. Insect populations, for example, can be reduced through habitat loss, pesticide applications, and other factors. Loss of insects also can have a domino effect on the total functioning of the ecosystem and can have ecological and economic repercussions. For example, use of the insecticide fenitrothion (used to control spruce budworm) appears to have caused native wild bee populations to plummet, affecting the success of pollination and cross-pollination.

Despite large and rapid losses of habitat, there are also gains and successes. The Rocky Mountain Arsenal in the United States is one such case where cumulative agents of change have begun to reverse some of the worst aspects of a highly contaminated site (see Chapter 10). This example illustrates how a concerted effort to restore natural processes and reduce urban pressures can work with the natural processes within an ecosystem to protect even some of our most degraded spaces. You may wish to contrast this example with that described in Enviro-Focus 14 (p. 562), where much work remains to be done.

SPECIES AT RISK

It is clear that without adequate and healthy habitat, wildlife (terrestrial and aquatic plants, animals, and microorganisms) cannot survive. Brief stories of four selected species at risk—the marbled murrelet, pink coreopsis, Peary caribou, and aurora trout—illustrate the threats from human actions facing wild species in ecosystems across Canada (the stories are based on information from Canadian Geographic Enterprises, 1997.

The threatened marbled murrelet is a small sea bird, a member of the auk family, whose nesting behaviour had been a mystery to researchers for nearly 100 years. It was not until 1993 that the first occupied murrelet nest in Canada was located in the dense coastal rain forest of British Columbia. Marbled murrelets forage for small schooling fish in nearshore areas (where they are at risk from gill nets and oil spills), and nest only on broad, moss-covered branches of mature conifers within 30 kilometres of the ocean (many similar species of sea birds nest in colonies on coastal cliffs). Only one egg is laid each year; to elude predators, the nest is relocated every year. As logging in the old-growth forests in valley bottoms continues, murrelet numbers have dropped as their prime nesting habitat has disappeared. As forest cover shrinks,

opportunistic ravens and Stellar's jays find the murrelet eggs and chicks easy prey; in Clayoquot Sound, the murrelet population has declined by about 20 percent since 1982.

First identified in Canada in 1920, the endangered pink coreopsis is a pink and yellow perennial herb that is scattered along the shorelines of Nova Scotia's southwestern lakes. In Canada, this coastal plain plant occurred exclusively in the Tusket River valley at six separate locations, all but one on private land. Three of those sites have been lost to residential development. The remaining sites are at risk because the hardy and stress-tolerant coreopsis thrives in gritty, sandy, and seasonally flooded soil on the shorelines of lakes. This locational preference makes the plant vulnerable to activities of cottagers and off-road drivers. Efforts are under way to educate landowners about this plant and to protect the pink coreopsis and other biologically associated plant species in remote areas where they are still found.

Living on the Queen Elizabeth Islands in the Northwest Territories, endangered Peary caribou are the only members of the deer family adapted to life in the Canadian High Arctic. During the summer, the Peary caribou graze river valleys and plains for grasses, sedges, herbs, and willows. During winter they move to higher areas where winds sweep snow away from vegetation; some travel across the frozen sea to search for food. Caribou numbers have dropped from 25 000 in 1961 to around 3000 in 2004 because heavier snowfall and freezing rain during the past decades have increased the caribou's vulnerability to starvation. On some islands, hunting and wolf predation have accelerated the herd's decline. Local Inuit communities that have relied on the caribou for generations have voluntarily (less awkward) reduced their hunting. A national park on Bathurst Island has been created to protect calving areas, and a captive breeding program at the Calgary Zoo also was initiated (but was not implemented because inclement weather prevented capture of the caribou).

The aurora trout is a colourful brook trout known to live only in two remote lakes (Whirligig and Whitepine) in the Temagami region north of Sudbury. By 1961, the aurora trout had been extirpated from both lakes because their high elevation and their sensitive geological setting made them prone to acidification that killed trout fry within weeks of hatching. Fortunately, the aurora trout escaped becoming the first casualty of acid precipitation because, a few years prior to 1961, researchers had collected over 3600 eggs to form the basis of a brood stock. This stock has been maintained for about 40 years. Attempts to introduce the species into lakes other than the species' native ones failed; rehabilitation of the trout's native lakes began prior to 1990 when water in the 11-hectare Whirligig was neutralized with 21 tonnes of powdered lime. In 1990, 950 fish were reintroduced to Whirligig, and today both lakes are successfully stocked with hatchery-raised aurora trout. As we know, emissions causing acid precipitation

Photo 12–7a

Photo 12–7b

Photo 12–7c

Among Canada's threatened and endangered species are the pink coreopsis (12–7a), aurora trout (12–7b), and Peary caribou (12–7c).

have been reduced substantially, but the water quality of the fish habitat is monitored constantly. Twice since 1990 the recovery team has had to intervene and add more lime to Whirligig.

Perhaps one of the best illustrations of the cumulative impacts of many human activity pressures is found in the case of grizzly bears in the Banff–Bow Valley area of Alberta. This saga, outlined briefly in Enviro-Focus 12 and Box 12–2 (p. 490), emphasizes the competition bears face with humans for critical montane habitat, and the habitat fragmentation and barriers that human development, land use, and transportation systems have on bear populations located within protected areas (in this case, a national park).

Since 1977, the Committee on the Status of Endangered Wildlife in Canada (COSEWIC) has been the agency responsible for identifying the status of all wild

ENVIRO-FOCUS 12

Grizzly Bears and Humans in Banff National Park and Area

In spite of the fact that national parks were created in part to protect wildlife, "Banff National Park is a dangerous place to live, if you are a grizzly bear. Researchers have learned that of the 73 grizzlies known to have died in the park from 1971 to 1995, 52 were either destroyed or removed in the interests of public safety. Ninety percent of the grizzlies died close to developed areas, and 56 percent of those were females, since females with curious cubs are the most likely to run into trouble with people" (Marty, 1997, p. 37). In a separate study that included Banff and Yoho national parks, it was discovered that between 1971 and 1998, 119 of 131 known mortalities were due to human-related causes. "Control of problem bears" gave rise to 85 of these 119 mortalities (Herrero, 2005, p. x).

These few statistics highlight some important dimensions of the competition between wild species and humans for habitat. Grizzly bears, whose numbers are estimated to be between 60 and 80 in Banff National Park, are 80 percent vegetarian and range widely in search of food sources such as berries, roots, grasses, and other plants, as well as carrion. Male bears require up to 2000 square kilometres to survive and females need between 200 and 500 square kilometres.

The Banff–Bow Valley area contains **montane** habitat (valley bottom and open forest of trembling aspen and Douglas fir) that is critical for wildlife survival, including that of grizzlies. Only 3 percent of Banff National Park's 6641 square kilometres is montane habitat, and half of that portion lies in the Bow Valley, where wildlife compete for the most productive habitat with humans and their developments. For instance, in the Bow Valley, people have built towns such as Banff, Lake Louise, and Canmore, and associated ski resorts, golf courses, shopping malls, industrial parks, campgrounds, and an airstrip, leaving only a remnant of their former range for bears to roam.

In placing their infrastructure within the valleys, humans have obstructed the traditional north–south

and east–west links or corridors that wild species have used for centuries to move north and south within their range between the Yukon and Yellowstone ecosystems. Genetic pathways for regional gene flow, these movement corridors also are fractured by the Trans-Canada Highway, which carries about 20 000 vehicles per day in the summer months and 14 000 per day year round (Parks Canada, 2007), and the Canadian Pacific Railway. Bears do not like crossing highways or using the underpasses that Parks Canada provided for big game animals (see Box 12–2 on p. 490 for further information on highway and railway impacts on wildlife).

Biologists working on the Eastern Slopes Grizzly Bear project are concerned about habitat fragmentation in Banff National Park and the Bow Valley area and have identified a general decline in bear numbers. Sensitive to human incursions, grizzly bears are an indicator species (when they are in trouble, the entire ecosystem usually is out of balance). Essentially, the Banff–Bow Valley area now provides only a fraction of its former potential for large mammals. While bears, wolves, and cougars still travel through the Banff–Bow

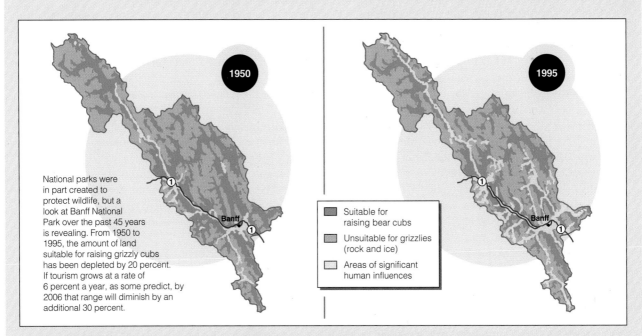

National parks were in part created to protect wildlife, but a look at Banff National Park over the past 45 years is revealing. From 1950 to 1995, the amount of land suitable for raising grizzly cubs has been depleted by 20 percent. If tourism grows at a rate of 6 percent a year, as some predict, by 2006 that range will diminish by an additional 30 percent.

■ Suitable for raising bear cubs

▨ Unsuitable for grizzlies (rock and ice)

□ Areas of significant human influences

Impacts of human development on grizzly bear habitat in Banff National Park and area.

SOURCE: "Homeless on the Range: Grizzlies Struggle for Elbow Room and Survival in Banff National Park," S. Marty, 1997, *Canadian Geographic, 117*(1), 35, 36. Reprinted by permission of The Royal Canadian Geographic Society.

(continued)

Valley movement corridors, biologists warn that more development will cause wary animals to avoid this area, potentially placing the continued survival of these populations at risk (Canadian Parks and Wilderness Society, 1997).

Human development and land use practices relating to "world class tourism" and the millions of visitors it draws annually to Banff National Park have had significant impacts on wild species, their behaviour and survival, and their habitat in the Banff–Bow Valley area. For instance, until improved garbage management systems were available in 1981, habituated bears (human-food addicts) frequently were relocated or destroyed. Although tourists feed bears less frequently than they did 20 years ago, finding finances and workers to deal effectively with habituated wildlife remains a problem.

Another example of human development impacts on wildlife is that, until recently, the policy of fire suppression to protect visitors and property in the park reduced the amount of feeding habitat for grizzly bears. The species remains slow to recover because mortality rates for female bears remain high (females do not breed until they are between four and eight years old, and average 0.5 cubs per year after that). Also, there is concern that the grizzly bear population on the east slopes of the Rocky Mountains could become genetically inbred and isolated from other subpopulations farther south as mate selection and other biological necessities are constrained by human barriers to bear movement.

In addition to the relatively recent developmental pressures being put on bears in the Banff–Bow Valley area, grizzlies were extirpated from the Prairies near the turn of the century. Current population estimates for Alberta suggest there are between 500 and 800 grizzlies in the province; at least one ENGO suggests that there may be fewer than 500 grizzlies remaining (Grizzly Bear Alliance, 2008). Even though grizzly bears were identified in 2002 as a threatened species in the

Photo 12–8

Critical habitat for grizzlies is shrinking because of human development and land use practices.

province, and are at risk of becoming endangered, the Alberta Fish and Wildlife Department allowed 150 individuals to obtain hunting licences for the annual Alberta grizzly bear hunt until 2006. The Alberta Sustainable Resource Development department has an ongoing program to manage human–bear interactions. This program includes educating landowners and recreationists to minimize food sources that may attract bears, collaborating with nongovernmental organizations that place conservation easements in key habitat, using aversion techniques in chronic problem areas, and placing road-killed ungulates in favourable feeding locations in spring.

Harmonizing human developments with wild species' habitat needs requires people to realize that some of their attitudes and actions are directly detrimental to the long-term survival of grizzly bears and other wild species. If we cannot make room for the grizzly bear in our national parks and surrounding lands, then where can the wilderness that sustains the grizzly find protection? If wild places cannot find protection, then biodiversity—and humans, too—clearly are threatened.

SOURCES: *Banff–Bow Valley: At the Crossroads. Technical Report of the Banff–Bow Valley Task Force,* Banff–Bow Valley Study (R. Page, S. Bayley, J. D. Cook, J. Green, & J. R. B. Ritchie), 1996, Ottawa: Department of Canadian Heritage; *The Bow Valley: A Very Special Place,* Canadian Parks and Wilderness Society (CPAWS), 1997, Calgary: Author; *Biology, Demography, Ecology and Management of Grizzly Bears in and around Banff National Park and Kananaskis Country: Final Report of the Eastern Slopes Grizzly Bear Project,* S. Herrero (Ed.), 2005, Calgary: Faculty of Environmental Design, University of Calgary, http://www.canadianrockies.net/Grizzly/final_report/Complete_ESGBP_FinalReport2005.pdf; "Province Defends Grizzly Bear Hunt," L. Lunman, March 28, 1997, *Calgary Herald,* p. B3; "Homeless on the Range: Grizzlies Struggle for Elbow Room and Survival in Banff National Park," S. Marty, 1997, *Canadian Geographic, 117*(1), 28–39; *The Banff Wildlife Crossings Project Report, 2002,* Parks Canada, 2007, http://www.pc.gc.ca/pn-np/ab/banff/docs/routes/chap1/routes1a_e.asp; Grizzly Bear Alliance, 2008. http://www.grizzlybearalliance.org/whatsnew.html

species in Canada and developing a list of Canadian species at risk. COSEWIC employs a seven-category set of status definitions (outlined in Table 12–3); these designations help to monitor the condition of wild species known to be at risk of eventual extinction from one or more agents of change.

In 1997, COSEWIC, identified a total of 281 mammal, bird, reptile, amphibian, fish, mollusc, lepidoptera (butterfly and moth), and plant species (including mosses and lichens) at risk across Canada. By 2007, COSEWIC had raised the number of plants and animals at risk of extinction to 521, an increase of about 85 percent in 10 years. Table 12–4 (on the next page) reveals increasing vulnerability of species over the last decade. Species on the list are found in every part of Canada, but most are found in the Okanagan Valley of south-central British Columbia; on the prairies of Alberta, Saskatchewan, and Manitoba; in southwestern Ontario; in southern Quebec; and on Nova Scotia's Atlantic coastal plain (World Wildlife Fund Canada, 2000c).

Table 12–4 provides a summary of the numbers of species at risk in Canada over time, as well as those known to be extinct.

SPACES AT RISK

The health, biodiversity, and sustainability of wild species is closely connected to the availability and quality of the natural spaces they occupy. Protecting regions makes sense because it protects all three kinds of biodiversity—genetic, species, and ecological diversity. Two quite different regions pose significant challenges for biodiversity protection: Canada's Arctic and Sage Creek, Alberta.

Canada's Arctic

Resource extraction, such as mineral and diamond mining in the Northwest Territories and oil and gas exploration in the Arctic, raises a variety of concerns related to wildlife. The Arctic National Wildlife Refuge (ANWR) in Alaska, often called the Serengeti of North America, sustains vast wildlife populations and also is a potential source of crude oil. Concerned about the fate of the Porcupine caribou herd that overwinters in Canada and migrates each spring to the coastal plain of the ANWR, Canadian conservationists have debated with U.S. government officials about whether oil exploration should be permitted there. Caribou show reduced calf production and lower calf survival rates around oil development areas; oil exploration could cause a 20 to 40 percent decline in the size of the herd, and cause economic hardship to the Aboriginal people who depend on the caribou for their survival ("Oil Exploration," 1997).

According to the Canadian Wildlife Federation, if the United States did open up the wildlife refuge to oil exploration and drilling, it would be violating four international accords: the Migratory Birds Convention (1916), the Agreement on the Conservation of Polar Bears (1976), the North American Waterfowl Management Plan (1986), and the Porcupine Caribou Agreement (1987) ("Oil Exploration," 1997). Yet, there has been pressure by the United States to do so to provide jobs and to increase domestic supplies of oil. In addition, as noted in Chapter 10, Canada's first diamond mine, the BHP Billiton diamonds project at Lac de Gras, Northwest Territories, received regulatory approval from the federal government in January 1997, followed by the EKATI, Diavik, and Snap Lake projects.

TABLE 12–3
THE COMMITTEE ON THE STATUS OF WILDLIFE IN CANADA (COSEWIC): STATUS DEFINITIONS (REVISED 2000)

Status Category		Definition
SC	special concern	• A species of special concern because of characteristics that make it particularly sensitive to human activities or natural events
T	threatened	• A species likely to become endangered if limiting factors are not reversed
E	endangered	• A species facing imminent extirpation or extinction
XT	extirpated	• A species no longer existing in the wild in Canada, but occurring elsewhere
X	extinct	• A species that no longer exists
NAR	not at risk	• A species that has been evaluated and found to be not at risk
DD	data deficient	• A species for which there is insufficient scientific information to support status designation

TABLE 12–4

THE COMMITTEE ON THE STATUS OF ENDANGERED WILDLIFE IN CANADA (COSEWIC): SUMMARY OF SPECIES AT RISK IN CANADA OVER TIME: 1997, 2001, 2007

					Number of Species			
	Mammals	Birds	Fish	Mollusks	Vascular plants, mosses, and lichens	Reptiles and Amphibians	Arthropods	Total
Extinct								
1997	1	3	5	1	0	0	0	10
2001	2	3	6	1	0	0	0	12
2007	2	3	6	1	1	0	0	13
Extirpated								
1997	3	2	4	0	2	1	1	13
2001	4	2	2	1	2	3	3	17
2007	3	2	4	2	3	5	3	22
Endangered								
1997	6	16	10	0	30	4	1	67
2001	16	20	10	7	52	10	3	118
2007	20	26	32	15	90	15	14	212
Threatened								
1997	5	7	16	1	38	3	0	70
2001	14	8	21	1	35	13	2	94
2007	17	12	26	3	54	18	6	136
Special Concern								
1997	18	21	47	0	35	9	1	131
2001	25	21	37	1	47	13	2	146
2007	26	22	37	4	42	17	3	151

SOURCE: *Canadian Species at Risk,* Committee on the Status of Endangered Wildlife in Canada (COSEWIC), November 2001, http://www.sararegistry. gc.ca/virtual_sara/files/species/clwsa%5F1101%5Fe%2Epdf; *Canadian Species at Risk,* Committee on the Status of Endangered Wildlife in Canada (COSEWIC), January 2007, http://www.cosewic.gc.ca/eng/sct0/rpt/rpt_csar_e.pdf; *List of Species at Risk in Canada as Designated by the Committee on the Status of Endangered Wildlife in Canada* (COSEWIC), 1997, Environment Canada, Canadian Wildlife Service, 1997, http://www.ec.gc.ca/envcan/docs/ endanger/table.html

The Canadian Arctic Resources Committee and the Canadian Wildlife Federation, among other organizations, are concerned about the cumulative effects that these future developments will have on wildlife and other resources, as well as on Aboriginal people. The Arctic already has experienced the environmental impacts of actions taken by people thousands of kilometres away. These impacts include pollutants, borne by wind and water currents, that enter the food chain, biomagnify, and end up in Inuit and other Aboriginal people who eat what they hunt. Pollutants such as pesticides from Southeast Asia, PCBs from Eastern Europe, mercury from the United States, and other persistent organic pollutants, heavy metals, and radionuclides have been found in the snow, ice, soil, animals, and even people of the Arctic. For example, mirex, a pesticide never registered for use in Canada, has made its way into breast milk of Inuit women. Nevertheless, if Inuit people turn away from the use of country foods, they risk becoming less physically active, less connected to cultural practices associated with hunting and eating local food, and more likely to get "southern" diseases such as heart disease, diabetes, and cancer.

As well, the predicted severe climatic consequences of global warming already are affecting wildlife. The summer sea ice required by polar bears is rapidly disappearing. Estimates suggest that the ice area may decline

Photo 12–9
Polar bears on dwindling sea ice.

by one-half or more over the next century, reducing their hunting range. Without the ice, the polar bear population is expected to decline from about 25 000 today to 17 500 in 45 years (Grahame-Rowe, 2006). Indeed, dead polar bears have been sighted among swimming polar bears, suggesting that more severe weather conditions, along with growing expanses of open water, have made survival more difficult.

Northern Aboriginal people consider sustainability as a means to safeguard their cultures and economies as well as the natural environment on which they depend so heavily. Even though involvement of the federal government provides some assurance that sustainability may be implemented domestically, there is a concern that action within Canada alone will not be sufficient to achieve the desired ends. The eight Arctic Inuit nations in Canada, Greenland, Alaska, and Chukotka agreed to implement an environmental protection strategy during their 1991 Circumpolar Conference. Their efforts illustrate the need for international and regional cooperation in order to provide the necessary conditions for biodiversity protection in the Arctic.

Photo 12–10
Inuit hunters during an annual whale hunt.

Sage Creek, Alberta

Principally because of the extent and natural character of its grasslands, as well as the concentration of rare, threatened, and endangered species it supports, Sage Creek, Alberta, is a nationally significant environmental area. Hundreds of species of prairie plants and animals occur in this contiguous, 5000-square-kilometre area in the southeastern part of Alberta, including such familiar threatened wildlife species as the burrowing owl, swift fox, and sage grouse, as well as rare plant species such as Pursh's milk vetch and the plains boisduvalia. Sage Creek also is recognized as one of the most diverse areas in North America for breeding grassland birds, and is home to the endangered mountain plover, fewer than 10 breeding pairs of which exist in Alberta (Wallis, Klimek, & Adams, 1996; Canadian Wildlife Service, 2000).

In March 1996, the Alberta Energy and Utilities Board (AEUB) recognized that Sage Creek's native prairie grassland ecosystems were important, vulnerable, and disappearing rapidly. In spite of awareness that the cumulative long-term impacts of all development in such grasslands, including that of oil and natural gas, can be very significant, the AEUB recommended to the National Energy Board (NEB) that Express Pipeline be granted approval to construct and operate a crude oil pipeline in the Sage Creek area. The NEB granted that approval. When the pipeline construction began in August 1996, one of the most extensive grasslands left in North America began to be fragmented.

Having opposed the approval of this pipeline proposal, the Alberta Wilderness Association (AWA) is "very concerned about further fragmentation and loss of threatened grassland ecosystems and is very disappointed in the apparent rubber stamping that seems to occur in regulatory hearing processes" (Wallis et al., 1996, p. 4). Calling the area one of the "crown jewels of prairie biodiversity," the AWA believes that the failure of the National Energy Board and the Canadian Environmental Assessment Agency's hearing process to deny Express Pipeline's application and reroute the pipeline through less sensitive terrain "demonstrates clearly the need to have a legislated system of areas that are protected from industrial activity" (Wallis et al., 1996, p. 4).

These areas are not the only ones where wild species are at risk because of human activities. A variety of threats face wildlife in ecosystems across Canada; while some species have been affected negatively by agricultural and industrial activities, acid precipitation, or contaminants, other species have been affected by hunting pressure and recreational and residential impacts. Some species, such as the peregrine falcon, have been brought back from the brink of extinction, while others, such as the whooping crane, remain at risk in their Canadian ranges.

Most biologists agree that the best way to protect species is to protect native habitats—that saving species starts with saving spaces for them. Island biogeography is a subfield of conservation biology. It was developed in the early 20th century to understand the rate of colonization by bird species in tropical islands in the South Pacific. This theory has been adapted and applied to many kinds of problems to predict the effects of fragmentation of habitat on the population success of different plant and animal species. Contemporary theories associated with island biogeography now attempt to predict the minimum viable area required by certain species and to determine whether and in what ways geographically separated groups should be interconnected to avoid population loss and species extinction. These predictions are very difficult to make and are subject to controversy. Biologists agree that fragmentation of habitat can have severe consequences, but the specific details of these consequences are not well understood. Furthermore, calculations of the habitat needs of one species may not reflect the needs of another species living within the same landscape. For species that move on a seasonal or other basis, protection may require a more extensive approach to conservation than simply setting individual areas aside. Changing climate also may affect areas that have been set aside. In these cases, connectivity of habitat patches (e.g., corridors) may be beneficial. Yet in other cases, isolation of species may be required to maintain their populations, and thus questions remain about how large these protected areas should be. In light of these uncertainties, it is clear that protection of biological diversity and promotion of sustainability will require a range of strategies. In the following section of this chapter, we examine some of these strategies.

Strategies to Protect Biodiversity

There is not one best way to protect biodiversity; rather, multiple strategies one required. In this section, we explore some basic approaches and then examine how these approaches have been applied in Canada.

IN SITU CONSERVATION

In situ conservation is the conservation of ecosystems and the maintenance and recovery of viable populations of species in their typical surroundings. Four main methods are associated with in situ conservation: protection of areas that are large enough to support ecosystem processes and species diversity; re-creation of those spaces through species recovery programs; sustainable use of biological resources; and improved understanding of biodiversity.

Protected Areas

Protected areas are known by a number of names, including ecological reserves wildlife management areas, parks, and conservation areas. Each type of protected area has a different set of management objectives, ranging from almost complete protection of biotic and abiotic components from human disturbance to protection that is offered only to selected ecosystem components (such as wildlife or soils). Conserving biodiversity through the use of protected areas involves careful management of human activities and prohibition of activities that could harm ecological processes or ecosystem integrity.

The World Conservation Union (IUCN) is the only global organization that unites nations, government agencies, and ENGOs in conserving the integrity and diversity of nature. The IUCN has categorized protected areas into six types (I to VI). Table 12–5 identifies these categories, their defining characteristics, and the management goals or practices associated with each type. Comparison of

Photo 12–11
The black-tailed prairie dog—listed by COSEWIC as a species of special concern—is protected in Grasslands National Park, Saskatchewan.

Photo 12–12
Point Pelee National Park, on the north shore of Lake Erie, is known around the world for its bird and monarch butterfly migrations. The marsh boardwalk provides people of all ages with the opportunity to discover nature.

TABLE 12–5
IUCN CATEGORIES OF PROTECTED AREA

IUCN Category	Defining Characteristics	Management Goals or Practices	Canadian Example
I. Natural reserve or wilderness area			
a. Nature reserve	• Areas possessing some outstanding or representative ecosystems, geological or physiographic features, or species	• Scientific research or ecological monitoring primarily	Oak Mountain Ecological Reserve (New Brunswick)
b. Wilderness area	• Large areas, unmodified or slightly modified, retaining their natural character and influence, without permanent or significant habitation	• Preservation of natural conditions	Bay du Nord Wilderness Area (Newfoundland)
II. National park (or equivalent)	• Areas designated to sustain the integrity of one or more ecosystems, exclude exploitation or intensive occupation, and provide a foundation for scientific, educational, recreational, and visitor opportunities, all of which must be ecologically and culturally compatible	• Ecosystem protection and recreation	Banff National Park (Alberta)
III. Natural monument	• Areas containing one or more specific natural or cultural features of outstanding or unique value because of inherent rarity, representation of aesthetic qualities, or cultural significance	• Protection of specific outstanding natural features, provision of opportunities for research and education, and prevention of exploitation or occupation	Parrsboro Fossil Cliffs (Nova Scotia)
IV. Habitat/species management areas	• Areas important for ensuring the maintenance of habitats or for meeting the requirements of certain species	• Securement and maintenance of habitat conditions necessary to protect species and ecosystem features where these require human manipulation for optimum management	Watshishou Migratory Bird Sanctuary (Quebec)
V. Protected landscape or seascape	• Areas where interactions of people and nature have produced a distinct character with significant cultural or ecological value and often with high biodiversity	• Conservation, education, recreation, and provision of natural products aimed at safeguarding the integrity of harmonious interactions of nature and culture	Algonquin Provincial Park (Ontario)
VI. Managed resource and protected areas	• Predominantly natural areas that are large enough to absorb sustainable resource uses without harming long-term maintenance of biodiversity	• Long-term protection and maintenance of biodiversity and other natural values and the promotion of sound management practices for sustainable production purpose	Battle Creek Community Pasture (Saskatchewan)

SOURCE: *The State of Canada's Environment—1996,* © Her Majesty the Queen in Right of Canada, Environment Canada, 1996, Box 14.4. Reprinted with permission of the Minister of Public Works and Government Services Canada, 2008.

various types of protected areas found in Canada with those found in other countries shows slightly more protected areas in Canada are in IUCN classes IV to VI than in categories I to III, which involve the highest level of protection. This means the Canadian system affords a slightly lower level of biodiversity protection than might be suggested by simple designation of protected areas.

Most of Canada's protected areas traditionally have been held in public ownership. Provincial parks and our national park system (see Figure 12–4) constitute the largest portion of protected land in Canada. ENGOs, however, have made important contributions to conserving biodiversity. The success of the North American Waterfowl Management Plan in protecting thousands of hectares of productive wetland ecosystems has been generated partly through incentives to private landowners to conserve wetlands for wildlife, and partly by the stewardship actions of partner ENGOs such as Ducks Unlimited Canada and the Nature Conservancy of Canada. By 2000, ENGOs owned or managed over 8 million hectares of conservation lands in relation to Canadian biodiversity efforts (Nature Conservancy, 2000, personal communication).

Growth in protected areas is one measure of the commitment to protect ecosystems. From the mid-1970s until 1994, protected lands more than doubled in area and represented approximately 8 percent of our total land mass. According to a document produced by the IUCN and the World Conservation Monitoring Centre (WCMC) in 1997 and reanalyzed in 2000, more than 9.5 percent of Canada, or more than 950 000 square kilometres, was protected area. Only about half that land will not be subject to major resource extraction activities, however, as less than half the area is protected under designations that correspond roughly to IUCN categories I to III (Government of Canada, 1996; World Conservation Monitoring Centre, 2000). Proportions of different types of federally and provincially protected areas, and other conservation areas, are shown in Figure 12–5 on page 506.

Canada's National Parks

Canada has relied on provincial and national parks as cornerstones of protecting biodiversity. Although national parks take up only 3 percent of Canada's land mass, "they contain over 70 percent of the native terrestrial and freshwater vascular plant species and over 80 percent of the vertebrate species" (Dearden & Dempsey, 2004, p. 233). The Canadian national parks system protects environments representative of Canada's natural and cultural heritage. Since Canada's first national park was established in Banff, Alberta, in 1885, the system has evolved to include parks, reserves, and marine conservation areas. These protected spaces are public lands administered by the federal government under the provisions of specific legislation. For instance, the Canada

National Parks Act (and regulations), proclaimed in February 2001, provides for the protection and management of these natural areas of Canadian significance for the long-term benefit, education, and enjoyment of present and future generations.

In the past, parks management principles promoted natural resource development and permitted multiple-use activities such as forestry, mining, and agriculture to take place within park boundaries. The Parks Act strengthens and places first priority on the ecological integrity of parks. This means that protecting **ecological integrity**—those conditions that are characteristic of a park's natural regions and likely to persist, including abiotic components, native species and biological communities, rates of change, and supporting processes—is the prime focus of park management efforts (Parks Canada Agency, 2001). A parallel concept important in parks management is that of the **ecological health** of an ecosystem in which native species are present at viable population levels (Searle, 2000). So that human activity does not impair ecological integrity, extractive industries are now prohibited within park boundaries (but such developments adjacent to park boundaries can prove problematic).

In 2007 there were 43 national parks and park reserves in Canada, located in all parts of Canada and varying in area from 8.7 to more than 44 800 square kilometres (see Figure 12–4). But it is not just the geographic space that is important. Other factors must be considered. For example, one might seek to protect areas where the highest levels of biodiversity exist. In Canada, some of these areas are in valley bottoms of old-growth forests that have competed for protection against the interests of forestry and urban development.

Another strategy may be to protect areas that keystone species require. Because of the ecological importance of such species, such a strategy may have a larger benefit for ecosystem protection than would be anticipated by their numbers. Canada's national parks were supposed to be established according to criteria of representation. Over 274 700 square kilometres (about 2.45 percent) of Canada's land mass is protected within the national park system. In 2007, 28 of the 39 terrestrial and 29 marine regions are under protection, up from 25 in 2003. If all of these regions were protected, about 364 000 square kilometres would be under protection (Parks Canada Agency, 2007). This idea of protecting representative environments derives from the 1971 Systems Planning Framework that set out a process by which new national parks could be designated and established. This framework classified Canada into 39 natural regions, each with its own combination of climate, vegetation, landforms, and internal biodiversity. The idea was that if each of the 39 regions could be represented adequately within the parks system, Canada's diversity of life forms, natural features, and natural processes would be protected. In 1992, Environment, Parks, and Wildlife ministers endorsed a Statement of Commitment to

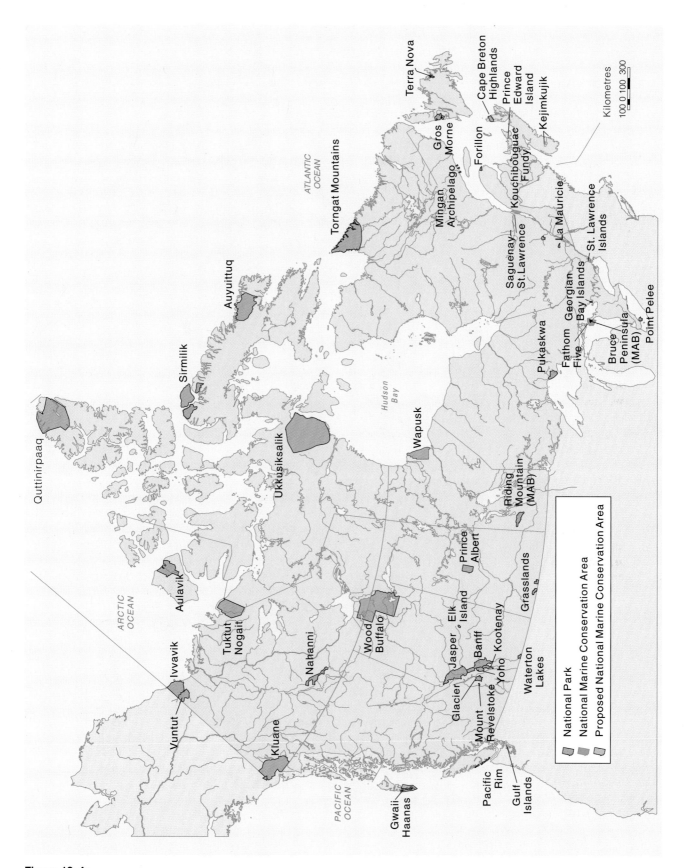

Figure 12–4a

National Parks and Marine Conservation Areas of Canada

SOURCE: Reproduced with the permission of Natural Resources Canada 2008, courtesy of the Atlas of Canada.

CHAPTER 12: BIODIVERSITY

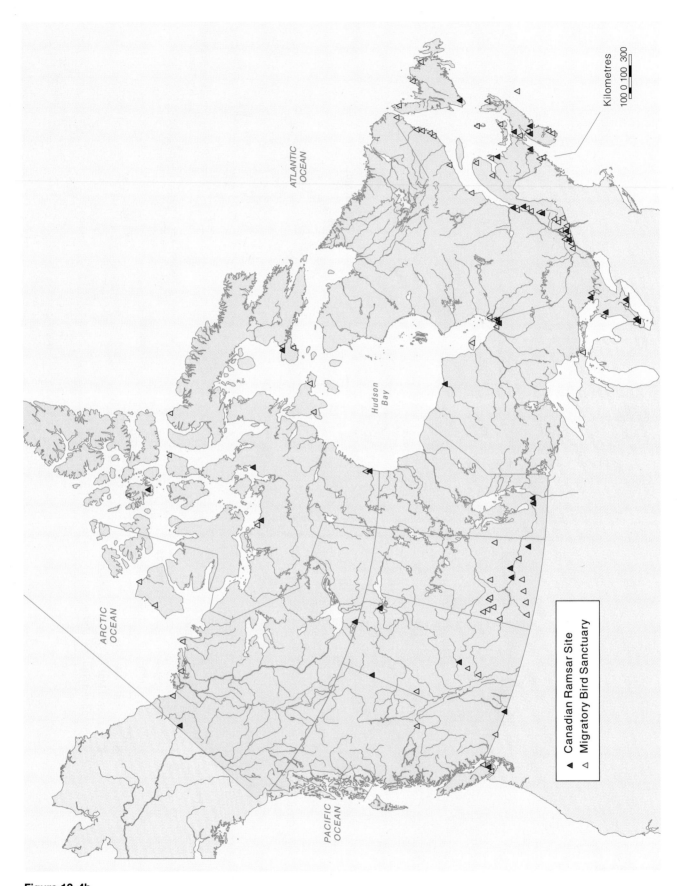

Figure 12–4b

Ramsar Sites and Migratory Bird Sanctuaries of Canada

SOURCE: Reproduced with the permission of Natural Resources Canada 2008, courtesy of the Atlas of Canada.

 NEL

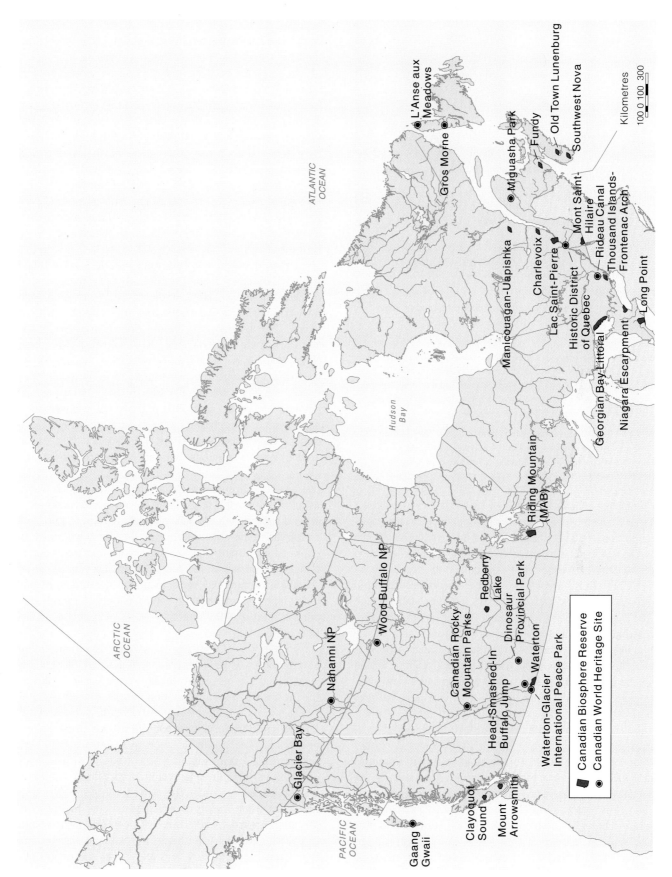

Figure 12–4c

Biosphere Reserves and World Heritage Sites of Canada

SOURCE: Reproduced with the permission of Natural Resources Canada 2008, courtesy of the Atlas of Canada.

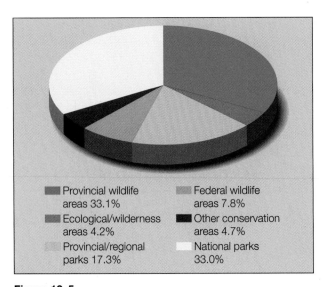

Figure 12–5

Proportion of federal, provincial, and other protected areas in Canada in the 1990s

Provincial wildlife areas 33.1%

Federal wildlife areas 7.8%

Ecological/wilderness areas 4.2%

Other conservation areas 4.7%

Provincial/regional parks 17.3%

National parks 33.0%

NOTE: These numbers are now outdated; however, there is no longer any central reporting or collating of these data. They illustrate the heavy reliance we have placed on provincial and national parks to be the repositories of wild species and natural spaces. There is a growing emphasis on environmental protection through increased involvement of private organizations (for-profit and nonprofit) in stewardship programs and projects.

SOURCE: *The State of Canada's Environment—1996,* © Her Majesty the Queen in Right of Canada, Environment Canada, 1996, Figure 14.8. Reprinted with permission of the Minister of Public Works and Government Services Canada, 2008.

Complete Canada's Networks of Protected Areas; in 2001, Parks Canada Agency (2001) recommended that implementation of that statement should be completed by 2003. While new areas were set aside after 2001, implementation of the network has not yet been completed.

The natural areas that are best represented within our national park system are the montane, boreal, and Arctic cordillera ecozones. Major gaps in ecosystem representation occur in the southern Prairies, most of the regions of the southern Arctic, the three taiga ecozones, and the most densely populated regions of Ontario and Quebec. In Nunavut, six natural regions lack representation, and in Quebec, four natural regions require national park status. Canada's efforts (along with those of other nations) have been criticized for selecting protected areas in regions based on economic or political criteria rather than ecological criteria. For example, in British Columbia and Alberta, the mountain ecosystems (particularly the Rockies) have far more of their ecosystems protected (and draw international tourists to Canada), while the interior boreal ecosystems (where timber, oil and gas, and mineral extraction take place) are grossly underrepresented in the provinces' protected areas network. Public opinion also has been influential. For example, setting aside areas to protect endangered insects does not get the same attention as setting aside areas to protect

endangered mammals. The old-growth forests of Canada's west coast have attracted far stronger public interest than the fescue grasslands of the Prairie provinces.

In some cases, it is very difficult to protect underrepresented ecosystems in southern Canada because frequently they have been highly modified through human settlement and economic activities. However, in 2003, the federal government created the Gulf Islands National Park Reserve to incorporate some of the islands and waterways located between Vancouver and Vancouver Island, in the most densely populated region in British Columbia. In 2008, the Naats'ihch'oh National Park Reserve in the Northwest Territories was announced, incorporating an area about 1.5 times the size of Prince Edward Island.

Urban development and other pressures have called for new strategies in the establishment and management of national parks. Many candidate lands are in private ownership; in these cases, the role of private stewardship is vital. For example, the Nature Conservancy of Canada has worked with landowners adjacent to Waterton Lakes National Park to establish conservation easements on land title to ensure that ranching and farming activities in the immediate area do not jeopardize important animal habitats or other environmental values. Conservation easements are purchased by the Nature Conservancy and attached to the property titles. They specify the location and/or types of activities that may be undertaken on land owned by private landowners. The Nature Conservancy has worked throughout Canada and the United States using this approach to promote private stewardship. The federal government also has a small program to purchase conservation easements from private landowners in an effort to encourage the protection of important ecosystems and species at risk. In northern Canada, in areas set aside as national parks pending settlement of any outstanding Aboriginal land claims, national park reserves permit traditional hunting, fishing, and trapping activities to continue.

Protection of marine ecosystems is as important as protection of terrestrial ecosystems, but Canada has lagged behind some other developed nations in achieving the desired level of protection. Parks Canada Agency has identified 29 marine regions (including the Atlantic, Pacific, and Arctic oceans as well as the Great Lakes) in Canada. The agency is seeking to ensure that each region will be represented in its network with at least one national marine conservation area. Marine conservation areas do not confer the same level of protection as national parks. The three existing national marine conservation areas—Gwaii Haanas (Queen Charlotte Islands in British Columbia), Fathom Five National Marine Park (Georgian Bay, Ontario), and an area at the confluence of the Saguenay and St. Lawrence rivers in Quebec—are intended to protect whales, marine mammals, and endemic plant species. Sustainable-use zones permit commercial fishing to continue. It is not clear whether future commercial activities will be allowed. In addition to Parks Canada Agency initiatives, the Canada Oceans Act provides for establishment of marine protected areas, and the provincial government of British Columbia also has established ecological reserves in marine areas. In 2002, the federal government announced the creation of five new national marine conservation areas in the following regions: Gwaii Haanas, British Columbia; western Lake Superior, Ontario; and the southern Strait of Georgia, British Columbia. As of 2008, these areas are still being negotiated. Regions for the remaining two marine conservation areas have yet to be chosen, although some discussions have been initiated to include part of the southern coast of Newfoundland.

The emphasis on **ecosystem management** within our national parks was reinforced by recommendations from two federal government task forces that examined the health of Canada's national parks. The Banff–Bow Valley Task Force (1996) and the Panel on the Ecological Integrity of Canada's National Parks (Parks Canada Agency, 2000) reported that our parks were under serious threat. Stressors (including habitat loss and fragmentation, losses of large carnivores, air pollution, pesticides, introduction of exotic species, and overuse by people) clearly had diminished the ecological integrity of these special places. Many stressors resulted from visitor or tourism facilities; these stressors, in particular, were difficult to address, as Parks Canada's budget was reduced by 25 percent between 1995 and 2000, and as a result, greater emphasis was placed on gaining revenue from visitors (Dearden & Dempsey, 2004).

In order to resolve such problems, Parks Canada's action plan for the future focuses on ways to (1) make ecological integrity central in legislation and policy that direct park management, (2) build partnerships with park neighbours and other stakeholders to cooperate in maintenance and protection of ecological integrity, (3) plan for ecological integrity by defining the direction for maintenance or restoration of ecological integrity and guiding appropriate public use, and (4) renew the Parks Canada organization to support more effectively the mandate of ecological integrity (Parks Canada Agency, 2001).

Other Protected Areas in Canada

Some of Canada's protected areas are designated under the terms of international treaties or agreements. The Ramsar Convention (see Chapter 7) protects wetlands of international importance within Canada, and sites (including areas of particular scientific or aesthetic value as well as the habitats of endangered species) are designated under the Convention Concerning the Protection of World Cultural and Natural Heritage. Ramsar and World Heritage sites may be designated without being protected formally (this helps identify candidate sites for formal protection in the future). By 2005, there were 13 World

Heritage sites in Canada (two shared with Canadian national parks), 15 biosphere reserves, and 37 Ramsar sites (see Figure 12–4). In addition, in British Columbia, a system of ecological reserves offers the highest degree of protection of any protected area. Ecological reserves were established in the 1970s for the protection of biodiversity. Their primary purpose is research and education, not outdoor recreation, although many are open to the public for nonconsumptive, observational uses such as nature appreciation, wildlife viewing, and photography. While large in number, they are very small in size.

Efforts by governments and nongovernmental organizations to increase the number and geographic extent of protected areas continue. In 2002–3, Quebec designated 27 new areas for protection, covering about 4 million hectares, that increased the proportion of protected areas from 2.9 to 5.3 percent. In April 2003, the Protected Natural Areas Act came into force in New Brunswick, providing more comprehensive legislation to manage and administer the province's entire network of protected natural areas. In February of the same year, Nova Scotia announced that four parcels of land would now be protected in an agreement that involved the Nature Conservancy of Canada (a nonprofit, NGO) and Bowmater Mersey Paper Company Limited (a forestry company).

Restoration and Rehabilitation

There is not much point in expending time, energy, and finances on species recovery or restoration if the ecosystem that is meant to support them is not rehabilitated also. This is why Canada reviews the status of certain classes of native flora and fauna under COSEWIC. A complementary program, Recovery of Nationally Endangered Wildlife (RENEW), develops recovery plans for more than 75 species that have been designated by COSEWIC as extirpated, endangered, or threatened. RENEW and similar programs recognize the need, but do not have the knowledge base, to respond effectively to threats to plants, invertebrates, fungi, and algae, even if many of these species perform more vital ecological functions than the vertebrates.

Encouraging results have been attained from several species protection or reintroduction programs. Sea otters have been reintroduced to Vancouver Island's west coast kelp forests; peregrine falcons have been restored to territories from which they had been extirpated; the ferruginous hawk has been downlisted from threatened to special concern; and the wood bison has been downlisted from endangered to threatened. The American white pelican and the prairie long-tailed weasel, two prairie species that had been listed as threatened, are among those that have been removed from the COSEWIC list. The trumpeter swan, formerly near extinction, is now successfully breeding in the Beaver Hills area of Alberta (see Box 12–4).

BOX 12-4
THE TRUMPETER SWAN

Photo 12-13
Trumpeter swan.

The trumpeter swan, North America's largest waterfowl, was almost extinct by the early 1930s. Habitat east of the Rocky Mountains had been destroyed during the 19th century. Swans were overharvested for their meat, skins (for tobacco pouches), and feathers (for hats). From 1853 to 1877, the Hudson Bay Company sold 17 671 swan skins, primarily from trumpeters. By 1935 (despite legislation of the Migratory Birds Convention Act), only 69 trumpeter swans were known to be alive. Wildlife officers in Alberta, along with wildlife officers across North America, began earnest efforts to restore these populations in the last half of the 20th century. In 1987, officers began to relocate swans from around Grande Prairie to the protected lakes of Elk Island National Park so the swans could bond with the Elk Island population. By 1998, a pair of reintroduced swans successfully raised four cygnets. These were the first to fledge in Elk Island in more than a century. Others continued in the same tradition. By 2006, there were seven breeding pairs in the region. Across North American, by 2000, there were approximately 23 647 trumpeter swans.

Sustainable Use of Biological Resources

Protected areas such as parks have dominated our thinking about biodiversity. There is no question that they have been important for protecting habitats and species in Canada. But parks are sometimes controversial. Their creation may displace people and disrupt traditional livelihoods. This concern has been raised by Aboriginal people in Canada and by residents of developing countries, who have accused ENGOs of a new form of colonialism by dictating where local people can and cannot extract the resources they need for survival. In some cases, the establishment of protected areas heightens illegal activities such as poaching or results in highly concentrated forms of degradation just outside the boundaries. Furthermore, protected areas that are established in "wilderness" locations may not help instill the understanding that people should have to use their own environments more sustainably.

Given the consensus that current and projected consumption levels are unsustainable (World Commission on Environment and Development, 1987), the best way to satisfy basic human economic needs without compromising biodiversity is the rigorous adoption of sustainability policies in all resource sectors. In Canada, this means that resource-consuming activities such as agriculture, forestry, fishing, and urban development are of particular significance in developing sustainable-use practices that will helps to conserve genetic resources.

Biosphere reserves offer a modified model for protecting biodiversity through a range of goals that include protection and sustainable use. These reserves are intended to be "living landscapes"—people work within local landscapes and demonstrate how they can earn a livelihood by living sustainably within their ecosystems. Biosphere reserves are established under the United Nations Educational, Scientific and Cultural Organization's (UNESCO) Man and the Biosphere (MAB) Programme. These reserves have a wide range of objectives in addition to conservation, including sustainable development, scientific research, training, monitoring, and demonstration. Biosphere reserves require a core area that is strictly protected by national legislation (e.g., national park, protective treaty, or convention) surrounded by a buffer in which activities that are consistent with the objective of conservation are permitted. Surrounding the core and buffer is a large transition area, where a wider range of human activities occurs and where ecological restoration and sustainable resource use can be demonstrated (see Figure 12–6 on page 510).

Biosphere reserves are important because they recognize and support cultural as well as biological diversity. They are created by local initiatives, coupled with provincial and federal support, and ultimately recognized by the United Nations. Once designated, they become part of an international network, and members participate in national and international meetings to discuss their common issues and progress. In 1999, there were six biosphere reserves in Canada; by 2007, this number had increased to 15, with more being proposed to UNESCO. Nevertheless, part of the challenge of the biosphere

Photo 12–14b

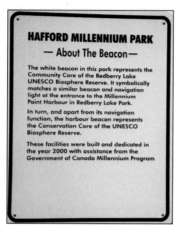

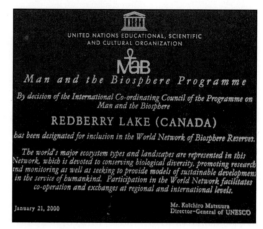

Photo 12–14a　　　　　**Photo 12–14c**　　　　　**Photo 12–14d**

This beacon (photo 12–14a) is located in the townsite of Hafford, a small community located within transition area of the Redberry Lake Biosphere Reserve, seven kilometres from the core area represented by the lake and its islands (photo 12–14b). Its plaques (photo 12–14c and photo 12–14d) remind residents of their commitment to protect their ecological and cultural heritage for present and future generations.

reserve concept is that outside the core area, the biosphere reserve is merely an area of recognition. This means that there are no laws or regulations that can be used to enforce or curb particular practices. Efforts to pursue conservation practices in support of sustainability are entirely voluntary, and financial and logistical support of provincial and federal governments has been minimal. Instead, volunteer members of biosphere reserve committees assist researchers and engage local communities in outreach activities that help to build understanding and commitment to the conservation objectives of the biosphere reserves. Where biosphere reserves are co-located with National Parks, cooperation plans have been developed between the two to allow for conservation and sustainable resource use.

In addition to the creation of biosphere reserves, private organizations such as Ducks Unlimited Canada (DUC) also undertake restoration of degraded habitats and encourage good stewardship practices of private landowners. While originally established to protect habitat for waterfowl species desirable for hunting, Ducks

Unlimited has expanded its role to habitat protection of wetlands. In some cases, DUC buys land outright to ensure that the property is not drained for agricultural or other purposes. In other cases, DUC works with current owners and other organizations (such as the Nature Conservancy of Canada and the Biosphere Programme) to identify important habitats and engage in agreements (some of which are cost-sharing agreements) to ensure that farming or ranching activities do not jeopardize important nesting, rearing, or overwintering areas.

EX SITU CONSERVATION

Ex situ conservation of biodiversity is the conservation of species or genetic materials under artificial conditions, away from the ecosystems to which they belong. As the supply of natural habitats has declined, maintaining captive populations (or cultivated populations in the case of plants) has been accepted as one of the few ways that survival of increasing numbers of species can be ensured

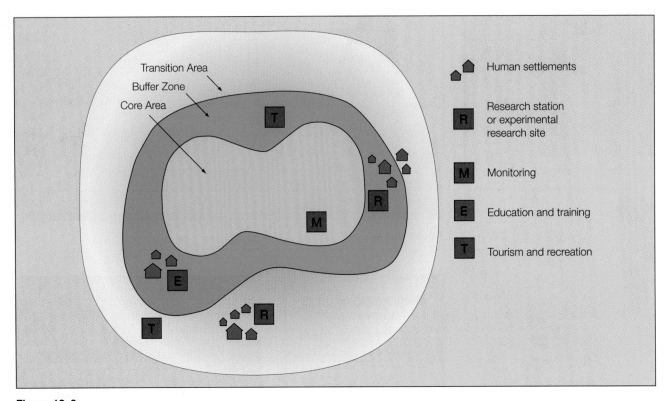

Figure 12–6

The three zones of a biosphere reserve

SOURCE: *Solving the Puzzle: The Ecosystem Approach and Biosphere Reserves,* UNESCO, 2000, Paris: Author, p. 6. Reprinted by permission of UNESCO.

until the long-term goal of restoring them to the wild (in at least some of their original ranges) is attained.

Among the advantages of ex situ facilities such as zoos, aquariums, aviaries, and botanical gardens are opportunities for scientific study as well as public education about species on display. In turn, this education can help build broader public support (and provide fundraising opportunities) for species conservation in situ. The majority of conservation biology opinion, however, indicates that captive breeding programs are not complete to conservation needs.

There are many reasons why they are not, including the fact that ex situ protection is expensive, and, as natural habitats continue to disappear, too many species require housing. Within ex situ facilities, animals often become domesticated and lose their wild behaviours. Lack of natural selection of mates is an issue that also may contribute to inbreeding problems such as depression. Another loss associated with ex situ facilities is the inability to pass on to captive-born young their hunting strategies or migration routes.

Plants

About 800 of the world's 1500 botanical gardens are committed to conserving rare, endemic, or other threatened plant species. Canada's 60 botanical gardens contain close to 40 000 plant species native to Canada and from around the world, including at least 11 endangered, rare, or vulnerable native plant species. In 1995, no plants were being propagated specifically for reintroduction.

Seed banks can be important ex situ facilities for conservation of plant species and genetic diversity. Around the world, seed banks help safeguard more than 6 million plant species against destruction by drought, war, climate change, or other disasters. However, only 35 of these facilities meet international standards for long-term storage ("Seeds in Threatened Soil," 2005). The most ambitious facility to date opened in February 2008 in Norway. The Svalbard Global Seed Vault was constructed underground on a remote Norwegian island and was designed to withstand global disaster including nuclear war or climate warming, and even failure of its freezers. Initially, 100 million seeds from more than 100 countries were sent to the facility for safekeeping. Species range from food staples of Africa and Asia such as rice, maize, wheat, and sorghum to European and South American types of lettuce, barley, and potato.

Both Agriculture and Agri-Food Canada and the Canadian Forest Service maintain seed stocks for use in plant breeding or in sustainable use programs. The Heritage Seed Program is a nongovernmental initiative that maintains a large variety of vegetable species, and "Seedy Saturday" (a concept that began in Vancouver and since

Photo 12–15

In Saskatchewan (as in this photo) and in other parts of Canada, Ducks Unlimited works with landowners and other ENGOs to protect wetland habitats.

has spread throughout Canada) promotes springtime sharing of seeds and seed stories among backyard gardeners, farmers, and others.

Animals

In the 1990s, Canada had about 50 zoos, 15 aquariums, and 15 aviaries; these facilities hold hundreds of species of mammals, birds, reptiles, fish, and invertebrates. More than 870 zoos and aquariums worldwide, housing over a million vertebrate specimens, are involved in global efforts to preserve both wild and native animal diversity ex situ. The focus in many of these institutions is no longer on entertainment but on providing living conditions that simulate various species' natural habitats accurately enough to promote breeding. This is seen to be particularly important for species whose numbers in the wild are so low that survival depends on captive breeding programs, called Species Survival Programs, to build up population

numbers to the point where species can be returned to their native ecosystems.

Canadian zoos hold at least 12 endangered, threatened, or vulnerable animal species, including the whooping crane, ferruginous hawk, eastern massasauga rattlesnake, spotted turtle, Vancouver Island marmot, grizzly bear, and polar bear. Canadian captive breeding programs have provided swift foxes and peregrine falcons for reintroduction programs (Government of Canada, 1996; Henry, 1994). Some Canadian zoos participate in international breeding programs of non-Canadian species for reintroduction to native ecosystems in other countries. Not all species can be propagated successfully in captivity, however.

At the University of Alberta, a poultry conservation program to conserve the genetic diversity of six breeds of chickens that contributed to our past or present meat and egg stocks has been ongoing since 1992. This program is a bit like an insurance policy; it is a conscious effort to sustain the genetic variability of the old-fashioned birds against the danger that today's commercially bred chickens are becoming more genetically uniform and may develop traits that will limit their viability (Robinson, 1997).

In spite of some benefits obtained through ex situ protection, it is not sufficient merely to save seeds, extract and freeze sperm, and protect some species in "stationary arks." A key challenge is that seeds and sperm saved do not continue to adapt to changing conditions in the real world, so it is not certain that they would be able to survive under future ecological conditions. Rather, we need to save wild species and natural ecosystems in intact, natural spaces if we hope to protect biodiversity and promote sustainability. Nevertheless, given the alterations in habitat that will arise from climate change, ex situ conservation or relocation may be a necessary alternative to protect specific species.

Photo 12–16

Captive breeding programs in zoos help conserve genetic diversity but are not a substitute for natural, functioning ecosystems. The black-footed ferret (above) is being reintroduced to North American grasslands.

Photo 12–17

The common pincushion cactus reaches the north end of its range on the Canadian prairie. Conservation efforts of private landowners and national parks are important to maintain the biodiversity of this region.

INTERNATIONAL STRATEGIES

Since 1980, a series of important documents have influenced international thinking about and responses to the issues of conservation of biodiversity and sustainable use of biological and other resources. Six of these documents are the following: *World Conservation Strategy* (1980); *Our Common Future* (1987); *Caring for the Earth* (1991); *Global Biodiversity Strategy* (1992); Agenda 21 (1992); and the Earth Charter (2000). These documents are covered in more detail in Box 1–2 (p. 17) and Table 1–3 (p. 18).

The United Nations Environment Programme–World Conservation Monitoring Centre (UNEP–WCMC) is an international centre of excellence devoted to the location and management of information on conservation and sustainable use of the world's living resources. Located in Cambridge, England, the centre is guided by a high-level Scientific Advisory Council (UNEP–WCMC, 2001). Of the more than 80 multilateral treaties the WCMC lists relating to conservation and management of biodiversity, Canada is involved in about 20, including nine out of 10 global conventions. The objectives of these nine international treaties are noted briefly in Table 12–6.

The 1992 United Nations Convention on Biological Diversity is the basis for much of the current international action on biodiversity. The objectives of the convention are to conserve biological diversity; to attain sustainable use of ecosystems, species, and genetic material; and to ensure the fair and equitable sharing of benefits arising from genetic resources.

As a leading proponent of the Convention on Biological Diversity, Canada (like all the other signatories) was responsible for developing a national strategy for the conservation and sustainable use of biological resources. The outcome—the Canadian Biodiversity Strategy—was derived by a working group comprising federal, provincial, territorial,

and nongovernmental representatives. The working group identified five strategic goals for the Canadian Biodiversity Strategy: to conserve biodiversity and use biological resources in a sustainable manner; to improve Canada's understanding of ecosystems and increase our resource management capacity; to promote public understanding of the need to conserve biodiversity and use biological resources in a sustainable manner; to maintain or develop incentives and legislation that support these goals; and to work with other countries to achieve the objectives of the convention (Environment Canada, 2000). The Canadian Biodiversity Information Network (CBIN) provides support for the Convention on Biological Diversity and Agenda 21.

Another important international treaty that deals with protection of wild species is the Convention on International Trade in Endangered Species of Wild Fauna and Flora (CITES). As signatories to CITES, Canadian and international law enforcement agents are able to target poaching, smuggling, and illegal trade in wildlife species, their parts and derivatives. For instance, the Canadian Wildlife Service is responsible for implementing CITES in Canada against poachers who illegally kill bears to obtain gall bladders and paws for sale to international markets. A Canadian federal law proclaimed in 1996, the Wild Animal and Plant Protection and Regulation of International and Interprovincial Trade Act (WAPPRIITA) protects Canadian and foreign species from illegal trade. It also protects Canadian ecosystems against the introduction of designated harmful species.

CANADIAN LAW, POLICY, AND PRACTICE

With the growth of international concern and action relating to biodiversity issues (species and spaces), and Canada's active participation in global efforts to preserve biodiversity, the national response has involved strengthening and augmenting existing laws, policies,

Photo 12–18

Bears killed illegally to satisfy a specific market are confiscated by authorities.

Global Treaty	Treaty Objectives
International Plant Protection Convention (Rome), 1951	• To maintain and increase international cooperation in controlling pests and diseases of plants and plant products; to prevent introduction and spread of these pests and diseases across national boundaries
Convention on Fishing and Conservation of the Living Resources of the High Seas (Geneva), 1958	• To improve conservation of the living resources of the high seas and prevent overexploitation
Convention on the High Seas (Geneva), 1958	• To codify the rules of international law relating to the high seas
Convention on Wetlands of International Importance Especially as Waterfowl Habitat (Ramsar), 1971	• To stem the progressive encroachment on and loss of wetlands; to recognize ecological functions of wetlands and their economic, cultural, scientific, and recreational value
Convention Concerning the Protection of the World Cultural and Natural Heritage (Paris), 1972	• To establish an effective system of collective protection of cultural and natural heritage of outstanding universal value, organized on a permanent basis and in accordance with modern scientific methods
Convention on International Trade in Endangered Species of Wild Fauna and Flora (Washington), 1973	• To protect, via import/export controls, certain endangered species from overexploitation
United Nations Convention on the Law of the Sea (Montego Bay), 1983	• To set up a comprehensive, new legal regime for the sea and oceans as far as environmental provisions are concerned; to establish material rules concerning environmental standards as well as enforcement provisions dealing with pollution of the marine environment
International Tropical Timber Agreement (Geneva), 1983	• To provide an effective framework for cooperation and consultation between countries producing and consuming tropical timber; to promote the expansion and diversification of international trade in tropical timber; to improve structural conditions in the tropical timber market; to promote research and development; to promote sustainable utilization and conservation of tropical forests and their genetic resources; to maintain the ecological balance in regions concerned
United Nations Convention on Biological Diversity (Rio de Janeiro), 1992	• To conserve biological diversity, the sustainable use of its components, and the fair and equitable sharing of the benefits arising out of use of genetic resources, including by providing appropriate access to genetic resources and transfer of relevant technologies, taking into account all rights over those resources and technologies, and by ensuring appropriate funding

SOURCE: *The State of Canada's Environment—1996,* © Her Majesty the Queen in Right of Canada, Environment Canada, 1996, Table 14.7. Reproduced with the permission of the Minister of Public Works and Government Services, 2008.

and practices as well as instituting new partnerships. Table 12–7 highlights selected examples of Canada's federal approach to protecting biodiversity. To illustrate Canadian efforts to protect Canadian species and spaces, the following sections comment briefly on the Endangered Species Protection Act, the Endangered Spaces Campaign of World Wildlife Fund Canada, and the Sierra Club's ratings of federal and provincial efforts.

Protecting Canadian Species

Wildlife management in Canada is "a complex, almost precarious system of shared responsibilities between the federal government and the provinces and territories" ("Protecting Canadian Species," 1996). The legislative basis of shared responsibility places migratory birds, fish, and marine mammals within federal jurisdiction; the

National/regional	Canadian Biodiversity Strategy
	Species at Risk Act
	Federal Policy on Wetland Conservation
	Canadian Environmental Protection Act
	National Accord for the Protection of Species at Risk
	Committee on the Status of Endangered Wildlife in Canada
	North American Waterfowl Management Plan
Wildlife (Flora and Fauna)	RENEW (Committee on the Recovery of Nationally Endangered Wildlife)
	Wildlife Policy for Canada
	Canada Wildlife Act
	CITES (Convention on International Trade in Endangered Species of Wild Fauna and Flora)
	WAPPRIITA (Wild Animal and Plant Protection and Regulation of International and Interprovincial Trade Act)
	Endangered Species Recovery Fund
	Migratory Birds Convention Act
	Canada Forest Accord
	National Forest Strategy
	Agricultural Weed Biocontrol Program

majority of wildlife protection responsibilities lie with the provincial and territorial governments. In spite of this, interjurisdictional cooperation (such as is seen in COSEWIC) and informal agreements have been a hallmark of wild species protection in Canada.

As useful as COSEWIC's designations of species at risk are in raising both public awareness and the political will to protect wildlife, the designations are less effective than they might be simply because they have no legal status. In 1996, a Canada Endangered Species Protection Act was tabled in Parliament. The original act was controversial, engendering opposition because some conservationists (including leading scientists) believed it was insufficient to protect endangered species and particularly their habitat, while landowners believed they risked losing their property and livelihood because of it. Not until December

2002 did the revised Species at Risk Act (SARA) receive royal assent. It came into full effect in June 2004. The Act is part of a three-part strategy for protecting biodiversity. The other components include a habitat stewardship program and the Accord for the Protection of Species at Risk—a Canada-wide agreement on federal–provincial–territorial cooperation. Environment Canada, Fisheries and Oceans Canada, and the Parks Canada Agency of Heritage Canada are the core departments responsible for implementing SARA. The Act prohibits killing species listed under the Act and destroying their critical habitat. The Act also established COSEWIC as a legal entity at arm's length from the government to ensure that species were designated by a scientific panel independent of government.

Protecting Canadian Spaces

Protecting our "natural capital" is essential if future generations of Canadians are to experience a healthy and prosperous environment. This is why the World Wildlife Fund Canada's Endangered Spaces Campaign continued to push governments to complete the promised nationwide system of protected areas (see Hummel, 1989). In this 10-year campaign, begun in 1989, conserving representative areas of the country's diverse lands and waters was considered a critical first step toward the necessary protection of biodiversity in support of sustainability (Hackman, 1996).

At the end of the campaign, 132 of Canada's 486 natural regions (or 6.8 percent of Canada's total area) were considered adequately or moderately protected (World Wildlife Fund Canada, 2000a, 2000b). Yet, information from different sources reveals discrepancies in the data and highlights some of the difficulties involved in measuring the success of protecting natural regions (see Table 12–8). In part, the impetus to protect areas representing all of Canada's natural regions came from the 1989 Canadian Wilderness Charter. Part of the Endangered Spaces Campaign of World Wildlife Fund Canada, the Canadian Wilderness Charter has a broad base of support—by the end of the campaign in 1999, more than 600 000 individuals and 300 organizations had signed the charter (World Wildlife Fund Canada, 2000a).

Several nongovernmental organizations attempt to keep track of Canadian biodiversity protection efforts. Each year, to measure progress in the Endangered Spaces Campaign, World Wildlife Fund Canada graded the provincial, territorial, and federal governments on their progress toward completing the goal. The 1998/1999 Report Card shows the final grades assigned to each jurisdiction for their progress in establishing the protected areas system (see Box 12–5 on page 516). Not only did this simple measure capture year-to-year differences in provincial, territorial, and federal progress in setting aside protected

TABLE 12-8

MEASURING SUCCESS IN PROTECTING CANADA'S NATURAL REGIONS?

Organization	Date	Area Protected (km²)	Percentage of Canada's Total Land Mass
Government of Canada	2003	820 000	8.2
Government of Canada	2001	660 003	6.6
Government of Canada	1996	800 000	8.0
WCMC	2000	950 000	9.6
WWF Canada	2000	683 000	6.8

NOTE: These statistics highlight the importance of being a critical thinker (see Chapter 2). The data above reflect inconsistencies in measuring Canada's protected areas. All the data are from respected sources. Some sources, such as Government of Canada, may have been published more recently (e.g., 2006) but relate to earlier time periods (e.g., 2003). The numerical values indicated above could suggest possible differences in the mandates and stated values of the three agencies represented. Thus, it is important to ask the following questions: What is the nature of the data? How were they collected? How were they interpreted? How were "protected areas" and "natural regions" defined?

SOURCES: *Canada's National Indicators Series, 2003,* Government of Canada, 2003, http://www.ec.gc.ca/soer-ree/English/ Indicators/default.cfm; *The State of Canada's Environment—1996,* Government of Canada, 1996, Ottawa: Supply and Services Canada; *Human Activity and the Environment, Annual Statistics 2003,* Statistics Canada, 2003, Ottawa: Ministry of Industry; *Human Activity and the Environment, Annual Statistics 2006,* Statistics Canada, 2006, http://www.statcan.ca/english/freepub/16-201-XIE/16-201-XIE2006000.pdf; *State of the World's Protected Areas, Annex 1: Summary of Protected Areas,* World Conservation Monitoring Center (WCMC), 2000, http://www.unep-wcmc.org/ protected_areas/albany_a1.pdf; *Endangered Spaces: The Wilderness Campaign That Changed the Canadian Landscape: 1989–2000,* World Wildlife Fund, 2000, pp. 22–23.

areas, it also was a means for Canadians to compare performance across and within political jurisdictions over time. For example, from 1997/98 to 1998/99, World Wildlife Fund downgraded British Columbia from C+ to C primarily because the government commitment to preserve 12 percent of British Columbia's lands did not allow for adequate representation of all of the province's natural areas: overall almost 20 percent remains inadequately represented (World Wildlife Fund Canada, 1999).

Every year since 1993, the Sierra Club of Canada has used a similar report card approach to rate the federal, provincial, and territorial governments on their progress in keeping the commitments they made at the 1992 Earth Summit regarding climate change and protection of biodiversity. In 2000, they gave the federal government a C for its commitment to reduce greenhouse gases and an F in protecting biodiversity (Sierra Club of Canada, 2006). By 2003, this rating had improved to A for its commitment to reduce greenhouse gases and B+ for its commitments to protect biodiversity (Sierra Club of Canada, 2003). Yet, in 2006, these fortunes changed: the federal government received an F rating for its efforts to reduce greenhouse gases and a D (for the Liberals) and an F (for the Conservatives) for their commitments to biodiversity. Individual provinces have faired at least as badly over the years. In 2006, Alberta had the worst record, receiving failing grades on both counts. Clearly, our efforts are uneven over time and space. In the concluding section, we examine some fundamental challenges facing the issue of biodiversity

protection and consider opportunities for meeting those challenges.

FUTURE CHALLENGES AND OPPORTUNITIES

As the rich heritage and diversity of Canada's wild species and natural landscapes continue to be placed at risk through human demands for expansion of urban, industrial, agricultural, recreational, and other activities, the importance of wildlife and wild spaces to the future sustainability of Canadian society cannot be underestimated. Yet, as pointed out throughout this chapter, climate change poses significant challenges to our efforts to protect biodiversity. Continued stewardship and actions on the part of individual Canadians, ENGOs, the private sector, and governments are vital if Canadians are to achieve completion of the national parks system and establishment of the network of protected areas across the country.

IMPLICATIONS OF CLIMATE CHANGE FOR BIODIVERSITY PROTECTION

Climate change calls into question whether or not the regions we protect will maintain the conditions necessary for sustaining biodiversity. Historically, our strategies for

The Endangered Spaces Campaign had a specific measurable goal: to help conserve Canada's biological diversity by protecting a representative sample of each of the country's terrestrial and one-third of its marine natural regions by the year 2000, and to complete the marine protected areas system by 2010. Following are the "grades" received by federal, provincial, and territorial governments from 1995/96 to 1998/99.

Federal Grades

Jurisdiction	1995/96	1996/97	1997/98	1998/99
Terrestrial	C	A–	D	C
Marine—Pacific	C	C–	D+	n/a
Marine—Arctic	D–	D–	D–	n/a
Marine—Atlantic	D+	D–	D+	n/a
Marine—Great Lakes	D	D	D	n/a

Provincial and Territorial Grades

Jurisdiction	1995/96	1996/97	1997/98	1998/99
Alberta	B	D+	F	F
British Columbia	A	C	C+	C
Manitoba	D–	B+	C	B–
New Brunswick	F	F	D	D
Newfoundland	D	C–	D	D+
Northwest Territories	D	C–	C	C–
Nova Scotia	A	C–	C+	C+
Ontario	F	C–	D+	B+
Prince Edward Island	C+	B	B	C
Quebec	C–	D–	F	F
Saskatchewan	C	F	B–	C
Yukon	D	C–	C+	C–

NOTE: The campaign is now over, so a national grading update is not available.

SOURCES: *The Endangered Species Campaign: 1997/98 Marine Grades and 1997/98 Terrestrial Grades,* World Wildlife Fund Canada, 1998, Author; *Grades: The 1998–99 Endangered Spaces Progress Report on Canada's Wild Lands,* World Wildlife Fund Canada, April 27, 1999, Author

the effects of climate change on European distributions of 1200 plant species. Their data indicated that 6 to 11 percent of species modelled potentially would be lost from selected reserves within 50 years. They asked "whether we should expect climate change to drive species out of reserves, if areas were not purposely selected to account for climate-change impacts on biodiversity. The answer is clearly yes" (p. 1623). Consequently, the idea that we can simply set aside protected areas and leave them alone may result in large and unintended losses.

Despite Canada's system of planning protected areas, many reserve areas have been established according to the spaces available or political feasibility. They are expected to remain in place in perpetuity. If we are serious about protecting biodiversity, climate change demands quite a different strategy. Species' ranges would be expected to move away from their current locations, and existing reserves may be inadequate to guarantee species' persistence in the long term (Araújo, 2004). Biodiversity protection may require improved understanding of the suitability of habitats and the establishment of large reserves, well connected into regional networks, rather than smaller, scattered reserves. Such strategies may require coordination and collaboration across political boundaries—even international boundaries. While Canada and the United States, as well as the European Union, have a history of collaboration on a range of interests, such efforts may be more challenging in places where institutional capacity for intergovernmental relations is more limited. We also may have to reconsider the desirability and viability of translocating populations or ex situ conservation to ensure the long-term survival of some species.

IMPROVING UNDERSTANDING OF AND ADVOCACY FOR BIODIVERSITY PROTECTION

If we are to be successful in conserving biodiversity and using biological resources sustainably, adopting ecological management principles is necessary. Ecological management directs human activities so that the biotic and abiotic components of ecosystems, and the processes that sustain them, continue. To manage effectively, it is necessary to have adequate understanding of ecosystems, species, and human impacts on them. Unfortunately, the current state of this knowledge is inadequate; thus, there needs to be a strong commitment to research.

Research needs include reliable baseline data, indicators for conserving biodiversity, standardized protocols for conducting surveys and inventories, and indicators of biodiversity change (for trend prediction). Gap analysis is a research tool used to evaluate and complete representative protected areas networks (Rowe, Kavanagh, & Iacobelli, 1995). Using ground surveys, inventories,

protecting and managing biodiversity have employed static understandings of climate. We have viewed climate of the future much like the climate of the recent past. Yet, recent research reveals this strategy may be misguided. A modelling study by Miguel Araújo and others (2004) examined

satellite imagery, and geographic information system (GIS) technology, gap analysis identifies missing dimensions in the representation of biodiversity. Hot spot analysis is a related tool that locates areas of species or endemic richness that should have priority for protection, sustainable use, or new biotechnologies. For example, 35 hot spots composing 2.3 percent of the Earth's surface hold almost one-half of all plants and vertebrate species (except fish) (Norman Myers, personal communication, 2008). Focusing on hot spots nationally and internationally may serve to protect the greatest proportion of biodiversity with the least effort and expense.

Efforts to monitor the status of biodiversity are ongoing. The federal Ecological Monitoring and Assessment Network (EMAN) program, for example, monitors a wide variety of ecosystem and species parameters to assess the interactions and sustainability of regional ecosystems. In addition to the research needs noted above, it is necessary to develop a dynamic program of public education that promotes awareness of biodiversity and develops strategies to reduce resource consumption levels. Indeed, scientific articles dealing with biodiversity losses (e.g., Hannah et al., 2002) have called for a closer relationship between science and public policy. Scientists, with specialized understanding, are in a key position to affect public awareness, policy, and actions. The "World Scientists' Warning to Humanity" noted in Chapter 1 is an example where scientists around the world believed so strongly in the challenges associated with global change that they joined together in a call for action.

PARTNERSHIPS FOR THE FUTURE

Growing concern over wildlife and wild spaces issues has caused a broad range of groups—government agencies, private-sector interests, ENGOs, and individuals—to work together to preserve and protect wildlife and to sustain Canada's ecosystems. The involvement of this range of groups helps ensure that resources are used wisely and that efforts are directed to the best possible use.

The policies, strategies, and legislation identified in Table 12–7, as well as numerous provincial and territorial conservation and sustainability strategies, wetland and wildlife policies, forest management plans, and protected areas strategies, are evidence that cooperation and collaboration can provide positive outcomes for wildlife and wild spaces.

Canada and the United States have signed several agreements to improve the management of birds that migrate between the two countries, and to deal with questions of fairness in regulating waterfowl harvests among Alaskan and Canadian Aboriginal peoples. A Framework for Cooperation to protect shared endangered species was signed by the Canadian environment minister and the U.S. interior secretary. Probably the best-recognized

Photo 12–19
The whooping crane is one species that has benefited from wildlife protection policies and strategies. It nests in Wood Buffalo National Park, in the Northwest Territories, and winters on the gulf coast of Texas.

cooperative effort, the billion-dollar North American Waterfowl Management Plan (NAWMP) is the combined initiative of Canada, the United States, and Mexico. The NAWMP is implemented through regionally based joint ventures that, in turn, involve federal, provincial, territorial, and state government agencies, ENGOs such as Ducks Unlimited Canada and Wildlife Habitat Canada, the private sector, and landowners all cooperating together. Regional habitat management in Canada is undertaken through the Prairie Habitat, the Eastern Habitat, and the Pacific Coast joint ventures. Initially conceived as a waterfowl plan, the NAWMP has expanded to include multispecies and biodiversity objectives.

The Canadian Coalition for Biodiversity, the Natural Heritage League, the Canadian Parks Partnership, Wildlife Habitat Canada, and the Canadian Parks and Wilderness Society (CPAWS) are among many citizen-based ENGO groups across Canada whose collaborative and cooperative efforts to preserve and protect wild species and spaces have made a difference at the national level. The

Yellowstone to Yukon Biodiversity Strategy (Y2Y) project involving CPAWS, and the reintroduction of the swift fox to the southern Alberta and Saskatchewan prairie, and the timber wolf to Montana, are projects that exemplify the range of actions possible through various forms of cooperation and collaboration.

On the provincial scale, organizations such as the Federation of Ontario Naturalists and the Nature Trust of British Columbia have helped coordinate efforts of multiple groups to magnify the effectiveness of local biodiversity conservation efforts. For example, acting as a partner with the Nature Trust of British Columbia, the Pacific Estuary Conservation Program was able to purchase Englishman River Flats on the east coast of Vancouver Island in 1992. This partnership, and the cooperation of the provincial government, enabled protection of a key feeding and resting area along British Columbia's coast for up to 30 000 brant (geese) that fly from Baja to Alaska and Russia. The Englishman River Estuary also is a wintering area for the trumpeter swan and other waterfowl; more than 110 bird species have been recorded in the estuary, which also provides essential rearing habitat for steelhead trout and salmon (Nature Trust of British Columbia, 1993). Parks Canada works with Aboriginal organizations to co-manage parks such as Haida Gwaii and Pacific Rim National Park Reserve. In Ontario, the greenbelt that includes the Niagara Escarpment from Tobermory to Niagara Falls, as well as agricultural land around Toronto and the Oak Ridges Moraine, is considered one of the largest and most successful in protecting lands from development and urban sprawl. The region is taking the first steps to be considered a biosphere reserve. If successful as a biosphere reserve, its spatial extent and partnerships among small rural municipalities and large urban centres would make it unique in the world. Presently, the amount of land in the greenbelt is 11 times larger than the City of Toronto (Mittelstaedt, 2008).

Two trends offer hope and challenges. Firstly, biodiversity protection is no longer the sole responsibility of government. The federal habitat stewardship program offers funding for private landowners to conserve biodiversity on private lands. Nongovernmental organizations (e.g., The Nature Conservancy and Ducks Unlimited) and private Canadian branches of the landowners are now participating alone, with one another, and with governments to provide education, incentives, and programs that invite individuals to undertake stewardship and conservation practices. Many banks and credit unions have environment funds that also support stewardship activities. For example, Vancity Credit Union, the largest credit union in the country, provides no-interest loans to landowners who seek to protect riparian habitats that occur on their property.

Secondly, biodiversity protection is to be achieved not only in wilderness areas far from the urban places in which the majority of Canadians live but also, wild

Photo 12–20
A stewardship project located on a farmer's property in Saskatchewan protects habitat for bird life.

species and natural spaces may occur in our own neighbourhoods and cities. For example, community gardens in Vancouver and Montreal (among other cities) are places that cultivate heritage apples, thereby protecting biodiversity of a species important for human consumption. Similarly, across the country, community organizations have undertaken campaigns to "liberate" streams (uncover streams that had been organized into systems of structured waterways and culverts for water provision, flood control, and sewage treatment) and demonstrate the effect of effluent disposal on fish populations of urban waterways. The movement to uproot grass lawns and promote indigenous plants also promotes biodiversity across the country. While initially rejected by municipal councils who enforced strict "weed" controls, such initiatives are now supported by governments. For example, the Saskatchewan Ministry of Environment publishes a

Photo 12–21
The sustainability of timber wolves depends partly on the cooperative and collaborative actions of groups and individuals.

book on planting species to attract birds and maintain "backyard biodiversity." The Trans Canada Trail, an initiative of an NGO, winds its way through urban parks and wilderness, reminding Canadians of their common natural and cultural heritage. These initiatives suggest that the protection of species and spaces does not take place solely in distant wilderness areas. Rather, urban areas are vital places for learning about and cultivating a love of nature and engaging in stewardship activities to protect biodiversity. Activities in urban places may help engender attitudes and commitments to halt the degradation of national parks and other protected areas, ensuring they are not "loved to death."

CONCLUDING COMMENTS

In part, the protection of biodiversity depends on continued development, application, and enforcement of legislation and regulation. International and national legislation, including Canada's Species at Risk Act, RENEW, CITES, WAPPRIITA, and the Migratory Birds Convention Act, provide important directions for protecting the future of biodiversity. These directions require continued monitoring, not only of the effectiveness of the legislation, but also of the species and spaces that are the subject of this legislation. As well, continued development of creative conservation programs and conservation research efforts (such as endangered species and spaces campaigns, and gap analysis) that include but are not lim-

ited to species currently protected under legislation will be necessary. Local stewardship initiatives are important in this regard.

If Canadians are to achieve balanced sustainable use and protection of wild species and spaces, in national parks or elsewhere, there is a need to shift from individual species management to a more holistic, creative, and dynamic landscape (and possibly airscape, see Box 12–6) management approach. Parks will continue to play an important role for Canadian to learn about and protect our natural capital endowment. The model of the biosphere reserve, with its philosophy of maintaining sustainable and living landscapes, and learning from our experiences, is an important contributor to contemporary conservation, bearing in mind that the core areas of biosphere reserves are also protected under national legislation (such as, but not restricted to, national parks)

The knowledge-building requirements to protect biodiversity are ongoing, from use of traditional and local ecological knowledge, to data collection by individual volunteers and scientists, to analysis and interpretation of data by academics in universities and research institutes, to the new information that GIS and other remote-sensing technologies generate. The contributions of both physical and social sciences to wild spaces and species in Canada must be supported and incorporated in actions from local to international scales if the global mission of conservation of biodiversity is to be attained.

Actions do not have to be big and expensive to be significant. As scores of Canadians have already found out,

making a big difference to Canada's species and spaces can start in our own backyards. Even urban environments contain important habitats for genetic diversity, and for plant and animal species in need of protection. Learning more about these spaces and species and translating that knowledge into action is a vital component of biodiversity protection. Such learning may translate also into a shift in societal priorities that will be necessary to remain vigilant in protecting "wilderness" spaces beyond urban borders. What we believe and what we do influence others around us; each of us can be stewards of Canada's wild species and natural spaces.

MAKING A DIFFERENCE 12
THE BIOSPHERE RESERVE OF MONT SAINT-HILAIRE

On April 28, 1978, UNESCO designated Mont Saint-Hilaire and its surrounding region a biosphere reserve, the first in Canada. (By 2008, there were 15 biosphere reserves in the country.) The decision was motivated by the great diversity of the flora and fauna of the Monteregian hill, the only intact remnant of the vast primeval forest that covered the whole region 500 years ago. Mont Saint-Hilaire is an exceptional centre for plant and animal diversity, with 600 species of higher plants, many of them rare; over 400-year-old trees; 250 types of minerals and 44 more discovered but not yet described; 200 bird species; 13 fish species; and 22 species of reptiles and amphibians. Of the 45 species of mammals, the deer, chipmunks, and squirrels are most numerous, but there are also a few families of foxes and coyotes. A lynx also has been seen.

Mont Saint-Hilaire had six different names during its long history, most of them to honour its various owners. The title "UNESCO biosphere reserve," given 30 years ago, does add a prestigious label, but, about 1000 years ago, Aboriginal people gave this mountain a name that is even richer and more eloquent, fully in accordance with the philosophy of the biosphere reserves. The first name given to the mountain by the Abenakis was "The Wigwam," or "The Long House." For this First Nation, the mountain represented a big open house that gathered under its roof all the creatures of the biosphere—the animals, the plants, the humans, the rocks, the lakes and creeks.

The Mont Saint-Hilaire Biosphere Reserve is only 12 square kilometres. But it is only 30 kilometres from Montreal, and is jealously protected by McGill University, its owner, and by the Nature Centre that manages the visitor services. However, it is also close to the hearts of thousands of citizens that live around mountain.

The reserve was established with the vision and enthusiasm of Alice Johannsen, the first director of the Nature Centre. The mountain is so popular today that 170 000 visitors come every year to enjoy the beauty

Photo 12–23
The Mont Saint-Hilaire Biosphere Reserve is a place where citizens work to protect their natural and cultural heritage simultaneously.

of its forest and the energy of a good walk. As is true for every biosphere reserve, citizens living within the reserve region, researchers from McGill and other universities, and staff associated with Mont St-Hilaire have worked together to protect and to restore their wooded and wet areas, their cultural heritage, and their landscape. This cooperation is demonstrated by new municipal and provincial legislation to protect lands and ecosystems within the biosphere reserve, activities to retain forest corridors, and efforts to maintain the viability of agricultural producers in the region. The mountain is also a powerful source of inspiration for the local culture, through poems, tales, paintings, photos, music, and festivities.

In highlighting this biosphere reserve, we illustrate the interconnections between protecting cultural diversity and biological diversity and the role of committed individuals and groups to protect our natural heritage. To visit the biosphere reserve and see how nature and culture work together, visit www.museevirtuel .ca/Exhibitions/Hilaire/flash-en/index.html

With thanks to Kees Vanderheyden and the people who inspired this documentation.

Chapter Questions

1. Review the ways in which habitat alteration can occur. In your neighbourhood, identify examples of current habitat alteration. Which types or sources of habitat alteration do you think are most important in your region? Justify your choice.

2. Go to your backyard (or the backyard of a friend). What plants or animals can you identify? What plants or animals are indigenous to the bioregion in which you live? What ones are introduced? What do you need to know to bring back more indigenous species to the yard?

3. Discuss the reasons why saving larger tracts of habitat is necessary to protect (endangered) species. Does "saving" mean not allowing any human activity? If not, what types and levels of human activities are acceptable? What types and levels are not acceptable?

4. Using Environment Canada's lists of Canadian species at risk (check the URLs in the References section) and other sources that are available to you, try to identify examples of species that are at risk in the region where you live. Are there any activities under way to try to protect, preserve, or rehabilitate these species and their habitats? If so, who is undertaking these efforts, what specific actions are being taken, and what is the rationale for these actions? If not, describe what you think needs to be done to achieve protection for these species.

5. What are the implications of climate change for biodiversity in your region? What methods of protection do you recommend?

6. Discuss the pros and cons of in situ and ex situ conservation approaches. In what circumstances is ex situ conservation justified?

7. Is Canada a leader or a laggard with respect to the protection of biodiversity? Explain your response.

references

Amphibiaweb, 2008. *Worldwide Amphibian Declines.* http://amphibiaweb.org/declines/declines.html

Bishop, C., et al. (1994). *A proposed North American amphibian monitoring program.* http://www.open.ac.uk/daptf/froglog/FROGLOG-11.html

Brooks, R. J., & MacDonald, C. J. (1996). Ranid population monitoring in Algonquin Provincial Park. *Froglog, 16* (February). http://acs-info.open.ac.uk/info/newsletters/FROGLOG-16-5.html

Campbell, A. (1999). Declines and disappearances of Australian frogs. *Environment Australia, 229.* http://www.environment.gov.au/bg/threaten/information/frogs/frogs.pdf

Canadian Geographic Enterprises. (1997). *Wildlife at risk.* Vanier, ON: Author.

Canadian Wildlife Service. (2000). *Species at risk.* http://www.cws-scf.ec.gc.ca/theme.cfm?lang=e&category=12

Committee on the Status of Endangered Wildlife in Canada. (2007, January). *Canadian species at risk.* http://www.cosewic.gc.ca/eng/sct0/rpt/rpt_csar_e.pdf

Costanza, R., D'Arge, R., & Groot, R. D. (1997). The values of the world's ecosystem services and natural capital. *Nature, 387*(6630), 253–260.

Dearden, P., & Dempsey, J. (2004). Protected areas in Canada: A decade of change. *The Canadian Geographer, 48*(2), 225–239.

Declining Amphibian Populations Task Force. (n.d.). *What are amphibian declines and their causes?* http://www.open.ac.uk/OU/Academic/Biology/J_Baker/DAPTF.What_are_ADs.html

Declining Amphibian Populations Task Force. (2000). Home pages. http://www.mnh.si.edu/biodiversity/daptf.htm

Drost, C. A., & Fellers, G. M. (1996). Collapse of a regional frog fauna in the Yosemite area of the California Sierra Nevada, USA. *Conservation Biology, 10,* 414–425.

Dunn, P. (1996). The need for amphibian monitoring in protected areas. *Research Links, 4*(3), 4, 10.

Eidsvik, H. (1989). Canada in a global context. In M. Hummel (Ed.), *Endangered spaces: The future for Canada's wilderness* (pp. 30–45). Toronto: Key Porter.

Environment Canada. (1996). *The state of Canada's environment.* Ottawa: Minister of Public Works and Government Services.

Environment Canada. Canadian Biodiversity Network. (2000). Home page. http://www.cbin.ec.gc.ca/cbin/HTML/en/default.cfm

Fisheries and Oceans Canada. (2007). *Commercial landings: Summary table.* http://www.dfo-mpo.gc.ca/communic/statistics/commercial/landings/seafisheries/index_e.htm

Government of Canada. (1996). *The state of Canada's environment—1996.* Ottawa: Supply and Services Canada.

Graham-Rowe, D. (2006). New Red List paints bleak picture of extinction. *New Scientist.* http://www.newscientist.com/channel/life/endangered-species/dn9096-new-red-list-paints-bleak-picture-of-extinction.html

Hackman, A. (1996). Protecting wild places. *World Conservation, 3,* 13–14.

Hannah, L., et al. (2002). Conservation of biodiversity in a changing climate. *Conservation Biology, 16*(1), 264–268.

Henry, J. D. (1994, August). Home again on the range. *Equinox, 76*, 46–53.

Hummel, M. (Ed.). (1989). *Endangered spaces: The future for Canada's wilderness.* Toronto: Key Porter.

McGill University. (2007). Gaining and losing biodiversity. *The Canadian biodiversity web site.* http://canadianbiodiversity.mcgill.ca/english/theory/gainingandlosing.htm

Mittelstaedt, M. (2008, April 10). Ontario's greenbelt a model for the world. *The Globe and Mail,* p. A9.

National Parks Service. (2000). Chapter IV: Existing environment, table K-2. *Yosemite Valley plan: Final. Vol. II.* http://www.nps.gov/yose/planning/yvp/seis/vol_II/appendix_k_c4p1.html

Nature Trust of British Columbia. (1993, Summer). PCEP purchase of Englishman River Flats "jewel" triggers creation of rare wildlife management area. *Natural Legacy, 6,* 1–3.

Oil exploration in the Arctic. (1997). *Canadian Wildlife Federation Bulletin, 6,* 7.

Parks Canada Agency. (2000). *Unimpaired for future generations? Protecting ecological integrity within Canada's national parks: Vol. 1, A call to action. Vol. 2, Setting a new direction for Canada's national parks. Report of the Panel on the Ecological Integrity of Canada's National Parks.* Ottawa: Minister of Public Works and Government Services.

Parks Canada Agency. (2001). *First priority: Progress report on implementation of the recommendations of the Panel on the Ecological Integrity of Canada's National Parks.* Ottawa: Minister of Public Works and Government Services.

Parks Canada Agency. (2007). *Parks Canada Agency performance report for the period ending March 31, 2007.* http://www.pc.gc.ca/docs/pc/rpts/rmr-dpr/archives/2006-07/cap-eng.pdf

Pounds, A. J., et al. (1999). Biological response to climate change on a tropical mountain. *Nature, 398,* 611–615.

Protecting Canadian species. (1996). *World Conservation, 3,* 9.

Robinson, F. E. (1997). Where have all the chickens gone? *Environment Views/Environment Network News, 1*(1), 15.

Rowe, S., Kavanagh, K., & Iacobelli, T. (1995). *A protected areas gap analysis methodology: Planning for the conservation of biodiversity.* Toronto: World Wildlife Fund Canada.

Searle, R. (2000). *Phantom parks: The struggle to save Canada's national parks.* Toronto: Key Porter.

Seeds in threatened soil [Editorial]. (2005). *Nature, 435*(2), 537–538.

Sierra Club of Canada. (2000). *Eighth annual Rio report card.* http://www.sierraclub.ca/national/rio/rio00-summary.html

Sierra Club of Canada. (2003). *Rio + 11: The eleventh annual Rio (Report on International Obligations) report card, 2003—summary of grades. Grading the Government of Canada and the provinces on their environmental commitments.* http://www.sierraclub.ca/national/rio

Sierra Club of Canada. (2006). *Rio + 14: The annual Rio (Report on International Obligations) report card, 2003—summary of grades. Grading the Government of Canada and the provinces on their environmental commitments.* http://www.sierraclub.ca/national/rio/rio-report-card-2006.pdf

United Nations Environment Programme–World Conservation Monitoring Centre (UNEP-WCMC). (2001). *About UNEP-WCMC.* http://www.unep-wcmc.org/aboutWCMC/

Wallis, C., Klimek, J., & Adams, W. (1996). Nationally significant Sage Creek grassland threatened by Express Pipeline. *Action Alert, 7*(4), 4 pp.

World Commission on Environment and Development. (1987). *Our common future.* Toronto: Oxford University Press.

World Conservation Monitoring Center (WCMC). (2000). *State of the world's protected areas.* Annex 1: Summary of Protected Areas. http://www.unep-wcmc.org/protected_areas/albany_a1.pdf

World Wildlife Fund Canada. (1999). *Endangered Spaces campaign: 1998–1999 Endangered Spaces progress report on Canada's wild lands, Number 9, British Columbia.* www.wwfcanada.org

World Wildlife Fund Canada. (2000a). *Endangered spaces.* Toronto: World Wildlife Fund. http://www.wwfcanada.org/

World Wildlife Fund Canada. (2000b). *Endangered Spaces campaign.* http://www.wwfcanada.org/

World Wildlife Fund Canada. (2000c). *Species at Risk campaign.* http://www.wwfcanada.org/

Zolkewich, S. (1995). Leopard frogs abound at DU project. *Ducks Unlimited Canada Conservator, 16*(1), 3.

Photo 12–24
Excess nitrogen in water supplies contributes to algal blooms. See the Canada and the World section for more about nitrogen loading.

Photo 12–25
Over 13 percent of South Africa's Fynbos biome is protected. The Convention on Biological Diversity requires countries to protect at least 10 percent of each ecological region within their borders; see Table C/W-13 in the Canada and the World section for some national comparisons.

Getting to Tomorrow

"Improving the quality of the environment in Canadian cities will not only enrich the quality of life and health of the vast majority of city residents, but also significantly contribute to the amelioration of global environmental problems such as climate change."

NRTEE (2003)

CHAPTER 13

Sustainability and the City

Chapter Contents

Chapter Objectives

After studying this chapter you should be able to

- understand the main issues and concerns relating to urbanization and ecosystems in Canada

- identify the effects of urbanization on the environment around us

- appreciate the complexity and interrelatedness of environmental, social, and economic issues relating to urbanization and their effects on our environment

- appreciate the effects our lifestyle choices have on our environment

- understand the types of efforts Canadians have made toward more sustainable communities

INTRODUCTION

The issue of how to create sustainable cities has emerged as one of the most critical environmental and developmental challenges of the new millennium. Today, just over one-half the global human population lives in urban areas. Although Canada's cities occupy only about 0.2 percent of the country's total land area, already almost 80 percent of Canadians live in communities of over 1000 people—Canada's definition of an urban place. Cities are part of the ecosystem, and urbanization has had a great impact on productive land, aquatic systems, forested lands, and other valued components of regional and local ecosystems. Furthermore, the ecological health of urban places is inextricably linked to human health. This connection has been demonstrated from the early days of urbanization, when advancement in public health services such as clean water improved the health outcomes for urban dwellers, to concerns today over the respiratory effects of air pollution caused by the increased use of motorized vehicles. Up to this point in this book, individual sectors such as water and air have been treated as separate entities. By discussing these elements again in this chapter, we emphasize how a key and uniquely human process—urbanization—transforms natural processes; illustrate how these processes have simultaneous environmental, social, and economic effects; and explore integrative strategies that are being developed to promote sustainable urban regions.

More specifically, in this chapter we identify some of the major kinds of effects our urban ways of life have on the environment, consider what efforts have been made to take the sustainability of the environment into account in urban planning, and comment on future directions for more sustainable communities.

AN URBANIZING GLOBE

The twentieth century witnessed the rapid urbanization of the world's population. In 2005, China, India, and the United States had the largest numbers of urban dwellers in the world. The global proportion of urban population increased from 13 percent (220 million) in 1900 to 29 percent (732 million) in 1950 and 49 percent (3.2 billion) in 2005 (United Nations Population Division, 2008). This rate of growth represents a quadrupling of the urban population since 1950. By 2030, the United Nations estimates that 60 percent of the global population will live in cities (Figure 13–1, on the next page).

While these figures are striking, it is important to realize that the definition of "urban" varies from one country to another. The United Nations does not provide

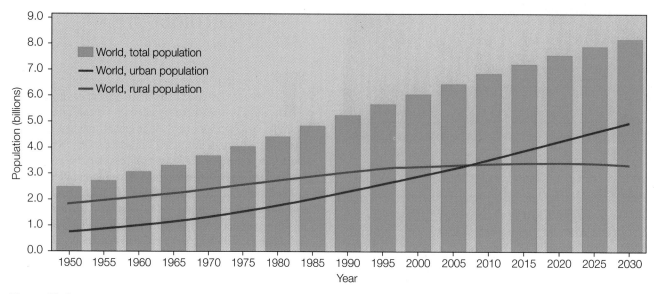

Figure 13–1

The rural and urban population of the world, 1950–2030

SOURCE: *World Urbanization Prospects, 2005.* Copyright © United Nations. Used with permission. http://www.un.org/esa/population/publications/WUP2005/2005wup.htm

a uniform definition, but uses the definitions provided by member countries to calculate its estimates. A city or an urban place can be defined by its form, its function, or its population density. The most common practice is to use population measures to define an urban place. As illustrated in Table 13–1, however, there is no agreement from one country to another about what constitutes urban. Thus, when we think of an urbanizing world, we must realize that in many cases, we are putting small towns and large metropolises in the same category.

TABLE 13–1
WHAT IS URBAN?

Country	Definition of Urban
Canada	Places of 1000 or more inhabitants, having a population density of 400 or more per square kilometre
United States	Agglomerations of 2500 or more inhabitants, generally having population densities of 1000 persons per square mile or more
Chile	Populated centres with definite urban characteristics such as certain public and municipal services
Botswana	Agglomeration of 5000 or more inhabitants where 75 percent of the economic activity is nonagricultural
Mexico	Localities of 2500 or more inhabitants
India	Towns (places with municipal corporation, municipal area committee, town committee, notified area committee, or cantonment board); also, all places having 5000 or more inhabitants, a density of no less than 1000 persons per square mile or 400 per square kilometre, pronounced urban characteristics, and at least three-fourths of the adult male population employed in pursuits other than agriculture
France	Communes containing an agglomeration of more than 2000 inhabitants living in contiguous houses or with no more than 200 metres between houses; also communes of which the major portion of the population is part of a multicommunal agglomeration of this nature
Japan	City *(shi)* having 50 000 or more inhabitants with 60 percent or more of the houses located in the main built-up areas and 60 percent or more of the population (including their dependants) engaged in manufacturing, trade, or other urban type of business; alternatively, a *shi* having urban facilities and conditions as defined by the prefectural order

SOURCE: *Table 6. Urban and total population by sex: 1995–2004 (Notes)*, United Nations Statistical Division, 2004, http://unstats.un.org/unsd/demographic/products/dyb/DYB2004/NotesTab06.pdf

PART 4: GETTING TO TOMORROW

ENVIRONMENT AND URBANIZATION IN HISTORICAL PERSPECTIVE

Urbanization is not a new form of human settlement, but the scale and rate of urban growth in the 20th century are unprecedented. The earliest forms of urbanized settlement took place in Mesopotamia and the Nile Valley about 3500 years ago. Most cities were much smaller than those of today; however, Rome is likely the first city to grow to 1 million people, during the third century A.D. Two important features of Rome's ability to support such a large population were the city's provision of clean water and its effective waste disposal system. The history of urbanization illustrates that wealth and poverty have characterized city life, so that the benefits and costs of urban living, and its environmental and social consequences, have been unevenly distributed across the urban landscape.

During the growth of industrial capitalism, from the late 18th to late 19th century, industrial cities began to grow rapidly. Cities were viewed as places offering higher wages and a variety of employment opportunities. In Europe, the rate of population growth escalated as the introduction of modern medicines and improvements in public health reduced the death rate. European countries moved through the second and third stages of demographic transition (see Chapter 4), characterized by declining death and birth rates. This transition was aided in part, by massive emigration from Europe to many other countries and regions, including Australia, Canada, New Zealand, South America, and the United States.

Urbanization, environmental quality, and public health are inextricably linked. While rich people in European countries had their water provided by private companies during the 19th century, the poor had to rely on public taps, wells, and local rivers. The poor were most susceptible to water-borne diseases, in part, because of ignorance of how these diseases were transmitted. In 1849, physician John Snow proposed that cholera was spread through contamination of food or water. His theory went against the conventional thinking of his time that disease was spread through inhalation of noxious vapours. His theory remained unproven until 1854, when an epidemic of cholera hit London. At that time, Dr. Snow traced the source of the disease to one of the water intakes located downstream from the city and, in particular, to one pump that serviced a large population where it was believed that approximately 500 people had died in 10 days. His findings revolutionized thinking about disease in urban places and encouraged the widespread establishment of publicly financed water systems. Providing and maintaining clean, affordable, and accessible water remains a major environmental and social issue confronting urban centres today.

Even today, rich and poor people have markedly different access to potable water in urban areas. In Mexico City, for instance, 60 percent of urban potable water is distributed to 3 percent of the households, whereas 50 percent of the inhabitants survive on 5 percent of the water (Speake & Gismondi, 2005). Our experience with providing safe drinking water in Canada is uneven, as well: Aboriginal people have less secure supplies of drinking water than any other social group (see Chapter 7), and some rural areas also face challenges in provision of high-quality drinking water. For cities, providing access to safe and affordable water is key to both ecological and human health.

The changing technologies of transportation have had an enormous influence on how cities took shape. In Canada and the United States, industrial cities (built in the mid-19th to early 20th century, primarily to manufacture goods for export) were relatively compact. Most of the employment was located in the central business district, and residents lived within walking distance of the downtown core. Manufacturing and warehouses were located near railway lines and terminals, and growth in the urban area followed streetcar lines. Most employment remained in the central core, because the primary modes of transportation were streetcars and walking.

From 1945 onward, as automobile use became widespread, cities grew dramatically in population and in area. Residential suburbs were established and included shopping centres and industrial parks. In automotive-based cities, central business districts declined in importance, while suburban employment grew. Public transportation declined overall; however, during the last two decades we have seen a revival in public transportation and in the (re)creation of walking and cycling pathways. Both of these actions help to address the multiple concerns of providing accessibility to housing, employment, and services, and the adverse effects of city life, including noise, congestion, land conversion, and poor air quality. Postindustrial processes, including people's ability to commute to suburban locations for employment or to work from home, have once again altered assumptions about transportation patterns and methods. Some cities emphasize suburban centres for shopping, business, and recreation rather than downtown city cores; the implications of such decisions are discussed in the following sections.

THE RISE OF MEGA-CITIES

Mega-cities, defined as those cities with 10 million or more inhabitants, are creatures of the 20th century. The first city to become a mega-city was New York in about 1940. By 2005, there were 20 mega-cities worldwide, accounting for about 9.3 percent of the world's population. In 2005, Tokyo was by far the most highly populated urban centre in the world with 35.2 million residents, followed by Mexico City (19.4 million), New York–Newark (18.7 million), São Paulo (18.3 million), Mumbai (18.2 million), Delhi (15.0 million), and Shanghai (14.5 million) (United Nations Population Division, 2008).

Because of their enormous size and rapid growth, mega-cities often lack adequate transportation, freshwater and sanitation systems, and housing for residents. They also may lack sufficient regulation of industrial processes, compounding problems of waste disposal and chemical contamination. These interconnected problems are environmental, social, and economic in character. Lack of housing has resulted in the rapid growth of substandard housing in slums. At the beginning of the 21st century, one in six of the world's inhabitants lived in slums where basic needs were inadequately met (see Table 4–4 on page 126). Many regions that are experiencing rapid urban growth are unable or unwilling to document rates of consumption, waste disposal, and slum creation. Without documentation, it is difficult to understand the scope of, and to take measures to address, these problems. Nevertheless, these obstacles should not prevent us from addressing the environmental and health problems of the world's poor who live in urban areas.

While mega-cities are large and their problems daunting, it is important to realize that most urban dwellers do not live in mega-cities. Most urban dwellers live in cities with populations under 50 000, while mega-cities house less than 10 percent of the world's population and their growth rates are declining.

Urban Environmental Conditions and Trends

From an environmental point of view, urban development both concentrates and exemplifies human use of the Earth's resources. For example, although urban areas take up only 2 percent of the Earth's surface area, they account for 75 percent of global resource use. Transformation of the landscape to urban uses often places enormous pressure on lands for food production. For example, Bangkok pushed its city limits outwards from 56 square kilometres in the 1950s to 426 square kilometres by the early 1990s. Similarly, the City of Toronto estimates that 330 square kilometres of land were converted to urban uses between 1966 and 1986 (City of Toronto, 2000). Changes in the physical landscape that accompany urbanization typically alter the hydrologic cycle and reduce the absorptive capacity of the Earth's surface by increasing the number and size of impermeable surfaces, channelling natural streams, and converting bogs and wetlands to building sites and roadways. Vehicles emit air pollutants that also may enter waterways via runoff and contaminate streams, rivers, and oceans. How to address the enormous waste generated by the concentration of human populations is another issue facing urban places, both rich and poor. Social issues may occur as communities become disrupted or destroyed through urban development; safety and crime issues may arise, and health concerns such as respiratory problems and inadequate exercise may increase.

Clearly urban development is not all bad. Concentrating people and production in cities can help reduce costs of services because of people's proximity to one another and because of economies of scale. Opportunities increase for improvements in water and wastewater services, all-weather roads and footpaths, electricity delivery, public transport, health care, enforcement of regulations dealing with occupational health and pollution control, and social and emergency services (e.g., schools, fire fighting). Certainly, a strong correlation exists between the proportion of urbanization and the rating of the country in the human development index (explained in Chapter 4): the top 10 countries in the human development ratings are all highly urbanized. In the more developed regions of the world, about 74 percent of the population live in urban settlements, whereas about 43 percent of less developed regions were urbanized in 2005 (United Nations Population Division, 2008). In the following sections, the stresses cities place on the environment and strategies to achieve urban sustainability are discussed.

ATMOSPHERE AND CLIMATE

Cities, because of their structure and form, and because of the results of various activities taking place within them, modify the local climate and create their own microclimates.

Microclimate

Five main factors shape a city's microclimate. These are the storage and reradiation of heat by buildings and streets, reduction of wind speed (which reduces the wind's cooling effect in summers), human-made sources of heat, rapid runoff of precipitation (which reduces the cooling effect of evaporation), and the effects of atmospheric pollutants. Most of these effects result from the loss of vegetation and construction of landscapes made of nonpermeable materials. The net result of the influence of these factors is the urban **heat island** effect, in which temperatures are 1 to 2°C higher in the city than in the surrounding rural area. Two implications of the heat island effect are that cities need less energy for heating but more for cooling (see Box 13–1), and that in using cooling devices that contain chlorofluorocarbons (CFCs) or CFC substitutes, we generate emissions with known (and unknown) impacts on the ozone layer.

Air Quality

Canada's National Air Pollution Surveillance (NAPS) program has collected air quality data throughout the country since 1970 (see Chapter 5). The air quality indicators track the exposure of Canadians to ground-level ozone and fine particulate matter ($PM_{2.5}$), two of the most pervasive and widespread air pollutants, and key components of smog.

Cities create heat, and Toronto is heating up. Since 1975, summer temperatures in the city have increased steadily. With the rising temperatures come health risks to residents. These include

- heat-related illness and mortality during heat waves, especially for senior citizens;
- exacerbation of pulmonary disease due to concentrations of ozone and particulate matter;
- increased risk of some infectious diseases, such as encephalitis, which spread more readily in hot weather.

Toronto Public Health, the Clean Air Partnership (CAP), and the Toronto Atmospheric Fund (TAF), with the financial assistance of the Government of Canada Climate Change Action Fund (CCAF), undertook a project to establish municipal policies and practices that would help protect Torontonians from the adverse effects of summer heat. The project had three parts; each is described briefly below.

Part 1: A Monitoring and Alert System

The Heat–Health Watch/Warning System, tailored to Toronto's unique climate, is based on an analysis of climate and mortality data for Toronto. It provides 48–60 hours' notice of the arrival in the city of an oppressive air mass—an air mass associated with predicted or actual morbidity and mortality rates well above the mean value for a given period. Developed by Laurence Kalkstein of the Center for Climatic Research at the University of Delaware, the system has been in place for several years in Philadelphia and Washington, D.C. In those two cities the system is credited with saving hundreds of lives during heat waves. Toronto's Health Department uses the system to implement mitigation plans based on estimates of the predicted number of people at risk of illness and death, a number that varies according to the number of consecutive days of the oppressive air, the time of year, the minimum temperature, and other criteria.

As an additional part of the project, the City of Toronto became a participant in the United Nations Showcase Project, along with Rome, Shanghai, and other cities, to develop this system for vulnerable cities around the world.

Part 2: Longer-Term Adaptation

The second part of the project focuses on mitigating the heat island effect in Toronto through the use of lighter-coloured surfaces on streets and buildings and the strategic placement of urban vegetation. Toronto is warmer than surrounding rural areas due to the urban heat island effect. The city's dark surfaces and infrastructure amplify the heating capacity of incoming solar radiation. Over the long term, municipal policies and measures that encourage urban reforestation and more reflective roofs and streets can cool ambient temperatures, creating more healthful

microclimates for people, reducing the hot air that air conditioning pumps into the environment, and ameliorating heat-induced smog levels (see Enviro-Focus 13 for information on "green roof" infrastructure).

This part of the project was designed to provide greater scientific understanding of Toronto's heat island and the benefits of mitigation strategies by:

- quantifying the direct and indirect benefits of shade trees, vegetation, and reflective (high-albedo) surfaces for several residential and commercial building types, using computer simulations of typical Toronto days in various seasons and under various conditions;
- conducting simulations that quantify the impact of heat island mitigation measures on building energy use and on Toronto's smog;
- developing the scientific basis for new municipal practices and policies that will help cool the city and reduce smog in the long term.

Part 3: North American Summit on Urban Adaptation

The third part of the project aimed to increase understanding of climate change on urban health with a conference on the urban heat island. In May 2002, leading scientists from Canada and the United States were invited to a conference to present the scientific basis of intervention and mitigation strategies, and municipal representatives from North American cities were asked to describe effective implementation practices.

The conference provided a status report on current research related to urban heat islands, exploring how research can inform policy and practices designed to reduce and respond to extreme summer heat. Also, challenges and barriers to change were identified, as well as best practices. Finally, the summit examined methods of addressing urban heat island and health issues.

Following Up with CAP

The Clean Air Partnership has continued to study climate change impacts and adaptation in Toronto. In 2007, CAP produced a report entitled *Time to Tackle Toronto's Warming*, a document that analyzes the options for coping with urban heat island effects and climate change in the Toronto region. The report identifies three areas of action to reduce vulnerability to heat:

- Changes in urban planning that reduce the urban heat island
- Programs that reduce heat-related illness
- Activities that reduce electricity demand and hot weather strains on the power generation and transmissions system

You can view CAP's report at www.cleanairpartnership.org/pdf/time_to_tackle_toronto_warming.pdf.

SOURCES: "Climate Focus in Toronto," Health Canada, January 2008, *Environmental and Workplace Health Newsletter, 6*, http://www.hc-sc.gc.ca/ewh-semt/pubs/climat/newsletter-bulletin-6/impacts_e.html; *Toronto Atmospheric Fund*, 2002, http://www.toronto.ca/taf/ Adapted with permission from Eva Ligeti, Manager, Cool Toronto Project. http://www.cleanairpartnership.org/cool_toronto.htm#contact Phone: 416-392-6672

While stratospheric ozone serves an important protective function, tropospheric or ground-level ozone is harmful to plants and animals because of its extremely strong oxidant properties. Ground-level ozone is considered the criterion for measuring photochemical smog, and it is the component most responsible for smog-related respiratory problems and eye irritations.

Ground-level ozone is produced by a series of chemical reactions involving hydrocarbons, nitrogen oxides, and sunlight. Almost all anthropogenic NO_x arrives in the troposphere as automobile exhaust, the result of incomplete combustion of fossil fuels in internal combustion engines. NO_x and sunlight react to produce ozone. Because of the reaction's dependence on sunlight, ground-level ozone problems are most severe during Canadian summers.

In December 2000, the United States and Canada committed to vigorous reductions in transboundary NO_x emissions as part of the Ozone Annex of the Canada–United States Air Quality Agreement. Canada was to implement new regulations for vehicle and fuel standards that were aligned with more exacting U.S. standards, and the Canada-Wide Standard for Ozone. Projections are that Canada's NO_x emissions in the transboundary area (which includes the Windsor–Quebec corridor) will be reduced by 44 percent by 2010.

SOURCES: *SOE Bulletin* No. 99-1, 1999, Environment Canada; *Environmental Chemistry* (6th ed.), S. E. Manahan, 1994, Boca Raton, FL: Lewis Publishers.

These two pollutants most seriously affect human health, with effects ranging from minor respiratory problems, to asthma attacks, and to premature death (see Box 13–2).

The seriousness of air pollution varies regionally across Canada. Between 1990 and 2005, the national ozone exposure indicator increased an average of 0.8 percent per year, equivalent to a 12 percent increase overall; ozone concentrations were highest in southern Ontario, increasing by 17 percent between 1990 and 2005. This upward trend would suggest that Canadians in locations where ozone exposure is greatest could experience an increased health risk. Conversely, while the highest concentrations of fine particulate matter were measured in southern Ontario and southern Quebec, the $PM_{2.5}$ exposure indicator showed no statistically significant increasing or decreasing trends, either nationally or regionally, between 1990 and 2005. This finding suggests that Canadians experienced no change in health risk from exposure to fine particulates during that time period (Government of Canada, 2007).

Although many sources of air pollution are located outside cities (refineries, pulp mills, forest fires), there is a concentration of different pollution sources in cities. Since the 1970s, emission reductions across a variety of sectors have led to national improvements (decreases) in average and peak levels for some air pollutants, including nitrogen dioxide, carbon monoxide, and sulphur dioxide. However, cities across the country continue to face different air pollution challenges. For instance, Calgary and Edmonton do not have problems with sulphur dioxide, but particulate levels remain a concern, as do ground-level ozone concentrations. Vancouver has reduced its total suspended particulates to well below the annual average desirable standard, while Windsor and Hamilton, among other cities, frequently have readings above the desirable level (McKitrick, 2007). Nevertheless, in cities such as Vancouver and Toronto, summers continue to be characterized by several smog alerts.

High local emissions that contribute to air pollution typically derive from motor vehicle use. Table 13–2 demonstrates that vehicle emissions vary according to the model of the car. One of the challenges facing policymakers is that even though motor vehicles are less polluting than they were a decade or two ago, more vehicles are on the road due to local population increases, and more vehicles are being used on a per capita basis, continuing to contribute to atmospheric emissions.

TABLE 13-2
VEHICLE EMISSIONS BY CAR MODEL

Car Model (2008) (Automatic/ Regular gas)	Greenhouse Gas Emissions (tons/year)
Toyota Tundra (4WD, 5.7L)	13.1
Dodge Durango (4WD, 5.7L)	12.2
GMC Envoy (4WD, 5.3L)	11.4
Jeep Grand Cherokee (4WD, 3.7L)	10.8
Ford Escape (4WD, 3L)	9.6
Chrysler PT Cruiser (2.4L)	8.7
Honda Element (4WD, 2.4L)	8.7
Volkswagen New Beetle (2.5L)	8.0
Honda Accord (automatic, 2.4L)	7.7
Chevrolet Malibu (2.4L)	7.3
Pontiac Vibe (1.8L)	6.8
Ford Focus (2L)	6.6
Toyota Yaris (1.5L)	5.9

SOURCE: *Find a Car*, U.S. Department of Energy, 2008, http://www.fueleconomy.gov/feg/findacar.htm

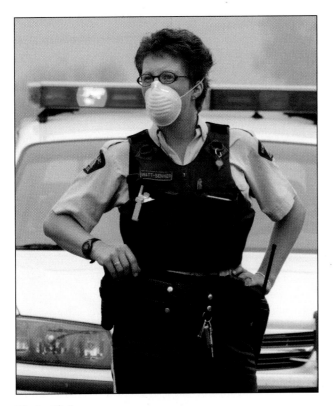

Photo 13–1

An RCMP officer wears a mask to filter the polluted air caused by forest fires in British Columbia in 2003. Around the world, many motorcyclists, cyclists, and commuters wear similar masks to minimize the effects of polluted air during their daily travels.

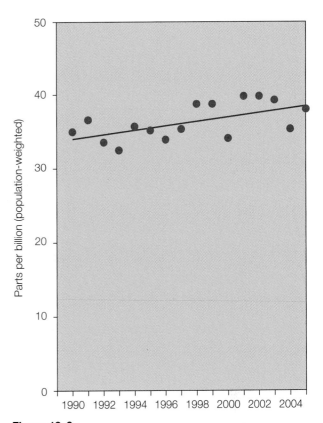

Figure 13–2a

Ground-level ozone exposure indicator, Canada, 1999–2005

NOTE: Based on data from 76 monitoring stations, the trend line represents an average rate of change of 0.8 percent per year. From 1990 to 2005, the indicator shows a statistically significant increase of 12 percent (plus or minus 10 percentage points, meaning the possible increase could range from 2 to 22 percent at a 90 percent confidence level).

SOURCE: *Canadian Environmental Sustainability Indicators, 2007.* © Her Majesty the Queen in Right of Canada, Environment Canada, Statistics Canada, Health Canada, page 6. Reproduced with permission of the Ministry of Public Works and Government Services Canada, 2008.

NOISE

Modern society is getting louder. From high-powered stereo systems in cars to leaf blowers, vacuums, dishwashers, highway traffic, personal watercraft, helicopters, snowmobiles, "surround-sound" big-screen TVs, and portable stereos and earphones, the Canadian population is exposed to more noise than ever before. Noise-induced hearing loss is the most common occupational health hazard in industry today, affecting more men than women. The British Columbia Workers' Compensation Board stated that one-quarter of all B.C. workers are exposed to occupational noise loud enough to damage their hearing (Workers' Compensation Board of B.C., 2003).

One of the factors leading to increased hearing loss is the ability to make much more powerful sound equipment; the sound at rock concerts today is more powerful than it was 20 or 30 years ago. Rock concerts frequently

Air quality in some Canadian cities is affected by the long-range transport of pollutants from other areas, principally the United States. The Lower Fraser Valley (affected by Vancouver-area ozone), the Windsor–Quebec corridor (affected by local and U.S. Great Lakes and Midwest sources), and the Fundy region of southern New Brunswick and western Nova Scotia (affected by sources in the northeastern United States) are the three ozone problem areas in Canada (Canadian Council of Ministers of the Environment, 1990). Neither Victoria, British Columbia, nor Prairie cities have the density of vehicles or the prevailing winds from industrial areas needed for ozone problems to develop. Figures 13–2a and 13–2b (p. 532) illustrate the changing ozone and fine particulate matter exposure levels for Canada from 1990 to 2005.

Canada has made progress in reducing air pollution, but we fared very poorly when compared to 30 other OECD nations in 2005. For instance, on emissions of carbon monoxide and volatile organic compounds, Canada was the worst, emitting two to three times as much as the OECD average. Canada's per capita emissions of sulphur dioxide were reduced over 30 percent between 1992 and 2002, yet they remained almost three times the OECD average (David Suzuki Foundation, 2005). Canadians must focus on strengthening our public policies to help improve our performance in air quality indicators.

CHAPTER 13: SUSTAINABILITY AND THE CITY

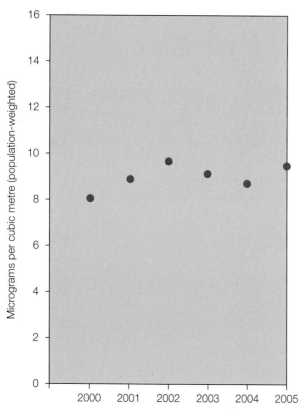

Figure 13–2b

Fine Particulate Matter Exposure Indicator, Canada, 2000 to 2005

NOTE: A trend line is not shown because data (from 2000 to 2005) from 65 monitoring stations showed no statistically significant increase or decrease in fine particulate matter at a 90 percent confidence level.

SOURCE: *Canadian Environmental Sustainability Indicators, 2007.* © Her Majesty the Queen in Right of Canada, Environment Canada, Statistics Canada, Health Canada, page 9. Reproduced with permission of the Ministry of Public Works and Government Services Canada, 2008.

are measured at 110 to 128 decibels—about the same level as a pneumatic drill or military jet, respectively. The higher the decibel level, the less time it takes before sound receptor cells start dying and permanent hearing damage occurs. At 130 decibels, after 75 seconds, you are at risk for permanent damage to your hearing; at 135 decibels, exposure time for permanent damage drops to 37.5 seconds (Shideler, 1997). Sound levels from car stereos have been measured at up to 138 decibels. In addition to loudness, both the length of exposure and the proximity to the source increase the damaging effects.

Most noise-induced hearing loss is preventable with proper use of protective ear devices. However, because hearing damage may not show up until years later, promoting safe hearing is a "tough sell," particularly among high school students, and especially when advertisers encourage young adults to play music and video games at loud levels. Even though the idea of earplugs at rock concerts has little appeal, Hearing Education and Awareness for Rockers (HEAR) worked with radio stations around the United States and Canada to give out over 60 000 earplugs during the 1996 Lollapalooza Tour, the first major music tour ever to give out earplugs. Some rock bands now sell ear protectors at their concerts (see Box 13–3).

Ironically, noise, or unwanted sound, may be considered a "silent" environmental issue. Second-hand noise (experienced by people who did not produce it), just like second-hand smoke, can have negative effects on people without their consent. Although people do not bleed, limp, or get sick as a result of noise exposure, there is evidence that noise causes increased stress and blood pressure levels, disrupted sleep patterns, altered heart function, and difficulties in concentrating (Fried, 1996; Patterson, 1995). Hearing loss caused by noise and the natural aging

BOX 13-3
HEARING EDUCATION AND AWARENESS FOR ROCKERS (HEAR), AND HEARNET

Hearing Education and Awareness for Rockers (HEAR) is a nonprofit organization dedicated to raising awareness of the real dangers of repeated exposure to excessive noise levels that can lead to permanent and sometimes debilitating hearing loss and tinnitus (ringing sensation). Founded in 1988 by Executive Director Kathy Peck (successful rocker and former bass player for the San Francisco punk band the Contractions), and Flash Gordon, M.D., HEAR is linked to both the music world and the medical community. As noted in the section on noise, HEAR was able to provide tens of thousands of earplugs to rock concert musicians and audiences during a major music tour in 1996.

HEAR's achievements include the launch of the "HEAR RECORDS Project," which works with record labels and artists from around the globe to celebrate music and musicians while promoting the value of protecting your ears. Sales from releases

go to help HEAR increase public awareness of the importance of hearing health and tinnitus prevention worldwide. HEAR recordings feature established recording artists and rising stars. Some spokespersons have included DJ Qbert, Les Claypool of Primus, Lars Ulrich from Metallica, and Todd Rundgren. In 1998 Virgin Megastores sponsored a national co-promotion with HEAR called "Stick It in Your Ear," a humorous campaign in which customers received a free pair of earplugs.

HEARNET is HEAR's interactive online publication that works to educate musicians, engineers, music manufacturers, promoters, and music fans, particularly young people, about the dangers of loud music. This interactive publication, which is updated regularly, provides information and resources on tinnitus, hearing loss, and hearing protection, has links to HEAR affiliates, and includes entertainment links. Check it out, whether your hearing is fine or not!

SOURCE: *HEARNET,* 2001, http://www.hearnet.com

process is cumulative over a lifetime, so people over 50 years of age are affected particularly severely.

Although noise pollution is not often thought of as an air quality problem, particularly in comparison with the ozone hole or the greenhouse effect, it is an increasingly serious problem for urban populations. Warning labels on noisy appliances are virtually nonexistent, and while we are admonished about wearing safety equipment while riding a bike we rarely think to wear earplugs while mowing the lawn.

WATER

Cities and the Hydrologic Cycle

The relationship of cities to the hydrologic cycle is a good illustration of how cities are linked to the larger eco-system. Generally, a city withdraws water (which may be contaminated) from a lake or river and treats the water to make it potable. As it is used, the water receives pollutants, including human wastes, that require the water to be treated again prior to its return to the hydrologic system (where natural processes further clean the water). Downstream, other communities that depend on the river or lake for their water supply put the water they withdraw through a similar succession of treatment processes. Some, perhaps, discharge untreated wastewater. Eventually the river carries the water and any remaining pollutants into the ocean. There, the natural processes of evaporation, transportation (as clouds), and precipitation, continue the hydrologic cycle (recall Figures 3–16 and 7–3).

The construction of cities also affects the water cycle, which, in turn, affects soils, plants, and animals. Cities may receive 5 to 10 percent more rainfall than the surrounding areas because the particulates and dust above cities provide nuclei for condensation of raindrops. But the concrete, stone, and asphalt streets, and other impervious building materials, prevent water infiltration and induce rapid runoff directly into stormwater systems. Local flooding events may increase, and the frequency of downstream flooding may increase also. It is estimated that because of the surfaces such as pavement and rooftops, there is nine times more runoff from a city block than from a woodland area of the same size (Taus & McClure, 2002). In addition, hard surfaces prevent water in the soil from evaporating; in natural ecosystems, evaporation is an important process that cools the surface. Changes in the built form of the city and the activities within a city increase the runoff and the pollutant loads that are introduced into urban waterways.

Water Supply and Water Quality

Surface water supplies most Canadian cities, although nearly 10 percent of the population is served by municipal systems that rely on groundwater (you may recall that 30 percent of all Canadians use groundwater for domestic purposes; however, much of this use is for small rural systems). As we saw in Chapter 7, supplies of both surface water and groundwater are susceptible to problems of availability and quality. City residents who rely on surface water, such as Victoria, sometimes face seasonal and temporary shortages of or restrictions on water use, whereas residents of cities that rely on groundwater, such as in Prince Edward Island and southern Ontario, may face the possibility of a long-term decline in supply. In Kitchener–Waterloo, Ontario, for example, the search for alternative water supply sources has led to consideration of a 120-kilometre water pipeline from Georgian Bay, part of Lake Huron. Cities such as Regina, where supply sources of surface water are of questionable or declining quality, also may need to find a new supply source or raise the treatment levels of the water they use.

Many sources of contamination may affect both surface water and groundwater supplies: drainage or seepage from industrial, commercial, residential, and recreational land uses, including waste disposal sites; runoff or seepage from chemical fertilizers and other agricultural chemicals; spills and discharges from shipping; and deposition of atmospheric pollutants. The Walkerton case is instructive here: to be safe for human consumption, water that is likely to be affected by such contamination must be filtered and treated chemically before it enters a city's distribution system.

Although water quality in Canadian cities is generally good, quality does vary across the country, since it is regulated at the provincial rather than the national level. On August 26, 2000, Ontario's Drinking Water Protection Regulation came into effect (Government of Ontario, 2001). The regulation established a new Ontario Drinking Water Standard (ODWS) that is legally enforceable. As per the regulation, the City of Toronto has committed to issuing quarterly reports on water quality. (For additional information on new provincial and territorial water quality initiatives, see Chapter 14.)

Water Use and Wastewater Treatment

Over 10 percent of the water withdrawn from natural sources in Canada supplies municipal systems used by residents, businesses, and some industries. More than half the water in municipal systems supplies residential consumption; between 1989 and 1996, residential consumption increased by 103 percent! As noted in Chapter 7, most water within the home is used in the bathroom, but on peak days in the summer, lawn and garden watering and car washing can drive water use up by 50 percent.

Our low water prices and flat-rate pricing have contributed to our profligate use. Since water consumption declines as its cost increases, it may be possible to reduce consumption by having water charges reflect the amount of water used. In the past, for example, when most Calgary residents

Photo 13–2a

Photo 13–2b

Leaking water supply systems and overwatered lawns and gardens create economic and environmental costs for Canadians.

paid a flat rate for their water, they consumed up to 60 percent more water per capita than did residents of Edmonton, a similar-sized city that used water meters to charge for water according to the volume people used. Since 1989, however, Calgary waterworks officials have been encouraging reduced wastage through a water meter incentive program and are working toward having 100 percent of residential properties on water meters. Through the program, Calgary Waterworks personnel install a water meter with a remote readout in single-family homes. Residents are billed for water and sewer charges for 12 consecutive months based on meter readings. After 12 months, a comparison is sent to the resident outlining the difference between the metered charge and the flat rate charge for the period. If the flat rate is more economical, residents can revert back and the difference between the rates is credited to their account. If the metered service proves to be more economical, the resident continues to be billed on the amount of water used. Overall, the percentage of Canada's municipal population with water meters increased from 52 percent in 1991 to 63 percent in

Photo 13–3

The effects of localized urban flooding may range from the inconvenience of being unable to use a pathway to paying for costly repairs to residences and public property.

2004 and to 80 percent in early 2008 (Environment Canada, 2001b, 2007; City of Calgary, personal communication). In addition, many cities have imposed by-laws requiring that residents water their lawns and use water for gardens or car washing on specified days only.

Most of the water used in urban areas is employed to remove domestic, industrial, and commercial wastes, including human sewage. Treatment to remove impurities is needed to safeguard human health, but the large and increasing volumes of treated wastewater may stress aquatic ecosystems. Some cities, such as Vancouver, do not separate their storm and sanitary (sewage) waters. Even if separate storm and sewer systems exist, heavy storm drainage flows may overload a treatment plant's capacity and cause either or both storm and sewage discharges to leave the plant untreated or insufficiently treated.

The percentage of Canadians served by municipal wastewater treatment plants has been increasing steadily, but the level of treatment varies widely across regions (see Figure 13–3a). For instance, many coastal cities, as well as those on the lower St. Lawrence River, discharge their wastewater directly into oceans or rivers. Most Ontario cities discharge into smaller rivers or the Great Lakes, while Prairie cities discharge solely into river systems. By 2004, about 89 percent of Ontario residents, about 72 percent of residents in Alberta, and 99 percent of residents in Saskatchewan living in communities with treatment systems were served by secondary treatment systems or better (see Figure 13–3b, p. 536). Saskatchewan reported the highest proportion of systems with tertiary treatment, at 34.9 percent. Manitoba, Prince Edward Island, and Newfoundland and Labrador reported virtually no tertiary treatment in 2004. Nova Scotia fared little better. Typically, localities near the oceans, including Victoria, St. John's, and Halifax, discharge into the ocean large volumes of untreated wastewater or wastewater that received only primary treatment. As noted in Chapters 7 and 8, such practices often have adverse effects on local shellfish grounds, coastal wetlands, and shorelines. Today,

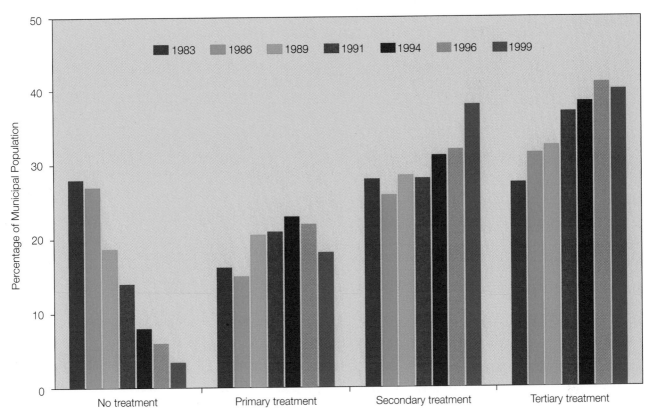

Figure 13–3a

Municipal population served by type of sewage system in Canada

SOURCE: *The State of Canada's Environment—1996*, © Her Majesty the Queen in Right of Canada, Environment Canada, 1996, Figure 12.13; Municipal Water Use Database (MUD) Survey, 2000, Environment Canada. Reprinted with permission of the Minister of Public Works and Government Services Canada, 2008.

efforts are being made to address the long-standing assumption that the ocean simply dilutes pollutants and offers a cheap means of disposing of human wastes.

Public or Private Water Provision Today, particularly for urban centres, there are serious debates about whether public or private enterprise is best suited to supply water and to provide wastewater treatment. In Canada, we are accustomed to public utilities that provide safe drinking water and wastewater services, but this has not always been the case. At the beginning of the 19th century, private companies were the main water providers for most of Europe and the United States. Typically, these systems supplied water to wealthier neighbourhoods, leaving aside those who could not afford to pay. By the end of the century, however, public municipal providers had been put in place because water had come to be viewed as vitally important to public health, national prosperity, and human progress (United Nations Development Program, 2007). Today, public water companies account for more than 70 percent of the total investment in water provision.

Public systems have been under scrutiny because they have been subject to failures to maintain their infrastructure and to provide safe and accessible water. For example, the United Nations reports that in Delhi, Dhaka,

and Mexico City, about 40 percent of the water pumped into public systems leaks out of corroded pipes or is sold illegally. The U.S. Environmental Protection Agency estimates that $68 billion will be needed over the next two decades just to restore and maintain existing water utility assets in major U.S. cities. More recently, in Canada, failures to protect water systems under public management at Walkerton and North Battleford (see Chapter 7) challenge us to reconsider our assumptions about the sanctity of public water provision and to consider how best to provide water that is safe, affordable, accessible, and accountable, and that promotes long-term sustainability.

At least three types of options are possible for supplying water and treating wastewater, along with combinations and variations (see Table 13–3, next page). To better understand what these options entail, it is important to understand two terms. *Commercialization* or *commodification* relates to creating a price and establishing market mechanisms for exchange; *privatization* entails the transfer of ownership of water supply systems to a private operator. Commercialization may take place in the absence of privatization; in fact, many water conservation strategies rely on the assumption that we must establish a price for use of water that reflects the true cost of delivery and disposal, to ensure that users conserve water resources

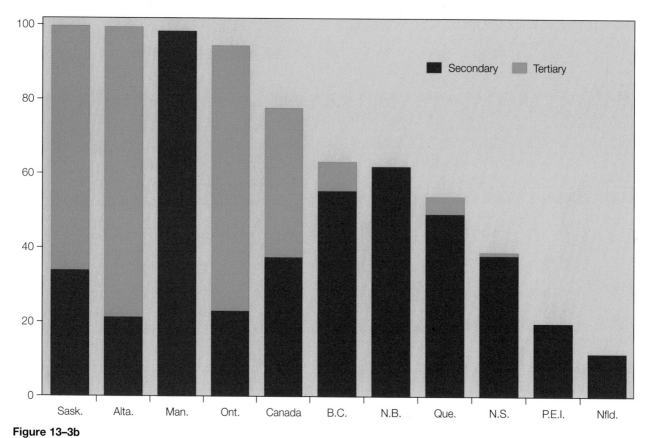

Figure 13–3b

Total population served by secondary and tertiary wastewater treatment in Canada, 1999

NOTE: Insufficient data to include Nunavut, the Northwest Territories, and Yukon.

SOURCE: *The State of Canada's Environment—1996*, © Her Majesty the Queen in Right of Canada, Environment Canada, 1996, Figure 12.14; Municipal Water Use Database (MUD) Survey, 2000, Environment Canada. Reprinted with permission of the Minister of Public Works and Government Services Canada, 2008.

TABLE 13–3
SUMMARY OF OPTIONS FOR WATER SUPPLY AND WASTEWATER TREATMENT

	Public utility	Private sector	Community/Co-operative
Consumer role	Citizen	Customer	Community member
Form of consumer participation	Collective, top-down	Individualistic	Collective, bottom-up
Accountability mechanism	Hierarchy	Contract	Community norms
Primary decision makers	Administrators, experts, officials	Households, experts, companies	Leaders and members of community organizations
Primary goals	Guardian of public interest Conformity with legislation/policy	Maximization of profit Efficient performance	Serving community interest Effective performance
Key incentives for water conservation or other goals	Expert/managerial feedback in public policy process Voter/ratepayer opinion	Price signals (share movements or bond ratings) Customer opinion	Agreements and shared goals Community opinion

SOURCE: Reprinted from Karen Bakker, "Liquid Asset," *Alternatives Journal, 29*:2 (2003) p. 19. Annual subscriptions $35.00 www.alternativesjournal.ca

over the long term. Commercialization frequently involves the introduction of metering and associated changes in water rates. Thus, commercialization can be undertaken by private or public operators.

Privatization A rare model of water system management, true privatization involves transferring the water resource to private companies that typically are answerable to shareholders with the overriding goal of profit maximization. If strongly regulated, some proportion of the profit may be required to be reinvested into maintaining and improving infrastructure. Those who favour privatization suggest that private companies can run water systems more efficiently and provide incentives for water conservation through pricing. As prices rise, consumers will become conservers. Fully privatized water supply utilities were created in England and Wales in 1989, where private companies own the assets and manage the infrastructure. Upon privatization, water consumption rates increased dramatically, and there were concerns that lower-income residents had no access to water. Furthermore, there were concerns that the water supply was accountable to shareholders rather than to general public.

More common are private–public partnerships (PPPs) that involve private corporations in the management of various aspects of municipally owned infrastructure, such as operating, managing, or even building water supply systems. The ownership of the water supply and the water system remains with the government. This arrangement is similar to tenure arrangements for timber harvesting on Crown land.

About 70 percent of the population in France is served through PPPs. In Canada, Hamilton, Ontario, was the first Canadian city to enter into a PPP when it contracted out the operations, maintenance, and management functions at its wastewater facilities in 1994. A private company now operates the water purification plant in Moncton, New Brunswick. Private companies that favour this system suggest that they are more efficient and can lower prices, improve performance, increase cost recovery, and thereby enable systems to be upgraded and improved as needed. While they appear successful in countries like France, they are not favoured in Canada. A recent bid in Vancouver to establish a PPP was scrapped after intense local opposition.

Communal Systems Community-run systems tend to be small in scale, usually are locally run, and often are managed as co-operatives where the users own and control the water supply system. Users also are involved in aspects of management and decision making to ensure that water use is in keeping with community norms and desires. Communal systems are based on the perspective that water is a common resource; water is essential for life, and converting it to a business opportunity is unethical. This view holds that private ownership inevitably conflicts with the public interest, as prices for water may be set at levels that are too high for low-income members of a population and too low for high-income earners.

Community systems exist mainly in Denmark, in Finland, and in many developing countries, although about 200 water supply cooperatives exist in Canada, primarily in Alberta, Manitoba, and Quebec (Bakker, 2003). Many of Canada's rural and Aboriginal water supplies are provided by community utilities.

Public Systems Public utilities generally attempt to meet basic human needs across all socioeconomic groups. In the past, they have tended to subsidize pricing to ensure affordability and also to encourage economic development within cities. Public ownership and management of the water supply often is argued on economic and ethical grounds. Economically, public water supply and wastewater services can reach economies of scale, particularly as the infrastructure is costly; ethically, public supply and services can ensure that water, a basic human need, is provided to all residents regardless of socioeconomic status. However, the history of subsidized pricing is that it has not met conservation objectives. Current efforts to achieve sustainability, then, often have focused on some level of commercialization. As documented above, municipalities across Canada increasingly have measured water consumption through meters to encourage sustainable use.

While economic efficiency, environmental conservation, and social equity objectives may be difficult to achieve in any system, efforts made by the municipal Department of Water and Sewerage in Porto Alegre, Brazil, demonstrate that reforms made to the public system can improve efficiency, accessibility, affordability, and accountability in water systems (see Box 13–4, next page). Key elements in Porto Alegre's success were improvements in accountability as well as in infrastructure.

Photo 13–4
Regulations prohibit houseboat users from discharging raw sewage wastes directly into Shuswap Lake, British Columbia.

With 1.4 million people, Porto Alegre, the capital of the state of Rio Grande do Sul in Brazil, has one of the lowest infant mortality rates in the country (14 deaths per 1000 live births in a country where the national average is 65) and a human development index comparable to that in rich countries. Effective municipal governance in water supply and sanitation has played a big part in this success story.

Municipal water providers have achieved universal access to water. Prices for water—$0.30 a litre—are among the lowest in the country. Meanwhile, wastewater treatment has increased from 2 percent in 1990 to almost 30 percent today, with a target of 77 percent in five years. Efficiency indicators are similar to those in the world's best performing private companies. The ratio of employees to household connections, one widely used efficiency indicator, is 3:1000. That ratio is 20 for Delhi and 5 for private companies in Manila.

The operating conditions of the Municipal Department of Water and Sewerage (DMAE), wholly owned by the municipality of Porto Alegre, help to explain the success

- a separate legal entity, it enjoys operational and financial autonomy
- ring-fenced, it receives no subsidies and is financially self-reliant
- financially independent, it can borrow for investment without municipal support.

The operating mandate combines social and commercial objectives. The utility pursues a no-dividend policy: all profits are reinvested into the system. Its tax exemption allows it to keep water rates low. And it is required to invest at least a quarter of its annual revenue in water infrastructure.

Why has Porto Alegre achieved universal access despite a high concentration of poverty among its customers? Partly because prices are low on average and partly because low-income households, welfare institutions, and residents of state and municipal housing projects for the disadvantaged are charged a social rate less than half the basic rate. The utility's governance structure combines regulatory oversight with a high level of public participation. The general director is appointed by the mayor, but a deliberative council—made up of engineers, medical staff, environmentalists, and representatives of a wide range of civil society organizations—exercises management oversight and has the power to rule on all major decisions.

Porto Alegre's participatory budget process provides a form of direct democracy with 44 public meetings each year in 16 areas of the city. Participants vote on their priorities and hear submissions from managers in six core areas, one of them water. As a prelude, billboards are placed in public places showing actual spending against planned spending, as well as the investment plan that follows the process. The public scrutiny of the municipal budget and the priority attached to water create strong incentives for high quality service delivery.

SOURCE: *Human Development Report 2006. Beyond Scarcity: Power, Poverty and the Global Water Crisis*, United Nations Development Programme, 2006, New York: Author.

Canadian municipalities are faced with aging infrastructure and new expectations with respect to water management in cities. The choice of delivery system is only one decision municipalities will have to consider over time. Pricing is another key issue. For example, the manufacturing sector within an urban setting has a vested interest in keeping the price of water as low as possible, and manufacturers may threaten to leave a location if costs increase substantially. Municipalities also may have to consider a form of progressive pricing to ensure that everyone can afford to meet their basic needs, while providing financial incentives for curbing consumption. Municipalities may consider other options, such as infrastructure that provides both potable water and grey water for different uses. Japan, for example, has long charged differential rates for potable and grey water. However, these choices also require changes to infrastructure.

ENERGY

Canadians use considerable energy to cope with our cold climate, to travel the long distances between population centres, and to satisfy our lifestyle choices (such as our preference for detached, single-family houses). Our overall energy consumption is not declining; data indicate that between 1980 and 1997, Canadian consumption of energy grew by 20 percent, slightly higher than the 18 percent average of the OECD countries. As noted in Chapter 11, the production and consumption of fuels and electricity in cities lead to local and global environmental stresses. Automobile use, home heating, resource and manufacturing industries, and other commercial enterprises cause local air pollution from emissions of NO_x, VOCs, SO_2, and particulate matter; as well, they contribute to global warming through release of CO_2. Ecosystems also experience stress from production, transport, and use of energy.

While it is difficult to compile a picture of municipal energy use in Canada (because the data are not collected by municipalities), it is known that per capita use of energy in the inner city is lower than in suburban areas, and lower still than in small towns and rural areas. This difference in energy use seems to suggest that, given its higher population density, the inner city is a more energy-efficient form of settlement, although this suggestion is tempered by the fact that many city neighbourhoods contain the poorest members of urban populations. The extensive, enclosed environments in large cities mean that people can travel from their homes and jobs to go shopping, dining, or to attend to business without ever going outdoors. While these environments provide convenience and comfort, they require heavy energy consumption for heating, cooling, and ventilating the system. Typically, industrial energy users do not locate in large cities, but in Toronto and Ottawa commercial and institutional sectors account for one-third of all energy use. This is double the national average and suggests that these businesses are good targets for energy management efforts.

Sustainable Housing

Examples of sustainable housing in Canada are growing. The concept of an ecologically friendly house has expanded beyond single dwellings and is being taken up by co-housing units as well as on some Canadian university campuses. Co-housing, a community planning model developed in Denmark more than 25 years ago, offers an alternative to current housing options. Co-housing projects are cooperative neighbourhoods designed, developed, and managed with a high degree of owner/resident participation (Kerr, 1998). Co-housing projects come in many forms. Some communities consist of single-family houses, although most are townhouse developments; a few are apartment buildings.

In many cases, sustainable housing also means affordable housing. Particularly in large urban centres where property values are high, affordable housing is a key issue that points to the need to pay attention to the social dimensions of sustainability. Housing cooperatives, Habitat for Humanity, and other initiatives provide opportunities to integrate design features that are environmentally friendly with those that are affordable, making urban living a sustainable option for a wider range of residents.

The Alberta Sustainable Home/Office in Calgary is a three-bedroom, 170-square-metre (1820-square-foot) house designed and built to demonstrate sustainability in cold-climate housing (see Photo 13–5). "An inventory of ideas," the house reflects concern for environmental stewardship, occupant health, resource conservation, the use of appropriate technologies and alternative energy sources, and self-sufficiency (Checora, 1996). The project was undertaken on the initiative of a small group of individuals who are partners in the business ASH—Autonomous and Sustainable Housing, Inc. To demonstrate its marketability and financial feasibility, the project was funded by a conventional mortgage without government assistance.

The project has three distinct phases: the sustainable stage, the autonomous stage (when the house no longer needs any city water or sewage treatment), and the energy-credit stage (when surplus electricity produced by the photovoltaic panels on the roof will be sold to the power company). The house was built to achieve these goals in

Photo 13–5
The solar panels and SunPipe are two of the features of ASH House in Calgary.

Calgary's cold climate without a conventional forced-air furnace or boiler—the house is not even connected to natural gas. Instead, the passive solar design of the home allows its occupants to take advantage of Alberta's year-round sunny climate. To keep the heat stored in the thermal mass in the house, the walls are insulated with cellulose to R-50 and the roof cavity to R-74 (well beyond the current building code). Any backup heat required comes from the highly efficient, wood-burning masonry heater that can be used for baking as well as future electrical generation. As of 2002, the ASH house was completely independent of public water, sewer, and gas utilities.

A similar demonstration project—the Toronto Healthy House—is a three-bedroom infill home that harvests its own energy, collects rainfall and purifies it for drinking, and biologically treats its own waste. Part of the Canada Mortgage and Housing Corporation's (CMHC) Healthy Housing initiative, the house has low operating costs and is affordable (see Figure 13–4, p. 540). In Red Deer, Alberta, in 1994, Healthy Housing principles were applied to the renovation of a 1905 home, demonstrating environmental responsibility through such elements as material selection, energy efficiency, airtightness, and equipment selection. One of the challenges of bringing these kinds of housing initiatives from demonstration into practice is that they cost more in the short run to design and build. If sustainability also means making them affordable to a wide range of income earners, then elements of environmental design need to be coupled with social policies to ensure that the environmental benefits are equitably distributed.

EcoResidence is an ecological living experiment at McGill University's agricultural campus. The renovated residence reuses many of the materials in the existing structure. Greenhouses attached to the fronts of all units are an essential feature of EcoResidence. Not only do they capture and store solar energy for redistribution by the passive solar heating system, but they also act as a natural

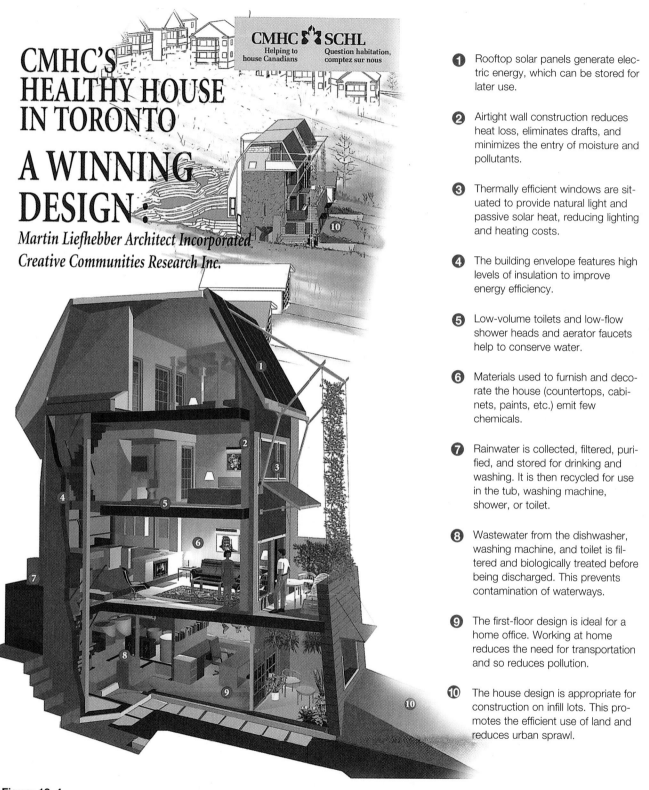

CMHC'S HEALTHY HOUSE IN TORONTO

A WINNING DESIGN:

Martin Liefhebber Architect Incorporated
Creative Communities Research Inc.

CMHC 💧 SCHL
Helping to house Canadians
Question habitation, comptez sur nous

❶ Rooftop solar panels generate electric energy, which can be stored for later use.

❷ Airtight wall construction reduces heat loss, eliminates drafts, and minimizes the entry of moisture and pollutants.

❸ Thermally efficient windows are situated to provide natural light and passive solar heat, reducing lighting and heating costs.

❹ The building envelope features high levels of insulation to improve energy efficiency.

❺ Low-volume toilets and low-flow shower heads and aerator faucets help to conserve water.

❻ Materials used to furnish and decorate the house (countertops, cabinets, paints, etc.) emit few chemicals.

❼ Rainwater is collected, filtered, purified, and stored for drinking and washing. It is then recycled for use in the tub, washing machine, shower, or toilet.

❽ Wastewater from the dishwasher, washing machine, and toilet is filtered and biologically treated before being discharged. This prevents contamination of waterways.

❾ The first-floor design is ideal for a home office. Working at home reduces the need for transportation and so reduces pollution.

❿ The house design is appropriate for construction on infill lots. This promotes the efficient use of land and reduces urban sprawl.

Figure 13–4
Toronto Healthy House

SOURCE: Canada Mortgage and Housing Corporation brochure, provided courtesy of CMHC and Martin Liefhebber Architects. Reproduced by permission. Actual house design may vary from design shown.

air filtration system. The roofs are designed to collect rainwater that is filtered into a central area in the buildings and stored in tanks. The next big step for the EcoResidence is an ecological wastewater treatment facility that would treat sewage using plants, animals, and microorganisms to purify wastewater in much the same way that wetlands do (Dupuis, 2000; McGill University, 1999).

Among other trends in sustainable housing are the use of straw bales, recycled tires, packed dirt, and mud. Straw bale construction is an old technology, used in Europe 300 years ago and pioneered in North America in the sandy, treeless Nebraska prairie in the 1890s. At that time, building homes from bales of straw was a necessity; now, as the world is concerned about running short of wood, straw bale construction of residences, workshops, and garages creates a new use for straw, normally an almost useless byproduct of such grains as wheat, oats, flax, and barley (see Photo 13–6). Straw bale construction has many advantages over conventional wood frame construction, including the fact that straw is a low-cost, renewable, easy-to-use material with high insulation value (see Table 13–4). In 2003, an ecovillage was built in Craik, Saskatchewan, using straw bale construction (among other features) to demonstrate the value of this form of insulation.

Sustainable houses leave a much smaller footprint on the ecosystem than do conventional single-family homes. Depending on their design and construction, sustainable houses may increase efficiency in land use, energy, and water consumption, and provide healthy indoor environments. By overcoming most of the environmental problems

TABLE 13–4
ADVANTAGES OF STRAW BALE CONSTRUCTION

- Straw bales are cheap to buy. Considered an agricultural waste product, straw is available annually. Rather than plow it under or burn it in the fields and thus create air pollution, farmers can bale straw and turn it into an energy-efficient resource.

- Straw bales have a high insulation value (R-2.7 per inch; an 18-inch-wide bale has an R value of 48).

- Straw bale buildings have lower heating and cooling requirements, resulting in reduced fossil fuel use and reduced CO_2 emissions.

- Straw bale construction is low-tech, easy, and requires few power tools.

- Lumber use is reduced.

- Straw bales are nontoxic and, when finished with natural plaster, allow a gradual transfer of air through the walls, promoting good indoor air quality.

- Straw bale buildings are soundproof: one Nebraska pioneer family, playing cards in the kitchen, was unaware that a tornado had just roared through the town.

- Straw bales resist combustion: because of the thickness and lack of oxygen available, it takes two hours to burn through a plaster, straw, and stucco wall (double the resistance of most wood-frame homes).

- With the proper foundation, roof, and finish plaster, straw bale buildings can last indefinitely (some Nebraska historic homes are still standing).

- Anecdotal evidence indicates that there are no problems with bugs in straw bale buildings.

SOURCES: *Straw Bale Construction*, Black Range Films, n.d., Kingston, NM; "Hay, There's a New Way to Build a House!" F. King, May 11, 1996, *Calgary Herald*, p. I10; "Piggy's Idea Recycled: Straw Replaces Scarce Wood," N. Oosterom, October 25, 1995, *Calgary Herald*, p. A2.

of single-family homes (such as high energy use and high costs of infrastructure services), as well as by being affordable, sustainable housing may become even more common in the future.

MATERIALS USE

Solid Waste

Throughout Canada, generating and managing solid wastes is an expensive environmental and social issue. From an ecosystem perspective, waste materials that enter landfills or are incinerated represent energy and resources that have not been used fully and that could have been recycled, reused, or reduced at their source, thereby reducing the need to extract and process new resources. From an economic perspective, solid wastes cost municipalities

Photo 13–6
A straw bale house under construction near Millarville, Alberta.

billions of dollars annually for their collection, transportation, and disposal. In community and environmental terms, continuing generation of waste leads to the need to find new landfill sites when the old ones fill up. Finding and approving new sites is becoming harder, in part because of the "NIMBY" (not in my backyard) syndrome.

One of the most controversial aspects of solid waste disposal is the location of disposal sites. Vancouver, for example, trucks waste to Cache Creek (over 300 kilometres north, in British Columbia's interior), while Toronto's shipment of garbage to the United States has generated much debate. Both cities are now examining new options for waste disposal; for example, the landfill at Cache Creek will close by the end of 2008. In the United States, activists have protested against "environmental racism." They point out that solid and hazardous waste sites are more likely to be located in or near neighbourhoods of poor people of colour than in or near white, middle-class areas. This is not solely an American problem. In the 1990s, the Halifax Regional Municipality (composed of Halifax, Dartmouth, Bedford, and Halifax County) was mired in a debate over environmental racism when it sought to replace its landfill site. In Halifax, African-Canadian residents historically have been subjected to residential segregation, systematic racism, deplorable living conditions, and ultimately, relocation without consultation. They feared that a similar story would be repeated with the creation of a new landfill. Their activism to protest the site became part of the push for Halifax to create one of the most comprehensive and successful waste resource management strategies in the country.

Landfilling and incinerating wastes almost always are controversial land use decisions because both incur environmental and socioeconomic effects. Even though technology has improved, landfills emit methane (a greenhouse gas) and other gases (some toxic), and there is as yet no method that is 100 percent efficient in capturing and containing these gases. Inadequate engineering, too,

can result in leachates (leaking liquid) contaminating surface water or groundwater. Incineration produces air emissions that contain toxic contaminants and particulates, and solid residues that are hazardous and require further disposal in specialized facilities. With a combination of high-temperature incineration methods and emission controls, problems of air emissions could be solved (Environment Canada, 1991). However, because high volumes of waste are required to make incineration economical, municipalities could have less incentive to "reduce, reuse, and recycle" their waste materials.

Although comparisons with other countries are difficult, Canadians have the dubious distinction of being among the world leaders in per capita waste production. In 2002, Canadians generated 30.4 million tonnes of solid waste (from residential, industrial, commercial, institutional, construction, and demolition sources); this is 971 kilograms per person, or almost 2.7 kilograms daily. Household garbage accounts for 40 percent of the solid waste generated in Canada, and in 2002, each Canadian generated 383 kilograms of residential waste (Statistics Canada, 2006). In comparison, waste generation in Sweden is estimated at less than one-third that of Canadians. Given these statistics, the Canadian Council of Ministers of the Environment established a Waste Resource Management Strategy, agreed on by all the provinces, which set a national target for a 50 percent per capita reduction in solid wastes from 1988 levels by 2000. At the end of 2000, Nova Scotia was the only province that had reached that goal. The goal was achieved through implementation of a recycling program, landfill reduction, and green bin doorstep pickup composting. It is estimated that the system in Halifax reduced annual GHGs by about 1.4 tonnes per resident. In 1999–2000, Halifax residents and businesses diverted 43 percent of the waste that

Photo 13–7
Of the material we send to landfills, how much could we reuse, recycle, or compost?

Photo 13–8
Easily accessible community facilities are one way Canadians may be encouraged to increase their recycling of solid wastes.

normally would have gone to landfill, including 36 000 tonnes of organics and 22 000 tonnes of other recyclables (including appliances). This system resulted in 125 new permanent jobs in a variety of occupations, and about

3000 jobs in Nova Scotia's recycling industry. Waste reduction in the workplace also may be an effective means to ensure that materials do not enter the landfill in the first place (see Box 13–5).

BOX 13–5
WASTE REDUCTION EFFORTS IN THE WORKPLACE

Provided that a company workplace is supportive of employee efforts to implement environmental initiatives, employees can have important effects on company practices. Whether as individuals, members of committees, or managers, many people have helped their companies to become greener in such areas as purchasing, environmental codes of practice, nonsmoking buildings, and conservation strategies for water, energy, and waste.

Support for bicycle commuting (including provision of shower facilities in the workplace) and contributions to events such as community tree planting and river cleanups have become meaningful company activities. Many of these activities have resulted from people sharing information about the importance of individual attitudes, actions, and impacts on our environment.

Within the workplace, individuals and environmental committees can influence other employees to participate in initiatives such as recycling programs. With the advent of computers in the workplace, the paperless office was predicted as the way of the future. However, as a result of people using more paper by printing more drafts of their work, paper use actually increased in 50 percent of Canadian companies surveyed in 1994. Fortunately, many companies and employees now participate in efforts to reduce paper use and to recycle used paper. In the same survey, it was noted that 83 percent of respondents participated in efforts to recycle paper, 60 percent used two-sided photocopying, 56 percent used the backs of paper sheets, and 55 percent used the computer for revisions to their documents rather than printing a new hard copy (Government of Canada, 1996; Pitney Bowes, 1994).

Telework or telecommuting is a trend that may be positive for the environment. As some corporations offer their employees the opportunity to work at home and connect to the office via computer and telecommunication technologies, reductions of air emissions and other environmental stresses due to commuting are expected. In addition, as employees spend less time in the office, telework can allow more people to share office space. This reduces the need for land for buildings as well as the heating and cooling costs associated with such real estate.

Environmental stewardship also is reflected in Canadian Pacific Hotels and Resorts (CPH&R) Green Program. In the fall of 1990, Canadian Pacific Hotels embarked on the project of developing a set of environmental standards for all of its hotels in Canada. The company conducted a detailed audit of all its operating hotels, asking hotel departments to submit information on every aspect of their impact on the environment. The program's goals are ambitious. Canadian Pacific Hotels is reducing the amount of waste sent to landfill by 50 percent across the chain,

running an extensive recycling program (including blue boxes for collecting recyclables in guest rooms), redesigning its purchasing policies to ensure that waste is reduced at source, and ensuring that supplies used in the hotels are nature-friendly. While every one of Canadian Pacific Hotels' properties has an environmental program, many individual hotels have developed some creative and unusual ways to become more nature-friendly. For example, Le Château Montebello uses its own composted soil as fertilizer; Hotel Vancouver now uses baking soda and salt instead of chlorine to maintain water clarity in its pool; and the Royal York donates leftover food to Second Harvest—a Toronto organization that collects and redistributes food to relief agencies.

In order to assess the effects of the environmental program and how its properties were responding to the 16-point plan, Canadian Pacific Hotels hired an outside environmental consultant to audit each property on overall compliance to the program. The results were very encouraging. Here are some of the highlights:

- Canadian Pacific Hotels has placed blue recycling boxes in every one of its hotel rooms at every property throughout Canada.

- 90 percent of all used soap is made available to local charities in Canada and in developing countries. The Queen Elizabeth Hotel alone sent 4200 pounds of soap to humanitarian agencies in less developed countries.

- 86 percent of all paper used in Canadian Pacific Hotels properties is recycled or is kraft paper that meets or exceeds Canadian Environmental Choice Standards. Over 80 percent of properties have succeeded in reducing their paper consumption by the 20 percent objective.

In 1996, Anne Checkley, director of communications and environmental affairs for CPH&R, indicated that there was "absolutely no down side to having an environmental program" (Beale, 1996, p. 24). Even though hotel occupancy has increased during the past decade, waste management costs have decreased. In fact, CPH&R publishes "The Green Partnership Guide," a collection of tips from its environmental committees that is sold around the world. This is an indication that greening of business can be profitable.

Growing numbers of companies have made changes in their operations and management in order to reduce the environmental impact of their activities. At the same time, companies are recognizing that there are business benefits to be realized by greening their operations. Business decision making that reflects environmental and social concerns and values is being termed corporate social responsibility (CSR).

SOURCES: "Canadian Pacific Hotel's Enviro-Initiatives," J. Beale, 1996, Winter, *Ecolutions*, 24–25; Canadian Pacific Hotels, home page, http://www. cphotels.com; *The State of Canada's Environment—1996*, Government of Canada, 1996; *Pitney Bowes Fourth Annual Green Office Survey*, Pitney Bowes, 1994, Toronto: Author.

Land Contamination

An important urban waste management problem has arisen on old industrial and other sites where toxic materials were deliberately dumped or accidentally spilled or leaked from underground storage tanks. On these sites, contamination levels of certain persistent compounds and metals, such as lead, cadmium, chromium, and nickel, prevent redevelopment for residential, recreational, or even commercial use without a costly cleanup. Numerous examples exist across the country, including the Expo 86 site in False Creek in Vancouver (see Photo 13–12 on page 549), and the Ataratiri housing project in Toronto (dropped in the late 1980s when cleanup costs were estimated to be over $30 million). Additionally, chemical fertilizers and pesticides, often applied to lawns and gardens in quantities greater than are applied in agricultural operations, enter the ecosystem by leaching into the ground or entering the wastewater disposal system. In response to public concerns about use of pesticides and herbicides, many municipal governments have developed integrated pest-management plans and reduced or eliminated use of chemicals on public lands such as parks.

URBANIZATION OF LAND

Green Space in the City

Historically, where green space was established in the city, the space was preserved primarily for recreational rather than ecological values. Natural areas and stream valleys, however, were used as convenient locations for dumping garbage and for highway routes, many watercourses were used as storm sewers, and many waterfronts were cut off from public access for use by industries, railways, and roads (Turner, 1996). Even the creation of parks in the city caused destruction of the natural environment as, for example, when productive wetlands were transformed into sports fields, playgrounds, manicured lawns, flower displays, and other planted areas using exotic species. Golf courses and other formal parks often are fertilized, treated with pesticides, and irrigated. Such treatments often eliminate remaining natural characteristics and add polluted runoff to lakes, streams, and rivers.

Apart from its important social benefits, most urban outdoor recreational space has very little conservation, ecological, or environmental value. Only when large "semi-wild" areas are preserved (such as Stanley Park in Vancouver or Nose Hill Park in Calgary) is there a potential for protection of environmental values. Even then, heavy use of Stanley Park has resulted in severe erosion of some of the area's original natural characteristics. Certain wildlife found in Nose Hill Park may not survive over the long term, as their corridors into the park now are virtually surrounded by urban development.

Some species of wildlife, wildflowers, and trees, however, are able to survive and even thrive in urban environments. Ravines, woods, and other vegetated areas within cities are important for providing habitat for a variety of wildlife and plants and for reducing or preventing soil erosion. In addition, natural areas help moderate urban microclimates, decrease air pollution (by trapping particles and absorbing carbon), and reduce storm flows (thus reducing the overload on sewers and treatment plants). Urban forests also are important recreational resources. Some of the benefits trees bring to human health and well-being are identified in Box 13–6.

As the ecosystem approach to green space within cities has developed, many communities have established systems of interconnected natural areas that permit reproduction and migration of many species of plants and wildlife and continuation of some or most ecosystem functions. While natural green spaces provide residents and visitors with aesthetically pleasing surroundings for recreation, relaxation, or contact with nature, the longer-term view is that such natural heritage systems would become the focus around which cities develop, rather than providing just a backdrop for development.

In spite of growing awareness of the multiple values of urban green space, city land use controls do not always afford green areas or natural spaces the protection they require to remain functional in an ecological or ecosystem sense. Many private developers and public agencies continue to view green space as unused or underused land and as prime sites for buildings and other facilities. Additional pressure on urban green space comes from efforts to increase the intensity of occupancy of urban land in order to reduce infrastructure costs and increase energy efficiency. From 1966 to 1986 (the last year for which Canada-wide data are available), the rate of conversion of rural and prime agricultural land to urban uses varied according to the population size of urban centres—the nine largest

Photo 13–9
While socially important, manicured green spaces in cities have fewer environmental benefits than natural areas.

BOX 13-6
URBAN FORESTS

Trees greatly influence the health of the urban environment; they are a source of beauty and help to purify the air, abate noise, modify heat, stabilize soil, reduce flood risks, and provide wildlife habitat as well as recreational settings for residents. For its regulatory services, an urban forest is an integral part of the hydrologic cycle in urban environments. The urban forest includes not only large stands of native trees, such as are found in Stanley Park in Vancouver, and in C. A. Pippy Park in St. John's, but also the millions of native and exotic trees lining our streets, in our yards, parks, and plant nurseries, and on the edges of some of our newest neighbourhoods.

One reality of life for urban trees is that many get a great deal less water than trees in rural settings do (streets, gutters, and sewer systems channel water away quickly). Urban trees also experience higher average temperatures, air and soil pollution, and the constant threat of root or stem damage from human traffic or heavy equipment. A tree planted in the black-top jungle of downtown Vancouver will survive an average of 13 years, while those planted in large treed gardens may survive up to 60 years (Forest Alliance of British Columbia, n.d., p. 2). Trees living in Toronto had a life expectancy of only five years (Jenish, 2004). While an average life expectancy of 32 years for trees in the Vancouver area is significantly less than the average life span of trees in rural areas, trees in urban areas naturalize built landscapes and provide important psychological benefits.

The benefits of trees (rural and urban) to human psychology are difficult to quantify, but they contribute noticeably to human health and well-being. Research has shown, for instance, that patients recover more quickly if their hospital room has a view of trees and natural landscapes (Ulrich, 1979). Urban trees shade and cool streets and buildings in summer, moderating the higher temperatures experienced in cities. If coniferous trees are placed strategically to buffer winter winds, they can help reduce heat loss from buildings in winter and contribute to fuel savings of 20 percent or more (Forest Alliance of British Columbia, n.d.).

Each tree in the urban forest removes pollutants and other particulates from city air. Carbon, chlorine, fluorine, ozone, sulphur dioxide, peroxyacetylnitrate (a component of photochemical smog), and other gases are absorbed by these trees. Trees function as carbon sinks. Every year, each city tree removes about 6 kilograms of carbon dioxide from the atmosphere. Because they are located in highly emitting areas, urban trees are five to 15 times more beneficial than wilderness trees with regard to the purification of the air we breathe. Similarly, trees filter airborne particulates, resulting in 27 to 42 percent less ground-level dust in treed areas than in open areas, an important health benefit for people sensitive to dust or allergic to pollen (Forest Alliance of British Columbia, n.d.). Ultimately, however, air pollution will damage forest health; the decline in the health of German forests (noted in Chapter 9) and the loss of ponderosa pine forests near Los Angeles due to smog attest to this fact.

For all of the above reasons, as well as the fact that they increase property values by 5 to 20 percent or more, "trees are not mere niceties, they're necessities" (Krakauer, 1990). We need to remember this as our cities grow—in Canada every day, forests are cleared to make way for new subdivisions, shopping centres, roadways, agriculture, and grazing lands. Population growth within cities means city trees also are lost to development changes designed to accommodate new residents. While not a total substitute for natural forests, urban tree planting, such as that encouraged by the Green Streets Canada Program (an initiative of Tree Plan Canada), is an important greening activity. Green Street Canada's objective is to create a partnership between the Tree Canada Foundation and municipalities across Canada to help improve their urban forests and provide citizens with a greater appreciation of how trees can contribute to the environment and the overall quality of life in their community (Tree Canada, 2001). By 1994, more than 40 million trees had been planted in rural and urban areas (Natural Resources Canada, 1995) and, since 1993, the Tree Canada Foundation has planted more than 75 million trees, in both urban and rural areas (Tree Canada Foundation, n.d.).

SOURCES: "The Urban Forest," Forest Alliance of British Columbia, n.d., *Choices*, 4(1), 2; "Trees Aren't Mere Niceties—They're Necessities," J. Krakauer, April 1990, *Smithsonian*, 21, 160–171; *The State of Canada's Forests 1994: A Balancing Act*, Natural Resources Canada, Canadian Forest Service, 1995; "Visual Landscapes and Psychological Well-Being," R. S. Ulrich, 1979, *Landscape Research, 4*, 17–23; Tree Canada Foundation, home page, 2001, http://www.treecanada.ca/index_e.htm

centres (over 500 000 population) accounted for 42.9 percent of the conversion (Warren, Kerr, & Turner, 1989).

Growth in urban populations during the coming decades is inevitable, as is continued urban expansion. The effects of continued expansion could be enormous; for example, a conservative estimate indicates that between 1988 and 2021, even if the most compact growth is pursued, the Greater Toronto area is expected to grow an additional 23 percent or 350 square kilometres (from a 1988 base area of 1520 square kilometres). If more dispersed trends were to continue, the increase would be 59 percent or 900 square kilometres (IBI Group, 1990).

One of the major contributing factors to this rate of land occupation is the popularity of the detached, single-family house surrounded by its own lot. Curvilinear street patterns (rather than the more compact grid layout) also have reinforced the spread-out form of urban development. Single-family detached housing remains popular. Prairie cities tend to have the highest proportion of single-family detached housing starts, with west coast and most Quebec centres slightly lower. However, there has been an increase in the average density of new residential developments, in part because frontage of single-family detached lots has decreased from the 15 to 18 metres

(50 to 60 feet) common up until the 1970s to about 9 to 12 metres (30 to 40 feet) in the 1990s.

LOSS OF AGRICULTURAL LAND

Both historically and today in Canada, much of the expansion of settlement has occurred on fertile agricultural land. About 25 percent of Canada's high-capability (class 1 to 3) agricultural land, including more than 50 percent of our prime, class 1 agricultural land, is located within 80 kilometres of Canada's 23 largest cities. While the amount of agricultural land lost to urbanization may seem quite small, we need to remember two important factors. One factor in this complex issue is that in some parts of Canada, urbanization affects specialty crop areas. The Okanagan Valley in British Columbia, the Niagara Peninsula in Ontario, and the horticultural lands adjacent to Vancouver and Montreal are areas that account for only a tiny proportion of the total amount of productive land in Canada. In these areas, however, urbanization permanently precludes the ability to grow specialty crops (see Chapter 6); thus, urbanization effects in these areas are highly significant.

The second factor is that urban growth affects agriculture in many indirect ways. Agricultural regions experience significant economic and social impacts when extensive industrial sites, gravel pits, golf courses, recreational facilities, and residential estates are developed. Sometimes called **urban shadow effects**, these impacts extend over large areas and cause declines in agriculture in urban regions

(Gertler, Crowley, & Bond, 1977). The problem seems to be that once agricultural production is discouraged, even land that is not needed for urban growth comes to be occupied by nonagricultural uses or is abandoned. In efforts to combat this problem, Quebec and British Columbia have had protective agricultural zoning in place for years, and other provinces have adopted policies that regulate urban expansion in agricultural areas.

In addition to agricultural land loss, removal of woodlands, disruption of wildlife corridors, destruction of habitat, and accelerated soil erosion, urban expansion has resulted in the loss of wetlands. Other environmentally sensitive areas may be threatened (and sometimes are destroyed) by urban expansion, including aquatic habitats, if groundwater and surface water bodies are polluted by stormwater runoff or septic tank and landfill seepage. Air quality, too, may be affected by the operation of gravel pits and landfills, including the frequent truck traffic they generate. These and previously noted effects of human activities associated with the city remind us that our ecological footprint (see Chapter 1) is impressed on the productive output of a land area many times larger than the geographic size of our cities. If we are to continue to support people's demands for food, water, forest products, and energy, and to assimilate the wastes resulting from our urban activities, then actions to ensure sustainability of our communities and to protect the environment that maintains them are vital. (See Enviro-Focus 13 for information on urban agriculture.)

ENVIRO-FOCUS 13

Urban Agriculture

For most Canadians, food is plentiful, and in terms of caloric intake, we are among the best-fed people in the world. However, Canadians living in urban areas rarely think about where their food comes from or about the environmental issues associated with the abundance of food seen in the supermarket. For instance, food prices tend not to incorporate fully the long-term environmental costs of production and transportation—it has been estimated that it takes three times as much energy to truck a head of lettuce from California to Toronto as it does to grow it locally in season (cited in Government of Canada, 1996).

Concerns about the sustainability of Canada's resource-intensive food production system, health concerns surrounding the use of additives and preservatives, the availability of fresh food for lower-income residents, as well as emerging issues concerning the use of genetically modified organisms (GMOs) as foodstuffs (see Chapter 6) have sparked increased interest in organic farming and in city gardening (urban agriculture). Since 1978, City Farmer, a nonprofit society, has promoted urban food production and environmental conservation from their small office in downtown Vancouver and from their demonstration food garden in a residential Kitsilano neighbourhood.

In 1996, Annex Organics of Toronto retrofitted an old warehouse building in order to grow tomatoes, peppers, eggplant, and herbs—on its roof! Rooftop

Photo 13–10
Community gardens bring people together to help meet economic, social, and environmental sustainability objectives.

gardening is an example of "green roof infrastructure," touted as a truly sustainable development technology (Kwik, 2000). Common in Europe, not only do rooftop gardens help improve urban air quality and moderate the urban heat island effect, they also insulate buildings and reduce the energy costs of heating and cooling. Urban food production is increased by the use of gardens on rooftops, where there is more space and sunlight than at ground level. City farmers find it advantageous to be so close to their customers; transport costs are minimized, and so are associated pollutants.

Another example of urban agriculture is the Hilton Montreal Bonaventure hotel, which boasts a 2.5-hectare landscaped rooftop, with winding brooks, birch trees, and many species of plants and animals, where guests can relax.

Vertical gardens (where vines and other vegetation are placed on or adjacent to interior or exterior walls) have many of the same benefits as horizontal rooftop gardens. These include reducing the cooling loads of buildings, moderating internal temperature variations, beautifying, assisting in food production, and providing additional green space (Bass & Hansell, 2000).

Community gardening is another strategy to help revive inner-city neighbourhoods. From an environmental standpoint, community gardening offers a way for urban residents to grow their own food organically, thereby reducing dependence on current methods of food production. Often, community gardens are places where new immigrants to Canada can cultivate foods from their countries of origin and share in the cultural diversity of the country. The Cultivating Communities project in Calgary began in 1996. The idea behind the establishment of a community garden within the grounds of a community association was to create a project in which people with disabilities, seniors, schoolchildren, and other neighbourhood residents could take part. Participants celebrate their success with a harvest of fresh vegetables (Pezzi, 1998).

Montreal's Community Gardening project is recognized as the largest and best-organized city gardening program in the country. The program's work in the 1990s involved composting research, food donations to community kitchens, access for gardeners with disabilities, and horticultural therapy projects. Vancouver's Strathcona Community Garden contains a heritage apple project, contributing to retaining the diversity of our food sources. Saskatoon combines a community garden program with its Child Hunger and Education Program, to encourage the production of healthy and inexpensive foods for the city's most vulnerable populations. Similar community garden initiatives have taken root in small and large centres across the country. Is there one in your community or on your campus? Perhaps you could help initiate a community garden!

SOURCES: "Climbing the Walls: Vertical Gardens Can Cool Buildings and Clear the Air," B. Bass & R. Hansell, 2000, *Alternatives Journal, 26*(3), 17–18; *Montreal's Community Gardening Program*, City Farmer, 1997, http://www.cityfarmer.org./Montreal13.html#ontreal; *Urban Agriculture Notes*, City Farmer, 1997, http://www.cityfarmer.org/urbagnotes1.html#notes; *Connections: Canadian Lifestyle Choices and the Environment*, Environment Canada, 1995, State of the Environment Fact Sheet No. 95-1; *The State of Canada's Environment—1996*, Government of Canada, 1996, Ottawa: Supply and Services Canada; "Gardens Overhead: Rooftop Culture Sprouts in North American Cities," J. Kwik, 2000, *Alternatives Journal, 26*(3), 16–17; "Community Gardens: Growing Communities," B. Pezzi, April 1998, *Encompass*, 11.

TOWARD SUSTAINABLE COMMUNITIES

We have come to appreciate that many consequences of urban growth can be avoided, or their impacts reduced, if we pay more careful attention to and incorporate stricter controls in land use planning. Before we consider examples of actual actions undertaken to move toward more sustainable communities, it is worthwhile outlining what is meant by sustainability in an urban context.

CITIES AND SUSTAINABILITY

Nigel Richardson (1989, p. 14) defined sustainable urban development as a "process of change in the built environment which fosters economic development while conserving resources and promoting the health of the individual, the community and the ecosystem." His definition illustrates the interconnections between ecosystem and human health and is consistent with definitions of sustainability we provided in Chapter 1. The strategies for sustainability discussed below illustrate efforts to place such definitions into specific practices.

Sustainable Calgary is a citizen-led, nonprofit society formed in 1996 as a result of educational workshops of the Arusha Centre (then a development education organization) and inspiration from the work of Sustainable

Photo 13–11
Increasingly heavy use of even large protected areas, such as Stanley Park in Vancouver, presents sustainability challenges.

Seattle. Sustainable Calgary's mission is to encourage and support action to influence policy, planning, and community processes. All of Sustainable Calgary's projects are guided by the following sustainability principles: ecological integrity, social equity, sustainable economic development, democratic participation in decision making, and intergenerational equity (Sustainable Calgary, n.d.a). This view of sustainability means that cities need to perform not only the economic functions that are the basis of their existence but also evolve to meet changing social and economic needs. In practice, citizens need to place a high priority on the condition of their environment and ensure that city administrators not only recognize the need for continuing economic and physical development and revitalization in the city but also provide water and sewage treatment plants, clean up contaminated land, and preserve open spaces. In short, environmental protection and resource conservation must be recognized as integral components of urban form and function.

Potentially, cities may be better for environmental protection and resource conservation than dispersed settlement patterns, because cities may achieve economies and efficiencies in water, sewage, and waste disposal (including recycling and reuse), in energy use (through **district heating**), in use of land (through compact development), and in transportation (substituting walking, bicycling, and transit for car use). However, obstacles to achieving these objectives exist.

Among the major obstacles is the fact that we still lack certain kinds of information on which to base long-term decisions about the future of our urban areas. For instance, we do not know the long-term consequences of climate change, or the implications of certain air and water pollutants for human and ecosystem health, or the best physical form or appropriate density for residential occupation. Lack of full knowledge, however, is never an excuse for inaction on any of these issues.

We do know that Canadians continue to prefer single-family detached housing over higher-density housing, and that they prefer to use their cars rather than public transit. Changing ingrained social values, personal lifestyles, and economic expectations of individuals is always difficult. And, as the oldest and relatively prosperous segment of the Canadian population continues to grow in number, resistance to change may increase (Government of Canada, 1996). Such social and demographic factors suggest that, to date, the concept of environmental sustainability has not been a significant influence for change in the complex field of urban development.

Another reason we have been slow to move to a sustainable communities approach to urbanization is because of the great expense and long life of the buildings, expressways, sewage treatment plants, public transit systems, and other facilities that make up our urban fabric. It would be very costly, both socially and financially, if we decided to quickly and radically alter this urban fabric.

An additional obstacle is that political control and administration of cities in Canada is not well suited to achieving sustainable communities. Different federal, provincial, and municipal policies and programs, the lack of coordination among them, and the lack of cooperation among the three levels of government affect communities differentially. In addition, during the 1990s, governments began to withdraw from providing services, or higher orders of government provided less money to provincial levels, which, in turn, provided fewer resources to municipalities. In many cases, critical infrastructures—roads, sewage systems—were not maintained regularly and now require considerable investment to meet new demands for sustainability. Fortunately, government departments and agencies are working to improve their cooperation and coordination so that progress toward sustainable communities may advance. Several federally supported sustainable community development initiatives attest to the changing scene. Interestingly, support for these initiatives has come from a variety of government departments, including Environment Canada, Health Canada, Natural Resources Canada, and Fisheries and Oceans Canada (New Economy Development Group, 2001). In addition, cities were placed on the list of priorities during federal elections in the early 2000s. Consequently, the federal government provides municipalities with some of the financial resources needed to maintain and upgrade their transportation and other urban infrastructure. Continuation of these investments is critical if we are to move toward more sustainable urban forms.

MAKING CANADIAN CITIES MORE SUSTAINABLE

In spite of the difficulties in striving for urban sustainability, there are signs of progress in urban form, conservation, reduction of environmental impacts, transportation, and planning. In the sections that follow, we consider some examples of actions that have been taken to help make Canadian cities more sustainable.

Urban Form

One approach to advancing urban sustainability is through a more compact urban form. A more compact urban form is expected to lead to more economical use of land, water, energy, and materials, and to reduce our dependence on cars in the city. Several municipalities across Canada, including the city of Halifax, the regional municipality of Hamilton-Wentworth, metropolitan Toronto, and the city of Regina, have revised their planning policies deliberately to support the shift to more compact urban forms. The kinds of changes that are envisioned for sustainable cities in Canada in the future are identified in Table 13–5 on the next page.

Photo 13–12
Urban redevelopment has transformed Vancouver's False Creek.

Intensification of land use (developing or redeveloping land at higher densities) also is being worked out through building conversions, neighbourhood rehabilitation, and infill construction. In cities as diverse as Toronto, St. John's, Sudbury, Montreal, and Vancouver, places of employment and residence are being integrated in mixed-use neighbourhoods. Higher-intensity land use also is being achieved through the use of infill housing, smaller lots in new suburban areas, and Main Street initiatives that encourage residential development above retail establishments. These initiatives are aimed, as well, at making housing affordable.

Conservation

Water Conservation Water and energy conservation programs have been put in place in many Canadian municipalities. Water conservation programs typically involve city programs such as leak detection and repair, metering, retrofitting, public education, and use restrictions. Major centres such as Toronto, Ottawa–Carleton, Laval, and Edmonton have broad water management plans in place, as do many smaller urban centres such as Cochrane, Ontario, and Rosemère, Quebec. In light of chronic water supply problems in Kitchener–Waterloo, a university student wrote a thesis that outlined a program for water conservation. His thesis was so convincing that he was awarded a new position with the municipal council—that of water conservation officer! Communities also contemplate alternatives: in considering how their area could move toward sustainability, the Greater Vancouver Regional District proposed that rainwater be collected for flushing toilets and for use in gardens (Balcom, 1997). Both municipal and community actions are important in water conservation.

Energy Conservation Like water conservation programs, energy conservation efforts focus both on reduction of city costs for fuel and electricity and on community-wide initiatives that contribute to economic, social, and

TABLE 13-5

CHARACTERISTICS OF CANADIAN "SUSTAINABLE CITIES" IN THE FUTURE

Changes to the form of the city (the pattern and density of its physical fabric) are expected to advance urban sustainability. In the future, sustainable cities in Canada would be expected to have the following characteristics:

- a substantially higher average density than today's city
  - land is used more fully; abandoned or underused sites are redeveloped
  - obsolete industrial and commercial buildings are converted to residential use
  - single-family detached housing (low-density) is largely replaced by more dense, compact forms
  - compact, affordable, and adaptable housing, such as the narrow, two-storey rowhouse (Grow Home) designed at McGill University's School of Architecture, provides ground-level access and some private outdoor space.

- a network of viable, linked subcentres
  - these subcentres and the downtown area are linked by mixed-use corridors and high-capacity rapid transit
  - each centre provides a range of services plus employment opportunities and moderate- to high-density housing.

- a mixed land use pattern
  - residential and other uses are mixed (more than we see now) with compatible, nonpolluting industries located in or adjacent to subcentres
  - this mixed-use development, including a mix of different housing types and sizes, reduces the need for travel.

- a citywide transit system and a network of bicycle routes
  - a convenient, efficient, and reliable city public transit system results in restrictions on the use of private cars, particularly in the downtown area and core of the subcentres
  - safe bicycle routes also are constructed.

- a range of housing choices in every residential district
  - all houses are built to high standards of energy and water efficiency
  - residents walk safely and conveniently to transit and cycle routes and to local schools, shops, and parks.

- corridors of open space
  - open-space corridors are left in their natural condition and run through the entire city
  - these provide recreational opportunities and ecological links to parks and the open countryside.

- a well-defined edge of the city
  - carefully planned urban expansion is compact and has no scattered urban infiltration into the surrounding rural area
  - expansion is mainly in the form of physically separate satellite communities developed around their own subcentres and served by the city's rapid transit system.

Planners feel that such reshaping of the city is attainable and would go a long way toward conserving land, natural ecosystems, energy, and water, and would reduce air pollution. As well, it would provide a highly livable urban environment.

SOURCE: *The State of Canada's Environment—1996*, © Her Majesty the Queen in Right of Canada, Environment Canada, 1996, Box 12.3. Reprinted with permission of the Minister of Public Works and Government Services Canada, 2008.

environmental objectives such as local economic development, improved air quality, and reduced CO_2 emissions. Energy audits and energy controls in municipal buildings, and energy reviews of newly designed municipal facilities, are among the ways both large and small communities can identify energy-saving possibilities. Common energy conservation initiatives include changing streetlighting, adopting energy standards for buildings, retrofitting municipal buildings, and converting municipal vehicles to alternative fuels.

Increasingly, municipalities have become involved in urban energy management, and have linked with broader community environmental efforts. Ontario's Green Communities program is one example in which the focus was on smaller urban centres such as Guelph, Sarnia, and Peterborough. Green Communities are nonprofit, community-based, multi-partner organizations (made up of businesses, institutions, and governments) that bring environmental solutions to homes. They are in the business of selling environmental action through behaviour change and uptake of green products and services (Green Communities Association, 2001). Domestic energy conservation measures also are being adopted both through retrofitting of older buildings and in new construction (including R-2000 and Built Green standards; see Chapter 11).

Conservation of Materials Many Canadian municipalities now offer recycling programs, compost collection, and other waste reduction services. Typically, emphasis is on the "3Rs"—reduction of the volume of waste at its source, reuse of materials, and recycling and composting. Some cities, including Sherbrooke, Montreal, Toronto, and Vancouver, have firm waste reduction targets; some, such as Toronto and Vancouver, are trying to establish controls on packaging; and still others have placed limits on the amount of garbage the city will collect from each dwelling.

Access to recycling programs of various types has increased throughout Canada. In 2006, 88 percent of Canadian households had access to a paper-recycling program, compared to 70 percent in 1994 (Statistics Canada, 1995; 2008). Recycling programs for glass bottles were equally accessible, at 88 percent. Eighty-seven percent of households had access to a plastic recycling program, 86 percent had access to a program to recycle metal cans, and many communities offered special hazardous-waste disposal facilities for paints, chemicals, and batteries. The greatest quantity of materials is recycled in Ontario and Quebec, but the

rates of recycling (amount recycled per person) are highest in British Columbia and Nova Scotia (Statistics Canada, 2007). Through 2006, more than 97 percent of households with access to recycling programs continued to use them (Statistics Canada, 2008).

In spite of its strong potential to reduce the amount of organic material entering the municipal waste stream, composting has not been accepted as readily as other recycling programs. In 2004, 23 percent of Canadian households composted their waste in some way; in 2006, 27 percent of households used a compost pile or bin for their food waste, leaves, and yard trimmings. The Maritime provinces divert the most organic waste per capita in Canada (Statistics Canada, 2008).

Conservation of Ecosystems and Natural Features

Cities are moving away from the traditional view of urban parks as green areas for recreation and toward conservation of natural areas, environmentally sensitive areas, and natural habitats. Although the biodiversity values of wetlands, shore zones, forests, and wildlife corridors have begun to be recognized, their protection is just beginning at the local level.

To encourage wildlife population growth and restoration of natural ecosystems, such cities as Ottawa, Edmonton, Toronto, and Montreal have begun to create or restore green corridors by linking small natural areas, cemeteries, waterfronts, transmission line right of ways, and other open spaces. Nationally, the Trans Canada Trail Foundation is overseeing the creation of a cross-country trail that conserves and preserves our natural heritage (see Box 14–3, p. 583). Calgary employs its Natural Area Management Plan to help protect existing natural environments and to identify potential areas for future conservation prior to their development. Many cities now practise

Photo 13–13
Readily available and affordable, recycled-plastic compost bins are an increasingly common sight.

Photo 13–14
Collecting rainwater in barrels or other containers is an effective way for individuals and communities to augment municipal water supply systems.

urban forestry, encourage naturalization of vegetation, and substitute integrated pest management for chemical pesticides. From Gander, Newfoundland, to Fort Saskatchewan, Alberta, experiments have been undertaken with sheep and other herbivores to replace gasoline-powered lawnmowers (Federation of Canadian Municipalities, 1995). Some initiatives have incorporated an ecosystem approach to land use planning within the urban field (Table 13–6). These include the Fraser River Estuary Management Program, Saskatoon's Meewasin Valley Authority, and the Hamilton Harbour Remedial Action Plan. These examples have placed a high value on understanding and protecting the interactions among air, land, water, and living organisms, ensuring that any specific projects are considered for their ecological, social, cultural, and economic considerations.

Reduction of Environmental Impacts

Ideally, cities should be free of activities that harm the health of other people or natural ecosystems. In reality, however, financial, jurisdictional, and behavioural barriers arise that affect progress toward air and water quality, waste management, and cleanups of harmful sites or substances.

Air and Water Quality The main way to lower concentrations of ground-level ozone (the leading urban air quality problem in Canada) is to reduce the emissions of its precursors (nitrogen oxides and VOCs) by motor vehicles. Federal and provincial governments largely control air pollution action—such as banning leaded gasoline

and regulating vehicle emissions—through the federal Motor Vehicle Safety Act and other provincial regulations. Federal and provincial governments continuously review quality standards and regulations (the NAAQOs), and some cities are taking action to improve air quality.

The Federation of Canadian Municipalities' (FCM) "20 percent club" merged with the International Council for Local Environmental Initiatives' (ICLEI) Canadian Cities for Climate Protection campaign. This united effort is named Partners for Climate Protection: For a Better Quality of Life. The goal of the merged program remains to support Canadian municipal governments and to prepare and implement local climate action plans. The ultimate goal is to reduce GHGs from municipal operations 20 percent below 1990 levels within 10 years of joining the program, and to reduce community-wide GHGs at least 6 percent below 1990 levels within 10 years of joining the program. The priorities of the program are to build capacity, support champions, provide up-to-date information, ensure access, create model plans, facilitate participation, generate feedback, and build partnerships (Federation of Canadian Municipalities, 2001).

Several cities have policies and programs relating to the use of alternative fuels as well as the reduction of emissions of SO_2, CO_2, and NO_x. Vancouver directs attention toward reduction of greenhouse gas and ozone-depleting emissions, Montreal's strategy focuses on reducing emissions and use of CFCs and halons, and Toronto has specific targets for reducing SO_2 emissions.

The report cards produced by Ecojustice (formerly the Sierra Legal Defense Fund), along with other public pressures, has spurred new investments in wastewater treatment. Although variable, the level of wastewater treatment has increased across Canada. Montreal recently completed a major sewage treatment scheme, while smaller centres such as Banff, Portage la Prairie, and others use innovative methods of sewage treatment, including biological processes and ultraviolet disinfection.

Transportation Because transportation decisions affect urban environments in so many ways, transportation is a key area for action. Some of the many ways cities have achieved greater sustainability in their transportation systems are outlined in Table 13–7. Public transit is an important component. Canadian transit systems already have made considerable efforts to increase ridership by improving their infrastructure (including new fleets of buses, bus shelters, and computerized information systems), their frequency, and their routing. Some public transit systems, such as in Saskatoon, are experimenting with the use of biofuels to reduce dependence on fossil fuels.

In some cases, residents are showing initiative to reduce their dependency on automobiles. In large cities, including Vancouver, car cooperatives are beginning to emerge. Car cooperatives typically operate on a nonprofit basis. Individuals buy a "share" at the outset and then

---

TABLE 13-6
CHARACTERISTICS OF AN ECOSYSTEM APPROACH TO LAND USE PLANNING

Since, in an ecosystem, everything is connected to everything else, an ecosystem approach should:

- encompass natural, physical, social, cultural, and economic considerations, and the relationships among them;
- focus on understanding interactions among air, land, water, and living organisms, including humans;
- emphasize the dynamic nature of ecosystems;
- recognize the importance of living species other than humans, and of future generations;
- work to restore and maintain the integrity, quality, and health of the ecosystem.

SOURCE: *The State of Canada's Environment—1996,* © Her Majesty the Queen in Right of Canada, Environment Canada, 1996, adapted from Box 12.4. Reproduced with permission of the Minister of Public Works and Government Services Canada, 2008.

Photo 13–15
Canada's millions of cars and light trucks emit over 4 tonnes of pollutants into the atmosphere every year.

TABLE 13–7
ACTIONS TO ACHIEVE MORE SUSTAINABLE URBAN TRANSPORTATION

- shift budget and program priorities from road systems to transit systems
- provide diverse transit options such as rapid transit, commuter rail, and surface transit networks; special facilities for high-occupancy vehicles such as car and van pools; and cycle and pedestrian pathways
- improve efficiency, speed, reliability, and general attractiveness of transit through dedicated lanes for buses, transit priority at intersections, schedule reliability, provisions of up-to-the-minute travel information, and integration of fares and schedules between routes and systems
- encourage more efficient use of infrastructure and vehicles such as travelling at off-peak times, combining trips, substituting transit for car use, sharing vehicles, and using less-congested routes
- discourage unnecessary automobile use in local residential areas by such means as traffic-calming street design
- provide public outreach, awareness, and education programs
- improve vehicle technology by designing lighter, more aerodynamic vehicles and smaller, more fuel-efficient engines, and by developing alternative fuels
- reduce the need for vehicular movement by implementing urban designs in which land use and transportation are integrated to create pedestrian-friendly streets and compact centres of intensive mixed activity linked by mixed-use corridors.

SOURCE: *The State of Canada's Environment—1996*, © Her Majesty the Queen in Right of Canada, Environment Canada, 1996. Reprinted with permission of the Minister of Public Works and Government Services Canada, 2008. http://www.ec.gc.ca/soer-ree/English/SOER/1996report/Doc/1-7-5-6-4-5-1.cfm

Photo 13–16
Bicycle paths for commuters and recreational cyclists promote pollution-free travel and physical fitness.

Photo 13–17
Although many Canadians are highly dependent on their vehicles, others are choosing to reduce their energy consumption by driving less and increasing their use of bicycles and public transit.

book a vehicle and pay for it on an as-use basis. Users are charged based on the amount of time the vehicle is booked and the distance travelled. These charges then pay for the insurance, maintenance, and other costs of the vehicles. For urban residents who do not require a car every day for commuting purposes, car cooperatives provide an affordable and convenient way to go shopping or take a day trip that is economical as well as environmentally and socially responsible.

Throughout the country, in both larger and smaller urban centres, a variety of government-led initiatives to improve transportation are under way. These initiatives may be categorized as urban structure and urban design policies, transportation infrastructure, demand management, traffic and transit management, and cleaner vehicle technology. Specific municipal policies and programs to improve transit services have been implemented in St. John's, Dartmouth, Montreal, and Toronto; reserved bus lanes have been established in Vancouver, Toronto, Ottawa, and Montreal; parking-related measures have been proposed in Montreal, Toronto, and Vancouver; and bicycle and pedestrian networks exist in Calgary, Vancouver, and other cities.

Planning Deliberate movement toward urban sustainability implies a more holistic, ecosystem-based approach to urban policy and governance than has been usual in Canada (Government of Canada, 1996). This kind of approach requires the development and implementation of urban sustainability goals, standards, and criteria that can be monitored and reported on in regular, municipal state-of-the-environment reports. Several municipalities, such as Calgary, have produced state-of-the-environment reports, while other cities have completed reports on the quality of life, state of the city, or environmental issues.

Since 1998, Sustainable Calgary has produced three "State of Our City" reports, with a fourth one due in 2008. Initially, dissatisfied with the narrow range of economic indicators that drove public policy making, a small group of Calgary citizens undertook the establishment of a set of community sustainability indicators. Over 2000 Calgarians eventually participated in researching, selecting, and documenting the sustainability indicators. Tracking of these indicators began in 1996, and by 2005, Sustainable Calgary's third report documented the status of 36 social, ecological, and economic indicators regarding the long-term health and vitality of the city (Sustainable Calgary, n.d.b). Sustainable Calgary has undertaken other successful endeavours, including the creation of a Calgary Green Map (the next Green Map is intended to be an online interactive version), a program to assess Calgary's ecological footprint, and "The Citizen's Agenda," an educational process enabling citizens to become engaged fully in policy design and action to achieve sustainability in their community.

Cities also are establishing new ways of working with local communities to advance sustainability. A redevelopment opportunity in Vancouver involving Southeast False Creek, a patch of former industrial land east of the present False Creek redevelopment, demonstrates the integration of sustainable development into urban design and planning processes. In 1991, Vancouver's City Council gave direction to explore the lands of Southeast False Creek as a model of sustainable development. In October 1999, Vancouver council approved the sustainable community policy for Southeast False Creek, which included five specific environmental plans for waste management, water management, energy, transportation, and urban agriculture. In May 2003, an official development plan proposal was prepared, followed by a public consultation process in the spring and summer of 2003. This is an example of sustainability principles being incorporated into specific design elements.

These kinds of initiatives can be considered part of the "smart growth" movement being adopted in many cities across Canada, the United States, and Europe. Smart growth, also known as new urbanism, refers to development principles and planning practices that create more efficient land use and transportation patterns intended to combat the establishment of urban sprawl and automobile-dependent land use patterns (see Table 13–8). Smart growth includes redeveloping and infilling existing city spaces, using existing infrastructure, improving accessibility around the city, and preserving greenspace within the city. Since 2003, many communities in British Columbia have worked to implement these ideas under the banner of Smart Growth on the Ground Initiative. This initiative has focused attention on compact communities, economic development, transportation, affordable housing, alternative development standards, agricultural land reserve, community involvement, and greenspace.

Canadian municipalities cannot achieve sustainability alone. Municipalities, through their umbrella organization, the Canadian Federation of Municipalities, have long argued that the reorganization of federal and provincial government finances and tax structure during the 1980s and 1990s has left them with insufficient resources to address aging infrastructure today. However, new programs established in the 2000s provided funding directly from the federal government to municipalities on the condition that urban plans be established that focus on long-term sustainability. Many cities have now signed agreements with the federal government. The goals and priorities for action of two Canadian cities, Vancouver and Saskatoon, listed in Table 13–9, illustrate that environmental, economic, and social concerns figure prominently and simultaneously in their plans.

Citizen action and the persistent, frequently well-informed, and skillful lobbying of environmental advocacy organizations often have helped bring about new or improved policies and programs within cities. For example,

TABLE 13-8
A COMPARISON OF CHARACTERISTICS OF SMART GROWTH AND URBAN SPRAWL

	Smart Growth	Urban Sprawl
Density	Higher-density, clustered activities	Lower-density, dispersed activities
Growth pattern	Infill development	Urban periphery growth
Land use mix	Mixed	Single use, segregated
Scale	Human scale, smaller buildings, blocks, and roads	Large scale, larger buildings, blocks, wide roads
Public services (shops, schools, parks)	Local, distributed, smaller; accommodates walking access	Regional, consolidated, larger; requires automobile access
Transport	Multimodal transportation and land use patterns that support walking, cycling, and public transit	Automobile-oriented transportation and land use patterns, poorly suited for walking, cycling, and transit
Connectivity	Highly connected roads, sidewalks, and paths, allowing more direct travel by motorized and nonmotorized modes	Hierarchical road network with many unconnected roads and walkways, and barriers to nonmotorized travel
Street design	Streets designed to accommodate a variety of activities	Streets designed to maximize motor vehicle traffic, volume, and speed
Planning process	Planned and coordinated between jurisdictions and stakeholders	Unplanned, with little coordination between jurisdictions and stakeholders
Public space	Emphasis on the public realm (streetscapes, pedestrian areas, public parks, public facilities)	Emphasis on the private realm (yards, shopping malls, gated communities, private clubs)

SOURCE: *Evaluating Criticism of Smart Growth,* T, Litman, 2005, Victoria, BC: Victoria Transport Policy Institute.

TABLE 13-9
SUSTAINABILITY GOALS AND PRIORITIES FOR ACTION IN VANCOUVER AND SASKATOON

Vancouver Sustainability Goals	Saskatoon Priorities for Action
• Growth in the numbers, size, and diversity of local businesses, and diversified employment opportunities for local residents	• Community-based approaches to affordable housing, homelessness, and the renewal of Saskatoon's older neighbourhoods
• Improved health outcomes for local residents, reflecting increased choices and ability to meet basic needs	• Developing cultural and recreational opportunities to enhance the quality of life in Saskatoon
• Improved safety and security and addressing the negative impacts of crime	• Supporting environmental protection and climate change solutions
• Improved and increased housing options, including affordable rental, supported, and transitional housing	• Enhancing Aboriginal participation in the economy
	• Promoting innovative initiatives for a positive business climate and enhanced competitiveness
	• Addressing strategic infrastructure necessary for the continued physical, social, and economic development of Saskatoon

SOURCES: *Saskatoon Urban Development Agreement,* 2000, http://www.wd.gc.ca/77_3005_ENG_ASP.asp; *The Vancouver Agreement,* 2000, http://www.city.vancouver.bc.ca/COMMSVCS/PLANNING/dtes/agreement.htm

Roadmap 2020 in Saskatoon is a citizen advisory group that has been working with the city to reduce GHGs, improve public transit, and establish a waste management plan. Municipalities now involve residents in specific environmental actions ranging from community cleanups, to tree planting and park naturalization efforts, to bird counts. Similarly, the healthy communities movement in Quebec, Ontario, and British Columbia has the common (and

In the mid-1990s, Bill Rees and Mathis Wackernagel developed the concept of the "ecological footprint," a term that has become part of the language surrounding sustainability. Dr. Rees first outlined the concept in a 1992 paper entitled "Ecological Footprints and Appropriated Carrying Capacity: What Urban Economics Leaves Out." Dr. Wackernagel further developed the concept in his PhD dissertation, and the two

Photo 13–18
Mathis Wackernagel.

Photo 13–19
Bill Rees.

co-authored the 1996 book *Our Ecological Footprint*. By 2007, the book was available in nine languages, and today many governments, communities, and businesses use the ecological footprint tool in monitoring current ecological resource balances and in planning for their future.

Mathis Wackernagel obtained a degree in mechanical engineering from the Swiss Federal Institute of Technology, then completed his PhD in community and regional planning at the University of British Columbia (UBC). Today, he is executive director of the Global Footprint Network (GFN), an organization that promotes a world where all people have the opportunity to live satisfying lives within the ecological capacity of the Earth. GFN is working to make the ecological footprint tool more scientifically rigorous and practically applicable, so that the ecological footprint will be as prominent a measuring device as is the gross domestic product. In 2005, the GFN began a 10-year project ("Ten in Ten Campaign") that, by 2015, aims to have 10 countries managing their ecological wealth in the same way as they manage their finances. GFN has identified 22 countries that are likely to be early adopters of the ecological footprint, including Canada, and over 70 organizations have become formal GFN partners. Some of the world's largest environmental agencies and NGOs already are using the footprint to promote

global sustainability, including the European Environment Agency, the International Council for Local Environmental Initiatives (now known as Local Governments for Sustainability, with 650 members), and the World Wildlife Fund (with 5 million global supporters).

Bill Rees earned his PhD in population ecology at the University of Toronto and has taught at UBC's School of Community and Regional Planning since 1969. Dr. Rees helped to establish the Canadian Society for Ecological Economics, and currently is a Fellow of the Post-Carbon Institute, a founding Fellow of the One Earth Initiative, and a co-investigator in the Global Integrity Project. In 2006, he was elected as a Fellow to the Royal Society of Canada. His teaching and research focus on human ecology and ecological economics, particularly how human demands for resources need to be managed so that sustainability may be achieved. Ecological footprint analysis has re-energized the debate on human carrying capacity, and Professor Rees studies its implications for public policy and sustainability planning. Drawing on several disciplines, Rees is working on a book that asks whether humanity is inherently unsustainable and whether our complex, increasingly knowledge-based society will be able to avoid the cycles of collapse that have characterized previous civilizations. His research examines why our decision-making processes seem unable to respond effectively and creatively to the growing knowledge of global change and crisis. These are difficult questions, but like Mathis Wackernagel, Bill Rees is tackling them head-on in order to accelerate global sustainability.

The challenge is for us to use the ecological footprint tool to shift our behaviours so that we may contribute to a healthy and "wealthy" planet for ourselves and for future generations.

SOURCES: *Global Footprint Network*, Global Footprint Network, 2007, http://www.rrfb.com/pdfs/global_footprint_network.pdf; *Our Team*, One Earth, 2007, http://www.oneearthweb.org/our-team.html; "Ecological Footprints and Appropriated Carrying Capacity: What Urban Economics Leaves Out," W. E. Rees, 1992, *Environment and Urbanization, 4*(2), 121–130; *William E. Rees*, University of British Columbia, School of Community and Regional Planning, 2007, http://www.scarp.ubc.ca/faculty%20profiles/rees.htm; *Our Ecological Footprint: Reducing human impact on the Earth*, M. Wackernagel & W. Rees, 1996, Gabriola Island, BC: New Society.

provincially supported) goal of socially, economically, and environmentally healthy communities. Hundreds of communities across Canada have developed a variety of achievable and practical sustainability strategies through involvement of local citizens and municipal representatives. Even universities, often significant corporate citizens within cities, are getting on board. In the past few years, several Canadian universities have developed sustainability plans to ensure that they demonstrate leadership in sustainable land and resource use, including pesticide and water use, energy generation and use, waste use and handling, emissions, and land use. Plans for upgrading of infrastructure and construction of new infrastructure often require the attainment of new sustainability standards as specified through their sustainability objectives.

Progress toward Urban Sustainability?

In 1976, Vancouver hosted the United Nations Conference on Human Settlements, called Habitat, the first UN forum to examine our response to urban populations. The Third World Urban Forum of the United Nations also was held in Vancouver, in June 2006, demonstrating internationally the ongoing interest of the city and of Canadians in addressing urban sustainability.

Although it is not possible to provide a definitive answer to the question of whether Canadian cities are being planned and managed in ways that are moving them toward greater sustainability, there are encouraging signs that some resource demands and some stresses on both local ecosystems and the global ecosphere are being reduced because of such actions. If we accept various reservations and exceptions, and acknowledge that more needs to be done, progress is evident in water, energy, and materials conservation, and in air and water quality and waste management. Municipalities are continuing to make substantial efforts to conserve and protect environmentally sensitive areas, green space, and natural systems.

As intensification has become a major policy goal, there has been increasing restraint on low-density expansion in the urban fringe. Cities are trying numerous approaches to encourage citizens to use transit, bicycles, and their feet instead of cars. And new techniques and approaches such as environmental assessment, sustainable development policies, and state-of-the-environment reporting are appearing more frequently in municipal operations.

In spite of these successes, there is concern that continuing improvement in energy conservation and in air quality depends on attaining a more compact urban form and a substantial shift in modes of transportation. Municipal and provincial action currently being taken may be insufficient to achieve the required changes. Given current and foreseeable future market forces and consumer preferences, how likely is it that large numbers of people will choose more compact types of housing, or switch from cars to buses or subway trains? Our cities, and the number of cars within them, continue to grow.

Potential effects of global warming for Canadian cities include flooding, depletion or degradation of water supplies, increased energy demands, and deteriorating air quality, all of which may have serious impacts on the economic base in some areas. Actions by individuals, groups, and private and public sectors will shape the extent to which our cities are sustainable. In the final chapter of this textbook, we examine our progress and assess the actions we are taking to advance or detract from sustainability.

Chapter Questions

1. In what ways do cities change their own environment and affect the environment of surrounding areas? How can we plan cities to minimize some of these effects?

2. In what ways is a high-quality life, with reduced waste, reduced energy use, and reduced pollution, both a goal and a challenge?

3. Discuss the ways in which sustainable housing can leave a smaller footprint on the ecosystem than conventional single-family homes. Are there ways in which existing housing in your community could be made more sustainable, environmentally, socially, and economically?

4. Comment on the following statement: natural area habitats in city parks will become more important as wilderness decreases.

5. All over Canada, people are taking action to encourage and promote healthy neighbourhoods. Consider your neighbourhood. What are some of the actions that have been taken—or could be

taken—to reduce the impact of "the car culture"? What could you do to take the lead in your neighbourhood to reduce the effects cars have on the environment and on our health?

6. One of the challenges facing Canadians in urban areas is to reduce the waste stream. How would you design a program for your community that would achieve a 50 percent reduction of the waste stream? What would be the most important factors to take into account?

7. Critically examine the city or town where you go to university. What are the top three priorities to meet economic, social, and environmental criteria for sustainability? Do priorities in one category make priorities in another category difficult to attain? Can you identify actions (e.g., tax systems, policies, programs) that can be used to help meet multiple priorities simultaneously?

8. Do an inventory of community gardens in the city or town where you currently live. How might this program be introduced or expanded? How might gardens help meet economic, social, and environmental objectives?

9. What elements might you include in a sustainability audit of your university?

references

Bakker, K. (2003). Liquid assets. *Alternatives Journal, 29*(2), 17–21.

Balcom, S. (1997, April 12). West Coast experiments with sustainable housing. *Calgary Herald,* p. I13.

Canadian Council of Ministers of the Environment. (1990). *Management plan for nitrogen oxides (NO$_x$) and volatile organic compounds (VOCs). Phase 1.* Winnipeg: Author.

Checora, G. (1996). Calgary house goes beyond sustainability. *Alternatives, 22*(4), 5–6.

City of Toronto. (2000). *Land: Background report. City of Toronto's environmental plan "Clean, Green and Healthy."* Toronto: Author.

David Suzuki Foundation. (2005). *The maple leaf in the OECD: Comparing progress toward sustainability 2005.* http://www .davidsuzuki.org/files/WOL/OECD_EngExec.pdf

Dupuis, O. (2000, Winter). The green housing effect. *Alternatives Journal, 26*(1), 7–8.

Environment Canada. (1991). *The national incinerator testing and evaluation program.* Ottawa: Author.

Environment Canada. (2001a). *The Green Lane: Vehicle Emissions Inspection Clinic program.* http://www.ec.gc.ca/special/emissions_e.htm

Environment Canada. (2001b). *Urban water: Municipal water use and wastewater treatment.* http://www.ec.gc.ca/Ind/English/Urb_H20/ Bulletin/uwind2_e.cfm

Environment Canada. (2007). *2007 municipal water use report.* http:// www.ec.gc.ca/water/en/info/pubs/sss/e_mun2004.pdf

Federation of Canadian Municipalities. (2001). *Partners for climate protection program.* http://www.fcm.ca

Fried, J. J. (1996, January 6). Noise. *Calgary Herald,* p. B4.

Gertler, L. O., Crowley, R. W., & Bond, W. K. (1977). *Changing Canadian cities: The next 25 years.* Toronto: McClelland & Stewart.

Government of Canada. (1996). *The state of Canada's environment— 1996.* Ottawa: Supply and Services Canada.

Government of Canada. (2007). *Canadian environmental sustainability indicators 2007.* http://www.ec.gc.ca/environmentandresources/ CESIFeature2007/CESI2007_e.pdf

Government of Ontario. (2001). *Environmental compliance reports.* http://www.ene.gov.on.ca/

Greater Vancouver Regional District. (1994). *Let's clear the air: Draft air quality management plan—Summary document.* Vancouver: Author.

Green Communities Association. (2001). http://www.gca.ca

IBI Group. (1990). *Greater Toronto area urban structure concepts study—Summary report.* Toronto: Greater Toronto Coordinating Committee.

Kerr, S. (1998, April). Cohousing: Build your own community. *Encompass Magazine,* 6–7.

McGill University. (1999, Summer). McGill news. *Alumni Quarterly.* www.mcgill.ca/alumni/news/s99/ecoresidence.htm

McKitrick, R. (2007). *Air pollution policy in Canada: Improving on success.* http://www.uoguelph.ca/~rmckitri/teaching/CdnAirPolicy.pdf

National Round Table on the Environment and the Economy (NRTEE). (2003). *Environmental quality in Canadian cities: The federal role.* Ottawa: Author.

New Economy Development Group. (2001, January). *Progress report on PRI's Sustainability Project on Sustainable Communities.*

Patterson, B. (1995, November 14). Sound off. *Victoria Times Colonist,* p. C1.

Richardson, N. (1989). *Land use planning and sustainable development in Canada.* Ottawa: Canadian Environmental Advisory Council.

Shideler, K. (1997, March 15). Common noise and "boom cars" cause hearing loss. *Calgary Herald,* p. C9.

Speake, S., & Gismondi, M. (2005). Water: A human right. In D. Davidson & K. Hatt (Eds.), *Consuming sustainability: Critical social analyses of ecological change* (pp. 47–69). Halifax: Fernwood.

Statistics Canada. (1995). *Households and the environment 1994.* Statistics Canada Cat. no. 11-526. Ottawa: Statistics Canada, Household Surveys Division.

Statistics Canada. (2006). *Earth Day … by the numbers.* http:// www42.statcan.ca/smr08/smr08_023_e.htm

Statistics Canada. (2007). *EnviroStats, 1*(1). http://www.statcan.ca/ english/freepub/16-002-XIE/16-002-XIE2007001.pdf

Statistics Canada. (2008, March 27). Study: Composting organic waste 2006. *The Daily.* http://www.statcan.ca/Daily/English/080327/ d080327c.htm

Sustainable Calgary. (n.d.a). *About us.* http://www.sustainablecalgary.ca/Page-3.html

Sustainable Calgary. (n.d.b). *Our projects: Sustainability indicator research.* http://www.sustainablecalgary.ca/Page-53.html

Taus, M., & R. McClure. (2002). When it rains, it pours pollutants into the waters. *Seattle Post.* http://seattlepi.nwsource.com/local/95883_sound20.shtml

Turner, J. (1996, August 28). Tide is turning against industrial waterfront. *The Globe and Mail,* p. A2.

United Nations Development Program (UNDP). (2007). *Human Development Report 2006. Beyond scarcity: Power, poverty and the global water crisis.* http://hdr.undp.org/hdr2006/statistics/countries/data_sheets/cty_ds_CAN.html

Warren, C. L., Kerr, A., & Turner, A. M. (1989). *Urbanization of rural land in Canada 1981–1986.* SOE Fact Sheet No. 89-1. Ottawa: Environment Canada, State of the Environment Directorate.

Workers' Compensation Board of B.C. (2003). *Hear for good: Preventing exposure at work.* http://www.worksafebc.com/publications/Health_and_Safety_Information/by_topic/assets/pdf/hear_for_good.pdf

CHAPTER 14

Meeting Environmental Challenges

Chapter Contents

"[Achieving sustainability] ... now requires harmonizing the insistent demands of poverty and capitalism with the quiet obligations of the biotic community. Heeding those obligations requires an uncommonly broad perspective, one that takes seriously the social institutions, human needs and biogeography. . . . I do not propose that single individuals embrace all these qualities. But how to organize the skills and commitments of a diverse human community to strive for these uncommon aims is a challenge we are only beginning to address."

Kai Lee (1999, n.p.)

Chapter Objectives

After studying this chapter you should be able to

- document progress made in safeguarding our environment
- consider challenges posed to action by the lack of systematic about information and trends regarding the environment
- discuss the increasing depth of understanding about environmental challenges and solutions
- describe multiple roles that citizens, governments, and the private sector might play in protecting the environment
- identify current models and practices that can help to achieve sustainability
- identify actions you can take to maintain momentum toward sustainability

INTRODUCTION

Every day, each Canadian makes lifestyle choices that have substantial environmental effects, choices that relate to the kind of housing we live in, the foods we eat, the appliances we use, the household products we select, and the means of transportation we favour. Every one of these choices may seem insignificant, but cumulatively these choices have an important influence on the sustainability of our future environment. The same is true of the kinds of decisions that local organizations, private firms, governments at all levels, and public agencies make in their daily operations.

Protecting and sustaining the quality of our environment is a serious challenge for all Canadians. Balancing economic and social well-being and the integrity of the ecological systems that support our economy and society requires all of us to come to grips with the fundamental issues involved in achieving sustainability. Not only do we need to think globally and act locally, cognizant of the impacts our actions may have on others and on our environment, but we also need to work together in a cooperative and collaborative fashion. Achieving sustainability goals requires new, "greener" ways of thinking, making decisions, and acting on these choices. We must rectify mistakes we made long ago that still have lasting effects today; we need to pass on better systems of management for our children's children. Will we meet these challenges?

After identifying environmental protection and sustainability as key challenges, this chapter describes the mixed progress we have made in safeguarding the Canadian environment. We suggest that there is a need to reconceptualize environmental problems to address questions related to our motivations, beliefs, and behaviours. We discuss how science, values, and public policymaking are often blended in decisions about the environment, and this mix creates challenges for taking action. Next, we describe how various groups—governments, Aboriginal peoples, private firms, and ENGOs—can and do take responsibility for the environment. Embedded in this discussion are strategies that have worked and can continue to improve our prospects for achieving sustainability. Our final section recounts some specific Canadian success stories and emphasizes how individuals and collectives can work together to pursue the goal of sustainability.

Excerpt from "Burying Hell," by Alex Gillis

Generations of the men in my family helped create hell on Earth at the gargantuan steel plant in Sydney, N.S., owned by the Dominion Iron and Steel Company. The sky-high smokestacks that my great-grandfather ... once patched are long gone, but the same cannot be said for one of Canada's most toxic sites: the Sydney tar ponds. They hold 700,000 tonnes of PCBs, dioxins and other pollutants. Nearby residents suffer some of Canada's highest rates of cancer, birth defects and miscarriages. They have seen orange liquid seeping through their basement walls, rain puddles turn fluorescent green and the lobsters they trap contaminated with coke-oven chemicals....

The furnaces emitted sticky mauve, white or red dust three times a day, the colour dependent on how hot the furnaces were running. Children would head indoors when they saw it blowing their way. It covered the city like a fine sand, stung the eyes and clung to cars....

My relatives in Sydney ... have long wondered where 700,000 tonnes of hell will go. Well, now they know. After decades of controversial negotiations, the federal and provincial governments are spending $400 million to cap the tar ponds. Intrepid souls will dig more than two kilometres of channels through the ponds and erect

Photo 14–1
A sign at the entrance to the Sydney tar ponds

immense underground walls, before capping the entire site with either layers of high-density polyethylene or clay and then gravel and oil. When completed, the old ponds will become 100 hectares of prime development property. Hell will have been paved over.

In the 21st century, Canadians have the opportunity to do better. Indeed, if we wish to achieve sustainability, we must.

SOURCE: Excerpt from "Burying Hell," by Alex Gillis. *Canadian Geographic*, May/June 2007, p. 98. © Alex Gillis. Used with permission.

PROGRESS IN SAFEGUARDING CANADA'S ENVIRONMENT

Enviro-Focus 14 is powerful and poignant. Rather than become depressed by this personal story of the Sydney tar ponds, however, we can use this message to stimulate action. In many cases across Canada, we *have* made progress in our understanding of how human activities affect the environment and in our ways of addressing these effects. Since the 1970s, environmental awareness, conservation, and protection have become increasingly important elements in economic and social decision making. As scientific understanding of ecosystem dynamics and complexity has grown, the need to take an ecosystem

approach to environmental issues has been impressed on many decision makers. As a result, in addition to seeking legislative and technical solutions, Canadians are promoting cooperation among governments, industry, ENGOs, and communities. Public education and action also are being fostered, various economic instruments developed, and voluntary codes of conduct established.

Environment Canada's 2003 report *Environmental Signals: Canada's National Environmental Indicator Series 2003* tracked key environmental issues through the use of various indicators. The list is not exhaustive and there are gaps, such as in tracking human health effects of environmental change. Furthermore, the findings may seem dated, as they illustrate trends from 1990 to 2000. We will have to wait a few more years to determine the trends in the first decade of the 21st century from this source. Nevertheless, the report does provide some guidance about where we are achieving positive results and what kinds of work remain to be done. Table 14–1 summarizes some of the key points in relation to air quality, water quality, biological diversity, and climate change.

AIR QUALITY

Regulatory changes by the federal and provincial/territorial governments, supported by technological advances in the private sector as well as by partnership actions involving industries, ENGOs, and communities, are among the efforts that have brought about reductions in the production and emission of many air contaminants. On an international level, for instance, Canada has exceeded its commitments to reduce ozone-depleting substances, and is meeting or exceeding both domestic and international targets for emissions that contribute to acidic precipitation.

Canada participates in other international efforts that are expected to improve air quality, including control

Photo 14–2
What are the long-term implications for human health of elevated smog and pollution levels (in this case, in Toronto)?

of the long-range transport of pollutants (heavy metals, pesticides such as DDT, and persistent organic contaminants such as PCBs). Domestically there have been some important improvements in air quality, such as the virtual

TABLE 14–1
SUMMARY OF CANADA'S ENVIRONMENTAL SIGNALS, 1990–2000

Environmental Issue Area	Improvement Trend and Indicator[1]	Challenges
Air quality		
Acid rain	Trend: Improving (+15%) Indicator: Trend in total emissions	• Critical loadings lower than originally understood, requiring further reductions • NO_x deposition rate threatens to override gains made by SO_x reduction • Interaction of acid deposition, climate change, and stratospheric ozone depletion emphasizes need for multi-issue approach
Stratospheric ozone	Trend: No change Indicator: Trend in Canadian values	• Global implications make problem resolution more difficult, despite Canada's proactive approach • Climate change may drive ozone loss • Lack of reporting • Smuggling of ODSs by some countries
Urban air quality	Trend: No change Indicator: Regional trends of ground-level ozone, total suspended particulate, NO_x and SO_x emissions	• Better understanding of chemistry of pollutants and consequences of synergistic effects is needed
Passenger transportation	Trend: Deteriorating (−10%) Indicator: Trend in automobile use	• Government initiatives to increase use of public transportation have been virtually ineffective • Automobile use has increased by 9% since 1990 • Decrease in this sector by 1.1% is attributed to popularity of SUVs and minivans

(continued)

TABLE 14–1
(CONTINUED)

Environmental Issue Area	Improvement Trend and Indicator[1]	Challenges
Water quality		
Municipal water use	Trend: Improving (+4%) Indicator: Percentage change in per capita water use	• Cost to municipal consumers does not reflect supply costs— Canadian water costs are currently among the lowest in the world • Increase in use efficiency is needed • Climate change effects on water quality and quantity are unknown • Most coastal municipalities have no water treatment
Municipal wastewater treatment	Trend: Improving (+20%) Indicator: Percentage change in proportion of population with secondary or tertiary sewage treatment	• Effects of treatment chemicals released into the environment are unknown • Existing water treatment infrastructure is "faltering"
Biological diversity	Trend: Improving (+70%) Indicator: Increase in strictly protected areas	• 64 percent of strictly protected areas are under 10 km^2 and are inadequate for large mammal protection • More than half of Canada's identified ecoregions have little or no protection • Trend assessment does not include other important indicators, including COSEWIC data • No reliable baseline data exist against which to measure habitat loss, species status, range, or population sizes, indicating the need for more research • Existing databases are difficult to compare
Climate change	Trend: Deteriorating (−20%) Indicator: Percentage change in greenhouse gas emissions	• Changing the energy and other resource consumption habits of individuals • Program tracking for successful initiatives • Better understanding of regional impacts
Sector industries		
Forestry	Trend: Improving (+30%) Indicator: Percent of strictly protected area in all four forest ecozones	• Forest contribution to overall ecosystem health not well quantified • Forest health indicators not encompassed in trend evaluation include change in forest species (no change) and harvesting rates (still increasing)
Agricultural soils	Trend: Improving (+20%) Indicator: Number of days soil left unprotected by vegetation	• Data collection excludes identification of smaller-scale degradation problems • Many soil health indicators are not included in trend assessment (e.g., residual nitrogen, soil organic matter, salinization, nutrient levels)
Energy	Trend: Deteriorating (−10%) Indicator: Canadian energy consumption	• Energy efficiency is improving, but energy use is still increasing • Fundamental shift in thinking is necessary to decrease fossil fuel dependency and expand use of alternative energies
Fisheries	Not included	
Mines and minerals	Not included	

[1] Numerical values are a description of one indicator only and are not necessarily a reflection of total issue trends. They are used by Environment Canada to highlight the rate of progress occurring on a specific issue.

SOURCE: *Environmental Signals: Canada's National Environmental Indicator Series 2003*, © Her Majesty the Queen in Right of Canada, Environment Canada, 2003. Reproduced with the permission of the Minister of Public Works and Government Services Canada, 2008. www.ec.gc.ca/soer-ree/English/Indicator_series/default.cfm

disappearance of lead from Canadian air following the 1990 phase-out of lead as a gasoline additive for road vehicles.

Nevertheless, smog levels and particulate matter remain important air quality issues. The Bay of Fundy, lower Fraser Valley, and Windsor–Quebec corridor are subjected to elevated smog levels partly because of their geographic locations and partly because of pollutants generated in industrial, transportation, and energy production activities. The expectation that use of the more than 15 million cars in Canada will increase means that ground-level ozone problems could worsen. Another important issue is the particulate matter in our air that constitutes a known public health issue. In order to have Canadian objectives for particulate levels in our air reflect current understanding of health effects, a federal–provincial working group recommended new objectives. In May 2000, additional national efforts to reduce particulate matter were announced. The federal ministers of both environment and health jointly announced their intention to declare toxic all particulate matter less than 10 microns in size. As well, federal, provincial, and territorial governments ratified the Canada-wide Standard for Particulate Matter less than or equal to 2.5 microns in diameter, and agreed to meet the standard by the year 2010 (Green Lane, 2001).

WATER QUALITY

Both freshwater bodies and oceans have benefited from efforts to clean up and prevent pollution from cities, industries, and agriculture. As a result of stronger laws, increasing demands for greener products, and behavioural changes, there have been important reductions in the levels of many emissions. The forest industry's reduction in discharges of dioxins and furans is an example of the improvements made. Some impacts of the minerals and metals industry on watersheds have been reduced also. Public participation in watershed management and rehabilitation efforts has been an important factor in reduction of pollutants entering fresh and ocean waters.

However, significant stresses on our aquatic ecosystems continue to challenge us. Our per capita levels of water use remain among the highest in the world, even though commercial and industrial users have improved their efficiency and reduced consumption. We still have untreated municipal and industrial wastewater entering water bodies, and both surface water and groundwater supplies continue to be subject to contamination. Fish and wildlife are known to be experiencing reproductive problems as a result of endocrine disruptors entering water bodies; this decrease in reproduction could endanger the survival of some species (Colborn, vom Saal, & Soto, 1993).

The Walkerton experience (see Chapter 7) provided an important impetus for Canadian jurisdictions to (re)assess their drinking water policies and standards.

Photo 14–3
We need to protect both our sources and our sinks of water.

Some provinces strengthened drinking water laws; however, no binding national standards exist (Boyd, 2003).

BIOLOGICAL DIVERSITY

Loss of biodiversity is a complex issue and is a consequence of most of the impacts discussed in this text. The decline in biodiversity in Canada is a continuing concern: in 2003, COSEWIC listed 431 species at risk, up from 380 in 2000 and from 402 in 2002. By 2007, 521 plant and animal species were identified as at risk in Canada and 13 are already extinct (see Chapter 12). Some of the reasons for these losses include direct overexploitation of species, such as those that have been hunted or fished to extinction. Others have declined because of indirect impacts: their habitat has been lost to urban or industrial processes or their habitat has been degraded through pollution.

The World Wildlife Fund conducted its first Nature Audit in 2003. The goal of the project was to assess Canada's success in meeting its national and international commitments to conserve biological diversity. The audit concluded that while significant commitments to conserve nature have been made, Canada has struggled to achieve "on-the-ground success at the scale of intervention required to adequately respond to the conservation need of the nation" (World Wildlife Fund, 2003, p. 2).

Although Environment Canada (2003) indicates that there has been a 70 percent increase in strictly protected area since 1992 (the indicator for biological diversity), 64 percent of that protected area is under 10 square kilometres in area and is inadequate for large mammal protection. The Canada Species at Risk Act (SARA), ratified in 2002, in conjunction with the National Accord for the Protection of Species at Risk, may help to provide the requisite protection for wildlife and their habitat. SARA is intended to fulfill part of Canada's obligations under the United Nations Convention on Biological Diversity.

Photo 14–4a

Photo 14–4b

With direct and dedicated action, we can protect the homes and species of those who share this planet. These photos depict the eastern loggerhead shrike and the plains bison.

Building on various existing initiatives, the Canadian Biodiversity Strategy draws on the commitment of a broad range of interests. Quebec and British Columbia were the first provinces to report formally on how they were implementing the strategy and the convention. However, there are inadequate baseline habitat data against which to measure changes in biological diversity, insufficient information on how humans affect ecosystem processes, and little knowledge to determine the critical thresholds. Indeed, information is lacking on most of Canada's species, their status, behaviours, ranges, population sizes, and trends (Environment Canada, 2003).

One challenge is that the species at risk legislation is limited in scope as it applies only to aquatic and terrestrial habitats within areas of federal jurisdiction. Additionally, SARA emphasizes cooperation among all

parties, from the territorial and provincial governments, to Aboriginal peoples, farmers, scientists, environmental groups, and industry, in establishing recovery programs for species at risk. While the involvement of a diversity of groups is key to achieving SARA'S aims the lack of real penalties provides no incentives for compliance. Also, as described later, firm application of this legislation requires the federal government to be assertive in claiming its mandate for environmental protection—something that it has been reluctant to do in the face of provincial interests.

Another example of progress in Canadian efforts to protect biodiversity has been the increase in protected space. In 1970, 23 parks made up the Canadian national parks system; by 2007, there were 42 national parks and six marine protected areas. Growth in establishment of protected areas in Canada over the period 1990–2000 is illustrated in Figure 14–1. Individual provinces have added or expanded over 285 park areas to their protected spaces systems; between 1995 and 2000, for instance, British Columbia added about 11.7 million hectares as part of its effort to preserve species at risk and conserve representative ecosystems (B.C. Parks, 2001). A challenge will be understand how best to set aside areas for habitat in a changing climate. Although federal tax law changes now encourage donations of ecologically sensitive land, many ecosystems (particularly in the more heavily populated parts of the country) continue to be unprotected. *Environmental Signals* (Environment Canada, 2003) indicates that more than half of Canada's identified ecoregions have little or no protection. We continue to lose lands due to urban expansion, and the protection of wetland habitats remains uncertain.

Yet, establishing parks is only one component to protecting biodiversity. Throughout the country, government agencies, landowners, ENGOs, and citizens are working together to protect habitat and establish recovery plans for species at risk. For example, significant efforts have been made to protect the eastern loggerhead shrike, located mainly (although not exclusively) in Ontario. This bird, which numbered only 17 breeding pairs in 1997, slowly has been making a comeback as a result of a range of strategies, including habitat maintenance, reduced use of chemicals on roads, road signs to reduce speed on roadways running through their habitat, and a captive breeding program that releases hatchlings into the wild. Similarly, in southern Saskatchewan, in the newly created Old Man on His Back Conservation Area, 50 plains bison were reintroduced in December 2003 from a purebred herd from Elk Island National Park in Alberta. This initiative required cooperation from local landowners, a large donation of land from a local family, government financial and logistical support, fundraising and long-term commitment to habitat protection by ENGOs, and sustained efforts by producers to maintain the grassland ecosystem in the region. The long-term

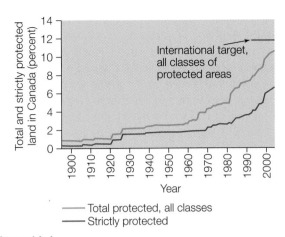

Figure 14–1

Growth in establishment of protected areas in Canada

NOTE: Strictly protected areas include nature reserves, wilderness areas, national parks, many provincial parks, and natural monuments. Other protected areas include habitat/species management areas, protected landscapes and seascapes, and managed resource areas.

SOURCE: *Environmental Signals: Canada's National Environmental Indicator Series 2003,* page ix. © Her Majesty the Queen in Right of Canada, Environment Canada, 2003. Reproduced with the permission of the Minister of Public Works and Government Services Canada, 2008. www.ec.gc.ca/soer-ree/English/Indicator_series/new_issues.cfm?issue_id=1&tech_id=1#bio_pic

Photo 14–5

Climate change may contribute to increased number and severity of storms affecting coastal regions in Canada. A storm in December 2006 in Vancouver caused extensive damage to the Seawall and the terrestrial ecosystem of Stanley Park, including many downed trees. (Compare with Photo 13–11, p. 548).

success of this reintroduction is still to be determined, but both examples demonstrate that commitment and creative collaboration *can* help to stem the biodiversity losses we have witnessed.

CLIMATE CHANGE

Canada's concerns regarding climate change have been addressed frequently throughout this text, particularly in the chapters on atmosphere (Chapter 5) and energy (Chapter 11). Climate change and sustainability are the focus here.

The Intergovernmental Panel on Climate Change has reported the international consensus that human activities clearly influence global climate. If projections are correct, and Canada experiences greater temperature changes than most regions of the world, the implications could be numerous. Among the potentially most severe consequences are more heat waves; increased storms, floods, and droughts; major shifts in fisheries, forestry, and agricultural resource bases; and damage to northern ecosystems.

The challenges we face in reducing anthropogenic sources of greenhouse gases are significant. With approximately 89 percent of total greenhouse gas emissions in Canada attributed to transportation and fossil fuel production and consumption, and with our large land mass, cold climate, and increasing population, reducing use of

fossil fuels is difficult. While progress has been made in fuel efficiency, Canada's greenhouse gas emissions have risen steadily since the 1980s (see Figure 14–2, next page). By the end of 2001, Canada's greenhouse gas emissions were 18.6 percent over 1990 levels and 26.9 percent higher than Kyoto Protocol target levels, precluding Canada from meeting its commitment under the UN Convention on Climate Change. By 2005, Canada's greenhouse gas emissions were 747 megatonnes, representing an increase of 25.3 percent over 1990 levels, and 32.7 percent above Kyoto targets (Environment Canada, 2007). While the rate of growth in emissions has been levelling off during a time when Canada's economy has been expanding, it is clear that Canada cannot continue to increase its emissions and maintain national and international credibility on climate change issues.

In an effort to improve Canada's performance in greenhouse gas reduction, the federal government introduced Action Plan 2000 to provide funding and education for individuals and businesses to help reduce their greenhouse gas emissions (Green Lane, 2003). Federal–provincial–territorial cooperation remains an important component in strengthening and expanding the Climate Change Plan for Canada. Climate change will be an increasingly critical political issue, as action to curb climate change will affect the oil and gas industry in Alberta (and other provinces) and the car manufacturing industry in Ontario. This issue will test the mettle of federal regulators against that of provincial governments, who argue that the Constitution places the right to exploit resources and to support industry firmly within their jurisdiction.

While Canadian governments may wrangle, other jurisdictions provide inspiration. In 2005, Sweden announced its ambitious strategy to be fossil fuel free

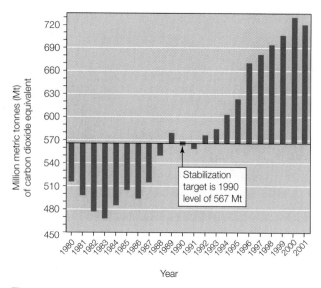

Figure 14–2

Greenhouse gas emissions 1980–2001: Comparison to stabilization target

SOURCES: *Building Momentum: Sustainable Development in Canada,* Government of Canada, Department of Foreign Affairs and International Trade, 1997, p. 5; *Canada's Greenhouse Gas Inventory, 1990–2001,* Greenhouse Gas Division, Environment Canada, August 2003, p. vii, http://www.ec.gc.ca/pdb/ghg/ 1990_0:_report/ 1990_01 report_e.pdf; *1990–2001 GHG Emission Estimates for Canada,* Greenhouse Gas Division, Environment Canada, July 2003, Summary Tables, http://www.ec.gc.ca/pdb/ghg/ canada_2001_e.cfm; *Canada's Greenhouse Gas Inventory: 1997 Emissions and Removals with Trends,* F. Neitzert, K. Olsen, & P. Collas, April 1999, Pollution Data Branch, Greenhouse Gas Division, Environment Canada, p. 73, http://www.ec.gc.ca/pdb/ghg/english/Docs/gh_eng.pdf; *Canada's Greenhouse Gas Inventory, 1990–1998: Final Submission to the UNFCC Secretariat,* Pollution Data Branch, Environment Canada, Greenhouse Gas Division, October 2000, pp. vii, ix, http://www.ec.gc.ca/pdb/ghg/english/ Docs/CGHGI_Vol1_Web_Eng.pdf

by 2020. According to Swedish reports, in the 1970s, 77 percent of Sweden's energy came from oil. By 2003, oil accounted for only 32 percent of Sweden's power supply, while renewable sources provided 26 percent of the country's energy requirements. The Swedish government aims to increase reliance on renewable sources by providing tax incentives, direct investments, and research to realign its economy. Vehicles are being manufactured to run on biofuels, and home heating systems are being converted to biomass and geothermal sources. Whether Sweden will meet its target is still uncertain. However, the Swedish example clearly shows that, in Canada, significant progress on climate change issues depends on finding ways for provincial, territorial, and federal governments to work together with citizens and private industry.

As noted in the preceding sections, loss of biodiversity, water quantity and quality, and climate change figure most prominently among the multiple environmental issues lacing Canada. Our renewable resource sectors— agriculture, forestry, and fishing—rely on the ongoing availability of our biological endowment. Overexploitation

of our renewable resources—be they soils, timber, or fish—will deplete resources and threaten the sustainability of our economy and society. For example, unsustainable harvesting practices contributed in large part to the declines in the fish resource off the Atlantic coast that subsequently led to the closure of some key fisheries, and resulted in severe socioeconomic effects in coastal communities. The seriousness of unsustainable harvesting practices became apparent in early 2003 when, after 10 years of closed commercial cod fisheries, two populations of Atlantic cod had failed to recover. In May 2003, COSEWIC placed both populations on the endangered species list (COSEWIC, 2003).

Collapse of the northern cod stocks provided concrete evidence of how important it is to live within our ecological endowment or biocapacity—to have resource management strategies and regulations that act to conserve resources. This is a challenge that, to some degree, has been reflected in the Atlantic Groundfish Strategy and the Oceans Management Strategy, as both have given important emphasis to conservation. Living within our means—finding economically and environmentally sound ways to use resources—results in challenges for the future such as generating adequate and scientifically sound knowledge on which to base decisions about sustainable use, undertaking appropriate measuring and monitoring, and strictly enforcing regulations regarding specific resources. If solutions to these sustainability challenges can be met, then it should not be necessary to take such drastic measures as closure of the fishery.

The availability of water is key to meeting our basic needs and to providing for ongoing resource use. Water is a limiting factor for several sectors, including agriculture, oil and gas development, and hydroelectric generation. It is also a key factor in the pattern and expansion of urban

Photo 14–6

Do we know where our water comes from and where our wastes go?

Photo 14–7

Consulting residents with knowledge of local ecosystems is a critical component of the decision-making process.

areas. Pressure will be placed on Canada to export its water resources, and some commentators have predicted that clean water will be as precious a commodity in the 21st century as oil is now. Infrastructure in Canadian cities and small towns is aging, and there is a need to invest in upgrading of facilities and training to ensure safe drinking water for future generations.

Finally, climate change will alter the availability and quality of all our resources, including our biodiversity and accessibility to water. We need to have both a better understanding of the regional changes that will take place and a stronger commitment to make the necessary changes in policies and lifestyles. Achieving this commitment is particularly difficult as, until recently, discussions about climate change have been fraught with rhetoric that climate change is a myth. The costs of doing nothing may be significant, but they are not yet clearly visible to consumers and policymakers. Pressures placed on all levels of government to expand industry in Canada make it particularly difficult to introduce policies and practices to change current lifestyles and job opportunities (recall the discussion of the staples trap in Chapter 4). And thus far, the Canadian public has not clearly articulated a desire to change. This challenge illustrates the complexity of understanding environmental problems and actions that can be taken to move toward a sustainable society.

RECONCEPTUALIZING ENVIRONMENTAL CHALLENGES

As we have described from the outset of this book, sustainability is a multifaceted concept that requires attention to environmental, social, and economic dimensions. Our strategies need to be integrative, adaptive, and

founded on good scientific and traditional or local knowledge (see Table 14–2 on the next page). Achieving sustainability will require collaboration among a range of stakeholders, as well as a reconceptualization of environmental challenges, so that we seek new ways of thinking about environmental problems and identify new kinds of solutions to address them.

MEASURING, MONITORING, AND REPORTING ON ENVIRONMENTAL CHANGE

Effective environmental management requires accurate and relevant information. Taking account of our environmental situation and reporting publicly about it are two key elements in understanding and addressing environmental challenges and change. The few key steps illustrated in Figure 14–3 (p. 570) helps us to raise awareness; identify trends; consider benefits and costs of (in)action; set baselines, goals, and targets; and monitor our successes and failures. Each of the strategies for environmental management described in Chapter 1—the ecosystem approach, environmental impact assessment and adaptive management, and shared governance—relies on measuring, monitoring, and reporting. Science has a key role to play as, in theory at least, having more information about our world and environmental change will help to ensure that future decision makers are better informed about potential consequences of actions than were their predecessors.

Environmental indicators can provide concise, understandable, scientifically credible information that profile the state of the environment and help measure progress toward the goal of sustainability. Indicators give us solid quantitative information, rather than impressions, allowing us to assess strategies and ask questions: Does this strategy or approach work? Can it be adapted successfully in other arenas? If not, what can we change to get better results?

Government cutbacks, reductions, and terminations to monitoring programs during the 1990s resulted in reduced availability of environmental data, reduced monitoring capability, and the loss of national baseline data and ecosystem-specific information required for decision making. These losses make it difficult to know with certainty whether Canada is on an environmentally, economically, and socially sustainable path. We have identified some of the existing information and data gaps in this book; notably, some of these gaps have been filled by ENGOs that have taken the initiative to keep the public and policymakers informed on specific issues. For example, Ecojustice publishes its review of water quality and wastewater every five years. The World Wildlife Fund now regularly calculates and publicly reports on the consumption of ecological capacity by country. These and other efforts are vital if we are to move forward to achieve sustainability.

TABLE 14-2
SUMMARIZING SUSTAINABILITY

Sustainability Characteristics	Sustainability Objectives	Sustainability Approaches	Sustainability Tools

• An ethical principle
• Commitment to equity
• Quality of life and well-being
• Integrated approach to planning and decision making
• Legacy left to future generations
• An international concept
• Respect for others (both humans and other elements of nature).
	• Sustain our natural resources
	• Protect the health of Canadians and ecosystems
	• Promote equity
	• Improve quality of life and well-being.
		• Integrated approach
		   – Involvement of all affected parties in decision making
		   – Full-cost accounting (social, economic, and environmental)
		   – Environmental assessment (social, economic, and environmental)
		• Ecosystem management
		• Measuring, monitoring and reporting
		• Sound science and analysis (regarding key issues, goals, etc.), including traditional (ecological) knowledge
		• Collaboration and cooperation among
		   – Citizens and organizations
		   – Private sector
		   – Governments and Aboriginal people
			•. Policy tools
			   – Voluntary actions of groups, individuals, industry, or communities
			   – Economic instruments
			   – Government expenditure
			   – Legal tools
			   – Environmental auditing
			• Information and awareness tools
			   – Labelling programs
			   – Technology sharing
			   – Sustainability indicators
			• Quality standards
			• Demonstrating sustainable practices

SOURCE: Adapted from *A Guide to Green Government,* Government of Canada, 1995, pp. 4–17.

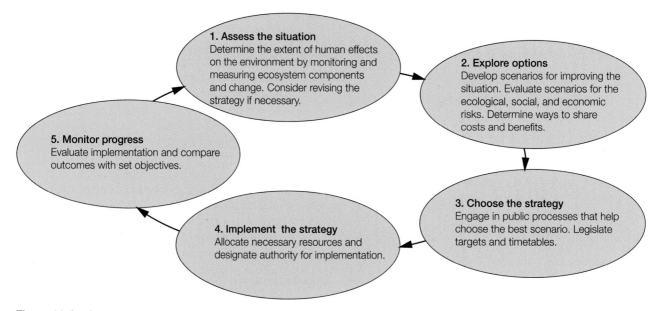

Figure 14–3

Key steps in understanding and taking action on environmental challenges and change

SOURCE: Adapted from *Living Planet Report—2006,* published in October 2006 by WWF–World Wide Fund for Nature (formerly World Wildlife Fund), Gland, Switzerland. © 2006 WWF. All rights reserved.

During the 2000s, however, the federal government began to regain some lost ground. The *Environmental Signals* report has been discussed already in this chapter. In 1995, the Auditor General Act was amended to require federal departments and agencies to establish sustainable development strategies every three years. In 2007, Environment Canada published its fourth strategy (for 2007–9) focusing on six goals related to protecting

Canadians from pollution and waste; providing weather and environmental predictions and services; managing Canada's natural capital; strengthening integrated decision making; helping communities enjoy a prosperous economy; ensuring sustainable development and use of natural resources; and strengthening federal governance and decision making.

Such efforts to measure, monitor environmental changes, establish public reports, and create action plans help to ensure that all steps to taking action, outlined in Figure 14–3, are completed, rather than ending with "monitoring progress" and "assessing situations."

The links between environment and public health also are being revealed. Following up from the World Summit on Sustainable Development in Johannesburg in 2002, an attempt to track environmental influences on children's health culminated in a 2006 report entitled *Children's Health and the Environment in North America*. This report tracks 13 indicators within three priority areas: asthma and respiratory diseases; lead and other chemicals, and waterborne diseases. While there are significant data gaps and concerns about the comparability of the information presented, the report is intended to raise awareness and induce action. Subsequently, in 2007, the ENGO Pollution Probe, along with the Canadian Partnership for Children's Health and Environment, organized a cross-Canada consultation about children's health and environment. This year-long process was designed to engage Canadian citizens in discussion and to produce a report recommending specific ways to reduce and eliminate exposure to toxic substances that may affect the health of Canadian children.

SCIENCE, VALUES, AND POLICYMAKING

Ultimately, addressing environmental challenges requires a reconceptualization of the problems we face. This re-imagining involves more than following a series of rational steps and stages—it requires a fundamental reorientation in our thinking about environmental challenges. Our experience in addressing environmental challenges demonstrates an increasing depth of understanding. Initially, we focused on making relatively simple adjustments to address the most obvious effects of environmental degradation without challenging the basic reasons for them. For example, during the 1960s, the effects of pollution might have been measured and companies might have been compelled to compensate directly government or those suffering from losses in environmental quality. If compensation proved costly, then improvements in technology may have been viewed as a means to address the pollution. Yet, the need for the specific industry or for the basic methods of achieving economic wealth went unchallenged.

Increasingly, we have begun to consider the negative effects of our practices on the health of people and ecosystems. The effects on people's health have been powerful motivators to identify indicators of change and observe the connections between multiple causes and effects. Health implications also have motivated the public to ask questions and prompted policymakers to take action to protect public health. Reconceptualization of environmental challenges means that we include our values and beliefs in understanding and addressing environmental change. Inclusion of values and beliefs is consistent with an ecosystem approach to environmental management.

By understanding human values, beliefs, and attitudes, and how these shape our behaviours toward the environment, we may be able to identify which environmental strategies are most likely to succeed or fail and why. Such understanding also helps to create awareness among decision makers and members of the public that will encourage new ways of thinking and working within our environmental limits. Although this third approach reflects a deeper understanding of environmental issues, it does not happen in isolation of the other two approaches. All three approaches (making adjustments; addressing ecosystem and human health; and understanding human

Photo 14–8

Measuring, monitoring, and reporting are important steps before selecting and implementing strategies for sustainability.

values, beliefs, and attitudes) are necessary to move toward sustainability.

If we are to move forward to address environmental challenges, we must understand at least five key points:

1. Environmental change is natural.

2. Changes, and their effects, occur at multiple levels (cross scales).

3. Environmental challenges are complex, uncertain, and rife with conflicting evidence and points of view.

4. Environmental science plays a key role in understanding environmental change.

5. Science is not sufficient; environmental management requires a judicious mix of science, policy, public debate, and ethics. In short, environmental management is a social challenge.

Environmental change is natural; however, humans have vastly accelerated the rate and scale of change on planet Earth. Within your lifetime, you will witness changes in climate and availability of resources that are unprecedented and unpredictable. The changes that you will witness will occur across temporal and geographic boundaries. Actions taken at one level will have ripple effects elsewhere. For example, what you throw away today may be carried off in waterways or across air currents to affect water or air quality some distance from the point of disposal. Decisions made in company boardrooms in Toronto may affect the ability of your friends to work in a resource industry in rural Canada. The fate of the Sydney tar ponds, and the people living alongside them, was determined largely in Ottawa and Halifax.

Environmental challenges are complex and our understanding is uncertain. In many cases, we lack basic information about the environment that might help inform our decisions. Even if this information is available, we lack understanding of how ecosystem processes work and how they interact with one another. "The fact is, we don't know. Don't have any idea. We don't know when we started doing many of the things we've done. We don't know what we are doing right now or how our present actions will affect the future" (Bryson, 2004, p. 594).

Because our knowledge of the environment is hampered by the lack of scientific understanding, we are unlikely to find simple solutions to environmental problems. We will need to deal with them in the absence of scientific consensus. This is the message behind the precautionary principle: we need to take action before full scientific understanding and consensus is achieved.

It is important to realize that environmental science operates within a highly charged sociopolitical system where "bad news" about the environment may not be addressed by policymakers until it becomes unavoidable. Today, scientists appreciate that their work may well be used in situations in which values and emotions can be as important as (or even more important than) theories, models, and quantitative evidence. Yet, scientists may be

Photo 14–9

Continuing international gatherings, such as the UN climate change conference, highlight growing scientific understanding of the global environment, and reinforce the need to make decisions and taken action with incomplete information.

unprepared for the gap between the principles and practices of "good science" and the realities of "public policy" and politics. The public delays in data releases, and the active silencing of scientists by politicians who refused to make hard decisions about Newfoundland cod populations until they finally crashed, illustrates this phenomenon. The fact that the Scientists' Warning to Humanity, first published in 1993, has resulted in relatively few changes is another case in point. Thus, while scientists and the technology they deliver may assist us to achieve sustainability, they alone cannot remedy environmental problems.

Since scientists tend to ask specific types of questions, science is limited in the kinds of answers it can provide regarding environmental issues. Thus, knowledge beyond scientific knowledge also may be valuable in understanding and addressing environmental challenges. To address many environmental problems, we need to study people's values, attitudes, and behaviours. Additionally, knowledge from other sources may be required for us to understand how environments have changed over time. For example, traditional knowledge has been used in the Arctic to help determine the rate, magnitude, and nature of climate change in that region and to develop land use strategies to address those changes (see Box 14–1). Furthermore, many problems involve political judgments as they require assessment of risks, costs, and benefits associated with different groups—human and nonhuman. These kinds of assessments may be made by social scientists or may be undertaken without reference to formal research.

While science plays a key role in understanding environmental change, advancing sustainability is not merely a technical or scientific exercise. Effective environmental management also requires the ability to recognize, identify, and incorporate different values and interests, while stimulating citizens and public policy decision makers into action.

Sustainable solutions invoke knowledge, innovation, action, interjurisdictional cooperation, and the participation and involvement of key stakeholders, affected communities, and individuals. Involvement of local communities and the incorporation of traditional knowledge in plans for sustainability are acknowledged as vital elements in successful strategies for sustainability. Two agencies in Northern Canada, one a nongovernmental organization (NGO), the other a territorial government, are successfully involving local communities and incorporating traditional knowledge to achieve sustainability objectives.

Devolution was completed in the Yukon in 2003. That means the authority for land and resource management, water rights, and other provincial-type programs and services was transferred from the federal Department of Indian and Northern Affairs to the Yukon territorial government. The NGO Council of Yukon First Nations (CYFN) was instrumental in the negotiations that achieved the necessary transfer of power.

The Council of Yukon First Nations is the "central political organization for the First Nations people of the Yukon" (CYFN, 2003). Originally convened to negotiate land claims and self-government agreements, the CYFN has facilitated First Nations' control over significant proportions of traditional lands. In essence, control of First Nations' traditional lands is now more firmly in their own hands.

The CYFN has expanded its mandate to work in partnership with other organizations that aim to protect and restore the natural environment and promote responsible resource development, particularly in northern Canada. Currently the CFYN is working with other agencies to ensure traditional foods are safe from contaminants introduced into the food chain by long-range transport of airborne pollutants. The CYFN is cooperating with other stakeholders to address climate change. Internationally, working with other Indigenous groups, the CFYN successfully lobbied to have the rights of local communities as holders of traditional knowledge recognized at the World Summit on Sustainable Development in South Africa in 2002.

The effects of climate change are predicted to have profound impacts on northern communities. The CFYN and many other organizations and governments are addressing the climate change issue at many levels. For instance, the territorial government of Nunavut has identified climate change as one of the two most important environmental issues it faces. In response,

the government of Nunavut has developed the Nunavut Climate Change Strategy that will address climate change through scientific research and the use of *Inuit Qaujimajatuqangit* (Inuit knowledge). The strategy embraces the dimensions of sustainability and includes the following principles:

- *Pijitsirniq*—action to control emissions
- *Aajiiqatigiingniq*—opportunities for affected parties to share ideas and be involved in decision making
- *Piliriqatigiingniq*—wise resource use through balance of Inuit knowledge and science
- *Pilimmaksarniq*—enhanced capacity, self-reliance, and empowerment through community involvement and plan implementation

Other principles of the strategy include an approach that is comprehensive, phased, and balanced; engages effective mitigation; and honours the precautionary principle.

Nunavut's other major environmental issue is land use planning. The primary purpose of the Nunavut Land Claim Agreement is "to protect and promote the future well-being of the residents and communities of the Nunavut Settlement Area ... and where necessary, to restore the environmental integrity of the Nunavut Settlement Area" (Nunavut Minister of Sustainable Development, 2003). Nunavut is using the opportunity to learn from mistakes made in southern Canada in developing its land use strategy. "A major flaw throughout much of Canada (with the exception of the north) has been the attempt to address cumulative effects through project specific review in the absence of regional land use plans that *a priori* would have established land use goals and thresholds by which project assessments could be judged as to their acceptability at all, and if acceptable, then under what conditions" (Nunavut Minister of Sustainable Development, 2003).

Land use planning to offset the negative implications of cumulative effects will include effective land use zoning; delineation of thresholds against which proposed project impacts (including small, less regulated projects) will be measured; identification of environmentally sensitive areas; stakeholder consultation to determine which environmental and cultural indicators will be subject to assessment monitoring; and broadened jurisdictional responsibility to reduce interference of wider regional mitigation measures.

SOURCES: Council of Yukon First Nations, personal communication, 2003; Nunavut Minister of Sustainable Development, personal communication, 2003.

PARTICIPANTS IN SAFEGUARDING OUR ENVIRONMENT

Every level of government in Canada is involved in sustainability actions, as are a multitude of nongovernmental organizations, other agencies, and individuals. To improve our performance, we must incorporate ideas of "shared governance" described in Chapter 1 whereby different

groups share in the responsibilities, decisions, and management activities associated with protecting the environment. Here, we briefly describe the potential roles of governments, firms, and organizations.

FEDERAL AND PROVINCIAL GOVERNMENTS

The federal government has an important role to play in environmental protection in Canada. The federal government has Constitutional responsibilities for all environmental components that cross provincial or national boundaries. Such responsibilities can be wide-ranging as they include freshwater lakes and rivers, oceans, air, and migratory animals (fish and birds). However, the government has struggled to implement new strategies in the face of environmental challenges.

In 2000, the Commissioner of Environment and Sustainable Development reported that the federal government had difficulty turning commitments into action. This difficulty is not unique to the federal government; the challenge arises partly because many environmental issues cross borders and affect areas of federal jurisdiction, while resource exploitation and development responsibilities rest primarily with the provincial governments. In a statement to the Canadian Bar Association in August 2007, Peter Lougheed, former premier of Alberta, declared that "a ferocious constitutional clash is all but inevitable, pitting the federal right to protect the environment against the provincial right to develop natural resources" (Makin, 2007, p. A1). Lougheed predicted that resource disputes concerning the right to develop the oil sands in Alberta versus the right of the federal government to use federal legislation to protect the environment will "very likely go before the Supreme Court as a constitutional reference, forcing the court to decide whether the British North

Photo 14–10
Will the federal government act on its authority to protect the environment? Holding a sign on which the globe is melting and a snowy owl proclaims in French, "I'm hot," this protester clearly hopes so.

America Act gives the province the right to develop its energy resources as it sees fit ... and [ultimately] threatening national unity" (Makin, 2007, p. A1).

This is a dire statement, yet it is supported by legal assessments of Canada's environmental efforts. For example, Holden argues that the Canadian federal government displays a degree of timidity in using its environmental powers as a result of concerns about aggravating Quebec nationalism and a desire to avoid confrontation with the provinces and territories about their jurisdiction over natural resources. Holden (2006, p. 74) goes on to say that "federal environmental law prevents a 'race to the bottom' situation where regional [provincial] governments within a nation compete for investment by lowering their environmental standards to attract investment into their borders; it overcomes the potential undue influence that resource extractive industries may have on regional governments; federal environmental law provides more access points for environmentalists who may be disregarded by a regional government; last, in a day and age where international cooperation has become the mantra of environmental protection, it is essential for a national government to have the ability to enforce the obligations it acquires through international agreements."

Both federal and provincial governments have an interest in promoting Canada's economic development. Much of this development is resource based. However, both levels of government also have responsibilities to protect our environment so that it may continue to provide for our economic and social well-being in the future. As explained in Chapter 4, powerful political pressures often favour resource exploitation over protection. Clearly, as Canadians, we need to be well informed and to keep our politicians accountable for decisions they make on our behalf about our environment and resource exploitation. We need to encourage our elected officials to demonstrate effective leadership so that they become part of the strategies for sustainability rather than one of the obstacles to be overcome.

ABORIGINAL PEOPLE

Aboriginal people in Canada have an important and growing role in environmental protection and management. Traditional Aboriginal knowledge, based on long-term occupation, also can help us better understand contemporary changes occurring in the environment.

The Constitutional and treaty rights of Aboriginal people make them "rightholders" in addition to "stakeholders." Governments and resource industries are required to ensure that Aboriginal people are consulted meaningfully about resource use. In some cases, Aboriginal people must retain access to resources (e.g., fish) before other user groups are permitted access. Many of the lands and reserves of Aboriginal people are located close to the sites of resource exploitation, and this proximity often places them at the heart of resource exploitation. Some

Aboriginal peoples work closely with governments and private firms to ensure that they share in the benefits of resource use (e.g., jobs and infrastructure) while ensuring that local ecosystems are not harmed. Other groups may oppose development until treaties have been signed or interim measures agreements between governments and Aboriginal peoples have been established.

Canada has a short history of involving Aboriginal people in environmental management decisions. In many cases, resource exploitation has been undertaken on or near Aboriginal territory without consultation. Sometimes the effects have been devastating, such as when the Bennett dam on the Peace River in northern British Columbia flooded Aboriginal reserves, hunting grounds, and burial sites, or when pollution from a pulp and paper mill contaminated the English-Wabigoon River in northern Ontario with mercury, destroying the Aboriginal food fishery and inflicting many members of the Grassy Narrows First Nation with Minamata disease.

Aboriginal people can use their relatively recent influence to ensure that resource exploitation does not do irreparable harm to the environment in the future. In some cases, they may enter strategic alliances with environmental organizations to have greater influence in decisions and practices affecting the environment. These alliances may be powerful as long as they respect the rights of Aboriginal people to self-determination. Since Aboriginal peoples' values and perspectives are variable, and since their decision making also occurs within a sociopolitical system, they too may encounter the social challenges of environmental management.

A promising trend has been the direct involvement of Aboriginal people in co-managing environmental resources and establishing impact-benefit agreements for resource exploitation. Aboriginal people are involved in co-management arrangements for national parks and protected areas, forestry, fishing, and wildlife management (see Chapters 8 and 9) and have negotiated impact-benefit agreements with mining companies (Chapter 10). These arrangements help to ensure that Aboriginal people are meaningful participants in the protection and use of Canada's environment and that our obligations to social sustainability and justice are met.

MUNICIPALITIES

Municipal governments have important roles to play in environmental protection and management. They are key providers of water and waste management services, and ensure protection of biodiversity within urban settings. Municipalities also take important actions to reduce the public's dependency on fossil fuels by establishing safe public transit and walking/cycling paths that encourage nonmotorized forms of transit, modelling behaviour by adopting biofuels in their buildings and transit fleets,

Photo 14–11
Aboriginal people have rights to resources and lands and will fulfill more significant roles as resource users and managers in the future.

reducing sprawl, and building compact subdivisions that can be accessed easily by foot or public transit. Providing clean water, effective sewage treatment systems, and recycling programs is easier, more efficient, and less costly when people are concentrated in smaller areas rather than dispersed. Recycling programs, for example, can run more efficiently in densely populated centres because large amounts of used glass, paper, plastic, and aluminum cans can be collected from a small area. Passionate local environmental leaders often emanate from large urban population bases; this is one reason why municipalities often have led the way in developing and implementing new initiatives and programs to promote environmental sustainability.

As we saw in previous chapters, there has been mixed success in efforts to improve the sustainability of urban environments. Some of the encouraging results include the trends toward smaller, more energy-efficient homes, more home-based businesses (reduced transportation demands), tighter land use controls, green infrastructure and community planning processes, and growing support of mixed land uses and intensification policies (such as infill and redevelopment of land to support higher population densities). Also, the increasing importance attached to protecting ecologically sensitive areas in urban landscapes has grown even though government resources have declined.

Some of the less encouraging trends include the continued Canadian preference for single-family, detached housing located in low-density neighbourhoods and the establishment of many new businesses in low-density business parks. These trends result in continued reliance on our vehicles and a transportation infrastructure focused less on public transit and more on the automobile. In fact,

Photo 14–12

Cities such as Victoria are building sustainability principles into new housing developments. "The Gorge" area shown here also incorporates walking and recreational pathways for local and regional benefit.

Photo 14–13

In cities such as Vancouver, where the population is growing rapidly, one challenge is to increase density while maintaining quality of life and affordable housing.

municipalities have made numerous efforts to increase use of public transportation. Many of these actions, including higher parking fees and preferential lanes for buses and car pools, have not been very effective in changing people's behaviour. As essential as transportation is to Canada's socioeconomic well-being, our transportation practices seem environmentally unsustainable, particularly with regard to pollution and fuel supply. Despite urban initiatives to reduce our reliance on cars, automobile use increased 9 percent between 1990 and 2000 (Environment Canada, 2003), and continues to rise.

The importance of environmentally sustainable transportation has been reflected in international agreements (such as the Nitrogen Oxide Protocol, the Volatile Organic Compounds Protocol, and the Canada–United States Air Quality Agreement), national efforts (such as the Canadian Environmental Protection Act [CEPA] regulations regarding benzene content of gasoline), as well as regional and local-level initiatives (such as the Air Care Program in British Columbia's Lower Mainland). The Commuter Connections (2001) website provides advice to people wanting to carpool as an alternative to other commuting methods. Commuter Connections supports a registry that matches would-be carpoolers at various postsecondary institutions, including one each in Alberta, Saskatchewan, Nova Scotia, and New Brunswick, nine in British Columbia, four in Ontario, and two in Quebec. The emergence of car cooperatives in larger urban centres (see Chapter 13) is another positive step toward reducing the number of vehicles on the road.

Canadians are among the world's leading producers of domestic waste. National, per capita nonhazardous solid waste generation has increased by 10 percent since 1998 (Environment Canada, 2003). However, since the early 1990s we have seen local gains in recycling through blue

box and other community programs, and small improvements in the amount of home composting. One challenge is to ensure there are markets for recycled materials so that the rates of recycling of paper, glass, metals, and plastics will continue to increase. Another challenge is to ensure recycling opportunities are convenient and readily available to all residents.

At the national level, a variety of targets have been established to stimulate waste reduction by households, industries, and government. For instance, the Canadian Council of Ministers of the Environment has developed the National Packaging Protocol and the National Solid Waste Management Program. By 1996 the National Packaging Protocol goal of a 50 percent reduction in packaging had been achieved by all signatories (Canadian Council of Ministers of the Environment, 2000). The National Solid Waste Management Program had as its objective the reduction in Canadian per capita output of solid waste to 50 percent of the 1988 level by the year 2000. Unfortunately, success has not come as quickly in the Solid Waste Management Program. At its conclusion in 2000, only Nova Scotia had achieved the target (Menyasz, Pole, & Ray, 2000). Nevertheless, the case of the Regional Municipality of Halifax illustrates how a single municipality can make a difference. Faced with the need to create a new landfill, residents and city officials opted to develop a comprehensive waste management strategy that involved a waste reduction and reuse campaign, a recycling program, landfill reduction, and green bin doorstep pickup composting. Halifax's efforts have earned it the distinction of having one of the most innovative waste management strategies in the country and possibly one of the best in North America.

Municipalities also offer opportunities for residents to participate face-to-face in urban planning. Regular council meetings typically are open to the public, while specific development initiatives usually request citizen

Photo 14–14
How can you get involved in your community?

Photo 14–15
Have we introduced our children to the wonders of nature?

involvement. Sustainable community initiatives, eco-developments, and smart growth efforts in cities across the country offer residents a direct voice in designing and shaping their cities for the future.

PRIVATE FIRMS

The private sector has a leadership role to play in sustainability. Indeed, Paul Hawken and Amory and L. Hunter Lovins (1999), among others, demonstrated convincingly that businesses can be profitable—indeed lucrative—by addressing environmental problems in developing their products and services. By taking account of natural capital—the natural resources and ecosystem services that underpin economic activity—private firms can assume leadership roles in environmental protection. Four linked principles have helped firms to protect the environment and improve their productivity: increasing resource productivity through conservation; redesigning industry on biological models with closed loops and zero waste; shifting from the sale of goods (for example, light bulbs) to the provision of services (illumination); and reinvesting in the natural capital that is the basis of future prosperity.

The private sector has developed some highly innovative waste management programs that illustrate these

principles. The 3M Corporation, for example, saved itself $1 million by reducing waste disposal volumes (from 2800 to 115 tonnes per year) at an Ontario manufacturing plant. A U.S. company, Malden Mills, developed fleece fabrics in which at least 89 percent of the material comes from recycled plastic pop bottles. Not only does it take less energy to make the fibres that go into this fabric, it creates 17 times fewer air pollutants. An average-sized jacket keeps 25 two-litre pop bottles out of landfills; every year a pile of pop bottles "the size of a few dozen Boeing 747s gets recycled instead of going to waste" (Malden Mills Industries, Inc., 1994).

New approaches to managing both benign and hazardous wastes are being developed; the life-cycle concept (see Box 14–2 on the next page) and "industrial ecology" (which manages industrial impacts from a more holistic perspective) are among these new developments.

Private firms have addressed, ineffectively, the effects of past industrial practices. Environment Canada reported that in 1989 an estimated 10 000 sites in Canada were potentially contaminated with environmentally harmful substances (Government of Canada, 1991). However, this estimate apparently has remained an estimate. Contaminated sites generally fall under provincial jurisdiction, and, in 2008, no consolidated national assessment of contaminated sites existed. In 1995–96, the office of the Auditor General estimated that potential cleanup costs were in the range of $2 billion (Pilgrim, 1998; Office of the Auditor General, 1996). Harbour bottoms, fuel storage areas, former gasoline stations, closed metal mines, former industrial facilities, railyards, former military bases, Distant Early Warning Line sites, and waste disposal areas are among these contaminated sites. Many are orphan sites; no responsible party can be found that is capable of paying for remediation. The remaining sites require rehabilitation by governments and local landowners. These are expensive exercises that may cost millions of dollars. As the Sydney tar ponds example illustrate, both industry and government provided weak environmental leadership.

BOX 14-2

THE LIFE-CYCLE CONCEPT

The life-cycle concept is a "cradle to grave" approach to thinking about products, processes, and services. The concept recognizes that all life-cycle stages (from extracting and processing raw materials to manufacturing, transportation and distribution, use and reuse, and recycling and waste management) have environmental and economic impacts.

Public policymakers as well as industrial and private organizations can use the life-cycle concept to help them make decisions about environmental design and to make improvements in resource efficiency and pollution prevention. In addition, the life-cycle approach can be used as a scientific tool for gathering quantitative data to inventory, weigh, and rank the environmental burdens of products, processes, and services.

In contrast to the specific approaches to environmental management that occur at the "end of the pipe" or "within the plant gate," decision makers can apply the life-cycle approach to all of the upstream and downstream implications of site-specific actions. For instance, decision makers could examine the changes in emission levels that would result from changing a raw material in the production process.

A variety of specific life-cycle tools have been developed to help decision makers make a difference, including life-cycle assessment (LCA), design for environment, life-cycle cost accounting, total energy cycle assessment, and total fuel cycle assessment. Industries increasingly are using LCA to improve their environmental performance. A life-cycle assessment quantifies energy and resource inputs and outputs at all stages of a life cycle, then determines and weighs the associated impacts to set the stage for improvements.

Box Figure 14–1 shows the division of a product life-cycle inventory (LCI) into inputs and outputs for material and energy, as well as environmental releases. An environmental engineer might use an LCI to baseline the operation's performance against generic data and help guide pollution prevention and process improvements. Similarly, a manufacturer might provide consumers with environmental profiles of finished products based on input/output accounts of its own activities, its materials and energy use, and external data. These environmental profiles could influence product users and also help manufacturers to meet changing customer requirements.

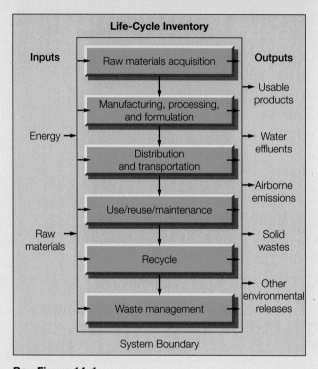

Box Figure 14–1

A product life-cycle inventory

The life-cycle concept has been developed into a framework called EPR, or Extended Producer Responsibility. EPR extends the responsibility for discarded byproducts and end products to the producer rather than to the individual and ultimately to governments. EPR has been used to create successful legislation in 15 Western European countries; in Poland, Hungary, and the Czech Republic; and in Korea, Japan, and Taiwan. The legislation is usually applied first to packaging—similar to the National Packaging Protocol in Canada—and then to electronic equipment and finally to vehicles.

SOURCES: *What Is Life-Cycle Management?* Environment Canada, 1996, http://www.ec.gc.ca/ecocycle/en/whatislcm.cfm; extended producer *responsibility* and *stewardship*, environment canada, *n.d.*, http://www.ec.gc.ca/epr/default.asp?lang=En&n=eebcc813-1

Clearly, industry and government must respond directly to such leadership challenges if the future sustainability of our environment is to be secured.

ENVIRONMENTAL NONGOVERNMENTAL ORGANIZATIONS

Despite the vocal protests against the logging of old-growth forests, not all environmental nongovernmental organizations (ENGOs) are focused on wilderness protection. Many Canadian ENGOs began by focusing attention on urban environmental issues. Now an organization with over 25 000 supporters, Pollution Probe was founded in 1969 by a small group of students at the University of Toronto. Their initial efforts focused on banning DDT from urban and agricultural applications, removing phosphates in detergents, and undertaking campaigns to improve air quality in Toronto. Pollution Probe currently focuses on key issues of air and water quality, climate change, and energy consumption. Similarly, the Society for Environmental Conservation (SPEC) was founded in 1969 in Coquitlam, British Columbia. While its primary focus is "urban sustainability," SPEC's activities have included lobbying against offshore oil expansion, reducing the use of hazardous pesticides, opposing freeway construction in favour of improved public forms of transit, and creating urban demonstration projects. Once considered the domain of "eco-freaks," ENGOs have now claimed a legitimate standing in environmental debates.

Increasingly, ENGOs are applying their members' energy and expertise to participatory planning mechanisms in which industry, government, community, and ENGOs work together to resolve environmental and land use issues. Many ENGOs view their major contributions to the environmental movement in terms of advocacy for environmental responsibility and leadership, education and building awareness of the possibility of various environmental initiatives, and research and monitoring. Others serve as watchdogs, catalysts, information providers, and nonpartisan observers. ENGOs also have the ability to work at various scales, and their small-scale and grassroots initiatives often serve as models for other agencies. Typically, ENGOs are not constrained by political frameworks and can be effective where politically restrained governments cannot. ENGOs also provide important voices in political decision making, sometimes through roundtables dealing with environmental, social, and economic issues, sometimes through formal hearings, and sometimes through local cleanup or other "action" days.

An important role of ENGOs, particularly as governments have reduced their monitoring efforts, has

been raising public awareness by establishing and publishing environmental indicators and reports. Many ENGOs have established credibility with industry and government as well as citizens, allowing them to work effectively as partners in identifying and implementing solutions to environmental challenges and to overcome perceptions that ENGOs are merely obstacles to economic development.

TOWARD SHARED GOVERNANCE FOR SUSTAINABILITY

Moving forward to address current and future environmental sustainability issues requires the inclusion of affected stakeholders in planning and implementing resource development projects. Not only does public involvement reduce the risk of community opposition and legal challenges, it also provides opportunities for the expression and inclusion of new ideas and innovative solutions to challenges we confront. Several initiatives involve the public in different ways. Some initiatives, such as public open houses related to Parks Canada management activities, are undertaken to ensure that the public is aware of actions being taken. Other initiatives may involve the public more directly, as in co-management approaches and practices in northern communities, or the Model Forest Program across the country. Such initiatives not only reflect public input but also provide opportunities to practise ecosystem and adaptive management.

Shared decision-making processes that integrate environmental, economic, and social considerations in the management of natural resources and ecosystems are the basis of achieving sustainability in Canada. Examples of the kinds of environmentally sensitive decision making required range from the Crombie Commission in Toronto; to Vision 2020 statements from such diverse communities as Hamilton, Ontario, and Canmore, Alberta; to the University of British Columbia's Task Force on Healthy and Sustainable Communities. These planning efforts, as well as concepts championed in such documents as the World Conservation Strategy, *Our Common Future*, and Agenda 21, have resulted in improved understanding of the need to make changes in consumption patterns, wealth distribution, and resource planning. Some of this understanding is reflected in Canada's annual reports to the United Nations Commission on Sustainable Development.

National and provincial roundtables, community-initiated programs, and voluntary initiatives by private industry are important signs that at least some environmental ethics have been internalized among Canadians and in the business world. In addition, more effort is devoted now to anticipating and preventing environmental

Photo 14–16
ENGOs undertake multiple activities to protect the environment.

Photo 14–17
Model forests are places where residents, government agencies, and private firms work together to support community sustainability. For example, thirteen Canadian and European universities have partnered with the Canadian Model Forest Network to convey over 10 years of research and implementation of SFM in model forests to improve international SFM practices. This group visited the Fundy Model Forest in 2005 as part of an intensive 2- to 3-week field course.

problems (rather than simply reacting to them). This new outlook is partly the result of more consistent public consultation on the design and implementation of decision-making strategies. Also, with better ways of disseminating information (such as Environment Canada's Green Lane and EcoAction websites), both the public and local decision makers are better informed and able to contribute significantly to decisions.

TAKING ACTION: CANADIAN MODELS OF SUSTAINABILITY

In this chapter, we have emphasized four types of strategies for meeting environmental challenges: measuring, monitoring, and reporting; the ecosystem approach; environmental impact assessment and adaptive management; and shared governance. How are these strategies put into action? Below we highlight a few models that have been applied in Canada. You may recognize some of these actions as having occurred in your home town.

Conceptually, the **ecological footprint** is a powerful metaphor to demonstrate the impact of our choices on the ecological carrying capacity of the Earth (Wackernagel & Rees, 1996). When the ecological footprint is calculated according to different socioeconomic status, it also illustrates how increasing wealth leads to increasing consumption and pressures on ecological systems. This metaphor is now taught from elementary school through to university level to encourage students to think in new ways about how our consumption patterns affect sustainability.

Photo 14–18
Making reports available publicly helps spur action by citizens and policymakers, including education and participation by children in environmental issues.

The ecological footprint model has been used to spur new actions. The City of Calgary, for example, determined in 2005 that it had the largest footprint of any Canadian city. In 2006, it developed an action plan to reduce its impact, including being the first North American city to power its public light rapid transit system entirely by wind generation, replacing all residential street lights and traffic lights with new energy-efficient lights, improving the building standards for all City buildings, and introducing methane gas recovery in its landfills (City of Calgary, n.d.).

The ecological footprint model also has spawned new ways to measure our impact on the Earth's systems. The efforts of GPI (Genuine Progress Index) Atlantic in Nova Scotia to establish a set of "genuine progress indicators" for the province has gained provincial and national attention. These measures, which span a range of environmental, social, and economic characteristics, have demonstrated new ways to move toward sustainability. These discussions have entered into government

Photo 14–19
The ecological footprint has been a powerful metaphor for raising awareness of our consumption of the Earth's natural capital and taking action to reduce our environmental impact.

Photo 14–20
National parks protect ecological integrity and form part of Canada's national identity.

Photo 14–21
Community gardens, often located on vacant land, offer city residents places to produce their own food.

circles, and the National Round Table on Environment and Economy has recommended extending the system of national accounts to include natural and social capital (Chapter 1) and a new Canadian index of wellbeing (Chapter 4).

Similarly, the Endangered Spaces Campaign of the World Wildlife Fund Canada (1989–2000) pressured the Canadian government to increase the number and size of protected areas across the country. The amount of land granted protected status over the course of the campaign increased from 3.0 percent to 6.8 percent of the total land mass in Canada. The percentages seem small, but the total represents a 127 percent increase (more than double), or an increase from 29.4 million to 68.3 million hectares, of protected land.

The community garden movement, which began in the 1970s, has grown larger during the past decade. Community gardens promote ecological and social sustainability as citizens work together to provide healthy, safe, and abundant food for themselves and others. They also promote cultural understanding as groups from different cultural backgrounds may share seeds, gardening tips, recipes, and a love of the outdoors in the city.

Consistent with the ecosystem approach, and operative at local to regional scales, biosphere reserves are

places where people seek to live out and demonstrate their commitment to sustainability. To create a biosphere reserve, local communities must come together and demonstrate the environmental, cultural, and economic significance of their area. Biosphere reserves must incorporate areas of environmental protection with areas in which sustainable development of local resources is promoted. Reserves are then recognized by provincial and federal levels of government before they gain biosphere status conferred by the United Nations Environmental, Scientific, and Cultural Organization (UNESCO). During the 1970s and 1980s, Canada had six biosphere reserves; by 2007, nine more had been created. This model has gained increasing appeal as a way to promote sustainable development within living and working landscapes. However, as biosphere reserves are areas of "recognition," not "regulation," they still require financial and logistical support from other levels

Photo 14–22

Biosphere reserves are initiated and maintained by local residents seeking to demonstrate how to live and work in the landscape sustainably.

of government in order to become functioning models of sustainability (see Chapter 12).

These models, among others, offer hope that environmental challenges can be met. What other models might you identify within your community? How can citizens work together and, in collaboration with government and industry, enhance the efficacy of individual choices?

THE IMPORTANCE OF INDIVIDUALS AND COLLECTIVES

From the outset of this book, we have identified the ecological realities of our individual actions and the challenges we face in shifting our thinking and actions toward sustaining our environment. Ultimately, because humans are connected inextricably to the Earth's ecosystems, we noted that individual and combined actions do make a difference to the environmental, social, and economic sustainability of our environment. Even though many people look to governments to show leadership and commitment in these areas, the responsibility for sustainability is shared among all members of Canadian society (Draper & Mitchell, 2001).

Canada's national environmental indicators tell us that some of our initiatives are working: we have seen improvements in the indicators for acid rain, water quality, protected spaces, energy efficiency, and soil management. However, Canada has more species at risk, we emit more greenhouse gases, we use more energy, and we generate more solid waste than ever before. Given these realities, each one of us faces a number of fundamental choices as we look toward the future of the Canadian environment: What kind of future do we want? How can we live a life that helps to sustain the Earth? How can we get where we want to be in the future? What kind

of legacy will we leave for our children, grandchildren, and succeeding generations? Knowing that each small action we take is important—because, fundamentally, healthy human communities and healthy environments are interdependent—we need to understand our own attitudes and values. If need be, we must change our view of the world and adopt new ways of thinking and acting. Canada's former Minister of the Environment, David Anderson, stated, "Our past experience has demonstrated that successful environmental management depends on our ability to fully engage individuals and communities in defining the problems, finding the solutions and taking action to improve the quality of our environment. In the end—whether the source of a problem is in our backyard or on the other side of the globe—the problem becomes a local one. As such, individuals and communities must do their part, and governments and others must support their efforts to do so" (Anderson, personal communication, 2003).

As stewards of our planet, we must ensure not only that we are (re)connected with the natural world, but also that we learn to understand, respect, and work with one another toward sustainability objectives. Out of the exercise of our individual and composite intelligence, insight, and innovation, we should be able to create many successful approaches to sustaining our Earth. The Trans Canada Trail, spanning the country from coast to coast, illustrates how individuals and groups can work together to build a positive legacy that improves environmental and social well-being for both present and future generations (see Box 14–3).

We can work together to make changes close to home. Many universities are now examining ways that they can become sustainable. Presidents and chancellors of many Canadian universities, along with their counterparts in more than 300 institutions, have signed the **Talloires Declaration**, committing their institutions to initiating and supporting mobilization of internal and external resources to address problems of environmental pollution and degradation and depletion of natural resources (Box 14–4, p. 584). By signing this declaration, the universities affirmed the importance of the environment as a foundation of their education and practice and committed their institutions to developing interdisciplinary approaches to curricula, research initiatives, operations, and outreach activities that support an environmentally sustainable future.

Despite this declaration, some universities have been slow to realize the impact they have as large-scale consumers of goods and as models for the built environment. Yet, new initiatives across university campuses are now directed toward reducing wastes (including hazardous wastes), improving commuter practices, establishing fair trade or sustainable procurement policies, demonstrating appropriate designs, and even modelling sustainable agricultural practices. Many of these activities have been spurred

When the main trunk of the 18 000-kilometre Trans Canada Trail is completed, it will be the longest trail in the world. A shared-use recreational trail that will link all provinces and territories and touch all three of our ocean shores, the Trans Canada Trail is a community-based project that will preserve and protect the environment, promote physical fitness and well-being, provide a safe and secure place for recreational activity, act as a stimulus for local businesses (such as bed-and-breakfast operations), educate people by bringing them closer to nature and their historical roots, and foster eco-tourism opportunities.

Since 1994, when the Trans Canada Trail Foundation was launched publicly as an independent registered charity, more than $12 million (of the estimated $42 million required) has been raised toward the building of the trail. Donations mainly come from private individuals. The goal of the foundation is to receive 83 percent of the donations required from individuals, 12 percent from corporations, 2 percent from merchandising and governments, and 1 percent from foundations. Through local trail and community groups, about 1.5 million people across Canada volunteer with the trail councils in their region, and their organizations have united to fulfill a shared vision of making the Trans Canada Trail a reality.

Built on provincial and federal park and Crown lands, on abandoned railway lines, alongside railway lines, and on private land, the trail will accommodate five core activities: walking, cycling, horseback riding, cross-country skiing, and (where possible or desired) snowmobiling. In 1996 about 800 kilometres were dedicated to the Trans Canada Trail, including the Galloping Goose Trail in Victoria, British Columbia (a 60-kilometre former rail line, considered the first "rails to trails" conversion in Canada); the Caledon Trailway, Jackson Creek Kiwanis Trail, Elora Cataract Trailway, and Grand River Trails in Ontario; several sections of trail in the National Capital Commission area (Ottawa–Hull); Le Petit Temis (between Cabano, Quebec, and Edmundston, New Brunswick); Guysborough Trail in Nova Scotia; and Confederation Trail in Prince Edward Island. By

Photo 14–23

The Trans Canada Trail network offers opportunities for Canadians to appreciate the wonders of nature in cities and in rural areas across the country.

2001, about 62 percent of trail length had been dedicated. Each year, about one dozen new projects across the country are added to the trail network.

On February 19, 2000, the 2000 Relay began in Tuktoyaktuk, Northwest Territories, to commemorate the official opening of the trail in the Ottawa area on September 9, 2000. Relay participants walked, cycled, cross-country skied, rode horseback, and sometimes snowmobiled the trail as an acknowledgment of the multi-use nature of the trail.

Although it is not yet complete, metre by metre, Canadians are making the Trans Canada Trail happen. If you would like to be a part of this important undertaking, you can find more information by e-mail (info@tctrail.ca) or by phone (1-800-465-3636), as well as at the website noted below.

SOURCE: *The Trans Canada Trail,* Trans Canada Trail Foundation, 2001, 2003, http://www.tctrail.ca. Reprinted by permission of the Trans Canada Trail.

Photo 14–24

What legacy do we want to leave for succeeding generations?

by the dedication and tenacity of students like you. What is happening on your campus? Can you get involved?

What other strategies might we advance? In this book, we have offered several avenues that suggest there are many creative ways to envision and to implement sustainability. Because there is no one right approach to achieving sustainability of our environment—indeed, in diversity we find the greatest potential to adapt to Earth's ever-changing conditions—our choices will be predicated on individuals learning about the place where they live, caring about the air, water, soil, wild plants, wild animals, wild places, and people of the place where they live (as well as beyond the immediate area), and acting on that caring (see Figure 14–4 on page 585). Since acting on one's own is not always sufficient or conducive to long-term change, many people find it important to get involved with locally

BOX 14–4
THE TALLOIRES DECLARATION

We, the presidents, rectors, and vice chancellors of universities from all regions of the world are deeply concerned about the unprecedented scale and speed of environmental pollution and degradation, and the depletion of natural resources. Local, regional, and global air and water pollution; accumulation and distribution of toxic wastes; destruction and depletion of forests, soil, and water; depletion of the ozone layer and emission of "greenhouse" gases threaten the survival of humans and thousands of other living species, the integrity of the earth and its biodiversity, the security of nations, and the heritage of future generations. These environmental changes are caused by inequitable and unsustainable production and consumption patterns that aggravate poverty in many regions of the world. We believe that urgent actions are needed to address these fundamental problems and reverse the trends. Stabilization of human population, adoption of environmentally sound industrial and agricultural technologies, reforestation, and ecological restoration are crucial elements in creating an equitable and sustainable future for all humankind in harmony with nature. Universities have a major role in the education, research, policy formation, and information exchange necessary to make these goals possible.

Thus, university leaders must initiate and support mobilization of internal and external resources so that their institutions respond to this urgent challenge. We, therefore, agree to take the following actions:

1. Increase Awareness of Environmentally Sustainable Development

Use every opportunity to raise public, government, industry, foundation, and university awareness by openly addressing the urgent need to move toward an environmentally sustainable future.

2. Create an Institutional Culture of Sustainability

Encourage all universities to engage in education, research, policy formation, and information exchange on population, environment, and development to move toward global sustainability.

3. Educate for Environmentally Responsible Citizenship

Establish programs to produce expertise in environmental management, sustainable economic development, population, and related fields to ensure that all university graduates are environmentally literate and have the awareness and understanding to be ecologically responsible citizens.

4. Foster Environmental Literacy for All

Create programs to develop the capability of university faculty to teach environmental literacy to all undergraduate, graduate, and professional students.

5. Practice Institutional Ecology

Set an example of environmental responsibility by establishing institutional ecology policies and practices of resource conservation, recycling, waste reduction, and environmentally sound operations.

Photo 14–25
Made entirely of discarded coffee cups from around campus, garlands strung from trees around the campus marked Sustainability Day, October 24, 2007, at the University of Saskatchewan. The display drew attention to the amount of waste generated by coffee drinkers. This student offers a simple solution—a reusable mug.

6. Involve All Stakeholders

Encourage involvement of government, foundations, and industry in supporting interdisciplinary research, education, policy formation, and information exchange in environmentally sustainable development. Expand work with community and nongovernmental organizations to assist in finding solutions to environmental problems.

7. Collaborate for Interdisciplinary Approaches

Convene university faculty and administrators with environmental practitioners to develop interdisciplinary approaches to curricula, research initiatives, operations, and outreach activities that support an environmentally sustainable future.

BOX 14-4
(CONTINUED)

8. Enhance Capacity of Primary and Secondary Schools

Establish partnerships with primary and secondary schools to help develop the capacity for interdisciplinary teaching about population, environment, and sustainable development.

9. Broaden Service and Outreach Nationally and Internationally

Work with national and international organizations to promote a worldwide university effort toward a sustainable future.

10. Maintain the Movement

Establish a secretariat and a steering committee to continue this momentum, and to inform and support each other's efforts in carrying out this declaration.

SOURCE: "Talloires Declaration," University Leaders for a Sustainable Future, www.ulsf.org

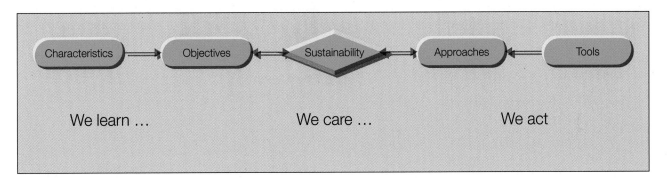

Figure 14–4
Toward environmental sustainability

based organizations or even local workplaces that are dedicated to helping and empowering local people bring about change in their own lives and communities.

Individual and cooperative actions matter when it comes to environmental sustainability. For instance, our individual and collective health may rely on simple choices, such as commuting by foot or bicycle. Such a choice will reduce traffic congestion and greenhouse gases while improving one's level of physical fitness and mental well-being. The interrelationship of environmental and social sustainability may induce people to make choices to improve their social well-being while improving conditions for the environment as well.

As we work toward reducing our imprint on the environment and improving environmental quality, it is important that we establish environmental sustainability strategies that ensure attention is paid to all groups in society. Carroll, Daniels, and Kusel (2000, p. 156) comment that "our collective future will likely consist of choices that test our ingenuity, our environmental ethic, and our compassion for one another." Similarly, Reed (2003, p. 230) concludes that "as a society, we will, in part be judged on what kind of environmental legacy we leave for future generations. But we will also be judged on the compassion that we have for people in the present. The choices between the two are not easy or clear. Nor are they mutually exclusive."

Developing compassion is an important part of ensuring that our strategies promote environmental protection and social justice. Environmental justice may mean considering the impacts of strategies on the livelihoods of others, in Canada and abroad; ensuring that safe and clean air and water are available and affordable to all; focusing attention on both present and future generations; and paying particular attention to groups that have been marginalized in the past to ensure that our decisions do not reproduce historical wrongs. In Canada, our ability to address the rights, improve the quality of life, and support the quest for self-determination of Aboriginal peoples is an important element of our commitment to environmental and social sustainability. The understanding we require to respect and work with one another ". . . may derive in part from education, but also may reflect an awareness of (and perhaps a change in) personal attitudes and values as well as social consciousness. Increasingly, community members are linking environmental concerns with concerns about local democracy, cultural continuity and economic independence.... Engaging in collaborative social and political actions in efforts to sustain the community and attain environmental justice within it retlects the importance of an active, informed and critical citizenry" (Draper and Mitchell, 2001, p. 97).

Born in 1979 to internationally renowned environmental scientist and activist David Suzuki (see Making a Difference 2) and English professor, writer, and activist Tara Cullis, Severn Cullis-Suzuki became a seasoned environmentalist at a young age. When she was nine, Cullis-Suzuki and a group of friends founded the Environmental Children's Organization (ECO) to learn and to teach other children about environmental issues. ECO raised funds to attend the 1992 Earth Summit in Rio de Janeiro, where Cullis-Suzuki addressed a plenary session. Cullis-Suzuki began by telling her audience that she and her group were there to try to make a difference and went on to say,

> I am only a child. . . . Yet I know that if all the money spent on war was spent on ending poverty and finding environmental answers, what a wonderful place this would be.... In school you teach us not to fight with others, to work things out, to respect others, to clean up our messes, not to hurt other creatures, to share, not be greedy. Then why do you go out and do the things you tell us not to do? You grownups say you love us, but I challenge you, please, to make your actions reflect your words.

When she finished, some in the audience were moved to tears, and many gave her a standing ovation. Cullis-Suzuki's book *Tell the World: A Young Environmentalist Speaks Out* (1993) includes the full text of her speech.

In 1993, Cullis-Suzuki received the UN Environment Programs Global 500 Award at a ceremony in Beijing. She also served on the UN Earth Charter Commission from 1997 to 2001. Later, as a member of a special advisory panel for Kofi Annan, seventh secretary-general of the United Nations, she worked with others to develop a pledge called the "Recognition of Responsibility" and presented it to the UN World Summit in Johannesburg in August 2002. (See the inside front cover for the pledge text.)

Photo 14–26
Severn Cullis-Suzuki.

In 2002, Cullis-Suzuki co-founded the Skyfish Project, an Internet-based discussion group that encouraged young people to speak out and to adopt a sustainable lifestyle. Due to members' other commitments, the Skyfish Project disbanded in 2006 and no longer maintains the website.

Schooled in ecology and evolutionary biology at Yale University (BSc) and ethnobotany at the University of Victoria (MSc), Cullis-Suzuki also has learned from the First Nations people of British Columbia, having been "adopted" and named by the Haida, Nu-chah-nulth, and Heiltsuk nations. In 2007, she became engaged to Judson Brown, a Haida park warden in the Gwaii Haanas National Park Reserve.

Active across a range of environmental causes, Cullis-Suzuki has hosted television shows for youth and families, has written books about the environment directed toward young people, and has been a motivational speaker in high demand. She speaks about the need to redefine our values and to act while considering the future.

Cullis-Suzuki describes herself as being most interested in motivating people "not with fear over the state of the world, but with hope for what can be done" (Hampson, 2007). Please take some time to consider how hope and action could "make a difference" in your own life, for the people you know, and for the environment in which you live.

SOURCES: *Notes from Canada's Young Activists: A Generation Stands Up for Change*, D. A. Cohen, S. Cullis-Suzuki, K. Frederickson, et al. (Eds.), 2007, Vancouver and Toronto: Douglas & McIntyre; *Tell the World: A Young Environmentalist Speaks Out*, S. Cullis-Suzuki, 1993, Toronto: Doubleday; "The Young Can't Wait," S. Cullis-Suzuki, August 26, 2002, *Time*, http://www.time.com/time/2002/greencentury/engeneration.html; "Born Green," S. Hampson, July 9, 2007, *The Globe and Mail*, http://www.theglobeandmail.com/servlet/story/RTGAM.20070709.wlhampson09/BNStory/lifeMain/?page=rss&id=RTGAM.20070709.wlhampson09; "Severn Cullis-Suzuki," *Top 20 Under Twenty*, n.d., http://www.top20under20.ca/en/MentorProgram/scsuzuki.htm

Whether we lead by example (for instance, by picking up litter from our streets, showing a neighbour how our backyard compost works, volunteering for a position in an ENGO, or speaking up against injustice), or whether we lead by "working within" to change existing economic and political institutions, the power of one-on-one communication to influence environmental change among political elites and other elected officials, and in our circle of friends, family, neighbours, and communities, should not be underestimated.

To ensure that we practise sustainability, a number of practical and philosophical considerations may guide our thinking and actions. These considerations include the following:

- *Critical assessment to determine how development proposals can be made sustainable:* Do they deplete Earth's capital? Do they preserve biodiversity? Do they enhance cultural diversity and self-determination? Do they promote self-reliance on the part of individuals and communities? Do they address equity issues that may arise by their proposals? Is the precautionary principle used to help ensure we use resources efficiently and live off Earth's income?

- *Use of appropriate technology:* To what degree are design-with-nature concepts employed? Are they simple, resource-efficient, and culturally adaptable technologies? Do they rely mostly on local sources of resources (recycled) and labour?

- *Information and education:* Are we teaching people (and learning, ourselves) how to think holistically, in a systematic, integrated, interdisciplinary fashion about planet Earth? Are we listening to the variety of sources of knowledge about Earth? Do we know where our water comes from, where our wastes go, what kinds of soils support our food production, and how long our growing season is? Do we use such information to spur action?

- *Demonstrating sustainability:* What models can we identify that are useful to demonstrate sustainability? Do they incorporate the dimensions of social equity, environmental sustainability, economic viability, and cultural diversity? How can we engage our families, universities, and communities to take up sustainability challenges?

- *Simplicity:* Have we reduced, reused, recycled, and refused (unnecessary products) wherever possible? Have we eliminated unnecessary consumption and waste of energy and other resources? Do we know what elements of our lifestyles are harmful or beneficial to the Earth?

Each small action we take in support of sustainability is important in helping to sustain Earth's life-support systems for ourselves and all life. Individual actions, however, must be coupled with strategic actions at higher levels to establish the conditions for effective societal change. Sustainability also means taking actions that maintain important elements of our social and cultural well-being. Protecting the environment is not a goal that can be achieved without recognizing the social context and cultural identity of people who live and work and are part of ecological systems. Actions that are taken without considering the effects on people who are affected by those decisions will, simply, be unsustainable. Perhaps, in working with others in our neighbourhoods and communities, our actions will help promote stewardship and encourage an acceptance by all groups of their role in promoting and implementing sustainability. It is not too late to learn how to work with Earth's ecosystems; if we really care, together our ingenuity and actions will help achieve a sustainable society.

Chapter Questions

1. Looking at the area where you live, identify examples of where progress has been achieved in reaching environmental goals, as well as examples where less progress has been achieved. What might some of the reasons be for the differential success? How have social and cultural issues been considered when deciding on sustainability strategies?

2. Identify any ENGOs or other community organizations that are active in your region. What are their objectives and what are some of the environmental issues they are concerned about? What kinds of actions do they take? Have they been successful in achieving their goals?

3. Comment on this statement: "A strong correlation is emerging between environmental and economic success." If you were to develop a complete response to this question, what additional information would you need to determine whether or not this statement is correct?

4. If you had the ear of the prime minister today, what environmental issues would you tell him/her to focus on in the next five years? What strategies would you suggest she/he adopt?

5. What is your university (church, family, volunteer organization) doing to promote sustainability? Does it have a sustainability policy? How can you get involved?

B.C. Parks. (2001). *Doubling the legacy.* http://www.env.gov.bc.ca/pac/foreverbc/home.html

Boyd, D. (2003). *Unnatural law: Rethinking Canadian environmental law and policy.* Vancouver: UBC Press.

British Columbia Minister of Environment, Lands and Parks. (1999). *Business plan, 2000–2001.*

Bryson, B. (2003). *A short history of nearly everything.* New York: Random House.

Canadian Council of Ministers of the Environment (CCME). (2000). *National Packaging Protocol 2000: Final report.* http://www.mbnet.mb/ccme/pdfs/NaPPFinalJun22_e.pdf

Carroll, M. S., Daniels, S. E., & Kusel, J. (2000). Employment and displacement among northwestern forest products workers. *Society and Natural Resources, 13,* 151–156.

City of Calgary. (n.d.). *Reducing the ecological footprint: A Calgary approach.* Calgary: Author. http://www.calgary.ca/docgallery/bu/environmental_management/ecological_footprint/footprint_a_calgary_approach.pdf

Colborn, T., vom Saal, F. S., & Soto, A. M. (1993). Developmental effects of endocrine-disrupting chemicals in wildlife and humans. *Environmental Health Perspectives, 101*(5), 378–384.

Committee on the Status of Endangered Wildlife in Canada (COSEWIC). (2003). *Committee on the Status of Endangered Wildlife in Canada: Results of the May 2003 COSEWIC Species Assessment Meeting.* http://www.cosewic.gc.ca/eng/sct0/index_e.cfm#sct0_2

Commuter Connections. (2001). *Find a carpool.* http://www.carpool.ca/carpool_find.asp

Draper, D. & Mitchell, B. (2001). Environmental justice considerations in Canada. *The Canadian Geographer, 45*(1), 93–98.

Environment Canada. (2003). *Environmental Signals: Canada's National Environmental Indicator Series 2003.* http://www.ec.gc.ca/soer-ree/English/Indicator_series/default.cfm

Environment Canada. (2006). *Species at risk.* http://www.speciesatrisk.ec.gc.ca/default_e.cfm

Environment Canada. (2007). *Latest greenhouse gas data show that Canada is still over 32% above Kyoto target.* News release. http://www.ec.gc.ca/default.asp?lang=En&n=714D9AAE-1&news=CCB1D619-7C62-408B-8785-A61FA84AEBFA

Government of Canada. (1991). *The state of Canada's environment—1991.* Ottawa: Supply and Services Canada.

Green Lane. (2001). *Particulate matter (PM<10).* http://www.ec.gc.ca/air/p-matter_e.shtml

Green Lane. (2003). *Government of Canada initiatives.* Fact sheet. http://www.ec.gc.ca/press/2002/020403_f_e.htm

Hawken, P., Lovins, A., & Lovins, L. H. (1999). *Natural capitalism: Creating the next industrial revolution.* Boston: Little, Brown & Co.

Holden, W. N. (2006). One concept and two countries: Federal government jurisdiction to make environmental law in Australia and Canada. *Australian Canadian Studies, 24*(1), 51–81.

Lee, K. N. (1999). Appraising adaptive management. *Conservation Ecology, 3*(2), 3. http://www.consecol.org/vol3/iss2/art3/

Makin, K. (2007, August 14). Clash over oil sands inevitable. *The Globe and Mail,* p. A1.

Malden Mills Industries, Inc. (1994). *Cool stuff to know about Polartec® fabrics.* Lawrence, MA: Author.

Menyasz, P., Pole, K., & Ray, R. (Eds.). (2000). Nova Scotia: Province alone in meeting goal of 50 percent garbage recycling by 2000. *Environment Policy and Law, 11*(8), 108.

Office of the Auditor General. (1996, November). *1996 report of the Auditor General.* Chapter 22. http://www.oag-bvg.gc.ca/domino/reports.nsf/html/9622ce.html#0.2.Q3O5J2.O25UY6.E9TLQE.DP

Office of the Auditor General. (1999). *1999 report of the Commissioner of the Environment and Sustainable Development.* http://www.oag-bvg.gc.ca/domino/reports.nsf/html/c904ce.html#0.2.2Z141Z1.NBS3AG.T8WQBF.52

Pilgrim, W. (1998). *The northeastern states and eastern Canadian provinces mercury study.* http://www.ceiw.ca/eman-temp/reports/publications/mercury/page78.html

Reed, M. G. (2003). *Taking Stands: Gender and the sustainability of rural communities.* Vancouver: UBC Press.

Wackernagel, M., & Rees, W. (1996). *Our ecological footprint: Reducing human impact on the earth.* Gabriola Island, BC: New Society.

World Wildlife Fund Canada. (2003). *The nature audit: Setting Canada's conservation agenda for the 21st century.* Report no. 1–2003. Toronto: Author.

Photo 14–27

An ozone red alert flag in metro Washington, D.C., warns residents when the air is considered too unhealthy to breathe for extended periods of time. Regional ozone levels may be affected by downwind emissions and by atmospheric chemistry. Look for our national ranking in the Canada and the World section.

Photo 14–28

Particulates in smog come mainly from burnt fossil fuels, and motorized vehicles such as these are a primary source of such emissions. The Canada and the World section shows Canada's place in the smog-ranking of urban particulates.

Canada and the World:
Using the Environmental Performance Index to Examine Canada's Performance Regarding Environmental Protection and Sustainability

How does Canada measure up with respect to its environmental performance? In countries across the world, including Canada, environmental management decisions frequently have been made without sufficient understanding of their consequences, which often are far-reaching in space and time. For instance, species have been introduced into ecosystems with disastrous results, and wilderness areas may be protected but are sometimes so fragmented that species continue to decline. In addition, policy development in the area of sustainability is lagging because policymakers do not have the tools to quantify environmental problems. Environmental policymakers within government agencies have had insufficient metrics to address issues comprehensively, and have lacked sufficient breadth and depth of baseline data to measure progress over time. The Environmental Performance Index (EPI) is one tool that helps to address this gap.

Countries often compare their gross national product, their export earnings, or other measures of economic performance to determine their success relative to other places. Yet, Canada's performance in achieving environmental protection and sustainability rarely is compared with that of other nations. We can use the EPI to compare Canada's environmental performance with the rest of the world.

As you read through this section, you may find some surprises and paradoxes that lead you to ask more questions of your professor, your peers, and your politicians. Canada is a leader in many categories of environmental performance, but it lags behind in others. Why is this the case? What do the data tell us? What do they omit? Can we truly compare our situation in Canada with that in other nations given significant differences in physical geography, socioeconomic status, and political circumstances? How do differences in data availability affect the results you see? Read through this section carefully; re-read Box 2–1, "Thinking Critically"; and consider the value and the limitations associated with the enormous effort to develop the EPI.

The EPI was created by the Yale Center for Environmental Law and Policy and the Center for International Earth Science Information Network at Columbia University, in collaboration with the World Economic Forum and the Joint Research Centre of the European Commission. The EPI focuses on two broad environmental protection objectives: the reduction of environmental stresses on human health and the promotion of ecosystem vitality and sound natural resources management. The environmental health objective recognizes that many environmental problems, such as indoor air pollution, have a direct impact on human health. Ecosystem vitality encompasses ecosystem functioning and resource management.

These two objectives are measured using 16 indicators that are combined into six policy categories; the categories were developed through consultation with experts, a review of relevant literature, and consideration of the United Nations' Millennium Development Goals (MDGs). As discussed in Chapter 4, the MDGs address poverty, health, and sustainability issues and identify specific targets for national governments to reach. By measuring how close each country comes to the specified targets, the EPI enables us to compare and evaluate the relative environmental performances of different nations. The creators of the EPI caution that this tool is in the pilot stage and will be refined over time.

The EPI team applied the following criteria when they were selecting the indicators:

- *Relevance:* Indicators are suitable for use on a global scale, and are relevant for all countries, no matter their location, climate, or stage of development.
- *Performance orientation:* Indicators measure outcomes, the "on-the-ground" conditions or results.
- *Transparency:* Data sources and methods used to develop indicators are clearly recognizable, and the collection of time-series data is possible.
- *Data quality:* Data used to construct indicators not only meet basic quality requirements but represent the best available measures.

Despite the EPI team's efforts to include the best-quality data, significant gaps existed: for instance, over 60 countries either did not maintain the data required for one or more of the 16 indicators, or the data that were available frequently were unreliable. Data were available to measure 16 indicators for 133 countries in the 2006 edition of the EPI (see Table C/W–1). The following indicators could *not* be included, due to insufficient data:

- Human exposure to toxic chemicals
- Waste management and disposal practices
- Sulphur dioxide emissions and acid rain
- Recycling and reuse rates
- Lead and mercury exposure
- Wetlands loss
- Soil productivity and erosion
- Greenhouse gas emissions (beyond CO_2)
- Ecosystem fragmentation

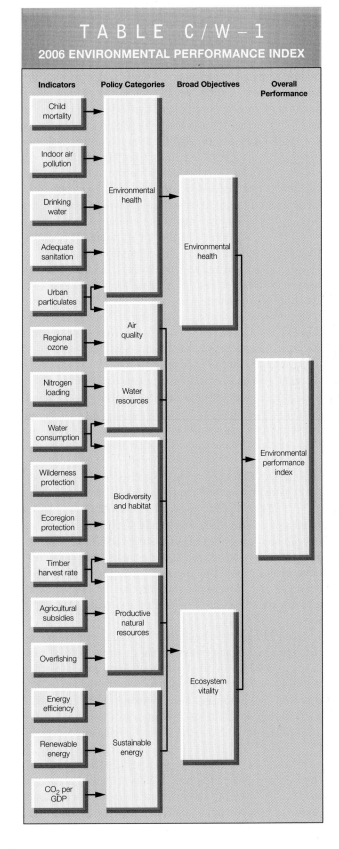

TABLE C/W–1
2006 ENVIRONMENTAL PERFORMANCE INDEX

For the 16 indicators included in the EPI, time-series data were not available in 2006; thus, a Rate of Progress Index could not be calculated.

After identifying targets for each indicator, the EPI team calculated a proximity-to-target value to measure how near each country was to each target. Targets were set after reviewing international agreements and national and international standards, and consulting with experts; the same targets were used for every country. Indicator data then were converted so that the higher the value a country obtained, the better its performance. Next, the proximity-to-target was determined; this involved calculating the difference between the observed value and the target value, then dividing by the difference between the worst observed value and the target value. This explanation is a simplification—for example, outliers had to be addressed, and results standardized so that the final proximity-to-target results ranged between 0 and 100. When indicator results were aggregated (combined) into policy categories, careful consideration was given to the method of data aggregation. Indicators were grouped, and weighted, using a principal component analysis (PCA) approach to identify patterns in the data.

EPI scores also can be aggregated according to a variety of characteristics, such as level of development, geographic location, political associations, climate, and demographics. The end results of working carefully with data are that the proximity-to-target results can be compared at each level of the EPI calculation (that is, the indicator, policy category, broad objective, or the EPI itself) for any country included in the analysis.

The 2006 Pilot Index provided a baseline, and further refinements have since been made. The 2008 EPI, under development, includes 25 indicators (see Table C/W–2). While the objectives remain the same, the indicators have been refined and the policy categories have been expanded. However, as country profiles are not yet available for the 2008 EPI, the results we consider are from the 2006 EPI.

The EPI is only a beginning—the EPI team compiling the index has made considerable progress toward providing a method to track environmental policy results, as has been done in areas such as poverty reduction. For example, 149 countries were included in the 2008 EPI, as data from an additional 16 countries (compared to the 2006 EPI) were added to the index. But challenges remain: for instance, until time-series data are collected, the EPI cannot be used to track progress (or lack thereof). When the 133 countries in the 2006 EPI were ranked according to EPI score, the top three countries were New Zealand, Sweden, and Finland, while Niger, Mauritania, and Chad ranked the lowest. Canada ranked eighth overall (but dropped to 12th in the 2008 EPI report). We selected 20 countries (see Figure C/W–1), which vary in geographic location and income group, to illustrate the remainder of this summary.

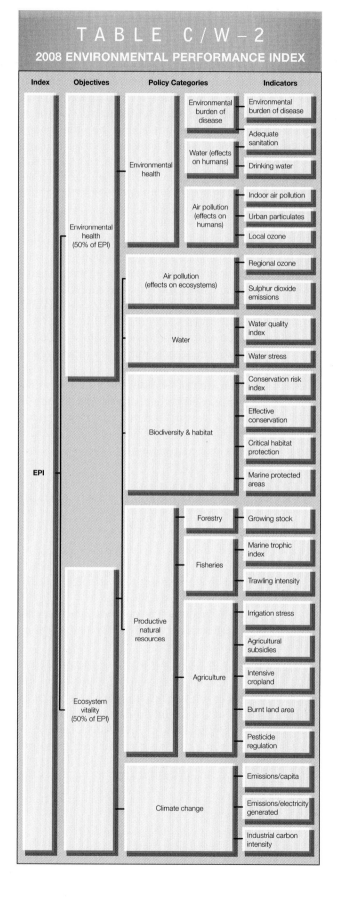

TABLE C/W–2
2008 ENVIRONMENTAL PERFORMANCE INDEX

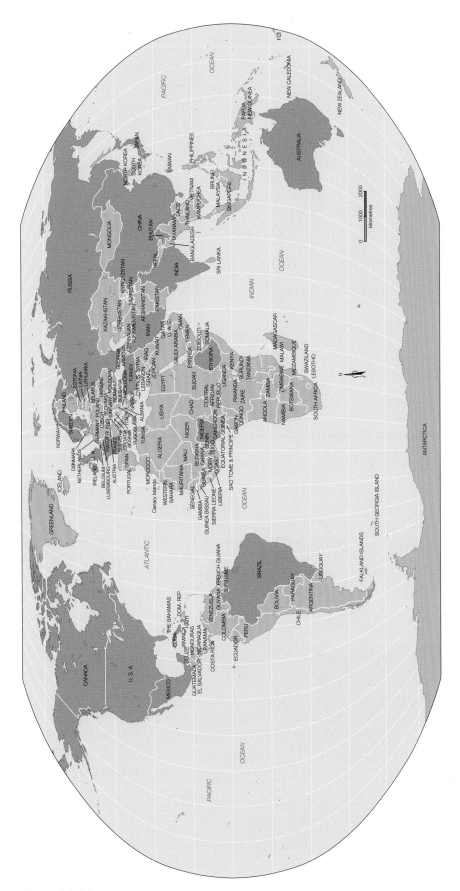

Figure C/W–1

Countries compared in the "Canada in the World" section

The Environmental Performance Index and the Human Development Index

The Human Development Index (HDI), an initiative of the United Nations Development Programme, provides an interesting comparison with the EPI. The HDI is a composite measure, encompassing life expectancy, adult literacy and enrolment in educational systems, and standard of living.

The EPI and HDI appear to be closely related: countries with higher EPI scores generally have higher HDI scores (Figure C/W–2). Higher scores on these measures relate to a nation's stage of development. For instance, as described by the HDI, Sweden, Canada, the United Kingdom, and the United States are all highly developed countries and members of the Organisation for Economic Co-operation and Development (OECD), while Ethiopia and Haiti are among the world's least developed countries (see also Chapter 4).

Canada's Performance on the EPI

Although Canada ranks eighth overall in the 2006 EPI, it does not rank highly in the policy categories in the Ecosystem Vitality objective. However, Canada ranks ninth in the policy category of Environmental Health, which constitutes 100 percent of the Environmental

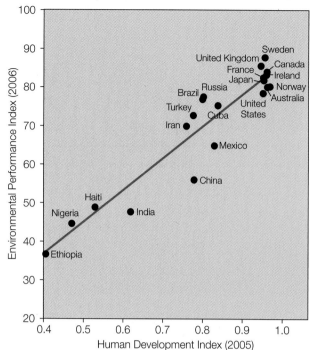

A Comparison of 2006 EPI and 2005 HDI Data

Figure C/W–2
Comparison of countries' 2006 EPI and 2005 HDI data

Health objective. As shown in Table C/W–1, the objectives consist of policy categories; the Environmental Health objective is made up of only one policy category, also entitled Environmental Health, and this objective constitutes half (50 percent) of the final EPI score. This weighting system is the reason why Canada places eighth in the overall ranking (Table C/W–3).

TABLE C/W–3
CANADA'S RANKINGS COMPARED TO COUNTRIES RANKED FIRST IN THE 2006 EPI POLICY CATEGORIES

Policy Category	Canada (Overall EPI Ranking: 8th)		Country Ranked First in Each Indicator	
	Indicator Value (Maximum: 100.0)	Ranking	Country (Overall EPI Ranking)	Indicator Value (Maximum: 100.0)
Environmental Health	98.6	9	Sweden (2)	99.4
Air Quality	56.2	60	Uganda (78)	98.0
Water	98.4	39	Sierra Leone (111)	100.0
Biodiversity and Habitat	55.1	59	Benin (84) and Venezuela (44)	88.0
Productive Natural Resources	73.9	72	17 countries have reached the target	100.0
Sustainable Energy	62.8	96	Uganda (78)	92.4

BROAD OBJECTIVES, POLICY CATEGORIES, AND INDICATORS

As explained above, the EPI consists of indicator data combined into policy categories, which, in turn, are aggregated into the broad objectives that make up the EPI. A more detailed explanation of the policy categories and indicators follows.

BROAD OBJECTIVE: ENVIRONMENTAL HEALTH

Policy Category: Environmental Health

This policy category includes indicators having a direct impact on human health, such as indoor air pollution, urban particulates, and access to drinking water and adequate sanitation. Child mortality also is an indicator. If data were available, exposure to lead would be another useful measure to include in this policy category.

Indicator: Child Mortality

This indicator measures the number of deaths per 1000 people aged one to four years (Table C/W–4). The target for this indicator is zero—that is, no children between the age of one and four years die.

The child mortality indicator does not include infant mortality, as its main determinants are not environmental. Young children, however, are very sensitive to environmental health stresses such as unsanitary water supply and poor air quality that may lead to respiratory and intestinal problems and disease. Tracking child mortality provides an important indicator of environmental conditions, rather than health care infrastructure. As is shown in Figure C/W–2, the four countries ranking the lowest on our selected EPI child mortality scores (India, Haiti, Ethiopia, and Nigeria) are among the world's least developed nations or have high population densities; they each rank within the lowest 25 percent on overall EPI scores.

Summary

Maximum Score: 41.63

Minimum Score: 0.09

Top Performers: Czech Republic, Sweden, Macao, Finland, Iceland

Bottom Performers: Sierra Leone, Niger, Angola, Afghanistan, Democratic Republic of the Congo

Indicator: Indoor Air Pollution

This indicator measures the percentage of households burning solid fuels indoors (including coal or biomass sources such as dung, charcoal, wood, or crop residues), with an adjustment for ventilation (Table C/W–5). The

TABLE C/W – 4
CHILD MORTALITY SCORES FOR SELECTED COUNTRIES

Country	Score (Deaths)[1]	Std'd. Prox. to Target[2]
Sweden	0.2	99.3
France	0.2	99.1
Canada	**0.3**	**98.9**
Japan	0.3	98.9
Norway	0.3	98.9
United Kingdom	0.3	98.9
Australia	0.3	98.8
Ireland	0.3	98.8
Cuba	0.4	98.5
United States	0.4	98.5
Mexico	1.1	95.9
Russia	1.2	95.3
Iran	1.4	94.4
China	1.5	94.1
Turkey	2.0	92.3
Brazil	2.1	91.9
India	8.5	67.1
Haiti	13.3	48.6
Ethiopia	21.2	18.3
Nigeria	26.0	0.0

NOTES:
[1] Deaths per 1000 population aged 1–4
[2] Standardized proximity to target (100 = target met)

SOURCE: *Pilot 2006 Environmental Performance Index*, D. C. Esty et al., 2006, New Haven: Yale Center for Environmental Law and Policy, pp. 117–249, 308–309, http://www.yale.edu/epi

target for this indicator is zero—no households burning fuels indoors.

Indoor air pollution is a major contributor to environmentally related disease and death; according to the 2006 EPI report, poor indoor air quality is the worst type of pollution, causing several million premature deaths annually. The correlation between poverty and environmental performance is clear; because people in countries at higher levels of development have little need to light indoor fires for heating and cooking, they tend to have significantly less indoor air pollution. Additionally, dealing with indoor air pollution requires resource capacity and investment that poorer nations cannot provide. Generally, little action has been taken to reduce indoor air pollution at regional, national, or international levels.

Summary

Maximum Score: 100.00

Minimum Score: 0.00

TABLE C/W–5
INDOOR AIR POLLUTION SCORES FOR SELECTED COUNTRIES

Country	Score (%)[1]	Std'd. Prox. to Target[2]
Australia	0	100.0
Canada	**0**	**100.0**
France	0	100.0
Ireland	0	100.0
Japan	0	100.0
Norway	0	100.0
Sweden	0	100.0
United Kingdom	0	100.0
United States	0	100.0
Russia	1	99.0
Iran	2	98.0
Turkey	11	89.0
Mexico	22	78.0
Brazil	27	73.0
China	30	70.0
Cuba	42	58.0
Nigeria	67	33.0
India	81	19.0
Haiti	82	18.0
Ethiopia	97	3.0

NOTES:

[1] Percentage of households using solid fuels, adjusted for ventilation

[2] Standardized proximity to target (100 = target met)

SOURCE: *Pilot 2006 Environmental Performance Index*, D. C. Esty et al., 2006, New Haven: Yale Center for Environmental Law and Policy, pp. 117–249, 310–311, http://www.yale.edu/epi

TABLE C/W–6
DRINKING WATER SCORES FOR SELECTED COUNTRIES

Country	Score (%)[1]	Std'd. Prox. to Target[2]
Australia	100	100.0
Canada	**100**	**100.0**
France	100	100.0
Ireland	100	100.0
Japan	100	100.0
Norway	100	100.0
Sweden	100	100.0
United Kingdom	100	100.0
United States	100	100.0
Russia	96	92.8
Iran	93	87.4
Turkey	93	87.4
Mexico	91	83.8
Cuba	91	83.8
Brazil	89	80.1
India	86	74.7
China	77	58.5
Haiti	71	47.7
Nigeria	60	27.8
Ethiopia	22	0.0

NOTES:

[1] Percentage population with access to an improved water source

[2] Standardized proximity to target (100 = target met)

SOURCE: *Pilot 2006 Environmental Performance Index*, D. C. Esty et al., 2006, New Haven: Yale Center for Environmental Law and Policy, pp. 117–249, 316–317, http://www.yale.edu/epi

Top Performers: 37 countries, including Canada, meet the target for this indicator

Bottom Performers: 11 countries have a score of 100 for this indicator

Indicator: Drinking Water

This indicator measures the percentage of the population with access to an improved water source: household connections, boreholes, public standpipes, protected springs, protected dug wells, and rainwater collections (Table C/W–6). The target for this indicator is 100 percent—the entire population having access to an improved water source. Additional discussion of freshwater issues is found in Chapter 7.

Access to drinking water, defined as access to an improved water source, is an MDG indicator. Lack of safe drinking water is another leading cause of environmentally related death and disease. Compared to indoor air quality, the provision of safe drinking water has received more international attention because of its inclusion in the MDGs.

Summary

Maximum Score: 100.00

Minimum Score: 13.00

Top Performers: 43 countries, including Canada, meet the target for this indicator

Bottom Performers: Afghanistan, Ethiopia, Somalia, Chad, Cambodia

Indicator: Adequate Sanitation

This indicator measures the percentage of the population with improved access to adequate sanitation (connections to public sewers and septic systems, simple pit latrines, pour-flush latrines, and ventilated improved pit latrines) (Table C/W–7). The target is 100 percent—the entire population having improved access. Typically, countries with per capita incomes above US$14 000 have 100 percent coverage. Additional

TABLE C/W-7
ADEQUATE SANITATION SCORES FOR SELECTED COUNTRIES

Country	Score (%)[1]	Std'd. Prox. to Target[2]
Australia	100	100.0
Canada	**100**	**100.0**
France	100	100.0
Ireland	100	100.0
Japan	100	100.0
Norway	100	100.0
Sweden	100	100.0
United Kingdom	100	100.0
United States	100	100.0
Cuba	98	97.6
Russia	87	84.2
Iran	84	80.5
Turkey	83	79.3
Mexico	77	72.0
Brazil	75	69.6
China	44	31.9
Nigeria	38	24.6
Haiti	34	19.8
India	30	14.9
Ethiopia	6	0.0

NOTES:

[1] Percentage population with improved access

[2] Standardized proximity to target (100 = target met)

SOURCE: *Pilot 2006 Environmental Performance Index,* D. C. Esty et al., 2006, New Haven: Yale Center for Environmental Law and Policy, pp. 117–249, 318–319, http://www.yale.edu/epi

discussion about freshwater and sanitation issues is found in Chapter 7.

Lack of access to adequate sanitation is a leading cause of environmentally related death and disease. As with drinking water, the provision of adequate sanitation is receiving more attention internationally because it is an MDG indicator.

Summary

Maximum Score: 100.00

Minimum Score: 6.00

Top Performers: 39 countries, including Canada, meet the target for this indicator

Bottom Performers: Ethiopia, Afghanistan, Chad, Congo, Eritrea

Indicator: Urban Particulates

This indicator measures particulates in micrograms per cubic metre (Table C/W–8). The 2006 EPI included countries with cities of more than 100 000 people and national capitals. The target for this indicator is 10 micrograms per cubic metre (10 μg/m³). The 10 μg/m³ target approximates the background level of particulates in most parts of the world. Additional discussion of particulate matter is found in Chapter 5, while information about sustainability and the city is found in Chapter 13.

No international targets exist for urban particulates, but some regional and national targets have been set. Target development has been more prevalent in countries where urban particulates are less problematic, however. Higher proximity-to-target scores for this indicator are found either in wealthy countries or in poor countries with little industrialization. People in countries with the worst urban particulate scores either may drive older vehicles or use dirtier fuels, or these nations may

TABLE C/W-8
URBAN PARTICULATE SCORES FOR SELECTED COUNTRIES

Country	Score (μg/m³)[1]	Std'd. Prox. to Target[2]
Sweden	15.3	96.2
France	16.7	95.2
Australia	18.6	93.9
United Kingdom	19.0	93.6
Norway	20.7	92.4
Canada	**22.4**	**91.2**
Ireland	22.6	91.0
United States	25.1	89.3
Cuba	25.0	89.3
Russia	25.8	88.8
Brazil	33.0	83.7
Japan	33.2	83.5
Haiti	49.9	71.6
Mexico	53.4	69.1
Turkey	54.1	68.6
Iran	71.2	56.4
China	87.8	44.7
Ethiopia	88.0	44.5
India	88.8	43.9
Nigeria	103.9	33.2

NOTES:

[1] Micrograms per cubic metre

[2] Standardized proximity to target (100 = target met)

SOURCE: *Pilot 2006 Environmental Performance Index,* D. C. Esty et al., 2006, New Haven: Yale Center for Environmental Law and Policy, pp. 117–249, 314–315, http://www.yale.edu/epi

be prone to dust storms, leading to high levels of natural particulates.

Summary

Maximum Score: 246.38

Minimum Score: 15.27

Top Performers: Belarus, Sweden, Antigua and Barbuda, Uganda, Venezuela

Bottom Performers: Sudan, Mali, Pakistan, Iraq, Uruguay

BROAD OBJECTIVE: ECOSYSTEM VITALITY

Policy Category: Air Quality

Urban particulates and regional ozone are the indicators for this category. While concentrations of reactive chemicals such as benzene, sulphur oxides and nitrogen oxides would be the most relevant indicators, they were not used because insufficient data were available. Urban particulate data serve as a proxy measure in the 2006 EPI assessment of urban air quality.

International policy initiatives regarding air pollution are becoming more prevalent. The Convention on Long-Range Transboundary Air Pollution (CLRTAP) is one such initiative, but it does not yet include developing countries. Additional information regarding atmospheric chemicals and policy initiatives is found in Chapter 5.

Indicator: Urban Particulates
The indicator is discussed under the preceding policy category of Environmental Health.

Indicator: Regional Ozone
Regional ozone measurements are included here because ground-level ozone is a threat both to public health and to ecosystem health, as this ozone can reduce the effectiveness of photosynthesis (Table C/W–9). This indicator measures regional ozone in parts per billion (ppb). The target for this indicator is set quite low, at 15 ppb, as epidemiological studies indicate that exposure to regional ozone is unsafe at any level. Additional discussion of ozone issues is found in Chapter 5.

Regional ozone levels may be affected by emissions from countries located downwind. Atmospheric chemistry also plays a role. While some national targets have been set, no international targets exist.

Summary

Maximum Score: 64.46

Minimum Score: 11.74

Top Performers: São Tomé and Principe, Gabon, Congo, Equatorial Guinea, Rwanda

Bottom Performers: Belize, Guatemala, Mexico, China, East Timor

TABLE C/W–9
REGIONAL OZONE SCORES FOR SELECTED COUNTRIES

Country	Score (ppb)[1]	Std'd. Prox. to Target[2]
Nigeria	24.1	78.7
Ethiopia	27.9	69.6
Brazil	38.7	44.3
Sweden	42.0	36.6
Norway	43.4	33.2
United Kingdom	44.9	29.6
Ireland	45.0	29.6
Turkey	45.0	29.5
France	45.7	27.7
Russia	48.0	22.4
Japan	48.3	21.8
Canada	**48.5**	**21.2**
India	52.1	12.9
Cuba	52.8	11.1
Haiti	53.4	9.7
Iran	55.1	5.8
United States	57.5	0.1
Australia	60.6	0.0
China	63.4	0.0
Mexico	64.2	0.0

NOTES:

[1] Parts per billion

[2] Standardized proximity to target (100 = target met)

SOURCE: *Pilot 2006 Environmental Performance Index*, D. C. Esty et al., 2006, New Haven: Yale Center for Environmental Law and Policy, pp. 117–249, 312–313, http://www.yale.edu/epi

Policy Category: Water Resources

Nitrogen loading and water consumption are the indicators in this policy category. Data for the nitrogen loading indicator were modelled, but there were insufficient data available to model other water pollutants (e.g., fecal coliform, phosphorus, and nitrogen). Targets for nitrogen loading and water consumption are unlikely to be met because demand for water and for agricultural products is increasing worldwide, and the MDGs set to alleviate hunger and shortages of water and sanitation will lead to an increase in water demand. However, as human impacts on water resources reach critical thresholds, there is growing awareness that water sources cannot be oversubscribed (consumed in excess of recharge) indefinitely. See Chapter 7 for additional discussion of freshwater resources.

Indicator: Nitrogen Loading

Derived from a modelled dataset, nitrogen load per average flow unit of a country's river basins is used as the indicator that captures pollutant emissions (Table C/W–10). Major landscape disturbances near water resources (such as urban development) can lead to an increased nitrogen load in the water body. Increased nitrogen levels also result from industrial fertilizer application and other byproducts of agricultural practices. The target for this indicator is 1 milligram per litre (1 mg/L). This target is located at the point where a water body changes from being considered oligotrophic, or nutrient-poor, to mesotrophic, or having a moderate level of nutrients. The nitrogren cycle is discussed in Chapter 3, and agroecosystems are discussed in Chapter 6.

Patterns in nitrogen loading values are difficult to discern, and unlike the environmental health indicators, nitrogen loading shows no clear relationship to GDP per capita. Countries with arid and semi-arid climates tend to score poorly, as do countries that are densely populated and those that export agricultural products. No internationally recognized targets exist for pollutant concentrations in water supplies; neither human nor ecosystem health are protected.

TABLE C/W–10
NITROGEN LOADING SCORES FOR SELECTED COUNTRIES

Country	Score (mg/l)[1]	Std'd. Prox. to Target[2]
Norway	6.2	99.9
Japan	12.8	99.8
Canada	**13.2**	**99.8**
Russia	16.4	99.7
Sweden	18.5	99.7
Brazil	19.7	99.6
Ireland	43.1	99.2
United Kingdom	45.1	99.2
Haiti	59.5	98.9
France	72.7	98.6
Nigeria	98.2	98.2
Cuba	134.7	97.5
Turkey	137.2	97.4
India	188.0	96.5
Ethiopia	335.3	93.7
Iran	476.3	91.0
United States	708.3	86.6
Australia	1159.3	78.0
China	3429.8	35.0
Mexico	8222.4	0.0

NOTES:

[1] Milligrams per litre

[2] Standardized proximity to target (100 = target met)

SOURCE: *Pilot 2006 Environmental Performance Index*, D. C. Esty et al., 2006, New Haven: Yale Center for Environmental Law and Policy, pp. 117–249, 320–321, http://www.yale.edu/epi

Summary

Maximum Score: 660 000.00

Minimum Score: 0.00

Top Performers: 9 countries meet the target for this indicator. Canada does not meet the target.

Bottom Performers: Algeria, Mali, Mauritania, Morocco, Libya

Indicator: Water Consumption

This indicator reflects the percentage of a country's territory affected by oversubscription of water resources. Accounting for domestic, industrial, and agricultural water withdrawals relative to the available water supply, this indicator points to a high degree of oversubscription when water consumption is more than 40 percent of the available supply (Table C/W–11). The target for this indicator is 0 percent, that is, no part of a country's area affected by oversubscription.

Depending on climatic factors and their natural water endowments, many countries with arid climates show more than half of their territory oversubscribed. Density of settlement does not appear to affect this indicator, but agricultural demands for water are the most important factor leading to oversubscription.

Summary

Maximum Score: 90.62

Minimum Score: 0.00

Top Performers: 39 countries meet the target for this indicator. Canada does not meet the target.

Bottom Performers: Kuwait, Israel, Jordan, Armenia, Somalia

Policy Category: Biodiversity and Habitat

This policy category includes water consumption, wilderness protection, ecoregion protection, and timber harvest rate. However, ecosystem monitoring is exceedingly complex: over 100 indicators may be needed to capture adequately the necessary information. The EPI uses the ecoregion protection indicator to measure how evenly biomes are protected in each country, while the wilderness protection indicator provides an indication of the degree to which the wildest areas of each country are protected. Unfortunately, the EPI designers lacked data with which they could monitor the effectiveness of protected areas management. The oversubscription of water resources and the timber harvest rate were included in this category to highlight the impact that deforestation has on habitat loss and the crucial role that water plays in sustaining aquatic ecosystems. Discussion of biodiversity and habitat is found in Chapter 12.

TABLE C/W–11
WATER CONSUMPTION SCORES FOR SELECTED COUNTRIES

Country	Score (%)[1]	Std'd. Prox. to Target[2]
Ireland	0.0	100.0
Norway	0.0	100.0
Sweden	0.4	99.4
Haiti	1.6	97.2
Canada	**1.7**	**97.0**
Russia	2.1	96.2
Brazil	2.3	95.8
Nigeria	4.7	91.5
Japan	5.6	89.7
France	8.4	84.7
United Kingdom	8.4	84.7
Turkey	13.9	74.6
Ethiopia	18.2	66.8
China	19.6	64.3
United States	21.3	61.1
Iran	25.3	53.7
Cuba	28.7	47.6
Mexico	31.5	42.4
India	33.5	38.8
Australia	45.7	16.6

NOTES:

[1] Percentage of territory in which consumption exceeds 40% of available water

[2] Standardized proximity to target (100 = target met)

SOURCE: *Pilot 2006 Environmental Performance Index*, D. C. Esty et al., 2006, New Haven: Yale Center for Environmental Law and Policy, pp. 117–249, 322–323, http://www.yale.edu/epi

Habitat destruction and species conservation measures would have been useful indicators for this category, but few data are available on an international level. While action regarding biodiversity conservation has been taken at international, national, and regional levels, better linkages with other goals, such as those dealing with development, are needed. The relationship of biodiversity to ecosystem functioning is not well understood, profoundly affecting conservation efforts.

Indicator: Water Consumption
This indicator was discussed under the policy category of Water Resources.

Indicator: Wilderness Protection
This indicator provides a measure of the percentage of a country's area that is protected formally as "wild" (Table C/W–12). While setting a global target for wilderness conservation is subjective, formal protection of larger areas clearly promotes greater success in attaining conservation goals. Given this knowledge, the EPI uses 90 percent as the target for remaining wild areas protection.

Summary

Maximum Score: 71.98

Minimum Score: 0.00

Top Performers: Brunei Darussalam, Venezuela, Burkina Faso, Benin, Botswana. Canada does not meet the target for this indicator.

Bottom Performers: 26 countries have a value of zero for this indicator

Indicator: Ecoregion Protection
The inclusion in protected areas of 10 percent of all major ecological regions is an internationally agreed-upon target in the Convention on Biological Diversity; consequently, the

TABLE C/W–12
WILDERNESS PROTECTION SCORES FOR SELECTED COUNTRIES

Country	Score (%)[1]	Std'd. Prox. to Target[2]
China	37.1	41.2
Cuba	29.5	32.8
United States	28.6	31.8
United Kingdom	26.0	28.9
Japan	24.0	26.7
Nigeria	14.2	15.8
Brazil	14.1	15.6
Ethiopia	13.4	14.9
Sweden	12.8	14.3
Australia	12.6	14.0
Mexico	12.5	13.9
Iran	10.7	11.9
India	10.3	11.5
Russia	9.6	10.6
Canada	**8.9**	**9.9**
Norway	7.2	8.0
France	6.4	7.1
Turkey	4.0	4.5
Ireland	3.2	3.5
Haiti	1.1	1.3

NOTES:

[1] Percentage of wild areas that are protected

[2] Standardized proximity to target (100 = target met)

SOURCE: *Pilot 2006 Environmental Performance Index*, D. C. Esty et al., 2006, New Haven: Yale Center for Environmental Law and Policy, pp. 117–249, 328–329, http://www.yale.edu/epi

EPI evaluates the level of inclusion of a country's ecological regions in its protected areas network, targeting protection of 10 percent of the area in every ecological region in a country. The focus is on terrestrial areas, as global targets for marine protected area coverage have not yet been accepted universally. This indicator is presented on a scale of 0 to 1, with 1 meaning that 10 percent of each biome is protected (Table C/W–13). The target for this indicator is 10 percent (a score of 1). Most of the countries that meet the target for this indicator are located in tropical climates.

Summary

Maximum Score: 1.00

Minimum Score: 0.00

Top Performers: 37 countries meet the target for this indicator. Canada does not meet the target.

Bottom Performers: Kiribati, Marshall Islands, Northern Mariana Islands, Monaco, Malta

Indicator: Timber Harvest Rate

This indicator measures timber harvest as roundwood production compared to the standing volume of forest (Table C/W–14). The target for this indicator is a 3 percent harvest rate; based on the judgment of forest experts, this harvest rate is considered sustainable for different forest types. Forest resources are discussed in Chapter 9.

Arid countries, those with large deforested areas, and those with high poverty levels scored poorly on this indicator. While countries have been discussing forest policy for decades, and acknowledge that forest management is an important element in sustainable development, no global, sustainable forest management frameworks exist yet.

The EPI team notes that the forest data employed in developing the indicator appear to contain artifacts—several countries show timber harvest rates over 30 percent, and some, such as Haiti, show a timber harvest rate

TABLE C/W–13
ECOREGION PROTECTION SCORES FOR SELECTED COUNTRIES

Country	Score (Scale 0–1)[1]	Std'd. Prox. to Target[2]
Japan	1.00	100.0
Russia	0.91	90.9
United States	0.91	90.6
Cuba	0.90	89.6
Ethiopia	0.86	85.8
China	0.84	84.3
Canada	**0.76**	**76.5**
Sweden	0.73	72.7
Australia	0.72	71.5
France	0.70	70.4
United Kingdom	0.69	68.7
Mexico	0.65	64.6
Iran	0.63	63.3
Brazil	0.59	58.7
India	0.57	57.1
Nigeria	0.42	42.0
Norway	0.28	28.0
Haiti	0.27	27.1
Turkey	0.26	25.6
Ireland	0.11	10.7

NOTES:
[1] 1 = 10% of each biome protected
[2] Standardized proximity to target (100 = target met)

SOURCE: *Pilot 2006 Environmental Performance Index*, D. C. Esty et al., 2006, New Haven: Yale Center for Environmental Law and Policy, pp. 117–249, 330–331, http://www.yale.edu/epi

TABLE C/W–14
TIMBER HARVEST SCORES FOR SELECTED COUNTRIES

Country	Score (%)[1]	Std'd. Prox. to Target[2]
Iran	0.1	100.0
Russia	0.2	100.0
Brazil	0.3	100.0
Australia	0.4	100.0
Japan	0.4	100.0
Canada	**0.7**	**100.0**
Norway	1.1	100.0
Turkey	1.1	100.0
France	1.2	100.0
United States	1.5	100.0
Mexico	1.6	100.0
Cuba	2.1	100.0
Sweden	2.3	100.0
United Kingdom	2.3	100.0
China	3.4	98.7
Ireland	5.1	92.8
Nigeria	6.3	88.6
India	11.8	69.6
Ethiopia	36.9	0.0
Haiti	111.6	0.0

NOTES:
[1] Percentage of standing forest
[2] Standardized proximity to target (100 = target met)

SOURCE: *Pilot 2006 Environmental Performance Index*, D. C. Esty et al., 2006, New Haven: Yale Center for Environmental Law and Policy, pp. 117–249, 324–325, http://www.yale.edu/epi

greater than 100 percent. These data artifacts may result from using two different data sets to calculate the timber harvest rate, or they may relate to the different ways countries measure forested areas.

Summary

Maximum Score: 225.17

Minimum Score: 0.00

Top Performers: 69 countries, including Canada, meet the target for this indicator

Bottom Performers: Niger, Mauritania, Egypt, Haiti, Bangladesh

Policy Category: Productive Natural Resources

Given limited data that reflect the state of forests, soils, freshwater, and fisheries, the three indirect, proxy indicators included in this policy category are timber harvest rate, agricultural subsidies, and overfishing. Agricultural subsidies in high-income OECD countries result in increased use of agricultural chemicals, and may lead to sensitive or marginal lands being used for agricultural purposes, thus reducing agricultural sustainability. In contrast, low-income countries may outperform high-income countries because they use productive natural resources less intensively. National performances on these indicators reflect the size of their natural resource endowment, and either effective management or less intense use of resources.

Deforestation and unsustainable agriculture practices are not receiving international attention at the level required. Fisheries data, such as fish landings within the exclusive economic zones of nations, are becoming more readily available (see Chapter 8 for more details).

Indicator: Timber Harvest Rate

This indicator is discussed under the policy category of Biodiversity and Habitat.

Indicator: Agricultural Subsidies

This indicator measures agricultural subsidies as a percentage of agricultural output (GDP) (Table C/W–15). The 0 percent target for this indicator was based on the General Agreement on Tariffs and Trade (GATT) and World Trade Organization (WTO) guidelines, which had the intention of promoting free trade. The target is useful when considering sustainability of land resources (see Chapter 6).

While 188 countries meet the target, subsidies remain high throughout Europe—many countries there use agricultural subsidies to protect their farmers' products from competition. However, high levels of subsidies can lead to unsustainable agricultural practices.

Summary

Maximum Score: 56.13

Minimum Score: –1.63

TABLE C/W–15
AGRICULTURAL SUBSIDIES SCORES FOR SELECTED COUNTRIES

Country	Score (%)[1]	Std'd. Prox. to Target[2]
India	–1.6	100.0
Australia	–0.8	100.0
Haiti	0.0	100.0
Ethiopia	0.0	100.0
China	0.0	100.0
Iran	0.0	100.0
Nigeria	0.0	100.0
Russia	0.0	100.0
Cuba	0.0	100.0
Sweden	0.6	93.0
Brazil	0.7	92.8
Ireland	0.8	91.4
Turkey	1.0	89.2
Mexico	1.5	84.0
United Kingdom	3.2	64.9
Canada	**4.1**	**55.0**
France	8.7	5.5
United States	10.9	0.0
Japan	22.3	0.0
Norway	40.1	0.0

NOTES:

[1] Agricultural subsidies as percent of agricultural output

[2] Standardized proximity to target (100 = target met)

SOURCE: *Pilot 2006 Environmental Performance Index*, D. C. Esty et al., 2006, New Haven: Yale Center for Environmental Law and Policy, pp. 117–249, 326–327, http://www.yale.edu/epi

Top Performers: 188 countries meet the target for this indicator. Canada does not meet the target.

Bottom Performers: Switzerland, Norway, Iceland, Japan, Slovakia

Indicator: Overfishing

This indicator calculated the ratio of biological productivity (tonnes of carbon per square kilometre [km^2] from each nation's exclusive economic zone per year) to tonnes of fish catch per km^2 of shelf per year (Table C/W–16); higher ratios indicate better results. The target of 3.2 millon tonnes of carbon per tonne of fish catch was set equal to a value of 1 (no overfishing). Higher ratios translated into higher scores, indicating increasing levels of overfishing (see Chapter 8).

The best performers for this indicator are small island nations, possibly because they employ small or traditional

TABLE C/W–16
OVERFISHING SCORES FOR SELECTED COUNTRIES

Country	Score (Scale 1–7)	Std'd. Prox. to Target[1]
Australia	2	83.3
Canada	**3**	**66.7**
Haiti	3	66.7
Brazil	4	50.0
Iran	4	50.0
Russia	4	50.0
Sweden	4	50.0
United Kingdom	4	50.0
Cuba	4	50.0
France	5	33.3
Ireland	5	33.3
Mexico	5	33.3
India	6	16.7
Nigeria	6	16.7
United States	6	16.7
Turkey	6	16.7
China	7	0.0
Japan	7	0.0
Norway	7	0.0
Ethiopia	–	–

NOTE:

[1] Standardized proximity to target (100 = target met)

SOURCE: *Pilot 2006 Environmental Performance Index,* D. C. Esty et al., 2006, New Haven: Yale Center for Environmental Law and Policy, pp. 117–249, 338–339, http://www.yale.edu/epi

fleets; conversely, those countries with large fleets consume large amounts of fish and thus score the worst.

Summary

Maximum Score: 7.00

Minimum Score: 1.00

Top Performers: 16 countries meet the target for this indicator. Canada does not meet the target.

Bottom Performers: 9 countries have the maximum value (7) for this indicator.

Policy Category: Sustainable Energy

Indicators in this policy category are energy efficiency, renewable energy, and carbon dioxide emissions per Gross Domestic Product. Energy use, in its current form, produces greenhouse gas (GHG) emissions and air pollution. Ideally, emissions for the six greenhouse gases included in the United Nations Framework Convention on Climate Change and the Kyoto Protocol would be included, but global data do not exist for several greenhouse gases.

Renewable energy currently is not addressed by any international agreement. However, the MDGs include a decrease in energy consumption per GDP as an indicator. (Energy matters are discussed in Chapter 11.)

Indicator: Energy Efficiency

While energy efficiency is being given increasing priority globally, and is also an MDG indicator (Table C/W–17), reaching a sustainable energy future requires the decoupling of energy consumption from economic activity and GDP growth. The world is not there yet, but some countries are making progress through conservation and shifts toward renewable energy sources.

Energy efficiency is reported in terajoules per million GDP in constant 2000 international purchasing power parity (PPP) dollars, that is, energy consumption divided by GDP. The target for this indicator is 1650 terajoules per million $GDP PPP. No industrialized nation ranks in the top 37 most energy efficient countries identified using

TABLE C/W–17
ENERGY EFFICIENCY SCORES FOR SELECTED COUNTRIES

Country	Score (Energy Efficiency)[1]	Std'd. Prox. to Target[2]
Ethiopia	1588	100.0
Haiti	1822	99.3
Ireland	4014	90.1
India	4571	87.8
United Kingdom	5668	83.2
Japan	6249	80.8
Brazil	6402	80.1
France	6685	79.0
Turkey	6690	78.9
Nigeria	6931	77.9
China	7079	77.3
Mexico	7153	77.0
Sweden	8238	72.5
Australia	8961	69.4
United States	9112	68.8
Norway	10689	62.2
Iran	13048	52.4
Canada	**14227**	**47.4**
Cuba	14968	44.3
Russia	22507	12.8

NOTES:

[1] Terajoules/million $GDP PPP

[2] Standardized proximity to target (100 = target met)

SOURCE: *Pilot 2006 Environmental Performance Index,* D. C. Esty et al., 2006, New Haven: Yale Center for Environmental Law and Policy, pp. 117–249, 332–333, http://www.yale.edu/epi

this indicator; the best performers are the world's poorest countries. However, no correlation exists between GDP per capita and energy efficiency.

Summary

Maximum Score: 48 332.41

Minimum Score: 288.26

Top Performers: 15 countries meet the target for this indicator. Canada does not meet the target.

Bottom Performers: Uzbekistan, Trinidad and Tobago, Tajikistan, United Arab Emirates, Bahrain

Indicator: Renewable Energy

As insufficient data exist regarding sustainable energy, this indicator measures renewable energy production as a percentage of total energy consumption and gauges energy diversification within a country (Table C/W–18). Renewable energy sources include hydroelectric, geothermal, solar, biomass, and wind. The target for this indicator is 100 percent renewable energy, which is the sustainable, long-term target.

Developing countries with considerable hydroelectric infrastructure scored well for this indicator. Members of the Organization of Petroleum Exporting Countries (OPEC) do not use renewable energy, nor do many African and island countries. Countries that export renewable energy may have values over 100 percent.

Summary

Maximum Score: 123.39

Minimum Score: 0.00

Top Performers: Paraguay, Bhutan, Mozambique, Zambia, Democratic Republic of the Congo

Bottom Performers: 61 countries have a value of zero for this indicator

Indicator: CO_2 per GDP

As targets for GHG emissions have yet to be developed, the EPI defines the UN Framework Convention on Climate Change's goal of "stabilization of greenhouse gas concentrations in the atmosphere at a level that would prevent dangerous anthropogenic interference with the climate system" (n.d., n.p.) as the reason to set emissions at 0 percent (or 0 tonnes/$GDP PPP). This indicator is measured in metric tonnes of carbon emissions per million GDP in constant 1995 U.S. dollars (Table C/W–19).

The major international agreement regarding GHG emissions is the Kyoto Protocol, but most signatory countries are unlikely to achieve the first set of targets for reducing CO_2 emissions between 2008 and 2012. The United States, one of the world's largest GHG emitters, and Australia have chosen not to sign the protocol. (See Chapters 5 and 11 for additional information on the Kyoto Protocol.) Data on CO_2 emissions from 1992 to 2000 are available; while some countries showed a decline in emissions, these declines resulted from economic collapse, not from GHG reduction policies.

Summary

Maximum Score: 4859.02

Minimum Score: 21.15

Top Performers: Chad, Cambodia, French Polynesia, Switzerland, Myanmar

Bottom Performers: North Korea, Turkmenistan, Ukraine, Uzbekistan, Mongolia

references

Esty, D. C., et al. (2006). *Pilot 2006 Environmental Performance Index.* New Haven: Yale Center for Environmental Law and Policy. http://www.yale.edu/epi

Esty, D. C., et al. (2008). *2008 Environmental Performance Index.* New Haven: Yale Center for Environmental Law and Policy. http://epi.yale.edu

United Nations Development Programme. (n.d.). *UNDP Human Development Reports.* http://hdr.undp.org/en/statistics.

United Nations Framework Convention on Climate Change (n.d.). *Full Text of the Convention.* http://unfccc.int/essential_background/convention/background/items/1349.php

World Health Organization. (n.d.). *Population with sustainable access to an improved water source (%), access to improved sanitation (%).* http://www.who.int/whosis/whostat2006ImprovedWaterImprovedSanitation.pdf

TABLE C/W-18
RENEWABLE ENERGY SCORES FOR SELECTED COUNTRIES

Country	Score (%)[1]	Std'd. Prox. to Target[2]
Norway	60.4	60.4
Brazil	37.0	37.0
Sweden	28.1	28.1
Ethiopia	26.8	26.8
Canada	**25.9**	**25.9**
Turkey	10.8	10.8
Haiti	9.5	9.5
Nigeria	8.4	8.4
China	6.3	6.3
Japan	6.2	6.2
Russia	6.1	6.1
France	5.7	5.7
India	5.3	5.3
Mexico	4.8	4.8
United States	4.0	4.0
Australia	3.7	3.7
Ireland	1.9	1.9
Cuba	1.8	1.8
Iran	1.7	1.7
United Kingdom	1.2	1.2

NOTES:

[1] Hydropower and renewable energy consumption as a percentage of total energy consumption

[2] Standardized proximity to target (100 = target met)

SOURCE: *Pilot 2006 Environmental Performance Index*, D. C. Esty et al., 2006, New Haven: Yale Center for Environmental Law and Policy, pp. 117–249, 334–335, http://www.yale.edu/epi

TABLE C/W-19
CO₂ PER GDP SCORES FOR SELECTED COUNTRIES

Country	Score (CO_2 Emissions)[1]	Std'd. Prox. to Target[2]
Sweden	44	96.2
France	56	95.1
Japan	57	95.0
Norway	77	93.3
Brazil	107	90.7
Ireland	109	90.5
United Kingdom	118	89.6
Haiti	136	88.1
Canada	**168**	**85.3**
United States	171	85.1
Ethiopia	204	82.1
Australia	209	81.7
Cuba	263	77.0
Turkey	294	74.3
Nigeria	305	73.3
Mexico	311	72.8
India	621	45.6
China	731	36.0
Iran	802	29.8
Russia	914	20.0

NOTES:

[1] Tonnes/million $GDP PPP

[2] Standardized proximity to target (100 = target met)

SOURCE: *Pilot 2006 Environmental Performance Index*, D. C. Esty et al., 2006, New Haven: Yale Center for Environmental Law and Policy, pp. 117–249, 336–337, http://www.yale.edu/epi

TABLE OF THE ELEMENTS

Element Name	Symbol	Atomic Number	Atomic Mass	Element Name	Symbol	Atomic Number	Atomic Mass
Actinium	Ac	89	(227)	Neon	Ne	10	20.1797
Aluminum	Al	13	26.981539	Neptunium	Np	93	(237)
Americium	Am	95	(243)	Nickel	Ni	28	58.6934
Antimony	Sb	51	121.757	Niobium	Nb	41	92.90638
Argon	Ar	18	39.948	Nitrogen	N	7	14.00674
Arsenic	As	33	74.92159	Nobelium	No	102	(259)
Astatine	At	85	(210)	Osmium	Os	76	190.2
Barium	Ba	56	137.327	Oxygen	O	8	15.9994
Berkelium	Bk	97	(247)	Palladium	Pd	46	106.42
Beryllium	Be	4	9.012182	Phosphorus	P	15	30.973762
Bismuth	Bi	83	208.98037	Platinum	Pt	78	195.08
Boron	B	5	10.811	Plutonium	Pu	94	(244)
Bromine	Br	35	79.904	Polonium	Po	84	(209)
Cadmium	Cd	48	112.411	Potassium	K	19	39.0983
Calcium	Ca	20	40.078	Praseodymium	Pr	59	140.90765
Californium	Cf	98	(251)	Promethium	Pm	61	(145)
Carbon	C	6	12.011	Protactinium	Pa	91	(231)
Cerium	Ce	58	140.115	Radium	Ra	88	(226)
Cesium	Cs	55	132.90543	Radon	Rn	86	(222)
Chlorine	Cl	17	35.4527	Rhenium	Re	75	186.207
Chromium	Cr	24	51.9961	Rhodium	Rh	45	102.90550
Cobalt	Co	27	58.93320	Rubidium	Rb	37	85.4678
Copper	Cu	29	63.546	Ruthenium	Ru	44	101.07
Curium	Cm	96	(247)	Samarium	Sm	62	150.36
Dysprosium	Dy	66	162.50	Scandium	Sc	21	44.955910
Einsteinium	Es	99	(252)	Selenium	Se	34	78.96
Erbium	Er	68	167.26	Silicon	Si	14	28.0855
Europium	Eu	63	151.965	Silver	Ag	47	107.8682
Fermium	Fm	100	(257)	Sodium	Na	11	22.989768
Fluorine	F	9	18.9984032	Strontium	Sr	38	87.62
Francium	Fr	87	(223)	Sulfur	S	16	32.066
Gadolinium	Gd	64	157.25	Tantalum	Ta	73	180.9479
Gallium	Ga	31	69.723	Technetium	Tc	43	(98)
Germanium	Ge	32	72.61	Tellerium	Te	52	127.60
Gold	Au	79	196.96654	Terbium	Tb	65	158.92534
Hafnium	Hf	72	178.49	Thallium	Tl	81	204.3833
Helium	He	2	4.002602	Thorium	Th	90	232.0381
Holmium	Ho	67	164.93032	Thulium	Tm	69	168.93421
Hydrogen	H	1	1.00794	Tin	Sn	50	118.710
Indium	In	49	114.82	Titanium	Ti	22	47.88
Iodine	I	53	126.90447	Tungsten	W	74	183.85
Iridium	Ir	77	192.22	Unnilennium	Une	109	(267)
Iron	Fe	26	55.847	Unnilhexium	Unh	106	(263)
Krypton	Kr	36	83.80	Unniloctium	Uno	108	(265)
Lanthanum	La	57	138.9055	Unnilpentium	Unp	105	(262)
Lawrencium	Lr	103	(262)	Unnilquadium	Unq	104	(261)
Lead	Pb	82	207.2	Unnilseptium	Uns	107	(262)
Lithium	Li	3	6.941	Uranium	U	92	238.0289
Lutetium	Lu	71	174.967	Vanadium	V	23	50.9415
Magnesium	Mg	12	24.3050	Xenon	Xe	54	131.29
Manganese	Mn	25	54.93805	Ytterbium	Yb	70	173.04
Mendelevium	Md	101	(258)	Yttrium	Y	39	88.90585
Mercury	Hg	80	200.59	Zinc	Zn	30	65.39
Molybdenum	Mo	42	95.94	Zirconium	Zr	40	91.224
Neodymium	Nd	60	144.24				

Atomic masses in parentheses are the mass number of the longest-lived isotope of the element.

abiotic. The nonliving components of an ecosystem, such as water, air, solar energy, and nutrients necessary to support life in a given area. Compare *biotic*.

Aboriginal peoples. In Canada, those people who may be considered First Nations (Registered or Treaty Indians), Métis, or Inuit.

acclimation. The adjustment of a species to slowly changing conditions in an ecosystem, such as temperature. See also *threshold effect*.

acid mine drainage. Acidic water that drains from mine sites and sometimes enters streams and lakes.

adaptation. Any genetically controlled characteristic—structural, physiological, or behavioural—that enhances the chance for members of a population to survive and reproduce in its environment. See also *mutation*.

aerobic respiration. A complex chemical process that drives the life processes of living things, by using oxygen to convert nutrients such as glucose back into carbon dioxide and water. The opposite of *photosynthesis*.

aesthetic arguments. A rationale for the conservation of nature based on its beauty and aesthetic qualities. Compare *ecological justification, moral justification, utilitarian justification*.

age-specific fertility rate. The number of live births per 1000 women of a specific age group per year.

agroecosystems. Communities of living organisms, together with the physical resources that sustain them (such as biotic and abiotic elements of the underlying soils and drainage networks), that are managed for the purposes of producing food, fibre, and other agricultural products.

agroforestry. The raising of trees or shrubs together with crops and/or animals on the same parcel of land.

alternative energy. Renewable energy sources, such as wind, flowing water, solar energy, and biomass, which create less environmental damage and pollution than fossil fuels, and offer an alternative to nonrenewable energy resources.

alternative livestock. The raising together of non-native animal species and domesticated native species.

anadromous. Fish that are born and develop in rivers and streams, migrate out to sea for as long as seven years or as short as a few months (depending on the species), and then return to their birthplace to spawn and die.

anthropogenic. Human-induced changes to the environment.

aquaculture. The breeding and raising of fish under controlled conditions, with the goal of high-level production for food or recreational purposes.

aquifer. Underground zone or layers of porous rock saturated with water from which an economically significant amount of groundwater can be obtained through a well.

assimilative capacity. The ability of a water body to accept sewage and other substances without significant harm to plants, organisms, and animals; human health; or other water uses.

atmosphere. A thin layer of gases consisting mostly of nitrogen and oxygen that completely surrounds the solid and liquid earth. See also *troposphere, stratosphere*.

atomic number. The number of protons in an atom's nucleus, which distinguishes it from the atoms of other elements.

atoms. The smallest particles that exhibit the unique characteristics of that particular element.

autotrophs. See *producers*.

background extinction. The continuous, low-level extinction of species that has occurred throughout much of history. Compare *mass extinction*.

barrier islands. Long, low, offshore islands of sediment that run parallel to much of North America's Atlantic and Gulf coasts and help protect coastal wetlands and habitats from storm damage.

benthic environment. The ocean floor, one of the two main divisions of the open sea environment. See also *pelagic environment*.

bioaccumulation. The uptake and retention of substances in organisms.

biocapital. See *natural capital*.

biodiversity. The diversity of life on earth, consisting of genetic diversity, species diversity, and ecosystem diversity.

bioenergy. Energy made available by the conversion of materials derived from sources of living organisms or their metabolic byproducts.

biofuels. See *ethanol*.

biogeochemical cycles. See *nutrient cycles*.

biological evolution. The change in inherited characteristics of a population from generation to successive generation.

biological oxygen demand (BOD). The amount of oxygen needed during the time it takes for waste material to be oxidized. Water quality is directly affected by this; some organisms thrive on a higher BOD and some suffocate for lack of oxygen.

biomagnification. The accumulation and concentration of certain substances in organisms, such as chlorinated organic compounds (DDT and PCBs) in the fatty tissues of predators in the Arctic marine system.

biomass. The dry weight of all organic matter contained in plants and animals in an ecosystem. Biomass can be converted into solid, liquid, or gaseous energy.

biomass burning. Using plant materials and animal wastes as fuel.

biome. A broad, regional type of ecosystem characterized by distinctive climate and soil conditions and a distinctive biological community adapted to those conditions.

bioremediation. A process that involves using naturally occurring or genetically modified microorganisms to break down or degrade hazardous substances into less hazardous or nontoxic substances.

biosphere. That part of the Earth inhabited by plants and animals, and their interactions with the atmosphere, hydrosphere, and lithosphere.

biotechnology. The use of a living organism (or a part thereof) to create some different product, whether cheese to eat, a vaccine to combat disease, or a plant or animal with novel attributes. Genetic engineering is a more recent aspect of biotechnology.

biotic. The living components of an ecosystem, including plants, animals, and their products (secretions, wastes, and remains) and effects in a given area. Compare *abiotic*.

biotic potential. The maximum rate a population can increase under ideal conditions.

bitumen. A black oil rich in sulphur that is found in oil sand. It can be treated and chemically upgraded into synthetic crude oil, though the net useful energy yield is lower than for conventional oil because more energy is required to extract and process it. See also *oil sand*.

carcinogen. A cancer-causing agent.

carnivores. Organisms that feed indirectly on plants by eating the meat of herbivores. Most carnivores are animals, but a few examples are in the plant kingdom, such as the Venus flytrap. See also *herbivores, omnivores*.

carrying capacity. The number of organisms that an ecosystem can support indefinitely while maintaining its productivity, adaptability, and capability for renewal.

cash crops. Crops grown to be traded in a marketplace.

catadromous. Species that spend most of their life cycle in fresh water, but enter the ocean to spawn.

certified organic. In Canada, a certified organic product has been produced using principles and methods outlined by the National Standard for Organic Production Systems. When producing or handling organic products, the national standard forbids the use of substances such as genetically engineered materials, synthetic pesticides, sewage sludge, synthetic growth regulators, food additives, ionizing radiation, forms of irradiation, synthetic fungicides, preservatives or fumigants. In addition, the content of any certified organic product must be at least 95 percent organic products,

chemical change. A change in which a chemical reaction is produced and a new substance created, as when gasoline is burned to produce carbon dioxide. Compare *physical change*.

chemical contamination. The presence of a chemical that makes something unfit for its intended use. Pesticide contamination, for example, makes soil unfit for food production.

chemical formula. A shorthand way to show the number of atoms (or ions) in the basic structural unit of a compound. Examples include NaCl, H_2O, and $C_6H_{12}O_6$.

chemosynthesis. The process in which some organisms (usually certain types of bacteria) convert, without sunlight, inorganic chemical compounds into organic nutrient compounds—food energy for their own use. Contrasts with *photosynthesis*.

chemotrophs. Producers, including algae and bacteria, that convert the energy found in inorganic chemical compounds into more complex energy without the use of sunlight. See also *consumers, producers*.

clear-cutting. A system of tree harvesting that removes all the trees in a given area, as opposed to selective cutting that leaves some trees standing. Replanting after clear-cutting can be difficult.

climax community. The mature stage of succession in a particular area, in which all organisms and nonliving factors are in balance.

closed system. See *systems*.

coal. The most abundant fossil fuel in the world, with reserves four to five times that of oil and gas combined. It has a relatively high net useful energy yield and is highly effective for providing industrial heat.

coastal wetlands. Coastal area that provides breeding grounds and habitats for many marine organisms as well as for waterfowl, shorebirds, and other wildlife.

coastal zone. The area where the ocean meets the land, which constitutes 10 percent of the ocean's area but contains 90 percent of all marine species.

co-generation. The production of two useful forms of energy from the same source, such as heat and power. See also *district heating*.

commensalism. An interaction between species in which one benefits and the other is neither helped nor harmed. See also *mutualism, symbiosis*.

community. An area where different species interact, such as an alpine community or a prairie community. See also *habitat*.

company towns. Small settlements that private firms involved in natural resource exploitation established to house their workers. In many company towns, these firms owned most of the businesses (e.g., grocery stories), public services (e.g., hospitals or clinics, recreational facilities), housing, and property. Although this level of ownership is not present today, the term *company towns* sometimes refers to towns where there is one primary employer, such as a mining or forestry company or major manufacturer.

competitive exclusion principle. When two species are competing for the same resources, one must migrate to another area if possible, shift its feeding habits or behaviour, suffer a sharp decline in population numbers, or become extinct.

compounds. One of the basic forms of chemical composition, which involves two or more different elements held together in fixed proportions by the attraction in the chemical bonds between their constituent atoms. See also *elements*.

conservation tillage. A soil conservation practice that involves leaving most of the crop residue on the soil surface to protect against erosion, reduce soil crusting, and increase the organic matter content of soil.

consumers. Those organisms that eat the cells, tissues, or waste products of other organisms. Animals are common consumers. Also called *heterotrophs*. See also *chemotrophs, producers*.

continuous clear-cutting. In timber harvesting, locating cut blocks adjacent to each other in successive years, a practice that rapidly lays bare much larger areas.

controlled experiment. An experiment designed to test the effects of independent variables on a dependent variable by changing one independent variable at a time.

conventional tillage. The practice of incorporating most of the crop residue after harvest into the soil.

coral reefs. Found in warm tropical and subtropical oceans, these formations are rich in life and may contain more than 3000 species of corals, fish, and shellfish.

country food. Food grown by people in small communities living in harmony with their local environment.

crude birth rate. The annual number of live births per 1000 population, without regard to age or sex composition.

crude death rate. The annual number of deaths per 1000 population.

crude growth rate. The net change, or difference, between the crude birth rate and the crude death rate.

cryosphere. Those portions of the Earth's surface where water is in a solid form, including snow, freshwater ice, sea ice, glaciers and permafrost. The Arctic and Antarctic, and many high-elevation places in between, are part of the cryosphere.

decomposers. See *microconsumers*.

deductive reasoning. Drawing conclusions from observations of the natural world by means of logical reasoning. Compare *inductive reasoning*.

deforestation. To clear an area of forests or trees, usually for lumber or agricultural uses.

demographic transition. A four-stage model of population change that links industrial development with zero population growth, and suggests a postindustrial phase that would focus more on sustainable forms of economic development.

demographic trap. A state in which a nation or population is stuck in the second stage of demographic transition, with a low death rate, a high birth rate, and increasing demand on available resources.

demography. The study of the characteristics and changes in the size and structure of human populations.

dependent variable. See *responding variable*.

desertification. A combination of human-induced environmental degradation (such as overgrazing of livestock) superimposed on a natural drought situation, causing expansion of desert conditions into areas that previously were more humid.

detritus feeders. See *detrivores*.

detrivores. Consumers that ingest fragments of dead organic material. Examples are earthworms and maggots.

differential reproduction. The ability to produce more offspring with the same favourable adaptations as the parents, which will allow them to survive under changed environmental conditions.

discharge. Refers to the amount of water returned to the original source. See also *withdrawal uses*.

dissolved oxygen content. The amount of oxygen dissolved in a given volume of water at a particular temperature and pressure. This can be a limiting factor on the growth of many aquatic populations.

district heating. An effort to maximize energy efficiency in power generating stations that involves a steam cycle that is modified so that the steam is extracted and used to produce hot water. The water is then pumped through pipes to surrounding buildings to supply heat. See also *co-generation*.

Dobson unit. One Dobson unit is equivalent to a layer of pure ozone 0.01 mm thick at standard temperature (0°C) and pressure (101.3 kPa) spread over Earth's surface.

doubling time. The length of time required for a population to double in size.

drainage basin. The area of land that contributes water and sediment to a river.

driftnetting. The placing of very long gillnets (2.5 km and longer) that drift with currents and wind for the purpose of entangling fish in webbed panel(s).

eco-certification. The independent testing and verification of a government agency, nongovernmental organization, or an industry consortium of environmental practices by a company, agency, or organization. Eco-certification has been pursued in several industries, including agriculture and forestry.

ecological diversity. The variety of biological communities, such as forests, deserts, grasslands, and streams, that interact with one another and with their physical and chemical (nonliving) environments. See also *species diversity*.

ecological footprint. A link between human lifestyles and ecosystems that allows people to visualize the impact of their consumption patterns and activities on ecosystems.

ecological health. An ecosystem where native species are present at viable population levels.

ecological integrity. A condition in which the structure and function of an ecosystem are unimpaired by human activity and are likely to persist into the future.

ecological justification. A rationale for the conservation of nature based on the idea that the environment provides specific functions necessary to the persistence of our life. Compare *aesthetic arguments, moral justification, utilitarian justification*.

ecological niche. The role an organism plays within the structure and functions of an ecosystem, and the way it interacts with other living things and with its physical environment.

ecology. The study of the interactions of living organisms with one another and with their nonliving environment of matter and energy.

ecosphere. See *biosphere*.

ecosystem. A community and its members interacting with each other and their nonliving environment.

ecosystem approach. Concentrates on managing entire ecosystems rather than managing individual parts of the systems.

ecosystem management. See *ecosystem approach*.

electrons. Negatively charged ions that continually orbit the nucleus of an atom and are held in orbit by attraction to the positive charge of the nucleus. See also *neutrons, protons*.

elements. One of the basic forms of chemical composition. All matter is built from the 109 known chemical elements; these are the simplest building blocks of all matter. See also *compounds*.

endemic species. A species that is native to a particular geographic region.

energy. The ability or capacity to do work. Energy enables us to move matter and change it from one form to another.

energy quality. The measure of an energy source's ability to perform useful work, such as running electrical devices or motors. See also *high-quality energy, low-quality energy*.

entropy. A measure of randomness or disorder. The higher the entropy, the greater its disorder. See *high-quality energy, high-quality matter, low-quality energy, low-quality matter*.

environment. The surroundings in which plants and animals live, affected by various physical factors such as temperature, water, light, and food resources.

environmental ethics. A new discipline that analyzes the issues regarding our moral obligations to future generations with respect to the environment.

environmental impact assessment (EIA). A process that aims to provide decision makers with scientifically researched and documented evidence to identify the likely consequences of undertaking new developments and changing natural systems. See also *environmental impact statement*.

environmental impact statement (EIS). A key component of an environmental impact assessment, an EIS provides a nontechnical summary of the study, including the main project characteristics, aspects of the environment likely to be affected, possible alternatives, and suggested measures and systems to monitor or reduce any harmful effects. See also *environmental impact assessment*.

environmental resistance. The limits set by the environment that prevent organisms from reproducing indefinitely at an exponential rate.

epiphytes. Plants that use their roots to capture nutrients and moisture from the air and to attach themselves to other plants, particularly in tropical forests (and some in temperate rain forests).

estuaries. A body of coastal water partly surrounded by land, with access to the open sea and a large supply of fresh water from rivers. These conditions provide excellent conditions for many important shellfish and fin fish species.

ethanol. A fuel converted from biomass materials and used to power motor vehicles, either directly as fuel or as an octane-enhancing gasoline additive. Ethanol can reduce carbon monoxide emissions from regular gasoline blends.

eukaryotic. Cells with a high degree of internal organization, including a nucleus (genetic material surrounded by a membrane) and several other internal parts surrounded by membranes. See also *prokaryotic*.

eutrophic. A lake enriched with nutrients in excess of what is required by producers. See also *mesotrophic, oligotrophic*.

eutrophication. An increase in the concentration of plant nutrients in water. Natural eutrophication is a slow process, but human-induced eutrophication (as from fertilizers used in agriculture) may accelerate the process and make water unfit for human consumption and for aquatic organisms.

exclusive economic zone (EEZ). The area of exclusive fishing rights granted to Canada in the 1982 United Nations Convention on the Law of the Sea. The zone came into force in 1994.

exotic species. A species that enters an ecosystem from a different part of the world through introduction (deliberately or accidentally) by humans.

exponential growth. Growth in a species that takes place at a constant rate per time period. When plotted on a graph, the exponential growth curve is J-shaped.

ex situ conservation. Conservation of species or genetic materials under artificial conditions, away from the ecosystems to which they belong.

extinction. The process whereby a species is eliminated from existence when it cannot adapt genetically and reproduce successfully under new environmental conditions. See also *background extinction, mass extinction*.

fact. An observation that all (or almost all) scientists agree is correct.

first law of energy. See *first law of thermodynamics*.

first law of thermodynamics. During a physical or chemical change, energy is neither created nor destroyed. See also *second law of thermodynamics*.

flaring. A method of disposing of unwanted, unprocessed natural gas. Gas is burned to release hydrogen sulphide (sour gas) and to avoid the buildup of potentially explosive levels of gas at work sites.

food chains. The sequence of who feeds on or decomposes whom in an ecosystem.

food web. A complex network of feeding relationships in which the flow of energy and materials through an ecosystem takes place. That flow occurs on the basis of a range of food choices on the part of each organism involved.

fossil fuels. The remains of prehistoric animals, forests, and sea floor life that have become buried in layers of sediment and decomposed very slowly, eventually being converted into crude oil. See also *hydrocarbons*.

fundamental niche. The full range of physical, chemical, and biological factors each species could use if there were no competition from other species. See also *interspecific competition*.

gene pool. The sum of all genes possessed by the individuals of a population.

general fertility rate. The number of live births per 1000 women of childbearing age per year.

generalist species. Species with the ability to live in many different places while tolerating a wide range of environmental conditions. Humans are considered a generalist species. See also *specialist species*.

genes. Segments of various deoxyribonucleic acid (DNA) molecules found in chromosomes. Genes impart certain inheritable traits to organisms.

genetic diversity. The diversity within a given population that shares common structural, functional, and behavioural traits but varies slightly in genetic makeup and so exhibits slightly different behaviours and appearances.

ghostfishing. The consequence of fish becoming entangled and drowning in lost and/or unmanned fishnets.

global warming potential. A concept developed to take into account the differing times that gases remain in the atmosphere and their individual radiative forcings in order to evaluate the potential climate effects of equal emissions of each of the greenhouse gases.

gross primary productivity. The rate at which producers in an ecosystem capture and store chemical energy as biomass. Compare *net primary productivity*.

gross water use. The total amount of water used (intake + recirculation).

groundwater. Water that has accumulated beneath the Earth's surface in underground aquifers (reservoirs) and in the saturation zone below the water table. Water percolates down through soils, gravel, and rock and rises up from below to slowly replenish aquifers and saturation zones. Compare *surface water*.

habitat. The place where an organism or population lives, such as an ocean, a forest, or a stream. See also *community*.

halocarbons. Any compound of carbon and a halogen (one of the chemical elements fluorine, chlorine, bromine, iodine, astatine) used especially as a refrigerant and propellant. CFC-11, for instance, was used widely in plastic foam blowing and CFC-12 was used in vehicle air conditioners and refrigerator coolants. Now being phased out because of potential to cause harm to stratospheric ozone layer.

halons. Compounds related to chlorofluorocarbons that contain bromine and are used in fire extinguisher systems. Implicated as ozone-destroying gases in the stratosphere.

heat island. A microclimate in which the air temperature is slightly higher than in the surrounding area. In an urban heat island, for example, the temperature in the city is 1–2°C higher than in the rural area around it.

herbivores. Organisms that eat green plants directly as a source of nutrients. Deer are common herbivores. See also *carnivores, omnivores.*

heterotrophs. See *consumers.*

highgrading. An unsound practice associated with selective cutting techniques that involves logging the highest-quality and most accessible timber first.

high-quality energy. Concentrated energy sources such as electricity, gasoline, and some food types that enable people and machines to perform useful tasks. See also *energy quality, low-quality energy.*

high-quality matter. Material such as coal or salt deposits commonly found near the Earth's surface in an organized or concentrated form, so that its potential for use as a resource is great. See *low-quality matter.*

human cultural diversity. The variety of human cultures that represent our adaptability and survival options in the face of changing conditions.

hydrocarbons. Any of a class of compounds containing only hydrogen and carbon, which include fossil fuels. See also *fossil fuels.*

hydroelectric power. Electrical power generated from the energy of falling water or any other hydraulic source.

hydrologic cycle. The movement of water between the atmosphere, terrestrial systems, and the oceans, through evaporation, runoff from streams and rivers, and precipitation.

hydrosphere. The Earth's supply of moisture in all its forms: liquid, frozen, and gaseous. This includes surface water, underground water, frozen water, water vapour in the atmosphere, and moisture in the tissues and organs of living things.

hypothesis. An explanation that is based on testable observations and experiments, and that can be accepted until it is disproved.

igneous rock. Rock formed from molten materials crystallizing at the Earth's surface (such as lava from volcanoes), or beneath the surface (such as granite). See also *metamorphic rock, sedimentary rock.*

immigrant species. Those species that migrate into or are introduced into an ecosystem, deliberately or accidentally, by humans.

impact-benefit agreements. Agreements undertaken in large-scale resource developments among industry, government, and affected communities. Normally they are undertaken where Aboriginal communities may be affected by resource extraction and production. Agreements may cover a range of social and economic concerns, including employment and training, economic development and business opportunities, community and social support, as well as implementation, coordination, and funding.

independent variable. A condition that is deliberately manipulated by scientists to test the response in an experiment. See also *operational definitions, responding variable.*

indicator species. Those species that provide early warnings of environmental damage to communities or ecosystems.

inductive reasoning. Drawing a general conclusion based on a limited set of observations. Compare *deductive reasoning.*

infant mortality rate. The ratio of deaths of infants under 12 months per 1000 live births.

inferences. Conclusions derived either by logical reasoning from premises and/or evidence, or by insight or analogy based on evidence.

inorganic compounds. Any compound not classified as an organic compound. Compare *organic compound.*

in situ conservation. Conservation of ecosystems and the maintenance and recovery of viable populations of species in their typical surroundings.

instream uses. Water used in its natural setting for hydroelectric power, transportation, fisheries, and other applications. See also *withdrawal uses.*

intake. The quantity of water withdrawn or used. See also *withdrawal uses.*

interspecific competition. Competition from other species for one or more of the same limited resources of food, sunlight, water, soil, nutrients, or space. See also *fundamental niche.*

intraspecific competition. Competition that occurs when individuals of the same species try to gain access to the same resources.

intrinsic value. A value placed on the inherent qualities of a species and/or an ecosystem, independent of its value to humans.

invertebrates. Animals without backbones, such as jellyfish, worms, insects, and spiders. Compare *vertebrates.*

ions. Subatomic, electrically charged particles in an atom. See also *protons, neutrons.*

ISO 14000. The series of management systems adopted by the International Organization for Standardization that address environmental quality. The purpose of these standards is to provide a holistic and strategic approach to an organization's environmental policies, programs, or activities. The standards do not address the quality of the products produced by the organization.

keystone species. Those species that play a crucial role in helping to maintain the ecosystems of which they are a part, by pollination, regulation of populations, or other activities.

kinetic energy. Energy associated with the movement of matter and mass. A moving air mass such as wind has kinetic energy, as do flowing streams, moving cars, heat, and electricity. See also *potential energy.*

law of conservation of matter. Matter is neither created nor destroyed, but is combined and rearranged in different ways.

law of tolerance. The presence, number, and distribution of a species in an ecosystem are determined by whether the levels of one or more physical or chemical factors fall within the range tolerated by the species. See also *limiting factor principle.*

limiting factor principle. Too much or too little of any abiotic factor can limit or prevent growth of a population, even if all other factors are at or near the optimum range of tolerance. See also *law of tolerance.*

limnetic zone. The open water area away from the shore of a lake or pond, with less light penetration and fewer producers. See also *littoral zone, profundal zone.*

lithosphere. The upper zone of the Earth's mantle and the inorganic mixture of rocks and mineral matter in the Earth's crust.

littoral zone. The shallow water and vegetated area along the shore of a lake or pond, and the most productive zone of the lake. See also *limnetic zone, profundal zone.*

long-distance commuting. The practice of flying miners into a mine to work for a designated period and then flying them back to their homes in larger communities for another period.

low-quality energy. Dispersed energy, such as the heat stored in the oceans, with little capacity to perform useful tasks. See also *energy quality, high-quality energy.*

low-quality matter. Hard-to-reach matter, such as that dispersed or diluted in the atmosphere or oceans. See also *high-quality matter.*

macroconsumers. Organisms that feed by ingesting or engulfing particles, parts, or entire bodies of other organisms, living or dead, including herbivores, carnivores, omnivores, scavengers, and detrivores.

macronutrients. The main constituents of the complex organic compounds required by all living organisms. The six major macronutrients are carbon, oxygen, hydrogen, nitrogen, phosphorus, and sulphur. See also *micronutrients.*

mangrove swamp. A collection of tropical evergreen trees with stiltlike aerial roots that cause thick undergrowth and provide habitat for marine organisms, waterfowl, and other coastal species.

mass. The amount of material in an object.

mass extinction. The disappearance of numerous species over a relatively short period of geological time. See also *background extinction.*

mass number. Sum of the number of protons and the number of neutrons in the nucleus of an atom. This sum gives the approximate mass of that atom.

matter. Anything that has mass and takes up space, including everything that is solid, liquid, or gaseous.

mesotrophic. A lake that falls in the mid-range between the two extremes of nutrient enrichment required by producers. See also *eutrophic, oligotrophic.*

metamorphic rock. Rock formed when existing rocks lying deep below the Earth's surface are subjected to high temperatures, high pressures, chemically active fluids, or a combination of these agents, causing the rocks' crystal structure to change. See also *igneous rock, sedimentary rock.*

microconsumers. Organisms that live on or within their food source, completing the breakdown of complex molecules into simpler compounds (which we call rot or decay).

micronutrients. The trace elements of complex organic compounds required by all living organisms. These include boron, copper, zinc, and others. See also *macronutrients.*

milling. In the processing of minerals, the crushing and grinding of ores to separate the useful materials from the nonuseful ones. See also *tailings.*

mineral exploration. Finding geological, geophysical, or geochemical conditions that differ from those of their surroundings.

mineral fuels. Crude oil and equivalents, including natural gas, coal, and natural gas byproducts. In 2002, they accounted for approximately 77 percent of the total value of Canadian mineral production.

mineral resources. Elements, chemical compounds, minerals, or rocks concentrated in a form that can be extracted to obtain a usable commodity.

molecules. Particle formed when two or more atoms of the same or different elements combine.

monoculture. Planting and cultivation of a single crop (or even a single strain or subspecies), usually on a large area of land.

montane. An ecozone in the Rocky Mountains dominated by coniferous trees. The region is important for its biodiversity and its comparatively mild microclimate that provides winter habitat for many mountain-dwelling species.

moral justification. A rationale for the conservation of nature based on the idea that elements of the environment have a right to exist, independent of human desires. Compare *aesthetic arguments, ecological justification, utilitarian justification.*

mutation. The random and unpredictable changes in DNA molecules that can be transmitted to offspring and produce variability. See also *adaptation.*

mutualism. A symbiotic relationship in which both interacting species benefit, as when honeybees pollinate flowers as they feed on the flower's nectar. See also *commensalism, symbiosis.*

native species. See *endemic species.*

natural capital. Earth's natural resources and ecological systems that provide vital life-support services, such as maintenance of soil fertility, flood control, and stabilization of climate. Natural capital refers to all aspects of our environment used to provide manufactured goods, to secure our quality of life, and to support a range of economic activities such as agriculture, forestry, tourism, and recreation. It includes stocks of resources such as minerals and timber, services from ecosystems such as fertile soils and clean water, and ecosystems such as wetlands and oceans. It can be depleted through human actions, such as poor agricultural practices, overharvesting, water pollution, toxic contamination, development, and other activities. *Natural capital* is sometimes used interchangeably with the term *natural resources,* although with its emphasis on ecosystems and their services, natural capital does have a broader meaning.

natural gas. A gaseous hydrocarbon mixture of methane combined with smaller amounts of propane and butane. The conventional or "associated" type is located underground above most reserves of crude oil, while the nonassociated type is found on its own in dry wells.

natural resources. The components of nature that are useful to us and are available at a price we are willing to pay, including stocks of resources such as minerals and timber. Natural resources are often classified into nonrenewable and renewable resources.

natural selection. The tendency for only the best adapted organisms to survive and reproduce in a given environment.

net primary productivity. The rate at which organic matter is incorporated into plant bodies so as to produce growth. See also *gross primary productivity.*

net useful energy. The usable amount of energy available from an energy source over its lifetime.

neutrons. Uncharged or electrically neutral ions, which cluster with protons in the centre of an atom and compose its nucleus. See also *electrons, ions, protons*.

nitrogen fixation. A part of the nitrogen cycle in which atmospheric nitrogen is converted into other chemical forms available to plants.

nonfuel minerals. Metallic minerals such as copper, gold, iron ore, nickel, and zinc, as well as nonmetallic minerals such as potash, sand, and gravel.

nonpoint sources. Pollutants discharged in an unconfined manner.

nonrenewable resources. Resources such as coal, oil, and other fossil fuels that are finite in supply or replaced so slowly that they are soon depleted. Compare *renewable resources*.

nuclear energy. The energy released by reactions within atomic nuclei, such as nuclear fission or nuclear fusion.

nutrient cycles. The means by which the nutrient elements and their compounds cycle continually through Earth's atmosphere, hydrosphere, lithosphere, and biosphere.

nutrients. The materials that an organism must take in to enable it to live, grow, and reproduce.

observations. Information gathered through any of our five senses or instruments that extend these senses.

oil sand. A combination of clay, sand, water, and bitumen. Canada is home to the largest known oil sand deposits in the world. See also *bitumen*.

oil shale. Rock that contains a solid mixture of hydrocarbon compounds called kerogen. Once crushed and heated, kerogen vapour is condensed to form heavy, slow-flowing oil shale.

oligotrophic. A lake with minimal levels of nutrients required for producers. See also *eutrophic, mesotrophic*.

omnivores. Consumers that eat both plants and animals, such as black bears, pigs, and humans. See also *carnivores, herbivores*.

one-industry town. A community whose existence depends on the exploitation of a single resource.

open-pit mining. A type of mining in which minerals are extracted from the earth by digging that leaves a large pit in the surface. Compare *strip mining*.

open system. See *systems*.

operational definitions. Set of criteria that tell scientists what to look for or what to do in order to carry out the measurement, construction, or manipulation of variables. See also *independent variable, responding variable*.

organic compound. Molecule that contains atoms of the element carbon, usually combined with each other and with atoms of one or more other elements such as chlorine, fluorine, hydrogen, nitrogen, oxygen, phosphorus, and sulphur. Compare *inorganic compound*.

organic farming. Producing crops and livestock naturally by using natural soil-forming processes, including organic fertilizer (compost, manure, legumes) and natural pest control (plants that repel bugs, bugs that eat harmful bugs, and environmental controls such as crop rotation), instead of using commercial inorganic fertilizers and synthetic pesticides and herbicides.

organism. A complex organization of cells, tissues, organs, and body systems that work together to create a multicellular individual such as a bear, whale, human, or orchid.

organochlorines. Carbon–hydrogen compounds in which one or more hydrogen atoms have been replaced by a chlorine atom.

organohalides. Carbon–hydrogen compounds that are bonded to a halogen (fluorine, chlorine, bromine, or iodine).

overburden. The layers of rock and soil that overlay mineral deposits. These layers are removed during surface mining.

ozone. An oxygen gas (O_3) that is an air pollutant in the lower atmosphere but beneficial in the upper atmosphere. See also *ozone layer*.

ozone layer. The layer of ozone in the stratosphere that filters out harmful ultraviolet radiation from the sun.

parasitism. A symbiotic relationship in which the parasite benefits by obtaining nourishment from the host and the host is weakened or killed by the parasite.

pelagic environment. The ocean water, one of the two main divisions of the open sea environment. The marine environment from the low-tide mark to the open ocean within the vertical division from the surface to floor. See also *benthic environment*.

permafrost. A permanently frozen layer of subsoil, characteristic of the tundra biome.

persistence. In reference to chemical compounds, those substances that do not break down easily in ecosystems and remain in the environment for long periods of time. Many organochlorine compounds are persistent.

phenology. The study of periodic occurrences in nature (such as timing of first and full bloom of plants, ripening of fruit, and migration of birds) and their relation to climate.

photochemical smog. The product of chemical reactions involving hydrocarbons and nitrous oxides in the presence of sunlight.

photosynthesis. The process by which living organisms—primarily plants and some bacteria—use water and carbon dioxide to convert the sun's energy into chemical energy (carbohydrates) and provide oxygen.

photovoltaics. The direct conversion of sunlight into electricity.

physical change. A change from one state to another, as when water changes from ice to its liquid state. Compare *chemical change*.

point sources. Pollution sources that discharge substances from a clearly identifiable or discrete pathway such as a pipe, ditch, channel, tunnel, or conduit.

polar stratospheric clouds. Formed in extremely cold temperatures within the polar vortex as it matures, cools, and descends, these clouds have been linked to depletion of the ozone layer.

polar vortex. An atmospheric condition that occurs during the polar winter night when the Antarctic air mass is partially isolated from the rest of the atmosphere and circulates around the pole.

pollutants. Substances that adversely affect the physical, chemical, or biological quality of the Earth's environment or that accumulate in the cells or tissues of living organisms in amounts that threaten the health or survival of these organisms.

polynyas. An area of unfrozen sea water, created by local water currents in northern oceans. They act as biological hotspots and serve as vital winter refuges for marine mammals.

population. A group of individuals of the same species living and interacting in the same geographic area at the same time.

population age structure. The distribution of the population by age, used in analysis of demographic trends.

population lag effect. See *population momentum.*

population momentum. When a population achieves replacement fertility, that population continues to grow for several generations before stabilizing.

potential energy. Energy stored and potentially available for use, such as the chemical energy stored in gasoline or food molecules. See also *kinetic energy.*

precautionary principle. A form of risk management that suggests that where there are threats of serious or irreversible damage to the environment, the absence of full scientific understanding or certainty about environmental change shall not be used as a reason for postponing measures or decisions to prevent environmental deterioration.

precious metals. Metals, such as gold and silver, that are valuable to humans because of their rarity or appearance.

predation. When members of a predator species feed on parts or all of an organism of a prey species.

predator. An organism, usually an animal, that feeds on other organisms, as when a turtle eats a fish in a freshwater pond ecosystem.

predator–prey relationships. The most obvious form of species interaction, which occurs when one organism (the predator) feeds on another (the prey).

prey. The organism consumed by a predator.

primary consumer. See *herbivores.*

primary energy use. The total requirements for all uses of energy, including energy used by the final consumer, energy in transforming one energy form to another, and energy used by suppliers in providing energy to the market.

primary succession. The development of biotic communities in a previously uninhabited and barren habitat with little or no soil. Compare *secondary succession.*

primary treatment. The lowest level of treatment in the management of municipal wastes that involves the mechanical removal of large solids, sediment, and some organic matter. See also *secondary treatment, tertiary treatment.*

principle of connectedness. Everything in the natural world is connected to and intermingled with everything else, and a change in environmental conditions will have multiple effects.

producers. Those self-nourishing organisms that perform photosynthesis by converting relatively simple inorganic substances such as water, carbon dioxide, and nutrients into complex chemicals such as carbohydrates, lipids, and proteins. Green plants and phytoplankton are common producers. See also *chemotrophs, consumers.*

profundal zone. The deepest zone of a lake, where lack of light means that no producers can survive. See also *limnetic zone, littoral zone.*

prokaryotic. Cells that lack a nuclear envelope and other internal cell membranes, including bacteria. Compare *eukaryotic.*

protons. Positively charged ions that cluster with neutrons in the centre of an atom and compose its nucleus. See also *electrons, ions, neutrons.*

qualitative data. Non-numerical records of independent and dependent variables kept during experiments.

quantitative data. Numerical records of independent and dependent variables kept during experiments.

realized niche. That portion of a fundamental niche actually occupied by a species, which results from the sharing of resources in a given ecosystem.

recirculation. Water that is reused in a particular distribution system. It may be used more than once in a specific process or used once and then recycled to another process.

reclamation. The rehabilitation of a site (a disused mine, for example) in order to make it a viable and, if possible, self-sustaining ecosystem that is compatible with a healthy environment.

regional sustainability. An alternative to the globalization of the food production system in which developing countries would be encouraged to grow food first for themselves and then for export.

renewable resources. Resources such as forests, solar energy, and fisheries that can be replaced by environmental processes in a time frame meaningful to humans. Also known as renewable natural capital. Compare *nonrenewable resources.*

replacement fertility. The fertility rate needed to ensure that the population remains constant as each set of parents is replaced by their offspring.

resource partitioning. The division of scarce resources in order that species with similar requirements can use the resources in different ways, in different places, and at different times.

riparian area. The "thin green line" along streams, rivers, and wetlands, formed as the result of water, soil, and vegetation interacting with one another. Part of extensive drainage basins, these productive green areas provide forage, shelter, fish, wildlife, and water.

salinity. The amounts of various salts dissolved in a given volume of water. This can be a limiting factor on the growth of both aquatic and terrestrial populations.

salinization. The accumulation of salts in soil—a process that may result in soil too salty to support plant growth.

scavengers. Consumers such as vultures and hyenas that eat dead organic material.

scientific method. Systematic methods used in scientific investigations of the natural world, which include designing controlled experiments, gathering data, and developing and testing hypotheses.

secondary consumers. See *carnivores.*

secondary energy use. Energy used by final consumers for residential, agricultural, commercial, industrial, and transportation purposes.

secondary succession. The development of biotic communities in an area where the natural vegetation has been removed or destroyed but where soil is present. See also *primary succession.*

secondary treatment. The second level of treatment in the management of municipal wastes that employs biological processes by which bacteria degrade most of the dissolved organics, about 30 percent of the phosphates, and about 50 percent of the nitrates. See also *primary treatment, tertiary treatment*.

second law of energy. See *second law of thermodynamics*.

second law of thermodynamics. With each change in form, some energy is degraded to a less useful form and given off into the surroundings, usually as low-quality heat. See also *first law of thermodynamics*.

sedimentary rock. Rock formed when small bits and pieces of matter and sediments are carried by wind or rain and then deposited, compacted, and cemented to form rock. See also *igneous rock, metamorphic rock*.

silviculture. The theory and practice of controlling the establishment, composition, growth, and quality of forest stands.

soil compaction. A form of structural degradation in soil in which soil is packed so tightly that its air spaces are closed, reducing aeration and infiltration and thus reducing the ability of the soil to support plant growth. Caused mainly by the repeated passing of heavy machinery over wet soil.

solar energy. Energy derived from the sun in the form of solar radiation.

specialist species. Species with the ability to live in only one type of habitat, eat only a few types of food, or tolerate a narrow range of climatic or environmental conditions. See also *generalist species*.

speciation. The formation of two or more species from one as the result of divergent natural selection and response to changes in environmental conditions.

species. A group of organisms that resemble one another in appearance, behaviour, chemical makeup and processes, and genetic structure, and that produce fertile offspring under natural conditions.

species diversity. The number of different species and the relative abundance of each in different habitats on Earth. See also *ecological diversity*.

stewardship. The concept that mankind has an ethical responsibility to care for plants, animals, and the environment as a whole, due to our superior intellect and power to change the natural world.

stratosphere. The layer above the troposphere that contains the ozone layer and protects life on Earth's surface by absorbing most incoming solar ultraviolet radiation. See also *atmosphere, troposphere*.

strip mining. Surface mining in which heavy machinery strips away the overlying layer of rock and soil to create a trench that exposes the mineral resource below. Compare *open-pit mining*.

succession. The process of community development over time, in which the composition and function of communities and ecosystems change.

summerfallow. Land left unsown and unharvested, usually for one season, to conserve moisture in the soil and to allow accumulation of nitrogen and other nutrients.

surface runoff. Precipitation that flows on the land (instead of soaking into it) and into bodies of surface water. May carry contaminants.

surface waters. All bodies of water, such as lakes, rivers, streams, and oceans, that lie on the surface of the Earth. Compare *groundwater*.

sustainability (economic). To promote diversified and efficient use of environmental resources that minimizes waste and provides environmentally sound economic activities for current and future generations.

sustainability (environmental). The ability of an ecosystem to maintain ecological processes, functions, biodiversity, and productivity over time. See also *sustainable development*.

sustainability (social). To use environmental resources in a way that improves our the ability to meet human needs equitably for present and future generations, encourages a high quality of life, and involves people directly in decisions that affect them.

sustainable development. Maintaining environmental resources so that they continue to provide benefits to living things and the larger environment of which they are a part. See also *sustainability*.

sustained yield. The practice of harvesting renewable resources so that an even flow of resources in perpetuity may be obtained.

symbiosis. Any intimate relationship between two or more different species. For example, the fur of the three-toed sloth is often occupied by algae and insects that feed on the algae. See also *commensalism, mutualism*.

synergistic effects. Outcomes in which the effects of two or more substances or organisms acting together are greater than the sum of their individual effects (they are multiplicative, not additive).

systems. Systems may be open or closed. A system that is open in regard to some factor exchanges that factor with other systems. An example of an open system is the ocean that exchanges water with the atmosphere. A system that is closed in regard to some factor does not exchange that factor with other systems. Earth is an open system in relation to energy and a closed system in regard to matter.

tailings. The nonuseful materials removed from the mill after the recoverable minerals have been extracted in the processing of minerals. See also *milling*.

Talloires Declaration. A statement signed by the presidents and chancellors of more than 300 institutions of higher education committing their institutions to addressing environmental pollution and degradation and depletion of natural resources. This declaration also committed these institutions to developing interdisciplinary approaches to curricula, research initiatives, operations, and outreach activities that support an environmentally sustainable future.

taxonomic. The classification of organisms according to evolutionary relationships.

tertiary consumers. Carnivores that eat other carnivorous (or secondary) consumers.

tertiary treatment. The third level of treatment in the management of municipal wastes that involves a chemical process to remove phosphates, nitrates, and other contaminants not removed during secondary treatment. See also *primary treatment, secondary treatment*.

theories. Models based on currently accepted hypotheses that offer broadly conceived, logically coherent, and well-supported concepts.

threshold effect. The harmful or even fatal reaction to exceeding the tolerance limit of a species in a given ecosystem. See also *acclimation, law of tolerance*.

tillage erosion. The movement of soil downhill during plowing operations that contributes to soil erosion and degradation on rolling or hummocky land.

total allowable catch (TAC). A limit set by the Northwest Atlantic Fisheries Organization (NAFO), an agency of the United Nations Food and Agricultural Organization, to ensure that groundfish stocks were not depleted.

total fertility rate (TFR). The average number of children expected to be born to a woman during her lifetime.

transitional. Operators of nonorganic production systems who wish to establish organic management practices follow a set of steps, set out by the National Standard for Organic Production Systems, to attain certification.

trophic level. The feeding level to which each organism belongs depending on whether it is a producer or a consumer and on what it eats or decomposes.

troposphere. The lowest layer of the atmosphere and the zone in which most weather events occur. See also *atmosphere, stratosphere*.

urban shadow effects. Urban impacts that extend over large areas and cause declines in agriculture in urban regions.

utilitarian justification. A rationale for the conservation of nature based on the idea that the environment provides individuals with direct economic benefits. Compare *aesthetic arguments, ecological justification, moral justification*.

vertebrates. Animals with backbones, including fish, amphibians, reptiles, birds, and mammals. Compare *invertebrates*.

volatile organic compounds (VOCs). Compounds that result primarily from the combustion of fossil fuels in motor vehicles. Most VOCs are hydrocarbons, such as methane, propane, chlorofluorocarbons, and benzene. They are also found in the vapours of substances such as gasoline, solvents, and oil-based paints.

water budget. The annual global fresh water budget is a balance among evaporation, atmospheric transport, precipitation, and storage. Scientists use factors in the hydrologic cycle, including amounts and rates of precipitation, evaporation, transpiration, stream flow, and subsurface flow to create a model called the water budget that is used to estimate the global water supply on the Earth's surface.

water resources. The network of rivers, lakes, and other surface waters that supply water for food production and other essential human systems.

watershed. An area of land in which all of the water under it or draining from its surface ends in the same place. Watersheds are separated from each other by the highest points of elevation in a region, for example, the Continental Divide, formed by the Rocky Mountains.

wetlands. Transitional areas between aquatic and terrestrial ecosystems, usually covered with fresh water for part of the year, with characteristic soils and vegetation.

withdrawal uses. Water removed from its natural setting by pipes or channels for a particular human use (human consumption, mineral extraction, irrigation, and other applications). Compare *instream uses*.

worldview. A set of commonly held values, ideas, and images concerning the nature of reality and the role of humanity within it.

zero tillage. The practice of leaving soil undisturbed between the harvest of one crop and planting of the next; includes direct seeding into stubble or sod. Also known as no tillage.

LIST OF ACRONYMS

ACAP, Atlantic Coastal Action Program
AECL, Atomic Energy of Canada Limited
AEUB, Alberta Energy and Utilities Board
AFS, Aboriginal Fishing Strategy
ANWR, Arctic National Wildlife Refuge
AOGCM, atmospheric-ocean general circulation models
APF, Agricultural Policy Framework
ARET, Accelerated Reduction/Elimination of Toxins
ASH, Autonomous and Sustainable Housing
ASWP, Atlantic Salmon Watch Program
ATES, aquifer thermal energy storage
AWA, Alberta Wilderness Association
BHP, Broken Hill Proprietary
BMP, best management practice(s)
BOD, biological oxygen demand
BSE, bovine spongiform encephalopathy
CAC, criteria air contaminant
CANDU, Canada Deuterium Uranium (nuclear reactor)
CANMET, Canada Centre for Mineral and Energy Technology
CARE, Conservation of Agriculture, Resources and Environment
CBD, United Nations Convention on Biological Diversity
CBIN, The Canadian Biodiversity Information Network
CBM, coalbed methane
CBR, crude birth rate
CCAF, Climate Change Action Fund
CCFM, Canadian Council of Forest Ministers
CCIW, Canada Centre for Inland Waters
CCME, Canadian Council of Ministers of the Environment
CCREM, Canadian Council of Resource and Environment Ministers
CDM, clean development mechanism
CDR, crude death rate
CEAA, Canadian Environmental Assessment Act
CEC, Commission for Environmental Cooperation
CEPA, Canadian Environmental Protection Act
CFC, chlorofluorocarbon
CFIA, Canadian Food Inspection Agency
CGR, crude growth rate
CHOPS, cold heavy oil production with sand
CHP, combined heat and power
CHRS, Canadian Heritage Rivers System
CIDA, Canadian International Development Agency
CITES, Convention on International Trade in Endangered Species of Wild Fauna and Flora
CIW, Canadian Index of Wellbeing
CLI, Canada Land Inventory
CMA, census metropolitan area(s)
CMHC, Canada Mortgage and Housing Corporation
COG, Canadian Organic Growers
COOGER, Centre for Offshore Oil and Gas Environmental Research
CoP 6, Sixth Conference of the Parties
CORE, Commission on Resources and Environment
COSEWIC, Committee on the Status of Endangered Wildlife in Canada
CPAWS, Canadian Parks and Wilderness Society
CPH&R, Canadian Pacific Hotels and Resorts
CPPI, Canadian Petroleum Products Institute
CSA, Canadian Standards Association
CSS, cyclic steam stimulation

CU, conservation unit
CWD, chronic wasting disease
CWS, Canada-wide standards
CYFN, Council of Yukon First Nations
CZM, coastal zone management
DAPTF, Declining Amphibian Populations Task Force
DDE, dichlorophenylethylene
DDT, dichlorodiphenyltrichloroethane
DFO, Department of Fisheries and Oceans
DGD, deep geological disposal
DNA, deoxyribonucleic acid
DNAPL, dense nonaqueous phase liquids
DSD, Duales System Deutschland
DU, Dobson units
dwt, deadweight tons
EA, environmental assessment
EARP, Canadian Environmental Assessment Review Panel
EC, European Community
EDC, endocrine-disrupting chemicals
EEZ, exclusive economic zone
EIA, environmental impact assessment
EIS, environmental impact statement
ELC, Environment Liaison Center
ELV, end-of-life vehicles
EMAN, Ecological Monitoring and Assessment Network
EMCBC, Environmental Mining Council of British Columbia
EMS, environmental management system
ENGO, environmental nongovernmental organization
ENSO, El Niño and the Southern Oscillation
EPR, extended producer responsibility
ESC, Ecological Science Cooperative
EU, European Union
EV, electric vehicles
FAO, Food and Agriculture Organization
FBMB, Fraser Basin Management Board
FCCC, United Nations Framework Convention on Climate Change
FCM, Federation of Canadian Municipalities
FNASWP, First Nations Atlantic Salmon Watch Program
FPB, Forestry Practices Board
FRAP, Fraser River Action Plan
FRCC, Fisheries Resources Conservation Council
FREMP, Fraser River Estuary Management
FSC, food, social, and ceremonial (purposes of Aboriginal harvest of fish)
FSC, Forest Stewardship Council
GATT, General Agreement on Tariffs and Trade
GBEI, Georgia Basin Ecosystem Initiative
GCM, general circulation model
GDP, gross domestic product
GE, genetic engineering
GHG, greenhouse gases
GIS, geographic information systems
GLWQA, Great Lakes Water Quality Agreements
GMF, genetically modified foods
GMO, genetically modified organism(s)
GNWT, Government of the Northwest Territories
GPI, genuine progress indicator
Gt, gigatonnes (billion tonnes)
GVRD, Greater Vancouver Regional District

GWP, global warming potential

HAB, harmful algal blooms

HBFC, hydrobromofluorocarbons

HCB, hexachlorobenzene

HCFC, hydrochlorofluorocarbons

HCHC, hexachlorocyclohexane

HDC, highly developed country

HDI, Human Development Index

HEAR, Hearing Education and Awareness for Rockers

HIV/AIDS, human immunodeficiency virus/acquired immune deficiency syndrome

ICLEI, International Council for Local Environmental Initiatives

ICME, International Council on Metals and the Environment

ICPD, International Conference on Population and Development

ICSC, International Centre for Sustainable Cities

IDRC, International Development Research Centre

IGBP, International Geosphere Biosphere Program

IHA, International Hydropower Association

IHDP, International Human Dimensions Program

IJC, International Joint Commission

ILO, intensive livestock operations

IPCC, The Intergovernmental Panel on Climate Change

IPM, integrated pest management

ISO, International Organization for Standardization

I-STOP, Integrated Satellite Tracking of Polluters

ITTA, International Tropical Timber Agreement

ITTO, International Tropical Trade Organization

IUCN, World Conservation Union (Formerly International Union for the Conservation of Nature and Natural Resources)

KPMG, Klynveld Peat Marwick Goerdeler

KWh, kilowatt-hours

LCA, life-cycle assessment

LCI, life-cycle inventory

LDC, less developed country

LNG, liquified natural gas

LOS, Law of the Sea

LRTAP, long-range transport of airborne pollutants

LRTP, long-range transport of pollutants

MAB, Man and the Biosphere

MDC, moderately developed country

MEND, Mine Environmental Neutral Drainage

MFT, mature fine tailings

MNR, Ministry of Natural Resources

MOE, Minister of the Environment

MOH, Minister of Health

MPA, marine protected area

Mt, megatonnes (million tonnes)

MW, megawatts

NAAMP, North American Amphibian Monitoring Program

NAAQO, National Ambient Air Quality Objective

NAEBA, North American Elk Breeders Association

NAFO, Northwest Atlantic Fisheries Organization

NAFTA, North American Free Trade Agreement

NAPS, Canada's National Air Pollution Surveillance

NASA, National Aeronautics and Space Administration

NASP, National Aerial Surveillance Program

NAWMP, North American Waterfowl Management Plan

NEB, National Energy Board

NGO, nongovernmental organization

NMCA, national marine conservation areas

NPA, National Program of Action (marine environment)

NPRI, National Pollutant Release Inventory

NPS, nonpoint source

NRBS, The Northern River Basins Study

NRC, Natural Resources Canada

NRTEE, National Round Table on the Environment and the Economy

ODS, ozone-depleting substance

ODWS, Ontario Drinking Water Standard

OECD, Organization for Economic Cooperation and Development

OEE, Office of Energy Efficiency

OPEC, Organization of Petroleum Exporting Countries

PAH, polyaromatic hydrocarbon

PAS, Protected Areas Strategy

PCB, polychlorinated biphenyl

PCP, pentachlorophenol

PDO, Pacific Decadal Oscillation

PECOS, Prairie Ecosystem Study

PEM, proton exchange membrane

PFC, perfluorocarbons

PFRA, Prairie Farm Rehabilitation Administration

PMF, plant molecular farming

POP, persistent organic pollutant

ppbv, parts per billion by volume

ppmv, parts per million by volume

PPP, purchasing power parity

PSA, Program for Sustainable Aquaculture

PSC, polar stratospheric clouds

PSkF, Pacific Streamkeepers Federation

PUC, Public Utilities Commission

PV, photovoltaics

RAP, Remedial Action Plan

RCMP, Royal Canadian Mounted Police

RENEW, Recovery of Nationally Endangered Wildlife

RPS, Renewable Portfolio Standards

SAGD, steam-assisted gravity drainage

SARA, Species at Risk Act

SCC, Standards Council of Canada

SOE, State of the Environment

SUV, sport utility vehicle

TAC, total allowable catch

TAF, Toronto Atmospheric Fund

TCDD, tetrachlorodibenzo-p-dioxin

TCDF, tetrachlorodibenzofuran

TEK, traditional ecological knowledge

TFL, tree farm licences

TFR, total fertility rate

THAI, toe to heel air injection

THM, trihalomethanes

TPC, Technology Partnerships Canada

TSS, total suspended solids

UCS, Union of Concerned Scientists

UN, United Nations

UNAIDS, the UN agency that tracks the AIDS epidemic

UNCCD, United Nations Convention to Combat Desertification

UNCED, United Nations Conference on Environment and Development

UNCLOS, United Nations Convention on the Law of the Sea

UNDP, United Nations Development Program

UNEP, United Nations Environment Programme

UNEP–WCMC, The United Nations Environment Programme–World Conservation Monitoring Centre

UNESCO, United Nations Educational, Scientific and Cultural Organization

UNFCCC, United Nations Framework Convention on Climate Change

UNICEF, United Nations Children's Fund
UV, ultraviolet
UV-A, ultraviolet-alpha
UV-B, ultraviolet-beta
UVI, Ultraviolet Index
VAPEX, vapour recovery extraction
VCR, Voluntary Challenge and Registry
VOC, volatile organic compound
VPA, Vancouver Port Authority

WAPPRIITA, Wild Animal and Plant Protection and Regulation of International and Interprovincial Trade Act
WCMC, World Conservation Monitoring Center
WCS, World Conservation Strategy
WHO, World Health Organization
WLED, white light–emitting diode
WMI, Whitehorse Mining Initiative
WMO, World Meteorological Organization
WWF, World Wide Fund for Nature (also, World Wildlife Fund)

PHOTO CREDITS

Front cover: Dianne Draper and Maureen Reed

Preliminary pages: page i: © Dianne Draper; iii: © Maureen Reed; iv: © Dianne Draper; v: © Kristiina Paul; vi: © Kristiina Paul; vii: © Kristiina Paul; viii: © Kristiina Paul; ix: Max Earey/Shutterstock; x: © Kristiina Paul; xi: © Kristiina Paul; xii: © Kristiina Paul.

Part 1: Opener: Pavel Cheiko/Shutterstock; **Chapter 1:** opener: Marko Kovacevic/Shutterstock; Photo 1–1: CP PHOTO/Chuck Stoody; 1–2: CP PHOTO/Troy Fleece; 1–3: CP PHOTO/Chuck Stoody; 1–4: Dejan Lazarevic/Shutterstock; 1–5: The Forest and Range Evaluation Program (FREP), Ministry of Forests and Range; 1–6: © Maureen Reed; 1–7a, b, c: © Dianne Draper; 1–7d: PhotoDisc/Getty Images; 1–8a, b: © Dianne Draper; 1–9: F. Lanting/First Light; 1–10a: S. Maslowski/CIDA; 1–10b: AP/CP Picture Archive; 1–11: © Al Harvey/The Slide Farm; 1–12a: UN/DPI photo; 1–12b: Ricardo Mazalan/CP Picture Archive; 1–13: © Al Harvey/The Slide Farm; 1–14: © Al Harvey/The Slide Farm; 1–15: Andrew Querner/Aurora/Getty Images; 1–16: Courtesy of Atlantic Coastal Action Program; 1–17: Blaise Edwards/CP Picture Archives; 1–18: Arthur Goss/Arts and Letters Club of Toronto; 1–19: Archives of Ontario.

Chapter 2: Opener: Andreas Gradin/SnapVillage; Photo 2–1: Library and Archives Canada, Acc. No. 1970-188-2243 Purchased through a grant from the Secretary of State/C-040293; 2–2: © Mary Evans Picture Library; 2–3: Ryan Remiorz/CP Picture Archive; 2–4: © Bill Banaszewski/Visuals Unlimited; 2–5: Associated Press/CP Picture Archive; 2–6: Clement Allard/CP Picture Archive; 2–7: © Mary Evans Picture Library; 2–8: Library and Archives Canada/C-061557; Figure 2–2: (John Muir, Gifford Pinchot) Hulton Archive/Getty Images; (Clifford Sifton) Turofsky/CP Picture Archive; (Aldo Leopold) University of Wisconsin-Madison Archives; (Rachel Carson) Comstock/Getty Images; Photo 2–9: © Todd Gipstein/CORBIS; 2–10: Kevin Lamarque/Reuters; 2–11: Ieva Geneviciene/Shutterstock; 2–12: © Dianne Draper; 2–13: CP PHOTO/Nathan Denette; 2–14: Anita/Shutterstock.

Part 2: Opener: Heather A. Craig/Shutterstock; **Chapter 3:** Opener: © Mike Dobel/Alamy; Photo 3–1a, b: © Dianne Draper; 3–2: Antonina Murawa/Shutterstock; 3–3: © PhotoDisc/Getty Images; 3–4: © PhotoDisc/Getty Images; 3–5: © Raymond Gehman/CORBIS; 3–6a: © Tom J. Ulrich/Visuals Unlimited; 3–6b, c: © PhotoDisc/Getty Images; 3–6d: Kevin Schafer/firstlight.ca; 3–7: © Dianne Draper; 3–8: © D. Cavagnaro/Visuals Unlimited; 3–9: © Dianne Draper; 3–10: © Michigan Sea Grant; 3–11: CP Picture Archive; 3–12: Peter K. Ziminski/Visuals Unlimited; Figure 3–11 (from top to bottom): Arthur Morris/Visuals Unlimited; S. Maslowski/Visuals Unlimited; S. Maslowski/Visuals Unlimited; S. Maslowski/Visuals Unlimited; Rudolf G. Arndt/Visuals Unlimited; Photo 3–13: Joe McDonald/Visuals Unlimited; 3–14: National Wildlife Federation; 3–15: © Dianne Draper; 3–16: Al Harvey/The Slide Farm; 3–17: F. Lanting/firstlight.ca; 3–18: © Dianne Draper; 3–19: Al Harvey/The Slide Farm; 3–20: Courtesy of C.S. Holling.

Chapter 4: Opener: Mark Horn/The Image Bank/Getty Images; Photo 4–1: Time Life Pictures/Getty Images; 4–2: Photos.com/Jupiter Images; 4–3: © Maureen Reed; 4–4: © Gideon Mendel/ActionAid/Corbis; 4–5: Saurabh Das/AP/CP Picture Archive; 4–6: CIDA Photo: Nancy Durrell McKenna; 4–7: UN/DPI photo;

4–8: UN/DPI photo; 4–9: © Lee Narraway; 4–10a: Photograph attributed to N.M. Hinshelwood/Library and Archives Canada/PA-028944; 4–10b: © Paul Henri, from Library and Archives Canada/PA-143463; 4–10c: Martin Chamberland/CP Picture Archive; 4–11: Les Bazso/The Province; 4–12: © Karen Kasmauski/Corbis; 4–13: Jurgen Ziewe/Shutterstock; 4–14: © Gaetano Images Inc./Alamy; 4–15: Christopher Pillitz/Reportage/Getty Images.

Part 3: Opener: Matthew Jacques/Shutterstock; **Chapter 5:** Opener: Armin Rose/Shutterstock; Photo 5–1a: Sia Chen How/Shutterstock; 5–1b: Henk Bentlage/Shutterstock; 5–2: © Dianne Draper; 5–3: CIDA Photo: Roger Lemoye; 5–4a: Sylvan H. Wittwer/Visuals Unlimited; 5–4b: John Meuser/Visuals Unlimited; 5–5a: Jasper National Park/Parks Canada; 5–5b: © Dianne Draper; 5–6: from Ozone depletion and climate change, Angus Fergusson, Environment Canada, 2001, page 5, Figure 3. Reprinted with permission of the Ministry of Public Works and Government Services Canada, 2008. http://exp-studies.tor.ec.gc.ca/e/ozone/OzoneDepletionClimateChange.pdf; 5–7: NASA; 5–8: © Reuters/CORBIS; 5–9: © Patrick Ward/CORBIS; Box 5–10: Photos.com/Jupiter Images; Photo 5–10: Victor Last/Geographical Visual Aids; 5–11: © Bert Klassen/Alamy; 5–12: © Dianne Draper; 5–13: © Dianne Draper; 5–14: © Al Harvey/The Slide Farm; 5–15: © Dick Hemingway; 5–16: THE CANADIAN PRESS/Chris Windeyer; 5–17: Logo and photo courtesy of Toronto Bike Month, City of Toronto.

Chapter 6: Opener: hougaard malan/Shutterstock; Photo 6–1a: © Al Harvey/The Slide Farm; 6–1b: © Dianne Draper; 6–2: CP PHOTO/Edmonton Sun-Brendon Dlouhy; 6–3: © Dianne Draper; 6–4: Agriculture and Agri-Food Canada; 6–5: © Dianne Draper; 6–6: R. Arndt/Visuals Unlimited; 6–7: Agriculture and Agri-Food Canada; 6–8: Ken Mantyla/CP Picture Archive; 6–9a: Agriculture and Agri-Food Canada; 6–9b,c: PhotoDisc/Getty Images; 6–9d,e: Photographer: R.J. W. Turner; Reproduced with the permission of Natural Resources Canada 2008, courtesy of Geological Survey of Canada; 6–10: Charlie Heidecker/Visuals Unlimited; 6–11: © Arco Images GmbH/Alamy; 6–12: © Ducks Unlimited Canada; 6–13: © Ducks Unlimited Canada; 6–14: © Dianne Draper; 6–15: Courtesy of Canadian Food Inspection Agency; 6–16: © Dianne Draper; 6–17: Len Rue, Jr./Visuals Unlimited; Figure 6–7 (photo): coko/Shutterstock; Photo 6–18: © Ducks Unlimited Canada; 6–19: Agriculture and Agri-Food Canada; 6–20: Courtesy of YEP Edmonton; 6–21: Photos.com/Jupiter Images; 6–22: Ulrike Hammerich/Shutterstock.

Chapter 7: Opener: Steve Rosset/Shutterstock; Photo 7–1: Al Grillo/AP/CP Picture Archive; 7–2: Tom Hanson/CP Picture Archive; 7–3: © Tourism Saskatchewan; 7–4: © Maureen Reed; 7–5: John Lehmann/CP Picture Archive; 7–6: Joe Traver/CP Picture Archive; 7–7: CP PHOTO/Larry MacDougal; 7–8: CP PHOTO/Larry MacDugal; 7–9a: © Hydro-Quebec; 7–9b: The Canadian Press/stf; 7–10: Frank M. Hanna/Visuals Unlimited; 7–11a: Courtesy of Department of Fisheries and Oceans Canada; 7–11b: Bob Semple; 7–12: © Vicki Gould; 7–13: © S.H. Draper; 7–14: Courtesy of Daivd Manz; 7–15: Courtesy of Daivd Manz; 7–16: © Liba Taylor/CORBIS; 7–17: © Martin Shields/Alamy.

Chapter 8: Opener: David William Taylor/Shutterstock; Photo 8–1: CP Picture Archive; 8–2: Vincent Dewitt/AP/CP Picture Archive; 8–3: © Al Harvey/The Slide Farm; 8–4: Vance Rodewalt/

The Calgary Herald, March 15, 1995, p. A4. Reprinted with permission of The Calgary Herald; 8–5: Richard Drew/AP/CP Picture Archive; 8–6: © Dianne Draper; 8–7: © Dianne Draper; 8–8: © Dianne Draper; 8–9: Courtesy of Department of Fisheries and Oceans Canada; 8–10: Paul Nicklen/National Geographic/Getty Images; 8–11: NASA; 8–12: © Dianne Draper; 8–13: © Natalie Fobes/CORBIS; 8–14: © Dianne Draper; 8–15: Courtesy of Trout Unlimited Canada; 8–16: © Dianne Draper; 8–17: © Dianne Draper; 8–18: Peter Ziminski/Visuals Unlimited; 8–19: Courtesy of Department of Fisheries and Oceans Canada; 8–20: Ray Smith/Victoria Times Colonist, September 17, 1995, p. A1; 8–21: © Dianne Draper; 8–22: Roger Watanabe/The Vancouver Sun; 8–23: © Al Harvey/The Slide Farm; 8–24: © Martin Leclerc, Courtesy of Glacialis Productions Inc.; 8–25: Bill Curtsinger/National Geographic/Getty Images.

Chapter 9: Opener: Natalia Bratslavsky/Shutterstock; Photo 9–1: © IRDC; 9–2: Associated Press/CP Picture Archive; 9–3: John Oohlden/Visuals Unlimited; 9–4: Ivy Images; 9–5: Natural Resources Canada; 9–6: © Keith Douglas/Alamy; 9–7: © Tracy Ferrero/Alamy; 9–8: © Maureen Reed; 9–9: Allen H. Benton/Visuals Unlimited; 9–10: Mary Cummins/Visuals Unlimited; 9–11a: Steve McCutcheon/Visuals Unlimited; 9–11b: Brooking Tatum/Visuals Unlimited; 9–11c: Steve McCutcheon/Visuals Unlimited; 9–11d: Kirtley-Perkins/Visuals Unlimited; 9–11e: Berndt Wittich/Visuals Unlimited; 9–12: © Laurie Wierzbicki; 9–13, 9–14, 9–15: Photo sequence compiled by Richard G. Thomas, Alberta Environmental Protection - Air Photo Services, Alberta Sustainable Resource Development, Edmonton; 9–16: Arthur R. Hill/Visuals Unlimited; 9–17: © Dianne Draper; 9–18: Courtesy of the Museum of Anthropology, UBC; 9–19: Courtesy of The Land Conservancy; 9–20: P. Marck/The Calgary Herald, June 23, 1997, p. C4. Reprinted with permission of The Calgary Herald; 9–21: © Jeff Amos; 9–22: © Kristiina Paul.

Chapter 10: Opener: Brian Milne/First Light; Photo 10–1: © Image A-00355, BC Archives; 10–2: © Maureen Reed; 10–3: © Russ Merne/Alamy; 10–4: City of Elliot Lake; 10–5: Natural Resources Canada – Photolibrary; 10–6: © Al Harvey/The Slide Farm; 10–7: © Erik Schaffer; Ecoscene/CORBIS; 10–8: Natural Resources Canada – Photolibrary; 10–9: Natural Resources Canada – Photolibrary; 10–10: © Maureen Reed; 10–11: Reprinted with permission of Alcan, Inc.; 10–12: © Patrice Halley; 10–13: CP PICTURE ARCHIVE/Fred Chartrand; 10–14: Reprinted with permission of Alcan, Inc.; 10–15: © Dianne Draper; 10–16: © Robert Harding Picture Library Ltd/Alamy.

Chapter 11: Opener: Marinko Tarlac/Shutterstock; Photo 11–1: © Dianne Draper; 11–2: © University of Calgary – Light Up The World Fund; 11–3: © Al Harvey/The Slide Farm; 11–4: The ENERGY STAR® mark is administered and promoted in Canada by Natural Resources Canada and is registered in Canada by the United States Environmental Protection Agency; 11–5a, b, c, d: Toronto Transit Commission; 11–6: © Mark Long; 11–7: © Lowell Georgia/CORBIS; 11–8: Eriko Sugita/Reuters; 11–9: Reprinted with permission of The Calgary Herald; 11–10: Photo David Dodge, Canadian Parks and Wilderness Society (CPAWS); Figure 11–6b, d: Gerry Langille, Courtesy of Sydney Tar Ponds Agency, www.tarpondscleanup.ca; Figure 11–6c: CP PHOTO/Len Wagg; Photo 11–11: J. Jacquemain/Comstock/Getty Images; 11–12: © Bettmann/Corbis; 11–13: Efrem Lukatsky/AP/CP Picture Archive; 11–14: R-2000 logo: R-2000 is an official mark of Natural Resources Canada. R-2000 house photo: NRCan/RNCan; 11–15: Courtesy of The EcoLogo Program, TerraChoice Environmental Marketing; 11–16: CP PHOTO/Richard Lam; 11–17: NASA.

Chapter 12: Opener: © Danita Delimont/Alamy; 12–1a: Thomas Gula/Visuals Unlimited; 12–1b: John Gerlach/Visuals Unlimited; 12–1c: R. Lindholm/Visuals Unlimited; 12–1d: Joe McDonald/Visuals Unlimited; 12–2: Victor Last/Geographical Visual Aids; 12–3: John Gerlach/Visuals Unlimited; 12–4: © Dianne Draper; 12–5: © Dianne Draper; 12–6: Arthur Morrison/Visuals Unlimited; 12–7a: William J. Weber/Visuals Unlimited; 12–7b: Bernd Wittich/Visuals Unlimited; 12–7c: Nada Pecnik/Visuals Unlimited; 12–8: © PhotoDisc/Getty Images; 12–9: © Juniors Bildarchiv/Alamy; 12–10: Steve McCutcheon/Visuals Unlimited; 12–11: Ivy Images; 12–12: Ivy Images; 12–13: © Kristiina Paul; 12–14a, b, c, d: © Maureen Reed; 12–15: © MARK DUFFY/Alamy; 12–16: Toronto Zoo; 12–17: Ivy Images; 12–18: Kao Sod Sub/AP/CP Picture Archive; 12–19: © Francis Lepine/biospherephotographie.ca; 12–20: Arthur Morris/Visuals Unlimited; 12–21: © Maureen Reed; 12–22: Joe McDonald/Visuals Unlimited; 12–23: © Design Pics Inc./Alamy; 12–24: © Ryan McGinnis/Alamy; 12–25: © Martin Harvey/CORBIS.

Part 4: Opener: Tootles/Shutterstock; **Chapter 13:** Opener: Tannis Toohey/Toronto Star; Photo 13–1: CP PHOTO/Richard Lam; 13–2a: © Dianne Draper; 13–2b: © Al Harvey/The Slide Farm; 13–3: © Dianne Draper; 13–4: © Al Harvey/The Slide Farm; 13–5: © Dianne Draper; 13–6: Reprinted with permission of The Calgary Herald; 13–7: © Dianne Draper; 13–8: © Dianne Draper; 13–9: © Al Harvey/The Slide Farm; 13–10: © Maureen Reed; 13–11: © Al Harvey/The Slide Farm; 13–12: © Dianne Draper; 13–13: © Dick Hemingway; 13–14: John Cunningham/Visuals Unlimited; 13–15: Kevin Frayer/CP Picture Archive; 13–16: © Dianne Draper; 13–17: © Al Harvey/The Slide Farm; 13–18: Courtesy of Gobal Footprint Network, 2006. National Footprint Accounts, 2006 Edition. Available at www.footprintnetwork. org; 13–19: Courtesy of Bill Rees.

Chapter 14: Opener: © Chris Cheadle/Alamy; Photo 14–1: © Malcolm McBain; 14–2: Dick Loek/Toronto Star/First Light; 14–3: © Annie Griffiths Belt/CORBIS; 14–4a: © Robert Shantz/Alamy; 14–4b: CP PHOTO/Troy Fleece; 14–5: © Al Harvey/Slide Farm; 14–6: © Dianne Draper; 14–7: Steve McCutcheon/Visuals Unlimited; 14–8: Courtesy of the Commission for Environmental Cooperation; Photo © Choppy/iStockphoto; 14–9: AP Photo/Ed Wray; 14–10: THE CANADIAN PRESS/Peter McCabe; 14–11: Courtesy of Cameco Corporation; 14–12: © Maureen Reed; 14–13: Karoline Cullen/Shutterstock; 14–14: © Maureen Reed; 14–15: The Orleans Preschool; 14–16: Courtesy of SPEC: Society Promoting Environmental Conservation, www.spec.bc.ca; 14–17: © Severn Cullis-Suzuki; 14–18: Courtesy of Fundy Model Forest; 14–19: Courtesy of the Fraser Basin Council, www.fraserbasin. bc.ca; 14–20: © moodboard/Corbis; 14–21: © NORMA JOSEPH/Alamy; 14–22: © Maureen Reed; 14–23: © Maureen Reed; 14–24: © World Stat International; 14–25: © Dianne Draper; 14–26: © University of Saskatchewan; photograph by Colleen McPherson; 14–27: © Michael Ventura/Alamy; 14–28: Ken Straiton/First Light.

Canada and the World: Opener: NASA; Table C/W–4: © Gaetano Images Inc./Alamy; C/W–5: Christopher Pillitz/Reportage/Getty; C/W–6: © Liba Taylor/CORBIS; C/W–7: © Karen Kasmauski/Corbis; C/W–8: Ken Straiton/First Light; C/W–9: © Michael Ventura/Alamy; C/W–10: © Ryan McGinnis/Alamy; C/W–11: © Martin Shields/Alamy; C/W–12: Ulrike Hammerich/Shutterstock; C/W–13: © Martin Harvey/CORBIS; C/W–14: © Jeff Amos; C/W–15: Photos.com/Jupiter Images; C/W–16: Bill Curtsinger/National Geographic/Getty Images; C/W–17: NASA; C/W–18: © Robert Harding Picture Library Ltd/ Alamy; C/W–19: © Kristiina Paul.

qualitative and quantitative data, 39–40

rain forests, temperate, 91, 375–76
Ramsar Convention/sites, 291, 504, 507
realized niche, 82
recycling
   cities and, 551
   extended producer responsibility
      and, 432–33
   Green Dot System, 432–33
   mining and, 428, 429, 432
Red River, 264–65
Rees, William, 556
Remedial Action Plan, 291
renewable resources, 14, 129, 459
   technologies and, 10, 11
research
   on mining, 432, 435
   on offshore drilling, 449–50
resource development
   government responsibility for, 130–31
resource extraction, 129
resource partitioning, 80, 82
resources
   biological, capacity vs. consumption
      of, 20–21
   consumption of, 5, 11, 12, 145
   defined, 13–14
   and ecological footprint, 21
   energy, 445–65 (see also energy)
   forest, in developing countries, 360–61
   forests (see forests/forestry)
   human population and, 11
   land (see agriculture; soil)
   measuring, monitoring, and reporting,
      27–28
   mining (see mining)
   nonrenewable, 14
   over-consumption of, 11
   renewable (see energy, renewable;
      renewable resources)
   sustainability of (see sustainability)
   water (see water)
rivers and streams, 261
   flooding of, 264–65
   freshwater, 96
   heritage, 263
   water runoff and, 261, 262
rock cycle, 407–408
R-2000 home program, 468

safety
   logging and, 368
   mining and, 414
   nuclear power and, 462–63
   water and, 264
Sage Creek, Alberta, 499–500
Saguenay River, 264
salmon. *See under* fish/fisheries
A Sand Country Almanac, 57
sanitation, EPI scores, 596–97
satellite remote, 38
scavengers, 75
science, 35–43
   assumptions in, 37
   complexity, values, worldviews, and,
      36, 42

correlation and, 37
critical thinking and, 36, 41
deductive reasoning and, 37
defined, 36
environmental decision making and,
   36, 43–45, 571–73
inductive reasoning and, 37
language use and, 40
measurement in, 37–38
methods of, 38–40
misunderstandings about, 40–42
probability and, 37
research models and, 40
theory and, 37, 40
value-free, 36, 40–42
scientific method, 42
sea levels, 310
sedimentary rock, 407
self-realization, principle of, 53
sewage treatment. *See under* water
shared governance, 29–31, 579–80
Sierra Legal Defence Fund
   drinking water and, 274, 277
Sifton, Clifford, 47, 48, 50
Silliman, Joel, 105
silviculture, 368
smog, 175–80
social norms, 25
soil
   agriculture and, 211, 232–33, 564
   capability, 211
   carbon content of, 211, 212, 232–33
   chemical contamination, 216
   contamination of, 215–16
   desertification and, 216–17
   erosion of, 212–13
   forests and, 373
   levels of organic matter in, 211–12
   salinization of, 214–15
   structure of, 214
solar energy, 466
   autotrophs and, 74–75
Southern Oscillation, 168, 170–71
Sparrow, Ron, Jr., 135
Sparrow decision, 132, 135
specialist species, 79
speciation, 99–100
species. *See also individual species*
   amphibians, environmental sensitivity
      of, 481–83
   biodiversity of, 73, 485–87
   birds (see birds)
   Canadian, at risk, 322–23, 493–97
   defined, 70
   ecological succession and, 100
   endangered, 322–23, 494, 518–20
   in forests, 373, 374, 379, 380–81, 383,
      384, 385
   generalist, 79
   humans vs. other, 10
   interaction among, 79–80, 82–83
   intrinsic value of, 484
   keystone, 79, 502
   loss of, 8
   natural selection, adaptation, and, 99
   number and organization of, 70, 71
   plants (see plants)

population of, 70
protecting Canadian, 513–14
reproduction strategies of, 98
speciation and extinction of, 99–100
specialist, 79
tolerance ranges of, 77
types and roles of, in ecosystems,
   78–83
types of, in biomes, 90–97
ultraviolet radiation and, 143–44
Species at Risk Act (SARA), 322, 565–66
St. Lawrence Action Plan/Vision,
   333, 335
standard error, 38
staples trap, 413, 414–15
starvation, 11
statistical significance, 38
stewardship, environmental, 30–31,
   147, 352
stratosphere, 67, 143
succession, 100
sun sensitivity test, 169
supply and demand, 26
sustainability, 15–31
   actions and objectives for, 17, 570
   adaptive management, 28–29
   agriculture and, 234, 236–48
   Arctic ecosystems and, 499
   of biological resources, 508–509
   of cities, 12–13, 548–57
   costs, benefits, and, 26
   defined, 15
   ecological (see ecological sustainability)
   economic (see economic sustainability)
   ecosystem approach to, 26–31
   environmental assessments 28–29
   environmental stewardship and, 30–31
   First Nations and, 25
   fresh water and, 290–94
   housing and, 539–41
   lifecycle concept and, 579
   made-in-Canada models for, 580–82
   milestones in, 18–19
   monitoring for, 27–28
   of ocean environment, 310–11, 313,
      314, 317, 352
   precautionary principle of, 26
   principles of, 17, 20–26
   of resources, 11
   social, 21, 25
sustainable development, 15–17,
   18–19, 459
   deep ecology, green alternatives,
      and, 52–54
   mining and, 417–18
   worldviews and, 45–48, 54–55
Suzuki, David, 58
Swan Lake, B.C., 295
Sydney tar ponds, 455–56, 562
Sweden, 567–68
symbiosis, 82
synergistic effects, 285

taiga. *See* boreal forest
Talloires Declaration, 582, 584–85
Technology Partnerships Program, 45
temperate grasslands, 91